D0269091

Sunday EXPRESS

GUIDE TO

GOLF

COURSES

— 1995 —

*Golfers seeking fresh challenges want to know
where they can play, what it will cost and the kind
of facilities they can expect. This book provides
every piece of information they need.*

PETER WATSON
Sports Editor, *Sunday Express*

Produced by the Automobile Association

PRODUCED BY AA PUBLISHING

Maps prepared by the Cartographic Department of The
Automobile Association

Maps © The Automobile Association 1994

Directory generated by the AA Establishment Database,
Information Research, Hotel and Touring Services

Cover design by The Paul Hampson Partnership

Cover photograph by Peter Dazeley

Editorial contributors: Features contributed by Ian Riach,
former Sports Editor of the *Scottish Sunday Express*.
Highlighted Irish courses selected with the help of
Charlie Mulqueen of the *Cork Examiner*

Illustrations by Alan Roe

Head of Advertisement Sales
Christopher Heard: Tel 0256 20123 (ext 21544)

Advertisement Production
Karen Weeks: Tel 0256 20123 (ext 21545)

Typeset by Avonset, Midsomer Norton, Nr Bath

Printed and bound in Great Britain by William Clowes Ltd,
Beccles and London

The contents of this book are believed correct at the time
of printing. Nevertheless, the Publisher cannot be held
responsible for any errors or omissions or for changes in
the details given in this guide or for the consequences of
any reliance on the information provided in the same.
Although every effort has been made to ensure accuracy
we always welcome any information from readers to assist
in such efforts and to keep the book up to date.

© The Automobile Association 1995

All rights reserved. No part of this publication may be
reproduced, stored in a retrieval system, or transmitted in
any form or by any means - electronic, mechanical,
photocopying, recording, or otherwise - unless the
written permission of the publisher has been given
beforehand. This book may not be lent, resold, hired out
or otherwise disposed of by way of trade in any form of
binding or cover other than that in which it is published,
without the prior consent of the publisher.

A CIP catalogue record for this book is available from the
British Library

Published by AA Publishing, which is a trading name
of Automobile Association Developments Limited
whose registered office is Norfolk House, Priestley
Road, Basingstoke, Hampshire RG24 9NY, Registered
number 1878835.

ISBN 0 7495 0906 6

CONTENTS

IMPORTANT

National Phone Codes Change - 16 April 1995

Increasing use of telecommunications services has meant an increase in the demand for numbers. In the current telephone numbering system only a few codes remain unused. To satisfy demand and create a more flexible structure for the future a new code system is being introduced.

LOCAL CODES

All local codes (usually 2 or 3 figures) will be changed to the national code number. This has already happened in many parts of the country.

When you use the national code for a local call, you will still only be charged the local rate.

REMEMBER If your call is to another number with the same code, there is no need to dial the code – just the number.

AREA CODES

From 16 April 1995 all area codes starting with 0 (with five exceptions – see below) will be changed to start with 01, for example:

York	0904	will be	01904
Basingstoke	0256	will be	01256
London	071	will be	0171

BRISTOL, LEEDS, LEICESTER, NOTTINGHAM AND SHEFFIELD

These five cities will have a completely new national code and one extra digit will be added to the individual subscribers number, for example:

Leeds	0532	will be	0113 2 + *old subscriber number*
Sheffield	0742	will be	0114 2 + *old subscriber number*
Nottingham	0602	will be	0115 9 + *old subscriber number*
Leicester	0533	will be	0116 2 + *old subscriber number*
Bristol	0272	will be	0117 9 + *old subscriber number*

The new '01' codes will be available on the BT and Mercury systems from August 1994 but callers will be able to go on using the existing '0' codes as well until 16 April 1995. After this date, all the old '0' codes will be changed to '01'

INTERNATIONAL CODES

On 16 April 1995 the code to dial abroad from the UK will also change from 010 to 00. This is part of a move to provide a single code for all European countries to access the international network.

Changes to phone codes will not affect:

- Individual subscribers numbers or local calls except in Bristol, Leeds, Leicester, Nottingham and Sheffield (see above)
- FreeFone or reduced rate services - eg 0800 or 0345 numbers
- Information and entertainment lines - eg 0891 or 0898 numbers
- Mobile phone numbers

For further information call Freefone 0800 01 01 01

4

HOW TO USE THIS *G*UIDE

●●●

THIS guide contains well over 2000 of those golf courses in Britain and Ireland that welcome visiting golfers. This includes some 250 newly-built courses.

*A*LL YOU NEED TO KNOW

We have endeavoured to supply all the information you need to know before your visit by telling you what kind of course you can expect, what club facilities are available, including catering, any leisure facilities and the green fees you can expect to pay. We have also included AA-recommended accommodation - whether it be at the course itself or slightly further away.

*A*RRANGING A VISIT

Some courses want advance notice of any visit, and possibly a letter of introduction from your own club. They may also require a handicap certificate. If this is the case the directory will include this information. However, it is always a good idea to check with any course in advance as details in the directory can change, particularly green fees, during the currency of the guide.

*C*OURSES OF NOTE

Courses that are considered to be of particular merit or interest have been placed within a shaded box and given a more detailed description. They may be very historic clubs or they may have been chosen because their courses are particularly testing or enjoyable to play. Some have been included because they are in holiday areas and have proved popular with visiting golfers. Such a selection cannot be either exhaustive or totally objective, and these courses do not represent any formal category on quality or other grounds.

Major Championship courses have special treatment with a full page entry, including a selection of places at which to eat as well as to stay.

*T*HE DIRECTORY

The directory is arranged in country and county order. Each country is divided by county and within each county, the courses are in alphabetical order of the towns under which they are listed. If you are not sure where your chosen course may be, there is an alphabetical index of courses at the end of the directory. The maps at the end of the book will also help to locate any golf course.

*M*AP REFERENCES

Should you be travelling in an unfamiliar part of the country and want to know the choice of courses available to you, consult the atlas at the end of the book. In its directory entry, each course has a map number and National Grid reference and there are directions to the course giving the nearest place located on the map.

*S*YMBOLS AND ABBREVIATIONS

In order to maximise the space available, we have used certain symbols and abbreviations within the directory entries and these are explained in the panel below.

04 TQ21	atlas page and National Grid reference
☎	telephone number
IR£	Irish Punts (Republic only - the rates of exchange between Punts and pounds sterling are liable to fluctuate)
⊗	lunch
⫰	dinner
🍴	bar snacks
☕	tea/coffee
♀	bar open midday and evenings
🛏	accommodation at club
👕	changing rooms
🏪	well-stocked shop
⚐	clubs for hire
(	professional at club
★	hotel classification
✕❀	restaurant classification (applicable to championship course entry only)
Q	Guest house classification
B	AA Branded group hotels

●●●

ENTRIES IN BOLD ITALICS

NB Although we make every effort to obtain up-to-date information from golf clubs, in some cases we have been unable to verify details with the club's management. Where this is the case the course name is shown in bold italics and you would be strongly advised to check with the club in advance of your visit

TELEPHONE CODES

Telephone codes throughout Britain are due to change - see the details on page 4.

The area codes shown against telephone numbers under Republic of Ireland courses are applicable within the Republic only. Similarly the area codes shown for entries in Great Britain and Northern Ireland cannot be used direct from the Republic. Check your telephone directory for details.

ACCOMMODATION

For each course listed, we recommend a nearby AA-appointed hotel, giving its classification, full name and address, telephone number and total number of bedrooms, including the number with private bath or shower. In some cases the hotel will be with the grounds of the golf course itself. The hotels recommended in the Golf Guide are mostly in the ★★, ★★★, and ★★★★ star categories. Where there is no AA-appointed hotel nearby, we have recommended an AA-inspected Guest House. Guest houses are classified by a quality assessment or Q rating of 1-5 Q's.

CLUB ACCOMMODATION

Some courses offer accommodation at their club. Where this facility exists, the 'bed' symbol (🛏) will appear in the entry under club facilities. This has been listed as a further option for those who might wish to stay at the course. However, unless the club accommodation has an AA star-rating, the only accommodation appointed by the AA is the star-rated hotel that appears at the foot of each entry.

KEY TO HOTEL CLASSIFICATION

The AA system of star rating from one to five stars is the market leader in hotel classifications and has long been universally recognised as an accurate, objective indication of the facilities one can expect to find at any hotel in the AA scheme.

★ Black stars indicate the level of facilities and services available at a hotel. One-star hotels are generally small hotels and inns, with good but often simple furnishings, facilities and food.

★★ Small to medium-sized hotels offering more facilities(telephones and televisions etc), and at least half the bedrooms will have en-suite bath or shower.

★★★ Medium-sized hotels with more spacious accommodation and a greater range of facilities and services; all rooms have en-suite bath or shower.

★★★★ Large hotels with spacious accommodation and high standards of comfort, service and food; all rooms have full en suite facilities.

★★★★★ Large luxury hotels offering the highest international standards of accommodation, facilities, services and cuisine.

🛏 This denotes an AA Country House hotel with a relaxed informal atmosphere and offering a personal welcome. Often secluded, they are not always rurally situated but are quiet.

Branded Hotels Hotels belonging to large groups do not carry star ratings as they reach a common level of comfort and facilities. They are indicated by a B prior to the hotel name.

PERCENTAGE RATINGS FOR QUALITY

Our inspectors give percentage scores to hotels with black stars as a way of comparing hotels of the same star rating in terms of quality. This covers all aspects of a hotel's operation, including hospitality, service, cleanliness, food, and overall presentation of bedrooms and public areas. A high percentage score indicates superior standards within the star rating.

RED STARS

The AA recognises hotels that consistently provide outstanding levels of hospitality, service, food and comfort through its prestigious red-star award scheme. These are given to a select group of hotels considered to be of the very best within their star rating. In such cases, a percentage score for quality is considered unnecessary. Red-star hotels in this guide are indicated by the word 'red' after the star classification.

ROSETTES

❀ Rosettes are awarded to restaurants and hotels achieving notable excellence for quality of cuisine, from one rosette – indicating carefully prepared food reflecting a high level of culinary skill – to a maximum of five rosettes indicating outstanding cuisine reaching the highest international standards.

ENGLAND

Golf as the ultimate leisure experience

ONE of the appealing sides to golf is that you can tee up where the great players have played and where some of the games most dramatic events have taken place. For instance, where Sam Torrance's birdie at the 18th in 1985 gave Europe victory over the Americans for the first time for 28 years – The Belfry.

That triumph put the Sutton Coldfield course firmly in the folklore of the game and, following two further Ryder Cups there, thousands have flocked to take advantage of its play and stay facilities. Every year more people are playing golf and looking for somewhere to stay that provides after game facilities. The Belfry offers everything a golfer would want. Two courses – the Brabazon, designed by Dave Thomas and Peter Allis, at 6,905 yards, and the Derby, which is a bit easier to take

at 6,103 yards. When the day's battle against par is over, hotel guests can unwind in the leisure club, which has an indoor swimming pool, sauna, steam room, gymnasium, squash courts and a tennis court.

The Belfry is one of five golfing centres in the De Vere group, which offer some of the best golf in England and off-course amenities to match. There is Belton Woods Hotel and Country Club, near Grantham, which has three courses offering panoramic views of the Lincolnshire parkland. You have the choice of playing on The Lakes course, with plenty of bunkers and water hazards to catch wayward shots, The Woodside, with several blind holes, and the nine-hole Spitfire.

The Mottram Hall Hotel course, deep in

the heart of Cheshire, was also designed by Dave Thomas and is as beautiful as it is tough. The front nine are set in flat, tree-lined parkland and the back nine winds its way through mature, rolling woodland. The course has hosted the Northern PGA Championship and was used as a qualifier for the Glenmuir PGA Club Championship.

Golf breaks are also offered by Britain's biggest hotel and leisure company, the Country Club Hotel group. Four of its courses are being used this year for top events on the PGA European Tour, the PGA Seniors' Tour, the Women's European Tour and Scotland's Tartan Tour. Nine Country Club hotels have 18-hole courses. There are six in England, plus St Pierre in Wales, Dalmahoy in Scotland and Treudelberg in Hamburg.

At Breadsall Priory Hotel, in Derby, a mansion dating back to the 1200s, there are two courses. There is the original Priory course or the new challenge of the Moorland course. Another of the group's centres, the Meon Valley Hotel, near Southampton, has a 6,519-yard course stretching round trees, lakes and streams and there is a nine-hole course for those making their way in the game. John Stirling, the hotel professional, who was captain of the PGA in 1989 – the last time Europe won the Ryder Cup – says 'a lot of people come here for seminars and want something to do at the end of the day. We have tennis, squash, a swimming pool and the golf courses are a big attraction. The outward and inward nines on our 18-hole course start at the same point, which is handy, and there is the nine-hole course to take the pressure off if we are busy.'

The Forest of Arden Golf and Country Club, Warwickshire, is again the venue for the Murphy's English Open, won last year by Ian Woosnam as he confirmed his place in the European Ryder Cup team. Deer roam free in the 10,000 acre parkland and fishermen can take advantage of the Packington trout lakes in the Forest of Arden for an additional charge. For the golfer there are the delights of two outstanding courses, the Arden and Aylesford. The Arden was re-developed by architect Donald Steel and the European Tour in readiness for the Murphy's tournament.

IAN RIACH,
Golf correspondent, *Scottish Sunday Express*

ENGLAND

AVON

BACKWELL   Map 03 ST46

Tall Pines ☎ Lulsgate (0275) 472076
Parkland course with views over the Bristol Channel.
18 holes, 5800yds, Par 70, SSS 68.
Club membership 600.
Visitors   must contact in advance.
Societies   apply in writing.
Green Fees £10 per round (£13 weekends & bank holidays).
Facilities   ⊗ ⅷ Ⅲ ७ ♥ ♀ ☍ ⌂ ⌐ { Terry Murray.
Location   Cooks Bridle Path, Downside
Hotel   ★★★63% Walton Park Hotel, Wellington Ter,
                  CLEVEDON ☎ (0275) 874253 41 ⇆ ⅏

BATH   Map 03 ST76

Bath ☎ (0225) 463834
Considered to be one of the finest courses in the west,
this is the site of Bath's oldest golf club. An interesting
course situated on high ground overlooking the city and
with splendid views over the surrounding countryside.
The rocky ground supports good quality turf and there
are many good holes. The 17th is a dog-leg right past, or
over the corner of an out-of-bounds wall, and thence on
to an undulating green.
18 holes, 6369yds, Par 71, SSS 70, Course record 65.
Club membership 675.
Visitors   must contact in advance and have a
                  handicap certificate.
Societies   must apply in writing.
Green Fees £25 per day (£30 weekends & bank
                  holidays).
Facilities   ⊗ ⅢⅢ by prior arrangement ७ ♥ ♀ ☍ ⌂ ⌐
                  { Peter J Hancox.
Location   Sham Castle, North Rd (1.5m SE city centre
                  off A36)
Hotel   ★★★65% Francis Hotel, Queen Square,
                  BATH ☎ (0225) 424257 93 ⇆ ⅏

Lansdown ☎ (0225) 422138
A flat parkland course in open situation.
18 holes, 6299yds, Par 71, SSS 70, Course record 65.
Club membership 790.
Visitors   must contact in advance & have handicap
                  certificate.
Societies   must contact in advance.
Green Fees £18 per round (£30 weekends & bank holidays).
Facilities   ⊗ ⅢⅢ by prior arrangement ७ ♥ ♀ ☍ ⌂ ⌐
                  { Terry Mercer.
Leisure   practice ground.
Location   Lansdown (6m SW of exit 18 of M4)
Hotel   ★★★65% Lansdown Grove Hotel, BATH
                  ☎ (0225) 315891 44 ⇆ ⅏

BRISTOL   Map 03 ST57

Bristol and Clifton ☎ (0275) 393474
A downland course with splendid turf and fine tree-lined
fairways. The 222-yard (par 3) 13th with the green well
below, and the par 4 16th, with its second shot across an
old quarry, are outstanding. There are splendid views
over the Bristol Channel towards Wales.
18 holes, 6292yds, Par 70, SSS 70, Course record 65.
Club membership 835.
Visitors   must contact in advance & have a handicap
                  certificate.
Societies   must book in advance.
Green Fees £30 per round (£38 weekends & bank
                  holidays).
Facilities   ⊗ ⅢⅢ by prior arrangement ७ ♥ ♀ ☍ ⌂ ⌐
                  { Peter Mawson.
Leisure   snooker.
Location   Beggar Bush Ln, Failand (4m W on B3129
                  off A369)
Hotel   ★★★68% Redwood Lodge Hotel &
                  Country Club, Beggar Bush Ln, Failand,
                  BRISTOL ☎ (0275) 393901 108 ⇆ ⅏

Filton ☎ (0272) 694169
Parkland course with a par 4 testing hole 'dog-leg' 383 yds.
18 holes, 6300yds, Par 70, SSS 70.
Club membership 800.
Visitors   must have handicap certificate but may not play
                  at weekends unless with member.
Societies   must contact in advance.
Green Fees £25 per day; £20 per round.
Facilities   ⊗ ⅢⅢ by prior arrangement ७ ♥ ♀ ☍ ⌂ ⌐
                  { Nicky Lumb.
Location   Golf Course Ln, Filton (5m NW off A38)
Hotel   B Forte Crest, Filton Rd, Hambrook, BRISTOL
                  ☎ (0272) 564242 197 ⇆ ⅏

Henbury ☎ (0272) 500044
A parkland course tree-lined and on two levels. The
River Trym comes into play on the 7th drop-hole with its
green set just over the stream. The last nine holes have
the beautiful Blaise Castle woods for company.
18 holes, 6039yds, Par 70, SSS 70, Course record 62.
Club membership 800.
Visitors   with member only weekends. Handicap
                  certificate usually required.
Societies   Tue & Fri only (minimum 20 players).
Green Fees £21 per round.
Facilities   ⊗ ⅢⅢ by prior arrangement ७ ♥ ♀ ☍ ⌂
                  { Nick Riley.
Location   Henbury Hill, Westbury-on-Trym (3m NW
                  of city centre on B4055 off A4018)
Hotel   ★★★56% St Vincent Rocks Hotel, Sion
                  Hill, Clifton, BRISTOL
                  ☎ (0272) 739251 46 ⇆ ⅏

Knowle ☎ (0272) 770660
A parkland course with nice turf. The first five holes
climb up and down hill but the remainder are on a more
even plane.
18 holes, 6016yds, Par 69, SSS 69.
Club membership 800.

▶

Visitors	must have handicap certificate. Must play with member at weekends.
Societies	Thu only. Must contact in advance.
Green Fees	not confirmed.
Facilities	⊗ 〗Ⅲ by prior arrangement ⌂ ♥ ♀ ⚲ 🏠 ♟ Gordon Brand.
Location	Brislington (3m SE of city centre off A37)
Hotel	★★★(red)🏨 Hunstrete House Hotel, CHELWOOD ☎ (0761) 490490 13 ⇆ ♞Annexe11 ⇆ ♞

Mangotsfield ☎ (0272) 565501
An easy hilly parkland course. Caravan site.
18 holes, 5337yds, Par 68, SSS 66, Course record 65.
Club membership 500.

Visitors	may not play on competition days. Must contact in advance.
Societies	weekdays only, must contact 2 weeks in advance.
Green Fees	not confirmed.
Facilities	⊗ ⌂ ♥ ♀ ⚲ 🏠 ♟ ♟ Craig Trewin.
Location	Carsons Rd, Mangotsfield (6m NE of city centre off B4465)
Hotel	B Forte Crest, Filton Rd, Hambrook, BRISTOL ☎ (0272) 564242 197 ⇆ ♞

Shirehampton Park ☎ (0272) 822083
A lovely course in undulating parkland comprising two loops.
There are views over the Portway beside the River Avon,
where sliced balls at the opening hole are irretrievable.
18 holes, 5600yds, Par 67, SSS 68.
Club membership 600.

Visitors	with member only at weekends.
Societies	Mon (if booked).
Green Fees	£18 per round (£25 weekends).
Facilities	⊗ 〗Ⅲ by prior arrangement ⌂ ♥ ♀ ⚲ 🏠 ♟ ♟ Brent Ellis.
Location	Park Hill, Shirehampton (4m NW of city centre on A4)
Hotel	★★★68% Redwood Lodge Hotel & Country Club, Beggar Bush Ln, Failand, BRISTOL ☎ (0275) 393901 108 ⇆ ♞

Woodlands ☎ Almondsbury (0454) 618121
Interesting parkland course, featuring five testing par 3's set
around the course's six lakes.
18 holes, 5477yds, Par 69, SSS 67.
Club membership 70.

Visitors	no restrictions.
Societies	contact in advance.
Green Fees	not confirmed.
Facilities	⊗ ⌂ ♥ ♀ ⚲ 🏠 ♟ ♟ Tony Isaacs.
Leisure	fishing.
Location	Trench Ln, Almondsbury (N of Bristol off A38)
Hotel	B Forte Crest, Filton Rd, Hambrook, BRISTOL ☎ (0272) 564242 197 ⇆ ♞

A golf course name printed in ***bold italics*** means we have been unable to verify information with the club's management for the current year

---

CHIPPING SODBURY   Map 03 ST78

Chipping Sodbury ☎ (0454) 319042
Parkland courses of Championship proportions. The old
course may be seen from the large opening tee by the
clubhouse at the top of the hill. Two huge drainage dykes
cut through the course and form a distinctive hazard on
eleven holes.
New Course: 18 holes, 6912yds, Par 73, SSS 73, Course record 67.
Old Course: 9 holes, 6184yds, Par 70, SSS 69.
Club membership 770.

Visitors	must have a handicap certificate and may only play after 12.30pm at weekends.
Societies	must contact in writing.
Green Fees	New course £25 per day; £20 up to 27 holes (£30/£25 weekends). Old course £4 per day (£5 weekends).
Facilities	⊗ 〗Ⅲ ⌂ ♥ ♀ ⚲ 🏠 ♟ ♟ Mike Watts.
Location	0.5m N
Hotel	★★66% Cross Hands Hotel, OLD SODBURY ☎ (0454) 313000 24rm(3 ⇆17 ♞)

CLEVEDON   Map 03 ST47

Clevedon ☎ (0275) 874057
Situated on the cliff-top overlooking the Severn estuary
and with distant views of the Welsh coast. Excellent
parkland course in first-class condition overlooking the
Severn estuary. Magnificent scenery and some
tremendous 'drop' holes. Strong winds.
18 holes, 5998yds, Par 69, SSS 69, Course record 64.
Club membership 700.

Visitors	must contact in advance & have a handicap certificate. No play Wed morning.
Societies	Mon & Tue only. Apply in writing.
Green Fees	£22 (£35 weekends & bank holidays).
Facilities	⊗ 〗Ⅲ ⌂ ♥ ♀ ⚲ 🏠 ♟ ♟ Martin Heggie.
Leisure	snooker, carts for hire.
Location	Castle Rd, Walton St Mary (1m NE of town centre)
Hotel	★★★63% Walton Park Hotel, Wellington Ter, CLEVEDON ☎ (0275) 874253 41 ⇆ ♞

CONGRESBURY   Map 03 ST46

Mendip Spring ☎ (0934) 852322
The 18-hole Brinsea course includes lakes and numerous
water hazards covering some 12 acres of the course. The 12th
is an island green surrounded by water and there are long
drives on the 7th and 13th. The 9-hole Lakeside course is an
easy walking course, mainly par 4. Floodlit driving range.
Brinsea: 18 holes, 6335yds, Par 71, SSS 70.
Lakeside: 9 holes, 2287yds, Par 68, SSS 65.
Club membership 500.

Visitors	must contact in advance.
Societies	apply in writing.
Green Fees	not confirmed.
Facilities	⊗ 〗Ⅲ ⌂ ♥ ♀ ⚲ 🏠 ♟ ♟ Christine Holt.
Leisure	heated indoor swimming pool, gymnasium, floodlit driving range.

Location	Honeyhall Ln (8m E of Weston-Super-Mare)
Hotel	★★★★♨♨69% Daneswood House Hotel, Cuck Hill, SHIPHAM ☎ (0934) 843145 & 843945 9 ⇌ ☞Annexe3 ⇌ ☞

KEYNSHAM   Map 03 ST66

Stockwood Vale ☎ Bristol (0272) 866505
Undulating public course with interesting par 3s and good views.
9 holes, 4010yds, Par 64, SSS 61.
Club membership 250.

Visitors	no restrictions, but booking system is available. Pay as you play Public Course.
Societies	must contact in advance.
Green Fees	£9 per 18 holes, £5 per 9 holes (£11/£5.50 weekends).
Facilities	⊗ ⓑ ♥ Ⓨ ⚘ 📷 ⛳ (Kelvin Aitken.
Leisure	covered driving range.
Location	Stockwood Ln
Hotel	★★73% Chelwood House Hotel, CHELWOOD ☎ (0761) 490730 11 ⇌ ☞

LONG ASHTON   Map 03 ST57

Long Ashton ☎ (0275) 392316
A high downland course with nice turf, some wooded areas and a spacious practice area. Good drainage ensures pleasant winter golf.
18 holes, 6077yds, Par 70, SSS 70.
Club membership 800.

Visitors	must contact in advance and have a handicap certificate.
Societies	must contact the secretary in advance.
Green Fees	£22 per round; £28 per 36 holes (£30 weekends & bank holidays).
Facilities	⊗ ⓑ ♥ Ⓨ ⚘ 📷 ⛳ (Denis Scanlan.
Leisure	snooker.
Location	The Clubhouse (0.5m N on B3128)
Hotel	★★★68% Redwood Lodge Hotel & Country Club, Beggar Bush Ln, Failand, BRISTOL ☎ (0275) 393901 108 ⇌ ☞

West Bristol ☎ Bristol (0275) 393707
A new course for 1993, designed by Peter Alliss and Clive Clark. In undulating hills south of Bristol, with lakes, pools and a rising landscape to give a challenging course.
18 holes, 6288yds, Par 72.
Club membership 780.

Visitors	must contact in advance and have handicap certificate, weekends may be limited.
Societies	must contact in advance.
Green Fees	not confirmed.
Facilities	⊗ ⅏ ⓑ ♥ Ⓨ ⚘ 📷 ⛳ (
Hotel	★★★68% Redwood Lodge Hotel & Country Club, Beggar Bush Ln, Failand, BRISTOL ☎ (0275) 393901 108 ⇌ ☞

MIDSOMER NORTON   Map 03 ST65

Fosseway Country Club ☎ (0761) 412214
Very attractive parkland course, not demanding but with lovely views.
9 holes, 4278yds, Par 68, SSS 65.
Club membership 350.

Visitors	may not play on Wed evenings, Sat & Sun mornings & competitions days.
Societies	by arrangement.
Green Fees	£12 per day (£15 weekends & bank holidays).
Facilities	⊗ ⓑ ♥ Ⓨ ⚘ 📷 (all day) 🏌 ◀
Leisure	heated indoor swimming pool, squash, snooker, outdoor bowling green.
Location	Charlton Ln (SE of town centre off A367)
Hotel	★★★68% Centurion Hotel, Charlton Ln, MIDSOMER NORTON ☎ (0761) 417711 44 ⇌ ☞

SALTFORD   Map 03 ST66

Saltford ☎ (0225) 873220 & 872043
Parkland course with easy walking and panoramic views over the Avon Valley. The par 4, 2nd and 13th are notable.
18 holes, 6081yds, Par 69, SSS 69.
Club membership 800.

Visitors	must contact in advance & have handicap certificate.
Societies	must telephone in advance.
Green Fees	not confirmed.
Facilities	⊗ ⅏ ⓑ ♥ Ⓨ ⚘ 📷 ⛳ (Dudley Millinstead.
Leisure	caddy cars.
Location	Golf Club Ln (S side of village)
Hotel	★★★(red)♨♨ Hunstrete House Hotel, CHELWOOD ☎ (0761) 490490 13 ⇌ ☞Annexe11 ⇌ ☞

WESTON-SUPER-MARE   Map 03 ST36

Puxton Park ☎ (0934) 876942
A Pay and Play course built on flat moorland dissected by a network of waterways.
18 holes, 6636yds, Par 72, SSS 71.
Club membership 250.

Visitors	must contact in advance.
Societies	apply in advance.
Green Fees	not confirmed.
Facilities	ⓑ (in summer) ♥ Ⓨ ⚘ 📷 ⛳ (Colin Ancsell.
Location	Puxton Ln, Hewish (2m junc 21 of M5 on A370)
Hotel	★★★65% Commodore Hotel, Beach Rd, Sand Bay, Kewstoke, WESTON-SUPER-MARE ☎ (0934) 415778 12 ⇌ ☞Annexe6 ⇌ ☞

Weston-super-Mare ☎ (0934) 626968
A compact and interesting layout with the opening hole adjacent to the beach. The sandy, links-type course is slightly undulating and has beautifully maintained turf and greens. The 15th is a testing 455-yard, par 4.
18 holes, 6251yds, Par 70, SSS 70.
Club membership 900.

Visitors	may not play on competition days. Must contact in advance.
Societies	must contact in advance.
Green Fees	£20 (£28 weekends & bank holidays).
Facilities	⊗ ⅏ ⓑ ♥ Ⓨ ⚘ 📷 ⛳ (Paul Barrington.
Leisure	snooker.
Location	Uphill Rd North (S side of town centre off A370)
Hotel	★★64% Beachlands Hotel, 17 Uphill Rd North, WESTON-SUPER-MARE ☎ (0934) 621401 18 ⇌ ☞

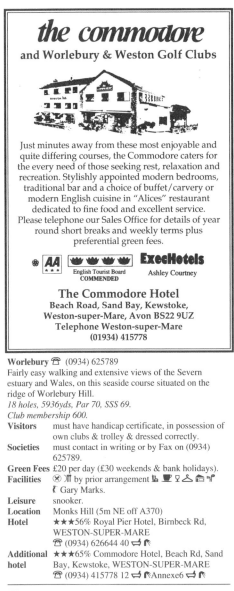

the commodore
and Worlebury & Weston Golf Clubs

Just minutes away from these most enjoyable and quite differing courses, the Commodore caters for the every need of those seeking rest, relaxation and recreation. Stylishly appointed modern bedrooms, traditional bar and a choice of buffet/carvery or modern English cuisine in "Alices" restaurant dedicated to fine food and excellent service. Please telephone our Sales Office for details of year round short breaks and weekly terms plus preferential green fees.

❀ **AA** ★★★ 🐾🐾🐾 **ExecHotels**
English Tourist Board
COMMENDED   Ashley Courtney

The Commodore Hotel
Beach Road, Sand Bay, Kewstoke,
Weston-super-Mare, Avon BS22 9UZ
Telephone Weston-super-Mare
(01934) 415778

Worlebury ☎ (0934) 625789
Fairly easy walking and extensive views of the Severn estuary and Wales, on this seaside course situated on the ridge of Worlebury Hill.
18 holes, 5936yds, Par 70, SSS 69.
Club membership 600.

Visitors	must have handicap certificate, in possession of own clubs & trolley & dressed correctly.
Societies	must contact in writing or by Fax on (0934) 625789.
Green Fees	£20 per day (£30 weekends & bank holidays).
Facilities	⊗ 🍴 by prior arrangement 🏌 💺 ♀ ⛳ 🏠 🍴 ໃ Gary Marks.
Leisure	snooker.
Location	Monks Hill (5m NE off A370)
Hotel	★★★56% Royal Pier Hotel, Birnbeck Rd, WESTON-SUPER-MARE ☎ (0934) 626644 40 ⇆ ໃ
Additional hotel	★★★65% Commodore Hotel, Beach Rd, Sand Bay, Kewstoke, WESTON-SUPER-MARE ☎ (0934) 415778 12 ⇆ ໃAnnexe6 ⇆ ໃ

WICK   Map 03 ST77

Tracy Park ☎ Bristol (0272) 372251
This course, situated on the south-western escarpment of the Cotswolds, is undulating with fine views. The clubhouse dates back to 1600 and is a building of great beauty and elegance, set in the 220 acre estate of this golf and country club. Natural water hazards affect a number of holes.
27 holes, 6850yds, Par 72, SSS 73.
Club membership 1000.

Visitors	must contact in advance.
Societies	must telephone in advance and confirm in writing.
Green Fees	£30 per day; £20 per round (£40/£30 weekends).
Facilities	⊗ 🍴 🏌 💺 ♀ ⛳ 🏠 🍴 ໃ Richard Berry.
Leisure	hard tennis courts, heated outdoor swimming pool, squash, snooker, caddy cars, croquet.
Location	Tracy Park, Bath Rd (S side of village off A420)
Hotel	★★★65% Lansdown Grove Hotel, BATH ☎ (0225) 315891 44 ⇆ ໃ

• BEDFORDSHIRE

ASPLEY GUISE   Map 04 SP93

Aspley Guise & Woburn Sands
☎ Milton Keynes (0908) 583596
A fine undulating course in expansive heathland interspersed with many attractive clumps of gorse, broom and bracken. Some well-established silver birch are a feature. The 7th, 8th and 9th are really tough holes to complete the first half.
18 holes, 6135yds, Par 71, SSS 70.
Club membership 580.

Visitors	with member only at weekends. Must have a handicap certificate
Societies	normally booked 12 mths ahead.
Green Fees	£27 per day; £22 per round.
Facilities	⊗ 🍴 by prior arrangement 🏌 💺 ♀ ⛳ 🏠 ໃ Trevor Hill.
Location	West Hill (2m W of M1 junc 13)
Hotel	★★★69% Moore Place Hotel, The Square, ASPLEY GUISE ☎ (0908) 282000 39 ⇆ Annexe15 ⇆

BEDFORD   Map 04 TL04

Bedford & County ☎ (0234) 352617
Pleasant parkland course with views over Bedford and surrounding countryside. The 15th is a testing par 4.
18 holes, 6347yds, Par 70, SSS 70.
Club membership 600.

Visitors	handicap certificate required, weekends with member only.
Societies	welcome Mon,Tue,Thu & Fri, telephone in advance.
Green Fees	not confirmed.
Facilities	⊗ 🍴 🏌 💺 ♀ ⛳ 🏠 ໃ E Bullock.
Location	Green Ln, Clapham (2m N off A6)
Hotel	★★★72% Woodlands Manor Hotel, Green Ln, Clapham, BEDFORD ☎ (0234) 363281 22 ⇆ ໃAnnexe3 ⇆ ໃ

Bedfordshire ☎ (0234) 261669

An easy walking, parkland course with tree hazards.

18 holes, 6196yds, Par 70, SSS 69, Course record 63.

Club membership 700.

Visitors   may not play at weekends except with member. Must contact in advance.

Societies   must telephone in advance/confirm in writing.

Green Fees £24 per day; £20 per round.

Facilities   ⊗ ⅲ by prior arrangement ㋒ 🍷 ♀ ⚲ 🏠 ♪ Gary Buckle.

Location   Bromham Rd, Biddenham (1m W on A428)

Hotel   ★★★72% Woodlands Manor Hotel, Green Ln, Clapham, BEDFORD ☎ (0234) 363281 22 ⇄ ♪Annexe3 ⇄ ♪

Mowsbury ☎ (0234) 771041 & 216374

Parkland municipal course in rural surroundings. Long and testing 14-bay driving range and squash facilities.

18 holes, 6514yds, Par 72, SSS 71, Course record 66.

Club membership 800.

Visitors   no restrictions.

Societies   apply in writing.

Green Fees £7.65 (£9.70 weekends & bank holidays).

Facilities   ⊗ ⅲ by prior arrangement ㋒ 🍷 ♀ ⚲ 🏠 ⅋ ♪ Malcolm Summers.

Leisure   squash, driving range.

Location   Cleat Hill, Kimbolton Rd (2m N of town centre on B660)

Hotel   ★★★72% Woodlands Manor Hotel, Green Ln, Clapham, BEDFORD ☎ (0234) 363281 22 ⇄ ♪Annexe3 ⇄ ♪

COLMWORTH   Map 04 TL15

Colmworth ☎ (0234) 378181

An easy walking course with well-bunkered greens, opened in 1991. The course is often windy and plays longer than the yardage suggests. Water comes into play on 3 holes.

18 holes, 6459yds, Par 71, SSS 71.

9 holes, 611yds, Par 27.

Club membership 270.

Visitors   advisable to contact in advance, tee reserved for members Sat & Sun until 10am & between 1-1.30pm.

Societies   welcome with prior arrangement.

Green Fees £10 per 18 holes (£15 weekends); £6 per 9 holes (£8 weekends).

Facilities   ⊗ ⅲ by prior arrangement ㋒ 🍷 ♀ ⚲ 🏠 ⅋ ♪ John MacFarlane.

Leisure   trolley hire, pool table.

Location   New Rd (7m NE of Bedford, off B660)

Hotel   ★★★67% The Barns Hotel, Cardington Rd, BEDFORD ☎ (0234) 270044 49 ⇄ ♪

DUNSTABLE   Map 04 TL02

Dunstable Downs ☎ (0582) 604472

A fine downland course set on two levels with far-reaching views and frequent sightings of graceful gliders. The 9th hole is one of the best short holes in the country. There is a modernised clubhouse.

18 holes, 6255yds, Par 70, SSS 70, Course record 64.

Club membership 600.

Visitors   weekends with member only.

Societies   telephone in advance.

Green Fees £25; winter £15.

Facilities   ⊗ ⅲ (Tue Thu & Fri) ㋒ 🍷 ♀ ⚲ 🏠 ♪ Michael Weldon.

Location   Whipsnade Rd (2m S off B4541)

Hotel   ★★★66% Old Palace Lodge Hotel, Church St, DUNSTABLE ☎ (0582) 662201 49 ⇄

LEIGHTON BUZZARD   Map 04 SP92

Leighton Buzzard ☎ (0525) 373811

Parkland course with easy walking.

18 holes, 6101yds, Par 71, SSS 70.

Club membership 595.

Visitors   may not play Tue pm. With member only weekends and bank holidays. Must contact in advance and have an introduction from own club.

Societies   apply in writing.

Green Fees not confirmed.

Facilities   ⊗ ⅲ ㋒ 🍷 ♀ ⚲ 🏠 ♪

Location   Plantation Rd (1.5m N of town centre off A4146)

Hotel   ★★★60% Swan Hotel, High St, LEIGHTON BUZZARD ☎ (0525) 372148 38 ⇄ ♪

LUTON   Map 04 TL02

South Beds ☎ (0582) 591500

27-hole downland course, slightly undulating.

Galley Course: 18 holes, 6342yds, Par 71, SSS 71, Course record 66.

Warden Course: 9 holes, 2424yds, Par 32.

Club membership 960.

Visitors   must contact in advance, restricted Tue.

Societies   apply in writing.

Green Fees not confirmed.

Facilities   ⊗ ⅲ ㋒ 🍷 ♀ ⚲ 🏠 ♪ Eddie Cogle.

Leisure   snooker.

Location   Warden Hill (3m N off A6)

Hotel   ★★★70% Strathmore Thistle Hotel, Arndale Centre, LUTON ☎ (0582) 34199 150 ⇄ ♪

Stockwood Park ☎ (0582) 413704

Municpal parkland course.

18 holes, 6049yds, Par 69, SSS 69.

Club membership 750.

Visitors   no restrictions.

Societies   Mon, Tue & Thu only.

Green Fees £7.30 per round (£9.60 weekends).

Facilities   ⊗ ⅲ (by prior arrangement summer only) ㋒ 🍷 ♀ ⚲ 🏠 ⅋ ♪ Glyn McCarthy.

Leisure   pool tables.

Location   London Rd (1m S)

Hotel   ★★★62% The Chiltern, Waller Av, Dunstable Rd, LUTON ☎ (0582) 575911 91 ⇄ ♪

MILLBROOK   Map 04 TL03

Millbrook ☎ Ampthill (0525) 840252

Long parkland course, on rolling countryside high above the Bedfordshire plains, with several water hazards. Laid out on well-drained sandy soil with many fairways lined with silver birch, pine and larch.

18 holes, 6530yds, Par 74, SSS 71.

Club membership 400. ▶

Visitors	must contact in advance unless with member.
Societies	weekdays except Thu.
Green Fees	£35 per day; £25 per round (£40 weekends).
Facilities	⊗ ⅷ (Wed, Fri & Sat or by prior arrangement) ⓗ ⲷ ♀ ⌂ 🖻ⓕ T K Devine.
Location	E side of village off A507
Hotel	★★★72% Flitwick Manor Hotel, Church Rd, FLITWICK ☎ (0525) 712242 15 ⇆ ⋔

SANDY   Map 04 TL14

John O'Gaunt ☎ Potton (0767) 260360
Two tree-lined parkland courses.
18 holes, 6214yds, Par 71, SSS 71.
Carthagena Course: 18 holes, 5590yds, Par 69, SSS 67.
Club membership 1300.

Visitors	must contact in advance and have handicap certificate.
Societies	apply in writing.
Green Fees	£40 per day/round (£50 weekends & bank holidays).
Facilities	⊗ ⅷ ⓗ ⲷ ♀ ⌂ 🖻ⓕ Peter Round.
Location	Sutton Park (3m NE of Biggleswade on B1040)
Hotel	★★64% Abbotsley Golf Hotel, Eynesbury Hardwicke, ST NEOTS ☎ (0480) 474000 15 ⇆ ⋔

SHEFFORD   Map 04 TL13

Beadlow Manor Hotel & Golf & Country Club
☎ (0525) 860800
A 27-hole golf and leisure complex. The golf courses are undulating with water hazards on numerous holes.
18 holes, 6231yds, Par 71, SSS 70.
Club membership 750.

Visitors	must have an introduction from own club.
Green Fees	not confirmed.
Facilities	♀ ⌂ 🖻ⓕ
Location	2m W on A507
Hotel	★★★72% Flitwick Manor Hotel, Church Rd, FLITWICK ☎ (0525) 712242 15 ⇆ ⋔

TILSWORTH   Map 04 SP92

Tilsworth ☎ Leighton Buzzard (0525) 210721
An undulating parkland course upgraded from 9 to 18 holes in 1992. 30-bay floodlit driving range.
18 holes, 5443yds, Par 70, SSS 66, Course record 66.
Club membership 350.

Visitors	must contact in advance but may not play Sun mornings
Societies	apply in writing.
Green Fees	£8 per 18 holes; £5 per 9 holes (£10/£6 weekends & bank holidays).
Facilities	⊗ ⅷ ⓗ ⲷ (no catering Sun) ♀ ⌂ 🖻ⓕ ⓕ Nick Webb.
Leisure	30 bay floodlite driving range.
Location	Dunstable Rd (0.5m NE off A5)
Hotel	★★★66% Old Palace Lodge Hotel, Church St, DUNSTABLE ☎ (0582) 662201 49 ⇆

WHIPSNADE   Map 04 TL01

Whipsnade Park ☎ Dagnall (044284) 2330
Parkland course situated on downs overlooking the Chilterns adjoining Whipsnade Zoo. Easy walking, good views.
18 holes, 6800yds, Par 72, SSS 72.
Club membership 500.

Visitors	with member only at weekends. Must contact in advance.
Societies	must contact in advance.
Green Fees	£31 per day; £21 per round.
Facilities	⊗ ⅷ ⓗ ⲷ ♀ ⌂ 🖻ⓕ
Location	Studham Ln, Dagnall (1m E off B4506)
Hotel	★★★66% Old Palace Lodge Hotel, Church St, DUNSTABLE ☎ (0582) 662201 49 ⇆

WOBURN   Map 04 SP93

For Woburn Golf Course see Bow Brickhill, Buckinghamshire.

WYBOSTON   Map 04 TL15

Wyboston Lakes ☎ Huntingdon (0480) 219200 & 212501
Parkland course, with narrow fairways, small greens, set around four lakes and a river.
18 holes, 5721yds, Par 69, SSS 69.
Club membership 300.

Visitors	must contact in advance at weekends.
Societies	must telephone in advance.
Green Fees	£10 per day/round (£14 weekends & bank holidays).
Facilities	⊗ ⅷ ⓗ ⲷ ♀ ⌂ 🖻 ⓕ ⤣ⓕ Paul Ashwell.
Leisure	fishing, driving range.
Location	NE side of village off A1
Hotel	★★★72% Woodlands Manor Hotel, Green Ln, Clapham, BEDFORD ☎ (0234) 363281 22 ⇆ ⋔Annexe3 ⇆ ⋔

● BERKSHIRE

ASCOT   Map 04 SU96

Berkshire ☎ (0344) 21496
Two heathland courses with splendid tree-lined fairways.
Red Course: 18 holes, 6369yds, Par 72, SSS 71.
Blue Course: 18 holes, 6260yds, Par 71, SSS 71.
Club membership 950.

Visitors	only on application to secretary.
Societies	must telephone in advance.
Green Fees	£65 per day; £50 per round.
Facilities	⊗ ⓗ ⲷ ♀ ⌂ 🖻 ⤣ⓕ P Anderson.
Leisure	caddy cars.
Location	Swinley Rd (2.5m NW of M3 jct 3 on A332)
Hotel	★★★★62% The Berystede, Bagshot Rd, Sunninghill, ASCOT ☎ (0344) 23311 91 ⇆ ⋔

Lavender Park ☎ (0344) 884074
Public parkland course. Driving range with 9-hole par 3 course, floodlit until 22.30 hrs.
9 holes, 1102yds, Par 28, SSS 29.
Club membership 50.
Visitors   no restrictions.
Societies   welcome.
Green Fees £4.50 per 18 holes; £3.25 per 9 holes (£7/£4.25 weekends & bank holidays).
Facilities   ⓑ (lunchtimes) 🍴 ♀ (ex Sun) 🏠 ⌂
              ⌂ David Johnson.
Leisure   snooker, floodlit golf driving range.
Location   Swinley Rd (3.5m SW on A332)
Hotel   ★★★★62% The Berystede, Bagshot Rd,
              Sunninghill, ASCOT ☎ (0344) 23311 91 ⇆ 🌰

Mill Ride ☎ Winkfield Row (0344) 886777
Opened for play in 1991, this 18-hole course combines good golfing country and attractive surroundings with a challenging design. The holes require as much thinking as playing.
18 holes, 6833yds, Par 72, SSS 72, Course record 68.
Visitors   must contact in advance.
Societies   apply in advance.
Green Fees £50 per day; £35 per round (£50 weekends).
Facilities   ⊗ ⌇ ⓑ 🍴 ♀ 🅰 🏠 ⌂ 🏌 ⌂
Leisure   sauna, driving range & practice facilities.
Location   Mill Ride Estate, North Ascot (1.5m NW of Ascot)
Hotel   ★★★★62% The Berystede, Bagshot Rd,
              Sunninghill, ASCOT ☎ (0344) 23311 91 ⇆ 🌰

Royal Ascot ☎ (0344) 25175
Heathland course exposed to weather.
18 holes, 5709yds, Par 68, SSS 68, Course record 65.
Club membership 600.
Visitors   must be guest of member.
Societies   Wed & Thu only, must contact in advance.
Green Fees on request.
Facilities   ⊗ ⌇ ⓑ 🍴 ♀ 🅰 🏠 ⌂ Garry Malia.
Leisure   snooker.
Location   Winkfield Rd (0.5m N on A330)
Hotel   ★★★★62% The Berystede, Bagshot Rd,
              Sunninghill, ASCOT ☎ (0344) 23311 91 ⇆ 🌰

Swinley Forest ☎ (0344) 20197
An attractive and immaculate course of heather and pine situated in the heart of Swinley Forest. The 17th is as good a short hole as will be found, with a bunkered plateau green. Course record holder is P. Alliss.
18 holes, 6001yds, Par 68, SSS 69, Course record 64.
Club membership 350.
Visitors   by invitation only.
Societies   must contact in writing.
Green Fees £50 per day (£60 weekends & bank holidays).
Facilities   ⊗ 🍴 ♀ 🅰 🏠 ⌂ 🏌 R C Parker.
Location   1.5m S, off A330
Hotel   ★★★★62% The Berystede, Bagshot Rd,
              Sunninghill, ASCOT
              ☎ (0344) 23311 91 ⇆ 🌰

BINFIELD   Map 04 SU87

Blue Mountain Golf Centre ☎ (0344) 300200
An 18-hole Pay and Play course.
18 holes, 6097yds, Par 70, SSS 70.
Club membership 950.
Visitors   no restrictions.
Societies   must contact in advance.
Green Fees £14 (£18 weekends).
Facilities   ⊗ ⌇ ⓑ 🍴 ♀ 🅰 🏠 ⌂ 🏌 Neil Dainton.
Leisure   covered driving range.
Location   Wood Ln (5m SE of Reading, on B3048)
Hotel   ★★★66% Reading Moat House, Mill Ln,
              Sindlesham, WOKINGHAM
              ☎ (0734) 351035 96 ⇆

CHADDLEWORTH   Map 04 SU47

West Berkshire ☎ (0488) 638574
Challenging and interesting downland course with testing 635 yds (par 5) 5th hole.
18 holes, 7069yds, Par 73, SSS 74.
Club membership 650.
Visitors   must contact in advance but are restricted weekends.
Societies   by arrangement.
Green Fees not confirmed.
Facilities   ⊗ ⓑ 🍴 ♀ 🅰 🏠 ⌂ 🏌 Wraith Grant.
Leisure   caddy cars available.
Location   1m S of village off A338
Hotel   ★★★61% The Chequers, Oxford St,
              NEWBURY
              ☎ (0635) 38000 45 ⇆ Annexe11 ⇆

COOKHAM   Map 04 SU88

Winter Hill ☎ Bourne End (0628) 527613
Parkland course set in a curve of the Thames with wonderful views across the river to Cliveden.
18 holes, 6408yds, Par 72, SSS 71, Course record 69.
Club membership 800.
Visitors   not permitted weekends. Must contact in advance.
Societies   must apply in writing.
Green Fees £24 per day (Mon-Fri).
Facilities   ⊗ 🍴 by prior arrangement ⓑ 🍴 ♀ 🅰 🏠
              ⌂ David Hart.
Leisure   trolleys.
Location   Grange Ln (1m NW off B4447)
Hotel   ★★★★70% The Compleat Angler, Marlow
              Bridge, MARLOW ☎ (0628) 484444 62 ⇆ 🌰

CROWTHORNE   Map 04 SU86

East Berkshire ☎ (0344) 772041
An attractive heathland course with an abundance of heather and pine trees. Walking is easy and the greens are exceptionally good. Some fairways become tight where the heather encroaches on the line of play. The course is testing and demands great accuracy.
18 holes, 6345yds, Par 69, SSS 70, Course record 64.
Club membership 700.
▶

Visitors	must contact in advance and have a handicap certificate; must play with member at weekends & bank holidays.
Societies	Thu & Fri only; must contact in advance.
Green Fees	£33 per day.
Facilities	⊗ ⅃ ☕ ♀ ⚲ 🏠 ℓ Arthur Roe.
Location	Ravenswood Ave (W side of town centre off B3348)
Hotel	★★★★(red)♨ Pennyhill Park Hotel, London Rd, BAGSHOT ☎ (0276) 471774 22 ⇥ ⚑Annexe54 ⇥ ⚑

DATCHET · Map 04 SU97

Datchet ☎ (0753) 543887 & 541872
Meadowland course, easy walking.
9 holes, 5978yds, Par 70, SSS 69, Course record 63.
Club membership 405.

Visitors	may play weekdays before 3pm.
Societies	Tue only.
Green Fees	£24 per day; £16 per round.
Facilities	⊗ ⅃ ☕ ♀ ⚲ 🏠 ℓ Bill Mainwaring.
Leisure	trolleys.
Location	Buccleuch Rd (NW side of Datchet off B470)
Hotel	★★59% The Manor Hotel, The Village Green, DATCHET ☎ (0753) 543442 30 ⇥ ⚑

HURLEY · Map 04 SU88

Temple ☎ Maidenhead (0628) 824248
An open parkland course with many excellent, fast greens relying on natural slopes rather than heavy bunkering. On one 'blind' punchbowl hole there is actually a bunker on the green. Good drainage assures play when many other courses are closed.
18 holes, 6206yds, Par 70, SSS 70.
Club membership 650.

Visitors	must contact in advance.
Societies	must book one year in advance.
Green Fees	£40 per day (£45 weekends).
Facilities	⊗ ⅃ ☕ ♀ ⚲ 🏠 ┅ ℓ Alan Dobbins.
Leisure	squash, putting green & practice ground.
Location	Henley Rd (1m SE on A4130)
Hotel	★★★★70% The Compleat Angler, Marlow Bridge, MARLOW ☎ (0628) 484444 62 ⇥ ⚑

MAIDENHEAD · Map 04 SU88

Maidenhead ☎ (0628) 24693
A pleasant parkland course on level ground with easy walking to good greens. Perhaps a little short but there are many natural features and some first-rate short holes.
18 holes, 6364yds, Par 70, SSS 70.
Club membership 650.

Visitors	may not play after noon on Fri or at weekends. Must contact in advance and have a handicap certificate.
Societies	must contact in writing.
Green Fees	not confirmed.
Facilities	⅃ ☕ ♀ ⚲ 🏠 ┅ ℓ

Location	Shoppenhangers Rd (S side of town centre off A308)
Hotel	★★★★74% Fredrick's Hotel, Shoppenhangers Rd, MAIDENHEAD ☎ (0628) 35934 37 ⇥ ⚑

NEWBURY · Map 04 SU46

Donnington Valley ☎ (0635) 551199
Undulating, short, but testing course with mature trees and elevated greens, some protected by water.
18 holes, 4029yds, Par 61, SSS 62.
Club membership 520.

Visitors	must book in advance.
Societies	booking required in advance.
Green Fees	£20 per day; £12 per round (£25/£15 weekends).
Facilities	⊗ ⅃ ⅃ ☕ ♀ ⚲ 🏠 ┅ ⋈ ℓ Nick Mitchell.
Leisure	fishing, clay pigeon shooting.
Location	Old Oxford Rd, Donnington (2m N of Newbury)
Hotel	★★★★63% Donnington Valley Hotel & Golf Course, Old Oxford Rd, Donnington, NEWBURY ☎ (0635) 551199 58 ⇥ ⚑

Newbury & Crookham ☎ (0635) 40035
A well-laid out, attractive course running mostly through woodland, and giving more of a challenge than its length suggests.
18 holes, 5880yds, Par 68, SSS 68.
Club membership 800.

Visitors	must play with member on weekends & bank holidays. Handicap certificate required.
Societies	must contact in advance.
Green Fees	£27.50 per day/round.
Facilities	⊗ ⅃ ⅃ ☕ ♀ ⚲ 🏠 ℓ David Harris.
Location	Bury's Bank Rd, Greenham (2m SE off A34)
Hotel	★★★61% The Chequers, Oxford St, NEWBURY ☎ (0635) 38000 45 ⇥Annexe11 ⇥

READING · Map 04 SU77

Calcot Park ☎ (0734) 427124
A delightfully sporting parkland course just outside the town. Hazards include a lake and many trees. The 6th is the longest, 497 yard par 5, with the tee-shot hit downhill over cross-bunkers to a well-guarded green. The 13th (188 yards) requires a big carry over a gully to a plateau green.
18 holes, 6283yds, Par 70, SSS 70.
Club membership 735.

Visitors	must have handicap certificate, but may not play weekends & bank holidays.
Societies	must apply in writing.
Green Fees	£30 per day/round; £20 after 4pm.
Facilities	⊗ ⅃ ⅃ ☕ ♀ ⚲ 🏠 ┅ ℓ Albert MacKenzie.
Location	Bath Rd, Calcot (2.5m W on A4)
Hotel	★★★55% The Copper Inn, Church Rd, PANGBOURNE ☎ (0734) 842244 22 ⇥ ⚑

$\mathcal{S}$UNNINGDALE

SUNNINGDALE ☎ ASCOT (0344) 21681   Map 04 SU96

John Ingham writes: Many famous golfers maintain that Sunningdale, on the borders of Berkshire, is the most attractive inland course in Britain. The great Bobby Jones once played the 'perfect' round of 66 made up of threes and fours on the Old Course. Later, Norman von Nida of Australia shot a 63 while the then professional at the club, Arthur Lees, scored a 62 to win a huge wager.

To become a member of this club takes years of waiting. Maybe it is the quality of the courses, maybe the clubhouse atmosphere and perhaps the excellence of the professionals shop has something to do with it; but added up, it has to be the most desirable place to spend a day.

Founded just over ninety years ago, the Old Course was designed by Willie Park, while H.S. Colt created the New Course in 1923. Most golfers will agree that there isn't one indifferent hole on either course. While the Old Course, with silver birch, heather and perfect turf, is lovely to behold, the New Course alongside is considered by many to be its equal. But just as golfers want to play the Old Course at St Andrews, and miss the redesigned Jubilee, so visitors to Sunningdale opt for the Old, and fail to realise what they are overlooking by not playing the New.

The classic Old Course is not long, measuring just 6341 yards, and because the greens are normally in excellent condition, anyone with a 'hot' putter can have an exciting day, providing they keep teeshots on the fairway and don't stray into the gorse and the pine trees that lie in wait. On a sunny day, if you had to be anywhere in the world playing well, then we opt for the elevated 10th tee on the Old. What bliss!

Membership 850

Visitors May not play Fri, Sat, Sun or public holidays. Must contact in advance and have a handicap certificate

Societies one year's notice required

Green fees £84 per day

Facilities ⊗ ⊾ ☕ ♀ ♨ 🏠 ⚷ (Keith Maxwell)

Location Ridgemount Rd (1m S of Sunningdale, off A30)

36 holes. Old Course: 18 holes, 6586yds, Par 72, SSS 70, Course record 62 (Nick Faldo)
New Course: 18 holes 6676yds, Par 70, SSS 72, Course record 64 (Gary Player)

WHERE TO STAY AND EAT NEARBY

HOTELS:

ASCOT
★★★★ 62% The Berystede, Bagshot Rd, Sunninghill. ☎ (0344) 23311. 91 European cuisine

★★ 71% Highclere, 19 Kings Rd, Sunninghill. ☎ (0344) 25220. 12 European cuisine

BAGSHOT
★★★★(red)❀❀❀ ♨♨ 80% Pennyhill Park, London Rd. ☎ (0276) 471774 22 Annexe 54 ⇆ 🐾. English & French cuisine

RESTAURANTS:

BRAY
✗✗✗✗❀❀❀❀ The Waterside, River Cottage, Ferry Road. ☎ Maidenhead (0628) 20691. French cuisine

EGHAM
✗✗❀❀ La Bonne Franquette, 5 High St ☎ (0784) 439494. French cuisine

Mapledurham ☎ (0734) 463353
18-hole course designed by Bob Sandow. Flanked by
hedgerows and mature woods, it is testing for players of all
levels.
18 holes, 5621yds, Par 69, SSS 67.
Club membership 600.

Visitors	no restrictions.
Societies	must contact in advance.
Green Fees	not confirmed.
Facilities	⊗ ⅷ ⅃ �L ♥ ♀ ⅍ 🖻 ⛳ 𝄞 Douglas Burton.
Location	Chazey Heath, Mapledurham (on A4074 to Oxford)
Hotel	★★★★61% Holiday Inn, Caversham Bridge, Richfield Av, READING ☎ (0734) 391818 112 ⇌ 🖛

Reading ☎ (0734) 472909
Tree-lined Parkland course, part hilly and part flat.
18 holes, 6212yds, Par 70, SSS 70.
Club membership 700.

Visitors	must have handicap certificate. With member only Fri & weekends.
Societies	advisable to book one year in advance.
Green Fees	£27 per day/round.
Facilities	⊗ & ⅷ (ex Mon) �L ♥ ♀ ⅍ 🖻 𝄞 Andrew Wild.
Location	17 Kidmore End Rd, Emmer Green (2m N off B481)
Hotel	★★★★60% Ramada Hotel, Oxford Rd, READING ☎ (0734) 586222 196 ⇌ 🖛

SINDLESHAM   Map 04 SU76

Bearwood ☎ Arborfield Cross (0734) 760060
Flat parkland course with one water hazard - over part of a
lake. Also 9-hole pitch and putt.
9 holes, 2802yds, Par 35, Course record 69.
Club membership 570.

Visitors	must have handicap certificate. With member only on weekends & bank holidays.
Green Fees	£8 per 9 holes; £15 per 18 holes.
Facilities	⊗ ⅷ �L ♥ (catering 10.30-dusk) ♀ ⅍ 🖻 𝄞 Mark Griffiths.
Leisure	riding, 9 hole pitch & putt course.
Location	Mole Rd (1m SW on B3030)
Hotel	★★★66% Reading Moat House, Mill Ln, Sindlesham, WOKINGHAM ☎ (0734) 351035 96 ⇌

SONNING   Map 04 SU77

Sonning ☎ (0734) 693332
A quality parkland course and the scene of many county
championships. Wide fairways, not overbunkered, and
very good greens. Holes of changing character through
wooded belts.
18 holes, 6366yds, Par 70, SSS 70, Course record 65.

Visitors	weekdays only. Handicap certificate required.
Societies	must apply in writing.
Green Fees	not confirmed.
Facilities	⊗ & ⅷ by prior arrangement �L ♥ ♀ ⅍ 🖻 𝄞 R McDougall.

Location	Duffield Rd (1m S off A4)
Hotel	★★★★60% Ramada Hotel, Oxford Rd, READING ☎ (0734) 586222 196 ⇌ 🖛

STREATLEY   Map 04 SU58

Goring & Streatley ☎ Goring (0491) 873229
A parkland/moorland course that requires 'negotiating'.
Four well-known first holes lead up to the heights of the
5th tee, to which there is a 300ft climb. Wide fairways,
not overbunkered, with nice rewards on the way home
down the last few holes.
18 holes, 6308yds, Par 71, SSS 70, Course record 65.
Club membership 750.

Visitors	with member only at weekends.
Societies	must telephone in advance.
Green Fees	£28 per day; £19 after 4pm.
Facilities	⊗ ⅷ �L ♥ ♀ ⅍ 🖻 ⛳ 𝄞
Location	N of village off A417
Hotel	★★★★66% Swan Diplomat Hotel, High St, STREATLEY ☎ (0491) 873737 46 ⇌ 🖛

SUNNINGDALE   Map 04 SU96

SUNNINGDALE See page 17

Sunningdale Ladies ☎ Ascot (0344) 20507
A short 18-hole course with a typical Surrey heathland
layout. Avery tight course, making for a challenging game.
18 holes, 3616yds, Par 60, SSS 60.
Club membership 350.

Visitors	telephone in advance.
Societies	Ladies societies only.
Green fees	£17/£22 (£19/£27 weekends & bank holidays).
Facilities	⊗ & �L (ex Sun) ♥ ♀ ⅍
Location	Cross Rd (1m S off A30)
Hotel	★★★★62% The Berystede, Bagshot Rd, Sunninghill, Ascot ☎ (0344) 23311 91 ⇌ 🖛

WOKINGHAM   Map 04 SU86

Downshire ☎ Bracknell (0344) 422708 & 302030
Municipal parkland course with many water hazards, easy
walking. Testing holes: 7th (par 4), 15th (par 4), 16th (par 3).
18 holes, 6382yds, Par 73, SSS 70.
Club membership 600.

Visitors	must contact in advance.
Societies	must telephone in advance.
Green Fees	not confirmed.
Facilities	⊗ ⅷ �L ♥ ♀ ⅍ 🖻 ⛳ 𝄞 Paul Watson.
Leisure	buggies, driving range.
Location	Easthampstead Park (3m SW of Bracknell)
Hotel	★★★★71% Coppid Beech, John Nike Way, BRACKNELL ☎ (0344) 303333 205 ⇌ 🖛

Sand Martins ☎ (0734) 792711
Two different 9-hole loops: the front nine is mostly tree-lined
with ponds and the back nine is similar to a links course.
18 holes, 6235yards, Par 70.
Club membership 850.

Visitors	no restrictions.
Societies	must apply in writing.
Green Fees	£40 per 36 holes; £25 per 18 holes.

Facilities ⊗ ⅢⅢ ⓑ ☖ ♀ ⚇ ⌂ ⑂ Willie Milne.
Leisure caddy cars.
Location Finchampstead Rd
Hotel ★★★66% Reading Moat House, Mill Ln,
Sindlesham, WOKINGHAM
☎ (0734) 351035 96 ⇆

BUCKINGHAMSHIRE

AYLESBURY   Map 04 SP81

Ellesborough ☎ Wendover (0296) 622114
Once part of the property of Chequers, and under the
shadow of the famous monument at the Wendover end of
the Chilterns. A downland course, it is rather hilly with
most holes enhanced by far-ranging views over the
Aylesbury countryside.
18 holes, 6276yds, Par 71, SSS 71, Course record 64.
Club membership 780.
Visitors must have a handicap certificate, but may
not play Tue mornings. With member only
at weekends. Must contact in advance.
Societies Wed & Thu only.
Green Fees £30 per day; £20 per round. Weekends &
holidays with member only.
Facilities ⊗ ⅢⅢ (12-2.30 & by arrangement 7-9pm) ⓑ
☖ ♀ ⚇ ⌂ ⑂ Paul Warner.
Leisure putting green, practice ground & net.
Location Butlers Cross (1m E of Ellesborough on
B4010)
Hotel ★★★74% Bell Inn, ASTON CLINTON
☎ (0296) 630252 6 ⇆ ⒭Annexe15 ⇆ ⒭
See advertisement on page 20

BEACONSFIELD   Map 04 SU99

Beaconsfield ☎ (0494) 676545
An interesting and, at times, testing tree-lined and
parkland course which frequently plays longer than
appears on the card! Each hole differs to a considerable
degree and here lies the charm. Walking is easy, except
perhaps to the 6th and 8th. Well bunkered.
18 holes, 6487yds, Par 72, SSS 71.
Club membership 862.
Visitors must contact in advance and have a
handicap certificate. Must play with member
at weekends and bank holidays
Societies must contact in writing
Green Fees £42 per day; £34 per round.
Facilities ⊗ ⅢⅢ by prior arrangement ⓑ ☖ ♀ ⚇ ⌂
⑂ ⑂ Michael Brothers.
Location Seer Green (2m E,S of Seer Green)
Hotel ★★★58% Bellhouse Hotel, Oxford Rd,
BEACONSFIELD
☎ (0753) 887211 136 ⇆ ⒭

BLETCHLEY   Map 04 SP83

Windmill Hill ☎ Milton Keynes (0908) 378623
Long, open-parkland course designed by Henry Cotton and
opened in 1972. Municipal.
18 holes, 6773yds, Par 73, SSS 72.
Club membership 430.
Visitors no restrictions.
Societies bookings for tee times: contact Sandie Hayward.
Green Fees £6.10 (£9 weekends).
Facilities ⊗ ⓑ ☖ ♀ ⚇ ⌂ ⑂ ⑂ Colin Clingan.
Leisure floodlit driving range, pool table.
Location Tattenhoe Ln (W side of town centre on A421)
Hotel ★★★60% Swan Hotel, High St, LEIGHTON
BUZZARD ☎ (0525) 372148 38 ⇆ ⒭

BOW BRICKHILL   Map 04 SP93

WOBURN See page 21

BUCKINGHAM   Map 04 SP63

Buckingham ☎ (0280) 815566
Undulating parkland course cut by a stream.
18 holes, 6082yds, Par 70, SSS 69, Course record 67.
Club membership 680.
Visitors with member only at weekends. Must contact in
advance.
Societies must book in advance
Green Fees £28 (weekdays).
Facilities ⊗ ⅢⅢ & ⓑ (ex Mon) ☖ ♀ ⚇ ⌂ ⑂ Tom Gates.
Leisure snooker.
Location Tingewick Rd (1.5m W on A421)
Hotel ★★★66% Buckingham Lodge Hotel, Ring Rd
South, BUCKINGHAM
☎ (0280) 822622 70 ⇆ ⒭

BURNHAM   Map 04 SU98

Burnham Beeches ☎ (0628) 661448
In the centre of the lovely Burnham Beeches countryside.
Wide fairways, carefully maintained greens, some hills,
and some devious routes to a few holes. A good finish.
18 holes, 6449yds, Par 70, SSS 71.
Club membership 670.
Visitors must contact in advance. May play on
weekdays only and must have a handicap
certificate or introduction from own club.
Societies welcome
Green Fees not confirmed.
Facilities ⚇ ⌂ ⑂ ⑂
Location Green Ln (0.5m NE)
Hotel ★★★64% Burnham Beeches Moat House,
Grove Rd, BURNHAM
☎ (0628) 603333 75 ⇆

Lambourne ☎ Maidenhead (0628) 662936 & 666755
A championship standard 18-hole course.
18 holes, 6765yds, Par 72, SSS 72.
Club membership 600.
Visitors must contact in advance, with introduction from
own club. With member only at weekends. ▶

The Bell Inn
Woburn

⊛
★ ★
69%

21 Bedford Street, Woburn, Beds MK17 9QD
Telephone: 01525 290280 Fax: 01525 290017

This friendly family owned Inn is a mixture of
Tudor, Georgian and Victorian architecture. The
beamed Elizabethan restaurant serves excellent
food and wine or try real ale and bar food with
the locals in our pub. Bedrooms are individual
with tasteful fabrics and furnishings. Woburn
Abbey with its beautiful park is close by, as is
Woburn Golf Club, home to the Dunhill Masters.

Best Western Hotel   *Egon Ronay listed*

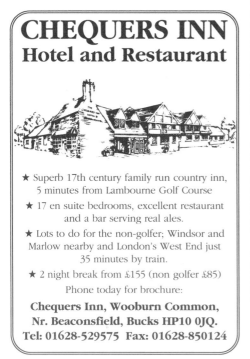

CHEQUERS INN
Hotel and Restaurant

★ Superb 17th century family run country inn,
5 minutes from Lambourne Golf Course

★ 17 en suite bedrooms, excellent restaurant
and a bar serving real ales.

★ Lots to do for the non-golfer; Windsor and
Marlow nearby and London's West End just
35 minutes by train.

★ 2 night break from £155 (non golfer £85)

Phone today for brochure:

Chequers Inn, Wooburn Common,
Nr. Beaconsfield, Bucks HP10 0JQ.
Tel: 01628-529575 Fax: 01628-850124

Green Fees not confirmed.
Facilities ⊗ ⅲ ᴸ ♨ ♀ ↀ 🏠 ⚐ 🏌 ⏄ R A Newman.
Leisure sauna, hairdressing salon, massage room.
Location Dropmore Rd
Hotel ★★★64% Burnham Beeches Moat House,
Grove Rd, BURNHAM
☎ (0628) 603333 75 ⇆
Additional ★★67% Chequers Inn, Kiln Ln, WOOBURN
hotel COMMON ☎ (0628) 529575 17 ⇆ 🏠

CHALFONT ST GILES   Map 04 SU99

Harewood Downs ☎ Little Chalfont (0494) 762308 &
764102
A testing undulating parkland course with sloping greens and
plenty of trees.
18 holes, 5958yds, Par 69, SSS 69, Course record 64.
Club membership 750.
Visitors must contact in advance & have handicap
certificate.
Societies apply by phone then confirm in writing.
Green Fees £27 per day; £20 per round (£30 weekends &
bank holidays).
Facilities ⊗ ⅲ by prior arrangement ᴸ ♨ ♀ ↀ 🏠
⏄ G C Morris.
Location Cokes Ln (2m N off A413)
Hotel ★★★★58% Bellhouse Hotel, Oxford Rd,
BEACONSFIELD ☎ (0753) 887211 136 ⇆ 🏠

CHARTRIDGE   Map 04 SP90

Chartridge Park ☎ High Wycombe (0494) 791772
Parkland course set in idyllic surroundings. Currently the
UK's longest 9-hole course.
18 holes, 5516yds, Par 68, SSS 69, Course record 66.
Club membership 600.
Visitors no restrictions.
Societies must telephone in advance.
Green Fees £25 per day.
Facilities ⊗ ⅲ ᴸ ♨ ♀ ↀ 🏠 ⚐ 🏌 ⏄ Peter Gibbins.
Leisure petrol golf buggies available.
Location 3m NW of Chesham
Hotel ★★★62% The Crown Hotel, High St,
AMERSHAM
☎ (0494) 721541 19 ⇆ 🏠Annexe4 ⇆ 🏠

CHESHAM   Map 04 SP90

Chesham & Ley Hill ☎ (0494) 784541
Heathland course on hilltop with easy walking. Subject to
wind.
9 holes, 5296yds, Par 67, SSS 66, Course record 64.
Club membership 430.
Visitors may play Mon & Thu, Wed after noon, Fri
before 1.30pm.
Societies subject to approval, Thu only.
Green Fees not confirmed.
Facilities ⊗ & ⅲ by prior arrangement ᴸ ♨ ♀ ↀ
Location Ley Hill Common (2m E)
Hotel ★★★62% The Crown Hotel, High St,
AMERSHAM
☎ (0494) 721541 19 ⇆ 🏠Annexe4 ⇆ 🏠

WOBURN

BOW BRICKHILL ☎ (0908) 370756   Map O4 SP93

John Ingham writes: Come off the M1 motorway at Junction 13 and you are quickly at Woburn, with its magnificent stately home, wildlife safari park and surrounding echoes of Henry VIII and the Dukes of Bedford. Within the last 20 years two new attractions have been added - two golf courses designed by the famed Charles Lawrie of Cotton Pennink.

To create these beautiful courses, the bulldozers got among pine and chestnut and literally cut fairways through some of the most picturesque country in all England - but it had been country seen by very few. From the very back tees, both courses are somewhat long for the weekend amateur. The Duke's measures 6940 yards and makes for a stiff test for any class of golfer, while the 'easier' Duchess, measuring a very respectable 6616 yards, requires a high degree of skill on its fairways guarded by towering pines.

Today, under the direction of Alex Hay, a Scottish TV golf commentator, the two courses are best known as the home of the British Masters, a golf tournament sponsored by Dunhill, who also sponsor the club.

The town of Woburn and the Abbey are both within Bedfordshire, while the golf and country club actually lie over the border in Buckinghamshire. Although just 45 miles from London, you will feel very much in the wilds and the local pubs and people, plus some wonderful countryside, make this area an excellent place to stay for a few days.

And, if you can hit the ball straight, you might get near the course record of 64 achieved by professional Peter Mitchell and Andrew Murray!

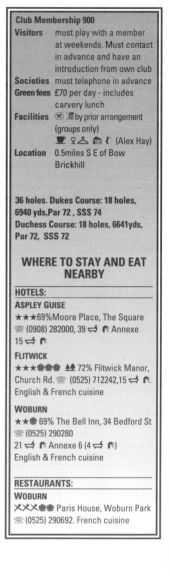

Club Membership 900

Visitors	must play with a member at weekends. Must contact in advance and have an introduction from own club
Societies	must telephone in advance
Green fees	£70 per day - includes carvery lunch
Facilities	⊗ ⌇ by prior arrangement (groups only) 🍺 ♀ 👥 🏌 ✆ (Alex Hay)
Location	0.5miles S E of Bow Brickhill

36 holes. Dukes Course: 18 holes, 6940 yds, Par 72 , SSS 74
Duchess Course: 18 holes, 6641yds, Par 72, SSS 72

WHERE TO STAY AND EAT NEARBY

HOTELS:

ASPLEY GUISE
★★★69%Moore Place, The Square
☎ (0908) 282000, 39 ⇋ 🛏 Annexe 15 ⇋ 🛏

FLITWICK
★★★❀❀❀ ♨♨ 72% Flitwick Manor, Church Rd. ☎ (0525) 712242,15 ⇋ 🛏. English & French cuisine

WOBURN
★★❀ 69% The Bell Inn, 34 Bedford St
☎ (0525) 290280
21 ⇋ 🛏 Annexe 6 (4 ⇋ 🛏)
English & French cuisine

RESTAURANTS:

WOBURN
✗✗✗❀❀ Paris House, Woburn Park
☎ (0525) 290692. French cuisine

DENHAM

Map 04 TQ08

Buckinghamshire ☎ Uxbridge (0895) 835777
A John Jacobs designed championship-standard course.
Visitors only welcome as guests of members to this beautiful
course in 269 acres of lovely grounds including mature trees,
lakes and rivers.
18 holes, 6880yds, Par 72, SSS 73.
Club membership 324.

Visitors	with member only or introduced by member.
Societies	must contact in advance.
Green Fees	not confirmed.
Facilities	⊗ ⅏ ⅃ ⬤ ♀ ♨ 🏠 🕴 ℓ John O'Leary.
Leisure	fishing.
Location	Denham Court
Hotel	★★★★58% Bellhouse Hotel, Oxford Rd, BEACONSFIELD ☎ (0753) 887211 136 ⇥ 📷

Denham ☎ Uxbridge (0895) 832022
A beautifully maintained parkland/heathland course,
home of many county champions. Slightly hilly and
calling for good judgement of distance in the wooded
areas.
18 holes, 6440yds, Par 70, SSS 71, Course record 66.
Club membership 550.

Visitors	must contact in advance & have handicap certificate. Must play with member Fri-Sun.
Societies	must book in advance.
Green Fees	£48 per day; £32 per round. Mon-Thu only.
Facilities	⊗ (Sun & Tue-Fri) ⬤ ⅃ ♀ ♨ 🏠 🕴 ℓ John Sheridan.
Location	Tilehouse Ln (2m NW)
Hotel	★★★★58% Bellhouse Hotel, Oxford Rd, BEACONSFIELD ☎ (0753) 887211 136 ⇥ 📷

FLACKWELL HEATH

Map 04 SU89

Flackwell Heath ☎ Bourne End (0628) 520027
Open heath and tree-lined course on hills overlooking
Loudwater and the M40. Quick drying.
18 holes, 6207yds, Par 71, SSS 70, Course record 63.
Club membership 800.

Visitors	with member only at weekends. A handicap certificate is usually required.
Societies	Wed & Thu only. Must contact in writing.
Green Fees	£27 per day.
Facilities	⊗ ⬤ ⅃ ♀ ♨ 🏠 ℓ Stephen Bryan.
Location	Treadaway Rd, High Wycombe (NE side of town centre)
Hotel	★★★★58% Bellhouse Hotel, Oxford Rd, BEACONSFIELD ☎ (0753) 887211 136 ⇥ 📷

GERRARDS CROSS

Map 04 TQ08

Gerrards Cross ☎ (0753) 883263
A wooded parkland course which has been modernised in
recent years and is now a very pleasant circuit with
infinite variety. The best part lies on the plateau above
the clubhouse where there are some testing holes.
18 holes, 6295yds, Par 69, SSS 70.
Club membership 820.

Visitors	must contact in advance & have a letter of introduction from their club or a handicap certificate.
Societies	must book one year ahead.
Green Fees	£36 per day; £29 per round.
Facilities	⊗ ⅏ by prior arrangement ⬤ ⅃ ♀ ♨ 🏠 ℓ Matthew Barr.
Location	Chalfont Park (NE side of town centre off A413)
Hotel	★★★★58% Bellhouse Hotel, Oxford Rd, BEACONSFIELD ☎ (0753) 887211 136 ⇥ 📷

HALTON

Map 04 SP81

Chiltern Forest ☎ Aylesbury (0296) 630899 & 631817
Extended to 18 holes in 1992, this very hilly wooded
parkland course is on two levels. The surrounding woodland
makes the course very scenic.
18 holes, 5765yds, Par 70, SSS 70.
Club membership 670.

Visitors	must play with member at weekends.
Societies	must contact in advance.
Green Fees	£22 per day.
Facilities	⊗ ⅏ ⬤ ⅃ ♀ (Mon-Fri) ♨ 🏠 ℓ C Skeet.
Location	Aston Hill (1m NE off A4011)
Hotel	★★ Rose & Crown Hotel, High St, TRING ☎ (0442) 824071 27 ⇥ 📷

HIGH WYCOMBE

Map 04 SU89

Hazlemere Golf & Country Club ☎ (0494) 714722
Undulating parkland. Two long par 5s.
18 holes, 5873yds, Par 70, SSS 68, Course record 64.
Club membership 700.

Visitors	weekdays all day. Weekends in the afternoon by prior arrangement through Pro. shop telephone (0494) 718298.
Societies	apply in advance.
Green Fees	£35 per day; £26 per round (£40 per round subject to availability at weekends).
Facilities	⊗ ⅏ ⬤ ⅃ ♀ ♨ 🏠 🕴 ℓ Steve Morvell.
Leisure	buggies, powered & pull trolleys.
Location	Penn Rd, Hazlemere (2m NE, A404 towards Amersham)
Hotel	★★★62% The Crown Hotel, High St, AMERSHAM ☎ (0494) 721541 19 ⇥ 📷 Annexe4 ⇥ 📷

IVER

Map 04 TQ08

Iver ☎ (0753) 655615
Pay and play parkland course; fairly flat.
9 holes, 2994yds, Par 72, SSS 70.
Club membership 500.

Visitors	no restrictions.
Societies	must contact in advance.
Green Fees	not confirmed.
Facilities	⊗ ⬤ ⅃ ♀ ♨ 🏠 🕴 ℓ Gerry Isles.
Leisure	practice range.
Location	Hollow Hill Ln, Langley Park Rd (1.5m SW off B470)
Hotel	B Marriott Hotel, Ditton Road, Langley, SLOUGH ☎ (0753) 544244 350 ⇥ 📷

IVINGHOE   Map 04 SP91

Ivinghoe ☎ Cheddington (0296) 668696
Testing parkland course with water on three holes. Easy walking on rolling countryside.
9 holes, 4508yds, Par 62, SSS 62, Course record 59.
Club membership 250.
Visitors   may only play after 8am.
Societies   must contact in advance.
Green Fees   £7 per round (£8 weekends).
Facilities   ⊗ 🄱 💺 ♀ 👤 🄰 ⫙ 🥂 Bill Garrad.
Leisure   caddy car for hire.
Location   Wellcroft (N side of village)
Hotel   ★★★74% Bell Inn, ASTON CLINTON
                 ☎ (0296) 630252 6 ⇄ 🐾Annexe15 ⇄ 🐾

LITTLE CHALFONT   Map 04 SU99

Little Chalfont ☎ (0494) 764877
Gently undulating flat course surrounded by woods.
9 holes, 5852yds, Par 68, SSS 68.
Club membership 300.
Visitors   no restrictions.
Societies   must contact in advance.
Green Fees   not confirmed.
Facilities   ⊗ ⫙ 🄱 💺 ♀ 👤 🄰 ⫙ 🥂
Leisure   practice area.
Location   Lodge Ln (Between Little Chalfont & Chorleywood)
Hotel   ★★★62% The Crown Hotel, High St, AMERSHAM
                 ☎ (0494) 721541 19 ⇄ 🐾Annexe4 ⇄ 🐾

LOUDWATER   Map 04 SU89

Wycombe Heights Golf Centre ☎ Penn (049481) 2862
Opened in 1991 and designed by the John Jacobs Partnership. The golf centre includes a 24-bay driving range.
18 holes, 6200yds, Par 70, SSS 72.
Club membership 1000.
Visitors   no restrictions.
Societies   apply in writing.
Green Fees   not confirmed.
Facilities   ⊗ ⫙ 🄱 💺 ♀ 👤 🄰 ⫙ 🥂 Wayne Owers.
Leisure   driving range.
Location   Rayners Ave
Hotel   B Forte Posthouse, Handy Cross, HIGH WYCOMBE ☎ (0494) 442100 106 ⇄ 🐾

MENTMORE   Map 04 SP91

Mentmore Golf & Country Club ☎ Aylesbury (0296) 662020
Two 18-hole courses in the wooded parkland of Mentmore House. Long par 5 at the 9th on the Rosebery Course.
Rosebery: 18 holes, 6777yds, Par 72, SSS 72.
Rothschild: 18 holes, 6763yds, Par 72, SSS 72.
Club membership 880.
Visitors   must have handicap certificate & contact in advance, weekends subject to competitions.
Societies   by prior arrangement.
Green Fees   £40 per day; £30 per round.
Facilities   ⊗ ⫙ 🄱 💺 ♀ 👤 🄰 ⫙ 🥂 Pip Elson.

Leisure   heated indoor swimming pool, sauna, steam room, jacuzzi.
Location   4m S of Leighton Buzzard
Hotel   ★★★60% Swan Hotel, High St, LEIGHTON BUZZARD ☎ (0525) 372148 38 ⇄ 🐾

MILTON KEYNES   Map 04 SP83

Abbey Hill ☎ (0908) 563845
Undulating municipal course within the new city. Tight fairways and well-placed bunkers. Stream comes into play on five holes. Also Par 3 course.
18 holes, 6177yds, Par 68, SSS 69.
Club membership 600.
Visitors   no restrictions.
Societies   must telephone (0908) 562408 in advance
Green Fees   £6.10 (£9 weekends).
Facilities   ⊗ ⫙ 🄱 💺 ♀ 👤 🄰 ⫙ 🥂
Leisure   pool table, darts.
Location   Two Mile Ash (2m W of new town centre off A5)
Hotel   ★★64% Swan Revived Hotel, High St, Newport Pagnell, MILTON KEYNES
                 ☎ (0908) 610565 42rm(40 ⇄ 🐾)

PRINCES RISBOROUGH   Map 04 SP80

Whiteleaf ☎ (0844) 274058
Short, 9-hole parkland course requiring great accuracy, fine views.
9 holes, 5391yds, Par 66, SSS 66.
Club membership 350.
Visitors   with member only at weekends.
Societies   on Thu only, must contact the secretary in advance.
Green Fees   £25 per day; £18 per round.
Facilities   ⊗ ⫙ 🄱 💺 ♀ 👤 🄰 🥂 Ken Ward.
Location   Whiteleaf (1m NE off A4010)
Hotel   ★★★74% Bell Inn, ASTON CLINTON
                 ☎ (0296) 630252 6 ⇄ 🐾Annexe15 ⇄ 🐾

STOKE POGES   Map 04 SU98

Farnham Park ☎ (028814) 3332
Fine, public parkland course in pleasing setting.
18 holes, 6172yds, Par 71, SSS 69.
Club membership 900.
Visitors   no restrictions.
Societies   must contact in advance.
Green Fees   not confirmed.
Facilities   🄱 💺 ♀ 👤 🄰 ⫙ 🥂 Paul Harrison.
Leisure   pool table, darts.
Location   Park Rd (W side of village off B416)
Hotel   B Marriott Hotel, Ditton Road, Langley, SLOUGH ☎ (0753) 544244 350 ⇄ 🐾

Stoke Poges ☎ Slough (0753) 526385
Judgement of the distance from the tee is all important on this first-class parkland course. There are many outstanding par 4's of around 440 yds, several calling for much thought. Fairways are wide and the challenge seemingly innocuous.
18 holes, 6654yds, Par 71, SSS 72, Course record 65.
Club membership 720.
                                                              ▶

Visitors	may not play weekends and Tue mornings and limited Wednesdays. Must contact in advance and have a handicap certificate.
Societies	must contact in advance.
Green Fees	£50 per day; £35 per round.
Facilities	⊗ ⅲ ⅬⅬ ♥ ♀ ⌂ ⟟ ℂ Tim Morrison.
Leisure	hard tennis courts, snooker, sauna, caddy cars.
Location	Park Rd (1.5m W off B416)
Hotel	B Marriott Hotel, Ditton Road, Langley, SLOUGH ☎ (0753) 544244 350 ⊨ ℝ

WAVENDON   Map 04 SP93

Wavendon Golf Centre ☎ Milton Keynes (0908) 281811
Pleasant parkland course set in 96 acres of mature trees.
18 holes, 5479yds, Par 67, SSS 67.
Club membership 550.

Visitors	must book 3 days in advance. Casual smart dress required.
Societies	must contact in advance by telephone.
Green Fees	£9 per 18 holes (£12 weekends). Par 3 £3.75 (£4.75 weekends).
Facilities	⊗ ⅲ ⅬⅬ ♥ ♀ ⌂ ⟟ ℂ Greg Iron.
Leisure	9 hole Par 3 course,36 bay driving range.
Location	Lower End Rd (just off A421)
Hotel	★★★69% Moore Place Hotel, The Square, ASPLEY GUISE ☎ (0908) 282000 39 ⊨ Annexe15 ⊨

WESTON TURVILLE   Map 04 SP81

Weston Turville Golf & Squash Club ☎ Aylesbury (0296) 24084 & 25949
Parkland course, with views of the Chiltern Hills. Flat easy walking with water hazards.
18 holes, 6008yds, Par 69, SSS 69.
Club membership 600.

Visitors	no restrictions.
Societies	must contact in advance.
Green Fees	£25 per day; £15 per round (£20 per round weekends & bank holidays).
Facilities	⊗ ⅲ by prior arrangement ⅬⅬ ♥ ♀ ⌂ ⟟ ℂ Tom Jones.
Leisure	squash.
Location	New Rd (0.5m N off B4544)
Hotel	★★★74% Bell Inn, ASTON CLINTON ☎ (0296) 630252 6 ⊨ ℝAnnexe15 ⊨ ℝ

WEXHAM STREET   Map 04 SU98

Wexham Park ☎ (0753) 663271
Gently undulating parkland course. Two courses.
18 holes, 5836yds, Par 69, SSS 68 or 9 holes, 2283yds, Par 32, SSS 32.
Club membership 500.

Visitors	no restrictions.
Societies	may not play at weekends; must contact in advance.
Green Fees	not confirmed.
Facilities	⊗ ⅲ by prior arrangement ⅬⅬ ♥ ♀ ⌂ ⟟ ℂ
Location	0.5m S
Hotel	B Marriott Hotel, Ditton Road, Langley, SLOUGH ☎ (0753) 544244 350 ⊨ ℝ

WING   Map 04 SP82

Aylesbury Vale ☎ Leighton Buzzard (0525) 240196
The course, which is gently undulating and played over water, was opened in the autumn of 1991. There are five ponds to add interest. In addition there is a 10-bay driving range, a practice fairway and practice putting green as well as an In-Golf Simulator.
18 holes, 6622yds, Par 72, SSS 72.
Club membership 510.

Visitors	must adhere to dress regulations. Not suitable for beginners.
Societies	telephone to book in advance.
Green Fees	£12 per round (£18.50 weekends and bank holidays).
Facilities	⊗ ⅲ by prior arrangement ⅬⅬ ♥ ♀ ⌂ ⟟ ℂ Lee Scarbrow.
Leisure	10 bay covered driving range.
Location	Wing Rd (2m NW on unclassified Stewkley road)
Hotel	★★★60% Swan Hotel, High St, LEIGHTON BUZZARD ☎ (0525) 372148 38 ⊨ ℝ

CAMBRIDGESHIRE

BAR HILL   Map 05 TL36

Cambridgeshire Moat House ☎ Cambridge (0954) 780098 & 780555
Undulating parkland course with lake and water hazards, easy walking. Many leisure facilities. Course record holders, Paul Way and Peter Townsend.
18 holes, 6734yds, Par 72, SSS 72.
Club membership 500.

Visitors	must book in advance.
Societies	must telephone in advance.
Green Fees	£20 per day; £15 per round (£25 per round weekends & bank holidays).
Facilities	⊗ ⅲ ⅬⅬ ♥ ♀ ⌂ ⟟ ℂ ⟊ David Vernon.
Leisure	hard tennis courts, heated indoor swimming pool, squash, sauna, solarium, gymnasium, buggies.
Location	Moat House Hotel (5m NW of Cambridge on A604)
Hotel	★★★63% Cambridgeshire Moat House, BAR HILL ☎ (0954) 780555 100 ⊨ ℝ

BRAMPTON   Map 04 TL27

Brampton Park ☎ Huntingdon (0480) 434700
Set in truly attractive countryside, bounded by the River Great Ouse and bisected by the River Lane. Great variety with mature trees, lakes and water hazards. One of the most difficult holes is the 4th, a Par 3 island green, named 'Fowler's Folly'.
18 holes, 6403yds, Par 72, SSS 73.
Club membership 600.

| Visitors | contact in advance. |
| Societies | must telephone in advance. |

Green Fees £24 per day; £18 per round (£36 per day weekend, includes lunch).
Facilities ⓑ 🍺 ♀ ♈ 🏨 ⋈ ℂ Alisdair Currie.
Location Buckden Rd
Hotel ★★64% Grange Hotel, 115 High St, BRAMPTON ☎ (0480) 459516 9rm(1 ⇆7 ℝ)

CAMBRIDGE   Map 05 TL45

Gog Magog ☎ (0223) 247626
Situated just outside the centre of the university town, Gog Magog, established in 1901, is known as the nursery of Cambridge undergraduate golf. The course is on high ground, and it is said that if you stand on the highest point and could see far enough to the east the next highest ground would be the Ural Mountains! The courses (there are two of them) are open but there are enough trees and other hazards to provide plenty of problems. Views from the high parts are superb. The nature of the ground ensures good winter golf.
Old Course: 18 holes, 6354yds, Par 70, SSS 70.
New Course: 9 holes, 5873yds, Par 69, SSS 68.
Club membership 1100.
Visitors must contact in advance & have handicap certificate. With member only at weekends.
Societies by reservation.
Green Fees Old Course: £35 per day; £29 per round. New Course £19 per day/round.
Facilities ⊗ ⑉ ⓑ ♀ ♈ 🏨 ℂ Ian Bamborough.
Location Shelford Bottom (3m SE on A1307)
Hotel ★★★68% Gonville Hotel, Gonville Place, CAMBRIDGE ☎ (0223) 66611 64 ⇆ ℝ

ELY   Map 05 TL58

Ely City ☎ (0353) 662751
Parkland course slightly undulating with water hazards formed by lakes and natural dykes. Magnificent views of Cathedral. Lee Trevino is the professional record holder.
18 holes, 6602yds, Par 72, SSS 72, Course record 66.
Club membership 1000.
Visitors must have handicap certificate. It is advisable to contact the club in advance.
Societies must contact club in advance.
Green Fees £22 per day (£30 weekends & bank holidays).
Facilities ⊗ ⑉ ⓑ 🍺 ♈ 🏨 ⋔ ℂ Andrew George.
Location Cambridge Rd (SW side of city centre on A10)
Hotel ★★64% Lamb Hotel, 2 Lynn Rd, ELY ☎ (0353) 663574 32 ⇆ ℝ

GIRTON   Map 05 TL46

Girton ☎ Cambridge (0223) 276169
Flat, open parkland course with easy walking.
18 holes, 6088yds, Par 69, SSS 69, Course record 67.
Club membership 750.
Visitors with member only at weekends. Must contact in advance.
Societies by arrangement.
Green Fees £25 per weekday (£20 with handicap certificate).
Facilities ⊗ ⑉ ⓑ 🍺 (no catering Mon) ♀ ♈ 🏨 ⋔ ℂ Scott Thomson.
Location Dodford Ln (NW side of village)

Hotel B Forte Posthouse, Lakeview, Bridge Rd, Impington, CAMBRIDGE ☎ (0223) 237000 118 ⇆ ℝ

MARCH   Map 05 TL49

March ☎ (0354) 52364
Nine-hole parkland course.
9 holes, 6210yds, Par 70, SSS 70, Course record 67.
Club membership 400.
Visitors with member only at weekends.
Societies apply in writing.
Green Fees £15 per round.
Facilities 🍺 (licensing hours) ♀ ♈ 🏨 ℂ Nigel Pickerell.
Leisure pool table.
Location Frogs Abbey, Grange Rd (0.5m off A141, March bypass)
Hotel ★67% Olde Griffin Hotel, High St, MARCH ☎ (0354) 52517 20rm(16 ⇆3 ℝ)

PETERBOROUGH   Map 04 TL19

Elton Furze ☎ (0832) 280189
A new course opened in 1993. Wooded parkland 18-hole course in lovely surroundings.
18 holes, 6291yds, Par 70, SSS 70.
Club membership 400.
Visitors on Tue and Thu only, without member.
Societies apply in writing, Tue & Thu only.
Green Fees not confirmed.
Facilities 🍺 ♀ ♈ 🏨 ℂ Frank Kiddie.
Location Bullock Rd, Haddon (4m SW of Peterborough, off A605)
Hotel ★★★★67% Swallow Hotel, Lynchwood, ALWALTON ☎ (0733) 371111 163 ⇆ ℝ

Orton Meadows ☎ (0733) 237478
Municipal, parkland course on either side of the Nene Valley Railway, with lakes and water hazards. Also 12-hole pitch and putt course.
18 holes, 5800yds, Par 68, SSS 68, Course record 67.
Club membership 850.
Visitors no restrictions.
Societies must telephone in advance.
Green Fees not confirmed.
Facilities ♈ 🏨 ⋔ ℂ Neil Grant.
Leisure 12 hole pitch & putt.
Location Ham Ln, Oundle Rd (3m W of town on A605)
Hotel ★★★70% Orton Hall Hotel, Orton Longueville, PETERBOROUGH ☎ (0733) 391111 49 ⇆ ℝ

Peterborough Milton ☎ (0733) 380489
Well-bunkered parkland course set in the grounds of the Earl Fitzwilliam's estate. Easy walking.
18 holes, 6221yds, Par 72, SSS 70.
Club membership 800.
Visitors handicap certificate required.
Societies Tue-Thu only, must contact in advance.
Green Fees £30 per day; £20 per round (£25 weekends).

▶

Facilities ⊗ ⍂ ⓛ ♥ ♀ ⚿ ⌂ ✦ Michael Gallagher.
Leisure caddy cars available for hire.
Location Milton Ferry (2m W on A47)
Hotel ★★★66% Butterfly Hotel, Thorpe Meadows, Off Longthorpe Parkway, PETERBOROUGH ☎ (0733) 64240 70 ⇆ ✦

Thorpe Wood ☎ (0733) 267701
Gently undulating, municipal parkland course designed by Peter Alliss and Dave Thomas.
18 holes, 7086yds, Par 71, SSS 74.
Club membership 850.
Visitors phone for reservations.
Societies must telephone in advance.
Green Fees not confirmed.
Facilities ⚿ ⌂ ⛳ ✦ Dennis & Roger Fitton.
Location Thorpe Wood (3m W of city centre on A47)
Hotel ★★★68% Peterborough Moat House, Thorpe Wood, PETERBOROUGH ☎ (0733) 260000 125 ⇆ ✦

PIDLEY   Map 05 TL37

Lakeside Lodge ☎ Ramsey (0487) 740540
A well designed, spacious course incorporating eight lakes and a modern clubhouse. Also 9-hole Par 3 and 25-bay driving range.
18 holes, 6600yds, Par 72, SSS 73.
Par 3: 9 holes, 820yds, Par 27.
Club membership 500.
Visitors no restrictions.
Societies must telephone in advance.
Green Fees £15.50 per 36 holes; £8.50 per 18 holes; £5 per 9 holes; £2 par 3 (weekends & bank holidays £14 per 18 holes; £8 per 9 holes).
Facilities ⊗ ⍂ ⓛ ♥ ♀ ⚿ ⌂ ⛳ ✦ Alistair Headley.
Leisure fishing, driving range, caddy cars.
Location Fen Rd
Hotel ★★★65% Slepe Hall Hotel, Ramsey Rd, ST IVES ☎ (0480) 463122 16rm(15 ⇆ ✦)

RAMSEY   Map 04 TL28

Ramsey ☎ (0487) 812600
Flat, parkland course with water hazards.
18 holes, 6133yds, Par 71, SSS 70, Course record 66.
Club membership 750.
Visitors must have a handicap certificate; must play with member at weekends & bank holidays.
Societies must contact secretary in advance.
Green Fees £20 per day/round.
Facilities ⊗ ⍂ ⓛ ♥ ♀ ⚿ ⌂ ⛳ ✦ Stuart Scott.
Leisure bowling green.
Location 4 Abbey Ter (S side of town)
Hotel ★★★72% The Old Bridge Hotel, HUNTINGDON ☎ (0480) 52681 26 ⇆ ✦

ST IVES   Map 05 TL37

St Ives (Cambs) ☎ (0480) 468392
Picturesque parkland course.
9 holes, 3302yds, Par 70, SSS 69.
Club membership 305.

Visitors telephone for details.
Societies welcome.
Green Fees £20 per day.
Facilities ⚿ ⌂ ✦ Darren Glasby.
Location Westwood Rd (W side of town centre off A1123)
Hotel ★★★65% Slepe Hall Hotel, Ramsey Rd, ST IVES ☎ (0480) 463122 16rm(15 ⇆ ✦)

ST NEOTS   Map 04 TL16

Abbotsley Golf & Squash Club ☎ Huntingdon (0480) 215153 & 474000
Two courses - main Abbotsley course (parkland with tree-lined fairways) hosts County Championship. Cromwell course, opened in 1991, is maturing well. Courses surround moated country house and hotel. Residential golf schools 30 weeks of the year plus floodlit, covered driving range.
Abbotsley: 18 holes, 5829yds, Par 70, SSS 72.
Cromwell: 18 holes, 6311yds, Par 73.
Club membership 650.
Visitors may not play before 10am at weekends.
Societies must contact by telephone.
Green Fees Abbotsley: £20 per day (£25 weekends); Cromwell: £10 per day (£14 weekends).
Facilities ⊗ ⍂ ⓛ ♥ ♀ ⚿ ⌂ ⛳ ⍾ ✦ Vivien Saunders.
Leisure squash, snooker, sauna, solarium, floodlit covered driving range.
Location 2m SE off B1046
Hotel ★★64% Abbotsley Golf Hotel, Eynesbury Hardwicke, ST NEOTS ☎ (0480) 474000 15 ⇆ ✦

St Neots ☎ Huntingdon (0480) 472363
Undulating parkland course with lake and water hazards, close to the Kym and Great Ouse rivers. Easy, level walking.
18 holes, 6027yds, Par 69, SSS 69, Course record 65.
Club membership 600.
Visitors must have handicap certificate. With member only at weekends.
Societies must contact in advance.
Green Fees £30 per day; £20 per round.
Facilities ⊗ ⍂ ⓛ ♥ ♀ ⚿ ⌂ ⛳ ✦ Graham Bithrey.
Leisure snooker.
Location Crosshall Rd (W side of town centre on A45)
Hotel ★★64% Grange Hotel, 115 High St, BRAMPTON ☎ (0480) 459516 9rm(1 ⇆7 ✦)

TOFT   Map 05 TL35

Cambridge Meridian ☎ Cambridge (0223) 264700
Opened in 1993. Set in 207 acres to a Peter Allis/Clive Clark design with sweeping fairways, lakes and well bunkered greens. The 4th hole has bunker complexes, a sharp dog-leg and a river with the green heavily guarded by bunkers.
18 holes, 6651yds, Par 73, SSS 72.
Club membership 600.
Visitors must contact in advance, must have handicap card, weekends are limited.
Societies applications in writing.
Green Fees £15 (£18 weekends & bank holidays).
Facilities ⓛ ♥ ♀ ⚿ ⌂ ⛳ ✦ Neil Harvey.
Location Comberton Rd (3m W of Cambridge, on B1046)
Hotel ★★★63% Royal Cambridge Hotel, Trumpington St, Cambridge ☎ (0223) 351631 46 ⇆ ✦

CHESHIRE

ALDERLEY EDGE — Map 07 SJ87

Alderley Edge ☎ (0625) 585583
Well-wooded, undulating pastureland course. A stream crosses 7 of the 9 holes.
9 holes, 5828yds, Par 68, SSS 68.
Club membership 400.
Visitors may not play Tue and Sat.
Societies Thu only.
Green Fees £18 per day; (£22 weekends).
Facilities ⊗ ⅏ ⓑ ☕ (no catering Mon) ♀ ⌂ 🖿
⅃ A Sproston.
Leisure snooker.
Location Brook Ln (1m NW on B5085)
Hotel ★★★73% Alderley Edge Hotel, Macclesfield Rd, ALDERLEY EDGE
☎ (0625) 583033 32 ⇶ 🖚

ALSAGER — Map 07 SJ75

Alsager Golf & Country Club ☎ (0270) 875700
An 18-hole parkland course situated in rolling Cheshire countryside. Clubhouse is well appointed with good facilities and a friendly atmosphere.
18 holes, 6206yds, Par 70, SSS 70, Course record 69.
Club membership 600.
Visitors must play with member at weekends. Must contact in advance.
Societies Mon, Wed & Thu only; must contact in writing.
Green Fees £21 per day Mon-Fri..
Facilities ⊗ ⅏ ⓑ ☕ ♀ (variable times) ⌂ 🖿 ⚘
⅃ Paul Preston.
Leisure snooker, limited number of caddy cars for hire.
Location Audley Rd (2m NE of M6 junct 16)
Hotel ★★★66% Manor House Hotel, Audley Rd, ALSAGER ☎ (0270) 884000 57 ⇶ 🖚

CHESTER — Map 07 SJ46

Chester ☎ (0244) 677760
Meadowland course on two levels contained within a loop of the River Dee. The car park overlooks the racecourse across the river.
18 holes, 6500yds, Par 72, SSS 71, Course record 66.
Club membership 700.
Visitors must contact in advance.
Societies must telephone in advance.
Green Fees £21 per day (£26 weekends).
Facilities ⊗ ⅏ by prior arrangement ⓑ ☕ ♀ ⌂ 🖿 ⚘ ⅃
Leisure snooker.
Location Curzon Park (1m W of city centre)
Hotel ★★★★67% Moat House International, Trinity St, CHESTER ☎ (0244) 322330 150 ⇶

Upton-by-Chester ☎ (0244) 381183
Pleasant, tree-lined, parkland course. Not easy for low-handicap players to score well. Testing holes are 2nd (par 4), 14th (par 4) and 15th (par 3).
18 holes, 5808yds, Par 69, SSS 68, Course record 62.
Club membership 700.

Visitors restricted competition days Sat & Sun. Must contact in advance.
Societies apply in writing.
Green Fees not confirmed.
Facilities ⊗ ⅏ ⓑ ☕ ♀ ⌂ 🖿 ⅃ P A Gardner.
Leisure snooker.
Location Upton Ln, Upton-by-Chester (N side off A5116)
Hotel ★★★★64% Mollington Banastre Hotel, Parkgate Rd, CHESTER
☎ (0244) 851471 64 ⇶

Vicars Cross ☎ (0244) 335174
Tree-lined parkland course, with undulating terrain.
18 holes, 6243yds, Par 72, SSS 70.
Club membership 660.
Visitors Mon-Thu day ticket only. Advisable to contact in advance.
Societies Apr-Oct, Tue & Thu only.
Green Fees not confirmed.
Facilities ⊗ ⅏ ⓑ ☕ (no catering Monday) ♀ ⌂ 🖿 ⅃ J A Forsythe.
Leisure snooker.
Location Tarvin Rd, Great Barrow (4m E on A51)
Hotel ★★★66% Rowton Hall Hotel, Whitchurch Road, Rowton, CHESTER
☎ (0244) 335262 42 ⇶ 🖚

CONGLETON — Map 07 SJ86

Astbury ☎ (0260) 272772
Parkland course in open countryside, bisected by a canal. Large practice area.
18 holes, 6269yds, Par 71, SSS 70.
Club membership 700.
Visitors with member only at weekends. Must have a handicap certificate. Must have an introduction from own club.
Societies Thu by written request.
Green Fees not confirmed.
Facilities ⊗ ⅏ by prior arrangement ⓑ ☕ ♀ ⌂ 🖿 ⅃ Nigel Griffith.
Leisure snooker.
Location Peel Ln, Astbury (1.5m S between A34 and A527)
Hotel ★★★65% Lion & Swan Hotel, Swan Bank, CONGLETON ☎ (0260) 273115 21 ⇶ 🖚

Congleton ☎ (0260) 273540
Superbly-manicured parkland course with views over three counties from the balcony of the clubhouse.
9 holes, 5103yds, Par 68, SSS 65.
Club membership 400.
Visitors may not play during competitions.
Societies must apply in writing to Secretary.
Green Fees £14 per day (£20 weekends).
Facilities ⊗ ⅏ ⓑ & ☕ ♀ ⌂ 🖿 ⅃ John Colclough.
Leisure snooker.
Location Biddulph Rd (1.5m SE on A527)
Hotel ★★★65% Lion & Swan Hotel, Swan Bank, CONGLETON ☎ (0260) 273115 21 ⇶ 🖚

Phoneday - remember from 16 April 1995 all phone codes in the UK will change - see page 4 for details

CREWE

Map 07 SJ75

Crewe ☎ (0270) 584099
Undulating parkland course.
18 holes, 6229yds, Par 70, SSS 70, Course record 66.
Club membership 600.

Visitors with member only weekends and bank holidays.
Societies Tue only, telephone to arrange.
Green Fees not confirmed.
Facilities ⊗ ⅢҜ by prior arrangement ⅃ ⬤ ♀ ☆ ☎
Leisure snooker.
Location Fields Rd, Haslington (2.25m NE off A534)
Hotel ★★★62% Hunters Lodge Hotel, Sydney Rd, Sydney, CREWE
☎ (0270) 583440 & 588216 42 ⇄ ♠

DELAMERE

Map 07 SJ56

Delamere Forest ☎ Sandiway (0606) 883264
Played mostly on open heath there is great charm in the way this course drops down into the occasional pine sheltered valley.
18 holes, 6305yds, Par 72, SSS 70, Course record 63.
Club membership 600.

Visitors restricted weekends and bank holidays. Must contact in advance.
Societies telephone to arrange and confirm in writing.
Green Fees £35 per day; £25 per round (£30 per round weekends and bank holidays).
Facilities ⊗ & ⅢҜ by prior arrangement ⅃ ⬤ ♀ ☆ ☎ ♠ Ellis B Jones.
Leisure caddy cars for hire.
Location Station Rd (1.5m NE, off B5152)
Hotel ★★★(red)♨ Nunsmere Hall Country House Hotel, Tarporley Rd, SANDIWAY
☎ (0606) 889100 32 ⇄ ♠

DISLEY

Map 07 SJ98

Disley ☎ (0663) 62071
Parkland/moorland course with trees. Often breezy. Good views. Testing hole: 5th (par 5).
18 holes, 6015yds, Par 70, SSS 69, Course record 63.
Club membership 400.

Visitors restricted Thu, Fri, weekends & bank holidays.
Societies must contact in advance.
Green Fees £25 per day (£30 weekends).
Facilities ⊗ ⅃ ⬤ (no catering Mon) ♀ ☆ ☎ ♩ ♠ Andrew Esplin.
Leisure snooker.
Location Stanley Hall Ln, Jacksons Edge (NW side of village off A6)
Hotel ★★70% Red Lion Inn, 112 Buxton Rd, High Ln, STOCKPORT ☎ (0663) 765227 6 ⇄ ♠

ELLESMERE PORT

Map 07 SJ47

Ellesmere Port ☎ 051-339 7689
Municipal parkland course with natural hazards of woods, brook and ponds.
18 holes, 6384yds, Par 70, SSS 72, Course record 66.
Club membership 300.

Visitors must contact in advance.
Societies by arrangement with professional.

Green Fees not confirmed.
Facilities ♀ ☆ ☎ ♩ ♠ David John Yates.
Leisure squash.
Location Chester Rd, Hooton (NW side of town centre on A41)
Hotel ★★★66% Woodhey Hotel, Welsh Rd, Little Sutton, HOOTON
☎ 051-339 5121 53 ⇄ ♠Annexe1 ⇄

FRODSHAM

Map 07 SJ57

Frodsham ☎ (0928) 732159
Undulating inland course with pleasant views from all parts. Crossed by two footpaths so extreme care needed.
18 holes, 6289yds, Par 70, SSS 70.
Club membership 600.

Visitors must contact in advance.
Societies telephone for bookings.
Green Fees £18 per day (£25/£20 weekends & bank holidays).
Facilities ⊗ ⅢҜ ⅃ ⬤ ♀ ☆ ☎ ♩ ♠♣ Graham Tonge.
Location Simons Ln (1.5m SW)
Hotel ★★★66% Forest Hills Hotel & Leisure Complex, Bellemonte Rd, Overton Hill, FRODSHAM ☎ (0928) 735255 58 ⇄ ♠

HELSBY

Map 07 SJ47

Helsby ☎ (0928) 722021
Quiet parkland course with natural hazards.
18 holes, 6049yds, Par 70, SSS 69.
Club membership 600.

Visitors weekends and bank holidays with member only. Must contact in advance.
Societies Tue & Thu.
Green Fees not confirmed.
Facilities ♀ ☆ ☎ ♩ ♠
Leisure snooker.
Location Towers Ln (1m S off A56)
Hotel ★★★★(red) The Chester Grosvenor Hotel, Eastgate St, CHESTER
☎ (0244) 324024 86 ⇄ ♠

KNUTSFORD

Map 07 SJ77

Heyrose ☎ Pickmere (0565) 733664 & 733623
An 18-hole course in wooded and gently undulating terrain. Both the course and the comfortable clubhouse have attractive views.
18 holes, 6510yds, Par 73, SSS 71.
Club membership 700.

Visitors by arrangement with secretary, handicap certificate may be required, advisable to contact in advance.
Societies must contact in advance.
Green Fees £23 per day; £18 per round (£28/£23 weekends & bank holidays).
Facilities ⊗ ⅢҜ ⅃ ⬤ ♀ ☆ ☎ ♠ Martin Redrup.
Leisure snooker.
Location Budworth Rd, Tabley (1.5m from junc 19 on M6)
Hotel ★★★70% Cottons Hotel, Manchester Rd, KNUTSFORD ☎ (0565) 650333 82 ⇄ ♠

Knutsford ☎ (0565) 633355
Parkland course set in a beautiful old deer park. It demands some precise iron play.
9 holes, 6288yds, Par 70, SSS 70.
Club membership 230.
Visitors   are not permitted weekends and restricted Wed. Must contact in advance.
Green Fees not confirmed.
Facilities   ⊗ ⅢⅢ by prior arrangement ⅃ 💷 ♀ ⚒
Location   Mereheath Ln (N side of town centre off A50)
Hotel   ★★★70% Cottons Hotel, Manchester Rd, KNUTSFORD ☎ (0565) 650333 82 ⊨ ⬧

Mere Golf & Country Club
☎ Bucklow Hill (0565) 830155
A gracious parkland championship course designed by James Braid in the Cheshire sand belt, with several holes close to a lake. The round has a tight finish with four testing holes.
18 holes, 6817yds, Par 71, SSS 73, Course record 64.
Club membership 540.
Visitors   must contact in advance.
Societies   Mon,Tue & Thu only by prior arrangement.
Green Fees £50 per day (Apr-Oct); £25 per day (Nov-Mar).
Facilities   ⊗ ⅢⅢ ⅃ 💷 ♀ ⚒ 🏠 ⚓ Peter Eyre.
Leisure   hard tennis courts, heated indoor swimming pool, squash, fishing, snooker, sauna, solarium, gymnasium, floating ball drive range,petrol buggies.
Location   Chester Rd, Mere (1m E of junc 19 of M6)
Hotel   ★★★70% Cottons Hotel, Manchester Rd, KNUTSFORD ☎ (0565) 650333 82 ⊨ ⬧

LYMM   Map 07 SJ68

Lymm ☎ (092575) 5020
First ten holes are gently undulating with the Manchester Ship Canal running alongside the 9th hole. The remaining holes are comparatively flat.
18 holes, 6304yds, Par 71, SSS 70, Course record 68.
Club membership 620.
Visitors   must have a handicap certificate, may not play on Thu mornings, weekends or bank holidays unless guest of member. Must contact in advance.
Societies   Wed only, must contact in writing.
Green Fees not confirmed.
Facilities   ⊗ ⅢⅢ ⅃ 💷 ♀ ⚒ 🏠 ⚓ ⚓ Steve McCarthy.
Leisure   snooker.
Location   Whitbarrow Rd (0.5m N off A6144)
Hotel   ★★★61% Lymm Hotel, Whitbarrow Rd, LYMM ☎ (092575) 2233 22 ⊨ ⬧Annexe47 ⊨ ⬧

MACCLESFIELD   Map 07 SJ97

Macclesfield ☎ (0625) 615845 & 423227
Very hilly heathland course recently extended to 18-holes. Situated on the edge of the Pennines with excellent views.
18 holes, 5625yds, Par 70, SSS 69.
Club membership 600.
Visitors   must have a club or EGU handicap certificate.
Societies   by arrangement.
Green Fees £17 per day (£20 weekends & bank holidays).

Facilities   ⊗ ⅢⅢ ⅃ 💷 ♀ ⚒ 🏠 ⚓ Tony Taylor.
Leisure   snooker.
Location   The Hollins (SE side of town centre off A523)
Hotel   ★★65% Crofton Hotel, 22 Crompton Rd, MACCLESFIELD ☎ (0625) 434113 8 ⊨ ⬧

Tytherington ☎ (0625) 434562
Modern championship course in beautiful, mature parkland setting. Headquarters of the Women's European Tour and venue of the WPGET English Open and County matches. Country club facilities.
18 holes, 6737yds, Par 72, SSS 72, Course record 68.
Club membership 2000.
Visitors   must contact in advance & have handicap certificate.
Societies   weekdays only, apply in writing up to one year in advance.
Green Fees £25 per 18 hole weekdays (£30 weekends).
Facilities   ⊗ ⅢⅢ ⅃ 💷 ♀ ⚒ 🏠 ⚓ ⚓
Leisure   hard tennis courts, heated indoor swimming pool, squash, snooker, sauna, solarium, gymnasium, bowls, clay shot, creche.
Location   1m N of Macclesfield on A523
Hotel   ★★★★61% Shrigley Hall Golf & Country Club, Shrigley Park, POTT SHRIGLEY ☎ (0625) 575757 156 ⊨

POTT SHRIGLEY   Map 07 SJ97

Shrigley Hall Hotel ☎ Bollington (0625) 575755 & 575757
Parkland course set in 262-acre estate with breathtaking views over the Peak District and Cheshire Plain. Designed by Donald Steel, this championship standard course provides a real sporting challenge while the magnificent hotel provides a wealth of sporting facilities as well as accommodation and food.
18 holes, 6305yds, Par 71, SSS 71, Course record 68.
Visitors   must contact in advance by telephone.
Societies   contact in advance.
Green Fees not confirmed.
Facilities   ⊗ ⅢⅢ ⅃ 💷 ♀ ⚒ 🏠 ⚓ ⚓ ⚓ Granville Ogden.
Leisure   hard tennis courts, heated indoor swimming pool, squash, fishing, snooker, sauna, solarium, gymnasium.
Location   Shrigley Park
Hotel   ★★★★61% Shrigley Hall Golf & Country Club, Shrigley Park, POTT SHRIGLEY ☎ (0625) 575757 156 ⊨

POYNTON   Map 07 SJ98

Davenport ☎ (0625) 876951
Undulating parkland course. Extensive view over Cheshire Plain from elevated 5th tee. Testing 17th hole, par 4.
18 holes, 6065yds, Par 69, SSS 69, Course record 64.
Club membership 600.
Visitors   no restrictions but advance booking advised.
Societies   Tue and Thu only. Must contact in writing.
Green Fees £24 (£30 weekends).
Facilities   ⊗ ⅢⅢ ⅃ 💷 ♀ ⚒ 🏠 ⚓ ⚓ Wyn Harris.
Leisure   snooker.
Location   Worth Hall, Middlewood Rd (1m E off A523)
Hotel   ★★★67% Bramhall Moat House, Bramhall Ln South, BRAMHALL ☎ 061-439 8116 65 ⊨ ⬧

PRESTBURY   Map 07 SJ97

Prestbury ☎ (0625) 828241

Rather strenuous parkland course, undulating hills, with many plateau greens looked after by one of only 7 Master Greenkeepers in the world. The 9th hole has a challenging uphill 3-tier green and the 17th is over a valley. Host to county and inter-county championships as well as England v USA competitions.

18 holes, 6143yds, Par 71, SSS 70, Course record 64. Club membership 723.

Visitors	must contact in advance and play with member weekends.
Societies	Mon pm & all day Thu, apply by tel or letter.
Green Fees	£30 per round or day.
Facilities	⚐ ▲ ⚑ ⚏ Nick Summerfield.
Leisure	snooker, pull trolleys only.
Location	Macclesfield Rd (S side of village off A538)
Hotel	★★★★63% Mottram Hall Hotel, Wilmslow Rd, Prestbury, WILMSLOW ☎ (0625) 828135 133 ⇆ 🐾

RUNCORN   Map 07 SJ58

Runcorn ☎ (0928) 574214

Parkland course with tree-lined fairways and easy walking. Fine views over Mersey and Weaver valleys. Testing holes: 7th par 5; 14th par 5; 17th par 4.

18 holes, 6035yds, Par 69, SSS 69. Club membership 575.

Visitors	welcome except between 9-10am, noon-1.30pm and Tue afternoon.
Societies	apply in writing.
Green Fees	not confirmed.
Facilities	⊗ �𝄞 ▲ ▬ ⚐ ▲ 🏠 ⚏ Steve Dooley.
Leisure	snooker.
Location	Clifton Rd (1.25m S of Runcorn Station)
Hotel	B Forte Posthouse, Wood Ln, Beechwood, RUNCORN ☎ (0928) 714000 135 ⇆ 🐾

SANDBACH   Map 07 SJ76

Malkins Bank ☎ Crewe (0270) 765931

Parkland course. Tight 13th hole with stream running through.

18 holes, 6071yds, Par 70, SSS 69. Club membership 500.

Visitors	no restrictions. Advisable to book in advance.
Societies	apply for booking form to course professional
Green Fees	£6 (£7 weekends).
Facilities	⊗ �𝄞 ▲ ▬ ⚐ ▲ 🏠 ⚏ David Wheeler.
Leisure	practice ground, lessons, trolley hire.
Location	Betchton Rd, Malkins Bank (1.5m SE off A533)
Hotel	★★★63% Saxon Cross Hotel, Holmes Chapel Rd, SANDBACH ☎ (0270) 763281 52 ⇆ 🐾

Sandbach ☎ Crewe (0270) 762117

Meadowland, undulating course with easy walking. Limited facilities.

9 holes, 5094yds, Par 68, SSS 67. Club membership 570.

Visitors	weekdays except Tue, and with member only weekends & bank holidays. Must contact in advance.
Societies	apply by letter.
Green Fees	£16 per day/round.
Facilities	⊗ �𝄞 ▲ ▬ ⚐ ▲
Location	Middlewich Rd (0.5m W on A533)
Hotel	★★★63% Saxon Cross Hotel, Holmes Chapel Rd, SANDBACH ☎ (0270) 763281 52 ⇆ 🐾

SANDIWAY   Map 07 SJ67

Sandiway ☎ (0606) 883247

Delightful undulating woodland and heath golf with long hills up to the 8th, 16th and 17th holes. Many dog-legged and tree-lined holes give opportunities for the deliberate fade or draw.

18 holes, 6435yds, Par 70, SSS 72. Club membership 750.

Visitors	must contact in advance and have a handicap certificate.
Societies	apply by letter.
Green Fees	£35 per day; £30 per round (£40/£35 weekends).
Facilities	⊗ ⟭ ▲ ▬ ⚐ ▲ 🏠 ⚑ ⚏ William Laird.
Location	1m E on A556
Hotel	★★★64% Hartford Hall Hotel, School Ln, Hartford, NORTHWICH ☎ (0606) 75711 20 ⇆

TARPORLEY   Map 07 SJ56

Oaklands Golf & Country Club ☎ (0829) 733884

Opened in Spring 1990, this pleasant course has lovely views over the Cheshire Plain plus many leisure facilities.

18 holes, 6508yds, Par 71, SSS 70, Course record 69. Club membership 550.

Visitors	no societies at weekend, visitors must book tee times in advance.
Societies	must contact in advance.
Green Fees	£18 per round (£22 weekends & bank holidays).
Facilities	⊗ ▲ ▬ ⚐ ▲ 🏠 ⚏ J Statham.
Leisure	snooker, sauna.
Location	Forest Rd (N of Tarporley off A49)
Hotel	★★★♨62% Willington Hall Hotel, Willington, TARPORLEY ☎ (0829) 752321 10 ⇆

Portal Golf & Country Club ☎ (0829) 733933

Opened in 1991, this course is set in mature, wooded parkland. There are fine views over the Chesire Plain and numerous water hazards. The 13th is just a short iron through trees, but its green is virtually an island surrounded by water.

18 holes, 7145yds, Par 73, SSS 73. Club membership 100.

Visitors	must contact in advance.
Societies	must contact at least 2 weeks in advance.
Green Fees	not confirmed.
Facilities	⊗ ⟭ ▲ ▬ ⚐ ▲ 🏠 ⚏ David John Clare.
Leisure	hard tennis courts, croquet & polo.
Location	Cobbler's Cross Ln
Hotel	★★★67% The Wild Boar, Whitchurch Rd, Beeston, TARPORLEY ☎ (0829) 260309 37 ⇆ 🐾

WARRINGTON   Map 07 SJ68

Birchwood ☎ (0925) 818819
Very testing parkland course with natural water hazards. The
11th hole is particularly challenging.
18 holes, 6808yds, Par 71, SSS 73, Course record 65.
Club membership 1150.
Visitors   welcome except Sun.
Societies   Mon, Wed & Thu.
Green Fees   not confirmed.
Facilities   ⊗ ⅀ ⅂ 🍴 ♀ ☂ 🏠 ⌇ Paul McEwan.
Leisure   snooker, sauna, electric trolleys for hire.
Location   Kelvin Close, Birchwood (4m NE on A574)
Hotel   B Forte Posthouse, Lodge Ln, Newton-Le-
                  Willows, HAYDOCK
                  ☎ (0942) 717878 136 ⊭ ⌇

Leigh ☎ Culcheth (0925) 762943
A pleasant, well-wooded parkland course. Any
discrepancy in length is compensated by the wide variety
of golf offered here. The course is well maintained and
there is a comfortable clubhouse.
18 holes, 5853yds, Par 69, SSS 68, Course record 64.
Club membership 750.
Visitors   may not play during competitions and before
                  9.30am or 12-1.30pm. Must have a handicap
                  certificate, unless with member.
Societies   must contact in writing.
Green Fees   £25 per day/round (£32 weekends & bank
                  holidays).
Facilities   ⊗ ⅀ ⅂ 🍴 ♀ ☂ 🏠 ⌇ Andrew Baguley.
Leisure   snooker, caddy cars.
Location   Kenyon Hall, Kenyon (5m NE off A579)
Hotel   ★★★64% Fir Grove Hotel, Knutsford Old
                  Rd, WARRINGTON
                  ☎ (0925) 267471 40 ⊭ ⌇

Poulton Park ☎ Padgate (0925) 812034
Tight, flat parkland course with good greens and many trees.
A straight drive off each tee is important. The 4/13th has a
fairway curving to the left with water and out-of-bounds on
left and trees on right.
9 holes, 5379yds, Par 68, SSS 66, Course record 66.
Club membership 350.
Visitors   may not play between 5-6pm weekdays and
                  noon-1.30pm Sat.
Societies   contact in writing.
Green Fees   £16 per day (£18 weekends).
Facilities   ⊗ ⅀ by prior arrangement ⅂ 🍴 ♀ ☂ 🏠
                  ⌇ Darren Newing.
Leisure   practice nets & putting green.
Location   Dig Ln, Cinnamon Brow, Padgate (3m from
                  Warrington on A574)
Hotel   ★★★64% Fir Grove Hotel, Knutsford Old Rd,
                  WARRINGTON ☎ (0925) 267471 40 ⊭ ⌇

Walton Hall ☎ (0925) 63061
Wooded, municipal parkland course on Walton Hall estate.
18 holes, 6843yds, Par 72, SSS 73, Course record 69.
Club membership 420.
Visitors   no restrictions.
Societies   must contact in writing.
Green Fees   not confirmed.
Facilities   ⅂ 🍴 ♀ ☂ 🏠 ☂

Location   Warrington Rd, Higher Walton (2.5m S off A56)
Hotel   ★★★64% Fir Grove Hotel, Knutsford Old Rd,
                  WARRINGTON ☎ (0925) 267471 40 ⊭ ⌇

Warrington ☎ (0925) 261620
Meadowland, with varied terrain and natural hazards.
18 holes, 6305yds, Par 72, SSS 70.
Club membership 400.
Visitors   no restrictions.
Societies   apply in writing.
Green Fees   £23 (£35 weekends & bank holidays).
Facilities   ⊗ ⅀ by prior arrangement ⅂ 🍴 ♀ ☂ 🏠
                  ⌇ Reay Mackay.
Location   The Hill Warren, London Rd, Appleton (2.5m S
                  on A49)
Hotel   ★★70% Rockfield Hotel, Alexandra Rd,
                  Grappenhall, WARRINGTON
                  ☎ (0925) 262898 6 ⊭ ⌇Annexe6 ⊭ ⌇

WAVERTON   Map 07 SJ46

Eaton ☎ Chester (0244) 335885 & 335826
Eaton Golf Club has moved to a new course. Designed by
Donald Steel, the course was opened in 1993 and is parkland
with a liberal covering of both mature trees and new planting
enhanced by natural water hazards. The old course at
Eccleston has been returned to nature.
18 holes, 6562yds, Par 72, SSS 71.
Club membership 550.
Visitors   must contact in advance & have handicap
                  certificate.
Societies   must contact in advance.
Green Fees   £21 per round/day (£27 weekends & bank
                  holidays).
Facilities   ⊗ ⅀ ⅂ 🍴 ♀ ☂ 🏠 ⌇ A Mitchell.
Location   Guy Ln (2.5m outside Chester on A41)
Hotel   ★★★★(red) The Chester Grosvenor Hotel,
                  Eastgate St, CHESTER
                  ☎ (0244) 324024 86 ⊭ ⌇

WIDNES   Map 07 SJ58

St Michael Jubilee ☎ 051-424 6230
Municipal parkland course dominated by the 'Stewards
Brook'. It is divided into two sections which are split by the
main road and joined by an underpass.
18 holes, 2648yds, Par 69, SSS 68.
Visitors   must be accompanied by member, contact in
                  advance and have an introduction from own
                  club.
Societies   must contact in writing.
Green Fees   not confirmed.
Facilities   ♀ ☂ 🏠 ⌇
Leisure   snooker.
Location   Dunalk Rd (W side of town centre off A562)
Hotel   ★58% Rockland Hotel, View Rd, RAINHILL
                  ☎ 051-426 4603 10rm(9 ⊭)

Widnes ☎ 051-424 2440
Parkland course, easy walking.
18 holes, 5719yds, Par 69, SSS 68.
Visitors   may play after 9am & after 4pm on competition
                  days. Must contact in advance.
Societies   must contact in writing.

►

Green Fees not confirmed.
Facilities ⊗ ⋙ by prior arrangement ⛏ ♣ ♀ ♨ 🏠
    ⚑ S Forster.
Leisure snooker.
Location Highfield Rd
Hotel ★58% Rockland Hotel, View Rd, RAINHILL
    ☎ 051-426 4603 10rm(9 ⇆)

WILMSLOW   Map 07 SJ88

Mottram Hall ☎ Macclesfield (0625) 80064 & 828135
Championship standard course with flat meadowland on the
front nine and undulating woodland on the back with well
guarded greens. The course was designed in 1989 and opened
in May 1991. The course is unusual as each half opens and
closes with Par 5's. The hotel offers many leisure facilities.
18 holes, 6905yds, Par 72, SSS 72, Course record 66.
Club membership 600.
Visitors must have current handicap certificate or letter
    of introduction from own club. Must contact in
    advance.
Societies must contact in advance.
Green Fees £30 (£35 weekends & bank holidays).
Facilities ⊗ ⋙ ⛏ ♣ ♀ ♨ 🏠 ⚑ 🏌 ⚑ Tim Rastall.
Leisure hard tennis courts, heated indoor swimming
    pool, squash, snooker, sauna, solarium,
    gymnasium, jacuzzi, caddies, beauty treatment.
Location Wilmslow Rd, Mottram St Andrew (on A538
    between Wilmslow and Preston)
Hotel ★★★★63% Mottram Hall Hotel, Wilmslow Rd,
    Prestbury, WILMSLOW
    ☎ (0625) 828135 133 ⇆ ⚑

Wilmslow ☎ Mobberley (0565) 872148
A fine parkland championship course, of middle length,
fair to all classes of player and almost in perfect
condition.
18 holes, 6607yds, Par 72, SSS 72.
Club membership 830.
Visitors restricted Wed, weekends & bank holidays.
    Must contact in advance.
Societies must contact in advance.
Green Fees £37.50 per day (£50 weekends); £25 per
    round (£40 weekends).
Facilities ⊗ ⋙ ⛏ ♣ ♀ ♨ 🏠 ⚑ John Nowicki.
Location Great Warford, Mobberley (2m SW off
    B5058)
Hotel ★★★73% Alderley Edge Hotel,
    Macclesfield Rd, ALDERLEY EDGE
    ☎ (0625) 583033 32 ⇆ ⚑

WINSFORD   Map 07 SJ66

Knights Grange ☎ (0606) 552780
Municipal parkland course with water hazards.
9 holes, 2860yds, Par 35, SSS 68.
Visitors no restrictions. Advisable to book day before,
    especially in summer.
Societies must contact the Manager in writing.
Green Fees £2.70 (£3.95 weekends & bank holidays) for 9
    holes; £3.50 (£5.10 weekends & bank holidays)
    for 18 holes.
Facilities ♣ ♨ 🏠 ⚑
Leisure hard and grass tennis courts.
Location Grange Ln (N side of town off A54)

Hotel ★★★64% Hartford Hall Hotel, School Ln,
    Hartford, NORTHWICH
    ☎ (0606) 75711 20 ⇆

♦ CLEVELAND ♦

BILLINGHAM   Map 08 NZ42

Billingham ☎ Stockton (0642) 533816
Parkland course on edge of urban-rural district, with hard
walking and water hazards; testing 15th hole.
18 holes, 6460yds, Par 73, SSS 71, Course record 66.
Club membership 1000.
Visitors with member only at weekends & bank holidays.
    Must have a handicap certificate.
Societies must contact in writing.
Green Fees under review.
Facilities ⊗ ⋙ ⛏ ♣ (by prior arrangement) ♀ ♨ 🏠
    ⚑ P S Bradley.
Leisure snooker.
Location Sandy Ln (1m W of town centre E of A19)
Hotel ★★★57% Billingham Arms Hotel, The
    Causeway, Billingham, STOCKTON-ON-TEES
    ☎ (0642) 553661 & 360880 69 ⇆ ⚑

EAGLESCLIFFE   Map 08 NZ41

Eaglescliffe and District ☎ (0642) 780098
This hilly course offers both pleasant and interesting golf
to all classes of player. It lies in a delightful setting on a
rolling plateau, shelving to the River Tees. There are fine
views to the Cleveland Hills.
18 holes, 6275yds, Par 72, SSS 70.
Club membership 550.
Visitors restricted Tue, Thu, Fri & weekends.
Societies must contact in advance.
Green Fees £22 per day (£28 weekends & bank
    holidays).
Facilities ⊗ ⋙ ⛏ ♣ ♀ ♨ 🏠 ⚑ Nic Gilks.
Leisure snooker.
Location Yarm Rd (E side of village off A135)
Hotel ★★★58% Swallow Hotel, 10 John
    Walker Square, STOCKTON-ON-TEES
    ☎ (0642) 679721 125 ⇆ ⚑

HARTLEPOOL   Map 08 NZ53

Castle Eden & Peterlee ☎ Wellfield (0429) 836510
Beautiful parkland course alongside a nature reserve. Hard
walking but trees provide wind shelter.
18 holes, 6262yds, Par 70, SSS 69, Course record 66.
Club membership 750.
Visitors with member only during 12-1.30pm & 4-
    6.30pm. Must contact in advance.
Societies must contact in advance on (0429) 836689.
Green Fees £20 per day (£30 weekends & bank holidays).
Facilities ⊗ ⋙ by prior arrangement ⛏ ♣ ♀ ♨ 🏠 ⚑
    ⚑ Graham J Laidlaw.
Leisure snooker, buggies, trolleys.

Location   Castle Eden (2m S of Peterlee on B1281 off A19)
Hotel   ★★69% Hardwicke Hall Manor Hotel, HESLEDEN ☎ (0429) 836326 11 ⇌ ☞

Hartlepool ☎ (0429) 274398
A seaside course, half links, overlooking the North Sea. A good test and equally enjoyable to all handicap players. The 10th, par 4, demands a precise second shot over a ridge and between sand dunes to a green down near the edge of the beach, alongside which several holes are played.
18 holes, 6255yds, Par 70, SSS 70.
Club membership 600.
Visitors   with member only on Sun.
Societies   must apply in writing.
Green Fees   £17 per day (£24 weekends).
Facilities   ⊗ & ☰ by prior arrangement ⮕ ☕ ♀ ⛳ 🏠 ☾ Malcolm E Cole.
Leisure   snooker.
Location   Hart Warren (N side off King Oswy Drive)
Hotel   ★★73% Ryedale Moor, 3 Beaconsfield St, Headland, HARTLEPOOL ☎ (0429) 231436 13 ⇌ ☞

MIDDLESBROUGH   Map 08 NZ41

Middlesbrough ☎ (0642) 311515
Undulating parkland course, prevailing winds. Testing 9th, 16th and 17th holes.
18 holes, 6167yds, Par 70, SSS 70.
Club membership 900.
Visitors   restricted Tue & Sat.
Societies   Wed, Thu & Fri only. Must contact the club in advance.
Green Fees   £26 per day (£32 weekends & bank holidays).
Facilities   ⛳ 🏠 ☾ Don Jones.
Leisure   snooker.
Location   Brass Castle Ln, Marton (4m S off A172)
Hotel   ★★★59% Marton Way Toby Hotel, Marton Rd, MIDDLESBROUGH ☎ (0642) 817651 53 ⇌ ☞

Middlesbrough Municipal ☎ (0642) 315533
Parkland course with good views. The front nine holes have wide fairways and large, often well-guarded greens while the back nine demand shots over tree-lined water hazards and narrow entrances to subtley contoured greens. Driving range.
18 holes, 6326yds, Par 71, SSS 70.
Club membership 575.
Visitors   tees should be booked in advance.
Societies   must contact in advance, in writing.
Green Fees   £7.50 per round (£9.50 weekends).
Facilities   ⊗ (Sun only) ⮕ ☕ ♀ ⛳ 🏠 ⛏ ☾ Alan Hope & Dave Symington.
Leisure   20 bay floodlit driving range.
Location   Ladgate Ln (2.5m S of town centre on B1380 off A172)
Hotel   ★★★59% Marton Way Toby Hotel, Marton Rd, MIDDLESBROUGH ☎ (0642) 817651 53 ⇌ ☞

For an explanation of symbols and abbreviations, see page 5

REDCAR   Map 08 NZ62

Cleveland ☎ (0642) 471798
Links championship course.
18 holes, 6707yds, Par 71, SSS 70, Course record 68.
Club membership 890.
Visitors   must contact in advance & have handicap certificate.
Societies   must apply in writing.
Green Fees   £18 per day/round (£27 weekends & bank holidays).
Facilities   ⊗ ☰ ⮕ ☕ ♀ ⛳ 🏠 ☾ Stephen Wynn.
Leisure   snooker.
Location   Queen St (8m E of Middlesborough)
Hotel   ★★★59% Marton Way Toby Hotel, Marton Rd, MIDDLESBROUGH ☎ (0642) 817651 53 ⇌ ☞

Wilton ☎ (0642) 465265
Parkland course with some fine views.
18 holes, 6104yds, Par 70, SSS 69.
Club membership 750.
Visitors   restricted Sat.
Societies   must telephone in advance.
Green Fees   not confirmed.
Facilities   ⊗ ☰ by prior arrangement ⮕ ☕ ♀ ⛳ 🏠 ☾ R Smith.
Location   Wilton Castle (3m W on A174)
Hotel   ★★★59% Marton Way Toby Hotel, Marton Rd, MIDDLESBROUGH ☎ (0642) 817651 53 ⇌ ☞

SALTBURN-BY-THE-SEA   Map 08 NZ62

Saltburn by the Sea ☎ (0287) 622812
Undulating meadowland course surrounded by woodland. Particularly attractive in autumn. There are fine views of the Cleveland Hills and of Tees Bay.
18 holes, 5803yds, Par 70, SSS 68.
Club membership 850.
Visitors   may not play Sat & occasional Sun.
Societies   apply in writing.
Green Fees   £19 (£22 weekends).
Facilities   ⊗ ☰ ⮕ ☕ ♀ ⛳ 🏠 ⛏ ☾ David Forsythe.
Leisure   snooker.
Location   Hob Hill, Guisborough Rd (S side of town centre on B1268)
Hotel   ★★★59% Marton Way Toby Hotel, Marton Rd, MIDDLESBROUGH ☎ (0642) 817651 53 ⇌ ☞

SEATON CAREW   Map 08 NZ52

Seaton Carew ☎ Hartlepool (0429) 261040 & 266249
A championship links course taking full advantage of its dunes, bents, whins and gorse. Renowned for its par 4 (17th); just enough fairway for an accurate drive followed by another precise shot to a pear-shaped, sloping green that is severely trapped.
The Old Course: 18 holes, 6604yds, Par 72.
Brabazon Course: 18 holes, 6849yds, Par 73.
Club membership 650.
Visitors   restricted after 10am at weekends & bank holidays. ▶

Societies	must apply in writing.
Green Fees	£24 per day (£32 weekends & bank holidays).
Facilities	⊗ ⊞ ⊾ ⬛ ♀ ⚙ 🏠 ℓ W Hector.
Leisure	snooker.
Location	Tees Rd (SE side of village off A178)
Hotel	★★73% Ryedale Moor, 3 Beaconsfield St, Headland, HARTLEPOOL ☎ (0429) 231436 13 ⇆ ℝ

STOCKTON-ON-TEES
Map 08 NZ41

Norton ☎ Stockton (0642) 676385 & 674636
An interesting parkland course with long drives from the 7th and 17th tees. Several water hazards.
18 holes, 5870yds, Par 71, SSS 71.

Visitors	no restrictions.
Societies	apply in advance.
Green Fees	not confirmed.
Facilities	⊗ ⊞ ⊾ ⬛ ♀ ⚙ 🏠 ℓ Ernest Scott.
Location	Norton (at Norton 2m N off A19)
Hotel	★★★57% Billingham Arms Hotel, The Causeway, Billingham, STOCKTON-ON-TEES ☎ (0642) 553661 & 360880 69 ⇆ ℝ

Teesside ☎ (0642) 676249
Flat parkland course, easy walking.
18 holes, 6472yds, Par 72, SSS 71.
Club membership 600.

Visitors	with member only weekdays after 4.30pm, weekends after 11am.
Societies	must contact in writing.
Green Fees	£20 per day (£26 weekends & bank holidays).
Facilities	⊗ ⊞ ⊾ ⬛ ♀ ⚙ 🏠 ℓ
Location	Acklam Rd, Thornaby (1.5m SE on A1130)
Hotel	B Forte Posthouse, Low Ln, Thornaby-on-Tees, STOCKTON-ON-TEES ☎ (0642) 591213 135 ⇆ ℝ

CORNWALL & ISLES OF SCILLY

BODMIN
Map 02 SX06

Lanhydrock ☎ (0208) 73600
Championship standard parkland/moorland course. Picturesque but not hilly.
18 holes, 6185yds, Par 71, SSS 71.
Club membership 200.

Visitors	no restrictions.
Societies	welcome.
Green Fees	£35 per 36 holes; £22 per 18 holes.
Facilities	⊗ ⊞ ⊾ ⬛ ♀ ⚙ 🏠 ⛳ ℓ (from May'94).
Leisure	practice area,buggies/trolleys for hire.
Location	Lostwithiel Rd, Lanhydrock (2m SE)
Hotel	★★★63% Restormel Lodge Hotel, Hillside Gardens, LOSTWITHIEL ☎ (0208) 872223 21 ⇆ ℝAnnexe12 ⇆
Additional hotel	★★69% Port Gaverne Hotel, PORT GAVERNE ☎ (0208) 880244 16 ⇆ ℝAnnexe3 ⇆ ℝ

PORT GAVERNE HOTEL

COMMENDED ・ Hospitality Hotels ・ AA ★ ★ ✿

WHY NOT PLAY
THE PORT GAVERNE WAY?
Inclusive golf at four of Cornwall's finest courses – St. Enodoc, St. Mellion, Bowood Park and Lanhydrock.

Stay in early 17c Cornish coastal inn situated in unique position on sheltered cove. Fine food and wine, fully licensed bar.

For details – Telephone: 01208 880 244

Fax: 01208 880 151

Mrs M. Ross,

Port Gaverne Hotel,
Port Isaac, Cornwall

BUDE
Map 02 SS20

Bude & North Cornwall ☎ (0288) 352006
Seaside links course with natural sand bunkers, superb greens and breathtaking views. Club established in 1891.
18 holes, 6222yds, Par 71, SSS 70.
Club membership 900.

Visitors	must contact in advance, restricted weekdays 9.30am-12.30pm, 2-5pm & from 6.30pm onwards. Closed Sat & Sun mornings.
Societies	weekdays only by arrangement.
Green Fees	not confirmed.
Facilities	⊗ ⊞ ⊾ ⬛ ♀ ⚙ 🏠 ℓ John Yeo.
Leisure	snooker.
Location	Burn View (N side of town)
Hotel	★★66% Camelot Hotel, Downs View, BUDE ☎ (0288) 352361 21 ⇆ ℝ

BUDOCK VEAN
Map 02 SW73

Budock Vean Hotel ☎ Falmouth (0326) 250288
Undulating parkland course.
9 holes, 5007yds, Par 68, SSS 65.

Visitors	restricted for morning play.
Societies	welcome if resident in hotel.
Green Fees	£14 per day (£18 Sun & bank holidays).
Facilities	⊗ ⊞ ⊾ ⬛ ♀ ⚙ 🏠 ⛳
Leisure	hard tennis courts, heated indoor swimming pool, snooker, buggies, trolleys.
Location	Mawnan Smith (1.5m SW)
Hotel	★★★72% Budock Vean Hotel, MAWNAN SMITH ☎ (0326) 250288 58 ⇆ ℝ

CAMBORNE   Map 02 SW64

Tehidy Park ☎ Portreath (0209) 842208
A well-maintained parkland course providing good holiday
golf.
18 holes, 6241yds, Par 72, SSS 71.
Club membership 1000.

Visitors	must contact in advance and have a handicap certificate.
Societies	must apply in writing.
Green Fees	£27 per day; £21 per round (£32/£26 Sun & bank holidays).
Facilities	⊗ ⅷ ⅃ ⅃ ♥ ♀ ⅃ 🏠 ⅆ ⅋ James Dumbrock.
Leisure	snooker.
Location	2m NE off A30
Hotel	★★★65% Penventon Hotel, REDRUTH ☎ (0209) 214141 50 ⇥ 🐾

CARLYON BAY   Map 02 SX05

Carlyon Bay Hotel ☎ (0726) 814228
Championship-length, cliff-top course moving into
parkland. Magnificent views surpassed only by the
quality of the course. The 230-yard (par 3) 18th with
railway and road out-of-bounds, holds the player's
interest to the end.
18 holes, 6501yds, Par 72, SSS 71.
Club membership 550.

Visitors	no restrictions.
Societies	must contact in advance.
Green Fees	not confirmed.
Facilities	⊗ ⅷ ⅃ ♥ ♀ ⅃ 🏠 ⅋ Nigel Sears.
Location	2.5m E of St Austell off A3082
Hotel	★★★★71% Carlyon Bay Hotel, Sea Rd, Carlyon Bay, ST AUSTELL ☎ (0726) 812304 73 ⇥ 🐾

CONSTANTINE BAY   Map 02 SW87

Trevose ☎ Padstow (0841) 520208
A pleasant holiday seaside course with early holes close
to the sea on excellent springy turf. It is a good and
enjoyable test. Self-catering accommodation is available
at the club.
18 holes, 6608yds, Par 71, SSS 71.
Short Course: 9 holes, 1360yds, Par 29, SSS 29.
New Course: 9 holes, 3031yds, Par 35, SSS 35.
Club membership 650.

Visitors	must contact in advance & have handicap certificate for main course.
Societies	must apply in writing.
Green Fees	Main course: £20-£28 per day. New Course: £14-£18 per day. Short Course: £8-£14 per day.
Facilities	⊗ ⅷ ⅃ ♥ ♀ ⅃ 🏠 ⅾ ⅋ Gary Alliss.
Leisure	hard tennis courts, heated outdoor swimming pool, snooker, Par 3 course, caddy cars.
Location	N side of village off B3276
Hotel	★★★76% Treglos Hotel, CONSTANTINE BAY ☎ (0841) 520727 44 ⇥ 🐾

FALMOUTH   Map 02 SW83

Falmouth ☎ (0326) 311262
Seaside/parkland course with outstanding coastal views.
Sufficiently bunkered to punish any inaccurate shots. Five
acres of practice grounds.
18 holes, 5680yds, Par 70, SSS 68, Course record 61.
Club membership 600.

Visitors	restricted play on competition days. Must contact in advance.
Societies	must contact in advance.
Green Fees	£25 per day; £20 per round.
Facilities	⊗ ⅷ ⅃ ♥ ♀ ⅃ 🏠 ⅋ David J Short.
Leisure	practice fields, putting green, trolleys.
Location	Swanpool Rd (SW side of town centre)
Hotel	★★★75% Penmere Manor Hotel, Mongleath Rd, FALMOUTH ☎ (0326) 211411 39 ⇥ 🐾

LAUNCESTON   Map 02 SX38

Launceston ☎ (0566) 773442
Undulating parkland course with views over Tamar Valley to
Dartmoor and Bodmin Moor. Dominated by the 'The Hill' up
which the 8th and 11th fairways rise, and on which the 8th,
9th, 11th and 12th greens sit.
18 holes, 6407yds, Par 70, SSS 71.
Club membership 800.

Visitors	with member only at weekends. Must contact in advance and have an introduction from own club.

▶

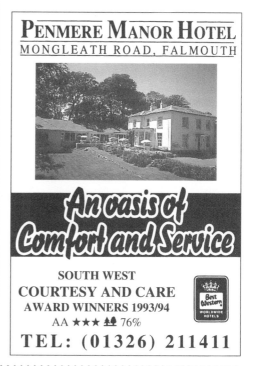

PENMERE MANOR HOTEL
MONGLEATH ROAD, FALMOUTH

An oasis of Comfort and Service

SOUTH WEST
COURTESY AND CARE
AWARD WINNERS 1993/94

AA ★★★ ⚜ 76%

TEL: (01326) 211411

Societies must apply in writing.
Green Fees not confirmed.
Facilities ⌂ 🏠 ⌖ ⌖
Location St Stephens (NW side of town centre on B3254)
Hotel ★★★68% Arundell Arms, LIFTON
☎ (0566) 784666 24 ⇆ 🐾Annexe5 ⇆ 🐾

LELANT — Map 02 SW53

West Cornwall ☎ Penzance (0736) 753401
A seaside links with sandhills and lovely turf adjacent to the Hayle estuary and St Ives Bay. A real test of the player's skill, especially 'Calamity Corner' starting at the 5th on the lower land by the River Hayle. A small (3 hole) course is available for practice.
18 holes, 5884yds, Par 69, SSS 69, Course record 65.
Club membership 900.
Visitors must have handicap certificate.
Societies must apply in writing.
Green Fees £20 per day (£25 weekends).
Facilities ⊗ ⧻ ⌂ 🍺 ♀ ⌂ 🏠 ⌖ ⌖ Paul Atherton.
Leisure snooker.
Location N side of village off A3074
Hotel ★★66% Boskerris Hotel, Boskerris Rd, Carbis Bay, ST IVES ☎ (0736) 795295 13rm(11 ⇆ 🐾)Annexe5 ⇆ 🐾

Phoneday - remember from 16 April 1995 all phone codes in the UK will change - see page 4 for details

LOOE — Map 02 SX25

Looe ☎ Widegates (0503) 240239
Exposed and somewhat windy course on high moorland; designed by Harry Vardon in 1934. Easy walking. Fine views over Looe coastline.
18 holes, 5940yds, Par 70, SSS 68, Course record 64.
Club membership 620.
Visitors no restrictions.
Societies apply one week in advance.
Green Fees £17 per round.
Facilities ⊗ ⧻ (in summer) ⌂ 🍺 ♀ ⌂ 🏠 ⌖
⌖ Alistair Macdonald.
Leisure caddy cars, trolleys.
Location Widegates (3.5m NE off B3253)
Hotel ★★68% Commonwood Manor Hotel, St Martin's Rd, LOOE ☎ (0503) 262929 10 ⇆ 🐾
Additional QQQQ Coombe Farm Guest House, Widegates,
hotel LOOE ☎ (0503) 240223 7 🐾Annexe3 🐾

LOSTWITHIEL — Map 02 SX15

Lostwithiel Golf & Country Club ☎ Bodmin (0208) 873550
An undulating, parkland course with water hazards. Overlooked by Restormel Castle and the Rover Fowey flows alongside the course. Driving range.
18 holes, 6098yds, Par 72, SSS 70.
Club membership 650.
Visitors must have handicap certificate. Must contact in advance.

ENGLISH TOURIST BOARD
HIGHLY COMMENDED

AA
QQQQ

Coombe Farm

WIDEGATES, Nr LOOE
CORNWALL PL13 1QN
Telephone:
Widegates (01503) 240223

WINNER
AA Guest
House
of the Year
Award West of
England 1981

A warm
welcome
assured by
Alexander
and
Sally Low

A lovely country house surrounded by lawns, meadows, woods and streams with superb views to the sea. Log fires. Delicious home cooking. Candlelit dining. Licensed. All bedrooms are en-suite and have colour TV, radio, tea and coffee-making facilities and direct dial telephone.

In the grounds – many animals and flowers, a swimming pool (heated in summer), croquet lawn and a stone barn for snooker and table tennis. Nearby golf, fishing, tennis, horse riding and glorious walks and beaches.

The perfect centre for visiting all parts of Cornwall and Devon.

Bed and breakfast from £18.00. Four course dinner from £12.00.

Special short break discounts.

LOSTWITHIEL Hotel
GOLF & COUNTRY CLUB

Set in richly wooded hills above the banks of the River Fowey. An 18-hole parkland golf course, tennis courts, heated indoor swimming pool, bar and restaurant facilities. Eighteen bedrooms of great charm and character converted from Cornish stone farm buildings.

FREE GOLF, TENNIS & SWIMMING AVAILABLE TO ALL RESIDENTS

Tel: 01208 873550
Lostwithiel, Cornwall PL22 1HQ

Societies	contact in advance.
Green Fees	summer £15 per round (£19 weekend); winter £10 per round (£15 weekend).
Facilities	⊗ ⅏ ⓛ ♨ ♀ ⏦ 🏠 ⛳ ⌸ ⏏ Martin Hammond.
Leisure	hard tennis courts, heated indoor swimming pool, fishing, snooker, floodlit undercover driving range.
Location	Lower Polscoe (1m outside Lostwithiel off A390)
Hotel	★★66% Lostwithiel Golf & Country Club, Lower Polscoe, LOSTWITHIEL ☎ (0208) 873550 18 ⌸ ⏏

MAWNAN SMITH   See **Budock Vean**

MULLION   Map 02 SW61

Mullion ☎ (0326) 240685
Founded in 1895, a clifftop and links course with panoramic views over Mounts Bay. A steep downhill slope on 6th and the 10th descends to the beach with a deep ravine alongside the green. Most southerly course in the British Isles.
18 holes, 6022yds, Par 69, SSS 69.
Club membership 700.

Visitors	must have handicap certificate.
Societies	must contact in advance.
Green Fees	£20 per day (£16 Apr-Sep).
Facilities	⊗ ⅏ ⓛ ♨ ♀ ⏦ 🏠 ⛳ ⏏ Robin Goodway.
Leisure	caddy cars, trolleys.

Location	Cury Cross Lanes (1.5m NW off A3083)
Hotel	★★★74% Polurrian Hotel, MULLION ☎ (0326) 240421 40rm(38 ⌸ ⏏)

NEWQUAY   Map 02 SW86

Newquay ☎ (0637) 874354
Seaside course close to the beach and open to wind.
18 holes, 6140yds, Par 69, SSS 69.
Club membership 500.

Visitors	must have a handicap certificate.
Societies	must contact in advance.
Green Fees	not confirmed.
Facilities	⊗ ⅏ (Wed, Fri, Sat & Sun) ⓛ ♨ ♀ ⏦ 🏠 ⏏
Leisure	hard tennis courts, snooker.
Location	Tower Rd (W side of town)
Hotel	★★62% Philema Hotel, 1 Esplanade Rd, Pentire, NEWQUAY ☎ (0637) 872571 37rm(32 ⌸ ⏏)

Treloy ☎ (0637) 878554
An Executive course constructed in 1991 to American specifications with large contoured and mounded greens. Offers an interesting round for all categories of player.
9 holes, 2143yds, Par 32, SSS 31.

Visitors	no restrictions.
Societies	must contact in advance.
Green Fees	£11.50 per 18 holes; £7.50 per 9 holes.
Facilities	ⓛ ♨ ♀ ⏦ 🏠 ⛳ ⏏
Location	On A3059 Newquay to St Columb Major Road
Hotel	★★70% Whipsiderry Hotel, Trevelgue Road, Porth, NEWQUAY ☎ (0637) 874777 24rm(5 ⌸14 ⏏)

PADSTOW   See **Constantine Bay**

PERRANPORTH   Map 02 SW75

Perranporth ☎ Truro (0872) 572454
There are three testing par 5 holes on the links course (2nd, 5th, 11th) and a fine view over Perranporth Beach from all holes.
18 holes, 6286yds, Par 72, SSS 70.
Club membership 600.

Visitors	must contact in advance & have handicap certificate. Restricted Sun mornings & competition days.
Societies	must apply in writing.
Green Fees	£30 per day (£25 weekends & bank holidays).
Facilities	⊗ ⅏ ⓛ ♨ ♀ ⏦ 🏠 ⛳ ⏏
Leisure	snooker.
Location	Budnick Hill (0.75m NE on B3285)
Hotel	★65% Beach Dunes Hotel, Ramoth Way, Reen Sands, PERRANPORTH ☎ (0872) 572263 6rm(5 ⌸ ⏏)Annexe3 ⌸ ⏏

PRAA SANDS   Map 02 SW52

Praa Sands ☎ Penzance (0736) 763445
A beautiful parkland course with outstanding sea views from every tee and green.
9 holes, 4104yds, Par 62, SSS 60.
Club membership 300.   ▶

Visitors	restricted Fri afternoon & Sun morning (May-Sep).
Societies	must contact in advance.
Green Fees	not confirmed.
Facilities	⊗ ⍟ 🏌 ♥ ♀ ♨ 🏠 ⛳ ♬ Mike Singleton.
Leisure	pool table & darts.
Location	Germoe Cross Roads (N side of village on A394)
Hotel	★★♣♣73% Nansloe Manor Hotel, Meneage Rd, HELSTON ☎ (0326) 574691 7rm(6 ⇋ ♠)

ROCK   Map 02 SW97

St Enodoc ☎ Trebetherick (0208) 863216
Classic links courses with huge sand hills and rolling fairways. James Braid laid out the original 18 holes in 1907 and changes were made in 1922 and 1935. English County Final and English Ladies Closed Amateur Championships held recently. On the Church, the 10th is the toughest par 4 on the course and on the 6th is a truly enormous sand hill known as the Himalayas.
Church Course: 18 holes, 6207yds, Par 69, SSS 70, Course record 67.
Holywell Course: 18 holes, 4142yds, Par 63, SSS 61.
Club membership 1400.

Visitors	may not play on bank holidays. Must have a handicap certificate of 24 or below for Church Course. Must contact in advance.
Societies	must contact in writing.
Green Fees	Church: £35 per day; £22 per round (£40/£27 weekends). Holywell: £18 per day; £12 per round.
Facilities	⊗ ⍟ 🏌 ♥ ♀ ♨ 🏠 ⛳ ♬ Nick Williams.
Leisure	practice ground, putting green.
Location	W side of village
Hotel	★★67% St Enodoc Hotel, ROCK ☎ (0208) 863394 13 ⇋ ♠

ST AUSTELL   Map 02 SX05

Porthpean ☎ (0726) 64613
A challenging 9-hole course which plays out at over 6500 yards. There are spectacular views over St Austell Bay. There is also an 8-bay covered and floodlit driving range.
9 holes, 3266yds, Par 37, SSS 37.
Club membership 180.

Visitors	no restrictions
Societies	telephone in advance.
Green Fees	£10 per 18 holes; £6.50 per 9 holes.
Facilities	🏌 ♥ ♀ ♨ 🏠 ⛳
Leisure	8 bay covered & floodlit driving range.
Location	Porthpean (1.5m from St Austell by-pass)
Hotel	★★66% The Pier House, Harbour Front, Charlestown, ST AUSTELL ☎ (0726) 67955 12 ⇋ ♠

St Austell ☎ (0726) 72649
Very interesting inland parkland course designed by James Braid. Undulating, well-covered with tree plantations and well-bunkered. Notable holes are 8th (par 4) and 16th (par 3).
18 holes, 6007yds, Par 69, SSS 69.
Club membership 800.

Visitors	must have handicap certificate.
Societies	must apply in writing.
Green Fees	£15 per day (£18 weekends).

Facilities	⊗ ⍟ 🏌 ♥ ♀ ♨ 🏠 ⛳ ♬ Mark Rowe.
Location	Tregongeeves Ln (1m SW off A390)
Hotel	★★★63% Porth Avallen Hotel, Sea Rd, Carlyon Bay, ST AUSTELL ☎ (0726) 812802 & 812183 23rm(22 ⇋ ♠)

ST JUST (NEAR LAND'S END)   Map 02 SW33

Cape Cornwall Golf & Country Club ☎ Penzance (0736) 788611
Coastal parkland, walled course. The walls are an integral part of its design. Country club facilities.
18 holes, 5650yds, Par 70, SSS 68.
Club membership 830.

Visitors	may not play before 11.30am at weekends.
Societies	must contact in advance.
Green Fees	£20 per day; £16 per round (£22 weekends).
Facilities	⊗ ⍟ (Wed-Sat) 🏌 ♥ ♀ ♨ 🏠 ⛳ ♔ ♬ Bob Hamilton.
Leisure	heated indoor swimming pool, snooker, sauna, solarium, gymnasium, children's area.
Location	Cape Cornwall (1m W of St Just)
Hotel	★★★♣♣61% Higher Faugan Hotel, Newlyn, PENZANCE ☎ (0736) 62076 11 ⇋ ♠

ST MARY'S

Isle of Scilly ☎ (0720) 22692
Links course, glorious views.
9 holes, 6001yds, Par 73, SSS 69.
Club membership 300.

Visitors	only with member on Sun.
Societies	must apply in writing
Green Fees	£15 per day.
Facilities	♀ ♨ 🏠 ⛳
Location	1m N of Hugh Town
Hotel	★★71% Tregarthens Hotel, Hugh Town, ST MARY'S ☎ (0720) 22540 28 ⇋ ♠Annexe1 ⇋ ♠

ST MELLION   Map 02 SX36

St Mellion International Golf & Country Club ☎ Liskeard (0579) 50101
St Mellion is a delightful family-run golfing complex put together by brothers Martin and Hermon Bond. They decided the Tamar Valley, made famous by Sherlock Holmes, deserved a championship golf course - so they chose to convert one of their farms. Their hearts were set on securing Jack Nicklaus as course architect. So they sent him a massive cheque, said to be £1 million, with a letter. It did the trick!
Today the rugged course, seen on TV for several professional events, certainly needs an expert touch if low scores are to be achieved. Without doubt a picturesque setting in Cornwall, some of the holes look inviting, but are dangerous. Maybe none more so than the short 11th, with the green nestling at the bottom of a valley guarded by sand bunkers and a stream! There are four holes in excess off 500 yards with the 16th, at 554 yards, being the longest. Not a course for the meek and mild.
Nicklaus Course: 18 holes, 6626yds, Par 72, SSS 72.
The Old Course: 18 holes, 5927yds, Par 70, SSS 68.
Club membership 4500.

Visitors	must contact in advance and have a handicap certificate.
Societies	must apply in writing.
Green Fees	Nicklaus Course: £42 per round; Old Course: £22 per round.
Facilities	⊗ ⅢⅢ ㏒ ♨ ♀ ⚲ 🏠 ⚑ 🏌 (Tony Moore.
Leisure	hard tennis courts, heated indoor swimming pool, squash, snooker, sauna, solarium, gymnasium, jacuzzi, caddy cars.
Location	0.5m NW off A388
Hotel	★★★65% St Mellion Hotel, St Mellion Golf & County Club, ST MELLION ☎ (0579) 50101 Annexe24 ⇆ 🌑

TORPOINT — Map 02 SX45

Whitsand Bay Hotel Golf & Country Club ☎ St Germans (0503) 30276
Seaside course laid-out on cliffs overlooking Whitsand Bay. Easy walking after 1st hole. The par 3 (3rd) hole is well-known.
18 holes, 5850yds, Par 68, SSS 69.
Club membership 450.

Visitors	must have handicap certificate.
Societies	must contact in advance.
Green Fees	£15 weekdays (£17.50 weekends & bank holidays).
Facilities	⊗ ⅢⅢ ㏒ ♨ ♀ ⚲ 🏠 ⚑ 🏌 (
Leisure	heated indoor swimming pool, riding, sauna, solarium, games room, masseur, hairdresser.
Location	Portwrinkle (5m W off B3247)
Hotel	★★64% Whitsand Bay Hotel, Golf & Country Club, Portwrinkle, TORPOINT ☎ (0503) 30276 34rm(32 ⇆ 🌑)

TRURO — Map 02 SW84

Killiow Park ☎ (0872) 70246
Picturesque parkland course with mature oaks and woodland and five holes played across or around water hazards. Floodlit, all-weather driving range.
18 holes, 3542yds, Par 60.
Club membership 450.

Visitors	may not play until after 10.30am at weekends. Must contact in advance.
Green Fees	not confirmed.
Facilities	♨ ⚲ 🏠 ⚑
Location	Killiow, Kea (3m SW of Truro, off A39)
Hotel	★★★66% Brookdale Hotel, Tregolls Rd, TRURO ☎ (0872) 73513 & 79305 22 ⇆

Truro ☎ (0872) 72640
Undulating parkland course.
18 holes, 5347yds, Par 66, SSS 66.
Club membership 900.

Visitors	must contact in advance & have handicap certificate.
Societies	must apply in writing.
Green Fees	£18 per day (£22 weekends & bank holidays).
Facilities	⊗ ⅢⅢ ㏒ ♨ ♀ ⚲ 🏠 ⚑ 🏌 (Nigel Bicknell.
Leisure	snooker, buggy.
Location	Treliske (1.5m W on A390)
Hotel	★★★66% Brookdale Hotel, Tregolls Rd, TRURO ☎ (0872) 73513 & 79305 22 ⇆

WADEBRIDGE — Map 02 SW97

St Kew ☎ (0208) 84500
An interesting 9-hole course with 3 holes with water and 15 bunkers. In a picturesque setting there are 5 par 4s and 4 par 3s. No handicap certificate required but some experience of the game is essential.
9 holes, 2200yds, Par 32, SSS 31, Course record 27.
Club membership 220.

Visitors	no restrictions.
Societies	apply in writing or by telephone.
Green Fees	£11 per 18 holes; £7 per 9 holes.
Facilities	⊗ ㏒ ♨ ♀ ⚲ 🏠 ⚑ (Tony Pitts.
Leisure	fishing, riding, 1 caddy car for hire.
Location	St Kew Highway (2m N, main A39)
Hotel	★★69% Port Gaverne Hotel, PORT GAVERNE ☎ (0208) 880244 16 ⇆ 🌑Annexe3 ⇆ 🌑

CUMBRIA

ALSTON — Map 12 NY74

Alston Moor ☎ (0434) 381675
Parkland course with lush fairways and naturally interesting greens.
10 holes, 5780yds, Par 66, SSS 66, Course record 67.
Club membership 180.

Visitors	no restrictions.
Societies	must contact in advance.
Green Fees	not confirmed.
Facilities	⊗ ⅢⅢ ㏒ ♨ (catering by arrangement) ♀ ⚲ ⚑
Location	The Hermitage (1.75m SE on B6277)
Hotel	★★68% Lowbyer Manor Country House Hotel, ALSTON ☎ (0434) 381230 8 ⇆ 🌑Annexe4 ⇆

APPLEBY-IN-WESTMORLAND — Map 12 NY62

Appleby ☎ (07683) 51432
This remotely situated heather and moorland course offers interesting golf with the rewarding bonus of several long par-4 holes that will be remembered. There are superb views.
18 holes, 5901yds, Par 68, SSS 68, Course record 63.
Club membership 830.

Visitors	restricted weekends and bank holidays.
Societies	must contact in advance by letter.
Green Fees	£12 per day (£16 weekends & bank holidays).
Facilities	⊗ & ⅢⅢ by prior arrangement ㏒ ♨ ♀ ⚲ 🏠
Leisure	snooker.
Location	Brackenber Moor (1m E of Appleby 0.5m off A66)
Hotel	★★★★♨71% Appleby Manor Country House Hotel, Roman Rd, APPLEBY-IN-WESTMORLAND ☎ (07683) 51571 23 ⇆ 🌑Annexe7 ⇆ 🌑 *See advertisement on page 40*

Swim, Bubble and Golf!

Enjoy your par 68 round on Appleby's eighteen beautiful moorland holes (5915 yds), then it's 5-minutes by car to return to your favourite Country House Hotel for a refreshing swim and a relaxing jacuzzi in the indoor leisure club.

Phone now for a free colour brochure with full details of the hotel, restaurant, leisure club and prices.

APPLEBY MANOR COUNTRY HOUSE HOTEL
Roman Road, Appleby-in-Westmorland
Cumbria, CA16 6JD. Facsimile (017683) 52888
Telephone (017683) 51571

★★★ BEST WESTERN HOTELS

ASKAM-IN-FURNESS Map 07 SD27

Dunnerholme ☎ Dalton-in-Furness (0229) 462675
Unique 10-hole (18 tee) links course with view of Lakeland hills, and a stream running through.
10 holes, 6162yds, Par 72, SSS 69.
Club membership 450.

Visitors restrictions during competitions.
Societies must contact in advance.
Green Fees £10 per round (£15 weekends & bank holidays).
Facilities (lunchtimes)
Leisure pool table.
Location Duddon Rd (1m N on A595)
Hotel ★★63% Eccle Riggs Hotel, Foxfield Rd, BROUGHTON IN FURNESS
☎ (0229) 716398 & 716780 12

BARROW-IN-FURNESS Map 07 SD26

Barrow ☎ (0229) 825444
Pleasant course laid out on meadowland with extensive views of the nearby Lakeland fells.
18 holes, 6209yds, Par 71, SSS 70.
Club membership 850.

Visitors must contact in advance & be members of a recognised golf club. Handicap certificate advisable.
Societies must contact in advance.
Green Fees £15 per day/round (£25 weekends & bank holidays).
Facilities Neale Hyde.
Location Rakesmoor Ln, Hawcoat (2m N off A590)
Hotel ★★64% Lisdoonie Hotel, 307/309 Abbey Rd, BARROW-IN-FURNESS
☎ (0229) 827312 12

Furness ☎ (0229) 471232
Links golf with a fairly flat first half but a much sterner second nine played across subtle sloping ground. There are good views of the Lakes, North Wales and the Isle of Man.
18 holes, 6363mtrs, Par 71, SSS 71.
Club membership 775.

Visitors must be a member of a recognised Golf Club with current handicap certificate. Restricted, Ladies Day Wed, competition days and members only Fri from 12-2pm
Societies must contact in writing.
Green Fees not confirmed.
Facilities
Leisure snooker.
Location Central Dr, Walney Island (1.75 W of town centre off A590)
Hotel ★★64% Lisdoonie Hotel, 307/309 Abbey Rd, BARROW-IN-FURNESS
☎ (0229) 827312 12

BOWNESS-ON-WINDERMERE Map 07 SD49

Windermere ☎ Windermere (05394) 43123
Enjoyable holiday golf on a short, slightly hilly but sporting course in this delightful area of the Lake District National Park, with superb views of the mountains as the backcloth to the lake and the course.
18 holes, 5006yds, Par 67, SSS 65, Course record 58.
Club membership 943.

Birdie, Eagle, Albatross . . .

. . . or even if you're looking for the elusive 'hole in one', Windermere is the place.

Situated only a mile from this 18 hole golf course, The Wild Boar Hotel with it's olde worlde charm offers you a friendly and welcome atmosphere.

Reflect, whilst sampling our excellent cuisine and extensive wine list, on the 67 par round.

All our rooms are ensuite and are equipped with every modern day facility to ensure your stay is an enjoyable one!

Discounted Green Fees for Residents
For your free colour brochure
telephone Windermere (015394) 45225

Wild Boar Hotel AA★★★ 71%

Crook, Nr. Windermere, Cumbria LA23 3NF.

Visitors	must contact in advance & be member of recognised club with a handicap certificate.
Societies	must contact in writing.
Green Fees	£23 per day (£28 weekends & bank holidays).
Facilities	⊗ ⅲ ⓛ ⓔ ♀ ⚑ 亼 ⓕ ⓘ W S M Rooke.
Leisure	snooker.
Location	Cleabarrow (1m E on B5284)
Hotel	★★★71% Wild Boar Hotel, Crook, WINDERMERE ☎ (05394) 45225 36 ⇥ ⋔

BRAMPTON   Map 12 NY56

Brampton ☎ (06977) 2255 & 2000
Challenging golf across glorious rolling fell country demanding solid driving and many long second shots. A number of particularly fine holes, the pick of which may arguably be, the 3rd and 11th. The course offers unrivalled panoramic views from its hilly position.
18 holes, 6420yds, Par 72, SSS 71, Course record 68.
Club membership 750.

Visitors	some restrictions on Mon, Wed & Thu.
Societies	must contact in writing.
Green Fees	not confirmed.
Facilities	⊗ ⅲ by prior arrangement ⓛ ⓔ ♀ 亼 ⚑ ⓕ ⓘ Stephen Harrisson.
Leisure	snooker.
Location	Talkin Tarn (1.5m SE of Brampton on B6413)
Hotel	★★★(red)ⓐ Farlam Hall Hotel, Hallbankgate, BRAMPTON ☎ (06977) 46234 12 ⇥ ⋔Annexe1 ⇥ ⋔

CARLISLE   Map 11 NY35

Carlisle ☎ (0228) 513303
Majestic looking parkland course with great appeal. A complete but not too severe test of golf, with fine turf, natural hazards, a stream and many beautiful trees.
18 holes, 6080yds, Par 71, SSS 70, Course record 63.
Club membership 950.

Visitors	with member on Sat, restricted Tue afternoons and competition days. Must contact in advance and have a handicap certificate.
Societies	contact in advance for details.
Green Fees	£27.50 per day; £25 per round (Sun £35).
Facilities	⊗ ⅲ ⓛ ⓔ ♀ 亼 ⚑ ⓕ ⓘ John Smith More.
Leisure	snooker.
Location	Aglionby (On A69 1m E of M6 junc 43)
Hotel	★★★63% Central Plaza Hotel, Victoria Viaduct, CARLISLE ☎ (0228) 20256 84 ⇥ ⋔

Stony Holme Municipal ☎ (0228) 34856
Municipal parkland course, bounded on three sides by the River Eden.
18 holes, 5783yds, Par 69, SSS 68, Course record 68.
Club membership 350.

Visitors	must contact in advance.
Societies	must telephone in advance.
Green Fees	not confirmed.
Facilities	⊗ ⅲ ⓛ ⓔ ♀ 亼 ⚑ ⓕ ⓘ S Ling.
Location	St Aidans Rd (3m E off A69)

Hotel	B Forte Posthouse, Parkhouse Rd, Kingstown, CARLISLE ☎ (0228) 31201 93 ⇥ ⋔

COCKERMOUTH   Map 11 NY13

Cockermouth ☎ Bassenthwaite Lake (07687) 76223
Fell-land course, fenced, with exceptional views and a hard climb on the 3rd and 11th holes. Testing holes: 10th and 16th (rearranged by James Braid).
18 holes, 5496yds, Par 69, SSS 67, Course record 65.
Club membership 586.

Visitors	restricted Wed, Sat & Sun.
Societies	must contact in advance.
Green Fees	£12 per day/round (£15 weekends & bank holidays).
Facilities	ⓛ ⓔ (weekends only) ♀ 亼
Leisure	snooker.
Location	Embleton (3m E off A66)
Hotel	★★★64% The Trout Hotel, Crown St, COCKERMOUTH ☎ (0900) 823591 23 ⇥ ⋔

CROSBY-ON-EDEN   Map 12 NY45

Eden ☎ Carlisle (0228) 573003
Open, championship-length course following the River Eden.
18 holes, 6368yds, Par 72, SSS 72.
Club membership 550.

Visitors	dress code e.g. no jeans or T-shirts etc. is strictly applied.
Societies	must contact in advance.
Green Fees	£15 per day (£20 weekends & bank holidays).
Facilities	⊗ ⅲ ⓛ ⓔ ♀ 亼 ⚑ ⓕ ⓘ Philip Harrison.
Leisure	16 bay floodlit driving range.
Location	5m from M6 junc 44, on A689 towards Brampton
Hotel	★★★★71% Crosby Lodge Country House Hotel, High Crosby, CROSBY-ON-EDEN ☎ (0228) 573618 9 ⇥ ⋔Annexe2 ⇥

GRANGE-OVER-SANDS   Map 07 SD47

Grange Fell ☎ (05395) 32536
Hillside course with magnificent views over Morecambe Bay and the surrounding Lakeland mountains.
9 holes, 4826mtrs, Par 70, SSS 66, Course record 67.
Club membership 300.

Visitors	may normally play Mon-Sat.
Green Fees	£10 per day (£15 weekends & bank holidays).
Facilities	ⓔ ♀ 亼
Location	Fell Rd (1m W)
Hotel	★★73% Netherwood Hotel, Lindale Rd, GRANGE-OVER-SANDS ☎ (05395) 32552 29 ⇥ ⋔

Grange-over-Sands ☎ (05395) 33180 or 33754
Parkland course with trees, ditches and easy walking.
18 holes, 5958yds, Par 70, SSS 69.
Club membership 600.

Visitors	must be members of golf clubs or recognised societies. May not play 8.30-9.30am & 11.45-1.15pm on Sat & Sun.
Societies	must contact in writing.
Green Fees	£20 per day; £15 per round (£25/£20 weekends & bank holidays). ▶

Facilities ⊗ & ⅲ by prior arrangement 🏌 (ex Tue) 🍺 ♀
🏃 🏠 ⚐ ⚒ Steve Sumner-Roberts.
Location Meathop Rd (NW of town centre off B5277)
Hotel ★★★63% Grange Hotel, Station Square,
GRANGE-OVER-SANDS
☎ (05395) 33666 41 ⇆ ☞

KENDAL
Map 07 SD59

Kendal ☎ (0539) 724079 & 733708
Elevated moorland course affording breathtaking views of
Lakeland fells and surrounding district.
18 holes, 5534yds, Par 66, SSS 67, Course record 60.
Club membership 700.
Visitors must have a handicap certificate.
Societies must contact in advance.
Facilities ⊗ ⅲ 🏌 🍺 ♀ 🏃 🏠 ⚐ ⚒
Location The Heights (W side of town centre)
Hotel ★★★60% Woolpack Hotel, Stricklandgate,
KENDAL ☎ (0539) 723852 54 ⇆ ☞

KESWICK
Map 11 NY22

Keswick ☎ Threlkeld (07687) 79324
Varied fell and tree-lined course with commanding views of
Lakeland scenery.
18 holes, 6175yds, Par 71, SSS 72.
Club membership 900.
Visitors must contact in advance, restricted on
competition days.
Societies must contact in advance.
Green Fees £15 per day (£20 weekends & bank holidays).
Facilities ⊗ ⅲ 🏌 🍺 ♀ 🏃 🏠 ⚐ ⚒ Craig Hamilton.
Leisure fishing, bowling green.
Location Threlkeld Hall (4m E off A66)
Hotel ★★★73% Brundholme Country House Hotel,
Brundholme Rd, KESWICK
☎ (07687) 74495 12 ⇆ ☞

KIRKBY LONSDALE
Map 07 SD67

Kirkby Lonsdale ☎ Barbon (05242) 76365
Parkland course on the east bank of the River Lune and
crossed by Barbon Beck. Mainly following the lie of the land,
the gently undulating course uses the beck to provide water
hazards.
18 holes, 6283yds, Par 70, SSS 70, Course record 73.
Club membership 600.
Visitors may not play before 9.30am. Restricted Sun am.
Societies telephone in advance.
Green Fees £16 per day (£20 weekends).
Facilities ⊗ ⅲ 🏌 🍺 ♀ 🏃 🏠 ⚒ Chris Barret.
Location Scaleber Ln, Barbon, Carnforth (6m S of
Sedbergh)
Hotel ★★66% Pheasant Inn, CASTERTON
☎ (05242) 71230 10 ⇆ ☞

MARYPORT
Map 11 NY03

Maryport ☎ (0900) 812605
A tight seaside links course exposed to Solway breezes. Fine
views across Solway Firth.
18 holes, 6088yds, Par 70, SSS 69.
Club membership 380.

Visitors no restrictions.
Societies must apply in writing.
Green Fees £15 per day/round (£20 weekends & bank
holidays).
Facilities ⊗ & ⅲ by prior arrangement 🏌 🍺 ♀ 🏃
Location Bank End (1m N on B5300)
Hotel ★★62% Ellenbank Hotel, Birkby,
MARYPORT ☎ (0900) 815233 26 ⇆ ☞

PENRITH
Map 12 NY53

Penrith ☎ (0768) 891919
A beautiful and well-balanced course, always changing
direction, and demanding good length from the tee. It is
set on rolling moorland with occasional pine trees and
some fine views.
18 holes, 6026yds, Par 69, SSS 69, Course record 64.
Club membership 870.
Visitors restricted at weekends. Must contact in
advance and have a handicap certificate.
Societies restricted at weekends.
Green Fees £20 per round (£25 weekends).
Facilities ⊗ ⅲ 🏌 🍺 ♀ 🏃 🏠 ⚐ ⚒ C B Thomson.
Leisure snooker.
Location Salkeld Rd (0.75m N off A6)
Hotel ★★65% George Hotel, Devonshire St,
PENRITH ☎ (0768) 62696 31 ⇆ ☞

ST BEES
Map 11 NX91

St Bees ☎ (0946) 824300
Links course, down hill and dale, with sea views.
9 holes, 5082yds, Par 64, SSS 65.
Club membership 275.
Visitors no restrictions.
Green Fees not confirmed.
Location 0.5m W of village off B5345
Hotel ★★★56% Blackbeck Bridge Inn, EGREMONT
☎ (0946) 841661 22 ⇆ ☞

SEASCALE
Map 06 NY00

Seascale ☎ (09467) 28202
A tough links requiring length and control. The natural
terrain is used to give a variety of holes and considerable
character. Undulating greens add to the challenge. Fine
views over the Western Fells, the Irish Sea and Isle of
Man.
18 holes, 6419yds, Par 71, SSS 71, Course record 65.
Club membership 750.
Visitors must contact in advance and normally may
not play before 9.30am.
Societies must contact in advance.
Green Fees £19 per day (£23 weekends & bank
holidays).
Facilities ⊗ ⅲ 🏌 🍺 ♀ 🏃 🏠 ⚐
Location The Banks (NW side of village off B5344)
Hotel ★★★56% Blackbeck Bridge Inn,
EGREMONT ☎ (0946) 841661 22 ⇆ ☞

For an explanation of symbols and
abbreviations, see page 5

SEDBERGH   Map 07 SD69

Sedbergh ☎ (05396) 20993
A grassland course with superb scenery.The permanent
greens were completed in May 1993.
9 holes, 5504yds, Par 70, SSS 68.
Club membership 300.
Visitors must book to play on weekends & bank holidays.
Societies must contact in advance.
Green Fees £12 (£15 weekends & bank holidays).
Facilities ⊗ ⅢⅢ ⅃ 🍺 ♀ 🛆 🖾 ⌐⌐
Leisure fishing.
Location Catholes, Abbot Holme (1m S off A683)
Hotel ★★70% Garden House Hotel, Fowl-ing Ln,
KENDAL ☎ (0539) 731131 10 ⇆ ♞

SILECROFT   Map 06 SD18

Silecroft ☎ Millom (0229) 774250
Seaside links course parallel to the coast of the Irish Sea.
Often windy. Easy walking. Spectacular views inland of
Lakeland hills.
9 holes, 5877yds, Par 68, SSS 68.
Club membership 365.
Visitors restricted weekends.
Societies must contact 14 days in advance.
Green Fees £10 per day (£15 weekends).
Facilities ♀ by prior arrangement 🛆
Location 1m SW
Hotel ★★63% Eccle Riggs Hotel, Foxfield Rd,
BROUGHTON IN FURNESS
☎ (0229) 716398 & 716780 12 ⇆ ♞

SILLOTH   Map 11 NY15

Silloth on Solway ☎ (06973) 31304
Billowing dunes, narrow fairways, heather and gorse and
the constant subtle problems of tactics and judgement
make these superb links on the Solway an exhilarating and
searching test. The 13th is a good long hole. Superb views.
18 holes, 6445yds, Par 72, SSS 71, Course record 66.
Club membership 600.
Visitors must contact in advance & have handicap
certificate. Restricted Sat & Sun mornings.
Societies must contact in advance.
Green Fees £22 per day (£27 per round weekends &
bank holidays).
Facilities ⊗ ⅢⅢ by prior arrangement 🍺 ♀ 🛆 🖾
♞ John Burns.
Leisure snooker.
Location S side of village off B5300
Hotel ★★62% Golf Hotel, Criffel St, SILLOTH
☎ (06973) 31438 22 ⇆ ♞

ULVERSTON   Map 07 SD27

Ulverston ☎ (0229) 582824
Inland golf with many medium length holes on
undulating parkland. The 17th is a testing par 4.
Overlooking Morecambe Bay the course offers extensive
views to the Lakeland Fells.
18 holes, 6142yds, Par 71, SSS 70.
Club membership 700.

Visitors must contact in advance and have a
handicap certificate. May not play on
competition days.
Societies must apply in writing.
Green Fees not confirmed.
Facilities 🛆 🖾 ♞
Location Bardsea Park (2m S off A5087)
Hotel ★★★69% Whitewater Hotel, The Lakeland
Village, NEWBY BRIDGE
☎ (05395) 31133 35 ⇆ ♞

WINDERMERE   See **Bowness-on-Windermere**

WORKINGTON   Map 11 NX92

Workington ☎ (0900) 603460
Meadowland course, undulating, with natural hazards created
by stream and trees. Good views of Solway Firth and Lakeland
Hills. 10th, 13th and 15th holes are particularly testing.
18 holes, 6200yds, Par 72, SSS 69.
Club membership 900.
Visitors must have a handicap certificate.
Societies must contact in advance.
Green Fees £17 per day (£22 weekends & bank holidays).
Facilities ⊗ ⅢⅢ & 🍺 (ex Mon) ♀ 🛆 🖾 ⌐⌐
♞ Aidrian Drabble.
Leisure snooker, caddy cars.
Location Branthwaite Rd (1.75m E off A596)
Hotel ★★★68% Washington Central Hotel,
Washington St, WORKINGTON
☎ (0900) 65772 40 ⇆ ♞

DERBYSHIRE

ALFRETON   Map 08 SK45

Alfreton ☎ (O773) 832070
A small parkland course with tight fairways and many natural
hazards.
9 holes, 5074yds, Par 66, SSS 65, Course record 62.
Club membership 340.
Visitors with member only Mon & weekends.
Societies apply in writing.
Green Fees £17 per day; £13 per round (18 holes).
Facilities ⊗ & ⅢⅢ (by prior arrangement, not Mon) 🍺 &
🍺 (ex Mon) ♀ (ex Mon) 🛆 🖾
Location Wingfield Rd, Oakerthorpe (1m W on A615)
Hotel ★★★★62% Swallow Hotel, Carter Ln East,
SOUTH NORMANTON
☎ (0773) 812000 161 ⇆ ♞

ASHBOURNE   Map 07 SK14

Ashbourne ☎ (0335) 42078
Undulating parkland course.
9 holes, 5359yds, Par 66, SSS 66.
Club membership 350.   ▶

Visitors	may not play on competition days. With member only at weekends.
Societies	telephone in advance.
Green Fees	£14.
Facilities	⊗ ⅢⅡ ⓑ ⌣ Ⓨ ⌂
Leisure	snooker.
Location	Clifton (1.5m SW on A515)
Hotel	★★♣♣75% Callow Hall, Mappleton Rd, ASHBOURNE ☎ (0335) 343403 & 342412 15 ⊂⌐ ℾ

BAKEWELL   Map 08 SK26

Bakewell ☎ (062981) 2307
Parkland course, hilly, with plenty of natural hazards to test the golfer. Magnificent views across the Wye Valley.
9 holes, 5240yds, Par 68, SSS 66, Course record 63.
Club membership 400.

Visitors	no restrictions.
Societies	must contact in advance.
Facilities	⊗ ⅢⅡ ⓑ ⌣ (no catering Mon) Ⓨ (ex Mon) ⌂ ⓑ
Location	Station Rd (E side of town off A6)
Hotel	★★66% Milford House Hotel, Mill St, BAKEWELL ☎ (0629) 812130 12 ⊂⌐ ℾ

BAMFORD   Map 08 SK28

Sickleholme ☎ Hope Valley (0433) 651306
Downland type course in the lovely Peak District. Fine views.
18 holes, 6064yds, Par 69, SSS 69, Course record 63.
Club membership 700.

Visitors	must contact in advance, restricted Wed mornings & weekends.
Societies	must contact in advance.
Green Fees	£22 per day/round.
Facilities	⊗ ⅢⅡ ⓑ ⌣ Ⓨ ⌂ ⓑ ℾ P H Taylor.
Location	Saltergate Ln (0.75m S on A6013)
Hotel	★★68% Yorkshire Bridge Inn, Ashopton Rd, Yorkshire Bridge, BAMFORD ☎ (0433) 651361 10 ⊂⌐ ℾ

BREADSALL   Map 08 SK33

Breadsall Priory Hotel, Golf & Country Club ☎ Derby (0332) 832235
Set in 200 acres of mature parkland, the Old Course is built on the site of a 13th-century priory. Full use had been made of natural features and fine old trees. In contrast the Moorland Course, opened in Spring 1992, designed by Donald Steel and built by Brian Piersen, features Derbyshire stone walls and open moors heavily affected by winds.
Priory: 18 holes, 5871yds, Par 72, SSS 68.
Moorland: 18 holes, 5820yds, Par 71, SSS 68.
Club membership 800.

Visitors	must contact in advance.
Societies	must contact in advance.
Green Fees	£36 per day; £27.50 per round (£30 per round weekends).
Facilities	⊗ ⅢⅡ ⓑ ⌣ Ⓨ ⌂ ⓑ ℾ↑ ℾ Andrew Smith.
Leisure	hard tennis courts, heated indoor swimming pool, squash, snooker, sauna, solarium, gymnasium, health & beauty salon.

Location	Moor Rd, Morley (0.75m W)
Hotel	★★★71% Breadsall Priory Hotel, Golf & Country Club, Moor Rd, MORLEY ☎ (0332) 832235 14 ⊂⌐ ℾAnnexe77 ⊂⌐ ℾ

BUXTON   Map 07 SK07

Buxton & High Peak ☎ (0298) 23453
Bracing, well-drained meadowland course; the highest in Derbyshire.
18 holes, 5980yds, Par 69, SSS 69, Course record 62.
Club membership 800.

Visitors	no restrictions.
Societies	apply in writing to Mrs S Arnfield.
Green Fees	£20 per day (£25 weekends & bank holidays).
Facilities	⊗ (ex Thu) ⅢⅡ by prior arrangement ⓑ & ⌣ (ex Thu) Ⓨ ⌂ ⓑ ℾ Andrew Hoyles.
Leisure	snooker.
Location	Town End (1m NE off A6)
Hotel	★★★62% Palace Hotel, Palace Rd, BUXTON ☎ (0298) 22001 122 ⊂⌐

Cavendish ☎ (0298) 23494
This parkland/moorland course with its comfortable clubhouse nestles below the rising hills. Generally open to the prevailing west wind, it is noted for its excellent surfaced greens which contain many deceptive subtleties. Designed by Dr Alastair McKenzie, good holes include the 8th, 9th and 18th.
18 holes, 5833yds, Par 68, SSS 68.
Club membership 600.

Visitors	must contact in advance. Must play with member at weekends.
Societies	must contact in advance in writing.
Green Fees	£35 per day; £25 per round (£35 per round weekends & bank holidays).
Facilities	⊗ ⅢⅡ ⓑ ⌣ Ⓨ ⌂ ⓑ ℾ↑ ℾ Paul Hunstone.
Leisure	snooker, hand trolley for hire.
Location	Gadley Ln (0.75m W of town centre off A53)
Hotel	★★★69% Lee Wood Hotel, 13 Manchester Rd, BUXTON ☎ (0298) 23002 & 70421 36 ⊂⌐ ℾAnnexe2 ⊂⌐ ℾ

CARSINGTON   Map 08 SK25

Carsington Water ☎ (062985) 650
Undulating meadowland course on the shores of Carsington Water Reservoir. This is a Pay as You Play course with limited membership available. There is a practice area and a golfing academy. From April 1995 the course will have 18 holes.
18 holes, 6130yds, Par 71.
Club membership 300.

Visitors	should adhere to dress code.
Societies	by prior arrangement in writing.
Green Fees	£11 per 18 holes; £6 per 9 holes (£13/£7 weekends).
Facilities	⊗ by prior arrangement ⓑ ⌣ (all catering from May'95) Ⓨ (from May'95) ⓑ ℾ↑
Leisure	practice area & golfing academy.
Location	Off B5035 Ashbourne/Wirlsworth rd
Hotel	★★★68% Ashbourne Oaks Hotel, Derby Rd, ASHBOURNE ☎ (0335) 346666 50 ⊂⌐ ℾ

CHAPEL-EN-LE-FRITH   Map 07 SK08

Chapel-en-le-Frith ☎ (0298) 812118
Scenic parkland course, with testing holes at the 15th (par 4)
and 17th (517 yds), par 5. Good views.
18 holes, 6119yds, Par 70, SSS 69.
Club membership 662.
Visitors   must contact professional in advance.
Societies   apply in writing.
Green Fees £20 per day (£30 weekends & bank holidays).
Facilities   ⊗ ℳ ⓑ ♟ (no catering Mon) ♀ ⚑ 🏠 ⚑ ⓕ
Location   The Cockyard, Manchester Rd (1m W on A6)
Hotel   ★★★69% Lee Wood Hotel, 13 Manchester Rd,
                  BUXTON ☎ (0298) 23002 & 70421
                  36 ⇆ ⓕAnnexe2 ⇆ ⓕ

CHESTERFIELD   Map 08 SK37

Chesterfield ☎ (0246) 279256
A varied and interesting, undulating parkland course with
trees picturesquely adding to the holes and the outlook alike.
Stream hazard on back nine. Views over four counties.
18 holes, 6326yds, Par 71, SSS 70, Course record 65.
Club membership 500.
Visitors   must contact in advance and must play with
                  member at weekends and bank holidays. A
                  handicap certificate is generally required.
Societies   apply in writing.
Green Fees £22 per round.
Facilities   ⊗ ℳ ⓑ ♟ ♀ ⚑ 🏠 ⓕ M McLean.
Location   Walton (2m SW off A632)
Hotel   ★★★62% Chesterfield, Malkin St,
                  CHESTERFIELD ☎ (0246) 271141 73 ⇆ ⓕ

Grassmoor Golf Centre ☎ (0246) 856044
An 18-hole heathland course with interesting and challenging
water features. 26-bay floodlit driving range, practice bunkers
and putting area.
18 holes, 5800yds, Par 69, SSS 69.
Club membership 400.
Visitors   may book in advance.
Societies   telephone in advance.
Green Fees £7.50 (£9 weekends).
Facilities   ⊗ ℳ ⓑ ♟ ♀ ⚑ 🏠 ⚑ ⓕ Jim Gallagher.
Leisure   sauna, driving range, practice bunkers.
Location   North Wingfield Rd, Grassmoor (between
                  Chesterfield & Grassmoor, off B6038)
Hotel   ★★★62% Chesterfield, Malkin St,
                  CHESTERFIELD ☎ (0246) 271141 73 ⇆ ⓕ

Stanedge ☎ (0246) 566156
Moorland course in hilly situation open to strong winds.
Some fairways are narrow. Accuracy is paramount.
9 holes, 4867yds, Par 64, SSS 64, Course record 64.
Club membership 300.
Visitors   with member only Sat & Sun, and may not play
                  after 2pm weekdays.
Societies   apply in writing.
Green Fees £15 per round (18 holes).
Facilities   ♟ ♀ ⚑
Leisure   pool table.
Location   Walton Hay Farm (5m SW off B5057 nr Red
                  Lion public house)
Hotel   ★★★62% Chesterfield, Malkin St,
                  CHESTERFIELD ☎ (0246) 271141 73 ⇆ ⓕ

Tapton Park ☎ (0246) 239500
Municipal parkland course with some fairly hard walking.
The 620 yd (par 5) 5th is a testing hole.
Tapton Main: 18 holes, 6013yds, Par 71, SSS 69.
Dobbin Clough: 9 holes, 2613yds, Par 34.
Club membership 750.
Visitors   must contact in advance. No caddies allowed.
Societies   telephone in advance.
Green Fees not confirmed.
Facilities   ⊗ ⓑ ♟ ♀ ⚑ 🏠 ⚑ ⓕ
Location   Murray House, Tapton (0.5m E of Chesterfield
                  Station)
Hotel   ★★★62% Chesterfield, Malkin St,
                  CHESTERFIELD ☎ (0246) 271141 73 ⇆ ⓕ

CODNOR   Map 08 SK44

Ormonde Fields ☎ Ripley (0773) 742987
Parkland course with undulating fairways and natural
hazards. The par 4 (4th) and the par 3 (11th) are notable.
There is a practice area.
18 holes, 6011yds, Par 69, SSS 69.
Club membership 500.
Visitors   restricted at weekends.
Societies   telephone in advance.
Green Fees £15 per day (£20 weekends).
Facilities   ⊗ ℳ ⓑ ♟ ♀ ⚑ 🏠 ⚑ ⓕ Peter Buttifant.
Location   Nottingham Rd (1m SE on A610)
Hotel   ★★★71% Makeney Hall Country House Hotel,
                  Makeney, Milford, BELPER
                  ☎ (0332) 842999 27 ⇆ ⓕAnnexe18 ⇆ ⓕ

DERBY   Map 08 SK33

Allestree Park ☎ (0332) 550616
Municipal parkland course in rather hilly country.
18 holes, 5749yds, Par 68, SSS 68, Course record 66.
Club membership 275.
Visitors   restricted weekends & bank holidays.
Societies   restricted at weekends & bank holidays.
Green Fees not confirmed.
Facilities   ⊗ & ℳ by prior arrangement ⓑ ♟ ♀ ⚑ 🏠 ⚑
                  ⓕ Colin Henderson.
Leisure   fishing.
Location   Allestree Hall (3m N on A6)
Hotel   ★★69% Kedleston Country House Hotel,
                  Kedleston Rd, DERBY
                  ☎ (0332) 559202 & 556507 14 ⇆ ⓕ

Derby ☎ (0332) 766323
Municipal parkland course. The front nine holes are rather
difficult.
18 holes, 6144yds, Par 70, SSS 69.
Club membership 450.
Visitors   starting time must be booked at weekends. Must
                  contact in advance.
Societies   apply in writing in advance.
Green Fees £8.90.
Facilities   ⊗ ℳ ⓑ ♟ ♀ ⚑ 🏠 ⚑ ⓕ Andrew Carnell.
Location   Shakespeare St, Sinfin (3.5m S of city centre)
Hotel   ★★★62% International Hotel, Burton Rd
                  (A5250), DERBY
                  ☎ (0332) 369321 41 ⇆ ⓕAnnexe21 ⇆ ⓕ

Mickleover ☎ (0332) 513339 or 512092
Undulating parkland course in pleasant setting.
18 holes, 5708yds, Par 68, SSS 68.
Club membership 700.

Visitors	no restrictions.
Societies	telephone (0332) 518662 in advance.
Green Fees	£20 per day/round (£25 weekends & bank holidays).
Facilities	⊗ ﹖ ﹐ 📖 ♥ ♀ ᚛ 🏠 ⌀ Paul Wilson.
Leisure	snooker.
Location	Uttoxeter Rd, Mickleover (3m W off A516/B5020)
Hotel	B Forte Posthouse, Pasture Hill, Littleover, DERBY ☎ (0332) 514933 62 ⇄

DRONFIELD   Map 08 SK37

Hallowes ☎ (0246) 413734
Attractive moorland/meadowland course set in the
Derbyshire hills. Several testing par 4's and splendid views.
18 holes, 6330yds, Par 71, SSS 70.
Club membership 600.

Visitors	may only play with member at weekends; restricted Wed. Must contact in advance and have a handicap certificate.
Societies	must contact in advance.
Green Fees	not confirmed.
Facilities	⊗ ﹖ ﹐ 📖 ♥ ♀ ᚛ 🏠 ⌀ Philip Dunn.
Leisure	snooker.
Location	Hallowes Ln (S side of town)
Hotel	★★62% Chantry Hotel, Church St, DRONFIELD ☎ (0246) 413014 7 ⇄ ↰

DUFFIELD   Map 08 SK34

Chevin ☎ (0332) 841864
A mixture of parkland and moorland, this course is rather
hilly which makes for some hard walking. The 8th calls for a
very hard drive, possibly the hardest in the area.
18 holes, 6057yds, Par 69, SSS 69.
Club membership 500.

Visitors	with member only weekends & bank holidays.
Societies	contact in advance.
Green Fees	not confirmed.
Facilities	♀ ᚛ 🏠 ⌀ ⌀
Leisure	snooker, practice ground.
Location	Golf Ln (N side of town off A6)
Hotel	★★69% Kedleston Country House Hotel, Kedleston Rd, DERBY ☎ (0332) 559202 & 556507 14 ⇄ ↰

GLOSSOP   Map 07 SK09

Glossop and District ☎ (0457) 865247
Moorland course in good position, excellent natural hazards.
11 holes, 5800yds, Par 68, SSS 68.
Club membership 250.

Visitors	may not play on bank holidays.
Societies	must apply in writing to professional.
Green Fees	not confirmed.
Facilities	⊗ ﹖ ﹐ 📖 ♥ (No catering Mon) ♀ (ex Mon) ᚛ 🏠 ⌀ Gary S Brown.
Location	Hurst Ln, off Sheffield Rd (1m E off A57)
Hotel	★★69% York House Hotel, York Place, Richmond St, ASHTON-UNDER-LYNE ☎ 061-330 5899 24 ⇄ ↰Annexe10 ⇄ ↰

HORSLEY   Map 08 SK34

Horsley Lodge ☎ Derby (0332) 780838
This course, opened in 1991 and set in 100 acres of
Derbyshire countryside, has some challenging holes. Also Par
3 course and floodlit driving range.
18 holes, 6434yds, Par 72, SSS 71, Course record 72.
Club membership 600.

Visitors	restricted during competitions at weekends.
Societies	must telephone in advance.
Green Fees	£25 per 36 holes, £17 per 18 holes, £12 per 9 holes.
Facilities	⊗ ﹖ ﹐ 📖 ♥ ♀ ᚛ 🏠 ⌀ ⌀ ⌀ Simon Berry.
Leisure	fishing, sauna, solarium, putting green, driving range.
Location	Smalley Mill Rd (4m NE of Derby, off A38)
Hotel	★★★71% Breadsall Priory Hotel,Golf & Country Club, Moor Rd, MORLEY ☎ (0332) 832235 14 ⇄ ↰Annexe77 ⇄ ↰

KEDLESTON   Map 08 SK34

Kedleston Park ☎ Derby (0332) 840035
The course is laid out in flat mature parkland with fine
trees and background views of historic Kedleston Hall
(National Trust). Many testing holes are included in each
nine and there is an excellent modern clubhouse.
18 holes, 6253yds, Par 70, SSS 70, Course record 65.
Club membership 954.

Visitors	welcome weekdays, must contact in advance & have handicap certificate. With member only at weekends.
Societies	telephone in advance.
Green Fees	£35 per day; £25 per round.
Facilities	⊗ ﹖ ﹐ 📖 ♥ ♀ ᚛ 🏠 ⌀ ⌀ Jim Hetherington.
Leisure	snooker, sauna, caddy cars.
Location	Kedleston Quarndon (2m SE)
Hotel	★★69% Kedleston Country House Hotel, Kedleston Rd, DERBY ☎ (0332) 559202 & 556507 14 ⇄ ↰

MATLOCK   Map 08 SK36

Matlock ☎ (0629) 582191
Moorland course with fine views of the beautiful Peak
District.
18 holes, 5991yds, Par 70, SSS 68.
Club membership 650.

Visitors	with member only weekends & bank holidays. Members only weekdays 12.30-1.30pm.
Societies	telephone in advance.
Green Fees	£25 per day/round.
Facilities	⊗ & ﹖ by prior arrangement 📖 ♥ ♀ ᚛ 🏠 ⌀ M A Whithorn.
Leisure	snooker, crown green bowling.
Location	Chesterfield Rd (1m NE of Matlock on A632)
Hotel	★★★70% New Bath Hotel, New Bath Rd, MATLOCK ☎ (0629) 583275 55 ⇄ ↰

> **Phoneday** - remember from 16 April
> 1995 all phone codes in the UK will
> change - see page 4 for details

MICKLEOVER

Map 08 SK33

Pastures ☎ Derby (0332) 521074
Small course laid-out on undulating meadowland in the
grounds of a psychiatric hospital, with good views across the
Trent valley. Fishing and snooker.
9 holes, 5005yds, Par 64, SSS 64, Course record 62.
Club membership 320.

Visitors	must be accompanied by a member, may not play on Sun. Must contact in advance.
Societies	must contact in advance.
Green Fees	on application.
Facilities	⬤⬤
Leisure	fishing, snooker, bowls, table tennis.
Location	Pastures Hospital (1m SW off A516)
Hotel	★★★62% International Hotel, Burton Rd (A5250), DERBY ☎ (0332) 369321 41 ⇆ ℝAnnexe21 ⇆ ℝ

NEW MILLS

Map 07 SK08

New Mills ☎ (0663) 743485
Moorland course with panoramic views and first-class greens.
9 holes, 5633yds, Par 68, SSS 67, Course record 67.
Club membership 350.

Visitors	must play with member at weekends & special days. Must contact in advance.
Societies	must contact in advance.
Green Fees	not confirmed.
Facilities	⊗ & ⫝̸ by prior arrangement ⬥ ⬤ ⬤⬤ ⬤ ⬤ ⬤ ⟨ Andrew Hoyles.
Location	Shaw Marsh (0.5m N off B6101)
Hotel	★★70% Red Lion Inn, 112 Buxton Rd, High Ln, STOCKPORT ☎ (0663) 765227 6 ⇆ ℝ

RENISHAW

Map 08 SK47

Renishaw Park ☎ Eckington (0246) 432044
Part parkland and part meadowland with easy walking.
18 holes, 5949yds, Par 71, SSS 68.
Club membership 500.

Visitors	no restrictions.
Societies	apply in writing.
Green Fees	£28 per day; £20 per round (£33 per round/day weekends & bank holidays).
Facilities	⊗ ⫝̸ by prior arrangement ⬥ ⬤ ⬤⬤ ⬤ ⬤ ⟨ Simon Elliot.
Leisure	snooker.
Location	Golf House (0.5m NW on A616)
Hotel	★★★57% Sitwell Arms Hotel, RENISHAW ☎ (0246) 435226 30 ⇆ ℝ

SHIRLAND

Map 08 SK45

Shirlands ☎ (0773) 834935
Rolling parkland and tree-lined course with extensive views
of Derbyshire countryside.
18 holes, 6072yds, Par 71, SSS 69, Course record 71.
Club membership 700.

Visitors	must contact in advance.
Societies	contact Professional.
Green Fees	not confirmed.
Facilities	⊗⫝̸⬥⬤⬤⬤⬤⬤⟨ N B Hallam.
Leisure	bowling green.

Location	Lower Delves (S side of village off A61)
Hotel	★★★★62% Swallow Hotel, Carter Ln East, SOUTH NORMANTON ☎ (0773) 812000 161 ⇆ ℝ

STANTON-BY-DALE

Map 08 SK43

Erewash Valley ☎ Sandiacre (0602) 323258
Parkland/meadowland course overlooking valley and M1.
Unique 4th and 5th in Victorian quarry bottom: 5th-testing
par 3.
18 holes, 6487yds, Par 72, SSS 71, Course record 67.
Club membership 860.

Visitors	no restrictions
Societies	contact in advance.
Green Fees	£27 per day; £22 per round (£27 per day/round weekends).
Facilities	⊗ ⫝̸ ⬥ ⬤ ⬤⬤ ⬤ ⬤ ⟨ M J Ronan.
Leisure	snooker, bowling green.
Location	1m W
Hotel	B Forte Posthouse, Bostocks Ln, SANDIACRE ☎ (0602) 397800 91 ⇆ ℝ

DEVON

AXMOUTH

Map 03 SY29

Axe Cliff ☎ Seaton (0297) 24371
Undulating links course with coastal views.
18 holes, 5057yds, Par 67, SSS 65.
Club membership 400.

Visitors	may only play after 11am on Wed & Sun.
Societies	must contact in advance.
Green Fees	on request.
Facilities	⊗ ⫝̸ ⬥ ⬤ ⬤⬤ ⬤ ⟨ Mark Dack.
Location	0.75m S on B3172
Hotel	★★64% Anchor Inn, BEER ☎ (0297) 20386 8rm(5 ⇆ ℝ)
Additional hotel	★★★68% Arundell Arms, LIFTON ☎ (0566) 784666 24 ⇆ ℝAnnexe5 ⇆ ℝ *See advertisement on page 48*

BIGBURY-ON-SEA

Map 03 SX64

Bigbury ☎ (0548) 810557
Clifftop, heathland course with easy walking. Exposed to
winds, but with fine views over the sea and River Avon. 7th
hole particularly tricky.
18 holes, 6048yds, Par 70, SSS 68.
Club membership 850.

Visitors	must have handicap certificate.
Societies	must apply in writing.
Green Fees	£20 per day (£24 weekends & bank holidays). Half price after 4pm.
Facilities	⊗ & ⫝̸ by prior arrangement ⬥ ⬤ ⬤⬤ ⬤ ⬤ ⟨ Simon Lloyd.
Leisure	caddy cars to hire.
Location	1m S on B3392
Hotel	★69% Henley Hotel, BIGBURY-ON-SEA ☎ (0548) 810240 8 ⇆ ℝ

THE ARUNDELL ARMS HOTEL

Lifton, Devon. PL16 0AA

★★★ ☺☺

Tel: 01566 784666 Fax: 01566 784494

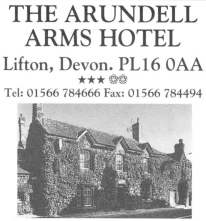

A famous sporting hotel on Devon/Cornwall border, offering a wide range of challenging championship courses including the Jack Nicklaus designed course at nearby St. Mellion. The Arundell Arms is a 250 year old former coaching inn, famed for its fishing on the river Tamar, shooting and golf, log fire comfort, superb food and wine in its 2 AA rosetted restaurant.

BUDLEIGH SALTERTON   Map 03 SY08

East Devon ☎ (0395) 443370
An interesting course with downland turf, much heather and gorse, and superb views over the bay. The early holes climb to the cliff edge. The downhill 17th has a heather section in the fairway, leaving a good second to the green.
18 holes, 6239yds, Par 70, SSS 70.
Club membership 850.
Visitors   must contact in advance and have an
              introduction from own club.
Societies   must contact in advance.
Green Fees not confirmed.
Facilities ⊗ ⅃ ⬤ ♀ ⚘ 🍴 ☂ ⚹ Trevor Underwood.
Location   North View Rd (W side of town centre)
Hotel   ★★★60% The Imperial, The Esplanade,
              EXMOUTH ☎ (0395) 274761 57 ⇄ ⛾

CHITTLEHAMHOLT   Map 03 SS62

Highbullen Hotel ☎ (0769) 540561
Mature parkland course with water hazards and outstanding scenic views to Exmoor and Dartmoor. Excellent facilities offered by the hotel.
9 holes, 2210yds, Par 31, SSS 29.
Club membership 100.
Visitors   no restrictions.
Green Fees £8 per day; £6 after 5pm (Free to residents).
Facilities ⊗ 🍴 ⅃ ⬤ ♀ ⚘ 🍴 ⚹ Paul Weston.
Leisure   hard tennis courts, outdoor and indoor heated
              swimming pools, squash, snooker, sauna,

---

solarium, gymnasium, indoor putting, steam room, tennis.
Location   0.5m SE of village
Hotel   ★★★♨70% Highbullen Hotel,
              CHITTLEHAMHOLT
              ☎ (0769) 540561 12 ⇄Annexe25 ⇄ ⛾

CHULMLEIGH   Map 03 SS61

Chulmleigh ☎ (0769) 580519
Challenging par 3 courses on undulating meadowland.
18 holes, 1485yds, Par 54, SSS 54, Course record 52.
Club membership 100.
Visitors   may play without restriction but juniors (under
              12 yrs) should be accompanied by an adult.
Societies   must contact in advance.
Green Fees £11 per day; £6 per round.
Facilities ⅃ ⬤ ♀ ⚘ 🍴 ☂
Leisure   trolleys.
Location   Leigh Rd (SW side of village just off A377)
Hotel   ★★★♨73% Northcote Manor,
              BURRINGTON ☎ (0769) 60501 11 ⇄ ⛾

CHURSTON FERRERS   Map 03 SX95

Churston ☎ Churston (0803) 842751
A cliff-top downland course with splendid views over Brixham harbour and Tor Bay. There is some gorse with a wooded area inland. A variety of shot is called for, with particularly testing holes at the 3rd, 9th and 15th, all par 4.
18 holes, 6219yds, Par 70, SSS 70.
Club membership 700.

Dainton Hotel and Licensed Restaurant

95 Dartmouth Road, Three Beaches, Goodrington, Paignton, Devon TQ4 6NA

Telephone: (01803) 550067
Fax No: (01803) 666339

Attractive hotel and licensed restaurant combining charm, warmth and character with modern facilities. Delightful olde worlde restaurant serving table d'hote, a la carte and bar meals. Wedding receptions and celebration meals also catered for. Well appointed bedrooms all ensuite and all with tea & coffee making facilities and colour TV plus views of Torbay. Beach 250 yards, Torquay 4 miles, Brixham 3 miles. Golf nearby. Bargain Breaks available. Ample parking.

♛ ♛ ♛

Visitors	must be members of recognised golf club & have handicap certificate, play is restricted at times.
Societies	must contact in advance.
Green Fees	£22 per day (£27 weekends).
Facilities	⊗ ⽶ by prior arrangement ⮂ ♨ ♀ ⛳ ⌂ 𝄞 R Penfold.
Location	NW side of village on A379
Hotel	★★62% Dainton Hotel, 95 Dartmouth Rd, Three Beaches, Goodrington, PAIGNTON ☎ (0803) 550067 & 525901 11 ⇆ ♞

CREDITON   Map 03 SS80

Downes Crediton ☎ (0363) 773025 & 774464
Converted farmhouse course with lovely views. Parkland with hilly back nine.
18 holes, 5920yds, Par 70, SSS 68.
Club membership 700.

Visitors	must contact in advance, restricted at weekends.
Societies	must contact in advance.
Green Fees	£16 per day (£22.50 weekends).
Facilities	⊗ (by prior arrangement Sun) ⽶ by prior arrangement ⮂ ♨ ♀ ⛳ ⌂ 𝄞 𝄞 Howard Finch.
Location	Hookway (1.5m SE off A377)
Hotel	★★★71% Barton Cross Hotel & Restaurant, Huxham, STOKE CANON ☎ (0392) 841245 & 841584 6 ⇆ ♞

CULLOMPTON   Map 03 ST00

Padbrook Park ☎ (0884) 38286
A 9-hole, 18 tee parkland course with much mature woodland and two small lakes.
9 holes, 6108yds, Par 70, SSS 69.
Club membership 450.

Visitors	must contact in advance.
Societies	apply by telephone.
Green Fees	not confirmed.
Facilities	⊗ ⽶ ⮂ ♨ ♀ ⛳ ⌂ 𝄞 Stewart Adwick.
Leisure	fishing, riding, indoor bowling centre.
Location	13m NE of Exeter, 1m from junc 28 of M5
Hotel	★★70% Parkway House, SAMPFORD PEVERELL ☎ (0884) 820255 10 ⇆ ♞

DAWLISH WARREN   Map 03 SX97

Warren ☎ (0626) 862255
Typical flat, genuine links course lying on spit between sea and Exe estuary. Picturesque scenery, a few trees but much gorse. Testing in windy conditions. The 7th hole provides the opportunity to go for the green across a bay on the estuary.
18 holes, 5973yds, Par 69, SSS 69.
Club membership 700.

Visitors	must contact in advance & have handicap certificate.
Societies	telephone in advance.
Green Fees	not confirmed.
Facilities	⊗ ⽶ ⮂ ♨ ♀ ⛳ ⌂ 𝄞 Andrew Naldrett.
Location	E side of village
Hotel	★★★62% Langstone Cliff Hotel, Dawlish Warren, DAWLISH ☎ (0626) 865155 64 ⇆ ♞

DOWN ST MARY   Map 03 SS70

Waterbridge ☎ (0363) 85111
A testing course of 9-holes set in a gently sloping valley. The Par of 31 will not be easily gained with 4 par-4's and 5 par-3's, although the course record holder has Par 29! The 3rd hole which is a raised green is surrounded by water and the 4th (439 yards) is demanding for beginners.
9 holes, 3908yds, Par 62, SSS 62, Course record 29.
Club membership 100.

Visitors	no restrictions.
Societies	telephone in advance.
Green Fees	£9 per 18 holes; £5 per 9 holes (£12/£6.50 weekends & bankholidays).
Facilities	♨ 𝄞 𝄞 Michael Blackwell.
Location	From Exeter on A377 towards Barnstaple
Hotel	★★★♨73% Northcote Manor, BURRINGTON ☎ (0769) 60501 11 ⇆ ♞

EXETER   Map 03 SX99

Exeter Golf & Country Club ☎ Topsham (039287) 4139
A sheltered parkland course with some very old trees and known as the flattest course in Devon. 15th & 17th are testing par 4 holes.
18 holes, 6000yds, Par 69, SSS 69.
Club membership 850.

Visitors	must contact in advance and have a handicap certificate.
Societies	welcome Thu only, must telephone in advance.
Green Fees	£22 per day.
Facilities	⊗ ⽶ (Fri & Sat evenings only) ⮂ ♨ ♀ ⛳ ⌂ 𝄞 Mike Rowlett.
Leisure	hard tennis courts, outdoor and indoor heated swimming pools, squash, snooker, sauna, solarium, gymnasium.
Location	Topsham Rd, Countess Wear (SE side of city centre off A379)
Hotel	★★★61% Travel Inn, 398 Topsham Rd, Exeter Bypass, EXETER ☎ (0392) 875441 44 ⇆ ♞

Woodbury Park ☎ Woodbury (0395) 33382
Two courses set in the lovely wooded parkland of Woodbury Castle.The 18-hole championship Oaks course is host to professional Championships and the 9-hole is a championship-standard training course.
Oaks: 18 holes, 6707yds, Par 72, SSS 72.
Acorn: 9 holes, 4582yds, Par 69, SSS 62.
Club membership 400.

Visitors	advisable to contact in advance.
Societies	contact in advance.
Green Fees	not confirmed.
Facilities	⊗ ⽶ by prior arrangement ⮂ ♨ ♀ (Mon-Sat) ⛳ ⌂ 𝄞
Leisure	fishing.
Location	Woodbury Castle, Woodbury
Hotel	★★71% Ebford House Hotel, Exmouth Rd, EBFORD ☎ (0392) 877658 17 ⇆ ♞

> Use the AA *Hotels* or *Bed and Breakfast* guides to extend your choice of accommodation

49

HIGH BICKINGTON
Map 02 SS52

Libbaton ☎ (0769) 60269
Parkland course on undulating land with no steep slopes.
Floodlit driving range.
18 holes, 5812yds, Par 72, SSS 68.
Club membership 400.

Visitors	may not play during competitions, advisable to phone in advance.
Societies	must contact in advance.
Green Fees	not confirmed.
Facilities	⊗ ⅧⅡ ᛒ ⬛ ♀ ♨ 🏠 🍴 ⚑ John Phillips.
Hotel	★★★⚑70% Highbullen Hotel, CHITTLEHAMHOLT ☎ (0769) 540561 12 ⇆Annexe25 ⇆ ⁿⓧ

HOLSWORTHY
Map 02 SS30

Holsworthy ☎ (0409) 253177
Pleasant parkland course.
18 holes, 6062yds, Par 70, SSS 69.
Club membership 700.

Visitors	may not play before 9.30am or 12-2.30pm Sat, before 2.30pm Sun or on competition days.
Societies	must contact in writing.
Green Fees	£15 per day (£20 weekends & bank holidays).
Facilities	⊗ ⅧⅡ ᛒ ⬛ ♀ ♨ 🏠 🍴 ⚑ Tim McSherry.
Location	Killatree (1.5m W on A3072)
Hotel	★★⚑70% Court Barn Country House Hotel, CLAWTON ☎ (040927) 219 8rm(4 ⇆3 ⁿⓧ)

HONITON
Map 03 ST10

Honiton ☎ (0404) 44422
Level parkland course on a plateau 850ft above sea level.
Easy walking and good views. The 4th hole is a testing par 3.
The club was founded in 1896.
18 holes, 5940yds, Par 69, SSS 68, Course record 68.
Club membership 800.

Visitors	must contact in advance & have handicap certificate.
Societies	must contact in writing.
Green Fees	£20 per round (£25 weekends).
Facilities	⊗ ⅧⅡ ᛒ ⬛ (Mon-Sat only) ♀ ♨ 🏠 ⚑ ⚑ Adrian Cave.
Leisure	touring caravan park adjacent.
Location	Middlehills (1.25m SE)
Hotel	★★68% Home Farm Hotel, Wilmington, HONITON ☎ (0404) 831278 & 831246 6 ⇆Annexe7 ⇆ ⁿⓧ

ILFRACOMBE
Map 02 SS54

Ilfracombe ☎ (0271) 862176
A sporting, clifftop, heathland course with views over the
Bristol Channel and moors from every tee and green.
18 holes, 5893yds, Par 70, SSS 69, Course record 66.
Club membership 706.

Visitors	must have handicap certificate, play is restricted at times.
Societies	must contact in advance.
Green Fees	not confirmed.
Facilities	⊗ ⅧⅡ ᛒ ⬛ ♀ ♨ 🏠 🍴 ⚑ David Hoare.
Leisure	pool & darts.

Location	Hele Bay (1.5m E off A399)
Hotel	★★67% Elmfield Hotel, Torrs Park, ILFRACOMBE ☎ (0271) 863377 12rm(11 ⁿⓧ)Annexe2 ⇆ ⁿⓧ

IVYBRIDGE
Map 02 SX65

Dinnaton Sporting & Country Club ☎ Plymouth (0752)
892512 & 892452
A 9-hole course, mainly par 3 but with four recently added
par 4 holes. Floodlit driving range.
9 holes, 3850yds, Par 62, SSS 56.
Club membership 300.

Visitors	a handicap certificate is required.
Societies	must telephone in advance.
Green Fees	weekdays £10 (£12.50 weekends & bank holidays).
Facilities	⊗ ⅧⅡ ᛒ ⬛ ♀ ♨ 🏠 🍴 ♨⚑ David Ridyard.
Leisure	heated indoor swimming pool, squash, snooker, sauna, solarium, gymnasium, badminton courts, volleyball courts.
Location	Blachford Rd
Hotel	★★⚑⚑74% Glazebrook House Hotel & Restaurant, SOUTH BRENT ☎ (0364) 73322 11 ⇆ ⁿⓧ

MORETONHAMPSTEAD
Map 03 SX78

Manor House Hotel ☎ (0647) 40355
This enjoyable parkland course is a sporting circuit with
just enough hazards (most of them natural) to make any
golfer think. The Rivers Bowden and Bovey meander
through the first eight holes. Driving range.
18 holes, 6016yds, Par 69, SSS 69, Course record 65.
Club membership 230.

Visitors	must contact in advance and pre-arrange starting times.
Societies	must contact in advance.
Green Fees	£30 per day; £22.50 per round (£35/£28 weekends).
Facilities	⊗ ⅧⅡ ᛒ ♀ ♨ 🏠 🍴 ♨⚑ Richard Lewis.
Leisure	hard tennis courts, squash, fishing, snooker, 6 hole pitch & putt, driving range.
Location	3m W off B3212
Hotel	★★70% The White Hart Hotel, The Square, MORETONHAMPSTEAD ☎ (0647) 40406 20 ⇆ ⁿⓧ

MORTEHOE
Map 02 SS44

Mortehoe & Woolacombe ☎ Woolacombe (0271) 870225
Attached to a camping and caravan site, this 9-hole course
has 2 par 3s and 7 par 4s. The gently sloping clifftop course
has spectacular views across Morte Bay.
9 holes, 2426yds, Par 34, SSS 32.
Club membership 250.

Visitors	no restrictions.
Societies	must telephone in advance.
Green Fees	£13 per day; £10 per 18 holes; £6 per 9 holes.
Facilities	⊗ ⅧⅡ ᛒ ⬛ (Apr-Nov) ♀ ♨ 🏠 ⚑
Leisure	heated indoor swimming pool, camping & caravan site.
Hotel	★★★75% Watersmeet Hotel, Mortehoe, WOOLACOMBE ☎ (0271) 870333 23 ⇆ ⁿⓧ

NEWTON ABBOT   Map 03 SX87

Newton Abbot (Stover) ☎ (0626) 52460
Wooded parkland course with a stream coming into play on eight holes. Fairly flat.
18 holes, 5886yds, Par 69, SSS 68.
Club membership 887.

Visitors	must have proof of membership of recognised club. Must contact in advance.
Societies	by arrangement on Thu only.
Green Fees	£22 per day.
Facilities	⊗ ℳ by prior arrangement 🍴 🍺 ♀ ⚲ 🏠 ♟ Malcolm Craig.
Location	Bovey Rd (3m N on A382)
Hotel	★★61% Queens Hotel, Queen St, NEWTON ABBOT
	☎ (0626) 63133 & 54106 24rm(20 ⇆ ♋)

OKEHAMPTON   Map 02 SX59

Okehampton ☎ (0837) 52113
Interesting and beautiful moorland course with true Dartmoor turf.
18 holes, 5223yds, Par 68, SSS 67, Course record 62.
Club membership 550.

Visitors	must contact in advance.
Societies	must contact in writing.
Green Fees	£15 per day (£20 Sat, £17 Sun).
Facilities	⊗ ℳ 🍴 🍺 ♀ ⚲ 🏠 🏁 ♟
Location	Tors Rd (1m S off A30)
Hotel	★★62% Oxenham Arms, SOUTH ZEAL
	☎ (0837) 840244 & 840577 8rm(7 ⇆ ♋)

PLYMOUTH   Map 02 SX45

Elfordleigh ☎ (0752) 336428
Charming, saucer-shaped parkland course with alternate tees for 18 holes. Tree-lined fairways and three lakes. Fairly hard walking.
9 holes, 5664yds, Par 68, SSS 67.
Club membership 450.

Visitors	must contact in advance & have handicap certificate.
Societies	by arrangement.
Green Fees	not confirmed.
Facilities	⊗ ℳ 🍴 🍺 ♀ ⚲ 🏠 🏁 ♋ ♟ Andrew Rickard.
Leisure	hard tennis courts, outdoor and indoor heated swimming pools, squash, snooker, sauna, solarium, gymnasium, games room, jacuzzi, croquet.
Location	Plympton (8m NE off B3416)
Hotel	★★★68% Elfordleigh Hotel & Country Club, Colebrook, Plympton, PLYMOUTH
	☎ (0752) 336428 18 ⇆ ♋
Additional hotel	★★★65% St Mellion Hotel, St Mellion Golf & County Club, ST MELLION
	☎ (0579) 50101 Annexe24 ⇆ ♋

Staddon Heights ☎ (0752) 402475
Seaside course that can be windy. Walking easy.
18 holes, 5874yds, Par 68, SSS 68.
Club membership 750.

Visitors	cannot play Sun.
Societies	must apply to the secretary.

▶

YOUR VERY OWN 19th
– WITH FREE GOLF

When you take a luxury lodge at St. Mellion – for a few days, a week or longer – these are just a few of the pleasures that await you.

Golf on either the Nicklaus Championship Course or the Old Course, the heated pool and all the other sports facilities at the Country Club and, not least, your choice of two excellent restaurants.

Add to that the tranquil Cornish countryside, nearby Plymouth and excellent beaches and your holiday will be complete.

Take the first step now. Find out about availability and rates – for parties of two to eight people – from our Reservation Staff on 01579 50101.

ST. MELLION GOLF & COUNTRY CLUB
DEPT AA · SALTASH · CORNWALL PL12 6SD
TEL 01579 50101   FAX 01579 50116

ST. MELLION

Harrabeer Country House Hotel
Harrowbeer Lane
Yelverton
Devon PL20 6EA
Telephone: Yelverton (01822) 853302

Harrabeer Country House is just the place to relax after a days golf. There are seven interesting courses, including St. Melion, within easy reach of this small, friendly, family run hotel. Enjoy excellent home cooked food and exchange golfing tales in the olde-worlde bar, where a log fire burns on cooler evenings. Special winter breaks.

Proprietors: Ron and Patsy Back

AA QQQ   COMMENDED

Green Fees £15 per day (£20 weekends).
Facilities ⊗ ⵘ ᴸ ♥ ⴹ ⵗ ⋒ (
Leisure snooker.
Location Plymstock (5m SW)
Hotel B Forte Posthouse, Cliff Rd, The Hoe,
PLYMOUTH ☎ (0752) 662828 106 ⇄ ꜰ
Additional ★★★65% St Mellion Hotel, St Mellion Golf &
hotel County Club, ST MELLION
☎ (0579) 50101 Annexe24 ⇄ ꜰ

SAUNTON   Map 02 SS43

> **Saunton** ☎ Braunton (0271) 812436
> Two traditional links courses (one championship).
> Windy, with natural hazards.
> *East Course: 18 holes, 6708yds, Par 71, SSS 73.*
> *West Course: 18 holes, 6356yds, Par 71, SSS 71, Course record 68.*
> *Club membership 1180.*
> **Visitors** must have handicap certificate and be
> member of recognised golf club.
> **Societies** must apply in writing.
> **Green Fees** £28 (£33 weekends).
> **Facilities** ⊗ ⵘ ᴸ ♥ ⴹ ⵗ ⋒ (
> **Location** S side of village off B3231
> **Hotel** ★★★★63% Saunton Sands Hotel,
> SAUNTON ☎ (0271) 890212 92 ⇄ ꜰ

SIDMOUTH   Map 03 SY18

Sidmouth ☎ (0395) 513451
Situated on the side of Peak Hill, offering beautiful coastal
views. Club founded in 1889.
18 holes, 5100yds, Par 66, SSS 65, Course record 59.
Club membership 700.
Visitors restricted on competition days. Must contact in
advance.
Societies must telephone in advance.
Green Fees £18 per day.
Facilities ⊗ ⵘ ♥ ⴹ ⋒ ⵗ (Haydn Barrell.
Location Cotmaton Rd, Peak Hill (W side of town centre)
Hotel ★★★★65% Victoria Hotel, Esplanade,
SIDMOUTH ☎ (0395) 512651 61 ⇄ ꜰ

SOUTH BRENT   Map 03 SX66

Wrangaton (S Devon) ☎ (0364) 73229
Moorland/parkland course within Dartmoor National Park.
Spectacular views towards sea and rugged terrain. Natural
fairways and hazards include bracken, sheep and ponies.
18 holes, 6040yds, Par 69, SSS 69, Course record 67.
Club membership 600.
Visitors must contact in advance & have evidence of
proficiency, restricted on competition days.
Usual dress rules apply.
Societies must give one months notice in writing.
Green Fees £16 per day (£20 weekends & bank holidays).
Facilities ⊗ & ⵘ (ex Mon) ᴸ ♥ ⴹ ⋒
(Adrian Whitehead.
Location Golf Links Rd, Wrangaton (2.25 m SW off A38)
Hotel ★★✦74% Glazebrook House Hotel &
Restaurant, SOUTH BRENT
☎ (0364) 73322 11 ⇄ ꜰ

TAVISTOCK   Map 02 SX47

Hurdwick ☎ (0822) 612746
This Executive parkland course with many bunkers and fine
views opened in 1990. The idea of Executive golf originated
in America and the concept is that a round should take no
longer than 3 hours whilst offering solid challenge, thus
suiting the busy business person.
18 holes, 4553yds, Par 67, SSS 62, Course record 67.
Club membership 175.
Visitors no restrictions.
Societies must contact in advance.
Green Fees £10 per day.
Facilities ᴸ ♥ ⴹ ⵗ
Leisure caddy cars.
Location Tavistock Hamlets (1m N)
Hotel ★★★62% Bedford Hotel, Plymouth Rd,
TAVISTOCK ☎ (0822) 613221 31rm(30 ⇄ ꜰ)

> **Tavistock** ☎ (0822) 612344
> Set on Whitchurch Down in south-west Dartmoor with
> easy walking and magnificent views over rolling
> countryside into Cornwall. Downland turf with some
> heather, and interesting holes on undulating ground.
> *18 holes, 6250yds, Par 70, SSS 70.*
> *Club membership 700.*
> **Visitors** may not play on competition days. Must contact
> in advance and have a handicap certificate.
> **Societies** must apply in writing.
> **Green Fees** weekdays £18; weekends £23.
> **Facilities** ⊗ ⵘ ᴸ ♥ ⴹ ⋒ ⵗ (Reg Cade.
> **Leisure** snooker.
> **Location** Down Rd (1m SE)
> **Hotel** ★★★62% Bedford Hotel, Plymouth Rd,
> TAVISTOCK
> ☎ (0822) 613221 31rm(30 ⇄ ꜰ)

TEDBURN ST MARY   Map 03 SX89

Fingle Glen ☎ (0647) 61817
9-hole course containing six par 4's and three par 3's set in
52 acres of rolling countryside. Testing 4th, 5th and 9th holes.
12-bay floodlit driving range.
9 holes, 2466yds, Par 33, SSS 31.
Club membership 450.
Visitors no restrictions.
Societies must telephone two weeks in advance.
Green Fees £11 per 18 holes; £7.50 per 9 holes (£13/£8.50
weekends).
Facilities ⊗ ⵘ ᴸ ♥ ⴹ ⋒ ⵗ ⴻ (Stephen Gould.
Leisure driving range.
Location 5m W of Exeter, off A30
Hotel ★★★61% Travel Inn, 398 Topsham Rd, Exeter
Bypass, EXETER ☎ (0392) 875441 44 ⇄ ꜰ

TEIGNMOUTH   Map 03 SX97

> **Teignmouth** ☎ (0626) 774194
> This fairly flat heathland course is high up with a fine
> seascape from the clubhouse. Good springy turf with
> some heather and an interesting layout makes for very
> enjoyable holiday golf.
> *18 holes, 5880yds, Par 70, SSS 69.*
> *Club membership 900.*

Visitors	must contact in advance & have handicap certificate & must use yellow tees.
Societies	must contact Secretary for details.
Green Fees	£22 per day/round.
Facilities	⊗ ⊮ by prior arrangement ⌿ ☕ ♀ ⚬ ⌂ ⊮ ℓ Peter Ward.
Location	Exeter Rd (2m NW off B3192)
Hotel	★★67% Ness House Hotel, Marine Dr, Shaldon, TEIGNMOUTH ☎ (0626) 873480 7 ⇆ ℟Annexe5rm

THURLESTONE   Map 03 SX64

Thurlestone ☎ Kingsbridge (0548) 560405
Situated on the edge of the cliffs with typical downland turf and good greens. The course, after an interesting opening hole, rises to higher land with fine seaviews, and finishes with an excellent 502-yard downhill hole to the clubhouse.
18 holes, 6303yds, Par 71, SSS 70, Course record 67.
Club membership 770.

Visitors	must contact in advance & have handicap certificate.
Green Fees	£24 per day/round.
Facilities	⊗ ⊮ ⌿ ☕ ♀ ⚬ ⌂ ⊮ ℓ Neville Whitley.
Leisure	hard and grass tennis courts.
Location	S side of village
Hotel	★★★★66% Thurlestone Hotel, THURLESTONE ☎ (0548) 560382 68 ⇆ ℟

TIVERTON   Map 03 SS91

Tiverton ☎ (0884) 252187
A parkland course where the many different species of tree are a feature and where the lush pastures ensure some of the finest fairways in the south-west. There are a number of interesting holes which visitors will find a real challenge.
18 holes, 6263yds, Par 71, SSS 71.
Club membership 900.

Visitors	must contact in advance & be member of a recognised golf club & have handicap certificate.
Societies	must contact in advance.
Green Fees	£21 per day/round (£27 weekends & bank holidays).
Facilities	⊗ ⊮ ⌿ ☕ ♀ ⚬ ⌂ ℓ David Sheppard.
Location	Post Hill
Hotel	★★65% Hartnoll Hotel, Bolham, TIVERTON ☎ (0884) 252777 11 ⇆ ℟Annexe5 ℟

TORQUAY   Map 03 SX96

Torquay ☎ (0803) 314591
Unusual combination of cliff and parkland golf, with wonderful views over the sea and Dartmoor.
18 holes, 6198yds, Par 69, SSS 70, Course record 66.
Club membership 700.

Visitors	must contact in advance & have handicap certificate.
Societies	must apply in writing.
Green Fees	£20 per day (£25 weekends & bank holidays).

Facilities	⊗ & ⊮ (ex Mon) ⌿ ☕ ♀ ⚬ ⌂ ⊮ ℓ M Ruth.
Location	30 Petitor Rd, St Marychurch (1.25m N)
Hotel	★★59% Norcliffe Hotel, 7 Babbacombe Downs Rd, Babbacombe, TORQUAY ☎ (0803) 328456 & 328023 28 ⇆ ℟

TORRINGTON   Map 02 SS41

Torrington ☎ Great Torrington (0805) 22229
Hard walking on hilly commonland course. Small greens and outstanding views.
9 holes, 4373yds, Par 64, SSS 61.
Club membership 398.

Visitors	cannot play Sat & Sun mornings & bank holidays. Must contact in advance.
Societies	by arrangement.
Green Fees	£12.50 per day/round (£15 weekends & bank holidays).
Facilities	⊗ ⊮ ⌿ ☕ ♀ ⚬ ⌂ ⊮
Leisure	practice area, putting green.
Location	Weare Trees, Great Torrington (1.25m NW)
Hotel	★★63% Beaconside Hotel, LANDCROSS ☎ (02372) 77205 9rm(4 ⇆2 ℟)

UPOTTERY   Map 03 ST20

Otter Valley Golf Centre ☎ (0404) 86266 (5m NW of Honiton off A30, on Upottery Rd) This is a golf school set in beautiful Devon countryside. There are practice facilities with driving range, approach and chipping green areas. 3-day courses are designed for established golfers and offer playing opportunities at Woodbury Park Golf Club, 1992 venue of the Devon Professional Championship and Mizuro Assistants Championship. A 5-day course gives instruction to establish all aspects of your game and takes you through the basics of sound swing technique, giving you a written record and a video analysis. Beginners are prepared for the Tony Jacklin Club Certificate of Competence and taken through their first round on a golf course. Self-catering accommodation is available at the course.

WESTWARD HO!   Map 02 SS42

Royal North Devon ☎ Bideford (0237) 473817
Links course with sea views.
18 holes, 6644yds, Par 71, SSS 72.
Club membership 1089.

Visitors	must have handicap certificate or letter of introduction from club.
Societies	must apply in advance.
Green Fees	on application.
Facilities	⊗ ⊮ by prior arrangement ⌿ ☕ ♀ ⚬ ⌂ ⊮ ℓ Graham Johnston.
Location	N side of village off B3236
Hotel	★★62% Culloden House Hotel, Fosketh Hill, WESTWARD HO! ☎ (0237) 479421 9rm(2 ⇆5 ℟)

See advertisement on page 54

For an explanation of symbols and abbreviations, see page 5

CULLODEN HOUSE HOTEL
WESTWARD HO! (01237) 479421

Victorian elegance – modern comforts – most rooms en-suite – views across Bideford Bay and Atlantic – friendly and comfortable atmosphere.

SPECIAL GOLFING HOLIDAYS AVAILABLE
– CHOICE OF 8 COURSES

AA ★★

YELVERTON
Map 02 SX56

Yelverton ☎ (0822) 852824
An excellent course on the moors with virtually no trees. It is exposed to high winds. The fairways are tight but there is plenty of room. The longest hole is the 8th, a 569-yard, par 5. Outstanding views.
18 holes, 6363yds, Par 71, SSS 70.
Club membership 800.

Visitors	must be member of a club & have handicap certificate. Must contact in advance.
Societies	by arrangement.
Green Fees	£20 per day.
Facilities	⊗ 〠 by prior arrangement 🝙 💺 ♀ ♨ 📠 ℓ Iain Parker.
Leisure	snooker, practice ground, caddy cars for hire.
Location	Golf Links Rd (1m S off A386)
Hotel	★★★69% Moorland Links Hotel, YELVERTON ☎ (0822) 852245 30 ➥ 🐾
Additional hotel	QQQ Harrabeer Country House Hotel, Harrowbeer Ln, YELVERTON ☎ (0822) 853302 7rm(4 ➥ 🐾) *See advertisement on page 51*

DORSET

BELCHALWELL
Map 03 ST70

Mid-Dorset ☎ Blandford (0258) 861386
Set in an area of outstanding natural beauty, rich in wildlife, which provides a picturesque backdrop to this stimulating, undulating course. Modern clubhouse with magnificent views.
18 holes, 5938mtrs, Par 70, SSS 71.
Club membership 350.

Visitors	no restrictions.
Societies	welcome by prior arrangement.
Green Fees	not confirmed.
Facilities	⊗ 〠 🝙 💺 ♀ ♨ 📠 ⚡ ℓ Andrew Pakes.
Hotel	★★★68% Crown Hotel, 8 West St, BLANDFORD FORUM ☎ (0258) 456626 32 ➥

BLANDFORD FORUM
Map 03 ST80

Ashley Wood ☎ (0258) 452253
Undulating downland course with superb views and excellent drainage.
18 holes, 6330yds, Par 71, SSS 70, Course record 68.
Club membership 550.

Visitors	Must contact in advance and have a handicap certificate.
Societies	contact in writing.
Green Fees	£17 per day (£24 weekends).
Facilities	⊗ 〠 🝙 💺 ♀ ♨ 📠 ℓ Spencer Taylor.
Leisure	caddy cars, practise ground.
Location	Wimborne Rd (2m E on B3082)
Hotel	★★★68% Crown Hotel, 8 West St, BLANDFORD FORUM ☎ (0258) 456626 32 ➥

BOURNEMOUTH
Map 04 SZ09

Knighton Heath ☎ (0202) 572633
Undulating heathland course on high ground inland from Bournemouth.
18 holes, 5987yds, Par 68, SSS 69.
Club membership 700.

Visitors	with member only weekends & bank holidays. Must have handicap certificate.
Societies	must book in advance.
Green Fees	£17 per day/round.
Facilities	⊗ (ex Mon) 〠 (ex Mon by prior arrangement) 🝙 💺 ♀ ♨ 📠 ℓ Jane Miles.
Location	Francis Av, West Howe (N side of town centre off A348)
Hotel	★★★57% Bournemouth Heathlands Hotel, 12 Grove Rd, East Cliff, BOURNEMOUTH ☎ (0202) 553336 116 ➥ 🐾

Queen's Park ☎ (0202) 396198
Undulating parkland course of pine and heather, with narrow, tree-lined fairways. Public course played over by 'Boscombe Golf Club' and 'Bournemouth Artisans Golf Club'.
18 holes, 6505yds, Par 72, SSS 72.

Visitors	must contact in advance.
Societies	must contact in advance.
Green Fees	not confirmed.
Facilities	⊗ 〠 🝙 💺 ♀ ♨ 📠 ℓ Richard Hill.
Location	Queens Park Dr West (2m NE of town centre off A338)
Hotel	★★64% Hotel Riviera, West Cliff Gardens, BOURNEMOUTH ☎ (0202) 552845 34 ➥ 🐾

For a Golfing Break in the New Forest

OUR OWN THREE, 18 HOLE COURSES

Come and stay at the 200 year old Bell Inn Hotel, ideally located 1½ miles off the M27 in a New Forest village, and play our **three** contrasting 18 hole courses.

The first tee is only a wedge away from the front door, with **reserved tee times** for all our guests.

For our full colour brochure please telephone: 01703 812214

AA ✿ ★ ★ ★

The Bell Inn
HOTEL AND GOLF CLUB

Brook, Lyndhurst, Hampshire SO43 7HE
Telephone: (01703) 812214 Fax: (01703) 813958

CHRISTCHURCH   Map 04 SZ19

Dudmoor Farm ☏ (0202) 483980
A non-membership golf course with tree-lined par 3 and 4 fairways.
9 holes, 1428mtrs, Par 31.
Visitors	no restrictions.
Societies	advisable to contact.
Green Fees	£4.50 per 18 holes.
Facilities	🍺 🏌 ⚑ 🛏
Leisure	squash, fishing.
Location	Farm Rd
Hotel	★★★75% Waterford Lodge Hotel, 87 Bure Ln, Friars Cliff, Mudeford, CHRISTCHURCH ☏ (0425) 272948 & 278801 20 ⇔

Iford Bridge ☏ (0202) 473817
Parkland course with the River Stour running through. Driving range.
9 holes, 2377yds, Par 34, SSS 32.
Club membership 350.
Visitors	no restrictions.
Societies	must contact in advance.
Green Fees	not confirmed.
Facilities	🍴 🏡 ⚑ ⚐
Leisure	hard and grass tennis courts, driving range, bowls.
Location	Barrack Rd (W side of town centre on A35)
Hotel	★★★75% Waterford Lodge Hotel, 87 Bure Ln, Friars Cliff, Mudeford, CHRISTCHURCH ☏ (0425) 272948 & 278801 20 ⇔

BRIDPORT   Map 03 SY49

Bridport & West Dorset ☏ (0308) 421095
Seaside links course on the top of the east cliff, with fine views over Lyme Bay and surrounding countryside. At the 13th hole (par 3), the green is 70 feet below the tee.
18 holes, 5246yds, Par 67, SSS 66, Course record 61.
Club membership 700.
Visitors	may not play 8-9.30am & noon-2pm or on competition days.
Societies	must contact in writing in advance.
Green Fees	£18 per day (after 2pm £12).
Facilities	⊗ 🍴🍺 🏌 ⚐🏡⚐ John Parish.
Leisure	putting green, pitch and putt.
Location	East Cliff, West Bay (2m S)
Hotel	★★★61% Haddon House Hotel, West Bay, BRIDPORT ☏ (0308) 23626 & 25323 13 ⇔ 🐾

BROADSTONE   Map 04 SZ09

Broadstone (Dorset) ☏ (0202) 692595
Typical heathland course.
18 holes, 6195yds, Par 70, SSS 71, Course record 66.
Club membership 800.
Visitors	may not play weekends & bank holidays. Must have handicap certificate.
Societies	contact in advance.
Green Fees	£33 per day; £27 per round (£40 weekends).
Facilities	⊗ 🍴🍺 🏌 ⚐🏡⚐ Nigel Tokely.
Location	Wentworth Dr (N side of village off B3074)
Hotel	★★★61% King's Head Hotel, The Square, WIMBORNE ☏ (0202) 880101 27 ⇔ 🐾

DORCHESTER   Map 03 SY69

Came Down ☏ (0305) 813494
Scene of the West of England Championships on several occasions, this fine course lies on a high plateau commanding glorious views over Portland. Three par 5 holes add interest to a round. The turf is of the springy, downland type.
18 holes, 6244yds, Par 70, SSS 71, Course record 66.
Club membership 700.
Visitors	must contact in advance & have handicap certificate. May play after 9am weekdays & after 11am Sun.
Societies	by arrangement on Wed only.
Green Fees	£20 per day (£25 per day weekends & bank holidays).
Facilities	⊗ 🍴🍺 🏌 ⚐🏡⚐ Robert Preston.
Location	Came Down (2m S off A354)
Hotel	★★★67% King's Arms Hotel, 30 High East St, DORCHESTER ☏ (0305) 265353 31 ⇔ 🐾 Annexe2 ⇔ 🐾

FERNDOWN   Map 04 SU00

Ferndown ☏ (0202) 872022
Fairways are gently undulating amongst heather, gorse and pine trees giving the course a most attractive appearance. There are a number of dog-leg holes and, on a clear day, there are views across to the Isle of Wight.
Old Course: 18 holes, 6452yds, Par 71, SSS 71.
Presidents: 9 holes, 5604yds, Par 70, SSS 68.
Club membership 700.

▶

Visitors	must contact in advance & have handicap certificate but may not play before 9.30am at weekends.
Societies	welcome Tue & Fri only, apply by letter.
Green Fees	Old Course: £35 per day (£40 weekends). Presidents: £15 per day (£20 weekends).
Facilities	⊗ ⑪ ℔ ➴ ♀ ⚲ 📠 🕪 𝄢 Doug Sewell.
Location	119 Golf Links Rd (S side of town centre off A347)
Hotel	★★★★65% The Dormy, New Rd, FERNDOWN ☎ (0202) 872121 128 ⊖ 🐾

HIGHCLIFFE

Map 04 SZ29

Highcliffe Castle ☎ (0425) 272210
Picturesque parkland course with easy walking.
18 holes, 4686yds, Par 64, SSS 63.
Club membership 500.

Visitors	must have handicap certificate or be a member of recognised club.
Societies	Tue only.
Green Fees	£18 per day; (£27 weekends).
Facilities	⊗ ℔ ➴ ♀ ⚲ 📠 𝄢
Location	107 Lymington Rd (SW side of town on A337)
Hotel	★★★75% Waterford Lodge Hotel, 87 Bure Ln, Friars Cliff, Mudeford, CHRISTCHURCH ☎ (0425) 272948 & 278801 20 ⊖

LYME REGIS

Map 03 SY39

Lyme Regis ☎ (0297) 442963
Undulating cliff-top course with magnificent views of Golden Cap and Lyme Bay.
18 holes, 6220yds, Par 71, SSS 70, Course record 68.
Club membership 575.

Visitors	must contact in advance & have handicap certificate or be a member of recognised golf club. No play on Thu & Sun mornings.
Societies	Tue, Wed & Fri; must contact in writing.
Green Fees	£24 per day (£20 after 2pm).
Facilities	⊗ ⑪ ℔ ➴ ♀ ⚲ 📠 𝄢 Andrew Black.
Leisure	trolleys.
Location	Timber Hill (1.5m N on A3052)
Hotel	★★★71% Alexandra Hotel, Pound St, LYME REGIS ☎ (0297) 442010 26rm(23 ⊖ 🐾)

LYTCHETT MATRAVERS

Map 03 SY99

Bulbury Woods ☎ Morden (0929) 459574
Parkland course in 40 acres of woodland, with extensive views over the Purbecks, Poole Bay and Wareham Forest. Not too hilly.
18 holes, 6065yds, Par 70, SSS 69.
Club membership 650.

Visitors	are advised to contact in advance.
Societies	must contact in advance.
Green Fees	£15.
Facilities	⊗ ⑪ by prior arrangement ℔ ➴ ♀ ⚲ 📠 🕪 𝄢 John Sharkey.
Location	Halls Rd (2m W of Lytchett Minster)
Hotel	★★★(red)🎖 Priory Hotel, Church Green, WAREHAM ☎ (0929) 552772 & 551666 15 ⊖ 🐾Annexe4 ⊖ 🐾

POOLE

Map 04 SZ09

Parkstone ☎ Canford Cliffs (0202) 707138
Very scenic heathland course with views of Poole Bay. Club founded in 1910.
18 holes, 6250yds, Par 72, SSS 70.
Club membership 800.

Visitors	must contact in advance and have handicap certificate.
Societies	by prior arrangement.
Green Fees	£34 per day; £25 per round (£40/£30 weekends & bank holidays).
Facilities	⊗ ⑪ by prior arrangement ℔ ➴ ♀ ⚲ 📠 🕪 𝄢 Mark Thomas.
Location	Links Rd, Parkstone (E side of town centre off A35)
Hotel	★★★80% Salterns Hotel, 38 Salterns Way, Lilliput, POOLE ☎ (0202) 707321 16 ⊖

SHERBORNE

Map 03 ST61

Sherborne ☎ (0935) 814431
A sporting course of first-class fairways with far-reaching views over the lovely Blackmore Vale and the Vale of Sparkford. Parkland in character, the course has many well-placed bunkers. The dog-leg 2nd calls for an accurately placed tee shot, and another testing hole is the 7th, a 194-yard, par 3. There is a practice area.
18 holes, 5949yds, Par 70, SSS 68.
Club membership 700.

Visitors	must contact in advance & have handicap certificate.
Societies	must contact well in advance.
Green Fees	£20 per day (£25 weekends).
Facilities	⊗ ⑪ ℔ ➴ ♀ ⚲ 📠 𝄢 Stewart Wright.
Location	Higher Clatcombe (2m N off B3145)
Hotel	★★★61% Sherborne Hotel, Horsecastles Ln, SHERBORNE ☎ (0935) 813191 59 ⊖ 🐾

STURMINSTER MARSHALL

Map 03 ST90

Sturminster Marshall ☎ Blandford (0258) 858444
Opened in June 1992, this 9-hole is Pay-and-Play. A membership scheme allows players to gain an official handicap. Course was designed by John Sharkey.
9 holes, 4650yds, Par 68, SSS 63.
Club membership 350.

Visitors	no restrictions.
Societies	welcome.
Green Fees	not confirmed.
Facilities	⊗ ℔ ➴ ♀ ⚲ 📠 🕪 𝄢 John Sharkey.
Location	Moor Ln
Hotel	★★★68% Crown Hotel, 8 West St, BLANDFORD FORUM ☎ (0258) 456626 32 ⊖

> A golf course name printed in ***bold italics*** means we have been unable to verify information with the club's management for the current year

SWANAGE
Map 04 SZ07

Isle of Purbeck ☎ Studland (092944) 361
A heathland course sited on the Purbeck Hills with grand
views across Swanage, the Channel and Poole Harbour.
Holes of note include the 5th, 8th, 14th, 15th, and 16th
where trees, gorse and heather assert themselves. The
very attractive clubhouse is built of the local stone.
Purbeck: 18 holes, 6295yds, Par 70, SSS 71.
Dene: 9 holes, 4014yds, Par 60, SSS 63.
Club membership 600.

Visitors	handicap certificate required for Purbeck course.
Societies	must contact in advance.
Green Fees	Purbeck: £30 per day; £22.50 round (£35/£27.50 weekends). Dene: £10 (£12 weekends).
Facilities	⊗ ⷨ by prior arrangement ⅏ ♛ ♀ ♙ ♟ ⚑ ⟊ Ian Brake.
Leisure	caddy cars & electric trolleys.
Location	2.5m N on B3351
Hotel	★★★65% The Pines Hotel, Burlington Rd, SWANAGE ☎ (0929) 425211 51rm(49 ⇌ ⋒)

VERWOOD
Map 04 SU00

Crane Valley ☎ (0202) 814088
Two secluded parkland courses set amid rolling Dorset
countryside and mature woodland - a 9-hole Pay and Play and
an 18-hole Valley course for golfers holding a handicap
certificate.The 6th nestles in the bend of the River Crane and
there are 4 long Par 5's ranging from 499 to 545 yards.
Valley: 18 holes, 6424yds, Par 72, SSS 71.
Woodland: 9 holes, 4120yds, Par 66, SSS 60.
Club membership 500.

Visitors	must have handicap certificate for Valley course.
Societies	contact in advance.
Green Fees	Valley, £25 per day;£17 per round (£30/£22 weekend) Woodland, £10.50 per 18 holes; £5.50 per 9 holes (£12/£6.50 weekends).
Facilities	⊗ ⷨ ⅏ ♛ ♀ ♙ ⚑ ⟊ Alan Egford.
Location	6m N of Ferndown
Hotel	★★★★65% The Dormy, New Rd, FERNDOWN ☎ (0202) 872121 128 ⇌ ⋒

Phoneday - remember from 16 April
1995 all phone codes in the UK will
change - see page 4 for details

WAREHAM
Map 03 SY98

East Dorset ☎ Bere Regis (0929) 472244
Long 18-hole parkland course with natural water
features. A second 9-hole, 18-tee course is set amongst
trees and rhododendrons. Floodlit 22-bay driving range,
club fitting centre, indoor putting area and extensive golf
shop.
*Lakeland: 18 holes, 6580yds, Par 72, SSS 73, Course
record 71.*
Woodland: 9 holes, 2440yards, Par 33.
Club membership 600.

Visitors	must contact in advance and handicap certificate required for Lakeland course.
Societies	apply in writing.
Green Fees	Lakeland: £18 (£25 weekends). Woodland: £13 (£18 weekends).
Facilities	⊗ ⷨ (by prior arrangement winter) ⅏ ♛ ♀ ♙ ⚑ ⟊ ⊷ ⟊ Kim Thomas.
Leisure	floodlit driving range.
Location	Hyde (5m NW on unclass Puddletown Rd,off A352)
Hotel	★★67% Kemps Country House Hotel, East Stoke, WAREHAM ☎ (0929) 462563 5rm(1 ⇌3 ⋒)Annexe10 ⇌ ⋒

Wareham ☎ (0929) 554147
Heathland/parkland course. The club was founded in 1926.
18 holes, 5603yds, Par 69, SSS 67.
Club membership 600.

Visitors	must have a handicap certificate & should contact the club in advance. Must be accompanied by a member at weekends & bank holidays.
Societies	must contact in advance.
Green Fees	£20 per day; £15 per round.
Facilities	⊗ ⷨ by prior arrangement ⅏ ♛ ♀ ♙
Location	Sandford Rd
Hotel	★★★71% Springfield Country Hotel, Grange Road, Stoborough, WAREHAM ☎ (0929) 552177 32 ⇌ ⋒

WEYMOUTH
Map 03 SY67

Weymouth ☎ (0305) 773981
Seaside parkland course. The 5th is played off an elevated
green over copse.
18 holes, 6030yds, Par 70, SSS 69, Course record 63.
Club membership 730.

Visitors	must contact in advance & have proof of membership or handicap certificate.
Societies	telephone in advance.
Green Fees	£20 per day (£26 weekends). ▶

EAST DORSET 🦌 GOLF CLUB
invites Society, Corporate and Group Golf Organisers
to stage your own event at Dorset's foremost Golf Resort.
Long 18-hole lakeland course with natural water features. The 9-hole woodland course is set amongst trees and
rhododendrons. Floodlight 22-bay driving range, club fitting centre and extensive golf shop. Luxury air conditioned
clubhouse. Stay 'n' play dormy bungalow. Visitors must contact in advance to book tee time. Society golf day
packages from £30 pp.
Call for details: Brian Lee, tel: 01929 472244
East Dorset Golf Club, Bere Regis, Nr. Wareham, Dorset BH20 7NT

Facilities	⊗ ⅷ by prior arrangement ☕ 🍺 ♀ ⚴ 🏠
	⚑ Des Lochrie.
Location	Links Rd, Westham (N side of town centre off
	B3157)
Hotel	★★64% Hotel Rex, 29 The Esplanade,
	WEYMOUTH
	☎ (0305) 760400 & 781004 31 ⇥ 🐾

CO DURHAM

Barnard Castle   Map 12 NZ01

> **Barnard Castle** ☎ Teesdale (0833) 38355
> Flat moorland course high above the River Tees and
> presenting fine views. A small stream runs in front of, or
> alongside, many of the holes adding challenge and
> enjoyment to the game.
> *18 holes, 5838yds, Par 71, SSS 68.*
> *Club membership 600.*
> | Visitors | must be member of recognised club. |
> | --- | --- |
> | Societies | by arrangement. |
> | Green Fees | not confirmed. |
> | Facilities | ⊗ ⅷ ☕ 🍺 ♀ ⚴ 🏠 ⚑⚑ |
> | Leisure | snooker. |
> | Location | Harmire Rd (0.75m N on B6278) |
> | Hotel | ★★71% Rose & Crown Hotel, |
> | | ROMALDKIRK |
> | | ☎ (0833) 50213 7 ⇥ 🐾Annexe5 ⇥ 🐾 |

Beamish   Map 12 NZ25

Beamish Park ☎ 091-370 1382
Parkland course. Designed by Henry Cotton and W
Woodend.
18 holes, 6205yds, Par 71, SSS 70.
Club membership 520.

Visitors	restricted except before 9am & 12.15-1.45pm.
Societies	by arrangement.
Green Fees	not confirmed.
Facilities	⊗ ⅷ ☕ 🍺 ⚴ 🏠 ⚑ C Cole.
Leisure	snooker.
Location	1m NW off A693
Hotel	★★★64% Beamish Park Hotel, Beamish Burn
	Rd, MARLEY HILL
	☎ (0207) 230666 47 ⇥ 🐾

Bishop Auckland   Map 08 NZ22

> **Bishop Auckland** ☎ (0388) 602198 & 663648
> A rather hilly parkland course with many well-
> established trees offering a challenging round. A small
> ravine adds interest to several holes including the short
> 7th, from a raised tee to a green surrounded by a stream,
> gorse and bushes. Pleasant views down the Wear Valley.
> *18 holes, 6420yds, Par 72, SSS 71.*
> *Club membership 820.*
> | Visitors | must contact in advance. |
> | --- | --- |
> | Societies | weekdays only; must contact in advance. |

> | Green Fees | £24 per day; £20 per round (£26 weekends). |
> | --- | --- |
> | Facilities | ⊗ ⅷ ☕ 🍺 (no catering Mon) ♀ ⚴ 🏠 ⚑ |
> | Leisure | snooker, driving range & practice fairway. |
> | Location | Durham Rd (1m NE on A689) |
> | Hotel | ★★★63% Park Head Hotel, New Coundon, |
> | | BISHOP AUCKLAND |
> | | ☎ (0388) 661727 8 ⇥ 🐾Annexe7 ⇥ |

Burnopfield   Map 12 NZ15

Hobson Municipal ☎ (0207) 271605
Meadowland course opened in 1981.
18 holes, 6403yds, Par 70, SSS 70.
Club membership 725.

Visitors	no restrictions.
Societies	must contact in advance.
Green Fees	£9 per round (£11.50 weekends & bank
	holidays).
Facilities	⊗ ⅷ ☕ 🍺 ♀ ⚴ 🏠 ⚑⚑ Jack Ord.
Leisure	practice area.
Location	Hobson (0.75m S on A692)
Hotel	★★★66% Swallow Hotel, High West St,
	GATESHEAD ☎ 091-477 1105 103 ⇥ 🐾

Chester-le-Street   Map 12 NZ25

Chester-le-Street ☎ Durham (091-388) 3218
Parkland course in castle grounds, good views, easy walking.
18 holes, 6054yds, Par 70, SSS 69, Course record 67.
Club membership 650.

Visitors	restricted weekends & bank holidays. Must
	contact in advance and have an introduction
	from own club or handicap certificate.
Societies	must apply in writing.
Green Fees	£20 per day/round (£25 weekends & bank
	holidays).
Facilities	⊗ ⅷ by prior arrangement ☕ 🍺 ♀ ⚴ 🏠 ⚑
	⚑ A Hartley.
Leisure	snooker, pool table.
Location	Lumley Park (0.5m E off B1284)
Hotel	★★★71% Ramside Hall Hotel, Carrville,
	DURHAM ☎ 091-386 5282 82 ⇥ 🐾

Consett   Map 12 NZ15

Consett & District ☎ (0207) 502186
Undulating parkland/moorland course.
18 holes, 6011yds, Par 71, SSS 69.
Club membership 650.

Visitors	advised to telephone for Wed and weekends.
Societies	must contact in advance.
Green Fees	£15 per day (£22 weekends & bank holidays).
Facilities	⊗ ⅷ ☕ 🍺 ♀ ⚴ 🏠 ⚑ S Watts.
Leisure	snooker.
Location	Elmfield Rd (N side of town on A691)
Hotel	★★★66% The Raven Hotel, Broomhill,
	EBCHESTER ☎ (0207) 560367 28 ⇥ 🐾

> For a full list of all the golf courses
> included in this guide, see the index at
> the end of the book

CROOK
Map 12 NZ13

Crook ☎ Bishop Auckland (0388) 762429
Meadowland/parkland course in elevated position with natural hazards, varied holes and terrain. Panoramic views over Durham and Cleveland Hills.
18 holes, 6079yds, Par 68, SSS 69.
Club membership 430.
Visitors welcome, but limited availability on weekends.
Societies must telephone in advance.
Green Fees £12 per day (£20 weekends).
Facilities ⊗ ㄴ ♥ ♀ ♨
Location Low Jobs Hill (0.5m E off A690)
Hotel ★★65% Kensington Hall Hotel, Kensington Ter, WILLINGTON
☎ (0388) 745071 10 ⇥ ♟

DARLINGTON
Map 08 NZ21

Blackwell Grange ☎ (0325) 464464
Pleasant parkland course with good views, easy walking.
18 holes, 5621yds, Par 68, SSS 67, Course record 63.
Club membership 950.
Visitors restricted Wed & Sun.
Societies must contact in writing.
Green Fees £20 per day (£20 per round weekends).
Facilities ⊗ ℿ ㄴ ♥ ♀ ♨ ☏ ⚐ Ralph Givens.
Location Briar Close (1m SW off A66)
Hotel ★★★67% Swallow King's Head Hotel, Priestgate, DARLINGTON
☎ (0325) 380222 86 ⇥ ♟

Darlington ☎ (0325) 355324
Fairly flat parkland course with tree-lined fairways, and large first-class greens. Championship standard.
18 holes, 6032yds, Par 70, SSS 72, Course record 64.
Club membership 750.
Visitors restricted weekends, bank holidays & competition days.
Societies must contact in advance.
Green Fees £22.
Facilities ⊗ ℿ ㄴ ♥ ♀ ♨ ⚐ Mark Rogers.
Leisure snooker.
Location Haughton Grange (N side of town centre off A1150)
Hotel ★★★♨67% Headlam Hall Hotel, Headlam, Gainford, DARLINGTON
☎ (0325) 730238 17 ⇥ ♟Annexe9 ⇥ ♟

Stressholme ☎ (0325) 461002
Picturesque municipal parkland course, long but wide, with 98 bunkers and a par 3 hole played over a river.
18 holes, 6511yds, Par 71, SSS 71.
Club membership 650.
Visitors must contact in advance.
Societies apply to the steward or professional.
Green Fees not confirmed.
Facilities ⊗ ㄴ ♥ ♀ ♨ ⚐ ☏ ⚐ Tim Jenkins.
Location Snipe Ln (SW side of town centre on A67)
Hotel ★★★67% Swallow King's Head Hotel, Priestgate, DARLINGTON
☎ (0325) 380222 86 ⇥ ♟

Hall Garth
Golf & Country Club Hotel
Coatham Mundeville, Nr. Darlington
Telephone: 01325 300400

The Hall Garth 40 Bedroom country house hotel has recently added a luxurious Leisure Club and Golf Course to its substantial estate.

Built to Championship standards, the Hall Garth Golf Course is acknowledged to be one of the finest 9-hole golf courses in the country.

This superb Par-74 course offers five spectacular water hazards and magnificent greens built to USGA specification, each averaging 700 sq. yds. It represents the ultimate challenge for the most demanding of golfers.

Without any doubt, the Hall Garth Golf Course forms a truly splendid golfing oasis in an idyllic setting spanning 70 acres of prime English countryside.

DURHAM
Map 12 NZ24

Brancepeth Castle ☎ 091-378 0075
Parkland course overlooked at the 9th hole by beautiful Brancepeth Castle.
18 holes, 6300yds, Par 70, SSS 70, Course record 64.
Club membership 780.
Visitors may be restrictions at weekends for parties.
Societies must contact in advance.
Green Fees £23 per day/round (£30 weekends & bank holidays).
Facilities ⊗ ℿ ㄴ ♥ ♀ ♨ ⚐ ☏ ⚐ D C Howdon.
Leisure snooker.
Location Brancepeth Village (4.5m SW on A690)
Hotel ★★★★70% Royal County Hotel, Old Elvet, DURHAM ☎ 091-386 6821 150 ⇥ ♟
Additional QQQBay Horse Inn, Brandon, DURHAM
hotel ☎ 091-378 0498 Annexe10 ⇥ ♟
See advertisement on page 60

Durham City ☎ 091-378 0806
Undulating parkland course bordered on several holes by the River Browney.
18 holes, 6326yds, Par 71, SSS 70.
Club membership 700.
Visitors restricted on competition days.
Societies must contact in advance.
Green Fees not confirmed.
Facilities ⊗ ℿ ㄴ ♥ ♀ ♨ ⚐ ☏ Steve Corbally.
Leisure pool table.
Location Littleburn, Langley Moor (1.5m S off A167)
Hotel ★★★68% Three Tuns Hotel, New Elvet, DURHAM ☎ 091-386 4326 47 ⇥ ♟

THE Bay Horse RESIDENTIAL

Brandon Village, County Durham DH7 8ST
Telephone: (091) 378 0498

Stone built accommodation, 3 double, 6 twin and 1 family room all en suite, centrally heated, attractively furnished, TV, tea/coffee making facilities, telephone and hair dryer. 50 cover restaurant and bar meals served in the Inn. Ample car parking. Beer garden. 3 golf courses and sports centre within 3 mile radius. Many places of interest, 3 mile from historic Durham City. Ideal for the business person or holiday maker. Children welcome.

Mount Oswald ☎ 091-386 7527
Flat, wooded parkland course with Georgian clubhouse.
18 holes, 6101yds, Par 71, SSS 69.
Club membership 150.
Visitors	must contact in advance for weekends but may not play before 10am on Sun.
Societies	must contact in advance.
Green Fees	£10 per round (£12 weekends & bank holidays).
Facilities	⊗ ⅢⅡ ⓛ ⬛ ♀ ♨ ⬛ ⌐
Location	Mount Oswald Manor, South Rd (1m S off A167)
Hotel	★★64% Bridge Toby Hotel, Croxdale, DURHAM ☎ 091-378 0524 46 ⇌ ⚲

MIDDLETON ST GEORGE Map 08 NZ31

Dinsdale Spa ☎ Dinsdale (0325) 332297
A mainly flat, parkland course on high land above the River Tees with views of the Cleveland Hills. Water hazards front the 8th, 9th and 18th tees and the prevailing west wind affects the later holes. There is a practice area by the clubhouse.
18 holes, 6090yds, Par 71, SSS 69.
Club membership 850.
Visitors	restricted Tue & weekends.
Societies	must contact in advance.
Green Fees	£20 per day; £16 per round.
Facilities	⊗ ⅢⅡ ⓛ ⬛ (no catering Mon) ♀ ♨ ⬛ ⌐ ⚲ Craig Imlah.

Location 1.5m SW
Hotel ★★★64% St George, Middleton St George, TEES-SIDE AIRPORT ☎ (0325) 332631 59 ⇌ ⚲

NEWTON AYCLIFFE Map 08 NZ22

Aycliffe ☎ Aycliffe (0325) 310820
A parkland course in a country setting.
18 holes, 5430yds, Par 68, SSS 66.
Visitors	must contact in advance.
Societies	apply in writing.
Green Fees	£6 per round (£7 weekends & bank holidays).
Facilities	ⓛ ⬛ ♀ ♨ ⬛ Robert Lister.
Leisure	squash, indoor bowls, badminton, indoor cricket.
Location	Oakleaf Sports Complex, School Aycliffe Ln (6m N of Darlington, off A6072)
Hotel	★★★★72% Redworth Hall Hotel & Country Club, REDWORTH ☎ (0388) 772442 100 ⇌ ⚲

SEAHAM Map 12 NZ44

Seaham ☎ 091-581 2354
Links course.
18 holes, 6017yds, Par 70, SSS 69, Course record 64.
Club membership 550.
Visitors	with member only weekends until 3.30pm.
Societies	must apply in writing.
Green Fees	not confirmed.
Facilities	⊗ & ⅢⅡ by prior arrangement ⓛ ⬛ ♀ ♨ ⬛
Leisure	snooker.
Location	Dawdon (S side of town centre)
Hotel	★★★★60% Swallow Hotel, Queen's Pde, Seaburn, SUNDERLAND ☎ 091-529 2041 66 ⇌ ⚲

STANLEY Map 12 NZ15

South Moor ☎ (0207) 232848
Moorland course with natural hazards designed by Dr Alistair McKenzie in 1926 and remains on of the most challenging of its type in north east England.
18 holes, 6445yds, Par 72, SSS 71, Course record 66.
Club membership 650.
Visitors	must contact in advance but may not play competition days.
Societies	must telephone in advance.
Green Fees	£21 per day; £14 per round (£25 per day/round weekends & bank holidays).
Facilities	⊗ ⅢⅡ ⓛ ⬛ ♀ ♨ ⬛ ⌐ ⚲ Shaun Cowell.
Leisure	snooker, caddy cars.
Location	The Middles, Craghead (1.5m SE on B6313)
Hotel	★★★64% Beamish Park Hotel, Beamish Burn Rd, MARLEY HILL ☎ (0207) 230666 47 ⇌ ⚲

A golf course name printed in ***bold italics*** means we have been unable to verify information with the club's management for the current year

EAST SUSSEX

BEXHILL
Map 05 TQ70

Cooden Beach ☎ Cooden (0424) 842040
The course is close by the sea, but is not real links in character. Despite that, it is dry and plays well throughout the year. There are some excellent holes such as the 4th, played to a built-up green, the short 12th, and three good holes to finish.
18 holes, 6450yds, Par 72, SSS 71, Course record 65.
Club membership 730.

Visitors	must have a handicap certificate. Restricted at weekends. Must contact in advance and have an introduction from own club.
Societies	must contact in advance by telephone to professional tel: (0424) 843938.
Green Fees	not confirmed.
Facilities	⊗ 〗 by prior arrangement 🍴 ☕ ♀ ⌂ 🖅 ⛏ 🏠 (Jeffrey Sim.
Leisure	snooker, bridge room.
Location	Cooden Sea Rd (2m W on A259)
Hotel	★★★66% Cooden Resort Hotel, COODEN BEACH ☎ (0424) 842281 40 ⇄ ℝ

Highwoods ☎ Bexhill-on-Sea (0424) 212625
Undulating course.
18 holes, 6218yds, Par 70, SSS 70, Course record 66.
Club membership 820.

Visitors	must play with member on Sun. Must contact in advance and have an introduction from own club.
Societies	must contact 6 months in advance.
Green Fees	not confirmed.
Facilities	⊗ (Sun only) 🍴 (Mon-Sat 10am-2pm) ☕ ♀ ⌂ 🖅 (M Andrews.
Leisure	snooker.
Location	Ellerslie Ln (1.5m NW)
Hotel	★★★58% Granville Hotel, Sea Rd, BEXHILL-ON-SEA ☎ (0424) 215437 50 ⇄ ℝ

BRIGHTON & HOVE
Map 04 TQ30

Brighton & Hove ☎ Brighton (0273) 556482
Downland course with sea views.
18 holes, 5722yds, Par 68, SSS 68.
Club membership 320.

Visitors	must contact in advance and may not play Sun mornings.
Societies	must contact in advance.
Green Fees	not confirmed.
Facilities	⌂ (
Leisure	snooker.
Location	Dyke Rd (4m NW)
Hotel	★★60% St Catherines Lodge Hotel, Seafront, Kingsway, Hove ☎ (0273) 778181 50rm(40 ⇄ ℝ)

> **Phoneday** - remember from 16 April
> 1995 all phone codes in the UK will
> change - see page 4 for details

Dyke ☎ Brighton (0273) 857296
This downland course has some glorious views both towards the sea and inland. The best hole on the course is probably the 17th; it is one of those teasing short holes of just over 200 yards, and is played across a gully to a high green.
18 holes, 6611yds, Par 72, SSS 72.
Club membership 700.

Visitors	restricted before noon on Sun.
Societies	must contact in advance.
Green Fees	£31 per day: £21 per round (£31 per round weekends).
Facilities	⊗ 〗 by prior arrangement 🍴 ☕ ♀ ⌂ 🖅 ⛏ (
Leisure	snooker.
Location	Dyke Rd (4m N between A23 & A27)
Hotel	★★60% St Catherines Lodge Hotel, Seafront, Kingsway, Hove ☎ (0273) 778181 50rm(40 ⇄ ℝ)

East Brighton ☎ Brighton (0273) 604838
Undulating downland course, overlooking the sea. Windy.
18 holes, 6346yds, Par 72, SSS 70.
Club membership 700.

Visitors	must contact in advance & have handicap certificate, but may not play before 9am on weekdays.
Societies	must contact at least 1 month in advance.
Green Fees	£21 per day; £16 per round (£30 per day weekends).
Facilities	⊗ 〗 🍴 ☕ ♀ ⌂ 🖅 (Wally Street.
Leisure	snooker.
Location	Roedean Rd (E side of town centre on B2118)
Hotel	★★★59% Norfolk Resort, 149 Kings Rd, BRIGHTON ☎ (0273) 738201 121 ⇄ ℝ

Hollingbury Park ☎ Brighton (0273) 552010
Municipal course in hilly situation on the Downs, overlooking the sea.
18 holes, 6500yds, Par 72, SSS 71.
Club membership 400.

Visitors	no restrictions
Societies	must book 1 month in advance
Green Fees	£10 weekday (£14 weekends & bank holidays).
Facilities	⊗ 🍴 ☕ ♀ ⌂ 🖅 ⛏ (
Location	Ditchling Rd (2m N of town centre)
Hotel	★★★59% Norfolk Resort, 149 Kings Rd, BRIGHTON ☎ (0273) 738201 121 ⇄ ℝ

Waterhall ☎ Brighton (0273) 508658
Hilly downland course with hard walking and open to the wind. Private club playing over municipal course.
18 holes, 5775yds, Par 69, SSS 68, Course record 66.
Club membership 400.

Visitors	may not play on competition days & before 8.30am at weekends.
Societies	must contact the secretary in writing.
Green Fees	£17 per day; £10 per round (£14 per round weekends).
Facilities	🍴 ☕ ♀ ⌂ 🖅 ⛏ (Paul Charman.
Location	Seddlescombe Rd, (Off Devils Dyke Road) (3m N off A27)
Hotel	★★60% St Catherines Lodge Hotel, Seafront, Kingsway, Hove ☎ (0273) 778181 50rm(40 ⇄ ℝ)

West Hove ☎ Brighton (0273) 419738 & 413411
A downland course designed by Hawtree & Sons.
18 holes, 6252yds, Par 72, SSS 70.
Club membership 500.

Visitors	tee times by arrangement.
Societies	by arrangement.
Green Fees	not confirmed.
Facilities	⊗ Ⅲ by prior arrangement ⅃ ♥ ♀ 🛆 🏠 ⌇ ⌇ David Mills.
Leisure	snooker.
Location	Church Farm, Hangleton
Hotel	★★60% St Catherines Lodge Hotel, Seafront, Kingsway, Hove ☎ (0273) 778181 50rm(40 ⇄ ſ)

CROWBOROUGH   Map 05 TQ53

Crowborough Beacon ☎ (0892) 661511
A picturesque course in pleasant heathland. Though most
fairways are wide and open, one or two are distinctly
tight where a wayward shot results in a lost ball. By no
means an easy course, with testing holes at the 2nd, 6th
and 16th.
18 holes, 6318yds, Par 71, SSS 70.
Club membership 700.

Visitors	must contact in advance & have handicap certificate but may not play at weekends & bank holidays.
Societies	telephone in advance.
Green Fees	£36 per day; £24 per round (£10 per round after 4pm).
Facilities	⊗ ⅃ ♥ ♀ 🛆 🏠 ⌇ ⌇ Dennis Newnham.
Location	Beacon Rd (1m SW on A26)
Hotel	★★★70% Spa Hotel, Mount Ephraim, TUNBRIDGE WELLS ☎ (0892) 520331 76 ⇄ ſ

Dewlands Manor ☎ Rotherfield (0892) 852266 & 853308
A pretty, moderately hilly, Pay and Play parkland course with
water features.
9 holes, 3186yds, Par 36, Course record 33.

Visitors	must contact in advance.
Societies	apply in writing.
Green Fees	£23 per 18 hole; £12.50 per 9 hole (£27/£14.50 weekends and bank holidays).
Facilities	⊗ ⅃ ♥ ♀ 🛆 🏠 ⌇
Leisure	electric & pull trolleys, caddy cars.
Location	Cottage Hill, Rotherfield (0.5m S of Rotherfield)
Hotel	★★⚑⚑70% Spindlewood Country House Hotel & Restaurant, Wallcrouch, WADHURST ☎ (0580) 200430 9 ⇄ ſ

EASTBOURNE   Map 05 TV69

Eastbourne Downs ☎ (0323) 720827
Downland/seaside course.
18 holes, 6635yds, Par 72, SSS 72.
Club membership 730.

Visitors	restricted after 1pm Sat & Sun.
Societies	must contact in advance.
Green Fees	£14 per round (£18 weekends).
Facilities	⊗ ⅃ ♥ ♀ 🛆 🏠 ⌇ ⌇ T Marshall.
Location	East Dean Rd (1m W of town centre on A259)
Hotel	★★★★56% Cavendish Hotel, Grand Pde, EASTBOURNE ☎ (0323) 410222 112 ⇄ ſ

Royal Eastbourne ☎ (0323) 729738
A famous club which celebrated its centenary in 1987.
The course plays longer than it measures. Testing holes
are the 8th, a par 3 played to a high green and the 16th, a
par 5 righthand dogleg.
Long Course: 18 holes, 6109yds, Par 70, SSS 69.
Short Course: 9 holes, 2147yds, Par 32, SSS 32.
Club membership 890.

Visitors	must have a handicap certificate for Long Course.
Societies	must telephone in advance.
Green Fees	on application.
Facilities	⊗ Ⅲ by prior arrangement ⅃ ♥ ♀ (ex Sun) 🛆 🏠 ⌇ ⋈ ⌇ Richard Wooller.
Leisure	snooker, putting green, caddy cars for hire.
Location	Paradise Dr (0.5m W of town centre)
Hotel	★★★74% Lansdowne Hotel, King Edward's Pde, EASTBOURNE ☎ (0323) 725174 127 ⇄ ſ

Willingdon ☎ (0323) 410981
Unique, hilly downland course set in oyster-shaped
amphitheatre.
18 holes, 6049yds, Par 69, SSS 69.
Club membership 570.

Visitors	by application.
Societies	Mon-Fri only. Must contact in advance by telephone.
Green Fees	£14/£24 per day/round (£16/£27 weekends & bank holidays).
Facilities	⊗ Ⅲ by prior arrangement ⅃ ♥ ♀ 🛆 🏠 ⌇ ⌇ James Debenham.

7 Courses to choose from!

Any 2 days - 1 September '94 - 31 December 1995

Your break includes 2 days' free golf (up to 36 holes
each day), accommodation, newspaper (except Sunday),
full English breakfast, light lunch at the golf club, with
a 4 course Dinner and coffee at the hotel. Guaranteed
tee-off times. Handicap certificates required.

All our 125 rooms are en suite with every modern
facility inc. Satellite TV.

The cost of your golf break from 1 Sep-31 Oct £148;
1 Nov-31 Mar £144; 1 Apr-31 May £146;
1 Jun-31 Oct £150; 1 Nov-31 Dec £143 Extra days pro rata.

You may, subject to availability, play at a selection of
7 golf clubs (all 18-hole) in this lovely area.

Please write or telephone for our Golfing Break folder.

Lansdowne Hotel   AA
                                        ★★★
King Edward's Parade · Eastbourne BN21 4EE   74%
Tel: (01323) 725174   **Fax: (01323) 739721**

Leisure   practice area.
Location   Southdown Rd (0.5m N of town centre off A22)
Hotel   ★★★63% Wish Tower Hotel, King Edward's
     Pde, EASTBOURNE
     ☎ (0323) 722676 65 ⇋ ⋔

FOREST ROW   Map 05 TQ43

Ashdown Forest Hotel ☎ (0342) 824866
Natural heathland and woodland course cut out of the
Ashdown Forest. The hotel specialises in catering for golf
breaks and societies.
18 holes, 5510yds, Par 68, SSS 67.
Club membership 150.
Visitors   are advised to contact in advance.
Societies   must contact in advance.
Green Fees on request.
Facilities   ⊗ ⋔ ⓛ ♥ ⓠ ⚐ ☖ ⋔ ⌂
      ⚑ Martyn Landsborough.
Leisure   pool, darts.
Location   Chapel Ln (4m S of East Grinstead off A22 &
     B2110)

Royal Ashdown Forest ☎ (0342) 822018
Undulating heathland course. Long carries off the tees
and magnificent views over the Forest. Not a course for
the high handicapper.
Old Course: 18 holes, 6477yds, Par 72, SSS 71.
New Course: 18 holes, 5549yds, Par 68, SSS 67.
Club membership 450.
Visitors   restricted weekends & Tue. Must have a
      handicap certificate on Old Course. No
      restrictions on New Course.
Societies   must contact in advance.
Green Fees £36 per day; £28 per round (£40/£34
      weekends & bank holidays).
Facilities   ⊗ ⓛ ♥ ⓠ (closes 8pm) ☖ ☖ ⋔
      ⚑ Martyn Landsborough.
Location   Chapel Ln (SE side of village)
Hotel   ★★★65% Woodbury House Hotel, Lewes
     Rd, EAST GRINSTEAD
     ☎ (0342) 313657 13 ⇋ ⋔Annexe1 ⋔
Additional ★★★★♨76% Ashdown Park Hotel, Wych
hotel   Cross, FOREST ROW
     ☎ (0342) 824988 96 ⇋ ⋔
     See Inside Back Cover

HASTINGS & ST LEONARDS   Map 05 TQ80

Beauport Park ☎ Hastings (0424) 852977
Played over Hastings Public Course. Undulating parkland
with stream and fine views.
18 holes, 6033yds, Par 70, SSS 70.
Club membership 290.
Visitors   no restrictions.
Societies   must contact in writing.
Green Fees not confirmed.
Facilities   ⓠ ☖ ☖ ⋔ ⚑
Location   St Leonards-on-Sea (3m N of Hastings on
     A2100)
Hotel   ★★★69% Beauport Park Hotel, Battle Rd,
     HASTINGS ☎ (0424) 851222 23 ⇋ ⋔

The Beauport Park Hotel
Hastings, Sussex TN38 8EA ★★★
Telephone: 01424 851222
Fax: 01424 852465

A Georgian country house hotel set in 33 acres of
parkland with its own swimming pool, tennis courts,
putting green, croquet lawn, French boules, outdoor
chess and country walks. Candle-lit restaurant and
open log fires. Adjacent to an 18 hole and 9 hole golf
course, floodlight driving range, riding stables and
squash courts. Convenient for East Sussex National
Golf Course – Home of the European Open.

Full inclusive golfing breaks available all year. Please send for our colour brochure and tariff.

HOLTYE   Map 05 TQ43

Holtye ☎ Cowden (0342) 850635
Undulating forest/heathland course with tree-lined fairways
providing testing golf. Difficult tees on back nine.
9 holes, 5289yds, Par 66, SSS 66, Course record 65.
Club membership 500.
Visitors   may not play weekend & Thu mornings. Must
      contact in advance.
Societies   Tue & Fri only, by arrangement.
Green Fees not confirmed.
Facilities   ⊗ ⋔ ⓛ ♥ ⓠ ☖ ⚑ Kevin Hinton.
Location   N side of village on A264
Hotel   ★★★(red)♨ Gravetye Manor Hotel, EAST
     GRINSTEAD ☎ (0342) 810567 18 ⇋

LEWES   Map 05 TQ41

Lewes ☎ (0273) 473245
Downland course. Fine views.
18 holes, 5951yds, Par 71, SSS 69, Course record 67.
Club membership 720.
Visitors   may not play at weekends before 2pm.
Societies   must contact in advance.
Green Fees £16.50 (£25 weekends).
Facilities   ⊗ ⋔ ⓛ ♥ ⓠ ☖ ⚑ Paul Dobson.
Location   Chapel Hill (E side of town centre off A26)
Hotel   ★★55% White Hart Hotel, 55 High St, LEWES
     ☎ (0273) 474676 & 476694 19rm(14 ⇋ ⋔)
     Annexe21 ⇋ ⋔

NEWHAVEN
Map 05 TQ40

Peacehaven ☎ (02739) 514049
Downland course, sometimes windy. Testing holes: 1st (par 3), 4th (par 4), 9th (par 3), 10th (par 3), 18th (par 3).
9 holes, 5305yds, Par 69, SSS 66, Course record 63.
Club membership 300.
Visitors no restrictions.
Societies telephone in advance.
Green Fees £10 per 18 holes (£16 weekends).
Facilities ⊗ ⅷ by prior arrangement ⅃ ☐ ♀ ⚎ 🏠 ⚑
(Gerry Williams.
Location Brighton Rd (0.75m W on A259)
Hotel ★★★65% The Star, ALFRISTON
☎ (0323) 870495 34 ⇆ 🐾

RYE
Map 05 TQ92

Rye ☎ (0797) 225241
Typical links course with superb greens and views.
Old Course: 18 holes, 6317yds, Par 68, SSS 71.
Jubilee Course: 9 holes, 6141yds, Par 71, SSS 70.
Club membership 1000.
Visitors must be invited/introduced by a member.
Green Fees on application.
Facilities ⊗ ☐ ♀ ⚎ 🏠 (Peter Marsh.
Location Camber (2.75m SE off A259)
Hotel ★★69% George Hotel, High St, RYE
☎ (0797) 222114 22 ⇆ 🐾

SEAFORD
Map 05 TV49

Seaford ☎ (0323) 892442
The great H. Taylor did not perhaps design as many courses as his friend and rival, James Braid, but Seaford's original design was Taylor's. It is a splendid downland course with magnificent views and some fine holes.
18 holes, 6233yds, Par 69, SSS 70.
Club membership 800.
Visitors must contact in advance, may play on weekdays only after 9.30am (ex Tue).
Societies must contact in advance.
Green Fees Apr-Oct: £25 per round (£15 after 4pm). Oct-Mar: £20.
Facilities ⊗ ⅷ⅃ ☐ ♀ ⚎ 🏠 ⇆ (Mark Smith.
Leisure snooker.
Location Firle Rd, East Blatchington (1m N)
Hotel ★★★65% The Star, ALFRISTON
☎ (0323) 870495 34 ⇆ 🐾

TICEHURST
Map 05 TQ63

Dale Hill ☎ (0580) 200112
Picturesque course with woodland, water and gently undulating fairways. Hotel and leisure centre within grounds.
18 holes, 6130yds, Par 70, SSS 70, Course record 68.
Club membership 550.
Visitors must play after 10am weekends.
Societies must contact in advance.
Green Fees £20 per round (£25 weekends).
Facilities ⊗ ⅷ⅃ ☐ ♀ ⚎ 🏠 ⚑ ⇆ (Liam Greasley.
Leisure heated indoor swimming pool, fishing, snooker, sauna, solarium, gymnasium, caddy cars for hire, driving range.

Location N side of village off B2087
Hotel ★★★71% Dale Hill Hotel & Golf Club, TICEHURST ☎ (0580) 200112 25 ⇆ 🐾

UCKFIELD
Map 05 TQ42

East Sussex National ☎ (0825) 880088
Created with a £30 million budget, the East Sussex National, which runs round the elegant Horsted Place Hotel, is a wonderful creation for golfers and is planned to be one of the most luxurious golf clubs in the world. Its two courses have been created with tournaments in mind and the 18th green has been designed so that 50,000 spectators can see.
East Course: 18 holes, 7081yds, Par 72, SSS 74, Course record 65.
West Course: 18 holes, 7154yds, Par 72, SSS 74, Course record 64.
Club membership 250.
Visitors must contact in advance and may require a handicap certificate. Must accompany a member on West Course.
Societies must contact the Corporate Hospitality Dept.
Green Fees Summer: £59.50 per round including lunch. Winter: £49.50 per day including lunch.
Facilities ⊗ ⅷ⅃ ⅃ ☐ ♀ ⚎ 🏠 ⚑ ⇆ (Ian Naylor.
Leisure hard tennis courts, heated indoor swimming pool, riding, sauna, 3 hole Academy course, croquet.
Location Little Horsted (S on A22)

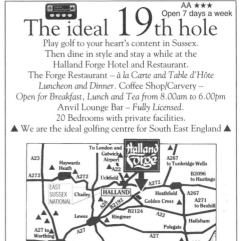

AA ★★★
Open 7 days a week

The ideal 19th hole

Play golf to your heart's content in Sussex.
Then dine in style and stay a while at the
Halland Forge Hotel and Restaurant.
The Forge Restaurant – *à la Carte and Table d'Hôte*
Luncheon and Dinner. Coffee Shop/Carvery –
Open for Breakfast, Lunch and Tea from 8.00am to 6.00pm
Anvil Lounge Bar – *Fully Licensed.*
20 Bedrooms with private facilities.
▲ We are the ideal golfing centre for South East England ▲

Hotel Restaurant and Coffee Shop/Carvery
Halland, nr. Lewes, East Sussex
On A22/B2192 roundabout,
4 miles south of Uckfield just beyond East Sussex National
Tel: Halland (01825) 840456 Fax: (01825) 840773

Hotel	★★★(red)🏌️ Horsted Place Sporting Estate & Hotel, Little Horsted, UCKFIELD ☎ (0825) 750581 17 ⇌ ➟
Additional hotel	★★★59% Halland Forge Hotel, HALLAND ☎ (0825) 840456 Annexe20 ⇌ ➟

Piltdown ☎ (0825) 722033
Natural heathland course with much heather and gorse. No bunkers, easy walking, fine views.
18 holes, 6070yds, Par 69, SSS 68.
Club membership 400.
Visitors   must telephone for details of restricted times.
Societies   must contact in writing.
Green Fees not confirmed.
Facilities ⊗ ⅲ by prior arrangement ⅼ ⬤ ♀ ⚲ 🏠 🍴 ⏿ John Amos.
Leisure   caddy cars, trolleys.
Location   3m NW off A272
Hotel   ★★★59% Halland Forge Hotel, HALLAND ☎ (0825) 840456 Annexe20 ⇌ ➟

ESSEX

ABRIDGE
Map 05 TQ49

Abridge Golf and Country Club ☎ Stapleford (0708) 688396
A parkland course with easy walking. The quick drying course is by no means easy to play. This has been the venue of several professional tournaments. Abridge is a Golf and Country Club and has all the attendant facilities.
18 holes, 6703yds, Par 72, SSS 72.
Club membership 600.
Visitors   must contact in advance. Play with member only at weekends.
Societies   Mon & Wed only; must contact in advance.
Green Fees not confirmed.
Facilities ⊗ (ex Fri) ⅼ ⬤ ♀ (ex Fri) ⚲ 🏠 ⏿ Mike Herbert.
Leisure   heated outdoor swimming pool, snooker, sauna.
Location   Epping Ln, Stapleford Tawney (1.75m NE)
Hotel   B Forte Posthouse, High Rd, Bell Common, EPPING ☎ (0992) 573137 Annexe79 ⇌ ➟

BASILDON
Map 05 TQ78

Basildon ☎ (0268) 533297
Undulating municipal parkland course. Testing 13th hole (par 4).
18 holes, 6153yds, Par 71, SSS 69.
Club membership 300.
Visitors   no restrictions.
Societies   must contact in advance.
Green Fees £8.50 per 18 holes (£13.50 weekends).
Facilities ⊗ ⅲ by prior arrangement ⅼ ⬤ ♀ ⚲ 🏠 🍴 ⏿ W Paterson.

Location   Clay Hill Ln, Kingswood (1m S off A176)
Hotel   B Forte Posthouse, Cranes Farm Rd, BASILDON ☎ (0268) 533955 110 ⇌ ➟

Pipps Hill Country Club ☎ (0268) 523456
Flat course with ditches and pond.
9 holes, 2829yds, Par 34, SSS 34.
Club membership 400.
Visitors   no restrictions.
Societies   must contact in advance.
Green Fees not confirmed.
Facilities ♀ ⚲
Location   Cranes Farm Rd (N side of town centre off A127)
Hotel   B Forte Posthouse, Cranes Farm Rd, BASILDON ☎ (0268) 533955 110 ⇌ ➟

BENFLEET
Map 05 TQ78

Boyce Hill ☎ (0268) 793625
Hilly parkland course with good views.
18 holes, 5377yds, Par 68, SSS 68.
Club membership 600.
Visitors   must have a handicap certificate. May only play with member at weekends.
Societies   Thu only.
Green Fees £25 per day/round.
Facilities ⊗ ⬤ ♀ ⚲ 🏠 🍴 ⏿ Graham Burroughs.
Location   Vicarage Hill, South Benfleet (0.75m NE of Benfleet Station)
Hotel   B Forte Posthouse, Cranes Farm Rd, BASILDON ☎ (0268) 533955 110 ⇌ ➟

BRAINTREE
Map 05 TL72

Braintree ☎ (0376) 346079
Parkland course with many rare trees.
18 holes, 6161yds, Par 70, SSS 69.
Club membership 750.
Visitors   may not play on Sun mornings. With member only Sat, Sun afternoon and bank holidays. Must contact in advance and have a handicap certificate.
Societies   must contact in advance.
Green Fees £25 per day, £18 after 2pm.
Facilities ⊗ ⅲ ⬤ ♀ ⚲ 🏠 ⏿ A K Parcell.
Location   Kings Ln, Stisted (1m E, off A120)
Hotel   ★★★61% White Hart Hotel, Bocking End, BRAINTREE ☎ (0376) 321401 31 ⇌ ➟

Towerlands ☎ (0376) 326802
Undulating, grassland course. Driving range and sports hall.
9 holes, 2703yds, Par 34, SSS 66.
Club membership 360.
Visitors   must not play before 12.30pm weekends. Correct dress at all times.
Societies   must contact in advance by telephone.
Green Fees 18 holes £10.50; 9 holes £8.50 (18 holes weekends & bank holidays £12.50).
Facilities ⊗ ⅲ ⅼ ⬤ ♀ ⚲ 🏠 🍴
Leisure   squash, sports hall, indoor bowls, driving range.
Location   Panfield Rd (on B1053)
Hotel   ★★★61% White Hart Hotel, Bocking End, BRAINTREE ☎ (0376) 321401 31 ⇌ ➟

BRENTWOOD   Map 05 TQ59

Bentley ☎ Coxtie Green (0277) 373179
Parkland course with water hazards.
18 holes, 6709yds, Par 72, SSS 72.
Club membership 550.
Visitors	may only play after 11am on bank holidays. Must contact in advance and have a handicap certificate.
Societies	must contact in advance.
Green Fees	£27 per day; £21 per round.
Facilities	⊗ ⅷ by prior arrangement ⅃ ☗ ⬓ ☖ 🖮 ⛏ Nick Garrett.
Location	Ongar Rd (3m NW on A128)
Hotel	B Forte Posthouse, Brook St, BRENTWOOD ☎ (0277) 260260 111 ⇥

Hartswood ☎ (0277) 218850
Municipal parkland course, easy walking.
18 holes, 6160yds, Par 70, SSS 69, Course record 69.
Club membership 800.
Visitors	must contact in advance.
Societies	must contact in advance.
Green Fees	not confirmed.
Facilities	Catering at the club by prior arrangement ⬓ ☖ 🖮 ⛏ John Stanion.
Location	King George's Playing Fields, Ingrave Rd (0.75m SE on A128)
Hotel	B Forte Posthouse, Brook St, BRENTWOOD ☎ (0277) 260260 111 ⇥

Warley Park ☎ (0277) 224891
Parkland course with reasonable walking. Numerous water hazards. There is also a golf-practice ground.
1st: 9 holes, 2950yds, Par 35, SSS 35.
2nd: 9 holes, 3132yds, Par 35.
3rd: 9 holes, 3240yds, Par 36.
Club membership 1000.
Visitors	must have handicap certificate, contact 24hrs in advance, with member only weekends.
Societies	must contact in advance.
Green Fees	£24 per 18 holes.
Facilities	⊗ ⅃ ☗ ⬓ ☖ 🖮 ⛏ P O'Connor.
Leisure	caddy cars.
Location	Magpie Ln, Little Warley (2.5m S off B186)
Hotel	B Forte Posthouse, Brook St, BRENTWOOD ☎ (0277) 260260 111 ⇥

BULPHAN   Map 05 TQ68

Langdon Hills Hotel & Golf Complex ☎ Basildon (0268) 548444
The complex is the base of the European School of Golf. The 18-hole course is of championship standard and there is also a 9-hole public course. Practice facilities include a 22-bay covered floodlit driving range, short game practice area with greens and bunkers and three-hole practice course.
Langdon: 18 holes, 6485yds, Par 72, SSS 71.
Horndon: 9 holes, 2861yds, Par 36, SSS 68.
Club membership 700.
Visitors	must have a handicap certificate & must contact the club in advance.
Societies	must book in advance.
Green Fees	not confirmed.
Facilities	⊗ ⅷ ⅃ ☗ ⬓ ☖ 🖮 ⛏

Leisure	22 bay floodlit covered driving range.
Location	Lower Dunton Rd
Hotel	★★★★65% Brentwood Moat House, London Rd, BRENTWOOD ☎ (0277) 225252 3 ⇥ ⛏Annexe30 ⇥ ⛏

BURNHAM-ON-CROUCH   Map 05 TQ99

Burnham-on-Crouch ☎ (0621) 782282 & 785508
Undulating meadowland course, easy walking, windy.
9 holes, 5918yds, Par 68, SSS 68.
Club membership 522.
Visitors	may only play Mon-Wed & Fri 9.30am-2pm, Thu noon-2pm. Must contact in advance.
Societies	Tue only. Must contact in writing.
Green Fees	not confirmed.
Facilities	⊗ ⅷ by prior arrangement ⅃ ☗ ⬓ ☖ 🖮 ⛏ Steve Parkin.
Leisure	3 caddy cars.
Location	Ferry Rd, Creeksea (1.25m W off B1010)
Hotel	★★64% Blue Boar Hotel, Silver St, MALDON ☎ (0621) 852681 21 ⇥ ⛏Annexe8 ⇥ ⛏

CANEWDON   Map 05 TQ99

Ballards Gore ☎ Southend (0702) 258917 & 258924
A parkland course with several lakes.
18 holes, 7062yds, Par 73, SSS 74.
Club membership 750.
Visitors	may not play at weekends.
Societies	apply in advance.
Green Fees	£22 per day; £16 per round.
Facilities	⊗ ⅷ by prior arrangement ⅃ ☗ ⬓ ☖ 🖮 ⛏ Ian Marshall.
Leisure	snooker, practice area, caddy cars in summer.
Location	Gore Rooad (2m NE of Rochford)
Hotel	★★★66% Hotel Renouf, Bradley Way, ROCHFORD ☎ (0702) 541334 24 ⇥ ⛏

CANVEY ISLAND   Map 05 TQ78

Castle Point ☎ (0268) 510830
A flat seaside links course with water hazards.
18 holes, 6176yds, Par 71, SSS 69, Course record 72.
Club membership 320.
Visitors	must book for weekends.
Societies	by prior arrangement.
Green Fees	not confirmed.
Facilities	⊗ ⅷ ⅃ ☗ ⬓ ☖ 🖮 ⛏ John Hudson.
Location	Somnes Av (SE of Basildon, A130 to Canvey Island)
Hotel	★★★63% Chichester Hotel, Old London Rd, Wickford, BASILDON ☎ (0268) 560555 2 ⇥ ⛏Annexe32 ⇥ ⛏

CHELMSFORD   Map 05 TL70

Channels ☎ (0245) 440005
Built on land from reclaimed gravel pits, 18 very exciting holes with plenty of lakes providing an excellent test of golf.
Channels: 18 holes, 6272yds, Par 71, SSS 71.
Belsteads: 18 holes, 4779yds, Par 67, SSS 63.
Club membership 750.

Visitors	must contact in advance & play with member at weekends.
Societies	must contact in advance.
Green Fees	£28 per day.
Facilities	⊗ ⟩⟩⟩ ㅑ ◆ ♀ ♨ 🏠 (Ian Sinclair.
Leisure	fishing, floodlit driving range, caddy cars.
Location	Belstead Farm Ln, Little Waltham (2m NE on A130)
Hotel	★★★55% South Lodge Hotel, 196 New London Rd, CHELMSFORD ☎ (0245) 264564 25 ⇥ (Annexe16 ⇥ (

Chelmsford ☎ (0245) 256483
An undulating parkland course, hilly in parts, with 3 holes in woods and four difficult par 4's. From the reconstructed clubhouse there are fine views over the course and the wooded hills beyond.
18 holes, 5944yds, Par 68, SSS 68.
Club membership 650.

Visitors	must contact in advance & have handicap certificate. visitors only at weekends.
Societies	must contact 9 months in advance.
Green Fees	£34 per day; £23 per round.
Facilities	⊗ (Tue-Sun) ⟩⟩⟩ by prior arrangement ㅑ ◆ ♀ ♨ 🏠 (
Location	Widford (1.5m S of town centre off A12)
Hotel	★★★55% South Lodge Hotel, 196 New London Rd, CHELMSFORD ☎ (0245) 264564 25 ⇥ (Annexe16 ⇥ (

CHIGWELL   Map 05 TQ49

Chigwell ☎ 081-500 2059
A course of high quality, mixing meadowland with parkland. For those who believe 'all Essex is flat' the undulating nature of Chigwell is a refreshing surprise. The greens are excellent and the fairways tight with mature trees.
18 holes, 6279yds, Par 71, SSS 70.
Club membership 657.

Visitors	must contact in advance & have handicap certificate, but must be accompanied by member at weekends.
Societies	must contact in writing
Green Fees	not confirmed.
Facilities	⊗ ㅑ ◆ ♀ ♨ 🏠 ⁒ (Ray Beard.
Location	High Rd (0.5m S on A113)
Hotel	★★59% Roebuck Hotel, North End, BUCKHURST HILL ☎ 081-505 4636 29 ⇥ (

CHIGWELL ROW   Map 05 TQ49

Hainault Forest ☎ 081-500 0385
Club playing over Borough of Redbridge public courses; hilly parkland subject to wind. Two courses, driving range.
No 1 Course: 18 holes, 5744yds, Par 70, SSS 67, Course record 65.
No 2 Course: 18 holes, 6600yds, Par 71, SSS 71.
Club membership 600.

Visitors	no restrictions.
Societies	must contact in writing.
Green Fees	not confirmed.
Facilities	⊗ ㅑ ◆ ♀ ♨ 🏠 ⁒ (T Dungate.
Location	Romford Rd, Chigwell Row (0.5m S on A1112)

Hotel	★★★68% Woodford Moat House, Oak Hill, WOODFORD GREEN ☎ 081-505 4511 99 ⇥ (

CLACTON-ON-SEA   Map 05 TM11

Clacton ☎ (0255) 421919
Windy, seaside course.
18 holes, 6494yds, Par 71, SSS 69.
Club membership 650.

Visitors	must contact in advance.
Societies	must contact in writing.
Green Fees	£20 (£30 weekends & bank holidays).
Facilities	⊗ & ⟩⟩⟩ (Tue,Wed,Fri & Sat) ㅑ ◆ ♀ ♨ 🏠 ⁒ (S J Levermore.
Leisure	buggy to hire by booking.
Location	West Rd (1.25m SW of town centre)
Hotel	★★65% Maplin Hotel, Esplanade, FRINTON-ON-SEA ☎ (0255) 673832 12rm(9 ⇥ 1 ()

COLCHESTER   Map 05 TL92

Birch Grove ☎ (0206) 734276
A pretty, undulating course surrounded by woodland - small but challenging with excellent greens.
9 holes, 4038yds, Par 62, SSS 60, Course record 58.
Club membership 250.

Visitors	restricted Sun mornings.
Societies	must contact in advance.
Green Fees	£10 (£12 weekends & bank holidays).
Facilities	⊗ ⟩⟩⟩ ㅑ ◆ ♀ ♨ 🏠
Location	Layer Rd, Kingsford (2.5m S on B1026)
Hotel	★★71% Kingsford Park Hotel, Layer Rd, Layer De La Haye, COLCHESTER ☎ (0206) 734301 10 ⇥ (

Colchester ☎ (0206) 853396
A fairly flat parkland course.
18 holes, 6319yds, Par 70, SSS 70.
Club membership 800.

Visitors	must contact in advance & have handicap certificate.
Societies	must contact in advance.
Green Fees	£22 per day or at secretary discretion (£25 per round weekends).
Facilities	⊗ ⟩⟩⟩ by prior arrangement ㅑ ◆ ♀ ♨ 🏠 (Mark Angel.
Location	Braiswick (1.5m NW of town centre on B1508)
Hotel	★★★60% George Hotel, 116 High St, COLCHESTER ☎ (0206) 578494 47 ⇥ (

Stoke-by-Nayland ☎ Nayland (0206) 262836
Two undulating courses (Gainsborough and Constable) situated in Dedham Vale. Some water hazards and hedges. On Gainsborough the 10th (par 4) takes 2 shots over a lake; very testing par 3 at 11th.
Gainsborough Course: 18 holes, 6516yds, Par 72, SSS 71.
Constable Course: 18 holes, 6544yds, Par 72, SSS 71.
Club membership 1460.

Visitors	restricted at weekends.
Societies	weekdays only . Must contact in advance.
Green Fees	£24 per 18 holes; £29 per 36 holes (£35/£28 weekends & bank holidays).
Facilities	⊗ ⟩⟩⟩ ◆ ♀ ♨ 🏠 ⁒ ⊨ (Kevin Lovelock.
Leisure	squash, fishing, sauna, buggies. ▶

Location   Keepers Ln, Leavenheath (1.5m NW of Stoke-by-Nayland on B1068)
Hotel   ★★★(red)♠♠ Maison Talbooth, Stratford Rd, DEDHAM ☎ (0206) 322367 10 ⇆ 🐾

EARLS COLNE   Map 05 TL82

Colne Valley ☎ Halstead (0787) 224233
An 18-hole course along the valley of the River Colne. Opened in 1991.
18 holes, 6272yds, Par 71, SSS 70.
Club membership 350.
Visitors   only after 10am at weekends, must dress correctly,no sharing of clubs.
Societies   apply in writing, minimum of 12 persons.
Green Fees   £22 per day; £12 per round (£18 per round weekends after 10am).
Facilities   ⊗ ⴾ 🍺 ♀ ♨ 🏠 (Mrs Kimberley Martin.
Location   Station Rd (off A604)
Hotel   ★★★67% White Hart Hotel, Market End, COGGESHALL ☎ (0376) 561654 18 ⇆ 🐾

Earls Colne Golf & Leisure Centre ☎ (0787) 224466
Created on the site of a World War II airfield, this challenging public course contains 14 lakes. Also 9-hole course and 4-hole instruction course as well as a variety of leisure facilities.
18 holes, 6900yds, Par 73, SSS 72, Course record 71.
Club membership 500.
Visitors   no restrictions.
Societies   must telephone in advance.
Green Fees   not confirmed.
Facilities   ⊗ ⴾ (Wed-Sat) ⴾ 🍺 ♀ ♨ 🏠 (Owen Mckenna.
Leisure   hard tennis courts, heated indoor swimming pool, fishing, sauna, solarium, gymnasium.
Hotel   ★★★67% White Hart Hotel, Market End, COGGESHALL ☎ (0376) 561654 18 ⇆ 🐾

FRINTON-ON-SEA   Map 05 TM22

Frinton ☎ (0255) 674618
Flat seaside links course, easy walking, windy. Also a short course.
Long Course: 18 holes, 6265yds, Par 71, SSS 70, Course record 66.
Short Course: 18 holes, 2508yds, Par 66.
Club membership 850.
Visitors   must have a handicap certificate for Long course.
Societies   must contact in writing.
Green Fees   £22 per day/round; £7.50 per day Short Course.
Facilities   ⊗ ⴾ by prior arrangement ⴾ 🍺 ♀ ♨ 🏠 ⴾ (Peter Taggart.
Leisure   snooker, buggies for hire.
Location   1 The Esplanade (SW side of town centre)
Hotel   ★★65% Maplin Hotel, Esplanade, FRINTON-ON-SEA ☎ (0255) 673832 12rm(9 ⇆1 🐾)

> **If you know of a golf course that welcomes visitors and is not already in this guide, we should be grateful for information**

GOSFIELD   Map 05 TL72

Gosfield Lake ☎ Halstead (0787) 474747 & 474488
Parkland course with bunkers, lake and water hazards. Designed by Sir Henry Cotton/Mr Howard Swan and opened in 1988. Also 9-hole course.
Lakes Course: 18 holes, 6707yds, Par 72, SSS 71.
Meadows Course: 9 holes, 4180yds, Par 64.
Club membership 850.
Visitors   a handicap certificate is required for Lakes Course. Telephone to book for weekends.
Societies   apply in writing. Telephone for information.
Green Fees   Lakes: £25 per day. Meadows: £10 per day.
Facilities   ⊗ ⴾ by prior arrangement ⴾ 🍺 ♀ ♨ 🏠 (Richard Wheeler.
Leisure   sauna.
Location   The Manor House, Hall Dr (4m N of Braintree on A1017)
Hotel   ★★★61% White Hart Hotel, Bocking End, BRAINTREE ☎ (0376) 321401 31 ⇆ 🐾

HARLOW   Map 05 TL40

Canons Brook ☎ (0279) 421482
Parkland course designed by Henry Cotton.
18 holes, 6728yds, Par 73, SSS 73.
Club membership 800.
Visitors   may not play at weekends.
Societies   must contact in advance.
Green Fees   £25 per day/round (weekdays).
Facilities   ⊗ (ex Mon) ⴾ ⴾ by prior arrangement 🍺 ♀ ♨ 🏠 ⴾ (Alan McGinn.
Location   Elizabeth Way (3m S of M11)
Hotel   ★★★67% Churchgate Manor Hotel, Churchgate St, Old Harlow, HARLOW ☎ (0279) 420246 85 ⇆

North Weald ☎ Epping (0992) 522118
Although only opened in November 1993, the blend of lakes and meadowland give this testing course an air of maturity.
18 holes, 6239yds, Par 71.
Club membership 780.
Visitors   must contact in advance and have handicap certificate, limited at weekends.
Societies   contact in advance.
Green Fees   not confirmed.
Facilities   ⊗ ⴾ ⴾ 🍺 ♀ ♨ 🏠 ⴾ (
Leisure   sauna.
Location   North Weald Bassett, Epping (M11 exit 7,off A414 towards Chipping Ongar)
Hotel   ★★★62% Harlow Moat House, Southern Way, HARLOW ☎ (0279) 422441 120 ⇆ 🐾

HARWICH   Map 05 TM23

Harwich & Dovercourt ☎ (0255) 503616
Flat moorland course with easy walking.
9 holes, 5742yds, SSS 68.
Club membership 420.
Visitors   with member only at weekends.
Societies   must contact in writing.
Green Fees   not confirmed.
Facilities   ⊗ ⴾ & ⴾ by prior arrangement 🍺 ♀ ♨ 🏠

Location	Station Rd, Parkeston, Dovercourt (W side 0.25m from docks on A120)
Hotel	★★55% Cliff Hotel, Marine Pde, Dovercourt, HARWICH ☎ (0255) 503345 & 507373 28 ➡ ♠

INGRAVE   Map 05 TQ69

Thorndon Park ☎ Brentwood (0277) 811666
Among the best of the Essex courses with a fine new purpose-built clubhouse and a lake. The springy turf is easy on the feet. Many newly planted young trees now replace the famous old oaks that were such a feature of this course.
18 holes, 6481yds, Par 71, SSS 71.
Club membership 680.

Visitors	must contact in advance and play with member at weekends.
Societies	must contact in advance.
Green Fees	£40 per day; £25 per round.
Facilities	⊗ ⅃ ♥ ♀ ⚘ 🏠 ⚑ ⚭
Location	Ingrave Rd (W side of village on A128)
Hotel	B Forte Posthouse, Brook St, BRENTWOOD ☎ (0277) 260260 111 ➡

LOUGHTON   Map 05 TQ49

Loughton ☎ 081-502 2923
Hilly 9-hole parkland course on the edge of Epping Forest.
9 holes, 4700yds, Par 64, SSS 63, Course record 65.
Club membership 350.

Visitors	must contact in advance.
Societies	telephone in advance.
Green Fees	£8 per 18 holes; £5 per 9 holes (£10/£6 weekends).
Facilities	⅃ ♥ ♀ ⚘ 🏠 ⚑ ⚭ S Layton.
Location	Clays Ln, Debden Green (1.5m SE of Theydon Bois)
Hotel	B Forte Posthouse, High Rd, Bell Common, EPPING ☎ (0992) 573137 Annexe79 ➡ ♠

MALDON   Map 05 TL80

Forrester Park ☎ (0621) 891406
Tight, undulating parkland course with tree-lined fairways and good views over the Blackwater estuary. Easy walking. Attractive 16th-century clubhouse.
18 holes, 6073yds, Par 71, SSS 69.
Club membership 1200.

Visitors	must contact in advance but may not play before 9.30am Tue & Wed or before 12.30pm weekends & bank holidays.
Societies	must apply in writing.
Green Fees	£22 per day; £17 per round (£17 per round weekends pm only).
Facilities	⊗ ⅃ ♥ ♀ ⚘ 🏠 ⚭ Gary Pike.
Leisure	hard tennis courts, practise ground.
Location	Beckingham Rd, Great Totham (3m NE of Maldon off B1022)
Hotel	★★64% Blue Boar Hotel, Silver St, MALDON ☎ (0621) 852681 21 ➡ ♠Annexe8 ➡ ♠

Maldon ☎ (0621) 853212
Flat, parkland course in a triangle of land by the River Chelmer, the Blackwater Canal and an old railway embankment. Alternate tees on 2nd nine holes.
9 holes, 6197yds, Par 71, SSS 69.
Club membership 480.

Visitors	may start after 2pm and at weekends only with member.
Societies	may play Mon & Thu. Must apply in writing.
Green Fees	£20 per day; £15 per round (Mon-Fri).
Facilities	⊗ & ⅃ by prior arrangement ⅃ ♥ ♀ ⚘ 🏠
Location	Beeleigh, Langford (1m NW off B1018)
Hotel	★★64% Blue Boar Hotel, Silver St, MALDON ☎ (0621) 852681 21 ➡ ♠Annexe8 ➡ ♠

ORSETT   Map 05 TQ68

Orsett ☎ Grays Thurrock (0375) 891352
A very good test of golf - this heathland course with its sandy soil is quick drying and provides easy walking. Close to the Thames estuary it is seldom calm and the main hazards are the prevailing wind and thick gorse. Any slight deviation can be exaggerated by the wind and a lost ball in the gorse results. The clubhouse has been modernised.
18 holes, 6614yds, Par 72, SSS 72.
Club membership 900.

Visitors	restricted weekends & bank holidays. Must contact in advance and have a handicap certificate.
Societies	must contact in advance.
Green Fees	£30 per day (£20 after 1pm).
Facilities	⊗ ⅃ ⅃ ♥ ♀ ⚘ 🏠 ⚑ ⚭ Robert Newberry.
Leisure	snooker, caddy cars.
Location	Brentwood Rd (1.5m SE off A128)
Hotel	B Forte Posthouse, Cranes Farm Rd, BASILDON ☎ (0268) 533955 110 ➡ ♠

PURLEIGH   Map 05 TL80

Three Rivers ☎ Maldon (0621) 828631
Parkland course.
Kings Course: 18 holes, 6348yds, Par 73, SSS 70.
Queens Course: 9 holes, 1071yds, Par 27.

Visitors	must contact in advance & have handicap certificate but may not play at weekends & bank holidays.
Societies	Tue-Fri only; must contact in advance.
Green Fees	not confirmed.
Facilities	⊗ ⅃ ⅃ ♥ ♀ ⚘ 🏠 ⚭ Graham Packer.
Leisure	hard tennis courts, heated outdoor swimming pool, squash, snooker, solarium.
Location	Stow Rd (1m from Purleigh on B1012)
Hotel	★★64% Blue Boar Hotel, Silver St, MALDON ☎ (0621) 852681 21 ➡ ♠Annexe8 ➡ ♠

ROCHFORD   Map 05 TQ89

Rochford Hundred ☎ (0702) 544302
Parkland course with ponds and ditches as natural hazards.
18 holes, 6292yds, Par 72, SSS 70.
Club membership 800.

Visitors	no restrictions.
Societies	must contact in writing.
Green Fees	not confirmed. ▶

Facilities ⊗ 🍴 ㊇ 🐴 ⛳ ♿ 📷 🏌

Location Hall Rd (W on B1013)

Hotel ★★★66% Hotel Renouf, Bradley Way, ROCHFORD ☎ (0702) 541334 24 ⇄ ☞

SAFFRON WALDEN   Map 05 TL53

Saffron Walden ☎ (0799) 522786
Undulating parkland course, beautiful views.
18 holes, 6609yds, Par 72, SSS 72 or 6371yds, Par 72, SSS 71.
Club membership 1000.

Visitors with member only at weekends. Must contact in advance and have a handicap certificate.

Societies must contact in advance.

Green Fees £28 per day/round.

Facilities ⊗ ㊇ 🐴 ⛳ ♿ 📷 🏌 Philip Davis.

Leisure buggies.

Location Windmill Hill (NW side of town centre off B184)

Hotel ★★65% Saffron Hotel, 10-18 High St, SAFFRON WALDEN ☎ (0799) 522676 21rm(8 ⇄8 ☞)

SOUTHEND-ON-SEA   Map 05 TQ88

Belfairs ☎ (0702) 525345
Municipal parkland course run by the Borough Council. Tight second half through thick woods, easy walking.
18 holes, 5795yds, Par 70, SSS 68.
Club membership 300.

Visitors restricted weekends & bank holidays.

Green Fees not confirmed.

Facilities 📷 🏌 🏌

Leisure hard tennis courts.

Location Eastwood Rd North, Leigh on Sea (3m W, N of A13)

Hotel ★69% Balmoral Hotel, 34 Valkyrie Rd, Westcliffe-on-Sea, SOUTHEND-ON-SEA ☎ (0702) 342947 22 ⇄ ☞

Thorpe Hall ☎ (0702) 582205
Parkland course.
18 holes, 6286yds, Par 71, SSS 71, Course record 66.
Club membership 1000.

Visitors must contact in advance & have handicap certificate. With member only weekends & bank holidays.

Societies must contact one year in advance.

Green Fees £30 per day/round.

Facilities ⊗ 🍴 ㊇ 🐴 (must be accompanied by member) ⛳ ♿ 📷 🏌 Bill McColl.

Leisure squash, snooker, sauna.

Location Thorpe Hall Av, Thorpe Bay (2m E off A13)

Hotel ★69% Balmoral Hotel, 34 Valkyrie Rd, Westcliffe-on-Sea, SOUTHEND-ON-SEA ☎ (0702) 342947 22 ⇄ ☞

SOUTH OCKENDON   Map 05 TQ58

Belhus Park Municipal ☎ (0708) 854260
Municipal parkland type course with easy walking.
18 holes, 5450yds, Par 68, SSS 67.
Club membership 250.

Visitors no restrictions. Must have proper golf shoes and shirts to be worn at all times.

Societies must contact in writing.

Green Fees not confirmed.

Facilities ⊗ 🍴 ㊇ 🐴 ⛳ ♿ 📷 🏌 🏌

Leisure heated indoor swimming pool, squash, sauna, solarium, gymnasium, 11 bay floodlit driving range.

Location Belhus Park (2m SW off B1335)

Hotel ★★★67% Stifford Moat House, High Rd, North Stifford, GRAYS ☎ (0375) 390909 96 ⇄ ☞

STAPLEFORD ABBOTTS   Map 05 TQ59

Stapleford Abbotts ☎ (0708) 381108
Two championship 18-hole courses and a 9-hole par 3. The main features of the Priors course are the numerous lakes and large sloping greeen. Abbots course has many hazards and will test players of all standards. It is rapidly maturing into one of the best in Essex.
Abbotts Course: 18 holes, 6431yds, Par 72, SSS 71.
Friars Course: 9 holes, 1140yds, Par 27.
Priors Course: 18 holes, 5771yds, Par 70, SSS 69.
Club membership 1400.

Visitors restricted at weekends. Must contact in advance.

Societies by arrangement.

Green Fees Abbotts £40; Priors £15; Friars £5.

Facilities ⊗ 🍴 ㊇ 🐴 ⛳ ♿ 📷 🏌 🏌 Dominic Eagle.

Leisure fishing, sauna, gymnasium, caddy cars.

Location Horsemanside, Tysea Hill (1m E off B175)

Hotel ★★59% Roebuck Hotel, North End, BUCKHURST HILL ☎ 081-505 4636 29 ⇄ ☞

THEYDON BOIS   Map 05 TQ49

Theydon Bois ☎ (0992) 813054
The course was originally a nine-hole built into Epping Forest. It was later extendend to 18-holes which were well-planned and well-bunkered but are situated out in the open on the hillside. The old nine in the Forest are short and have three bunkers among them, but even so a wayward shot can be among the trees. The autumn colours here are truly magnificent.
18 holes, 5472yds, Par 68, SSS 68.
Club membership 625.

Visitors must contact in advance and have a handicap certificate.

Societies Mon & Tue only. Must contact in advance.

Green Fees £23 (£20 weekends after 2pm).

Facilities ⊗ ㊇ ⛳ ♿ 📷 🏌 🏌 R Hall.

Location Theydon Rd (1m N)

Hotel B Forte Posthouse, High Rd, Bell Common, EPPING ☎ (0992) 573137 Annexe79 ⇄ ☞

TOLLESHUNT D'ARCY   Map 05 TL91

Quietwaters ☎ Maldon (0621) 868888
Two 18-hole courses. The Links is a seaside course with a number of greenside ponds and strategically placed bunkers, while the Lakes is a championship course with large water features and mounding between fairways.
Links Course: 18 holes, 6194yds, Par 71, SSS 70.
Lakes Course: 18 holes, 6767yds, Par 72, SSS 72.
Club membership 494.

Visitors	restricted at weekends.
Societies	must contact in advance.
Green Fees	Links: £25 per day; £18 per round (£30/£22.50 weekends & bank holidays). Lakes: £45 per day; £30 per round at all times.
Facilities	⊗ ⅲ by prior arrangement ⓑ 🍺 ♀ ♙ 🖾 ⋈
Leisure	hard tennis courts, heated indoor swimming pool, squash, fishing, snooker, sauna, solarium, gymnasium, 8 international bowling rinks.
Location	Colchester Rd (1.75m NE on B1026)
Hotel	★★71% Kingsford Park Hotel, Layer Rd, Layer De La Haye, COLCHESTER ☎ (0206) 734301 10 ⇆ 🐾

TOOT HILL　　　　　　　　　　Map 05 TL50

Toot Hill ☎ Ongar (0277) 365747
Pleasant course with several water hazards and sand greens.
18 holes, 6053yds, Par 70, SSS 69.
Club membership 400.

Visitors	welcome but may not play at weekends.
Societies	by prior arrangement.
Green Fees	£35 per day; £25 per round.
Facilities	⊗ ⓑ 🍺 ♀ ♙ 🖾 ⅰ 【 Geoff Bacon.
Leisure	practice range, caddy cars.
Location	School Rd (7m SE of Harlow, off A414)
Hotel	B Forte Posthouse, High Rd, Bell Common, EPPING ☎ (0992) 573137 Annexe79 ⇆ 🐾

WITHAM　　　　　　　　　　Map 05 TL81

Braxted Park Estate ☎ Maldon (0621) 892305
A Pay and Play course in ancient parkland, surrounded by lakes and extremely pretty countryside. Suitable for beginners and average players.
9 holes, 1980yds, Par 30.

Visitors	may play week days only.
Societies	apply in writing 8 weeks prior to visit.
Green Fees	£11 per 18 holes; £8 per 9 holes.
Facilities	⋈
Leisure	hard tennis courts, heated indoor swimming pool, fishing, snooker, sauna.
Location	7m SE of Braintree
Hotel	★★★64% Rivenhall Resort Hotel, Rivenhall End, WITHAM ☎ (0376) 516969 7 ⇆ 🐾Annexe48 ⇆ 🐾

WOODHAM WALTER　　　　　　Map 05 TL80

Bunsay Downs ☎ (0245) 222648
Attractive 9-hole public course. Also Par 3 course..
9 holes, 2932yds, Par 70, SSS 68.
Badgers: 9 holes, 1319yds, Par 54.
Club membership 350.

Visitors	no restrictions.
Societies	Mon-Fri only. Must contact in advance.
Green Fees	9 holes: £7.50/£8. 18 holes £9.50. (£9.50/£10.50 weekends).
Facilities	⊗ ⅲ ⓑ 🍺 ♀ ♙ 🖾 ⅰ 【 Mickey Walker.
Leisure	caddy cars, trolleys, practice area.
Location	Little Baddow Rd
Hotel	★★64% Blue Boar Hotel, Silver St, MALDON ☎ (0621) 852681 21 ⇆ 🐾Annexe8 ⇆ 🐾

Warren ☎ Danbury (0245) 223258
Attractive parkland course with natural hazards and good views.
18 holes, 6229yds, Par 70, SSS 70, Course record 65.
Club membership 840.

Visitors	must play with club member at weekends before 3pm. Must have a handicap certificate.
Societies	must contact in advance.
Green Fees	not confirmed.
Facilities	⊗ (Sun) ⓑ 🍺 ♀ ♙ 🖾 ⋈ 【 Miss Mickey Walker.
Leisure	snooker.
Location	0.5m SW
Hotel	★★64% Blue Boar Hotel, Silver St, MALDON ☎ (0621) 852681 21 ⇆ 🐾Annexe8 ⇆ 🐾

GLOUCESTERSHIRE

CHELTENHAM　　　　　　　　Map 03 SO92

Cotswold Hills ☎ (0242) 515264
A gently undulating course with open aspects and views of the Cotswolds.
18 holes, 6345yds, Par 70, SSS 72, Course record 67.
Club membership 750.

Visitors	no restrictions.
Societies	must apply in writing or telephone.
Green Fees	£26 per day; £21 per round (£31/£26 weekends).
Facilities	⊗ ⅲ ⓑ 🍺 ♀ ♙ 🖾 【 Noel Boland.
Location	Ullenwood (3m S off A436)
Hotel	B Forte Posthouse, Crest Way, Barnwood, GLOUCESTER ☎ (0452) 613311 123 ⇆ 🐾

Lilley Brook ☎ (0242) 526785
Undulating parkland course. Magnificent views over Cheltenham and surrounding coutryside.
18 holes, 6226yds, Par 69, SSS 70, Course record 63.
Club membership 800.

Visitors	must contact in advance and have handicap certificate. With member only at weekends.
Societies	by prior arrangement, except Tue.
Green Fees	£20 per day/round (weekdays).
Facilities	⊗ ⅲ ⓑ 🍺 ♀ ♙ 🖾 ⅰ 【
Leisure	caddy car for hire.
Location	Cirencester Rd, Charlton Kings (3m S on A435)
Hotel	★★★★56% The Queen's, Promenade, CHELTENHAM ☎ (0242) 514724 74 ⇆ 🐾

CIRENCESTER　　　　　　　　Map 04 SP00

Cirencester ☎ (0285) 652465
Undulating Cotswold course.
18 holes, 6002yds, Par 70, SSS 69.
Club membership 750.

Visitors	may not play on competition days. Must contact in advance and have a handicap certificate.
Societies	must contact in writing.
Green Fees	£20 per day (£25 weekends & bank holidays).
Facilities	⊗ ⅲ by prior arrangement ⓑ 🍺 ♀ ♙ 🖾 ⅰ 【 Geoff Robbins. ▶

Leisure caddy cars.
Location Cheltenham Rd, Bagendon (1.5m N on A435)
Hotel ★★★68% Stratton House Hotel, Gloucester Rd, CIRENCESTER ☎ (0285) 651761 41 ⇔ ⋔

CLEEVE HILL

Map 03 SO92

Cleeve Hill ☎ (024267) 2025 & 2592
Undulating heathland course.
18 holes, 6217yds, Par 69, SSS 70, Course record 64.
Club membership 650.
Visitors must contact in advance. Some restrictions weekends.
Societies must contact in advance.
Green Fees £8 (£10 weekends & bank holidays).
Facilities ⊗ ⫼ ⓑ ⬤ ♀ ⚲ 🏠 ⫐ ⓒ David Finch.
Leisure skittle alley.
Location nr Prestbury (1m NE on B4632)
Hotel ★★★61% Hotel De La Bere, Southam, CHELTENHAM ☎ (0242) 237771 32 ⇔ ⋔Annexe25 ⇔

COLEFORD

Map 03 SO51

Forest Hills ☎ (0594) 810620
A parkland course on a plateau with panoramic views of Coleford and Forest of Dean. Some testing holes with the par-5 13th hole sitting tight on a water hazard.
18 holes, 5600yds, Par 68, SSS 67.
Club membership 500.
Visitors no restrictions Mon-Sat, Sun by arrangement.
Societies contact in advance.
Green Fees £13 per day (£15 weekends).
Facilities ⊗ ⫼ ⓑ ⬤ ♀ ⚲ 🏠 ⫐
Location Mile End Rd
Hotel ★★71% The Speech House, Forest of Dean, COLEFORD ☎ (0594) 822607 14 ⇔ ⋔

Royal Forest of Dean ☎ Dean (0594) 832583
Established in 1973 and now matured into an extremely pleasant parkland course.
18 holes, 5459yds, Par 69, SSS 66, Course record 63.
Club membership 500.
Visitors are required to give Tee-off times.
Societies welcome Mon-Thu, must telephone in advance.
Green Fees £12 per round (£10 weekends & bank holidays).
Facilities ⊗ ⫼ ⓑ ⬤ ♀ ⚲ 🏠 ⫐ ⚑ ⓒ John Nicol.
Leisure hard tennis courts, outdoor swimming pool, bowling green.
Location Lords Hill
Hotel ★★71% The Speech House, Forest of Dean, COLEFORD ☎ (0594) 822607 14 ⇔ ⋔

DURSLEY

Map 03 ST79

Stinchcombe Hill ☎ (0453) 542015
High on the hill with splendid views of the Cotswolds, the River Severn and the Welsh hills. A downland course with good turf, some trees and an interesting variety of greens.
18 holes, 5734yds, Par 68, SSS 68.
Club membership 550.
Visitors restricted at weekends. Must contact in advance.

Societies must apply in writing.
Green Fees £20 per day; £15.50 per round (£25 weekends & bank holidays).
Facilities ⊗ ⫼ ⓑ ⬤ ♀ ⚲ 🏠 ⓒ Brendan Wynne.
Leisure pool table.
Location Stinchcombe Hill (1m W off A4135)
Hotel ★★59% Prince Of Wales Hotel, BERKELEY ROAD ☎ (0453) 810474 41 ⇔ ⋔

GLOUCESTER

Map 03 SO81

Gloucester Hotel & Country Club ☎ (0452) 411331
Undulating, wooded course, built around a hill with superb views over Gloucester and the Cotswolds. The 12th is a drive straight up a hill, nicknamed 'Coronary Hill'.
18 holes, 5613yds, Par 70, SSS 69.
Club membership 750.
Visitors must book at weekends. Handicap certificate required.
Societies by arrangement.
Green Fees not confirmed.
Facilities ⊗ & ⫼ (in hotel) ⓑ ⬤ ♀ ⚲ 🏠 ⫐ ⚑ ⓒ Peter Darnell.
Leisure hard tennis courts, heated indoor swimming pool, squash, snooker, sauna, solarium, gymnasium, table tennis, skittles, dry ski slopes.
Location Matson Ln, Robinswood Hill (2m SW off M5)
Hotel ★★★69% Bowden Hall Resort Hotel, Bondend Ln, Upton St Leonards, GLOUCESTER ☎ (0452) 614121 72 ⇔ ⋔

LYDNEY

Map 03 SO60

Lydney ☎ Dean (0594) 842614 & 841561
Flat parkland/meadowland course with prevailing wind along fairways.
9 holes, 5329yds, Par 66, SSS 66.
Club membership 350.
Visitors with member only at weekends & bank holidays.
Societies must telephone in advance.
Green Fees £12 per day.
Facilities ⓑ ⬤ (summer only) ♀ (summer only) ⚲
Location Lakeside Av (SE side of town centre)
Hotel ★★71% The Speech House, Forest of Dean, COLEFORD ☎ (0594) 822607 14 ⇔ ⋔

MINCHINHAMPTON

Map 03 SO80

Minchinhampton (New Course) ☎ (0453) 833866
The course is on an upland Costwold plateau. It is level and open in design. Very good golf is needed to achieve par of 72.
New Course: 18 holes, 6675yds, Par 72, SSS 72, Course record 66.
Club membership 1600.
Visitors must contact in advance & have handicap certificate.
Societies must contact by telephone.
Green Fees £24 per day; (£30 weekends & bank holidays).

Facilities ⊗)ℿ (Wed, Thu, Fri & Sat) ♨ ☕ ♀ ⛩ ⌂ ⚑ ⚐ Chris Steele.
Leisure snooker.
Location New Course (2m E)
Hotel ★★★65% Burleigh Court, Minchinhampton, STROUD ☎ (0453) 883804 11 ⇌ ⚑Annexe6 ⇌ ⚑

Minchinhampton (Old Course) ☎ Nailsworth (0453) 832642

An open grassland course 600 feet above sea level. There is a prevailing west wind that affects most holes. Panoramic Cotswold views.

Old Course: 18 holes, 6295yds, Par 71, SSS 70.
Club membership 600.

Visitors must contact in advance.
Societies must contact by telephone.
Green Fees £10 per day/round (£13 weekends & bank holidays).
Facilities ⊗ &)ℿ by prior arrangement ♨ (ex Mon) ☕ ♀ ⛩ ⌂ ⚑ ⚐ David Woodward.
Leisure snooker.
Location Old Course (1.5m W)
Hotel ★★★65% Burleigh Court, Minchinhampton, STROUD ☎ (0453) 883804 11 ⇌ ⚑Annexe6 ⇌ ⚑

NAUNTON Map 04 SP12

Naunton Downs ☎ (0451) 850090

New in 1993, Naunton Downs course plays over beautiful Cotswold countryside. A valley running through the course is one of the main features, creating 3 holes that cross over it. The prevailing wind adds extra challenge to the par 5's (which play into the wind), combined with small undulating greens.

18 holes, 6159yds, Par 71, SSS 69, Course record 76.
Club membership 750.

Visitors no restrictions but players must pre-book starting times at weekends.
Societies must pre-book.
Green Fees £19.95 per day.
Facilities ⊗)ℿ ♨ ☕ ♀ ⛩ ⌂ ⚑ ⛟ ⚐ Nigel Powell.
Leisure hard tennis courts, riding.
Location B4068 Stow/Cheltenham
Hotel ★★★♣♣79% Lords of the Manor, UPPER SLAUGHTER ☎ (0451) 820243 29 ⇌ ⚑

PAINSWICK Map 03 SO80

Painswick ☎ (0452) 812180

Downland course set on Cotswold Hills at Painswick Beacon, with fine views. Short course more than compensated by natural hazards and tight fairways.

18 holes, 4895yds, Par 67, SSS 64.
Club membership 420.

Visitors with member only on Sun.
Societies must apply in writing.
Green Fees not confirmed.
Facilities ⊗)ℿ ♨ ☕ ♀ ⛩ ⌂
Location 1m N on A46
Hotel ★★★71% Painswick Hotel, Kemps Ln, PAINSWICK ☎ (0452) 812160 19 ⇌ ⚑

TEWKESBURY Map 03 SO83

Puckrup Hall Hotel ☎ (0684) 296200

Set in 140 acres of undulating parkland with lakes, existing trees and marvellous views of the Malvern hills. There are water hazards at the 5th and a cluster of bunkers on the long 9th before the challnging tee shot across the water to the par-3 18th.

18 holes, 6431yds, Par 71, SSS 71.
Club membership 400.

Visitors must contact in advance, handicap certificate prefered.
Societies Tue & Thu by prior arrangement.
Green Fees £22.50 per 18 holes (£25 weekends & bank holidays).
Facilities ⊗)ℿ ♨ ☕ ♀ (11-11 ex Sun) ⛩ ⌂ ⛟ ⚐ Kevin Pickett.
Leisure heated indoor swimming pool, fishing, sauna, solarium, gymnasium, golf/leisure breaks, buggy hire.
Location Puckrup (4m N, on main A38)
Hotel ★★★74% Puckrup Hall Hotel and Golf Club, Puckrup, TEWKESBURY ☎ (0684) 296200 84 ⇌ ⚑

Phoneday - remember from 16 April 1995 all phone codes in the UK will change - see page 4 for details

PUCKRUP HALL HOTEL and GOLF CLUB

Puckrup, Tewkesbury,
Gloucestershire GL20 6EL
Telephone: (01684) 296200
Fax: (01684) 850788

Puckrup Hall Hotel and Golf Club is set amidst 140 acres of rolling parkland between the Cotswolds and Malvern Hills, just a few minutes from junction 8 of the M5. The 18 hole par 71 golf course, with the addition of lakes to the natural water sources and astute use of specimen trees, will satisfy the most discerning golfer. The 84 luxury bedrooms, superb cuisine and extensive conference and private dining facilities are all complemented by "Generations" Leisure Club which hosts swimming pool, spa bath and crêche. Altogether the ideal location for a touring base, golfing break or management retreat.

Tewkesbury Park Hotel Golf & Country Club
☎ (0684) 295405
A parkland course in a sheltered situation beside the
River Severn. The par 3, 5th is an exacting hole calling
for accurate distance judgment. The hotel and country
club offer many sports facilities.
18 holes, 6197yds, Par 73, SSS 70, Course record 68.
Club membership 553.

Visitors	must contact in advance and have an introduction from own club.
Societies	apply in writing.
Green Fees	not confirmed.
Facilities	⊗ ⊪ ⓛ ⓛ ♀ ♨ 🏠 ᵞ ⌐ ໐ Robert Taylor.
Leisure	hard tennis courts, heated indoor swimming pool, squash, snooker, sauna, solarium, gymnasium.
Location	Lincoln Green Ln (1m SW off A38)
Hotel	★★★66% Tewkesbury Park Hotel Golf & Country Club, Lincoln Green Ln, TEWKESBURY ☎ (0684) 295405 78 ➟ ໐

WESTONBIRT   Map 03 ST88

Westonbirt ☎ (066688) 242 & 333
A parkland course with good views.
9 holes, 4504yds, Par 64, SSS 64.
Club membership 150.

Visitors	no restrictions.
Societies	must apply in writing.
Green Fees	not confirmed.
Facilities	♨ (in summer) ⌂
Location	Westonbirt School (E side of village off A433)
Hotel	★★★64% Hare & Hounds Hotel, Westonbirt, TETBURY ☎ (0666) 880233 22 ➟ ໐Annexe8 ➟ ໐

WOTTON-UNDER-EDGE   Map 03 ST79

Cotswold Edge ☎ Dursley (0453) 844167 & 844398
Meadowland course situated in a quiet Cotswold valley. First
half flat and open, second half more varied.
18 holes, 5816yds, Par 71, SSS 68, Course record 68.
Club membership 800.

Visitors	preferable to contact in advance, at weekends may only play with member.
Societies	must contact in writing.
Green Fees	not confirmed.
Facilities	⊗ ⊪ by prior arrangement ⓛ ♨ ♀ ⌂ 🏠 ᵞ ⌐ David Gosling.
Location	Upper Rushmire (N of town on B4058 Wotton-Tetbury road)
Hotel	★★63% The Old Schoolhouse Hotel, Canonbury St, BERKELEY ☎ (0453) 811711 7 ➟ ໐

A golf course name printed in ***bold
italics*** means we have been unable to
verify information with the club's
management for the current year

GREATER LONDON

Those courses which fall within the confines
of the London Postal District area (ie have
London postcodes - W1, SW1 etc) are listed
under the county heading of **London** in the
gazetteer (see page 136).

ADDINGTON   Map 05 TQ36

Addington Court ☎ 081-657 0281
Challenging, well-drained courses designed by F. Hawtree.
Two 18-hole courses, 9-hole course and a pitch-and-putt
course.
Old: 18 holes, 5577yds, Par 67, SSS 67, Course record 63.
New Falconwood: 18 holes, 5360yds, Par 66, SSS 66.
Club membership 350.

Visitors	no restrictions.
Societies	must telephone in advance.
Green Fees	not confirmed.
Facilities	⊗ ⊪ by prior arrangement ⓛ ♨ ♀ ⌂ 🏠 ᵞ ⌐ Geoffrey A Cotton.
Location	Featherbed Ln (1m S off A2022)
Hotel	★★★★59% Selsdon Park Hotel, Sanderstead, CROYDON ☎ 081-657 8811 170 ➟ ໐

Addington Palace ☎ 081-654 3061
Hard-walking parkland course, with two (par 4) testing holes
(2nd and 10th).
18 holes, 6262yds, Par 71, SSS 71.
Club membership 600.

Visitors	must play with member at weekends & bank holidays.
Societies	Tue, Wed & Fri only.
Green Fees	£25 per day.
Facilities	⊗ ⓛ ♨ ♀ ⌂ 🏠 ⌐ Roger Williams.
Location	Gravel Hill (0.5m SW on A212)
Hotel	★★★★59% Selsdon Park Hotel, Sanderstead, CROYDON ☎ 081-657 8811 170 ➟ ໐

BARNEHURST   Map 05 TQ57

Barnehurst ☎ (0322) 523746
Parkland course, easy walking.
9 holes, 5320yds, Par 66, SSS 66.
Club membership 300.

Visitors	restricted Tue, Thu, Sat (pm) & Sun.
Societies	by arrangement.
Green Fees	£5.70 per 18 holes (£9.20 weekends & bank holidays).
Facilities	⊗ ⊪ ⓛ ♨ ♀ ⌂ 🏠 ⌐ Patrick Tallack.
Leisure	practice ground.
Location	Mayplace Rd East (0.75m NW of Crayford off A2000)
Hotel	B Forte Posthouse, Black Prince Interchange, Southwold Rd, BEXLEY ☎ (0322) 526900 102 ➟ ໐

BARNET

Map 04 TQ29

Arkley ☎ 081-449 0394
Wooded parkland course situated on highest spot in
Hertfordshire with fine views.
9 holes, 6045yds, Par 69, SSS 69.
Club membership 400.
Visitors with member only at weekends.
Societies Wed, Thu, Fri, by arrangement.
Green Fees not confirmed.
Facilities ⊗ ⫫ ⅃ ⬛ ♀ ♨ 🏠 ⌊ Mark Squire.
Location Rowley Green Rd (2m W off A411)
Hotel ★★★68% Edgwarebury Hotel, Barnet Ln,
ELSTREE ☎ 081-953 8227 50 ⇥ ⌐

Dyrham Park Country Club ☎ 081-440 3361
Parkland course.
18 holes, 6369yds, Par 71, SSS 70, Course record 65.
Club membership 1200.
Visitors must be guest of member.
Societies Wed only, must book in advance.
Green Fees not confirmed.
Facilities ⊗ ⫫ ⅃ ⬛ ♀ (all day) ♨ 🏠 ⌐ ⌊ Bill Large.
Leisure hard tennis courts, heated outdoor swimming
pool, fishing, snooker.
Location Galley Ln (3m NW off A1081)
Hotel B Forte Posthouse, Bignells Corner, SOUTH
MIMMS ☎ (0707) 643311 120 ⇥ ⌐

Old Fold Manor ☎ 081-440 9185
Heathland course, good test of golf.
18 holes, 6471yds, Par 71, SSS 71, Course record 66.
Club membership 522.
Visitors with member only weekends & bank holidays.
Handicap certificate/letter of introduction
required.
Societies must apply in writing.
Green Fees £20 per round; Mon & Wed £8 per round.
Facilities ⊗ ⫫ ⅃ ⬛ (no catering Mon & Wed) ♀ (ex
Mon & Wed) ♨ 🏠 ⌐ ⌊ Daniel Fitzsimmons.
Leisure snooker.
Location Old Fold Ln, Hadley Green (N side of town
centre on A1000)
Hotel ★★★★63% West Lodge Park Hotel,
Cockfosters Rd, HADLEY WOOD
☎ 081-440 8311 48 ⇥ ⌐Annexe2 ⇥ ⌐

BECKENHAM

Map 05 TQ36

Beckenham Place ☎ 081-658 5374
Picturesque course in the grounds of a public park. The
course is played over by the Braeside Golf Club.
18 holes, 5722yds, Par 68, SSS 68.
Club membership 200.
Visitors no restrictions.
Societies must contact in advance.
Green Fees not confirmed.
Facilities ♀ ♨ 🏠 ⌐ ⌊
Location The Mansion (0.5m N on B2015)
Hotel ★★★65% Bromley Court Hotel, Bromley Hill,
BROMLEY ☎ 081-464 5011 120 ⇥ ⌐

Langley Park ☎ 081-658 6849
This is a pleasant, but difficult, well-wooded, parkland
course with natural hazards including a lake at the 18th
hole.
18 holes, 6488yds, Par 69, SSS 71, Course record 65.
Club membership 650.
Visitors may not play before 9am or at weekends.
Must contact in advance & have handicap
certificate.
Societies Wed & Thu only, must apply in writing.
Green Fees £35 per day/round.
Facilities ⊗ ⅃ ⬛ ♀ ♨ 🏠 ⌐ ⌊ Colin Staff.
Location Barnfield Wood Rd (0.5 N on B2015)
Hotel ★★★65% Bromley Court Hotel, Bromley
Hill, BROMLEY
☎ 081-464 5011 120 ⇥ ⌐

BEXLEYHEATH

Map 05 TQ47

Bexleyheath ☎ 081-303 6951
Undulating course.
9 holes, 5239yds, Par 66, SSS 66.
Club membership 350.
Visitors may not play weekends & bank holidays.
Societies by arrangement.
Green Fees not confirmed.
Facilities ♀ ♨
Location Mount Dr, Mount Rd (1m SW)
Hotel B Forte Posthouse, Black Prince Interchange,
Southwold Rd, BEXLEY
☎ (0322) 526900 102 ⇥ ⌐

BIGGIN HILL

Map 05 TQ45

Cherry Lodge ☎ (0959) 572250 & 576712
Undulating parkland course with good views, 600feet above
sea level and affected by wind. 14th is 434 yards across a
valley and uphill. Requires two good shots to reach the green.
18 holes, 6652yds, Par 72, SSS 73.
Club membership 700.
Visitors must contact in advance but may not play at
weekends.
Societies must telephone in advance.
Green Fees £23 per day; £18 per round.
Facilities ⊗ ⫫ (Fri evening) ⅃ ⬛ ♀ ♨ 🏠 ⌊ Nigel Child.
Leisure sauna.
Location Jail Ln (1m E)
Hotel ★★★65% Kings Arms Hotel, Market Square,
WESTERHAM ☎ (0959) 562990 16 ⇥ ⌐

BROMLEY

Map 05 TQ46

Magpie Hall Lane ☎ 081-462 7014
Flat course, ideal for beginners.
9 holes, 2745yds, Par 70, SSS 67.
Club membership 100.
Visitors no restrictions.
Societies must contact in advance.
Green Fees not confirmed.
Facilities ♀ 🏠 ⌐ ⌊
Location Magpie Hall Ln (2m SE off A21)
Hotel ★★★65% Bromley Court Hotel, Bromley Hill,
BROMLEY ☎ 081-464 5011 120 ⇥ ⌐

Shortlands ☎ 081-460 2471
Easy walking parkland course with a brook as a natural hazard.
9 holes, 5261yds, Par 65, SSS 66, Course record 59.
Club membership 410.
Visitors   must be guest of member.
Green Fees not confirmed.
Facilities   ⛏ 🏠 (Jamie Bates.
Location   Meadow Rd, Shortlands (0.75m W off A222)
Hotel   ★★★65% Bromley Court Hotel, Bromley Hill,
                  BROMLEY ☎ 081-464 5011 120 ⇔ ⊫

Sundridge Park ☎ 081-460 0278
The East course is longer than the West but many think
the shorter of the two courses is the more difficult. The
East is surrounded by trees while the West is more hilly,
with good views. Both are certainly a good test of golf.
*East Course: 18 holes, 6467yds, Par 70, SSS 71, Course
record 64.*
*West Course: 18 holes, 6007yds, Par 68, SSS 69, Course
record 64.*
Club membership 1200.
Visitors   may only play on weekdays. Must contact in
                  advance and must have a handicap
                  certificate.
Societies   must contact in advance.
Green Fees £36 per day.
Facilities   ⊗ ⅃ ⬛ ♀ ⛏ 🏠 (Bob Cameron.
Location   Garden Rd (N side of town centre off
                  A2212)
Hotel   ★★★65% Bromley Court Hotel, Bromley
                  Hill, BROMLEY
                  ☎ 081-464 5011 120 ⇔ ⊫

CARSHALTON   Map 04 TQ26

Oaks Sports Centre ☎ 081-643 8363
Public parkland course with floodlit, covered driving range.
*18 holes, 6033yds, Par 70, SSS 69 or 9 holes, 1443yds, Par
28, SSS 28.*
Club membership 1000.
Visitors   no restrictions.
Societies   must apply in writing.
Green Fees £10 per round (£12 weekends). 9 hole: £4.50 per
                  round (£5.50 weekends).
Facilities   ⊗ ⅊ by prior arrangement ⅃ ⬛ ♀ ⛏ 🏠 ⸹
                  (G Horley, P Rees, M Pilkington.
Leisure   squash.
Location   Woodmansterne Rd (0.5m S on B278)
Hotel   B Forte Posthouse, Purley Way, CROYDON
                  ☎ 081-688 5185 83 ⇔ ⊫

CHESSINGTON   Map 04 TQ16

Chessington ☎ 081-391 0948
Tree-lined parkland course designed by Patrick Tallack.
9 holes, 1400yds, Par 27, SSS 28.
Club membership 250.
Visitors   must book 7.30am-noon weekends only.
Societies   must telephone 1 month in advance.
Green Fees not confirmed.
Facilities   ♀ ⛏ 🏠 ⸹ (
Location   Garrison Ln (opp Chessington South Station nr
                  Zoo)
Hotel   ★★63% Haven Hotel, Portsmouth Rd, ESHER
                  ☎ 081-398 0023 16 ⇔ ⊫Annexe4 ⇔ ⊫

CHISLEHURST   Map 05 TQ47

Chislehurst ☎ 081-467 2782
Pleasantly wooded undulating parkland/heathland course.
Magnificent clubhouse with historical associations.
18 holes, 5128yds, Par 66, SSS 65.
Club membership 800.
Visitors   must contact in advance. With member only
                  weekends.
Societies   must contact in writing.
Green Fees not confirmed.
Facilities   ♀ ⛏ 🏠 ⸹ (
Leisure   snooker.
Location   Camden, Park Rd
Hotel   ★★★65% Bromley Court Hotel, Bromley Hill,
                  BROMLEY ☎ 081-464 5011 120 ⇔ ⊫

COULSDON   Map 04 TQ25

Coulsdon Court ☎ 081-660 0468 & 081-668 0414
A public parkland course with good views. Clubhouse
formerly owned by the Byron family.
18 holes, 6037yds, Par 70, SSS 69.
Visitors   must book mid-week for weekends.
Societies   by arrangement.
Green Fees not confirmed.
Facilities   ⊗ ⅊ ⅃ ♀ ⛏ 🏠 ⸹ ⋈ (
Leisure   hard tennis courts, squash, solarium,
                  gymnasium.
Location   Coulsdon Rd (0.75m E off A23 on B2030)
Hotel   ★★★★59% Selsdon Park Hotel, Sanderstead,
                  CROYDON ☎ 081-657 8811 170 ⇔ ⊫

Woodcote Park ☎ 081-668 2788
Slightly undulating parkland course.
18 holes, 6337yds, Par 71, SSS 70.
Club membership 700.
Visitors   must contact in advance & have handicap
                  certificate but may not play at weekends.
Societies   must contact in advance.
Green Fees not confirmed.
Facilities   ⊗ ⅊ by prior arrangement ⅃ ⬛ ♀ ⛏ 🏠
                  (D Hudspith.
Leisure   snooker.
Location   Meadow Hill, Bridle Way (1m N of town centre
                  off A237)
Hotel   B Forte Posthouse, Purley Way, CROYDON
                  ☎ 081-688 5185 83 ⇔ ⊫

CROYDON   Map 05 TQ36

Croham Hurst ☎ 081-657 5581
Parkland course with tree-lined fairways and bounded by
wooded hills. Easy walking.
18 holes, 6274yds, Par 70, SSS 70.
Club membership 800.
Visitors   must contact in advance & have handicap
                  certificate. With member only weekends & bank
                  holidays.
Societies   must book 1 year in advance.
Green Fees not confirmed.
Facilities   ⊗ ⅊ by prior arrangement ⅃ ⬛ ♀ ⛏ 🏠 ⸹
                  (Eric Stillwell.
Location   Croham Rd (1.5m SE)

Hotel ★★★★59% Selsdon Park Hotel, Sanderstead, CROYDON ☎ 081-657 8811 170 ⇋ ⋔

Selsdon Park ☎ 081-657 8811
Parkland course. Full use of hotel's sporting facilities by residents.
18 holes, 6402yds, Par 71, SSS 69.
Visitors   restrictions at weekends for non-residents.
Societies must contact in advance.
Green Fees £20 per round (£30 weekends & bank holidays).
Facilities ⊗ ⋔ ⓑ 💺 ♀ ♨ 🏠 �🍴 ⟷ ⟨ Tom O'Keefe.
Leisure   hard and grass tennis courts, outdoor and indoor heated swimming pools, squash, snooker, sauna, solarium, gymnasium, croquet & boule.
Location   Addington Rd, Sanderstead (3m S on A2022)
Hotel   ★★★★59% Selsdon Park Hotel, Sanderstead, CROYDON ☎ 081-657 8811 170 ⇋ ⋔

Shirley Park ☎ 081-654 1143
This parkland course lies amid fine woodland with good views of Shirley Hills. The more testing holes come in the middle section of the course. The remarkable 7th hole calls for a 187-yard iron or wood shot diagonally across a narrow valley to a shelved green set right-handed into a ridge.
18 holes, 6210yds, Par 71, SSS 70.
Club membership 1000.
Visitors   should contact in advance. Handicap certificate preferred. With member only at weekends.
Societies by arrangement.
Green Fees £13 per day (£28 weekends & bank holidays).
Facilities ⊗ ⋔ ⓑ 💺 ♀ ♨ 🏠 ⍾ ⟨ Nick Allen.
Leisure   snooker, trolleys.
Location   Addiscombe Rd (E side of town centre on A232)
Hotel   ★★★★64% Croydon Park Hotel, 7 Altyre Rd, CROYDON ☎ 081-680 9200 214 ⇋ ⋔

DOWNE   Map 05 TQ46

High Elms ☎ (0689) 858175
Municipal parkland course. Very tight 13th, 230 yds (par 3).
18 holes, 6340yds, Par 71, SSS 70.
Club membership 570.
Visitors   no restrictions.
Green Fees not confirmed.
Facilities ⊗ ⓑ 💺 ♀ ♨ 🏠 ⍾
Location   High Elms Rd (1.5m NE)
Hotel   ★★★65% Bromley Court Hotel, Bromley Hill, BROMLEY ☎ 081-464 5011 120 ⇋ ⋔

West Kent ☎ Orpington (0689) 851323
Partly hilly downland course.
18 holes, 6399yds, Par 70, SSS 70.
Club membership 750.
Visitors   with member only at weekends. Must contact in advance and have a handicap certificate.
Societies must apply in writing at least two days in advance.
Green Fees £36 per day; £24 per round.
Facilities ⊗ ⓑ 💺 ♀ ♨ 🏠 ⟨ Roger Fidler.
Location   West Hill (0.75m SW)
Hotel   ★★★65% Bromley Court Hotel, Bromley Hill, BROMLEY ☎ 081-464 5011 120 ⇋ ⋔

ENFIELD   Map 05 TQ39

Crews Hill ☎ 081-363 6674
Parkland course in country surroundings.
18 holes, 6230yds, Par 70, SSS 70.
Club membership 603.
Visitors   Mon-Fri before 9am. Handicap certificate required.
Societies must apply in writing.
Green Fees not confirmed.
Facilities ⊗ & ⋔ by prior arrangement ⓑ 💺 (no catering Mon) ♀ ♨ 🏠 ⟨ J Reynolds.
Leisure   caddy cars.
Location   Cattlegate Rd, Crews Hill (3m NW off A1005)
Hotel   ★★60% Holtwhites Hotel, 92 Chase Side, ENFIELD ☎ 081-363 0124 30rm(28 ⇋ ⋔)

Enfield ☎ 081-363 3970
Public parkland course. Salmons Brook crosses 7 holes.
18 holes, 6137yds, Par 72, SSS 70 or 5924yds, Par 69, SSS 68.
Club membership 625.
Visitors   must contact in advance & have handicap certificate. With member only at weekends.
Societies Mon, Wed & Fri, must contact in advance.
Green Fees not confirmed.
Facilities ⊗ ⋔ ⓑ 💺 ♀ ♨ 🏠 ⟨ Lee Fickling.
Location   Old Park Rd South (W side of town centre off A110)
Hotel   ★★60% Holtwhites Hotel, 92 Chase Side, ENFIELD ☎ 081-363 0124 30rm(28 ⇋ ⋔)

Enfield Municipal ☎ 081-363 4454
Flat wooded parkland course. 9th hole is a left-hand dog-leg with second shot over a brook.
18 holes, 5755yds, Par 68, SSS 68.
Club membership 350.
Visitors   must play with member.
Societies must apply in writing to the secretary.
Green Fees not confirmed.
Facilities ⊗ ⋔ 💺 ♨ 🏠 ⍾ ⟨ David Lewis.
Location   Beggars Hollow, Clay Hill (N side of town centre)
Hotel   ★★60% Holtwhites Hotel, 92 Chase Side, ENFIELD ☎ 081-363 0124 30rm(28 ⇋ ⋔)

GREENFORD   Map 04 TQ18

Ealing ☎ 081-997 0937
Flat, parkland course relying on natural hazards; trees, tight fairways, and the River Brent which affects 9 holes.
18 holes, 6216yds, Par 70, SSS 70, Course record 64.
Club membership 700.
Visitors   Mon-Fri only on application to pro shop.
Societies Mon, Wed & Thu only by arrangement.
Green Fees £30 per day/round.
Facilities ⊗ ⓑ 💺 ♀ ♨ 🏠 ⟨ Arnold Stickley.
Leisure   caddy cars.
Location   Perivale Ln
Hotel   ★★★70% The Bridge Hotel, Western Av, GREENFORD ☎ 081-566 6246 68 ⇋ ⋔

For an explanation of symbols and
abbreviations, see page 5

Horsenden Hill ☎ 081-902 4555
A well-kept, tree-lined short course.
9 holes, 1618yds, Par 28, SSS 28.
Club membership 135.
Visitors no restrictions.
Societies telephone for details.
Green Fees not confirmed.
Facilities ⊗ 🏢 🍺 ♀ ♣ 🏠 ᵗ 𝄢 Anthony Ferrier.
Location Whitten Av, Woodland Rise (3m NE on A4090)
Hotel ★★★70% The Bridge Hotel, Western Av, GREENFORD ☎ 081-566 6246 68 ⇆ 🌾

Perivale Park ☎ 081-575 7116
Parkland course.
9 holes, 2600yds, Par 68, SSS 65.
Club membership 250.
Visitors no restrictions.
Green Fees £4.20 per 9 holes (£11.50 per 18 holes weekends).
Facilities ⊗ 🏢 🏢 🍺 ♣ 🏠 ᵗ 𝄢 Peter Bryant.
Leisure trolleys.
Location Stockdove Way (E side of town centre, off A40)
Hotel ★★★65% Carnarvon Hotel, Ealing Common, LONDON ☎ 081-992 5399 145 ⇆ 🌾

HADLEY WOOD
Map 04 TQ29

Hadley Wood ☎ 081-449 4328
A parkland course on the northwest edge of London. The gently undulating fairways have a friendly width inviting the player to open his shoulders, though the thick rough can be very punishing to the unwary. The course is pleasantly wooded and there are some admirable views.
18 holes, 6473yds, Par 72, SSS 71, Course record 66.
Club membership 600.
Visitors may not play Tue mornings & Sat. Must book in advance Sun.
Societies by arrangement.
Green Fees £40 per day; £30 per round (£35 Sun).
Facilities ⊗ 🏢 by prior arrangement 🍺 🍺 ♀ ♣ 🏠 ᵗ 𝄢 Peter Jones.
Leisure snooker.
Location Beech Hill (E side of village)
Hotel ★★★★63% West Lodge Park Hotel, Cockfosters Rd, HADLEY WOOD ☎ 081-440 8311 48 ⇆ 🌾Annexe2 ⇆ 🌾

HAMPTON
Map 04 TQ17

Fulwell ☎ 081-977 3844 & 081-977 2733
Championship-length parkland course with easy walking. The 575-yd, 17th, is notable.
18 holes, 6544yds, Par 71, SSS 71.
Club membership 750.
Visitors may not play Tue & weekends. Must contact in advance and have a handicap certificate.
Societies must apply in writing.
Green Fees £30 per day/round (£35 weekends).
Facilities ⊗ 🏢 by prior arrangement 🍺 🍺 ♀ ♣ 🏠 ᵗ 𝄢 David Haslam.
Location Wellington Rd, Hampton Hill (1.5m N on A311)
Hotel ★★★66% Richmond Hill, 146-150 Richmond Hill, RICHMOND ☎ 081-940 2247 & 081-940 5466 124 ⇆ 🌾

HAMPTON WICK
Map 04 TQ16

Home Park ☎ 081-977 2658
Flat, parkland course with easy walking.
18 holes, 6218yds, Par 71, SSS 71.
Club membership 573.
Visitors no restrictions.
Societies must contact in advance.
Green Fees not confirmed.
Facilities ⊗ 🏢 🏢 🍺 ♀ ♣ 🏠 𝄢 Len Roberts.
Location Off A308 on W side of Kingston Bridge
Hotel ★★★66% Richmond Hill, 146-150 Richmond Hill, RICHMOND ☎ 081-940 2247 & 081-940 5466 124 ⇆ 🌾

HILLINGDON
Map 04 TQ08

Hillingdon ☎ (0895) 233956
Parkland course west of London.
9 holes, 5490yds, Par 68, SSS 67.
Club membership 400.
Visitors may not play Thu, weekends, or bank holidays. Must have an introduction from own club.
Societies must apply in writing.
Green Fees not confirmed.
Facilities ⊗ 🏢 by prior arrangement 🍺 🍺 ♀ ♣ 🏠 𝄢
Location Dorset Way, Vine Ln (W side of town off A4020)
Hotel ★★★62% Master Brewer Hotel, Western Av, HILLINGDON ☎ (0895) 251199 106 ⇆ 🌾

HOUNSLOW
Map 04 TQ17

Airlinks ☎ 081-561 1418
Meadowland/parkland course designed by P. Allis and D. Thomas.
18 holes, 5885yds, Par 71, SSS 68, Course record 65.
Club membership 500.
Visitors may not play before noon at weekends.
Societies must apply in writing.
Green Fees not confirmed.
Facilities ⊗ 🏢 by prior arrangement in winter 🍺 🍺 ♀ ♣ 🏠 ᵗ 𝄢 Ken Wyckham.
Leisure 36 bay flood lit driving range.
Location Southall Ln (W of Hounslow off M4 junc 3)
Hotel ★★★62% Master Robert Hotel, Great West Rd, HOUNSLOW ☎ 081-570 6261 100 ⇆ 🌾

Hounslow Heath Municipal ☎ 081-570 5271
Parkland course in a conservation area, planted with an attractive variety of trees. The 15th hole lies between the fork of two rivers.
18 holes, 5820yds, Par 69, SSS 68.
Club membership 300.
Visitors may not play at weekends.
Societies must telephone in advance.
Green Fees not confirmed.
Facilities ♣ 🏠 ᵗ 𝄢
Location Staines Rd
Hotel B Forte Crest, Sipson Rd, WEST DRAYTON ☎ 081-759 2323 569 ⇆ 🌾

ILFORD

Map 05 TQ48

Ilford ☎ 081-554 2930
Fairly flat parkland course intersected five times by a river.
18 holes, 5702yds, Par 67, SSS 66.
Club membership 592.

Visitors	must contact in advance, restricted weekends & bank holidays.
Societies	must contact in advance.
Green Fees	£13.50 per round (£16 weekends).
Facilities	⊗ ∭ (Thu-Sat) 🍴 ♀ ♨ 🏠 ℓ S Dowsett.
Location	Wanstead Park Rd (NW side of town centre off A12)
Hotel	★★★68% Woodford Moat House, Oak Hill, WOODFORD GREEN ☎ 081-505 4511 99 ⇋ 🐾

ISLEWORTH

Map 04 TQ17

Wyke Green ☎ 081-560 8777
Fairly flat parkland course.
18 holes, 6242yds, Par 69, SSS 70, Course record 64.
Club membership 730.

Visitors	restricted weekends & bank holidays. Must contact in advance and a handicap certificate required.
Societies	must apply in writing.
Green Fees	£28 per day (£42 weekends).
Facilities	⊗ ∭ 🏌 🍴 ♀ ♨ 🏠 ℓ David Holmes.
Leisure	snooker, caddy cars.
Location	Syon Ln (1.5m N on B454 off A4)
Hotel	★★★62% Master Robert Hotel, Great West Rd, HOUNSLOW ☎ 081-570 6261 100 ⇋ 🐾

KINGSTON UPON THAMES

Map 04 TQ16

Coombe Hill ☎ 081-942 2284
A splendid course in wooded terrain. The undulations
and trees make it an especially interesting course of great
charm. And there is a lovely display of rhododendrons in
May and June.
18 holes, 6293yds, Par 71, SSS 71, Course record 64.
Club membership 550.

Visitors	must contact in advance. With member only at weekends.
Societies	must book in advance.
Green Fees	£45 per day/round; £25 after 3pm (weekdays).
Facilities	⊗ ∭ by prior arrangement 🏌 🍴 ♀ ♨ 🏠 ⛳ ℓ Craig Defoy.
Leisure	snooker, sauna, caddy cars for hire.
Location	Golf Club Dr, Coombe Ln West (1.75m E on A238)
Hotel	★★★66% Kingston Lodge Hotel, Kingston Hill, KINGSTON UPON THAMES ☎ 081-541 4481 62 ⇋ 🐾

Coombe Wood ☎ 081-942 0388
Parkland course.
18 holes, 5210yds, Par 66, SSS 66.
Club membership 650.

Visitors	must contact in advance & play with member at weekends.
Societies	Wed, Thu & Fri; must contact in advance.

Green Fees £26 per day (weekdays).
Facilities	⊗ ∭ by prior arrangement 🏌 🍴 ♀ ♨ 🏠 ⛳ ℓ David Butler.
Location	George Rd (1.25m NE on A308)
Hotel	★★★66% Kingston Lodge Hotel, Kingston Hill, KINGSTON UPON THAMES ☎ 081-541 4481 62 ⇋ 🐾

MITCHAM

Map 04 TQ26

Mitcham ☎ 081-648 4280
A wooded heathland course on a gravel base.
18 holes, 5935yds, Par 69, SSS 68.
Club membership 500.

Visitors	must telephone & book in advance.
Societies	must phone in advance.
Green Fees	£10.50 per round.
Facilities	⊗ 🏌 🍴 ♀ ♨ 🏠 ℓ Jeff Godfrey.
Location	Carshalton Rd (1m S)
Hotel	B Forte Posthouse, Purley Way, CROYDON ☎ 081-688 5185 83 ⇋ 🐾

NEW MALDEN

Map 04 TQ26

Malden ☎ 081-942 0654
Parkland course with the hazard of the Beverley Brook which
affects 4 holes (3rd, 7th, 8th and 12th).
18 holes, 6201yds, Par 71, SSS 70, Course record 65.
Club membership 800.

Visitors	restricted weekends. Must contact in advance.
Societies	must apply in writing.
Green Fees	not confirmed.
Facilities	⊗ 🏌 🍴 ♀ ♨ 🏠 ℓ Robert Hunter.
Location	Traps Ln (N side of town centre off B283)
Hotel	★★★66% Kingston Lodge Hotel, Kingston Hill, KINGSTON UPON THAMES ☎ 081-541 4481 62 ⇋ 🐾

NORTHWOOD

Map 04 TQ09

Haste Hill ☎ (0923) 822877 & 825224
Parkland course with stream running through. Excellent views.
18 holes, 5787yds, Par 68, SSS 68, Course record 64.
Club membership 350.

Visitors	no restrictions.
Societies	must apply in writing 2 months in advance.
Green Fees	£10 (£15 prior to noon, £12.50 after noon weekends).
Facilities	⊗ ∭ by prior arrangement 🏌 🍴 ♀ ♨ 🏠 ⛳
Leisure	caddy cars, tuition available.
Location	The Drive (0.5m S off A404)
Hotel	★★67% Harrow Hotel, Roxborough Bridge, 12-22 Pinner Rd, HARROW ☎ 081-427 3435 76 ⇋ 🐾

Northwood ☎ (0923) 821384
A very old club to which, it is said, golfers used to drive
from London by horse-carriage. They would find their
golf interesting as present-day players do. The course is
relatively flat although there are some undulations, and
trees and whins add not only to the beauty of the course
but also to the test of golf.
18 holes, 6493yds, Par 71, SSS 71.
Club membership 800. ▶

Visitors	with member only weekends.
Societies	Mon, Thu & Fri only, by arrangement.
Green Fees	not confirmed.
Facilities	⊗ Ⅲ ⅍ 💷 ⌺ 🏠 ⅞ ℂ Chris J Holdsworth.
Location	Rickmansworth Rd (SW side of village off A404)
Hotel	★★67% Harrow Hotel, Roxborough Bridge, 12-22 Pinner Rd, HARROW ☎ 081-427 3435 76 ⇌ 🐾

Sandy Lodge ☎ (0923) 825429

A links-type, very sandy, heathland course.
18 holes, 6081yds, Par 70, SSS 70.
Club membership 750.

Visitors	must contact in advance & have handicap certificate. Not permitted weekends & bank holidays.
Societies	must apply in writing.
Green Fees	not confirmed.
Facilities	⊗ Ⅲ⅍ 💷 ⌺ 🏠 ℂ Jeff Pinsent.
Location	Sandy Lodge Ln (N side of town centre off A4125)
Hotel	★★63% The White House, Upton Rd, WATFORD ☎ (0923) 237316 62 ⇌ 🐾Annexe26 ⇌ 🐾

ORPINGTON   Map 05 TQ46

Cray Valley ☎ (0689) 39677 & 31927

An open parkland course with two man-made lakes and open ditches.
18 holes, 5400yds, Par 70, SSS 67.
Club membership 640.

Visitors	no restrictions.
Societies	by arrangement.
Green Fees	not confirmed.
Facilities	⊗ ⅍ 💷 ⌺ 🏠 ⅞ ℂ John Gregory.
Location	Sandy Ln (1m off A20)
Hotel	★★★65% Bromley Court Hotel, Bromley Hill, BROMLEY ☎ 081-464 5011 120 ⇌ 🐾

Lullingstone Park ☎ (0959) 533793

Popular 27-hole public course set in 690 acres of undulating parkland. Championship length 18-holes, plus 9-hole course and a further 9-hole pitch and putt.
18 holes, 6759yds, Par 72, SSS 72 or 9 holes, 2432yds, Par 33.
Club membership 400.

Visitors	welcome.
Societies	must telephone in advance.
Green Fees	£9.10 per 18 holes; £5.80 per 9 holes (£11.40-£14/£7.80 weekends).
Facilities	⊗ Ⅲ by prior arrangement ⅍ 💷 ⌺ 🏠 ⅞ ℂ R Lee.
Leisure	caddy cars, driving range, pitch & putt.
Location	Parkgate, Chelsfield (Leave M25 junct 4 and take Well Hill turn)
Hotel	★★★65% Bromley Court Hotel, Bromley Hill, BROMLEY ☎ 081-464 5011 120 ⇌ 🐾

Ruxley Park Golf Centre ☎ (0689) 871490

Parkland course with public, floodlit driving range. Difficult 6th hole, par 4. Easy walking and good views.
18 holes, 5892yds, Par 71, SSS 68.
Club membership 500.

Visitors	may not play mornings on weekends & bank holidays. Must contact in advance.
Societies	must telephone two weeks in advance.
Green Fees	not confirmed.
Facilities	⊗ ⅍ 💷 ⌺ 🏠 ℂ Mark Woodman.
Leisure	driving range, covered bays (floodlit).
Location	Sandy Ln, St Paul's Cray (2m NE on A223)
Hotel	★★★65% Bromley Court Hotel, Bromley Hill, BROMLEY ☎ 081-464 5011 120 ⇌ 🐾

PINNER   Map 04 TQ18

Grims Dyke ☎ 081-428 4539

Pleasant, undulating parkland course.
18 holes, 5600yds, Par 69, SSS 67, Course record 64.
Club membership 590.

Visitors	with member only at weekends.
Societies	must apply in writing.
Green Fees	£25 per day; £20 per round.
Facilities	⊗ Ⅲ by prior arrangement ⅍ 💷 ⌺ 🏠 ℂ G Kemble.
Location	Oxhey Ln, Hatch End (3m N on A4008)
Hotel	★★67% Harrow Hotel, Roxborough Bridge, 12-22 Pinner Rd, HARROW ☎ 081-427 3435 76 ⇌ 🐾

Pinner Hill ☎ 081-866 0963 & 081-866 2109

A hilly, wooded parkland course.
18 holes, 6266yds, Par 72, SSS 70, Course record 63.
Club membership 770.

Visitors	are required to have handicap certificate on Mon, Tue & Fri. Public days Wed & Thu. Contact in advance.
Societies	Mon, Tue & Fri only, by arrangement.
Green Fees	£25 per round Mon, Tue & Fri; £8.10 per round Wed & Thu. (£32 weekends).
Facilities	⊗ & Ⅲ (Fri-Tue) ⅍ 💷 ⌺ 🏠 ⅞ ℂ Mark Grieve.
Location	Southview Rd, Pinner Hill (2m NW off A404)
Hotel	★★67% Harrow Hotel, Roxborough Bridge, 12-22 Pinner Rd, HARROW ☎ 081-427 3435 76 ⇌ 🐾

PURLEY   Map 05 TQ36

Purley Downs ☎ 081-657 8347

Hilly downland course. Notable holes are 6th and 12th.
18 holes, 6020yds, Par 70, SSS 69, Course record 65.
Club membership 700.

Visitors	must have a handicap certificate, & play on weekdays only with member.
Societies	must contact in advance.
Green Fees	£30 per round.
Facilities	⊗ ⅍ 💷 ⌺ 🏠 ℂ Graham Wilson.
Leisure	snooker.
Location	106 Purley Downs Rd (E side of town centre off A235)
Hotel	B Forte Posthouse, Purley Way, CROYDON ☎ 081-688 5185 83 ⇌ 🐾

Phoneday - remember from 16 April 1995 all phone codes in the UK will change - see page 4 for details

RICHMOND UPON THAMES Map 04 TQ17

Richmond ☎ 081-940-4351
A beautiful and historic wooded, parkland course on the edge of Richmond Park, with six par-3 holes. The 4th is often described as the best short hole in the south of England. Low scores are uncommon because cunningly sited trees call for great accuracy. The clubhouse is one of the most distinguished small Georgian mansions in England.
18 holes, 6007yds, Par 70, SSS 69.
Club membership 700.
Visitors may not play weekends.
Societies must apply in writing.
Green Fees £38 per day.
Facilities ⊗ ⓑ ⛴ ♀ △ 🏠 ⌁ ⌁ Nick Job.
Location Sudbrook Park, Petersham (1.5m S off A307)
Hotel ★★★66% Richmond Hill, 146-150 Richmond Hill, RICHMOND ☎ 081-940 2247 & 081-940 5466 124 ⇄ 🐾

Royal Mid-Surrey ☎ 081-940 1894
A long playing parkland course. The flat fairways are cleverly bunkered. The 18th provides an exceptionally good par 4 finish with a huge bunker before the green to catch the not quite perfect long second.
Outer Course: 18 holes, 6343yds, Par 69, SSS 70, Course record 64.
Inner Course: 18 holes, 5544yds, Par 68, SSS 67, Course record 70.
Club membership 1200.
Visitors may not play at weekends. Must contact in advance and be introduced by member or another club.
Societies must apply in writing.
Green Fees not confirmed.
Facilities ⊗ ⓑ ⛴ ♀ △ 🏠 ⌁ ⌁ David Talbot.
Leisure snooker.
Location Old Deer Park (0.5m N of Richmond upon Thames off A316)
Hotel ★★★66% Richmond Hill, 146-150 Richmond Hill, RICHMOND ☎ 081-940 2247 & 081-940 5466 124 ⇄ 🐾

ROMFORD Map 05 TQ58

Maylands Golf Club & Country Park ☎ Ingrebourne (0708) 342055
Picturesque undulating parkland course.
18 holes, 6351yds, Par 71, SSS 70.
Club membership 700.
Visitors with member only at weekends.
Societies Mon, Wed & Fri only, by arrangement.
Green Fees £30 per day; £20 per round.
Facilities ⊗ ⫿ (weekdays only) ⓑ ⛴ ♀ △ 🏠 ⌁ John Hopkin.
Leisure caddy cars & trollies for hire.
Location Colchester Rd, Harold Park
Hotel B Forte Posthouse, Brook St, BRENTWOOD ☎ (0277) 260260 111 ⇄

Romford ☎ (0708) 740986
A many-bunkered parkland course with easy walking. It is said there are as many bunkers as there are days in the year. The ground is quick drying making a good course for winter play when other courses might be too wet.
18 holes, 6374yds, Par 72, SSS 70.
Club membership 693.
Visitors with member only weekends & bank holidays. Must contact in advance & have handicap certificate.
Societies must telephone in advance.
Green Fees £23 per round.
Facilities ⊗ ⫿ by prior arrangement ⓑ ⛴ ♀ △ 🏠 ⌁ Harry Flatman.
Location Heath Dr, Gidea Park (1m NE on A118)
Hotel B Forte Posthouse, Brook St, BRENTWOOD ☎ (0277) 260260 111 ⇄

RUISLIP Map 04 TQ08

Ruislip ☎ (0895) 638835
Municipal parkland course. Many trees.
18 holes, 5703yds, Par 69, SSS 68.
Club membership 450.
Visitors no restrictions.
Societies must telephone in advance.
Green Fees £10 per day (£15 before noon, £12.50 after weekends).
Facilities ⊗ ⫿ ⓑ ⛴ ♀ △ 🏠 ⌁ Paul Glozier/Jeff Bradbrook.
Leisure snooker, 40 booth driving range.
Location Ickenham Rd (0.5m SW on B466)
Hotel ★★★62% Master Brewer Hotel, Western Av, HILLINGDON ☎ (0895) 251199 106 ⇄ 🐾

SIDCUP Map 05 TQ47

Sidcup ☎ 081-300 2150
Easy walking parkland course with natural water hazards.
9 holes, 2861yds, Par 68, SSS 68.
Club membership 400.
Visitors with member only weekends & bank holidays.
Societies must apply in writing.
Green Fees £18 per day/round.
Facilities ⊗ ⫿ by prior arrangement ⓑ ⛴ ♀ △ 🏠 ⌁
Leisure snooker.
Location 7 Hurst Rd (N side of town centre off A222)
Hotel ★★★★69% Swallow Hotel, 1 Broadway, BEXLEYHEATH ☎ 081-298 1000 142 ⇄ 🐾

SOUTHALL Map 04 TQ17

West Middlesex ☎ 081-574 3450
Gently undulating parkland course.
18 holes, 6242yds, Par 69, SSS 70.
Club membership 500.
Visitors restricted weekends & bank holidays.
Societies apply in writing.
Green Fees not confirmed.
Facilities △ 🏠 ⌁
Location Greenford Rd (W side of town centre on A4127 off A4020)
Hotel ★★★62% Master Robert Hotel, Great West Rd, HOUNSLOW ☎ 081-570 6261 100 ⇄ 🐾

STANMORE   Map 04 TQ19

Stanmore ☎ 081-954 2599
North London parkland course.
18 holes, 5860yds, Par 68, SSS 68, Course record 63.
Club membership 600.
Visitors   must contact in advance & have handicap
                 certificate. With member only at weekends &
                 bank holidays.
Societies   Wed & Thu only, by arrangement.
Green Fees   Mon & Fri £11.50 per day; £8.50 per round.
                 Tue-Thu £32 per day; £25 per round.
Facilities   ⊗ ⅢⅡ (ex Mon & Fri) ⅗ 🍺 🍵 ⏃ 🏠 ⌐ℾ 𝄢 V Law.
Location   29 Gordon Av (S side of town centre)
Hotel   ★★67% Harrow Hotel, Roxborough Bridge, 12-
                 22 Pinner Rd, HARROW
                 ☎ 081-427 3435 76 ⇆ ℾ

SURBITON   Map 04 TQ16

Surbiton ☎ 081-398 3101
Parkland course with easy walking.
18 holes, 6211yds, Par 70, SSS 70.
Club membership 750.
Visitors   with member only at weekends & bank holidays.
                 Must contact in advance and have a handicap
                 certificate.
Societies   must apply in writing.
Green Fees   £40.50 per day; £27 per round.
Facilities   ⊗ ⅢⅡ & ⅗ (in season) 🍺 ⏃ ⏃ 🏠
                 𝄢 Paul Milton.
Location   Woodstock Ln (2m S off A3)
Hotel   ★★63% Haven Hotel, Portsmouth Rd, ESHER
                 ☎ 081-398 0023 16 ⇆ ℾAnnexe4 ⇆ ℾ

TWICKENHAM   Map 04 TQ17

Strawberry Hill ☎ 081-894 0165
Parkland course with easy walking.
9 holes, 2381yds, Par 64, SSS 62.
Club membership 350.
Visitors   with member only at weekends.
Societies   must apply in writing.
Green Fees   £25 per day; £18 per round.
Facilities   ⊗ ⅢⅡ by prior arrangement ⅗ 🍺 ⏃ ⏃ 🏠
                 𝄢 Peter Buchan.
Location   Wellesley Rd (S side of town centre off A311)
Hotel   ★★★66% Richmond Hill, 146-150 Richmond
                 Hill, RICHMOND
                 ☎ 081-940 2247 & 081-940 5466 124 ⇆ ℾ

Twickenham ☎ 081-783 1748 & 1698
Municipal commonland course.
9 holes, 3180yds, Par 72, SSS 71.
Club membership 200.
Visitors   no restrictions.
Societies   apply in advance
Green Fees   not confirmed.
Facilities   ⊗ ⅢⅡ ⅗ 🍺 ⏃ ⏃ 🏠 ⌐ℾ 𝄢 Steve LLoyd.
Leisure   floodlit driving range.
Location   Staines Rd (2m W on A305)
Hotel   ★★★66% Richmond Hill, 146-150 Richmond
                 Hill, RICHMOND
                 ☎ 081-940 2247 & 081-940 5466 124 ⇆ ℾ

UPMINSTER   Map 05 TQ58

Upminster ☎ (0708) 222788
Parkland course adjacent to river.
18 holes, 5951yds, Par 68, SSS 69.
Club membership 800.
Visitors   with member only at weekends. Must have an
                 introduction from own club.
Societies   apply in writing.
Green Fees   not confirmed.
Facilities   ⏃ ⏃ 🏠 𝄢
Location   114 Hall Ln (N side of town centre)
Hotel   ★★★60% Palms Hotel, Southend Arterial Rd,
                 HORNCHURCH ☎ (0708) 346789 137 ⇆ ℾ

UXBRIDGE   Map 04 TQ08

Uxbridge ☎ (0895) 237287
Municipal parkland course, undulating and tricky.
18 holes, 5750yds, Par 68, SSS 68, Course record 66.
Club membership 700.
Visitors   no restrictions.
Societies   Thu by arrangment.
Green Fees   £10 (£15/£12.50 weekends).
Facilities   ⊗ ⅢⅡ ⅗ 🍺 ⏃ ⏃ 🏠 ⌐ℾ 𝄢 Phil Howard.
Leisure   buggies.
Location   The Drive, Harefield Place (2m N off B467)
Hotel   ★★★62% Master Brewer Hotel, Western Av,
                 HILLINGDON ☎ (0895) 251199 106 ⇆ ℾ

WEMBLEY   Map 04 TQ18

Sudbury ☎ 081-902 3713
Undulating parkland course very near centre of London.
18 holes, 6282yds, Par 69, SSS 70.
Club membership 650.
Visitors   must have handicap certificate. With member
                 only at weekends.
Societies   must apply in writing.
Green Fees   not confirmed.
Facilities   ⊗ ⅢⅡ by prior arrangement ⅗ 🍺 ⏃ 🏠
                 𝄢 Neil Jordan.
Leisure   snooker.
Location   Bridgewater Rd (SW side of town centre on
                 A4090)
Hotel   ★★★70% The Bridge Hotel, Western Av,
                 GREENFORD ☎ 081-566 6246 68 ⇆ ℾ

WEST DRAYTON   Map 04 TQ07

Holiday ☎ (0895) 444232
Fairly large, testing, hilly par 3 course suitable both for
beginners and scratch players.
9 holes, 1618yds, Par 28, Course record 50.
Club membership 120.
Visitors   restricted Sun morning.
Societies   by arrangement.
Green Fees   not confirmed.
Facilities   catering facilities at hotel ⏃ ⏃ 🏠 ⌐ℾ 🏌
Leisure   heated indoor swimming pool, sauna, solarium,
                 gymnasium.
Location   Stockley Rd (1m SE off A408)

Hotel ★★★★70% Holiday Inn Crowne Plaza,
Stockley Rd, West Drayton, WEST DRAYTON
☎ (0895) 445555 375 ⇥

WOODFORD GREEN   Map 05 TQ49

Woodford ☎ 081-504 0553 & 081-504 4254
Forest land course on the edge of Epping Forest. Views over
the Lea Valley to the London skyline.
9 holes, 5806yds, Par 70, SSS 68.
Club membership 400.

Visitors	must contact in advance. With member only Tue/Thu mornings, weekends & bank holidays.
Societies	must contact in advance.
Green Fees	£15 per day.
Facilities	⊗ (ex Sun & Mon) ⓑ 🍺 ♀ ⚷ 🏠 🥢 (Ashley Johns.
Location	Sunset Av (NW side of town centre off A104)
Hotel	★★★68% Woodford Moat House, Oak Hill, WOODFORD GREEN ☎ 081-505 4511 99 ⇥ 📞

GREATER MANCHESTER

ALTRINCHAM   Map 07 SJ78

Altrincham ☎ 061-928 0761
Municipal parkland course with easy walking, water on many
holes, rolling contours and many trees. Driving range in
grounds.
18 holes, 6162yds, Par 71, SSS 69.
Club membership 350.

Visitors	must book in advance.
Societies	by prior arrangement.
Green Fees	not confirmed.
Facilities	⚷ 🏠 🥢 (John Jackson.
Leisure	driving range.
Location	Stockport Rd (0.75 E of Altrincham on A560)
Hotel	★★★65% Cresta Court Hotel, Church St, ALTRINCHAM ☎ 061-927 7272 139 ⇥ 📞

Dunham Forest ☎ 061-928 2605
Attractive parkland course cut through magnificent beech
woods.
18 holes, 6636yds, Par 72, SSS 72.
Club membership 600.

Visitors	may not play weekends & bank holidays.
Societies	telephone for availability.
Green Fees	£27 per round £5 for extra 9 holes (£32 weekends).
Facilities	⊗ 🍺 by prior arrangement ⓑ 🍺 ♀ ⚷ 🏠 🥢 (Ian Wrigley.
Leisure	hard tennis courts, squash, snooker.
Location	Oldfield Ln (1.5m W off A56)
Hotel	★★★66% Bowdon Hotel, Langham Rd, Bowdon, ALTRINCHAM ☎ 061-928 7121 82 ⇥ 📞

Ringway ☎ 061-904 9609 & 061-980 8432
Parkland course, with interesting natural hazards. Easy
walking, good views.
18 holes, 6307yds, Par 71, SSS 70, Course record 67.
Club membership 720.

Visitors	may not play before 9.30am or between 1-2pm. Must have handicap certificate.
Societies	Thu only May-Sep.
Green Fees	£28 (£34 weekends & bank holidays).
Facilities	⊗ 🍺 (ex Mon) ⓑ 🍺 ♀ ⚷ 🏠 (Nick Ryan.
Leisure	snooker.
Location	Hale Mount, Hale Barns (2.5m SE on A538)
Hotel	★★★65% Cresta Court Hotel, Church St, ALTRINCHAM ☎ 061-927 7272 139 ⇥ 📞

ASHTON-IN-MAKERFIELD   Map 07 SJ59

Ashton-in-Makerfield ☎ (0942) 727267 & 719330
Well-wooded parkland course. Easy walking.
18 holes, 6250yds, Par 70, SSS 70.
Club membership 800.

Visitors	With member only weekends & bank holidays. No visitors Wed.
Societies	apply in writing.
Green Fees	£21 (weekdays).
Facilities	⊗ 🍺 ⓑ 🍺 ♀ ⚷ 🏠 🥢 (Peter Allan.
Leisure	snooker.
Location	Garswood Park, Liverpool Rd (0.5m W of M6 (Junc 24) on A58)
Hotel	B Forte Posthouse, Lodge Ln, Newton-Le-Willows, HAYDOCK ☎ (0942) 717878 136 ⇥ 📞

ASHTON-UNDER-LYNE   Map 07 SJ99

Ashton-under-Lyne ☎ 061-330 1537
A testing, varied moorland course, with large greens. Easy
walking. Three new holes have improved the course.
18 holes, 6300yds, Par 70, SSS 70, Course record 69.
Club membership 650.

Visitors	with member only weekends & bank holidays.
Societies	telephone in advance.
Green Fees	not confirmed.
Facilities	⊗ 🍺 ⓑ 🍺 ♀ ⚷ 🏠 (Colin Boyle.
Leisure	snooker.
Location	Gorsey Way, Higher Hurst (1.5m NE)
Hotel	★★69% York House Hotel, York Place, Richmond St, ASHTON-UNDER-LYNE ☎ 061-330 5899 24 ⇥ 📞Annexe10 ⇥ 📞

Dukinfield ☎ 061-338 2340
Recently extended, tricky hillside course with several
difficult Par 3s and a very long par 5.
18 holes, 5400yds, Par 67, SSS 67.
Club membership 400.

Visitors	may not play on Wed afternoons & must play with member at weekends. Must contact in advance.
Societies	must contact in advance.
Green Fees	£16.50 per day.
Facilities	⊗ 🍺 ⓑ 🍺 ♀ ⚷ 🏠 (Jason Peel.
Location	Lyne Edge, Yew Tree Ln (S off B6175)
Hotel	★★69% York House Hotel, York Place, Richmond St, ASHTON-UNDER-LYNE ☎ 061-330 5899 24 ⇥ 📞Annexe10 ⇥ 📞

BOLTON Map 07 SD70

Bolton ☎ (0204) 843067
This well maintained heathland course is always a pleasure to visit. The 12th hole should be treated with respect and so too should the final four holes which have ruined many a card.
18 holes, 6300yds, Par 70, SSS 70.
Club membership 600.
Visitors restricted at weekends.
Societies welcome Mon, Thu & Fri, apply in writing.
Green Fees not confirmed.
Facilities ⊗ ∭ by prior arrangement ⒝ 🍺 ♀ ☖ 🏠 ℓ R Longworth.
Leisure snooker.
Location Lostock Park, Chorley New Rd (3m W on A673)
Hotel ★★★59% Pack Horse Hotel, Bradshawgate, Nelson Square, BOLTON ☎ (0204) 27261 72 ⇄ ℕ

Bolton Municipal ☎ (0204) 842336
A parkland course.
18 holes, 6336yds, Par 71, SSS 69, Course record 68.
Club membership 300.
Visitors no restrictions
Societies telephone in advance.
Green Fees not confirmed.
Facilities ⊗ ∭ by prior arrangement ⒝ 🍺 ♀ ☖ 🏠 ℸ ℓ A K Holland.
Location Links Rd (3m W on A673)
Hotel ★★★62% Beaumont Hotel, Beaumont Rd, BOLTON ☎ (0204) 651511 96 ⇄ ℕ

Breightmet ☎ (0204) 27381
Long parkland course.
9 holes, 6416yds, Par 72, SSS 71.
Club membership 350.
Visitors may not play weekends.
Societies welcome Tue & Thu only, apply in advance in writing.
Green Fees £15 per round (£18 weekends & bank holidays).
Facilities ⊗ ∭ ⒝ 🍺 ♀ ☖
Leisure snooker.
Location Red Bridge, Ainsworth (E side of town centre off A58)
Hotel ★★★59% Pack Horse Hotel, Bradshawgate, Nelson Square, BOLTON ☎ (0204) 27261 72 ⇄ ℕ

Deane ☎ (0204) 61944 & 651808
Undulating parkland course with small ravines on approaches to some holes.
18 holes, 5583yds, Par 68, SSS 67, Course record 64.
Club membership 500.
Visitors must be a member of a golf club.
Societies must apply in writing.
Green Fees £18 per day/round (£22.50 weekend and bank holidays).
Facilities ⊗ ∭ ⒝ 🍺 (no catering Mon) ♀ ☖ 🏠 ℓ David Martindale.
Leisure snooker.
Location Broadford Rd, Deane
Hotel ★★★62% Beaumont Hotel, Beaumont Rd, BOLTON ☎ (0204) 651511 96 ⇄ ℕ

Dunscar ☎ (0204) 303321 & 301090
A scenic moorland course with panoramic views. A warm friendly club.
18 holes, 6085yds, Par 71, SSS 69, Course record 66.
Club membership 600.
Visitors may normally play after 9.30am & 1.30pm; some restrictions at weekends.
Societies must telephone in advance.
Green Fees prices on application.
Facilities ⊗ ∭ ⒝ 🍺 ♀ ☖ 🏠 ℸ ℓ Gary Treadgold.
Leisure snooker, caddy cars, golf lessons.
Location Longworth Ln, Bromley Cross (2m N off A666)
Hotel ★★★65% Egerton House Hotel, Blackburn Rd, Egerton, BOLTON ☎ (0204) 307171 32 ⇄ ℕ

Great Lever & Farnworth ☎ (0204) 656137
Downland course with easy walking.
18 holes, 5859yds, Par 70, SSS 69.
Club membership 600.
Visitors must contact in advance.
Societies contact in advance.
Green Fees £15 per day (£25 weekends & bank holidays).
Facilities ⊗ (ex Mon) ∭ by prior arrangement ⒝ (ex Mon) 🍺 by prior arrangement ♀ ☖ 🏠 ℓ Donald Stirling.
Leisure snooker.
Location Lever Edge Ln (SW side of town centre off A575)
Hotel ★★★59% Pack Horse Hotel, Bradshawgate, Nelson Square, BOLTON ☎ (0204) 27261 72 ⇄ ℕ

Harwood ☎ (0204) 22878
Mainly flat parkland course.
9 holes, 5993yds, Par 71, SSS 69, Course record 64.
Club membership 441.
Visitors with member only weekends.
Societies contact in writing.
Green Fees £15 per round.
Facilities 🍺 ♀ ☖ 🏠 ℓ M Dance.
Leisure snooker.
Location Springfield, Roading Brook Rd, Harwood (2.5m NE off B6196)
Hotel ★★★65% Egerton House Hotel, Blackburn Rd, Egerton, BOLTON ☎ (0204) 307171 32 ⇄ ℕ

Old Links ☎ (0204) 842307
Championship moorland course.
18 holes, 6408yds, Par 72, SSS 72.
Club membership 750.
Visitors welcome except championship days & Sat until 4pm.
Societies apply by letter.
Green Fees £25 per day (£30 weekends).
Facilities ⊗ ∭ ⒝ 🍺 ♀ ☖ 🏠 ℓ Paul Horridge.
Leisure snooker.
Location Chorley Old Rd (NW of town centre on B6226)
Hotel ★★★59% Pack Horse Hotel, Bradshawgate, Nelson Square, BOLTON ☎ (0204) 27261 72 ⇄ ℕ

Regent Park ☎ (0204) 844170
Parkland course.
18 holes, 6140yds, Par 70, SSS 71.
Club membership 230.
Visitors no restrictions.

Societies   application form from Club Pro or Bolton Metro
                 Leisure Services, The Wellsprings, Bolton,
                 Lancs.
Green Fees   £5 (£7 weekends & bankholidays).
Facilities   ⊗ ⅢⅢ ᒪ ᔕ 🍵 Ω ᐃ 🏠 ⚟ 𝄞 Mike Jones.
Leisure   trolleys available.
Location   Links Rd, Chorley New Rd (3.5m W off A673)
Hotel   ★★★62% Beaumont Hotel, Beaumont Rd,
                 BOLTON ☎ (0204) 651511 96 ⇨ 🐾

BRAMHALL   Map 07 SJ88

Bramall Park ☎ 061-485 3119
Well-wooded parkland course with splendid views of the
Pennines.
18 holes, 6043yds, Par 70, SSS 69, Course record 66.
Club membership 600.
Visitors   must contact in advance.
Societies   apply in writing.
Green Fees   £25 per day/round (£35 weekends).
Facilities   ⊗ & ⅢⅢ by prior arrangement ᒪ ᔕ Ω ᐃ 🏠 ⚟
Leisure   snooker.
Location   20 Manor Rd (NW side of town centre off
                 B5149)
Hotel   ★★★67% Bramhall Moat House, Bramhall Ln
                 South, BRAMHALL ☎ 061-439 8116 65 ⇨ 🐾

Bramhall ☎ 061-439 4057 & 061-439 6092
Undulating parkland course, easy walking.
18 holes, 6293yds, Par 70, SSS 70.
Club membership 720.
Visitors   welcome except Thu & Sat. Must contact in
                 advance.
Societies   Wed only, apply in writing.
Green Fees   £25 per day (£35 Fri-Sun).
Facilities   ⊗ & ⅢⅢ by prior arrangement ᒪ ᔕ Ω ᐃ 🏠
                 ⚟ Richard Green.
Leisure   snooker, trolleys for hire.
Location   Ladythorn Rd (E side of town centre off A5102)
Hotel   ★★★67% Bramhall Moat House, Bramhall Ln
                 South, BRAMHALL
                 ☎ 061-439 8116 65 ⇨ 🐾

BROMLEY CROSS   Map 07 SD71

Turton ☎ Bolton (0204) 852235
Moorland course.
9 holes, 5584yds, Par 68, SSS 67.
Club membership 325.
Visitors   with member only at weekends and bank
                 holidays. May not play Wed before 3pm.
Societies   must contact in writing.
Green Fees   not confirmed.
Facilities   (catering by prior arrangement) Ω ᐃ
Location   Wood End Farm, Chapeltown Rd (3m N on
                 A676)
Hotel   ★★★65% Egerton House Hotel, Blackburn Rd,
                 Egerton, BOLTON ☎ (0204) 307171 32 ⇨ 🐾

BURY   Map 07 SD81

Bury ☎ 061-766 4897
Hard walking on hilly moorland course.
18 holes, 5961yds, Par 69, SSS 69.
Club membership 650.

Visitors   must have a handicap certificate but may not
                 play at weekends.
Societies   contact in advance.
Green Fees   £20 per day (£26 weekends).
Facilities   ⊗ ⅢⅢ ᒪ ᔕ Ω ᐃ ⚟ S Crake.
Leisure   snooker.
Location   Unsworth Hall, Blackford Bridge (2m S on A56)
Hotel   ★56% Woolfield House Hotel, Wash Ln,
                 BURY ☎ 061-797 9775 16rm(3 ⇨7 🐾)

Lowes Park ☎ 061-764 1231
Moorland course, with easy walking. Usually windy.
9 holes, 6009yds, Par 70, SSS 69.
Club membership 350.
Visitors   may not play Wed & Sat, by appointment Sun.
                 Must contact in advance.
Societies   apply in writing.
Green Fees   £13.50 per round (£20 weekends).
Facilities   ⊗ ⅢⅢ ᒪ ᔕ (no catering Mon) Ω ᐃ 🏠
Location   Hill Top, Walmersley (N side of town centre off
                 A56)
Hotel   ★56% Woolfield House Hotel, Wash Ln,
                 BURY ☎ 061-797 9775 16rm(3 ⇨7 🐾)

Walmersley ☎ 061-764 1429
Moorland hillside course, with wide fairways, large greens
and extensive views. Testing holes: 2nd (484 yds) par 5; 4th
(444 yds) par 4.
9 holes, 6114yds, Par 72, SSS 70, Course record 64.
Club membership 450.
Visitors   must contact in advance & have handicap
                 certificate. Restricted at weekends.
Societies   telephone one month in advance.
Green Fees   £15 per day.
Facilities   ⊗ ⅢⅢ ᒪ ᔕ (no catering Mon) Ω (ex Mon) ᐃ
Location   Garretts Close, Walmersley (2m N off A56)
Hotel   ★★★63% Old Mill Hotel, Springwood,
                 RAMSBOTTOM ☎ (0706) 822991 36 ⇨

CHEADLE   Map 07 SJ88

Cheadle ☎ 061-491 4452
Parkland course with hazards on every hole, from sand
bunkers and copses to a stream across six of the fairways.
9 holes, 5006yds, Par 64, SSS 65.
Club membership 446.
Visitors   may not play Tue & Sat. Must contact in
                 advance and have a handicap certificate.
Societies   apply in writing.
Green Fees   £15 per round (£23 Sun & bank holidays).
Facilities   ⊗ (ex Tue & Thu) ⅢⅢ & ᒪ (ex Thu) ᔕ Ω ᐃ 🏠
                 ⚟ G J Norcott.
Leisure   snooker, trolleys.
Location   Cheadle Rd (S side of village off A5149)
Hotel   ★★63% Wycliffe, 74 Edgeley Rd, Edgeley,
                 STOCKPORT ☎ 061-477 5395 20 ⇨ 🐾

DENTON   Map 07 SJ99

Denton ☎ 061-336 3218
Easy, flat parkland course with brook running through.
Notable hole is one called 'Death and Glory'.
18 holes, 6541yds, Par 72, SSS 70.
Club membership 600.
Visitors   may not play at weekends.   ▶

Societies   apply to secretary Mr R Wickham.
Green Fees £20 (£25 bank holidays).
Facilities ⊗ ⅪⅢ ⅬⅬ ⅬⅬ ⅬⅬ ⅬⅬ Rodger Vere.
Location   Manchester Rd (1.5m W on A57)
Hotel   ★★69% York House Hotel, York Place,
                Richmond St, ASHTON-UNDER-LYNE
                ☎ 061-330 5899 24 ⇆ ⚑Annexe10 ⇆ ⚑

FAILSWORTH   Map 07 SD80

Brookdale ☎ 061-681 4534
Undulating parkland course, with river crossed 5 times in
play. Hard walking.
18 holes, 6040yds, Par 68, SSS 68.
Club membership 600.
Visitors   restricted Sun and Tue (ladies day). Must contact
                in advance and have a handicap certificate.
Societies   must contact in advance.
Green Fees not confirmed.
Facilities ⊗ ⅪⅢ ⅬⅬ ⅬⅬ (no catering Mon) ⅬⅬⅬⅬⅬ
                Jason Spibey.
Leisure   snooker.
Location   Ashbridge, Woodhouses (N side of Manchester)
Hotel   ★★69% York House Hotel, York Place,
                Richmond St, ASHTON-UNDER-LYNE
                ☎ 061-330 5899 24 ⇆ ⚑Annexe10 ⇆ ⚑

FLIXTON   Map 07 SJ79

William Wroe Municipal ☎ 061-748 8680
Parkland course, with easy walking.
18 holes, 4395yds, Par 64, SSS 61, Course record 60.
Club membership 225.
Visitors   must book in advance, only alternate tee times
                available at weekends 7.44am-11.28am.
Green Fees £6 per 18 holes; £3.50 per 9 holes (£8/£5
                weekends).
Facilities Catering at weekends ⅬⅬ (weekends) ⅬⅬⅬⅬ
                John Jackson.
Location   Pennybridge Ln (E side of village off B5158)
Hotel   ★61% Beaucliffe Hotel, 254 Eccles Old Rd,
                Pendleton, SALFORD
                ☎ 061-789 5092 21rm(2 ⇆15 ⚑)

GATLEY   Map 07 SJ88

Gatley ☎ 061-437 2091
Parkland course. Moderately testing.
9 holes, 5934yds, Par 68, SSS 68.
Club membership 400.
Visitors   may not play Tue & Sat. With member only
                weekends.
Societies   apply in writing.
Green Fees not confirmed.
Facilities ⊗ ⅪⅢ ⅬⅬ & ⅬⅬ by prior arrangement ⅬⅬⅬⅬⅬ
Leisure   squash, snooker.
Location   Waterfall Farm, Styal Rd, Heald Green (S side
                of village off B5166)
Hotel   ★★★★60% Belfry Hotel, Stanley Rd,
                HANDFORTH ☎ 061-437 0511 81 ⇆

┌───┐
│   **For an explanation of symbols and**   │
│   **abbreviations, see page 5**   │
└───┘

HALE   Map 07 SJ78

Hale ☎ 061-980 4225
Beautiful, undulating parkland course, with the River Bollin
winding round fairways.
9 holes, 5780yds, Par 70, SSS 68, Course record 65.
Club membership 300.
Visitors   may not play before 4.30pm Thu; with member
                only weekends.
Societies   apply in writing.
Green Fees £20 per day/round.
Facilities ⊗ & ⅪⅢ by prior arrangement ⅬⅬ ⅬⅬ ⅬⅬ ⅬⅬ
                Joy Jackson.
Location   Rappax Rd (1.25m SE)
Hotel   ★★★66% Bowdon Hotel, Langham Rd,
                Bowdon, ALTRINCHAM
                ☎ 061-928 7121 82 ⇆ ⚑

HAZEL GROVE   Map 07 SJ98

Hazel Grove ☎ 061-483 3978
Parkland course.
18 holes, 6300yds, Par 71, SSS 71.
Club membership 550.
Visitors   must contact in advance and have a handicap
                certificate.
Societies   must apply in writing.
Green Fees £22.50 per round (£27.50 weekends).
Facilities ⊗ ⅪⅢ ⅬⅬ ⅬⅬ ⅬⅬ ⅬⅬ ⅬⅬ ⅬⅬ
Leisure   snooker.
Location   Buxton Rd (1m E off A6)
Hotel   ★★★67% Bramhall Moat House, Bramhall Ln
                South, BRAMHALL
                ☎ 061-439 8116 65 ⇆ ⚑

HINDLEY   Map 07 SD60

Hindley Hall ☎ Wigan (0942) 55131
Parkland course with mostly easy walking.
18 holes, 5913yds, Par 69, SSS 68.
Club membership 500.
Visitors   restricted Wed and weekends.
Societies   apply in writing.
Green Fees £20 per day (£27 weekends & bank holidays).
Facilities ⊗ ⅪⅢ ⅬⅬ ⅬⅬ ⅬⅬ ⅬⅬ ⅬⅬ Neil Brazell.
Leisure   snooker.
Location   Hall Ln (1m N off A58)
Hotel   ★★61% Brocket Arms Hotel, Mesnes Rd,
                WIGAN ☎ (0942) 46283 27 ⇆ ⚑

HORWICH   Map 07 SD61

Horwich ☎ (0204) 696980
Parkland course with natural hazards and generally windy.
Hard walking.
9 holes, 5286yds, Par 67, SSS 67, Course record 64.
Club membership 400.
Visitors   restricted Wed and weekends.
Societies   must contact secretary in writing.
Green Fees £12 per day.
Facilities ⊗ ⅪⅢ ⅬⅬ & ⅬⅬ by prior arrangement ⅬⅬ ⅬⅬ
Location   Victoria Rd (SE side of village A673)
Hotel   ★★★62% Beaumont Hotel, Beaumont Rd,
                BOLTON ☎ (0204) 651511 96 ⇆ ⚑

HYDE   Map 07 SJ99

Werneth Low ☎ 061-368 2503
Hard walking but good views from this moorland course.
Exposed to wind.
9 holes, 5734yds, Par 70, SSS 68.
Club membership 350.
Visitors   may not play Tue mornings, weekends & bank
              holidays.
Societies   must contact in advance.
Green Fees not confirmed.
Facilities   ⊗ 🍽 by prior arrangement 🏌 🍺 ♀ 🛄 🏠
              🍸 Tony Bacchus.
Location   Werneth Low (2m S of town centre)
Hotel   ★★70% Red Lion Inn, 112 Buxton Rd, High
              Ln, STOCKPORT ☎ (0663) 765227 6 ⇆ 🐾

LEIGH   Map 07 SD60

Pennington ☎ (0942) 682852
Municipal parkland course, with natural hazards of brooks,
ponds and trees, and easy walking.
9 holes, 2919yds, Par 35, SSS 34.
Club membership 200.
Visitors   no restrictions.
Societies   must contact in advance.
Green Fees not confirmed.
Facilities   🍺 🏠 🏌🍸 Tim Kershaw.
Location   St Helen's Rd (SW side of town centre off
              A572)
Hotel   ★★63% Kirkfield Hotel, 2/4 Church St,
              NEWTON LE WILLOWS
              ☎ (0925) 228196 17 ⇆ 🐾

LITTLEBOROUGH   Map 07 SD91

Whittaker ☎ (0706) 378310
Moorland 9-hole course.
9 holes, 5632yds, Par 68, SSS 67.
Club membership 150.
Visitors   welcome except for Tue pm and Sun.
Societies   apply to Secretary.
Green Fees £10 per day (£12 weekends).
Facilities   🛄
Location   Whittaker Ln (3m NE of Rochdale, along A58)
Hotel   ★★★66% Norton Grange Hotel, Manchester
              Rd, Castleton, ROCHDALE
              ☎ (0706) 30788 50 ⇆ 🐾

MANCHESTER   Map 07 SJ89

Blackley ☎ 061-643 2980
Parkland course. Course crossed by footpath.
18 holes, 6237yds, Par 70, SSS 70, Course record 65.
Club membership 670.
Visitors   with member only Thu, weekends and bank
              holidays.
Societies   apply in advance.
Green Fees £17.50.
Facilities   ⊗ 🍽 by prior arrangement 🏌 🍺 ♀ 🛄 🏠
              🍸 Martin Barton.
Leisure   snooker, caddy cars.
Location   Victoria Ave East, Blackley (4m N of city
              centre, on Rochdale Rd)

Hotel   ★★★62% Bower Hotel, Hollinwood Av,
              Chadderton, OLDHAM   ·
              ☎ 061-682 7254 66 ⇆ 🐾

Chorlton-cum-Hardy ☎ 061-881 5830 & 061-881 3139
Meadowland course with trees, stream and several ditches.
18 holes, 6004yds, Par 70, SSS 69, Course record 63.
Club membership 780.
Visitors   handicap certificate required.
Societies   on Thu only by prior booking.
Green Fees £20 per day (£25 weekends).
Facilities   ⊗ 🍽 🏌 🍺 (snacks on Mon, times vary
              seasonally) ♀ 🛄 🏠 🏌🍸 D Screeton.
Leisure   snooker, practice area.
Location   Barlow Hall, Barlow Hall Rd, Chorlton-cum-
              Hardy (4m S of Manchester A5103/A5145)
Hotel   ★★★61% Willow Bank Hotel, 340-342
              Wilmslow Rd, Fallowfield, MANCHESTER
              ☎ 061-224 0461 116 ⇆ 🐾

Davyhulme Park ☎ 061-748 2260
Parkland course.
18 holes, 6237yds, Par 72, SSS 70, Course record 67.
Club membership 500.
Visitors   may not play on Wed & Sat; must play with
              member on Sun. Must have an introduction from
              own club.
Societies   must contact in advance.
Green Fees not confirmed.
Facilities   ⊗ 🍽 by prior arrangement 🏌 🍺 ♀ 🛄 🏠 🏌
              🍸 Hugh Lewis.
Leisure   snooker.
Location   Gleneagles Rd, Davyhulme (8m S adj to Park
              Hospital)
Hotel   ★61% Beaucliffe Hotel, 254 Eccles Old Rd,
              Pendleton, SALFORD
              ☎ 061-789 5092 21rm(2 ⇆15 🐾)

Didsbury ☎ 061-998 9278
Parkland course.
18 holes, 6273yds, Par 70, SSS 70, Course record 66.
Club membership 700.
Visitors   restricted Tue, Wed & weekends.
Societies   must contact in advance.
Green Fees £22 per day (£25 weekends).
Facilities   ⊗ 🍽 🏌 🍺 ♀ 🛄 🏠 🏌🍸 Peter Barber.
Leisure   snooker.
Location   Ford Ln, Northenden (6m S of city centre off
              A5145)
Hotel   B Forte Posthouse, Palatine Rd, Northenden,
              MANCHESTER ☎ 061-998 7090 198 ⇆ 🐾

Fairfield ☎ 061-370 1641 & 061-370 2292
Parkland course set around a reservoir. Course demands
particularly accurate placing of shots.
18 holes, 5654yds, Par 70, SSS 68.
Club membership 400.
Visitors   may not play mornings at weekends & may be
              restricted on Wed & Thu.
Societies   apply in writing to Secretary.
Green Fees £16 per round (£22 weekends & bank holidays).
Facilities   ⊗ 🍽 by prior arrangement 🏌 🍺 ♀ 🛄 🏠
              🍸 Nick Harding.
Leisure   snooker.
Location   Booth Rd, Audenshaw (1.5m W of Audenshaw
              off A635)   ▶

Hotel ★★69% York House Hotel, York Place,
Richmond St, ASHTON-UNDER-LYNE
☎ 061-330 5899 24 ⇔ ੯Annexe10 ⇔ ੯

Northenden ☎ 061-998 4738
Parkland course surrounded by the River Mersey.
18 holes, 6469yds, Par 72, SSS 71.
Club membership 600.
Visitors Must contact in advance. Tee reserved for
members 8.30-9.15am & 12.30-1.15pm.
Societies Tue & Fri only, telephone in advance.
Green Fees not confirmed.
Facilities ⊗ ⊞ ੯ ⚑ ♀ ⚑ ੯ Bill McColl.
Leisure snooker.
Location Palatine Rd (6.5m S of city centre on B1567 off
A5103)
Hotel B Forte Posthouse, Palatine Rd, Northenden,
MANCHESTER ☎ 061-998 7090 198 ⇔ ੯

Pike Fold ☎ 061-740 1136
Picturesque, hilly course. Good test of golf.
9 holes, 5785yds, Par 70, SSS 68, Course record 66.
Club membership 200.
Visitors may not play Sun. Must be with member Sat &
bank holidays.
Societies apply in writing.
Green Fees not confirmed.
Facilities ⊗ & ⊞ by prior arrangement ੯ ⚑ ♀ ⚑
Leisure snooker.
Location Cooper Ln, Victoria Av, Blackley (4m N of city
centre off Rochdale Rd)
Hotel ★★★62% Bower Hotel, Hollinwood Av,
Chadderton, OLDHAM
☎ 061-682 7254 66 ⇔ ੯

Withington ☎ 061-445 9544
Flat parkland course.
18 holes, 6410yds, Par 71, SSS 71.
Club membership 600.
Visitors welcome except Thu, must contact in advance,
restricted at weekends.
Societies telephone in advance, welcome except Thu, Sat
& Sun.
Green Fees £25 per day; £22 per round.
Facilities ⊗ ⊞ by prior arrangement ੯ ⚑ ♀ ⚑ ⚑
੯ R J Ling.
Leisure snooker.
Location 243 Palatine Rd, West Didsbury (4m SW of city
centre off B5167)
Hotel B Forte Posthouse, Palatine Rd, Northenden,
MANCHESTER ☎ 061-998 7090 198 ⇔ ੯

Worsley ☎ 061-789 4202
Well-wooded parkland course.
18 holes, 6220yds, Par 72, SSS 70.
Club membership 700.
Visitors no restrictions.
Societies Mon, Wed & Thu only.
Green Fees £22 per day; £20 per round (£30 weekends &
bank holidays).
Facilities ⊗ ⊞ ੯ ⚑ ♀ ⚑ ⚑ ⚑ ੯ Ceri Cousins.
Leisure snooker.
Location Stableford Av, Monton Green, Eccles (6.5m NW
of city centre off A572)
Hotel ★★★60% Novotel, Worsley Brow, WORSLEY
☎ 061-799 3535 119 ⇔ ੯

MELLOR

Map 07 SJ98

Mellor & Townscliffe ☎ 061-427 2208
Scenic parkland and moorland course, undulating with some
hard walking. Good views. Testing 200 yd, 9th hole, par 3.
18 holes, 5925yds, Par 70, SSS 69, Course record 68.
Club membership 650.
Visitors with member only Sun.
Societies apply by letter.
Green Fees £20 per day (£27.50 weekends & bank holidays).
Facilities ⊗ & ⊞ by prior arrangement ੯ ⚑ ♀ ⚑ ⚑
੯ Gary R Broadley.
Location Gibb Ln, Tarden (0.5m S)
Hotel ★74% Springfield Hotel, Station Rd, MARPLE
☎ 061-449 0721 6 ⇔ ੯

MIDDLETON

Map 07 SD80

Manchester ☎ 061-643 3202
Moorland golf of unique character over a spaciously laid
out course with generous fairways sweeping along to
large greens. A wide variety of holes will challenge the
golfer's technique, particularly the testing last three
holes.
18 holes, 6464yds, Par 72, SSS 72.
Club membership 700.
Visitors must contact in advance, restricted
weekends.
Societies apply in writing.
Green Fees £26 per day/round (£32 weekends & bank
holidays).
Facilities ⊗ ⊞ by prior arrangement ੯ ⚑ ♀ ⚑ ⚑
੯ Brian Connor.
Leisure snooker, driving range.
Location Hopwood Cottage, Rochdale Rd (2.5m N off
A664)
Hotel ★★61% Midway Hotel, Manchester Rd,
Castleton, ROCHDALE
☎ (0706) 32881 24 ⇔ ੯

North Manchester ☎ 061-643 9033
A long, tight heathland course with natural water hazards.
Excellent views of the Yorkshire Wolds.
18 holes, 6527yds, Par 72, SSS 72.
Club membership 800.
Visitors no restrictions.
Societies telephone in advance.
Green Fees £25 per day; £22 per round.
Facilities ⊗ ⊞ ੯ ⚑ ♀ ⚑ ⚑ ⚑ ੯ Peter Lunt.
Leisure snooker.
Location Rhodes House, Manchester Old Rd (W side of
town centre off A576)
Hotel ★★★62% Bower Hotel, Hollinwood Av,
Chadderton, OLDHAM
☎ 061-682 7254 66 ⇔ ੯

MILNROW

Map 07 SD91

Tunshill ☎ (0706) 342095
Testing moorland course, particularly 6th and 15th (par 5's).
9 holes, 5804yds, Par 70, SSS 68.
Club membership 275.
Visitors must contact in advance, restricted weekends &
evenings.

Societies apply in writing.
Green Fees not confirmed.
Facilities 🏋 & 🍽 (ex Mon) ♀ 🏌
Leisure snooker, pool table.
Location Kiln Ln (1m NE M62 exit junc 21 off B6225)
Hotel ★★★66% Norton Grange Hotel, Manchester Rd, Castleton, ROCHDALE
☎ (0706) 30788 50 ⇆ ₨

OLDHAM   Map 07 SD90

Crompton & Royton ☎ 061-624 2154 & 061-624 0986
Undulating moorland course.
18 holes, 6222yds, Par 70, SSS 70, Course record 65.
Club membership 721.
Visitors must contact in advance and may not play at weekends, Tue or Wed.
Societies apply in advance
Green Fees £24 (£30 weekends).
Facilities ⊗ ≡ 🏋 & 🍽 (no catering Mon ex bank holidays) ♀ 🏌 🏠 ₨ David Melling.
Leisure snooker.
Location Highbarn (0.5m NE of Royton)
Hotel ★★★62% Bower Hotel, Hollinwood Av, Chadderton, OLDHAM
☎ 061-682 7254 66 ⇆ ₨

Oldham ☎ 061-624 4986
Moorland course, with hard walking.
18 holes, 5045yds, Par 66, SSS 65.
Club membership 400.
Visitors no restrictions.
Societies must contact in advance.
Green Fees not confirmed.
Facilities ⊗ ≡ 🏋 🍽 (catering by arrangement) ♀ 🏌 🏠 ₨ Michael S Hollongworth.
Location Lees New Rd (2.5m E off A669)
Hotel ★★69% York House Hotel, York Place, Richmond St, ASHTON-UNDER-LYNE
☎ 061-330 5899 24 ⇆ ₨Annexe10 ⇆ ₨

Werneth ☎ 061-624 1190
Semi-moorland course, with a deep gulley and stream crossing eight fairways. Testing hole: 3rd (par 3).
18 holes, 5363yds, Par 68, SSS 66, Course record 63.
Club membership 460.
Visitors may not play on Tue or Thu and weekends. Must contact in advance.
Societies must contact in advance.
Green Fees not confirmed.
Facilities ⊗ ≡ 🏋 🍽 ♀ 🏌 🏠 ₨
Leisure snooker.
Location Green Ln, Garden Suburb (S side of town centre off A627)
Hotel ★★69% York House Hotel, York Place, Richmond St, ASHTON-UNDER-LYNE
☎ 061-330 5899 24 ⇆ ₨Annexe10 ⇆ ₨

PRESTWICH   Map 07 SD80

Prestwich ☎ 061-773 2544
Parkland course, near to Manchester city centre.
18 holes, 4806yds, Par 64, SSS 63.
Club membership 450.
Visitors with member only at weekends.

Societies apply in writing.
Green Fees not confirmed.
Facilities ♀ 🏌 🏠 ₨
Leisure snooker.
Location Hilton Ln (N side of town centre on A6044)
Hotel ★61% Beaucliffe Hotel, 254 Eccles Old Rd, Pendleton, SALFORD
☎ 061-789 5092 21rm(2 ⇆15 ₨)

ROCHDALE   Map 07 SD81

Castle Hawk ☎ (0706) 40841
Two parkland courses, with challenging par 3s, and a driving range.
New: 9 holes, 5398yds, Par 68, SSS 68.
Old: 18 holes, 3158yds, Par 55, Course record 53.
Club membership 160.
Visitors no restrictions.
Societies must contact in advance.
Green Fees £6 (£8 weekends).
Facilities ⊗ ≡ 🏋 🍽 ♀ 🏌 🏠 ₨ Mike Vipond. 🏌
Leisure fishing, driving range.
Location Chadwick Ln, Castleton (S of Rochdale, nr junc 20 (M62))
Hotel ★★★66% Norton Grange Hotel, Manchester Rd, Castleton, ROCHDALE
☎ (0706) 30788 50 ⇆ ₨

Rochdale ☎ (0706) 43818
Parkland course with enjoyable golf and easy walking.
18 holes, 6034yds, Par 71, SSS 69, Course record 65.
Club membership 700.
Visitors must contact in advance for details of restricted times.
Societies apply in writing.
Green Fees £20 per round/day (£24 weekends & bank holidays).
Facilities ⊗ 🏋 🍽 ♀ 🏌 🏠 ₨ Andrew Laverty.
Leisure snooker.
Location Edenfield Rd, Bagslate (1.75m W on A680)
Hotel ★★61% Midway Hotel, Manchester Rd, Castleton, ROCHDALE
☎ (0706) 32881 24 ⇆ ₨

Springfield Park ☎ (0706) 56401 (weekend only)
Parkland-moorland course situated in a valley. The River Roch adds an extra hazard to the course.
18 holes, 5237yds, Par 67, SSS 66, Course record 67.
Club membership 270.
Visitors must book for weekends.
Societies telephone in advance.
Green Fees not confirmed.
Facilities 🏠 🏌 ₨ David Wills.
Location Springfield Park, Bolton Rd (1.5m SW off A58)
Hotel ★★61% Midway Hotel, Manchester Rd, Castleton, ROCHDALE
☎ (0706) 32881 24 ⇆ ₨

ROMILEY   Map 07 SJ99

Romiley ☎ 061-430 2392
Parkland course, well-wooded.
18 holes, 6421yds, Par 70, SSS 71.
Club membership 700.
Visitors must contact in advance.   ▶

Societies   apply in writing.
Green Fees £22 (£33 weekends & bank holidays).
Facilities ⊗ ℳ by prior arrangement 🝔 ⚑ ♀ 👥 🛏 ⚑ 🏌 🍴
Leisure   snooker.
Location   Goose House Green (E side of town centre off
                B6104)
Hotel   ★★70% Red Lion Inn, 112 Buxton Rd, High
                Ln, STOCKPORT ☎ (0663) 765227 6 ⇆ 🐾

SALE   Map 07 SJ79

Ashton on Mersey ☎ 061-973 3220
Parkland course with easy walking.
9 holes, 6146yds, Par 72, SSS 69.
Club membership 360.
Visitors   with member only Sun & bank holidays, not Sat.
Green Fees not confirmed.
Facilities ⊗ ℳ 🝔 ⚑ ♀ 👥 🛏 🍴 Paul Wagstaff.
Location   Church Ln (1m W of M63 junc 7)
Hotel   ★★★65% Cresta Court Hotel, Church St,
                ALTRINCHAM ☎ 061-927 7272 139 ⇆ 🐾

Sale ☎ 061-973 1638
Parkland course.
18 holes, 6346yds, Par 71, SSS 70, Course record 66.
Club membership 600.
Visitors   dress regulations in club house & on course.
Societies   apply by letter.
Green Fees £22 per round.
Facilities ⊗ ℳ 🝔 ⚑ (catering Mon-Fri only) ♀ 👥 🛏 🍴
                🍴 Mike Stewart.
Leisure   snooker.
Location   Golf Rd (NW side of town centre off A6144)
Hotel   ★★★65% Cresta Court Hotel, Church St,
                ALTRINCHAM ☎ 061-927 7272 139 ⇆ 🐾

SHEVINGTON   Map 07 SD50

Gathurst ☎ Appley Bridge (0257) 252861
Testing parkland course, slightly hilly.
9 holes, 6282yds, Par 72, SSS 70.
Club membership 350.
Visitors   after 5pm, with member only Wed, weekends &
                bank holidays.
Societies   apply in writing.
Green Fees not confirmed.
Facilities ⊗ ℳ 🝔 ⚑ ♀ 👥 🛏 🍴
Leisure   snooker.
Location   62 Miles Ln (W side of village B5375 off junc
                27 of M6)
Hotel   ★★★65% Almond Brook Moat House, Almond
                Brook Rd, STANDISH
                ☎ (0257) 425588 122 ⇆ 🐾

STALYBRIDGE   Map 07 SJ99

Stamford ☎ (0457) 832126
Undulating moorland course.
18 holes, 5701yds, Par 70, SSS 68.
Club membership 550.
Visitors   must telephone in advance.
Societies   must contact in advance.
Green Fees £17.50 per day (£23 weekends & bank holidays).
Facilities ⊗ ℳ 🝔 ⚑ (no catering Mon) ♀ 👥 🛏
Leisure   snooker.

Location   Huddersfield Rd (2m NE off A635)
Hotel   ★★69% York House Hotel, York Place,
                Richmond St, ASHTON-UNDER-LYNE
                ☎ 061-330 5899 24 ⇆ 🐾Annexe10 ⇆ 🐾

STOCKPORT   Map 07 SJ89

Heaton Moor ☎ 061-432 2134
Parkland course, easy walking.
18 holes, 5907yds, Par 70, SSS 69, Course record 66.
Club membership 400.
Visitors   restricted Tue & bank holidays.
Societies   apply in writing.
Green Fees not confirmed.
Facilities ⊗ ℳ by prior arrangement 🝔 ⚑ ♀ 👥 🛏 🏌
                🍴 C Loydall.
Location   Heaton Mersey (N of town centre off B5169)
Hotel   ★★66% Saxon Holme Hotel, 230 Wellington
                Rd, STOCKPORT ☎ 061-432 2335 30 ⇆ 🐾

Houldsworth ☎ 061-442 9611 & 061-442 1712
Flat parkland course, tree-lined and with water hazards.
Testing holes 9th (par 5) and 13th (par 5).
18 holes, 6209yds, Par 71, SSS 70.
Club membership 625.
Visitors   may not play weekends & bank holidays unless
                by prior arrangement with professional.
Societies   by prior arrangement.
Green Fees £20 per round/day (£25 weekends).
Facilities ⊗ ℳ by prior arrangement 🝔 ⚑ ♀ 👥 🛏
                🍴 David Naylor.
Leisure   snooker.
Location   Houldsworth Park, Reddish (4m SE of city
                centre off A6)
Hotel   ★★★61% Willow Bank Hotel, 340-342
                Wilmslow Rd, Fallowfield, MANCHESTER
                ☎ 061-224 0461 116 ⇆ 🐾

Marple ☎ 061-427 2311
Parkland course.
18 holes, 5475yds, Par 68, SSS 67, Course record 65.
Club membership 500.
Visitors   restricted Thu afternoon & weekend competition
                days.
Societies   must contact in advance.
Green Fees not confirmed.
Facilities ⊗ (ex Mon) ℳ by prior arrangement 🝔 (ex Mon
                in winter) ⚑ ♀ 👥 🛏 🍴 Nick Hamilton.
Location   Barnsfold Rd, Hawk Green, Marple (S side of
                town centre)
Hotel   ★★70% Red Lion Inn, 112 Buxton Rd, High
                Ln, STOCKPORT ☎ (0663) 765227 6 ⇆ 🐾

Reddish Vale ☎ 061-480 2359
Undulating heathland course designed by Dr. A Mackenzie
and situated in the River Thame valley.
18 holes, 6100yds, Par 69, SSS 69, Course record 64.
Club membership 550.
Visitors   must play with member at weekends.
Societies   must contact in writing.
Green Fees £22 per day/round.
Facilities ⊗ 🝔 ⚑ ♀ 👥 🛏 🍴 Richard Brown.
Leisure   snooker.
Location   Southcliffe Rd, Reddish (1.5m N off Reddish road)
Hotel   ★★63% Wycliffe, 74 Edgeley Rd, Edgeley,
                STOCKPORT ☎ 061-477 5395 20 ⇆ 🐾

Stockport ☎ 061-427 2001 & 061-427 2421
A beautifully situated course in wide open countryside. It is not too long but requires that the player plays all the shots, to excellent greens.
18 holes, 6326yds, Par 71, SSS 71.
Club membership 500.
Visitors	must contact in advance, restricted Ladies Day (Tue) and weekends.
Societies	Wed & Thu only, apply in writing.
Green Fees	not confirmed.
Facilities	⊗ ⅷ by prior arrangement ⓵ ⬤ by prior arrangement ⓵ ⬣ ⬜ ⅷ ⅼ T Le Brocq.
Leisure	snooker.
Location	Offerton Rd, Offerton (4m SE on A627)
Hotel	★★70% Red Lion Inn, 112 Buxton Rd, High Ln, STOCKPORT ☎ (0663) 765227 6 ⇥ ❦

SWINTON   Map 07 SD70

Swinton Park ☎ 061-794 1785
One of Lancashire's longest inland courses. Clubhouse extensions have greatly improved the facilities.
18 holes, 6712yds, Par 73, SSS 72, Course record 63.
Club membership 600.
Visitors	restricted at weekends. Must contact in advance and have handicap certificate.
Societies	by letter.
Green Fees	not confirmed.
Facilities	⊗ ⅷ ⓵ ⬤ ⓵ ⬣ ⬜ ⅼ James Wilson.
Leisure	snooker.
Location	East Lancashire Rd (1m W off A580)
Hotel	★★★60% Novotel, Worsley Brow, WORSLEY ☎ 061-799 3535 119 ⇥ ❦

UPPERMILL   Map 07 SD90

Saddleworth ☎ Saddleworth (0457) 873653
Moorland course, with superb views of Pennines.
18 holes, 5976yds, Par 71, SSS 69, Course record 62.
Club membership 743.
Visitors	must contact in advance, restricted at weekends.
Societies	apply in writing.
Green Fees	£23 per day (£26 weekends & bank holidays).
Facilities	⊗ (not Mon in winter) ⅷ by prior arrangement ⓵ ⬤ ⓵ ⬣ ⬜ ⅼ E T Shard.
Leisure	snooker, caddy car.
Location	Mountain Ash, Ladcastle Rd, Oldham (E side of town centre off A670)
Hotel	★★★70% Hotel Smokies Park, Ashton Rd, Bardsley, OLDHAM ☎ 061-624 3405 47 ⇥ ❦

URMSTON   Map 07 SJ79

Flixton ☎ 061-748 2116
Meadowland course bounded by River Mersey.
9 holes, 6410yds, Par 71, SSS 71.
Club membership 450.
Visitors	with member only weekends & bank holidays.
Societies	apply by letter to Steward.
Green Fees	£17.50 per day.
Facilities	⊗ ⅷ by prior arrangement ⓵ ⬤ ⓵ ⬣ ⬜ ⅼ J Watson.
Leisure	snooker, caddy cars.

Location	Church Rd, Flixton (S side of town centre on B5213)
Hotel	★★★58% Ashley Hotel, Ashley Rd, Hale, ALTRINCHAM ☎ 061-928 3794 47 ⇥ ❦

WALKDEN   Map 07 SD70

Brackley Municipal ☎ 061-790 6076
Mostly flat course.
9 holes, 3003yds, Par 35, SSS 69.
Visitors	no restrictions.
Green Fees	not confirmed.
Facilities	⬜ ⅼ
Location	2m NW on A6
Hotel	★★★60% Novotel, Worsley Brow, WORSLEY ☎ 061-799 3535 119 ⇥ ❦

WESTHOUGHTON   Map 07 SD60

Westhoughton ☎ (0942) 811085
Compact downland course.
9 holes, 2886yds, Par 35, SSS 68.
Club membership 280.
Visitors	with member only at weekends.
Societies	must apply in writing.
Green Fees	not confirmed.
Facilities	⊗ & ⅷ by prior arrangement ⓵ ⬤ ⓵ ⬣ ⬜ ⅼ P Wesselingh.
Leisure	snooker, pool table.
Location	Long Island (0.5m NW off A58)
Hotel	★★★62% Beaumont Hotel, Beaumont Rd, BOLTON ☎ (0204) 651511 96 ⇥ ❦

WHITEFIELD   Map 07 SD80

Stand ☎ 061-766 2388
A semi-parkland course with five moorland holes. A fine test of golf with a very demanding finish.
18 holes, 6426yds, Par 72, SSS 71.
Club membership 680.
Visitors	must contact in advance but may not play on Tue or weekends.
Societies	must contact in writing.
Green Fees	£25 per day (£30 weekends & bank holdays).
Facilities	⊗ ⅷ ⓵ ⬤ ⓵ ⬣ ⬜ ⅷ ⅼ Mark Dance.
Leisure	snooker.
Location	The Dales, Ashbourne Grove (1m W off A667)
Hotel	★56% Woolfield House Hotel, Wash Ln, BURY ☎ 061-797 9775 16rm(3 ⇥ 7 ❦)

Whitefield ☎ 061-766 3096
Fine sporting parkland course with well-watered greens.
18 holes, 6041yds, Par 69.
Club membership 500.
Visitors	must contact in advance and have an introduction from own club.
Societies	must contact in advance.
Green Fees	not confirmed.
Facilities	Catering on request ⓵ ⬣ ⬜ ⅷ ⅼ Paul Reeves.
Leisure	hard tennis courts, snooker.
Location	Higher Ln (N side of town centre on A665)
Hotel	★★★★54% Portland Thistle, 3/5 Portland St, Piccadilly Gdns, MANCHESTER ☎ 061-228 3400 205 ⇥ ❦

WIGAN
Map 07 SD50

Haigh Hall ☎ (0942) 831107
Municipal parkland course, with hard walking, and a canal forms the west boundary. Adjacent to 'Haigh Country Park' with many facilities.
18 holes, 6423yds, Par 70, SSS 71, Course record 66.
Club membership 150.
Visitors no restrictions.
Green Fees not confirmed.
Facilities ⊗ Ⅲ 🍺 ♀ (weekend afternoons) ☂ 🛍 ⚑
　　　　　 ℓ Ian Lee.
Location Haigh Country Park, Haigh (2m NE off B5238)
Hotel ★★61% Brocket Arms Hotel, Mesnes Rd, WIGAN ☎ (0942) 46283 27 ⇌ ℟

Wigan ☎ Standish (0257) 421360
Among the best of Lancashire's 9-hole courses. The fine old clubhouse is the original Arley Hall, and is surrounded by a moat.
9 holes, 6058yds, Par 70, SSS 69, Course record 64.
Club membership 320.
Visitors welcome except Tue. Must contact in advance.
Societies apply in writing.
Green Fees not confirmed.
Facilities ⊗ Ⅲↆ 🍺 ♀ ☂
Leisure snooker.
Location Arley Hall, Haigh (3m NE off B5238)
Hotel ★★★65% Almond Brook Moat House, Almond Brook Rd, STANDISH ☎ (0257) 425588 122 ⇌ ℟

WOODFORD
Map 07 SJ88

Avro ☎ 061-439 2709
An attractive, tight and challenging 9-hole course.
9 holes, 5735yds, Par 69, SSS 68.
Club membership 400.
Visitors restricted weekends and competition days.
Societies must contact The Hon Secretary, c/o 23 Meadowbank Avenue, Atherton, Manchester M49 9LB.
Green Fees £10 (£15 weekends & bank holidays).
Facilities 🍺 ☂
Location Old Hall Ln (W side of village on A5102)
Hotel ★★★67% Bramhall Moat House, Bramhall Ln South, BRAMHALL ☎ 061-439 8116 65 ⇌ ℟

WORSLEY
Map 07 SD70

Ellesmere ☎ 061-790 2122
Parkland course with natural hazards. Testing holes: 3rd (par 5), 9th (par 3), 13th (par 4). Hard walking.
18 holes, 5954yds, Par 69, SSS 69.
Club membership 550.
Visitors welcome except club competition days & bank holidays. Must contact in advance & have handicap certificate.
Societies Mon-Wed only, contact in advance.
Green Fees £24 per day; £18 per round (£25 per day/round weekends).
Facilities ⊗ Ⅲ (by arrangement in winter) ↆ 🍺 ♀ ☂ 🛍
　　　　　 ℓ Terry Morley.

Leisure snooker, electric golf trolleys for hire.
Location Old Clough Ln (N side of village off A580)
Hotel ★★★60% Novotel, Worsley Brow, WORSLEY ☎ 061-799 3535 119 ⇌ ℟

HAMPSHIRE

ALDERSHOT
Map 04 SU85

Army ☎ (0252) 540638
Picturesque heathland course with three par 3's, over 200 yds.
18 holes, 6550yds, Par 71, SSS 71.
Club membership 800.
Visitors must contact in advance & have handicap certificate.
Societies Mon & Thu only.
Green Fees not confirmed.
Facilities ⊗ Ⅲↆ 🍺 (catering all day) ♀ ☂ 🛍 ℓ
Location Laffans Rd (1.5m N of town centre off A323/A325)
Hotel B Forte Crest, Lynchford Rd, FARNBOROUGH ☎ (0252) 545051 110 ⇌ ℟

ALRESFORD
Map 04 SU53

Alresford ☎ (0962) 733746
A testing downland course on well drained chalk.Now expanded to 18 holes, incorporating the original 12, but changing direction of play to give two starting points and two closing greens near clubhouse.
18 holes, 5905yds, Par 69, SSS 68.
Club membership 640.
Visitors must contact in advance but may not play before noon on weekends & bank holidays.
Societies must telephone in advance.
Green Fees £15 per round (£30 weekends & bank holidays).
Facilities ⊗ Ⅲↆ 🍺 ♀ ☂ 🛍 ⚑ ℓ Malcolm Scott.
Location Cheriton Rd, Tichborne Down (1m S on B3046)
Hotel ★★59% Swan Hotel, 11 West St, ALRESFORD ☎ (0962) 732302 & 734427 23rm(10 ⇌)

ALTON
Map 04 SU73

Alton ☎ (0420) 82042
Undulating meadowland course.
9 holes, 5744yds, Par 68, SSS 68, Course record 66.
Club membership 340.
Visitors must have a handicap of 18 or less to play at weekends & bank holidays, or be accompanied by a member.
Societies weekdays only.
Green Fees £10 per round.
Facilities 🍺 ♀ ☂ 🛍 ℓ Andy Lamb.
Location Old Odiham Rd (2m N off A32)
Hotel ★★★62% Alton House Hotel, Normandy St, ALTON ☎ (0420) 80033 39 ⇌ ℟

Worldham Park ☎ (0420) 543151
The course is in a picturesque woodland setting with an
abundance of challenging holes (doglegs, water and sand).
Will be increased to 18-holes by early 1995 to offer a course
of some 6,000 plus yards and a par of 70.
9 holes, 2608yds, Par 34, SSS 34.
Club membership 475.

Visitors	no restrictions.
Societies	one months notice in writing.
Green Fees	£7.50 (£9.50 weekends & bank holidays).
Facilities	⊗ ⅃ ■ ♀ 🏠 ⭐ ⚑ Charles Troth.
Leisure	14 bay driving range.
Location	Cakers Ln, Worldham (B3004, 2mins from Alton)
Hotel	★★★64% Grange Hotel, 17 London Rd, Holybourne, ALTON ☎ (0420) 86565 26 ⇆ ☞Annexe4 ⇆ ☞

AMPFIELD　　　　　　　　　　　　　　　　　Map 04 SU42

Ampfield Par Three ☎ Braishfield (0794) 368480
Pretty parkland course designed by Henry Cotton in 1963.
Well-bunkered greens.
18 holes, 2478yds, Par 54, SSS 53.
Club membership 510.

Visitors	must contact in advance & have a handicap certificate to play at weekends & bank holidays. Golf shoes must be worn & no club sharing.
Societies	must contact in writing.
Green Fees	£15 per day; £9 per round (£15.50 per round weekends & bank holidays).
Facilities	⊗ ⅃ ■ ♀ ⅄ 🏠 ⭐ ⚑
Location	Winchester Rd (4m NE of Romsey on A31)
Hotel	★★★68% Potters Heron Hotel, AMPFIELD ☎ (0703) 266611 54 ⇆ ☞

ANDOVER　　　　　　　　　　　　　　　　　Map 04 SU34

Andover ☎ (0264) 358040
Hilly downland course, fine views.
9 holes, 5933yds, Par 69, SSS 68, Course record 65.
Club membership 500.

Visitors	restricted mornings at weekends and bank holidays.
Societies	must contact in writing.
Green Fees	£15 per day; £10 per round; (£22 Sun & bank holidays).
Facilities	⊗ (ex Sun) ⅃ by prior arrangement ⅃ ■ ♀ ⅄ 🏠 ⭐ ⚑ Andrea Timms.
Location	51 Winchester Rd (0.5m S on A3057)
Hotel	★★60% Danebury Hotel, High St, ANDOVER ☎ (0264) 323332 24 ⇆ ☞

BARTON-ON-SEA　　　　　　　　　　　　　　Map 04 SZ29

Barton-on-Sea ☎ New Milton (0425) 615308
Though not strictly a links course, it is right on a cliff
edge with views over the Isle of Wight and Christchurch
Bay. On a still day there is nothing much to it - but when
it blows the course undergoes a complete change in
character. Recently reconstructed to create 27 holes.
Becton-Needles: 18 holes, 6505yds, Par 72, SSS 71.
Needles-Stroller: 18 holes, 6444yds, Par 72, SSS 71.
Stroller-Becton: 18 holes, 6289yds, Par 72, SSS 70.
Club membership 700.

Visitors	after 8.30am Mon-Fri & 9.30am weekends & bank holidays. Must contact in advance and have a handicap certificate.
Societies	Mon-Fri. Must book well in advance.
Green Fees	£25 per day (£30 weekends & bank holidays).
Facilities	⊗ ⅃ by prior arrangement ⅃ ■ ♀ ⅄ 🏠 ⭐ ⚑ P Coombs.
Leisure	snooker, caddy carts.
Location	Milford Rd, New Milton (B3058 E side of town)
Hotel	★★★★★(red)🏨 Chewton Glen Hotel, Christchurch Rd, NEW MILTON ☎ (0425) 275341 58 ⇆ ☞
Additional hotel	★★★73% South Lawn Hotel, Lymington Rd, MILFORD ON SEA ☎ (0590) 643911 24 ⇆ ☞

BASINGSTOKE　　　　　　　　　　　　　　Map 04 SU65

Basingstoke ☎ (0256) 465990
A well-maintained parkland course with wide and
inviting fairways. You are inclined to expect longer
drives than are actually achieved - partly on account of
the trees. There are many two-hundred-year-old beech
trees, since the course was built on an old deer park.
18 holes, 6350yds, Par 70, SSS 70, Course record 67.
Club membership 700.　　　　　　　　　　　　　　　▶

South Lawn Hotel & Restaurant ★★★ ✿

Milford-on-Sea, Lymington, Hampshire SO41 0RF
Tel: Lymington (01590) 643911 Fax: (01590) 644820

*Delightful Country House Hotel in peaceful
surroundings where comfort and good food
predominate. Owner/Chef Ernst Barten
supervises excellent cuisine. Specially
imported wines from Germany.*

*All rooms en-suite, colour TV, phone and
trouser press. Facilities nearby include
windsurfing and sailing from Keyhaven,
Golf at Brockenhurst and Barton-on-Sea,
the Beach at Milford and walking or riding
in the beautiful New Forest.*

Visitors	must have a handicap certificate and play with member at weekends.
Societies	Wed & Thu only.
Green Fees	not confirmed.
Facilities	⊗ ⅷ ⅃ ♿ ♀ ⚘ 🏠 ∤ Ian Hayes.
Location	Kempshott Park (3.5m SW on A30 M3 exit 7)
Hotel	B Forte Posthouse, Grove Rd, BASINGSTOKE ☏ (0256) 468181 84 ⇨ 🐾

Dummer ☏ (0256) 397888
Opened in July 1993 and designed by Peter Alliss/Clive Clark to consist of two 9-hole loops with water hazards. Gentle terrain makes the course suitable for players of all ages.
18 holes, 6556yds, Par 72.
Club membership 830.

Visitors	must contact in advance, handicap card required, limited at weekends.
Societies	contact in advance.
Green Fees	not confirmed.
Facilities	⚘ 🏠 ∤ (
Leisure	sauna.
Location	Nr Basingstoke (off junc 7 of M3 towards Dummer village)
Hotel	★★★62% Wheatsheaf Hotel, NORTH WALTHAM ☏ (0256) 398282 28 ⇨ 🐾

Weybrook Park ☏ (0256) 20347
A course designed to be enjoyable for all standards of player.
18 holes, 6093yds, Par 72, SSS 69.
Club membership 350.

Visitors	telephone for availability. Sat after 11am, Sun after noon.
Societies	telephone in advance for availability and confirm in writing.
Green Fees	£12 (£14 weekends & bank holidays).
Facilities	♿ ⅃ ♀ ⚘
Location	Aldermaston Rd, Sherborne St John (2m W of town centre, entrance via A339)
Hotel	★★★58% Ringway Hotel, Popley Way, Aldermaston Roundabout, Ringway North (A339), BASINGSTOKE ☏ (0256) 20212 134 ⇨ 🐾

BORDON   Map 04 SU73

Blackmoor ☏ (0420) 472775
A first-class moorland course with a great variety of holes. Fine greens and wide pine tree-lined fairways are a distinguishing feature. The ground is mainly flat and walking easy.
18 holes, 6200yds, Par 69, SSS 70, Course record 65.
Club membership 700.

Visitors	must have a letter of introduction from their club or a handicap certificate; must be accompanied by a member at weekends. Must contact in advance.
Societies	must telephone in advance.
Green Fees	not confirmed.
Facilities	⊗ ⅷ ♿ ♀ ⚘ 🏠 ∤ (Andrew Hall.
Leisure	practice ground & nets.
Location	Whitehill
Hotel	★★★61% Bush Hotel, The Borough, FARNHAM ☏ (0252) 715237 66 ⇨ 🐾

BOTLEY   Map 04 SU51

Botley Park Hotel & Country Club ☏ (0489) 780888
Pleasantly undulating course with water hazards. Driving range and country club facilities.
18 holes, 6026yds, Par 70, SSS 70.
Club membership 750.

Visitors	must contact in advance & have handicap certificate.
Societies	contact in advance.
Green Fees	not confirmed.
Facilities	⊗ ⅷ ♿ ♀ ⚘ 🏠 ⛳ 🖐 (Tim Barter.
Leisure	hard tennis courts, heated indoor swimming pool, squash, snooker, sauna, solarium, gymnasium, croquet lawn & petanque.
Location	Winchester Rd, Boorley Green (1m NW of Botley on B3354)
Hotel	★★★★63% Botley Park Hotel & Country Club, Winchester Rd, Boorley Green, BOTLEY ☏ (0489) 780888 100 ⇨ 🐾

BROCKENHURST   Map 04 SU20

Brokenhurst Manor ☏ Lymington (0590) 23332
An attractive woodland/heathland course set at the edge of the New Forest, with the unusual feature of three loops of six holes each to complete the round. Fascinating holes include the short 5th and 12th, and the 4th and 17th, both dog-legged. A stream also features on seven of the holes.
18 holes, 6222yds, Par 70, SSS 70, Course record 64.
Club membership 800.

★★
The Watersplash Hotel
Brockenhurst in the New Forest

The Watersplash Hotel is recommended for its excellent food, friendly service and accommodation. Brokenhurst Manor Golf Club, situated just half a mile away, is one of ten courses within easy reach of the hotel. Personally supervised by resident proprietors Robin and Judy Foster who specialise in catering for the individual and small golf parties. Well-stocked bar and extensive wine list. All 23 bedrooms have private bathroom, colour TV, tea and coffee making facilities, direct dial telephone and radio. Heated outdoor pool in season. For further details ask for our colour brochure.

The Watersplash Hotel, The Rise, Brockenhurst, Hampshire SO42 7ZP. Tel: (01590) 22344 Fax: (01590) 24047

Visitors	must contact in advance and have a handicap certificate (maximum, men 24 and ladies 32).
Societies	small societies (16 maximum) Mon, Wed & Fri by arrangement.
Green Fees	£30 per day; £25 per round (£35 weekends & bank holidays).
Facilities	⊗ ⅷ by prior arrangement ⯅ 💺 ♀ ⛳ 🏠 ⟨ John Lovell.
Location	Sway Rd (1m S on B3055)
Hotel	★★★64% Balmer Lawn Hotel, Lyndhurst Rd, BROCKENHURST ☎ (0590) 23116 58 ⇥ 🐾
Additional hotel	★★63% Watersplash Hotel, The Rise, BROCKENHURST ☎ (0590) 22344 23 ⇥ 🐾

BURLEY
Map 04 SU20

Burley ☎ (0425) 402431
Undulating heather and gorseland. The 7th requires an accurately placed tee shot to obtain par 4. Played off different tees on second nine.
9 holes, 6149yds, Par 71, SSS 69, Course record 68.
Club membership 520.
Visitors must contact in advance & have a handicap certificate. May not play before 4pm Sat.
Green Fees £14 per day (£16 weekends).
Facilities ⊗ by prior arrangement ⯅ 💺 ♀ ⛳
Location E side of village
Hotel ★★★59% Moorhill House, BURLEY ☎ (0425) 403285 24 ⇥ 🐾

CORHAMPTON
Map 04 SU62

Corhampton ☎ Droxford (0489) 877279
Downland course.
18 holes, 6444yds, Par 71, SSS 71.
Club membership 650.
Visitors must contact in advance & must play with member at weekends & bank holidays.
Societies Mon & Thu only. Must telephone in advance.
Green Fees £30 per day; £20 per round.
Facilities ⊗ ⅷ by prior arrangement ⯅ 💺 ⛳ 🏠 ⟨ Garry Stubbington.
Location Sheep's Pond Ln (1m W off B3035)
Hotel ★★74% Old House Hotel, The Square, WICKHAM ☎ (0329) 833049 9 ⇥ 🐾 Annexe3 ⇥ 🐾

CRONDALL
Map 04 SU74

Oak Park ☎ Aldershot (0252) 850880
Gently undulating course overlooking pretty village. 16-bay floodlit driving range, practice green and practice bunker.
18 holes, 6437yds, Par 72, SSS 71, Course record 67.
Club membership 400.
Visitors no restrictions.
Societies must telephone in advance.
Green Fees £25 per day; £16 per round (£40/£22.50 weekends & public holidays).
Facilities ⊗ ⅷ ⯅ 💺 ♀ ⛳ 🏠 ⟨ Simon Coaker.
Leisure practice green & covered driving range.
Location Heath Ln (0.5m E of village off A287)
Hotel ★★★61% Bush Hotel, The Borough, FARNHAM ☎ (0252) 715237 66 ⇥ 🐾

DIBDEN
Map 04 SU40

Dibden ☎ Southampton (0703) 207508 & 845596
Municipal parkland course with views over Southampton Water. A pond guards the green at the par 5, 3rd hole. Twenty-bay driving range.
Course 1: 18 holes, 6206yds, Par 71, SSS 70.
Course 2: 9 holes, 1520yds, Par 29.
Club membership 600.
Visitors no restrictions.
Societies must contact in writing.
Green Fees £6.90 (£10 weekends).
Facilities ⊗ ⅷ by prior arrangement ⯅ 💺 ♀ ⛳ 🏠 ⟨ Alan Bridge.
Location Main Rd (2m NW of Dibden Purlieu)
Hotel ★★★60% Forest Lodge Hotel, Pikes Hill, Romsey Rd, LYNDHURST ☎ (0703) 283677 23 ⇥ 🐾

EASTLEIGH
Map 04 SU41

Fleming Park ☎ (0703) 612797
Parkland course with stream-'Monks Brook'-running through.
18 holes, 4436yds, Par 65, SSS 62.
Club membership 300.
Visitors no restrictions.
Societies must contact in advance.
Green Fees not confirmed.
Facilities ⯅ 💺 ♀ ⛳ 🏠 ⟨ Chris Strickett.
Location Magpie Ln (E side of town centre)
Hotel ★★★64% Southampton Park Hotel, Cumberland Place, SOUTHAMPTON ☎ (0703) 223467 72 ⇥ 🐾

EAST WELLOW
Map 04 SU32

Wellow ☎ Romsey (0794) 322872 & 323833
Parkland course around lake. Plenty of established and new trees.
18 holes, 5966yds, Par 70, SSS 69.
Club membership 400.
Visitors must contact in advance.
Societies apply in advance.
Green Fees £15 per day (£20 weekends & bank holidays).
Facilities ⊗ ⅷ ⯅ 💺 ♀ ⛳ 🏠 ⟨ Neil Bratley.
Location Ryedown Ln (1m N from A36 to Salisbury then 1m right)
Hotel ★★★62% White Horse Hotel, Market Place, ROMSEY ☎ (0794) 512431 33 ⇥ 🐾

FAREHAM
Map 04 SU50

Cams Hall ☎ (0329) 827222
Two Peter Alliss/Clive Clark designed golf courses opened in 1993. The Historic is in parkland and the Coastal has lakes and undulating hills.
Coastal: 18 holes, 6180yds, Par 71.
Historic: 9 holes, 3326yds, Par 36.
Club membership 1125.
Visitors must contact in advance, and have handicap certificate, restricted at weekends.
Societies must contact in advance.
Green Fees not confirmed. ▶

Facilities ⊗ ⅏ ⅃ ⊒ ♀ ⅍ 🏠 ⅂ ⅂ Jason Neves.
Leisure sauna.
Location M27 exit 11 to A27
Hotel ★★★67% Lysses House Hotel & Conference Centre, 51 High St, FAREHAM
☎ (0329) 822622 21 ⇔ 📠

FARNBOROUGH Map 04 SU85

Southwood ☎ (0252) 548700
Municipal parkland course with stream running through.
18 holes, 5738yds, Par 69, SSS 68, Course record 61.
Club membership 700.
Visitors must book in advance.
Societies must contact in advance.
Green Fees £11.50 (£14 weekends).
Facilities ⊗ ⅏ by prior arrangement ⅃ ⊒ ♀ ⅍ 🏠 ⅂
⅂ Bob Hammond.
Location Ively Rd (0.5m W)
Hotel B Forte Crest, Lynchford Rd, FARNBOROUGH
☎ (0252) 545051 110 ⇔ 📠

FLEET Map 04 SU85

North Hants ☎ (0252) 616443
Picturesque tree-lined course with much heather and gorse close to the fairways. A comparatively easy par-4 first hole may lull the golfer into a false sense of security, only to be rudely awakened at the testing holes which follow. The ground is rather undulating and, though not tiring, does offer some excellent 'blind' shots, and more than a few surprises in judging distance.
18 holes, 6257yds, Par 69, SSS 70, Course record 67.
Club membership 700.
Visitors must contact in advance & have handicap certificate. Must play with member at weekends.
Societies Tue & Wed only.
Green Fees £24 per round; £30 two rounds. With member only at weekends..
Facilities ⊗ ⅏ ⅃ ⊒ ♀ ⅍ 🏠 ⅂ Steve Porter.
Location Minley Rd (0.25m N of Fleet station on B3013)
Hotel ★★★57% Lismoyne Hotel, Church Rd, FLEET ☎ (0252) 628555 42 ⇔ 📠

GOSPORT Map 04 SZ69

Gosport & Stokes Bay ☎ (0705) 527941
A testing links course overlooking the Solent, with plenty of gorse and short rough. Changing winds.
9 holes, 5966yds, Par 71, SSS 69, Course record 65.
Club membership 500.
Visitors may not play at weekends & Thu.
Societies must telephone in advance.
Green Fees £15 per day (£20 weekends).
Facilities ⊗ & ⅏ by prior arrangement ⅃ ⊒ ♀ ⅍ 🏠 ⅂
Location Off Fort Rd, Haslar (A32 S from Fareham,E on Fort rd to Haslar)
Hotel ★★59% Anglesey Hotel, Crescent Rd, Alverstoke, GOSPORT
☎ (0705) 582157 & 523932 18 ⇔ 📠

HARTLEY WINTNEY Map 04 SU75

Hartley Wintney ☎ (0252) 844211 & 842214
Easy walking, parkland course in pleasant countryside. Played off different tees on back nine, with testing par 4s at 4th and 13th.
9 holes, 6096yds, Par 70, SSS 69.
Club membership 420.
Visitors must contact in advance.
Societies Tue & Thu only.
Green Fees not confirmed.
Facilities ⊗ & ⅏ by prior arrangement ⅃ ⊒ ♀ ⅍ 🏠
⅂ Martin Smith.
Location London Rd (NE side of village on A30)
Hotel ★★★57% Lismoyne Hotel, Church Rd, FLEET
☎ (0252) 628555 42 ⇔ 📠

HAYLING ISLAND Map 04 SU70

Hayling ☎ (0705) 464446
A delightful links course among the dunes offering fine sea-scapes and views across to the Isle of Wight. Varying sea breezes and sometimes strong winds ensure that the course seldom plays the same two days running. Testing holes at the 12th and 13th, both par 4. Club selection is important.
18 holes, 6489yds, Par 71, SSS 71.
Club membership 850.
Visitors must contact in advance and have a handicap certificate.
Societies welcome Tue & Wed, apply in writing.
X:Green Fees not confirmed.
Facilities ⊗ by prior arrangement ⅃ ⊒ ⅍ 🏠 ⅂ ⅂
Location Links Ln (SW side of island at West Town)
Hotel B Forte Posthouse, Northney Rd, HAYLING ISLAND
☎ (0705) 465011 92 ⇔ 📠

KINGSCLERE Map 04 SU55

Sandford Springs ☎ (0635) 297881
The course has unique variety in beautiful surroundings and offers three distinctive loops of 9 holes. There are water hazards, woodlands and gradients to negotiate, providing a challenge for all playing categories. From its highest point there are extensive views.
The Park: 9 holes, 2963yds, Par 35, SSS 34.
The Lakes: 9 holes, 3180yds, Par 35, SSS 34.
The Wood: 9 holes, 3042yds, Par 36, SSS 35.
Club membership 600.
Visitors must contact in advance. Must play with member at weekends.
Societies must contact in advance.
Green Fees £29 per 18+ holes, £23 per 18 holes, £15 per 9 holes.
Facilities ⊗ ⅏ ⅃ ⊒ ♀ ⅍ 🏠 ⅂ ⅂ Gary Edmunds.
Leisure caddy cars & practice ground.
Location Wolverton (on A339)
Hotel ★★★65% Millwaters, London Rd, NEWBURY ☎ (0635) 528838 30 ⇔ 📠

KINGSLEY

Map 04 SU73

Dean Farm ☎ Bordon (0420) 489478
Undulating downland course.
9 holes, 1350yds, Par 28.
Visitors no restrictions.
Green Fees £6.50 per 18 holes; £4 per 9 holes.
Facilities ⬛ 🍷🍴🏠
Leisure hard tennis courts.
Location W side of village off B3004
Hotel ★★★64% Grange Hotel, 17 London Rd,
Holybourne, ALTON
☎ (0420) 86565 26 ⇌ 🐾Annexe4 ⇌ 🐾

LECKFORD

Map 04 SU33

Leckford ☎ (0264) 810320
A testing downland course with good views.
9 holes, 6444yds, Par 70, SSS 71.
Club membership 200.
Visitors must be accompanied by member and contact in
advance.
Green Fees not confirmed.
Facilities 🛆
Location 1m SW off A3057
Hotel ★★★63% Grosvenor Hotel, High St,
STOCKBRIDGE ☎ (0264) 810606 25 ⇌ 🐾

LEE-ON-THE-SOLENT

Map 04 SU50

Lee-on-Solent ☎ Lee-on-Solent (0705) 551170
A modest parkland/heathland course, yet a testing one. The
five short holes always demand a high standard of play and
the 13th is rated one of the best in the country.
18 holes, 5959yds, Par 69, SSS 69, Course record 63.
Club membership 700.
Visitors must play with member at weekends.
Societies must contact in advance.
Green Fees £25 per day/round (£30 weekends & bank
holidays).
Facilities ⊗ 🍽 (summer Wed-Sat) ⬛ 🍷 🍴 🛆 🏠
🍷 John Richardson.
Location Brune Ln (1m N off B3385)
Hotel ★★★62% Belle Vue Hotel, 39 Marine Pde East,
LEE-ON-THE-SOLENT
☎ (0705) 550258 24 ⇌ 🐾Annexe3 ⇌ 🐾

LIPHOOK

Map 04 SU83

Liphook ☎ (0428) 723271
Heathland course with easy walking and fine views.
18 holes, 6250yds, Par 70, SSS 70, Course record 67.
Club membership 800.
Visitors must contact in advance, may not play Sunday
mornings, and must have a handicap certificate.
Societies must contact in advance.
Green Fees £35 per day; £25 per round (£45/£35 Sat,
£40 per round Sun after 2pm).
Facilities ⊗ 🍽 by prior arrangement ⬛ 🍷 🍴 🛆 🏠 🍴
🍷 Ian Large.
Location Wheatsheaf Enclosure (1.5m SW off A3)
Hotel ★★★72% Lythe Hill Hotel, Petworth Rd,
HASLEMERE ☎ (0428) 651251 40 ⇌ 🐾

Old Thorns ☎ (0428) 724555
A challenging 18-hole championship-standard course
designed around magnificent oaks, beeches and Scots pine.
18 holes, 6041yds, Par 72, SSS 70.
Visitors no restrictions.
Societies must telephone in advance.
Green Fees £40 per day; £25 per round (£35 per round
weekends).
Facilities ⊗ 🍽 ⬛ 🍷 🍴 🛆 🏠 🍴 🐾🍷 Philip Loxley.
Leisure hard tennis courts, heated indoor swimming
pool, sauna, solarium, caddy cars.
Location Griggs Green (1m W on B2131)
Hotel ★★★72% Lythe Hill Hotel, Petworth Rd,
HASLEMERE ☎ (0428) 651251 40 ⇌ 🐾

LYNDHURST

Map 04 SU20

Bramshaw ☎ Southampton (0703) 813433
Two 18-hole courses. The Manor Course is landscaped
parkland with excellent greens, and features mature trees
and streams. The Forest course is set amidst beautiful
open forest. Easy walking. The Bell Inn Hotel, attached to
the club, provides fine accommodation just a wedge shot
from the first tee, and reserved tee times for its guests.
Manor Course: 18 holes, 6233yds, Par 71, SSS 70,
Course record 66.
Forest Course: 18 holes, 5774yds, Par 69, SSS 68,
Course record 66.
Club membership 1200.
Visitors must contact in advance & be accompanied
by member at weekends.
Societies may not play at weekends. Must telephone
in advance.
Green Fees £30 per day; £20 per round.
Facilities ⊗ ⬛ 🍷 🍴 🛆 🏠 🍴🍷 Clive Bonner.
Leisure caddy cars, golfing rates at Bell Inn.
Location Brook (On B3079 1m W of M27 junc 1)
Hotel ★★★67% Bell Inn, BROOK
☎ (0703) 812214 22 ⇌
See advertisiement on page 55

New Forest ☎ (0703) 282450
This picturesque heathland course is laid out in a typical
stretch of the New Forest on high ground a little above
the village of Lyndhurst. Natural hazards include the
inevitable forest ponies. The first two holes are somewhat
teasing, as is the 485-yard (par 5) 9th. Walking is easy.
18 holes, 5742yds, Par 69, SSS 68, Course record 66.
Club membership 900.
Visitors must contact in advance.
Societies must contact in advance.
Green Fees not confirmed.
Facilities ⊗ ⬛ 🍷 (not Sun) 🍴 🛆 🏠🍷 Ken Gilhespy.
Location Southampton Rd (0.5m NE off A35)
Hotel ★★★70% Crown Hotel, High St,
LYNDHURST ☎ (0703) 282922 40 ⇌ 🐾

NEW MILTON

Map 04 SZ29

Chewton Glen Hotel ☎ Highcliffe (0425) 275341
A9-hole, Par 3 course with the hotel grounds plus a practice
area. ONLY open to residents of the hotel or as a guest of a
member of the club.
9 holes, Par 27, SSS 27.
Club membership 160.

▶

Visitors	members & residents only.
Green Fees	£10 per day with member.
Facilities	⊗ ▥ ■ ♀ ↑ ⋈ ⟨ George Smith.
Leisure	hard tennis courts, heated indoor plus outdoor swimming pool, snooker, sauna, solarium, gymnasium.
Location	Christchurch Rd
Hotel	★★★★(red)⛛ Chewton Glen Hotel, Christchurch Rd, NEW MILTON ☎ (0425) 275341 58 ⇔ ⋔

OVERTON   Map 04 SU54

Test Valley ☎ Basingstoke (0256) 771737
A new inland links course with fine turf fairways and greens laid out in traditonal links style with pot bunkers as a feature. There is strategic bunkering and ponds on this easy walking course on a well drained chalk subsoil. The 2nd, 4th, 12th, 14th and 17th holes are particularly challenging but every hole has its own appealing individual character. Host of the Hampshire Open in 1995.
18 holes, 6811yds, Par 72, SSS 73.
Club membership 600.

Visitors	advisable to ring in advance.
Societies	apply in writing or telephone in advance.
Green Fees	£22 per day; £14 per 18 holes (£32/£20 weekends).
Facilities	⊗ ▥ ▙ ■ ♀ ⌂ ⋈ ↑ ⟨ Terry Notley.
Leisure	trolley,power trolley,buggy available.
Location	Micheldever Rd (6m S of Kingsclere)
Hotel	★★★62% Wheatsheaf Hotel, NORTH WALTHAM ☎ (0256) 398282 28 ⇔ ⋔

PETERSFIELD   Map 04 SU72

Petersfield ☎ (0730) 262386
Part-heath, parkland course with a lake, and good views.
18 holes, 5603yds, Par 69, SSS 67, Course record 68.
Club membership 700.

Visitors	restricted weekends & bank holidays.
Societies	must contact in writing.
Green Fees	£21 per day; £15 per round (£21-£30 weekends & bank holidays).
Facilities	⊗ ▙ ■ ♀ ⌂ ⋒ ⟨ Greg Hughes.
Location	Heath Rd (E side of town centre off A3)
Hotel	★★★69% Spread Eagle Hotel, South St, MIDHURST ☎ (0730) 816911 37 ⇔ ⋔Annexe4 ⋔

PORTSMOUTH & SOUTHSEA   Map 04 SU60

Great Salterns Public Course ☎ Portsmouth (0705) 664549 & 699519
Easy walking, seaside course with open fairways and testing shots onto well-guarded, small greens. Testing 13th hole, par 4, requiring 130yd shot across a lake.
18 holes, 5610yds, Par 69, SSS 66, Course record 64.
Club membership 700.

Visitors	no restrictions.
Societies	must contact in advance.
Green Fees	£9.70 per 18 holes; £5.50 per 9 holes.
Facilities	♀ ⌂ ⋈ ↑ ⟨ Terry Healy.
Location	Eastern Rd (NE of town centre on A2030)
Hotel	★★★64% Hospitality Inn, St Helens Pde, SOUTHSEA ☎ (0705) 731281 115 ⇔ ⋔

Southsea ☎ Portsmouth (0705) 660945
Municipal, meadowland course.
18 holes, 5900yds, Par 72, SSS 68, Course record 64.
Club membership 550.

Visitors	no restrictions.
Societies	must contact in advance; telephone (0705) 664549
Green Fees	£10 per round.
Facilities	⌂ ↑ ⟨ Terry Healy.
Location	The Mansion, Great Salterns, Eastern Rd (0.5m off M27)
Hotel	★★★64% Hospitality Inn, St Helens Pde, SOUTHSEA ☎ (0705) 731281 115 ⇔ ⋔

ROMSEY   Map 04 SU32

Dunwood Manor ☎ Lockerley (0794) 340549
Undulating parkland course with fine views. Testing 1st hole: Reynolds Leap (par 4).
18 holes, 5905yds, Par 69, SSS 69.
Club membership 700.

Visitors	must contact in advance & have handicap certificate, restricted weekends.
Societies	must contact in advance.
Green Fees	£28 per day; £20 per round (£30 per round weekends).
Facilities	⊗ ▥ ▙ ■ ♀ ⌂ ⌂ ↑ ⋈ ⟨ Jonathan Simpson.
Leisure	caddy cars.
Location	Shootash Hill (4m W off A27)
Hotel	★★★62% White Horse Hotel, Market Place, ROMSEY ☎ (0794) 512431 33 ⇔ ⋔

Romsey ☎ Southampton (0703) 734637
Parkland/woodland course with narrow tree-lined fairways. Six holes are undulating, rest are sloping. There are superb views over the Test valley.
18 holes, 5851yds, Par 69, SSS 68.
Club membership 700.

Visitors	must play with member at weekends.
Societies	Mon, Tue & Thu, must contact in advance.
Green Fees	not confirmed.
Facilities	⊗ ▥ by prior arrangement ▙ ■ ♀ ⌂ ⌂ ⟨ Mark Desmond.
Location	Romsey Rd, Nursling (3m S on A3057)
Hotel	★★★62% New Forest Heathlands, Romsey Rd, Ower, ROMSEY ☎ (0703) 814333 52 ⇔ ⋔

ROTHERWICK   Map 04 SU75

Tylney Park ☎ Hook (0256) 762079
Parkland course. Practice area.
18 holes, 6109yds, Par 70, SSS 69, Course record 67.
Club membership 700.

Visitors	must be with member at weekends or have a handicap certificate.
Societies	must apply by phone in advance.
Green Fees	£20 per day (£28 per round weekends).
Facilities	⊗ ▥ by prior arrangement ▙ ■ ♀ ⌂ ⌂ ⟨ Chris De Bruin.
Location	0.5m SW
Hotel	★★★★(red)⛛ Tylney Hall Hotel, ROTHERWICK ☎ (0256) 764881 35 ⇔ Annexe56 ⇔

ROWLANDS CASTLE   Map 04 SU71

Rowlands Castle ☎ Portsmouth (0705) 412784
Exceptionally dry in winter, the flat parkland course is a
testing one with a number of tricky dog-legs and bunkers
much in evidence. The 7th, at 522yds, is the longest hole
on the course and leads to a well-guarded armchair green.
18 holes, 6381yds, Par 72, SSS 70.
Club membership 850.

Visitors	must play with member Sat; restricted Sun. Must contact in advance.
Societies	Tue & Thu only; must contact in writing.
Green Fees	£23 (£28 weekends and bank holidays).
Facilities	⊗ ⏁ ⓑ ☳ ♀ ⚎ ⌑ ⟮ P Klepacz.
Leisure	2 caddy cars for hire.
Location	Links Ln (W side of village off B2149)
Hotel	★★★67% Brookfield Hotel, Havant Rd, EMSWORTH ☎ (0243) 373363 & 376383 41 ⇄ ⋔

SHEDFIELD   Map 04 SU51

Meon Valley Hotel ☎ Wickham (0329) 833455
It has been said that a golf course architect is as good as
the ground on which he has to work. Here Hamilton Stutt
had magnificent terrain at his disposal and a very good and
lovely parkland course is the result. There are three holes
over water. The hotel provides many sports facilities.
Meon Course: 18 holes, 6519yds, Par 71, SSS 71.
Valley Course: 9 holes, 5770yds, Par 70, SSS 68.
Club membership 700.

Visitors	may book up to seven days in advance.
Societies	telephone in advance, written confirmation.
Green Fees	Meon Course: £40 per day; £25 per round (£30 per round weekends & bank holidays). Valley Course: per 18 holes £20 (£25 weekends & bank holidays).
Facilities	⊗ ⏁ ⓑ ☳ ♀ ⚎ ⌑ ☷ ⟮ John Stirling.
Leisure	hard tennis courts, heated indoor swimming pool, squash, snooker, sauna, solarium, gymnasium, health & beauty salon.
Location	Sandy Ln (off A334 between Botley and Wickham)
Hotel	★★★66% Meon Valley Hotel Golf & Country Club, Sandy Ln, SHEDFIELD ☎ (0329) 833455 83 ⇄ ⋔

SOUTHAMPTON   Map 04 SU41

Chilworth ☎ (0703) 733166 & 740544
A 9-hole course with a restricted booking system to allow
undisturbed play.
Manor Golf Course: 9 holes, 2347yds, Par 32, SSS 63.
Club membership 300.

Visitors	must book in advance.
Societies	must contact in advance.
Green Fees	not confirmed.
Facilities	⊗ ⏁ by prior arrangement ⓑ ⚎ ☷ ⌑ ⟮ Martin Butcher.
Leisure	floodlit driving range with 31 bays.
Location	Main Rd, Chilworth (A27 towards Romsey)
Hotel	★★★60% Southampton Moat House, Highfield Ln, Portswood, SOUTHAMPTON ☎ (0703) 559555 66 ⇄ ⋔

Southampton ☎ (0703) 760478
This beautiful municipal parkland course always ensures a
good game, fast in summer, slow in winter. Three par 4's
over 450 yds.
18 holes, 6213yds, Par 69, SSS 70.
Club membership 500.

Visitors	no restrictions.
Societies	welcome.
Green Fees	not confirmed.
Facilities	♀ ⚎ ☷ ⌑ ⟮
Location	Golf Course Rd, Bassett (4m N of city centre off A33)
Hotel	★★65% Star Hotel, High St, SOUTHAMPTON ☎ (0703) 339939 45rm(38 ⇄ ⋔)

Stoneham ☎ (0703) 769272
A hilly, heather course with sand or peat sub-soil; the
fairways are separated by belts of woodland and gorse to
present a varied terrain. The interesting 4th is a difficult
par 4 and the fine 11th has cross-bunkers about 150 yards
from the tee.
18 holes, 6310yds, Par 72, SSS 70, Course record 63.
Club membership 800.

Visitors	restricted at weekends. Must contact in advance.
Societies	must apply to secretary.
Green Fees	£27 per day/round (£30 weekends & bank holidays).
Facilities	⊗ ⏁ ⓑ ☳ ♀ (all day) ⚎ ☷ ⟮
Location	Monks Wood Close (4m N of city centre off A27)
Hotel	★★★60% The Polygon, Cumberland Place, SOUTHAMPTON ☎ (0703) 330055 119 ⇄ ⋔

SOUTHWICK   Map 04 SU60

Southwick Park Naval Recreation Centre ☎ Cosham
(0705) 380131
Set in 100 acres of parkland.
18 holes, 5972yds, Par 69, SSS 69.
Club membership 700.

Visitors	must contact in advance and may play weekday mornings only.
Societies	Tue only, telephone in advance.
Green Fees	£16 per round.
Facilities	ⓑ ⚎ ♀ ⚎ ☷ ⌑ ⟮ John Green.
Leisure	pitch & putt, skittle alley.
Location	Pinsley Dr (0.5m SE off B2177)
Hotel	★★74% Old House Hotel, The Square, WICKHAM ☎ (0329) 833049 9 ⇄ ⋔ Annexe3 ⇄ ⋔

TADLEY   Map 04 SU66

Bishopswood ☎ (0734) 815213 & 812200
Wooded course, fairly tight, with stream and natural water
hazards.
9 holes, 6474yds, Par 72, SSS 71.
Club membership 500.

Visitors	must contact in advance. No play weekends.
Societies	must contact by telephone.
Green Fees	9 holes £8; 18 holes £13.
Facilities	⊗ ⏁ ⓑ ⚎ ☷ ⟮ Steve Ward.
Leisure	floodlit driving range. ▶

Location	Bishopswood Ln (1m W off A340)
Hotel	★★★69% Romans Hotel, Little London Rd, SILCHESTER ☎ (0734) 700421 11 ⇄Annexe13 ⇄ ♟

Location	Cherry Tree Av, Cowplain (NE side of town centre off A3)
Hotel	B Forte Posthouse, Northney Rd, HAYLING ISLAND ☎ (0705) 465011 92 ⇄ ♟

WATERLOOVILLE   Map 04 SU60

Portsmouth ☎ (0705) 372210 & 372299
Hilly, challenging course subject to wind. Good views of Portsmouth Harbour.
18 holes, 6139yds, Par 69, SSS 69.
Club membership 600.
Visitors   must book in advance.
Societies   must book in advance, in writing, booking fee £12.
Green Fees £14 per day; £9.70 per 18 holes; £7.10 per round winter.
Facilities   ⊗)Ⅲ ⓑ ♥ ♀ ♨ 📷 ♈ ♟ ♍ Ian Roper.
Location   Crookhorn Ln, Purbrook (2m S, off A3)
Hotel   ★★★57% The Bear Hotel, East St, HAVANT ☎ (0705) 486501 42 ⇄ ♟

Waterlooville ☎ Portsmouth (0705) 263388
Parkland course, easy walking.
18 holes, 6647yds, Par 72, SSS 72, Course record 66.
Club membership 800.
Visitors   must contact in advance & may only play on weekdays.
Societies   Thu only; apply by letter.
Green Fees £30 per day; £20 per round.
Facilities   ⊗)Ⅲ (Fri only) ♥ ♀ ♨ 📷 ♍ John Hay.
Leisure   caddy cars.

WINCHESTER   Map 04 SU42

Hockley ☎ Twyford (0962) 713165
High downland course with good views.
18 holes, 6296yds, Par 71, SSS 70.
Club membership 700.
Visitors   must play with member at weekends.
Societies   must contact in writing.
Green Fees £25 per day.
Facilities   ⊗ &)Ⅲ (ex Mon) ⓑ ♥ ♀ ♨ 📷 ♍ ♈ Terry Lane.
Location   Twyford (2m S on A33)
Hotel   B Forte Crest, Paternoster Row, WINCHESTER ☎ (0962) 861611 94 ⇄ ♟

Royal Winchester ☎ (0962) 852462
The Royal Winchester course is a sporting downland course centred on a rolling valley, so the course is hilly in places. In the spring of 1994 the clubhouse was destroyed by fire but the course is still available for play and temporary facilities have been erected until the new clubhouse is completed. Royal Winchester Club must be included in any list of notable clubs, because of its age (it dates from 1888) and also because the club was involved in one of the very first professional matches.
18 holes, 6212yds, Par 71, SSS 70, Course record 7.
Club membership 772.

★★★★ ㊒㊓
LAINSTON HOUSE HOTEL

where English Tradition remains our hallmark

Set in sixty three acres of tranquil Hampshire downland, just 2½ miles from the Historic Cathedral City of Winchester. Lainston House is an elegant William and Mary House with thirty eight individually designed bedrooms and suites. The charm of the reception rooms is enhanced by the peace and serenity of this period house. The highly praised restaurant offers gourmet food freshly prepared with local ingredients and the superb service is complemented by breathtaking views over the tranquil parkland. Lainston House offers weekend tariffs and special events throughout the year.

Golf can be arranged at The Royal Winchester Golf Club which is 2 miles away

Lainston House Hotel & Restaurant, Sparsholt, Winchester, Hampshire SO21 2LT
Telephone: (01962) 863588 Fax: (01962) 776672.
Situated on the A272 Stockbridge Road out of Winchester

Visitors	must play with member at weekends. Must contact in advance and have a handicap certificate.
Societies	must contact in writing.
Green Fees	£26 per round/day weekdays.
Facilities	⊗ ⅢⅢ by prior arrangement ⅃ 🐟♀⚲🏠🍴 ⧘ Steven Hunter.
Location	Sarum Rd (1.5m W off A3090)
Hotel	★★★★♨74% Lainston House Hotel, Sparsholt, WINCHESTER ☎ (0962) 863588 38rm(37 ➪ 🐾)
Additional hotel	QQQQ Leckhampton, 62 Kilham Ln, WINCHESTER ☎ (0962) 852831 3rm(2 ➪ 🐾)

South Winchester ☎ (0962) 877800
Opened in September 1993, this Peter Alliss/Clive Clark course incorporates downland and meadows. Visitors are only welcome if playing with a memember.
18 holes, 7086yds, Par 72, SSS 74.
Club membership 850.

Visitors	members guests only.
Societies	must contact in advance.
Green Fees	not supplied..
Facilities	⊗ ⅢⅢ ⅃ 🐟♀⚲🏠🍴⧘ Richard Adams.
Leisure	driving range, caddies/buggies.
Location	Pitt (off A3090)
Hotel	★★★65% Royal Hotel, Saint Peter St, WINCHESTER ☎ (0962) 840840 75 ➪ 🐾

HEREFORD & WORCESTER

ALVECHURCH

Map 07 SP07

Kings Norton ☎ Wythall (0564) 826706	
An old club with three, 9-hole courses; the Blue, Red and Yellow. Parkland with some exacting water hazards, it has housed important events. There is also a 12-hole, par 3 course.	
27 holes, 7064yds, Par 72, SSS 74.	
Club membership 984.	
Visitors	may not play at weekends.
Societies	must telephone in advance.
Green Fees	£29.50 per day; £27 per 18 holes.
Facilities	⊗ ⅢⅢ ⅃ 🐟♀⚲🏠⧘ Kevin Hayward.
Leisure	snooker, practice area.
Location	Brockhill Ln, Weatheroak (3m NE)
Hotel	★★★73% Pine Lodge Hotel, Kidderminster Rd, BROMSGROVE ☎ (0527) 576600 118 ➪ 🐾

BEWDLEY

Map 07 SO77

Little Lakes Golf and Country Club ☎ (0299) 266385
A testing 9-hole undulating parkland course offering alternative tees for the second nine and some pleasing views.
9 holes, 6247yds, Par 73, SSS 72, Course record 70.
Club membership 500.

Visitors	must contact in advance but may not play at weekends.
Societies	must telephone in advance.
Green Fees	£10 per round.
Facilities	⊗ ⅢⅢ ⅃ 🐟♀⚲🏠⧘ Mark A Laing.
Leisure	hard tennis courts, outdoor swimming pool, fishing, snooker.
Location	Lye Head (2.25m W off A456)
Hotel	★★★67% Stourport Moat House, 35 Hartlebury Rd, STOURPORT-ON-SEVERN ☎ (0299) 827733 68 ➪ 🐾

Wharton Park ☎ (0299) 405222 & 405163
18-hole championship-standard course in 140 acres of countryside. Some long Par 5s on the 6th (577yds) and the 9th (525yds)as well as superb par 3 holes at 3rd, 7th, 12th make this a very challenging course.
18 holes, 6600yds, Par 73, SSS 72, Course record 68.
Club membership 600.

Visitors	advisable to telephone in advance.
Societies	apply in writing.
Green Fees	not confirmed.
Facilities	⊗ ⅢⅢ ⅃ 🐟⚲🏠🍴🎣⧘ Angus Hoare.
Leisure	fishing, snooker, trolleys & buggies for hire.
Location	Longbank (off A456 Bewdley bypass)
Hotel	★★★67% Stourport Moat House, 35 Hartlebury Rd, STOURPORT-ON-SEVERN ☎ (0299) 827733 68 ➪ 🐾

BISHAMPTON

Map 03 SO95

Vale Golf & Country Club ☎ (038682) 781
Opened in 1991 this course offers an American-style layout, with large greens, trees and bunkers and several water hazards. Its rolling fairways provide a testing round, as well as superb views of the Malvern Hills. Picturesque and peaceful. Also 9-hole course and 20-bay driving range.
International: 18 holes, 7114yds, Par 74, SSS 74.
Lenches: 9 holes, 2759yds, Par 35, SSS 35.
Club membership 700.

Visitors	may be restricted at peak times weekends. Booking preferred.
Societies	must apply in advance.
Green Fees	International: £20 per round (£24 weekends). Lenches: £12 per round (£16 weekends).
Facilities	⊗ ⅢⅢ ⅃ 🐟♀⚲🏠🍴⧘ Caroline Griffiths.
Leisure	tennis courts, fishing, riding, buggies, pitch & putt.
Location	Hill Furze Rd
Hotel	★★61% The Chequers Inn, Chequers Ln, FLADBURY ☎ (0386) 860276 & 860527 8 ➪ 🐾

BLAKEDOWN

Map 07 SO87

Churchill and Blakedown ☎ (0562) 700200 & 700454 (Pro)
Pleasant course on hilltop with extensive views.
9 holes, 6472yds, Par 72, SSS 71.
Club membership 365.

Visitors	with member only weekends & bank holidays. Handicap certificate required.
Societies	Mon-Fri, by arrangement through secretary.
Green Fees	£17.50 per day.
Facilities	⊗ ⅢⅢ ⅃ 🐟 (no catering Mon) ♀⚲🏠🍴 ⧘ K Wheeler.

▶

Leisure trolleys for hire.
Location Churchill Ln (W side of village off A456)
Hotel ★★70% Gainsborough House Hotel, Bewdley Hill, KIDDERMINSTER
☎ (0562) 820041 42 ⇥ ❧

BROADWAY
Map 04 SP03

Broadway ☎ (0386) 853683
At the edge of the Cotswolds this downland course lies at an altitude of 900 ft above sea level, with extensive views.
18 holes, 6216yds, Par 72, SSS 69.
Club membership 850.
Visitors must play with member Sat before 3pm. No ladies Sun (am). Must contact in advance.
Societies must contact in advance.
Green Fees £30 per day; £24 per round (£30 per round/day weekends & bank holidays).
Facilities ⊗ ℍ & ⅃ (ex Mon) ♥ ♀ ⏦ 🖻 ⚐ ⚑ Martyn Freeman.
Location Willersey Hill (2m NE)
Hotel ★★★70% Dormy House Hotel, Willersey Hill, BROADWAY
☎ (0386) 852711 26 ⇥ ❧Annexe23 ⇥

BROMSGROVE
Map 07 SO97

Blackwell ☎ 021-445 1994
Pleasantly undulating parkland with a variety of trees. Laid out in two 9-hole loops.
18 holes, 6202yds, Par 70, SSS 71.
Visitors must contact in advance, must have handicap certificate.
Societies must contact in advance.
Green Fees not confirmed.
Facilities ⊗ & ℍ by prior arrangement ⅃ ♥ ♀ ⏦ 🖻 ⚑ Nigel Blake.
Location Blackwell (2m W of Alvechurch)
Hotel ★★★73% Pine Lodge Hotel, Kidderminster Rd, BROMSGROVE ☎ (0527) 576600 118 ⇥ ❧

Bromsgrove Golf Centre ☎ (0527) 575886 & 570505
A Pay and Play, Hawtree-designed 9-hole course. Also 41 bay floodlit driving range and floodlit practice bunker.
9 holes, 3159yds, Par 35, SSS 70.
Club membership 300.
Visitors dress restriction, no T-shirts, jeans etc.
Societies weekdays only, apply in writing or telephone.
Green Fees £10 per 18 holes; £6 per 9 holes (£12/£7 weekends & bank holidays).
Facilities ♥ (vending machine) ⏦ 🖻 ⚑ Graeme Long.
Location Stratford Rd (E side of Bromsgrove, 6m W of Alvechurch)
Hotel ★★★73% Pine Lodge Hotel, Kidderminster Rd, BROMSGROVE ☎ (0527) 576600 118 ⇥ ❧

DROITWICH
Map 03 SO86

Droitwich ☎ (0905) 774344
Undulating parkland course.
18 holes, 6040yds, Par 70, SSS 69, Course record 63.
Club membership 785.
Visitors Mon-Fri handicap certificate required, with member only weekends & bank holidays.

Societies must apply by telephone or letter.
Green Fees £24 per day.
Facilities ⊗ ℍ ⅃ ♥ ♀ ⏦ 🖻 ⚑ C Thompson.
Leisure snooker.
Location Ford Ln (1.5m N off A38)
Hotel ★★★70% Chateau Impney Hotel, DROITWICH ☎ (0905) 774411 67 ⇥ ❧

Ombersley ☎ Worcester (0905) 620747
Undulating course in beautiful countryside high above the edge of the Severn Valley. Covered driving range and putting green.
18 holes, 6289yard, Par 72, SSS 68.
Club membership 600.
Visitors suitable dress expected, no jeans.
Societies telephone in advance.
Green Fees £9.60 per 18 holes (£12.80 weekends).
Facilities ⊗ ℍ ⅃ ♥ ♀ ⏦ 🖻 ⚐ ⚑ Graham Glenister.
Leisure driving range, putting green, caddy cars.
Location Bishops Wood Rd, Lineholt, Ombersley (3m W of Droitwich)
Hotel ★★★★60% Raven Hotel, St Andrews St, DROITWICH ☎ (0905) 772224 72 ⇥ ❧

FLADBURY
Map 03 SO94

Evesham ☎ Evesham (0386) 860395
Parkland, heavily wooded, with the River Avon running alongside 5th and 14th holes. Good views. Nine greens played from eighteen different tees.
9 holes, 6418yds, Par 72, SSS 71, Course record 69.
Club membership 400.

THE
CHEQUERS INN

AA
★★

An old English village Inn offering exceptional accommodation, good food and hospitality. Eight en suite rooms all with colour TV/Sky and tea/coffee facilities.
Golf Breaks – 3 days Dinner, Bed & Breakfast, 4 days golf (different courses) – £225 per person.
FLADBURY, PERSHORE, WORCESTERSHIRE WR10 2PZ
TELEPHONE: (01386) 860276

Visitors except Tue & competition days. With members only at weekends. Handicap certificate required. Must be a member of a E.G.U. affiliated club.
Societies must apply by letter.
Green Fees £15 per day/round.
Facilities ⊗ & ⅲ by prior arrangement ⅃ ▄ ♀ ☖ 🏠 🏌
  ♩ Charles Haynes.
Leisure trolleys.
Location Craycombe Links, Old Worcester Rd (0.75m N on B4084)
Hotel ★★★69% The Evesham Hotel, Coopers Ln, off Waterside, EVESHAM ☎ (0386) 765566 40 ⇔ 🏠

Additional ★★61% The Chequers Inn, Chequers Ln,
hotel FLADBURY
  ☎ (0386) 860276 & 860527 8 ⇔ 🏠

HEREFORD   Map 03 SO53

Belmont Lodge ☎ (0432) 352666
Partly wooded course, the second half of which is on the banks of the River Wye.
18 holes, 6480yds, Par 71, SSS 71.
Club membership 500.
Visitors advised to contact in advance at weekends.
Societies must contact in writing.
Green Fees £8/£16 per round (£20 weekends).
Facilities ⊗ ⅲ ⅃ ▄ ♀ ☖ 🏠 🏌 🏓 ♩ Mike Welsh.
Leisure hard tennis courts, fishing, snooker, bowling green, caddy cars.
Location Belmont (2m S off A465)
Hotel ★★★62% Belmont Lodge & Golf Course, Belmont, HEREFORD ☎ (0432) 352666

HOLLYWOOD   Map 07 SP07

Gay Hill ☎ 021-474 6001
A meadowland course, some 7m from Birmingham.
18 holes, 6532yds, Par 72, SSS 71, Course record 64.
Club membership 715.
Visitors must play with member at weekends.
Societies must contact in advance.
Green Fees £28.50 per day (weekdays).
Facilities ⊗ ⅲ by prior arrangement ⅃ ▄ ♀ ☖ 🏠 🏌
  ♩ Andrew Hill.
Leisure snooker.
Location Hollywood Ln (N side of village)
Hotel ★★★67% Regency Hotel, Stratford Rd, Shirley, SOLIHULL ☎ 021-745 6119 112 ⇔ 🏠

KIDDERMINSTER   Map 07 SO87

Habberley ☎ (0562) 745756
Very hilly, wooded parkland course.
9 holes, 5400yds, Par 69, SSS 68.
Club membership 300.
Visitors except competition days. Must contact in advance.
Societies must apply in writing.
Green Fees not confirmed.
Facilities ⊗ ⅲ ⅃ ▄ (all catering by prior arrangement) ♀ ☖ 🏠
Location 2m NW
Hotel ★★70% Gainsborough House Hotel, Bewdley Hill, KIDDERMINSTER ☎ (0562) 820041 42 ⇔ 🏠

Kidderminster ☎ (0562) 822303
Parkland course with natural hazards and some easy walking.
18 holes, 6405yds, Par 72, SSS 71, Course record 67.
Club membership 700.
Visitors must have a handicap, with member only weekends & bank holidays.
Societies must apply by letter.
Green Fees £22 per day/round.
Facilities ⊗ ⅲ ⅃ ▄ ♀ ☖ 🏠 🏌 ♩ Nick Underwood.
Location Russell Rd (0.5m SE of town centre)
Hotel ★★70% Gainsborough House Hotel, Bewdley Hill, KIDDERMINSTER ☎ (0562) 820041 42 ⇔ 🏠

KINGTON   Map 03 SO25

Kington ☎ (0544) 230340 & 231320
The highest 18-hole course in England, with magnificent views over seven counties. A natural heathland course with easy walking on mountain turf cropped by sheep. There is bracken to catch any really bad shots but no sand traps.
18 holes, 5840yds, Par 70, SSS 68.
Club membership 600.
Visitors except weekends 10.15am-noon & 1.45-2.45pm also competition days.
Societies must telephone in advance
Green Fees £16 per day; £13 per round (£20/£16 weekends & bank holidays).
Facilities ⊗ & ⅲ by prior arrangement ⅃ ▄ ♀ ☖ 🏠
  ♩ Dean Oliver.
Location Bradnor Hill (0.5m N off B4355)
Hotel ★★62% Talbot Hotel, West St, LEOMINSTER ☎ (0568) 616347 20 ⇔ 🏠

LEOMINSTER   Map 03 SO45

Leominster ☎ (0568) 611402
Sheltered parkland course alongside River Lugg with undulating land for nine holes.
18 holes, 6045yds, Par 69, SSS 69.
Club membership 600.
Visitors may not play Sun morning.
Societies must apply in advance.
Green Fees £17 per day; £12.50 per round (£21 weekends & bank holidays).
Facilities ⊗ ⅲ ⅃ ▄ ♀ ☖ 🏠 🏌 ♩ Gareth Bebb.
Leisure fishing.
Location Ford Bridge (3m S on A49)
Hotel ★★56% Royal Oak Hotel, South St, LEOMINSTER
  ☎ (0568) 612610 17 ⇔ 🏠Annexe1 ⇔ 🏠

MALVERN WELLS   Map 03 SO74

Worcestershire ☎ Malvern (0684) 575992
Fairly easy walking on windy downland course with trees, ditches and other natural hazards. Outstanding views of Malvern Hills and Severn Valley. 17th hole (par 5) is approached over small lake.
18 holes, 6449yds, Par 71, SSS 71.
Club membership 800.

▶

Visitors only after 10am at weekends or with a member. Must contact in advance & have handicap certificate.

Societies must apply in writing.

Green Fees £25 per day/round (£30 weekends & bank holidays).

Facilities ⊗ & 🍴 (ex Mon) 🍺 ▆ ♀ 🛆 🛍 ⎰

Leisure snooker.

Location Wood Farm, Hanley Rd (2m S of Gt Malvern on B4209)

Hotel ★★★58% Foley Arms Hotel, Worcester Rd, MALVERN
☎ (0684) 573397 26 ⇄ ⎰Annexe2 ⇄ ⎰

REDDITCH
Map 07 SP06

Abbey Park Golf & Country Club ☎ (0527) 68006
Young parkland course opened in 1985, with rolling fairways. A 'Site of Special Scientific Interest', the course includes two fly-fishing lakes and is pleasant to play.
18 holes, 6411yds, Par 71, SSS 71.
Club membership 1400.

Visitors welcome.

Societies must apply in writing.

Green Fees £10 per round (£12.50 weekends).

Facilities ⊗ 🍴 🍺 ▆ ♀ 🛆 🛍 🏌 ⎰ R K Cameron.

Leisure heated indoor swimming pool, fishing, snooker, sauna, solarium, gymnasium.

Location Dagnell End Rd (1.25m N off A441 on B4101)

Hotel ★★★61% Southcrest Hotel, Pool Bank, Southcrest, REDDITCH
☎ (0527) 541511 58 ⇄ ⎰

Pitcheroak ☎ (0257) 541054 & 541043
Woodland course, hilly in places. There is also a putting green and a practice ground.
9 holes, 4527yds, Par 66, SSS 62.
Club membership 200.

Visitors no restrictions.

Societies welcome.

Green Fees not confirmed.

Facilities ⊗ 🍴 🍺 ▆ ♀ 🛆 🛍 🏌 ⎰ David Stewart.

Leisure putting green, practice ground, caddy cart.

Location Plymouth Rd (SW side of town centre off A448)

Hotel ★★★61% Southcrest Hotel, Pool Bank, Southcrest, REDDITCH
☎ (0527) 541511 58 ⇄ ⎰

Redditch ☎ (0527) 543309
Parkland course, the hazards including woods, ditches and large ponds. The par 4, 14th is a testing hole.
18 holes, 6671yds, Par 72, SSS 72.
Club membership 1236.

Visitors with member only weekends & bank holidays.

Societies must apply in writing.

Green Fees £27.50 per day.

Facilities ⊗ 🍴 🍺 ▆ ♀ 🛆 🛍 ⎰ F Powell.

Leisure snooker.

Location Lower Grinsty Ln, Callow Hill (2m SW)

Hotel ★★★61% Southcrest Hotel, Pool Bank, Southcrest, REDDITCH
☎ (0527) 541511 58 ⇄ ⎰

ROSS-ON-WYE
Map 03 SO62

Ross-on-Wye ☎ Gorsley (0989) 720267
The undulating, parkland course has been cut out of a silver birch forest; the fairways being well-screened from each other. The fairways are tight, the greens good.
18 holes, 6500yds, Par 72, SSS 73, Course record 69.
Club membership 760.

Visitors must contact in advance, restricted at weekends.

Societies must telephone in advance.

Green Fees £25 per day (£30 weekends & bank holidays).

Facilities ⊗ 🍴 (ex Mon) 🍺 ▆ ♀ 🛆 🛍 ⎰ Nick Catchpole.

Leisure snooker, electric trolleys for hire.

Location Two Park, Gorsley (on B4221 N side of M50 junc 3)

Hotel ★★★♨68% Pengethley Manor, ROSS-ON-WYE
☎ (0989) 730211 11 ⇄ ⎰Annexe13 ⇄ ⎰

TENBURY WELLS
Map 07 SO56

Cadmore Lodge Hotel & Country Club ☎ (0584) 810044
A picturesque 9-hole course in a brook valley. Challenging holes include the 1st and 6th over the lake, 8th over the valley and 9th over hedges.
9 holes, 5129yds, Par 68, SSS 65.
Club membership 200.

Visitors no restrictions but check availability.

Societies telephone in advance.

Green Fees £7 (£10 weekends).

Facilities ⊗ 🍴 🍺 ▆ ♀ 🛆 🏌

Leisure hard tennis courts, fishing, bowling green.

Location Berrington Green

Hotel ★★61% Cadmore Lodge Hotel & Country Club, Berrington Green, Tenbury Wells
☎ (0584) 810044 8 ⇄ ⎰

UPPER SAPEY
Map 03 SO66

Sapey ☎ (0886) 853288
Parkland course with views of the Malvern Hills. Trees, lakes and water hazards. Not too strenuous a walk.
18 holes, 5900yds, Par 69, SSS 68, Course record 64.
Club membership 623.

Visitors no restrictions.

Societies must contact in advance.

Green Fees £15 (£20 per round weekends & bank holidays).

Facilities ⊗ 🍴 🍺 ▆ ♀ 🛆 🛍 🏌 ⎰ Chris Knowles.

Leisure fishing, buggies.

Location B4203 Bromyard/Whitley Rd

Hotel ★★★♨78% Elms Hotel, ABBERLEY
☎ (0299) 896666 16 ⇄ ⎰Annexe9 ⇄ ⎰

WORCESTER
Map 03 SO85

Tolladine ☎ (0905) 21074
Parkland course, hilly and very tight, but with excellent views of the surrounding hills and Worcester city.
9 holes, 2813yds, Par 68, SSS 67.
Club membership 350.

Visitors	with member only weekend & bank holidays.
Societies	must apply in writing.
Green Fees	£15 per 18 holes.
Facilities	⊗ ⅷ ⓑ 🍷 ♀ ♨ ⌂ ℓ Clare George.
Location	Tolladine Rd (1.5m E)
Hotel	★★★60% The Giffard, High St, WORCESTER ☎ (0905) 726262 103 ⇥ ⋔

Worcester Golf & Country Club ☎ (0905) 422555
Fine parkland course with many trees, a lake, and views of the Malvern Hills.
18 holes, 6119yds, Par 69, SSS 69.
Club membership 1100.

Visitors	with member only weekends. Must contact in advance and have a handicap certificate.
Societies	must apply in advance.
Green Fees	£23 per round/day.
Facilities	⊗ ⅷ ⓑ 🍷 ♀ ♨ ⌂ ℓ Colin Colenso.
Leisure	hard and grass tennis courts, squash, snooker.
Location	Boughton Park (SW side of city centre off A4103)
Hotel	★★★60% The Giffard, High St, WORCESTER ☎ (0905) 726262 103 ⇥ ⋔

WORMSLEY   Map 03 SO44

Herefordshire ☎ Canon Pyon (0432) 830219
Undulating parkland course with expansive views.
18 holes, 6100yds, Par 70, SSS 69.
Club membership 800.

Visitors	must contact in advance.
Societies	must apply in advance.
Green Fees	not confirmed.
Facilities	⊗ ⅷ ⓑ 🍷 ♀ ♨ ⌂ ⋔ ℓ
Location	Ravens Causeway (E side of village)
Hotel	★★★62% The Green Dragon, Broad St, HEREFORD ☎ (0432) 272506 87 ⇥ ⋔

WYTHALL   Map 07 SP07

Fulford Heath ☎ (0564) 824758 & 822806
A mature parkland course encompassing two classic par threes. The 11th, a mere 149 yards, shoots from an elevated tee through a channel of trees to a well protected green. The 16th, a 166 yard par 3, elevated green, demands a 140 yard carry over an imposing lake.
18 holes, 5971yds, Par 70, SSS 69.
Club membership 700.

Visitors	with member only weekend & bank holidays. Must contact in advance and have a handicap certificate.
Societies	must apply in writing.
Green Fees	£25 weekdays.
Facilities	⊗ ⅷ ⓑ 🍷 (no catering Mon) ♀ ♨ ⌂ ℓ
Leisure	snooker.
Location	Tanners Green Ln (1m SE off A435)
Hotel	★★★63% St John's Swallow Hotel, 651 Warwick Rd, SOLIHULL ☎ 021-711 3000 177 ⇥ ⋔

Phoneday - remember from 16 April 1995 all phone codes in the UK will change - see page 4 for details

HERTFORDSHIRE

ALDBURY   Map 04 SP91

Stocks Hotel & Country Club ☎ (0442) 851491 & 851341
An18-hole parkland course is one of the many facilities at this country club. The course plays off blue, white (6,804 yards), yellow and red tees. There is also a driving range.
18 holes, 6345yds, Par 72, SSS 73.
Club membership 500.

Visitors	welcome Mon-Fri, weekends by arrangement.
Societies	apply by telephone in advance.
Green Fees	£30 per round (£40 weekends by arrangement).
Facilities	⊗ ⅷ ⓑ 🍷 ♀ ♨ ⌂ ⋔ ⚑ ℓ Derwynne Honan.
Leisure	hard tennis courts, heated outdoor swimming pool, riding, snooker, sauna, solarium, gymnasium, croquet, caddy cars, driving range.
Location	Stocks Rd (2m from A41 at Tring)
Hotel	★★★★59% Pendley Manor, Cow Ln, TRING ☎ (0442) 891891 71 ⇥ ⋔

ALDENHAM   Map 04 TQ19

Aldenham Golf and Country Club ☎ Watford (0923) 853929
Undulating parkland course.
Old Course: 18 holes, 6455yds, Par 70, SSS 71.
New Course: 9 holes, 2403yds, Par 33.
Club membership 550.

Visitors	Old Course restricted weekends before 1pm. New Course no restrictions.
Societies	must contact in advance.
Green Fees	not confirmed.
Facilities	⊗ ⅷ by prior arrangement ⓑ 🍷 ♀ ♨ ⌂ ⋔ ℓ Alistair McKay.
Location	Church Ln (W side of village)
Hotel	★★★58% Dean Park Hotel, 30-40 St Albans Rd, WATFORD ☎ (0923) 229212 90 ⇥ ⋔

BERKHAMSTED   Map 04 SP90

Berkhamsted ☎ (0442) 865832
There are no sand bunkers on this Championship heathland course but this does not make it any easier to play. The natural hazards will test the skill of the most able players, with a particularly testing hole at the 11th, 568 yards, par 5. Fine Greens, long carries and heather and gorse. The clubhouse is very comfortable.
18 holes, 6605yds, Par 71, SSS 72, Course record 64.
Club membership 750.

Visitors	must have handicap certificate.
Societies	Wed & Fri only, by arrangement.
Green Fees	£30-£35 per day; £20 per round (£30-£35 weekends after 11am).
Facilities	⊗ ⅷ ⓑ 🍷 ♀ ♨ ⌂ ⋔ ℓ
Location	The Common (1.5m E)
Hotel	★★★★59% Pendley Manor, Cow Ln, TRING ☎ (0442) 891891 71 ⇥ ⋔

BISHOP'S STORTFORD   Map 05 TL42

Bishop's Stortford ☎ (0279) 654715
Parkland course, fairly flat.
18 holes, 6440yds, Par 71, SSS 71.
Club membership 700.
Visitors	must contact in advance & have handicap certificate but may not play weekends & bank holidays.
Societies	must contact in advance.
Green Fees	£21 per day.
Facilities	⊗ �𝄞 ⓑ ♥ ♀ ♨ ⓐ (Vince Duncan.
Leisure	snooker.
Location	Dunmow Rd (1m W of M11 junc 8 on A1250)
Hotel	★★★★66% Down Hall Country House Hotel, Hatfield Heath, BISHOP'S STORTFORD ☎ (0279) 731441 103 ⇄ (

BRICKENDON   Map 05 TL30

Brickendon Grange ☎ Bayford (0992) 511258
Parkland course.
18 holes, 6349yds, Par 71, SSS 70, Course record 66.
Club membership 680.
Visitors	must have handicap certificate. With member only at weekends & bank holidays.
Societies	by arrangement.
Green Fees	£30 per day; £24 per round (£15 per round Nov-Mar).
Facilities	⊗ ⓑ ♥ ♀ ♨ ⓐ (John Hamilton.
Leisure	caddy cars.
Location	W side of village
Hotel	★★★62% White Horse, Hertingfordbury, HERTFORD ☎ (0992) 586791 42 ⇄ (

BROOKMANS PARK   Map 04 TL20

Brookmans Park ☎ Potters Bar (0707) 652487
Brookman's Park is an undulating parkland course, with
several cleverly constructed holes. But it is a fair course,
although it can play long. The 11th, par 3, is a testing
hole which plays across a lake.
18 holes, 6454yds, Par 71, SSS 71.
Club membership 750.
Visitors	must contact in advance and have a handicap certificate; must play with member at weekends & bank holidays.
Societies	Wed & Thu only; must telephone in advance.
Green Fees	not confirmed.
Facilities	⊗ ⓑ ♥ ♀ ♨ ⓐ (Ian Jelley/Mike Plumbridge.
Leisure	fishing, snooker.
Location	Golf Club Rd (N side of village off A1000)
Hotel	B Forte Posthouse, Bignells Corner, SOUTH MIMMS ☎ (0707) 643311 120 ⇄ (

BUNTINGFORD   Map 05 TL32

East Herts ☎ Ware (0920) 821978
An attractive undulating parkland course with magnificent
specimen trees.
18 holes, 6185yds, Par 71, SSS 71.
Club membership 700.

Visitors	must contact in advance & have handicap certificate, but may not play on Wed & weekends.
Societies	must contact in advance.
Green Fees	not confirmed.
Facilities	⊗ �𝄞 by prior arrangement ⓑ ♥ ♀ ♨ ⓐ (Jim Hamilton.
Location	Hamels Park (1m N of Puckeridge off A10)
Hotel	★★★61% Vintage Court Hotel, Vintage Corner, PUCKERIDGE ☎ (0920) 822722 48 ⇄ (

BUSHEY   Map 04 TQ19

Bushey Hall ☎ (0923) 225802 & 222253
Parkland course.
18 holes, 6099yds, Par 70, SSS 69, Course record 66.
Club membership 500.
Visitors	may book 7 days in advance.
Societies	must contact in writing.
Green Fees	£12 (£16 weekends & bank holidays).
Facilities	⊗ �𝄞 ⓑ ♥ ♀ ♨ ⓐ ⓣ (Ken Wickham.
Leisure	practice area, caddy cars.
Location	Bushey Hall Dr (1.5m NW on A4008)
Hotel	★★★58% Dean Park Hotel, 30-40 St Albans Rd, WATFORD ☎ (0923) 229212 90 ⇄ (

Hartsbourne Golf & Country Club ☎ 081-950 1133
Parkland course with good views.
*18 holes, 6305yds, Par 71, SSS 70, Course record 62 or 9
holes, 4968yds, Par 68, SSS 66.*
Club membership 750.
Visitors	must be guest of a member.
Societies	must apply in writing.
Green Fees	not confirmed.
Facilities	⊗ ⒨ by prior arrangement ⓑ ♥ ♀ ♨ ⓐ (Geoff Hunt.
Location	Hartsbourne Ave (S off A4140)
Hotel	★★★58% Dean Park Hotel, 30-40 St Albans Rd, WATFORD ☎ (0923) 229212 90 ⇄ (

CHESHUNT   Map 05 TL30

Cheshunt ☎ (0992) 29777 & 24009
Municipal parkland course, well-bunkered with ponds, easy
walking.
18 holes, 6613yds, Par 71, SSS 71, Course record 65.
Club membership 510.
Visitors	must book Tee-times through Pro shop.
Societies	must apply in writing.
Green Fees	not confirmed.
Facilities	⊗ ♥ ♨ ⓐ ⓣ (Chris Newton.
Location	Cheshunt Park, Park Ln (1.5m NW off B156)
Hotel	B Marriott Hotel, Halfhide Ln, Turnford, BROXBOURNE ☎ (0992) 451245 150 ⇄ (

CHORLEYWOOD   Map 04 TQ09

Chorleywood ☎ (0923) 282009
Heathland course with natural hazards and good views.
9 holes, 5676yds, Par 68, SSS 67.
Club membership 300.
Visitors	must contact in advance, restricted Tue & Thu mornings & weekends.
Societies	must apply in writing.
Green Fees	not confirmed.

Facilities ⊗ ⅷ ⓛ ☕ 🍷 (all catering by prior arrangement) ♀
🍴🏡
Leisure snooker.
Location Common Rd (E side of village off A404)
Hotel ★★★68% Bedford Arms Thistle, CHENIES
☎ (0923) 283301 10 ⇆ ⓡ

ELSTREE
Map 04 TQ19

Elstree ☎ 081-953 6115
Parkland course.
18 holes, 6603yds, Par 73, SSS 72.
Club membership 650.
Visitors advisable to contact in advance, no restrictions
weekdays, may not play until after 2pm
weekends.
Societies telephone in advance.
Green Fees £30 per day; £20 per round (£40/£25 weekends
& bank holidays).
Facilities ⊗ ⅷ by prior arrangement ⓛ ☕ ♀ 🍴
🍷 Marc Warwick.
Leisure driving range, trolleys.
Location Watling St (E of Bushey, on A5)
Hotel ★★★68% Edgwarebury Hotel, Barnet Ln,
ELSTREE ☎ 081-953 8227 50 ⇆ ⓡ

ESSENDON
Map 04 TL20

Hatfield London Country Club ☎ Potters Bar (0707)
642624
Parkland course with many varied hazards, including ponds, a
stream and a ditch. 19th-century manor clubhouse. 9-hole
pitch and putt.
18 holes, 6854yds, Par 72, SSS 73.
Visitors must contact in advance.
Societies must apply in writing.
Green Fees £29 per day ticket, £16 per round Tue-Fri, £13 per
round Mon. (£32 weekends & bank holidays).
Facilities ⊗ ⅷ by prior arrangement ⓛ ☕ ♀ 🍴 🏡 🍷
🍷 Norman Greer.
Leisure hard tennis courts.
Location Bedwell Park (on B158 1m S)
Hotel ★★★56% The Homestead Court, Homestead
Ln, WELWYN GARDEN CITY
☎ (0707) 324336 58 ⇆ ⓡ

GRAVELEY
Map 04 TL22

Chesfield Downs Family Golf Centre ☎ Letchworth
(0462) 482929
A revolutionary new golf course with the emphasis on
facilities for the entire family. Its undulating, open downland
course has an inland links feel. There is a 25-bay floodlit,
covered driving range, a 9-hole Par 3 and many other
facilities.
Chesfield Downs: 18 holes, 6360yds, Par 71, SSS 72.
Lannock Links: 9 holes, 975yds, Par 27, SSS 27.
Club membership 650.
Visitors no restrictions.
Societies must telephone in advance.
Green Fees Chestfield Downs: £13.75 per round (£19.75
weekends). Links course; £2.50 per 9 holes
(£3.50 weekends.
Facilities ⊗ ⅷ ⓛ ☕ ♀ 🍴 🏡 🍷 🍷
Leisure 25 bay floodlit covered driving range.

Location Jack's Hill
Hotel ★★★61% Hertfordpark Hotel, Danestrete,
STEVENAGE ☎ (0438) 350661 100 ⇆ ⓡ

HARPENDEN
Map 04 TL11

Harpenden ☎ (0582) 712580
Gently undulating parkland course, easy walking.
18 holes, 6037yds, Par 70, SSS 70.
Club membership 800.
Visitors must contact in advance. May not play Thu &
weekends.
Societies must apply in writing.
Green Fees £30 per day; £20 per round (weekdays).
Facilities ⊗ ⅷ by prior arrangement ⓛ ☕ ♀ 🍴 🏡 🍷
🍷 D Smith.
Location Hammonds End, Redbourn Ln (1m S on B487)
Hotel ★★★68% Harpenden Moat House Hotel, 18
Southdown Rd, HARPENDEN
☎ (0582) 764111 18 ⇆ ⓡAnnexe35 ⇆ ⓡ

Harpenden Common ☎ (0582) 715959
Flat, easy walking, good greens, typical common course.
18 holes, 5651yds, Par 68, SSS 67.
Club membership 820.
Visitors must have handicap certificate. With member
only at weekends. Must contact in advance.
Societies Thu & Fri only, by arrangement.
Green Fees £25 per day; £20 per round (£25 per round
weekends).
Facilities ⊗ ⓛ ☕ ♀ 🍴 🏡 🍷 🍷 Barney Puttick.
Location Cravells Rd, East Common (1m S on A1081)
Hotel ★★★65% Glen Eagle Hotel, 1 Luton Rd,
HARPENDEN ☎ (0582) 760271 50 ⇆ ⓡ

HEMEL HEMPSTEAD
Map 04 TL00

Boxmoor ☎ (0442) 242434
Challenging, very hilly, moorland course with sloping
fairways divided by trees. Fine views. Testing holes: 3rd (par
3), 4th (par 4).
9 holes, 4812yds, Par 64, SSS 63.
Club membership 250.
Visitors may not play on Sun.
Societies must telephone in advance.
Green Fees not confirmed.
Facilities ⊗ & ⅷ by prior arrangement ⓛ & ☕ (Wed-Sat)
♀ 🍴
Location 18 Box Ln, Boxmoor (2m SW on B4505)
Hotel ★★66% The Two Brewers Inn, The Common,
CHIPPERFIELD ☎ (0923) 265266 20 ⇆ ⓡ

Little Hay ☎ (0442) 833798
Semi-parkland, inland links.
18 holes, 6678yds, Par 72, SSS 72.
Visitors no restrictions.
Societies must contact in advance.
Green Fees £7.50 per round (£11.25 weekends & bank
holidays).
Facilities ⊗ ⓛ ☕ ♀ 🍴 🏡 🍷 🍷 David Johnson.
Leisure floodlit golf range, 9 hole pitch & putt.
Location Box Ln, Bovingdon (1.5m SW on B4505 off
A41)
Hotel B Forte Posthouse, Breakspear Way, HEMEL
HEMPSTEAD ☎ (0442) 251122 146 ⇆ ⓡ

Shendish Manor ☎ (0442) 232220
A hilly course with plenty of trees and good greens. A tough course for any golfer.
9 holes, 6076yds, Par 70, SSS 69.
Visitors	no restrictions.
Societies	must contact in advance.
Green Fees	£10 per 18 holes; £6 per 9 holes (£14 per 18 holes weekends & bank holidays).
Facilities	⊗ ⅷ by prior arrangement ┗ ♥ ♀ ♈ 🏠 ⛳
Leisure	snooker, practice area.
Location	London Rd, Apsley
Hotel	★★★63% Aubrey Park Hotel, Hemel Hempstead Rd, REDBOURN ☎ (0582) 792105 119 ⇄ 🥾

KNEBWORTH   Map 04 TL22

Knebworth ☎ Stevenage (0438) 812752
Parkland course, easy walking.
18 holes, 6492yds, Par 71, SSS 71, Course record 69.
Club membership 900.
Visitors	must have handicap certificate , but may not play at weekends.
Societies	by arrangement.
Green Fees	£27 per day/round.
Facilities	⊗ ⅷ ┗ ♥ ♀ ♈ 🏠 ⛳ Bobby Mitchell.
Location	Deards End Ln (N side of village off B197)
Hotel	B Forte Posthouse, Old London Rd, Broadwater, STEVENAGE ☎ (0438) 365444 54 ⇄ 🥾

LETCHWORTH   Map 04 TL23

Letchworth ☎ (0462) 683203
Planned more than 50 years ago by Harry Vardon, this adventurous, parkland course is set in a peaceful corner of 'Norman' England. To its variety of natural and artificial hazards is added an unpredictable wind.
18 holes, 6181yds, Par 70, SSS 69.
Club membership 1000.
Visitors	with member only at weekends. Must contact in advance and have a handicap certificate.
Societies	Wed, Thu & Fri only, must telephone in advance.
Green Fees	not confirmed.
Facilities	┗ ♥ ♀ ♈ 🏠 ⛳
Location	Letchworth Ln (S side of town centre off A505)
Hotel	★★★61% Blakemore Thistle, Blakemore End Rd, Little Wymondley, HITCHIN ☎ (0438) 355821 82 ⇄ 🥾

LITTLE GADDESDEN   Map 04 SP91

Ashridge ☎ (0442) 842244
Good parkland course, challenging but fair. Good clubhouse facilities.
18 holes, 6217yds, Par 72, SSS 70, Course record 64.
Club membership 730.
Visitors	must contact in advance & have handicap certificate but may not play Thu, weekends & bank holidays.
Societies	weekdays except Thu, by arrangement.
Green Fees	£50 per day; £35 per round.
Facilities	⊗ ⅷ ┗ ♥ ♀ ♈ 🏠 ⛳ Geoff J Pook.

Location	B4507
Hotel	★★★74% Bell Inn, ASTON CLINTON ☎ (0296) 630252 6 ⇄ 🥾Annexe15 ⇄ 🥾

POTTERS BAR   Map 04 TL20

Potters Bar ☎ (0707) 652020
Undulating parkland course with water in play on many holes.
18 holes, 6273yds, Par 71, SSS 70.
Club membership 520.
Visitors	must contact in advance & have handicap certificate. With member only at weekends.
Societies	Mon-Fri only, by arrangement.
Green Fees	£27.50 per day; £18 per round.
Facilities	⊗ ┗ ♥ ♀ ♈ 🏠 ⛳ Kevin Hughes.
Leisure	caddy car,trolley & terrain vehicle hire.
Location	Darkes Ln (N side of town centre)
Hotel	B Forte Posthouse, Bignells Corner, SOUTH MIMMS ☎ (0707) 643311 120 ⇄ 🥾

RADLETT   Map 04 TL10

Porters Park ☎ (0923) 854127
A splendid, undulating parkland course with fine trees and lush grass. The holes are all different and interesting - on many accuracy of shot to the green is of paramount importance.
18 holes, 6313yds, Par 70, SSS 70, Course record 65.
Club membership 800.
Visitors	must have handicap certificate. With member only on Fri afternoons & weekends.
Societies	Wed & Thu only, must telephone in advance.
Green Fees	£42 per day; £28 per round.
Facilities	⊗ ┗ ♥ ♀ ♈ 🏠 ⛳ David Gleeson.
Location	Shenley Hill (NE side of village off A5183)
Hotel	★★★★64% Noke Thistle, Watford Rd, ST ALBANS ☎ (0727) 854252 111 ⇄ 🥾

REDBOURN   Map 04 TL11

Redbourn ☎ (0582) 792150
Testing parkland course (Five par 4's over 400 yds). Also 9-hole par 3 course.
18 holes, 6407yds, Par 70, SSS 71 or 9 holes, 2722yds, Par 27.
Visitors	must play with member at weekends & bank holidays until 3pm.
Societies	must telephone in advance.
Green Fees	not confirmed.
Facilities	⊗ ⅷ by prior arrangement ┗ ♥ ♀ ♈ 🏠 ⛳
Leisure	driving range.
Location	Kinsbourne Green Ln (1m N off A5183)
Hotel	★★★68% Harpenden Moat House Hotel, 18 Southdown Rd, HARPENDEN ☎ (0582) 764111 18 ⇄ 🥾Annexe35 ⇄ 🥾

RICKMANSWORTH   Map 04 TQ09

Moor Park ☎ (0923) 773146
Two parkland courses.
High Golf Course: 18 holes, 6713yds, Par 72, SSS 72.
West Golf Course: 18 holes, 5815yds, Par 69, SSS 68.
Club membership 1800.

Visitors	must contact in advance but may not play at weekends, bank holidays or before 10am on Tue & Thu.
Societies	must apply in writing.
Green Fees	High: £30 per round. West: £25 per round.
Facilities	⊗ ⓑ ♥ ♀ ♨ 🏠 ⛴ ⓒ Lawrence Farmer.
Leisure	hard and grass tennis courts.
Location	1.5m SE off A4145
Hotel	★★★58% Dean Park Hotel, 30-40 St Albans Rd, WATFORD ☎ (0923) 229212 90 ⇥ 🐾

Rickmansworth Public Course ☎ (0923) 775278
Undulating, municipal parkland course.
18 holes, 4492yds, Par 63, SSS 62, Course record 63.
Club membership 300.

Visitors	must contact the club in advance for weekend play.
Societies	must contact in advance.
Green Fees	not confirmed.
Facilities	⊗ ⏵ ⓑ ♥ ♀ ♨ 🏠 ⛴ ⓒ Iain Duncan.
Leisure	pool table.
Location	Moor Ln (2m S of town off A4145)
Hotel	★★★58% Dean Park Hotel, 30-40 St Albans Rd, WATFORD ☎ (0923) 229212 90 ⇥ 🐾

ROYSTON   Map 05 TL34

Royston ☎ (0763) 242696
Heathland course on undulating terrain and fine fairways.The 8th, 9th and 18th are the most notable holes.
18 holes, 5692yds, Par 70, SSS 67, Course record 65.
Club membership 650.

Visitors	with member only at weekends.
Societies	by arrangement Mon-Fri.
Green Fees	£20 per day.
Facilities	⊗ ⏵ ⓑ ♥ ♀ ♨ 🏠 ⓒ Mark Hatcher.
Leisure	snooker, putting green,practice area,elec trolley.
Location	Baldock Rd (0.5m W of town centre)
Hotel	★★★61% Blakemore Thistle, Blakemore End Rd, Little Wymondley, HITCHIN ☎ (0438) 355821 82 ⇥ 🐾

ST ALBANS   Map 04 TL10

Batchwood Hall ☎ (0727) 833349 & 844250
Municipal parkland course designed by J H Taylor and opened in 1935.
18 holes, 6489yds, Par 71, SSS 71.
Club membership 425.

Visitors	may not play on Sat & Sun mornings.
Green Fees	not confirmed.
Facilities	ⓑ ♥ ♀ ♨ 🏠 ⛴ ⓒ Jimmy Thompson.
Leisure	hard tennis courts, squash, solarium, gymnasium.
Location	Batchwood Dr (1m NW off A5183)
Hotel	★★★65% St Michael's Manor Hotel, Fishpool St, ST ALBANS ☎ (0727) 864444 22 ⇥

Verulam ☎ (0727) 853327
Parkland course with fourteen holes having out-of-bounds. Water affects the 5th, 6th and 7th holes. Samuel Ryder was Captain in 1927 when he began the now celebrated Ryder Cup Competition.
18 holes, 6457yds, Par 72, SSS 71.
Club membership 600.

Visitors	must contact in advance & have handicap certificate. With member only at weekends.
Societies	must contact one year in advance.
Green Fees	Mon: £20 per 36 holes, £12 per 18 holes. Tue-Fri: £30 per 36 holes, £25 per 18 holes.
Facilities	⊗ ⏵ by prior arrangement ⓑ ♥ ♀ ♨ 🏠 ⛴ ⓒ Nick Burch.
Leisure	practice ground/nets.
Location	London Rd (1m from junc 22 of M25 off A1081)
Hotel	★★★★74% Sopwell House Hotel & Country Club, Cottonmill Ln, Sopwell, ST ALBANS ☎ (0727) 864477 92 ⇥ 🐾

STEVENAGE   Map 04 TL22

Stevenage Golf Centre ☎ (0438) 880424
Municipal course designed by John Jacobs, with natural water hazards and some wooded areas.
18 holes, 6451yds, Par 72, SSS 71.
Club membership 600.

Visitors	no restrictions.
Societies	must contact 1 week in advance. Deposit required.
Facilities	⊗ ⓑ ♥ ♀ (all day) ♨ 🏠 ⛴ ⓒ Keith Bond.
Leisure	floodlit driving range.
Location	Aston Ln (4m SE off B5169)
Hotel	B Forte Posthouse, Old London Rd, Broadwater, STEVENAGE ☎ (0438) 365444 54 ⇥ 🐾

WARE   Map 05 TL31

Chadwell Springs ☎ (0920) 461447
Quick drying moorland course on high plateau subject to wind. The first two holes are par 5 and notable.
9 holes, 6042yds, Par 72, SSS 69.
Club membership 400.

Visitors	with member only at weekends.
Societies	apply in writing,
Green Fees	not confirmed.
Facilities	⊗ ⏵ by prior arrangement ⓑ ♥ ♀ ♨ 🏠 ⓒ A N Shearn.
Location	Hertford Rd (0.75m W on A119)
Hotel	★★★64% Ware Moat House, Baldock St, WARE ☎ (0920) 465011 50rm(43 ⇥6 🐾)

Hanbury Manor Golf & Country Club ☎ (0920) 487722
Superb parkland course designed by Jack Nicklaus II. Large oval tees, watered fairways and undulating greens make up the first 9 holes. Attractive lakes and deep-faced bunkers are strategically sited. Second 9 holes offer open panoramas and challenging holes.
18 holes, 7016yds, Par 72, SSS 74, Course record 71.
Club membership 600.

Visitors	with handicap certificate, members guest and hotel residents welcome.
Societies	strictly limited to Mon-Thu and restricted tee times, must be booked in advance.
Green Fees	Hotel guests £35 per round Mon-Th (£40 Fri-Sun & bank holidays).
Facilities	⊗ ⏵ ⓑ ♥ ♀ ♨ 🏠 ⛴ 🍴 ⓒ Peter Blaze.
Leisure	hard tennis courts, heated indoor swimming pool, squash, snooker, sauna, solarium, gymnasium, buggy,power trolly,jacuzzi,steam room. ▶

Location	Adjacent to A10
Hotel	★★★★★78% Hanbury Manor, WARE
	☎ (0920) 487722 69 ⇄ ℟Annexe27 ⇄ ℟

WATFORD   Map 04 TQ19

West Herts ☎ (0923) 236484
Another of the many clubs that were inaugurated in the 1890's when the game of golf was being given a tremendous boost by the the performances of the first star professionals, Baird, Vardon and Taylor. The West Herts course is close to Watford but its tree-lined setting is beautiful and tranquil. Set out on a plateau the course is exceedingly dry. It also has a very severe finish with the 17th, a hole of 378 yards, the toughest on the course. The last hole measures over 480 yards.
18 holes, 6488yds, Par 72, SSS 71, Course record 68.
Club membership 700.

Visitors	must contact in advance & have handicap certificate. No play at weekends.
Societies	Wed & Fri only, must apply in writing.
Green Fees	£30 per day; £20 per round.
Facilities	⊗ ⓑ ♥ ♀ ⚲ 🏠 ⛳ ℓ Charles Gough.
Location	Cassiobury Park (W side of town centre off A412)
Hotel	★★★58% Dean Park Hotel, 30-40 St Albans Rd, WATFORD
	☎ (0923) 229212 90 ⇄ ℟

WELWYN GARDEN CITY   Map 04 TL21

Mill Green ☎ (0707) 276900
Opened in autumn 1993, the 18-hole, Peter Alliss/Clive Clark designed, Mill Green course makes use of woodland and meadows. The par 3 9-hole gives a good test for improving the short game.
18 holes, 6615yds, Par 72, SSS 72.
Club membership 830.

Visitors	must contact in advance and have handicap certificate, restricted at weekends.
Societies	contact in advance.
Green Fees	£30 per round (£40 weekends).
Facilities	⊗ ⓜ ⓑ ♥ ♀ ⚲ 🏠 ℓ Alan Hall.
Leisure	par 3 course, caddy cars.
Location	Mill Green, Gypsy Ln (exit 4 of A1(M),A414 to Mill Green)
Hotel	★★★56% The Homestead Court, Homestead Ln, WELWYN GARDEN CITY
	☎ (0707) 324336 58 ⇄ ℟

Panshanger Golf & Squash Complex ☎ (0707) 333350
Municipal parkland course overlooking Mimram Valley. Squash.
18 holes, 6638yds, Par 72, SSS 70.

Visitors	no restrictions.
Societies	apply in writing.
Green Fees	not confirmed.
Facilities	⊗ ⓜ ⓑ ♥ (catering by prior arrangement) ♀ ⚲ 🏠 ⛳ ℓ
Leisure	squash.
Location	Herns Ln (N side of town centre off B1000)
Hotel	★★★56% The Homestead Court, Homestead Ln, WELWYN GARDEN CITY
	☎ (0707) 324336 58 ⇄ ℟

Welwyn Garden City ☎ (0707) 325243
Undulating parkland course with a ravine. Course record holder is Nick Faldo.
18 holes, 6100yds, Par 70, SSS 69.
Club membership 820.

Visitors	must contact in advance & have handicap certificate but may not play Sun.
Societies	Wed & Thu only, by arrangement.
Green Fees	not confirmed.
Facilities	⊗ ⓜ ⓑ ♥ ♀ ⚲ 🏠 ℓ Simon Bishop.
Location	Mannicotts (W side of city, exit 6 off A1)
Hotel	★★★56% The Homestead Court, Homestead Ln, WELWYN GARDEN CITY
	☎ (0707) 324336 58 ⇄ ℟

WHEATHAMPSTEAD   Map 04 TL11

Mid Herts ☎ (058283) 2242
Commonland, wooded with heather and gorse-lined fairways.
18 holes, 6060yds, Par 69, SSS 69.
Club membership 600.

Visitors	may not play Tue, Wed afternoons & weekends.
Societies	must contact in writing.
Green Fees	£31 per 36 holes; £21 per 18 holes.
Facilities	⊗ ⓑ ♥ ♀ ⚲ 🏠 ℓ
Location	Gustard Wood (1m N on B651)
Hotel	★★★68% Harpenden Moat House Hotel, 18 Southdown Rd, HARPENDEN
	☎ (0582) 764111 18 ⇄ ℟Annexe35 ⇄ ℟

HUMBERSIDE

BEVERLEY   Map 08 TA03

Beverley & East Riding ☎ (0482) 867190
Picturesque parkland course with some hard walking and natural hazards - trees and gorse bushes. Also cattle and sheep (spring to autumn); horse-riders are an occasional hazard in the early morning.
18 holes, 5949yds, Par 68, SSS 68, Course record 62.
Club membership 460.

Visitors	restricted weekends & bank holidays.
Societies	telephone(0482) 868757 to arrange.
Green Fees	not confirmed.
Facilities	⊗ ⓜ by prior arrangement ⓑ ♥ ♀ ⚲ 🏠 ℓ Ian Mackie.
Location	The Westwood (1m SW on B1230)
Hotel	★★★66% Beverley Arms Hotel, North Bar Within, BEVERLEY
	☎ (0482) 869241 57 ⇄ ℟

BRANDESBURTON   Map 08 TA14

Hainsworth Park ☎ Hornsea (0964) 542362
A parkland course with easy walking.
18 holes, 6003yds, Par 71, SSS 69.
Club membership 400.

| Visitors | welcome except competition days. Contact in advance. |

Societies   apply in writing.
Green Fees £15 per day; £10 per round (£15 per round
     weekends & bank holidays).
Facilities   ⊗ ⅷ by prior arrangement ⅙ 🍺 ♀ ♨ 🏠 ⛳ 🚣
Leisure   squash.
Location   Burton Holme (SW side of village on A165)
Hotel   ★★67% Burton Lodge Hotel,
     BRANDESBURTON
     ☎ (0964) 542847 8rm(7 ⇄ ↾)

BRIDLINGTON   Map 08 TA16

Bridlington ☎ (0262) 606367
Clifftop, seaside course, windy at times, with hazards of
bunkers, ponds, ditches and trees.
18 holes, 6491yds, Par 71, SSS 71, Course record 66.
Club membership 620.
Visitors   welcome except Sun until 11.15am and Wed 9-
     11.30am.
Societies   telephone secretary one week in advance.
Green Fees £15 per day; £10 per round (£20 weekends &
     bank holidays).
Facilities   ⊗ ⅷ ⅙ 🍺 ♀ ♨ 🏠 ⛳ ↾
Leisure   snooker.
Location   Belvedere Rd (1m S off A165)
Hotel   ★★67% Monarch Hotel, South Marine Dr,
     BRIDLINGTON
     ☎ (0262) 674447 40rm(36 ⇄ ↾)

BROUGH   Map 08 SE92

Brough ☎ Hull (0482) 667291 & 667374
Parkland course.
18 holes, 6159yds, Par 68, SSS 69.
Club membership 800.
Visitors   with member only at weekends. Must have
     handicap certificate and contact in advance.
Societies   apply by letter.
Green Fees not confirmed.
Facilities   ⊗ ⅷ ⅙ 🍺 ♀ ♨ 🏠 ⛳ ↾ Gordon Townhill.
Leisure   snooker.
Location   Cave Rd (0.5m N)
Hotel   B Forte Posthouse, Ferriby High Rd, NORTH
     FERRIBY ☎ (0482) 645212 95 ⇄ ↾

CLEETHORPES   Map 08 TA30

Cleethorpes ☎ (0472) 814060
Flat meadowland seaside course intersected by large dykes.
18 holes, 6018yds, Par 70, SSS 69, Course record 64.
Club membership 760.
Visitors   restricted Wed afternoons.
Societies   Tue,Thu or Fri only. Must contact in advance.
Green Fees not confirmed.
Facilities   ⊗ & ⅷ by prior arrangement ⅙ 🍺 ♀ ♨ 🏠
     ↾ Eric Sharp.
Location   Kings Rd (1.5m S off A1031)
Hotel   ★★★70% Kingsway Hotel, Kingsway,
     CLEETHORPES ☎ (0472) 601122 50 ⇄ ↾

Remember – replace all divots, and
repair ball-marks or damage by spikes
on completion of the hole

DRIFFIELD, GREAT   Map 08 TA05

Driffield ☎ Driffield (0377) 253116
An easy walking, parkland course.
18 holes, 6199yds, Par 70, SSS 69.
Club membership 633.
Visitors   no restrictions.
Societies   apply in writing or telephone.
Green Fees £15 per day/round (£20 weekends).
Facilities   ⊗ ⅷ by prior arrangement ⅙ 🍺 ♀ ♨ 🏠
     ↾ I Mackay.
Location   Sunderlandwick (2m S of off A164)
Hotel   ★★♨58% Wold House Country Hotel,
     Nafferton, DRIFFIELD ☎ (0377) 254242
     9rm(7 ⇄ ↾)Annexe1 ↾

ELSHAM   Map 08 TA01

Elsham ☎ Barnetby (0652) 680291
Parkland course in country surroundings. Easy walking.
18 holes, 6411yds, Par 71, SSS 71, Course record 69.
Club membership 600.
Visitors   with member only weekends & bank holidays.
Societies   must contact in advance.
Green Fees £22 per round/day.
Facilities   ⊗ ⅷ ⅙ 🍺 ♀ ♨ 🏠 ↾ Stuart Brewer.
Location   Barton Rd (2m SW on B1206)
Hotel   ★★★65% Wortley House Hotel, Rowland Rd,
     SCUNTHORPE ☎ (0724) 842223 38 ⇄ ↾

FLAMBOROUGH   Map 08 TA27

Flamborough Head ☎ Bridlington (0262) 850333
Undulating seaside course.
18 holes, 5438yds, Par 66, SSS 66, Course record 63.
Club membership 500.
Visitors   may not play before noon on Sun & must be
     member of recognised golf club.
Societies   must contact in advance.
Green Fees £12 per day; £10 per round (£16 weekends &
     bank holidays).
Facilities   ⊗ ⅷ ⅙ 🍺 (no catering Mon in winter) ♀ ♨
Leisure   snooker.
Location   Lighthouse Rd (2m E off B1259)
Hotel   ★64% Flaneburg Hotel, North Marine Rd,
     FLAMBOROUGH
     ☎ (0262) 850284 13rm(8 ↾)

GRIMSBY   Map 08 TA21

Grimsby ☎ (0472) 342630
Parkland course with easy walking.
18 holes, 6058yds, Par 70, SSS 69.
Club membership 725.
Visitors   restricted at weekends.
Societies   welcome Mon-Fri only, telephone in advance.
Green Fees not confirmed.
Facilities   ♀ ♨ 🏠 ↾
Location   Littlecoates Rd (W side of town centre off
     A1136)
Hotel   B Forte Posthouse, Littlecoates Rd, GRIMSBY
     ☎ (0472) 350295 52 ⇄ ↾

HESSLE   Map 08 TA02

Hessle ☎ Hull (0482) 650171
Well-wooded downland course, easy walking, windy.
18 holes, 6290yds, Par 72, SSS 70.
Club membership 650.
Visitors	must have a handicap certificate.
Societies	must contact in advance.
Green Fees	£23 per day; £18 per round (£25 per round weekends & bank holidays).
Facilities	⊗ & ⫙ by prior arrangement ⊾ ♥ ♀ ♨ ☖ ⎰ Grahame Fieldsend.
Leisure	snooker.
Location	Westfield Rd, Raywell (4m NW off A164)
Hotel	B Forte Posthouse, Ferriby High Rd, NORTH FERRIBY ☎ (0482) 645212 95 ⇆ ⬤

HORNSEA   Map 08 TA14

Hornsea ☎ (0964) 532020
Flat, parkland course with good greens.
18 holes, 6475yds, Par 71, SSS 71.
Club membership 600.
Visitors	with member only at weekends & after 3pm. Must contact in advance.
Societies	apply in writing.
Green Fees	£25 per day; £18 per round (£30 per round weekends).
Facilities	⊗ ⫙ ⊾ ♥ ♀ (all day) ☖ ⎰⎰ ⎰
Leisure	snooker, practice area.
Location	Rolston Rd (1m S on B1242)
Hotel	★★★66% Beverley Arms Hotel, North Bar Within, BEVERLEY ☎ (0482) 869241 57 ⇆ ⬤

HOWDEN   Map 08 SE72

Boothferry ☎ (0430) 430364
A heavily bunkered meadowland course with several dykes.
18 holes, 6600yds, Par 73, SSS 72, Course record 64.
Club membership 900.
Visitors	must contact in advance.
Societies	must contact for booking form.
Green Fees	not confirmed.
Facilities	⊗ ⫙ ⊾ ♥ ♀ ♨ ☖ ⎰⎰ ⎰ Stewart Wilkinson.
Location	Spaldington Ln, Goole (2.5m N of Howden off B1228)
Hotel	★★★64% Clifton Hotel, 1 Clifton Gardens, Boothferry Rd, GOOLE ☎ (0405) 761336 9rm(5 ⇆3 ⬤)

HULL   Map 08 TA02

Ganstead Park ☎ (0482) 811121
Parkland course, easy walking.
18 holes, 6801yds, Par 72, SSS 73, Course record 66.
Club membership 700.
Visitors	welcome except Sun & Wed mornings.
Societies	must contact in advance.
Green Fees	£20 per day; £15 per round (£24 weekends).
Facilities	⊗ ⫙ ⊾ ♥ ♀ ♨ ☖ ⎰⎰ ⎰ Michael J Smee.

Leisure	snooker.
Location	Longdales Ln, Coniston (6m NE off A165)
Hotel	★★65% Waterfront Hotel, Dagger Ln, HULL ☎ (0482) 227222 30 ⇆ ⬤

Hull ☎ (0482) 658919
Parkland course.
18 holes, 6242yds, Par 70, SSS 70.
Club membership 750.
Visitors	must contact in advance & have handicap certificate. With member only at weekends.
Societies	apply in writing.
Green Fees	£25 per day; £20 per round (£16 per day/round Nov-Mar).
Facilities	⊗ ⫙ ⊾ ♥ (all catering by prior arrangement) ♀ ♨ ☖ ⎰ David Jagger.
Leisure	snooker.
Location	The Hall, 27 Packman Ln (5m W of city centre off A164)
Hotel	★★★69% Willerby Manor Hotel, Well Ln, WILLERBY ☎ (0482) 652616 34 ⇆ ⬤

Springhead Park ☎ (0482) 656309
Municipal parkland course with tight, tree-lined, undulating fairways.
18 holes, 6402yds, Par 71, SSS 71.
Club membership 667.
Visitors	welcome ex Sun (tee reserved).
Green Fees	not confirmed.
Facilities	☖ ⎰⎰ ⎰ Barry Herrington.
Location	Willerby Rd (5m W off A164)
Hotel	★★★69% Willerby Manor Hotel, Well Ln, WILLERBY ☎ (0482) 652616 34 ⇆ ⬤

Sutton Park ☎ (0482) 74242
Municipal parkland course.
18 holes, 6251yds, Par 70, SSS 70.
Club membership 450.
Visitors	no restrictions.
Societies	apply to Hull Leisure Services, 79 Ferensway, Hull.
Green Fees	not confirmed.
Facilities	⊾ ♥ ♀ ♨ ☖ ⎰⎰ ⎰ Paul Rushworth.
Leisure	snooker.
Location	Salthouse Rd (3m NE on B1237 off A165)
Hotel	★★65% Waterfront Hotel, Dagger Ln, HULL ☎ (0482) 227222 30 ⇆ ⬤

IMMINGHAM   Map 08 TA11

Immingham ☎ (0469) 575298
Parkland course with some water hazards and a public footpath across holes 1, 2 & 8.
18 holes, 6161yds, Par 71, SSS 69.
Club membership 650.
Visitors	restricted Sat pm and Sun am.
Societies	must telephone and confirm in writing.
Green Fees	£20 per day; £15 per round (£20 weekend and bank holidays).
Facilities	⊗ & ⫙ by prior arrangement ⊾ ♥ ♀ ♨ ☖ ⎰⎰ ⎰ Geoffrey Norton.
Location	St Andrews Ln, off Church Ln (7m NW off Grimsby)
Hotel	★★63% Old Chapel Hotel & Restaurant, 50 Station Rd, IMMINGHAM ☎ (0469) 572377 14 ⇆ ⬤

NORMANBY

Map 08 SE81

Normanby Hall ☎ Scunthorpe (0724) 720226
Parkland course.
18 holes, 6548yds, Par 72, SSS 71, Course record 68.
Club membership 740.
Visitors restricted at certain times.
Societies may not play at weekends & bank holidays;
must contact in advance.
Green Fees £16 per day; £10 per round (£12 per round
weekends & bank holidays).
Facilities ⊗ ⅷ ⅃ 🍺 ♀ ♨ 🖻 🛉 ⸙ Christopher Mann.
Leisure trolleys.
Location Normanby Park (5m N of Scunthorpe adj to
Normanby Hall)
Hotel ★★64% Royal Hotel, Doncaster Rd,
SCUNTHORPE ☎ (0724) 282233 33 ⇥ 🐾

SCUNTHORPE

Map 08 SE81

Holme Hall ☎ (0724) 862078
Heathland course with sandy subsoil. Easy walking.
18 holes, 6475yds, Par 71, SSS 71, Course record 65.
Club membership 675.
Visitors must play with member at weekends & bank
holidays. Must contact in advance.
Societies must contact in advance.
Green Fees £20 per round/day.
Facilities ⊗ ⅃ 🍺 ♀ ♨ 🖻 🛉 ⸙ Richard McKiernan.
Leisure snooker.
Location Holme Ln, Bottesford (3m SE)
Hotel ★★64% Royal Hotel, Doncaster Rd,
SCUNTHORPE ☎ (0724) 282233 33 ⇥ 🐾

Kingsway ☎ (0724) 840945
Parkland course with many par 3's.
9 holes, 1915yds, Par 30, SSS 29.
Visitors no restrictions.
apply giving one week's notice.
Green Fees not confirmed.
Facilities ♨ 🖻 🛉
Location Kingsway (W side of town centre off A18)
Hotel ★★64% Royal Hotel, Doncaster Rd,
SCUNTHORPE ☎ (0724) 282233 33 ⇥ 🐾

Scunthorpe ☎ (0724) 866561
Very tight parkland course.
18 holes, 6281yds, Par 71, SSS 71, Course record 67.
Club membership 700.
Visitors may not play Sun. Handicap certificate required.
Must contact in advance.
Societies apply in writing.
Green Fees £24 per day; £20 per round.
Facilities ⊗ ⅷ by prior arrangement ⅃ 🍺 ♀ ♨ 🖻
⸙ Andrew Lawson.
Leisure snooker.
Location Ashby Decoy, Burringham Rd (2.5m SW on
B1450 nr Asda Superstore)
Hotel ★★64% Royal Hotel, Doncaster Rd,
SCUNTHORPE ☎ (0724) 282233 33 ⇥ 🐾

SOUTH CAVE

Map 08 SE93

Cave Castle Golf Hotel ☎ (0430) 421286 & 422245
A young but challenging course at the foot of the Wolds with
superb views. There is a keen interest in ladies golf and
tuition and golf clinics are available.
18 holes, 6409yds, Par 72, SSS 71.
Club membership 360.
Visitors no restrictions.
Societies by arrangement.
Green Fees £18 per day; £12.50 per round (£25/£18
weekends and bank holidays).
Facilities ⊗ ⅷ ⅃ 🍺 ♀ ♨ 🖻 🛉 ⛳ ⸙ Carl Worby.
Leisure fishing, par 3 pitch & putt.
Location South Cave
Hotel ★★65% Fox & Coney Inn, Market Place, South
Cave ☎ (0430) 422275 8 ⇥ 🐾

WITHERNSEA

Map 08 TA32

Withernsea ☎ (0964) 612078
Exposed seaside links with narrow, undulating fairways,
bunkers and small greens.
9 holes, 5112yds, Par 66, SSS 64.
Club membership 550.
Visitors with member only at weekends.
Societies apply in writing.
Green Fees £8 per day (Mon-Fri 5days £32).
Facilities ⅃ & 🍺 by prior arrangement ♀ ♨ 🖻
⸙ Graham Harrison.
Location Chesnut Av (S side of town centre off A1033)
Hotel ★★64% Pearson Park Hotel, Pearson Park,
HULL ☎ (0482) 43043 32 ⇥ 🐾

KENT

ADDINGTON

Map 05 TQ65

West Malling ☎ (0732) 844785
Two 18-hole parkland courses.
*Spitfire: 18 holes, 6142yds, Par 70, SSS 70, Course record
67.*
*Hurricane: 18 holes, 6011yds, Par 70, SSS 69, Course
record 70.*
Club membership 1000.
Visitors may not play Spitfire course unless accompanied
by member.
Societies must apply in writing.
Green Fees £28 per day; £20 per round (£30 per round after
noon at weekends).
Facilities ⊗ ⅷ by prior arrangement ⅃ 🍺 ♀ ♨ 🖻
⸙ Jonathan Foss.
Leisure squash, snooker, table tennis.
Location London Rd (1m S off A20)
Hotel ★★★63% Larkfield Priory Hotel, London Rd,
LARKFIELD
☎ (0732) 846858 52 ⇥ 🐾

ASHFORD   Map 05 TR04

Ashford ☎ (0233) 622655
Parkland course with good views and easy walking. Narrow fairways and tightly bunkered greens ensure a challenging game.
18 holes, 6246yds, Par 71, SSS 70.
Club membership 650.

Visitors	must contact in advance & have handicap certificate.
Societies	Tue & Thu only, by arrangement.
Green Fees	not confirmed.
Facilities	⊗ ┗ ♥ ♀ ♣ 🖼 ℓ Hugh Sherman.
Location	Sandyhurst Ln (1.5m NW off A20)
Hotel	★★★58% Master Spearpoint Hotel, Canterbury Rd, Kennington, ASHFORD ☎ (0233) 636863 35 ⇥ ℟

BARHAM   Map 05 TR25

Broome Park ☎ Canterbury (0227) 831701
Championship standard parkland course in a valley, with a 350-year-old mansion clubhouse.
18 holes, 6610yds, Par 72, SSS 72, Course record 66.
Club membership 600.

Visitors	must contact in advance & have handicap certificate, but may not play Sat/Sun mornings.
Societies	Mon-Fri only, by arrangement.
Green Fees	£30 per day; £25 per round (£37.50/£30 weekends & bank holidays).
Facilities	⊗ ∭ ┗ ♥ ♀ ♣ 🖼 ☂ ℓ Tienne Britz.
Leisure	hard tennis courts, heated outdoor swimming pool, squash, snooker, sauna, solarium, gymnasium, clay pigeon shooting, croquet, putting.
Location	1.5m SE on A260
Hotel	★★★60% Chaucer Hotel, Ivy Ln, CANTERBURY ☎ (0227) 464427 42 ⇥ ℟

BEARSTED   Map 05 TQ85

Bearsted ☎ Maidstone (0622) 738198
Parkland course with fine views of the North Downs.
18 holes, 6278yds, Par 72, SSS 68.
Club membership 700.

Visitors	must be member of recognised golf club & have handicap certificate, but may not play before 4pm at weekends unless with member.
Societies	must apply in writing.
Green Fees	£32 per day; £24 per round (£30 per round weekends).
Facilities	⊗ ∭ ┗ ♥ ♀ ♣ 🖼 ℓ Tim Simpson.
Leisure	practice area, putting green.
Location	Ware St (2.5m E of Maidstone off A20)
Hotel	★★★★60% Tudor Park Hotel, Golf & Country Club, Ashford Rd, Bearstead, MAIDSTONE ☎ (0622) 734334 119 ⇥ ℟

BOROUGH GREEN   Map 05 TQ65

Wrotham Heath ☎ (0732) 884800
Parkland course, hilly, good views.
18 holes, 6000yds, Par 70, SSS 69.
Club membership 549.

Visitors	with member only at weekends. Must contact in advance and have a handicap certificate.
Societies	Fri only, by arrangement.
Green Fees	not confirmed.
Facilities	⊗ (ex Mon) ∭ by prior arrangement ┗ ♥ ♀ ♣ 🖼 ℓ Harry Dearden.
Location	Seven Mile Ln (2.25m E on B2016)
Hotel	B Forte Posthouse, London Rd, Wrotham Heath, WROTHAM ☎ (0732) 883311 106 ⇥ ℟

BROADSTAIRS   Map 05 TR36

North Foreland ☎ Thanet (0843) 862140
A picturesque course situated where the Thames Estuary widens towards the sea. North Foreland always seems to have a breath of tradition of golf's earlier days about it. Perhaps the ghost of one of its earlier professionals, the famous Abe Mitchell, still haunts the lovely turf of the fairways. Walking is easy and the wind is deceptive. The 8th and 17th, both par 4, are testing holes. There is also an approach and putting course.
18 holes, 6382yds, Par 71, SSS 71.
Short Course: 18 holes, 1760yds, Par 54.
Club membership 1000.

Visitors	for Main course are required to book in advance & have handicap certificate. Short course has no restrictions.
Societies	Wed & Fri only, by arrangement.
Green Fees	Main course £35 per day; £25 per round (£35 per round weekends). Short course £5.50/£6.50 per day.
Facilities	⊗ ∭ ┗ ♥ ♀ ♣ 🖼 ℓ Mike Lee.
Leisure	hard tennis courts.
Location	Convent Rd, Kingsgate (1.5m N off B2052)
Hotel	★★66% Royal Albion Hotel, Albion St, BROADSTAIRS ☎ (0843) 868071 19 ⇥ ℟

CANTERBURY   Map 05 TR15

Canterbury ☎ (0227) 453532
Undulating parkland course, densely wooded in places, with elevated trees and difficult drives on several holes.
18 holes, 6249yds, Par 70, SSS 70.
Club membership 700.

Visitors	may only play after 3pm weekends & bank holidays.
Societies	by arrangement.
Green Fees	£36 per day; £27 per round (£36 per round weekends).
Facilities	⊗ ∭ by prior arrangement ┗ ♥ ♀ ♣ 🖼 ℓ Paul Everard.
Location	Scotland Hills (1.5m E on A257)
Hotel	★★★60% Chaucer Hotel, Ivy Ln, CANTERBURY ☎ (0227) 464427 42 ⇥ ℟

CHART SUTTON   Map 05 TQ84

The Ridge ☎ Maidstone (0622) 844382
Opened in 1993, the course was designed by Patrick Dawson around mature orchards to challenge all levels of player. The par 5, 18th has two lakes to negotiate.
18 holes, 6254yds, Par 71, SSS 70.
Club membership 650.

Visitors   by arrangement only, must have handicap
                  certificate.
Societies   by arrangement.
Green Fees   £25 (£30 weekends).
Facilities   ⊗ ⑂ 🏌 ⬛ ♀ ⚲ 🏠 🏧 Allen Robertson.
Location   Chartway St, East Sutton (5m S of Bearsted, off
                  A274)
Hotel   ★★★★60% Tudor Park Hotel, Golf & Country
                  Club, Ashford Rd, Bearstead, MAIDSTONE
                  ☎ (0622) 734334 119 ⇆ ☏

CRANBROOK   Map 05 TQ73

Cranbrook ☎ (0580) 712833
Scenic, parkland course with easy terrain, backed by
Hemstead Forest and close to Sissinghurst Castle (1m) and
Bodiam Castle (6m). The most testing hole is the 12th (530
yds par 5). Venue for the County Championships.
18 holes, 6351yds, Par 70.
Club membership 500.
Visitors   may not play at weekends before 11am.
Societies   must apply in writing.
Green Fees   not confirmed.
Facilities   ⊗ ⑂ by prior arrangement 🏌 ⬛ ♀ ⚲ 🏠
                  ☏ Alan Gillard.
Location   Benenden Rd (2m E)
Hotel   ★★68% Hartley Mount Country House, Hartley
                  Rd, CRANBROOK ☎ (0580) 712230 6 ⇆ ☏

DARTFORD   Map 05 TQ57

Birchwood Park ☎ Swanley (0322) 660554
18-hole course of two separate nines, reasonably demanding
for good golfers. Last four holes very interesting. Additional
9-hole simple beginners/practice course and 38-bay floodlit
driving range.
Eighteen Hole: 18 holes, 6364yds, Par 71, SSS 70.
Nine Hole: 9 holes, 1223yds, Par 28.
Club membership 400.
Visitors   advisable to contact in advance, restricted Sat &
                  Sun mornings.
Societies   apply in writing or telephone.
Green Fees   £18 (£23 weekends & bank holidays).
Facilities   ⊗ (Sun only) 🏌 ⬛ ♀ ⚲ 🏠 🏧 ☏ Martyn Hirst.
Leisure   38 bay floodlit driving range.
Location   Birchwood Rd, Wilmington (B258 between
                  Dartford & Swanley)
Hotel   ★★★★69% Swallow Hotel, 1 Broadway,
                  BEXLEYHEATH ☎ 081-298 1000 142 ⇆ ☏

Dartford ☎ (0322) 226455
Heathland course.
18 holes, 5914yds, Par 69, SSS 69, Course record 65.
Club membership 750.
Visitors   may not play at weekends. Must have a handicap
                  certificate.
Societies   Mon & Fri only. Must telephone in advance.
Green Fees   £28 per day.
Facilities   ⊗ ⑂ by prior arrangement 🏌 ⬛ ♀ ⚲ 🏠
                  ☏ Gary Cooke.
Location   Dartford Heath
Hotel   B Forte Posthouse, Black Prince Interchange,
                  Southwold Rd, BEXLEY
                  ☎ (0322) 526900 102 ⇆ ☏

DEAL   Map 05 TR35

Royal Cinque Ports ☎ (0304) 374007
Famous championship seaside links, windy but with easy
walking. Outward nine is generally considered the easier,
inward nine is longer and includes the renowned 16th,
perhaps the most difficult hole. On a fine day there are
wonderful views across the Channel.
18 holes, 6785yds, Par 72, SSS 72, Course record 65.
Club membership 850.
Visitors   restricted Wed mornings, weekends & bank
                  holidays. Must contact in advance and have
                  a handicap certificate.
Societies   must contact in advance.
Green Fees   £45 per day; £35 per round (after 1pm).
Facilities   ⑂ by prior arrangement 🏌 ⬛ ♀ ⚲ 🏠 🏧 ☏
                  Andrew Reynolds.
Location   Golf Rd (along seafront at N end of Deal)
Hotel   B Forte Posthouse, Singledge Ln, Whitfield,
                  DOVER ☎ (0304) 821222 67 ⇆ ☏

EDENBRIDGE   Map 05 TQ44

Edenbridge Golf & Country Club ☎ (0732) 865097
Gently undulating course with a driving range.
18 holes, 6257yds, Par 73, SSS 72.
Skeynes: 18 holes, 5671yds, Par 67.
Club membership 1100.
Visitors   must contact in advance, restricted at weekends.
Societies   must contact in advance.
Green Fees   not confirmed.
Facilities   ⊗ 🏌 ⬛ ♀ ⚲ 🏠 🏧 ☏ Keith Burkin.
Leisure   hard tennis courts, solarium, gymnasium.
Location   Crouch House Rd (1m W of town centre)
Hotel   ★★★(red)♨ Gravetye Manor Hotel, EAST
                  GRINSTEAD ☎ (0342) 810567 18 ⇆

EYNSFORD   Map 05 TQ56

Austin Lodge ☎ (0322) 868944
A well drained course designed to lie naturally in three
secluded valleys in rolling countryside. Over 7000 yds from
the medal tees. Practice ground, nets and a putting green add
to the features.
18 holes, 6600yds, Par 73, SSS 71.
Club membership 600.
Visitors   must contact in advance, may not play until after
                  1pm on weekends and bank holidays.
Societies   telephone for bookings.
Green Fees   £15 per round (£23 weekends).
Facilities   ⊗ ⑂ 🏌 ⬛ ♀ ⚲ 🏠 ☏ Nigel Willis.
Leisure   caddy cars, practice ground.
Location   Eynsford Station (6m S of Dartford)
Hotel   ★★★★59% Brands Hatch Thistle, BRANDS
                  HATCH ☎ (0474) 854900 140 ⇆ ☏

A golf course name printed in ***bold
italics*** means we have been unable to
verify information with the club's
management for the current year

FAVERSHAM

Map 05 TR06

Faversham ☎ (0795) 890561
A beautiful inland course laid out over part of a large estate with pheasants walking the fairways quite tamely. Play follows two heavily wooded valleys but the trees affect only the loose shots going out of bounds. Fine views.
18 holes, 6030yds, Par 70, SSS 69.
Club membership 800.

Visitors	must have handicap certificate. With member only at weekends. Contacting the club in advance is advisable.
Societies	must contact in advance.
Green Fees	£30 per day; £25 per round (£32/£25 weekends).
Facilities	⊗ ▥ ⅃ ♣ ♀ ⚑ 🏠 ℓ Stuart Rokes.
Location	Belmont Park (3.5m S)
Hotel	★★★★(red)🏅 Eastwell Manor Hotel, Eastwell Park, Boughton Lees, ASHFORD ☎ (0233) 635751 23 ⇌ 🐾

GILLINGHAM

Map 05 TQ76

Gillingham ☎ Medway (0634) 853017
Parkland course.
18 holes, 5879yds, Par 70, SSS 68, Course record 65.
Club membership 830.

Visitors	must be member of recognised golf club with a handicap certificate. Must contact in advance. With member only weekends & bank holidays.
Societies	must apply in writing.
Green Fees	not confirmed.
Facilities	⊗ & ▥ (ex Mon & Tue) ♣ ♀ ⚑ 🏠 ℓ Brian Impett.
Location	Woodlands Rd (1.5m SE on A2)
Hotel	B Forte Posthouse, Maidstone Rd, ROCHESTER ☎ (0634) 687111 135 ⇌ 🐾

GRAVESEND

Map 05 TQ67

Mid Kent ☎ (0474) 568035
A well-maintained downland course with some easy walking and some excellent greens. The first hole is short, but nonetheless a real challenge. The slightest hook and the ball is out of bounds or lost.
18 holes, 6199yds, Par 69, SSS 69.
Club membership 1200.

Visitors	must contact in advance & have handicap certificate. With member only at weekends.
Societies	Tue only; must contact in advance.
Green Fees	£30 per day; £20 per round.
Facilities	⊗ ▥ by prior arrangement ♣ ♀ ⚑ 🏠 ℓ Neil Hansen.
Location	Singlewell Rd (S side of town centre off A227)
Hotel	★★61% Royal Victoria & Bull Hotel, 16-18 High St, ROCHESTER ☎ (0634) 846266 28rm(21 ⇌ 🐾)

HAWKHURST

Map 05 TQ73

Hawkhurst ☎ (0580) 752396
Undulating parkland course.
9 holes, 5709yds, Par 70, SSS 68, Course record 69.
Club membership 480.

Visitors	must play with member at weekends. Advisable to contact in advance for weekday play.
Societies	must apply in writing.
Green Fees	£15 per round.
Facilities	⊗ ▥ by prior arrangement ♣ ♀ ⚑ 🏠 ℓ Tony Collins.
Leisure	squash, buggies, trolleys.
Location	High St (W side of village off A268)
Hotel	★★★68% Tudor Court Hotel, Rye Rd, HAWKHURST ☎ (0580) 752312 18 ⇌ 🐾

HERNE BAY

Map 05 TR16

Herne Bay ☎ (0227) 373964
Parkland course with bracing air.
18 holes, 5466yds, Par 68, SSS 67.
Club membership 350.

Visitors	may not play mornings at weekends.
Green Fees	not confirmed.
Facilities	♀ ⚑ 🏠 ℓ
Location	Thanet Way (1m S on A291)
Hotel	★★★61% Falstaff Hotel, St Dunstans St, CANTERBURY ☎ (0227) 462138 23 ⇌ 🐾

HOO

Map 05 TQ77

Deangate Ridge ☎ Medway (0634) 251180
Parkland, municipal course designed by Fred Hawtree. 18-hole pitch and putt.
18 holes, 6300yds, Par 71, SSS 70.
Club membership 950.

Visitors	no restrictions.
Societies	must apply in writing.
Green Fees	not confirmed.
Facilities	⚑ 🏠 🏐 ℓ
Leisure	hard tennis courts.
Location	4m NE of Rochester off A228
Hotel	B Forte Posthouse, Maidstone Rd, ROCHESTER ☎ (0634) 687111 135 ⇌ 🐾

HYTHE

Map 05 TR13

Hythe Imperial ☎ (0303) 267554
A 9-hole links course played off alternative tees on the second nine. Flat but interesting and testing. Hotel provides many leisure and sports facilities.
9 holes, 5533yds, Par 68, SSS 67, Course record 65.
Club membership 440.

Visitors	must have handicap certificate, but may not play at weekends.
Societies	must apply in writing.
Green Fees	£20 per day.
Facilities	▥ ♣ by prior arrangement ♀ ⚑ 🏠 🏐 ℓ Gordon Ritchie.
Leisure	hard and grass tennis courts, heated indoor swimming pool, squash, snooker, sauna, solarium, gymnasium, bowling, croquet, putting.
Location	Princes Pde (SE side of town)
Hotel	★★★★71% The Hythe Imperial Hotel, Princes Pde, HYTHE ☎ (0303) 267441 100 ⇌ 🐾
Additional hotel	★★★67% Stade Court Hotel, West Pde, HYTHE ☎ (0303) 268263 42 ⇌ 🐾

Sene Valley ☎ (0303) 268513
A two-level downland course which provides interesting golf over an undulating landscape with sea views.
18 holes, 6276yds, Par 71, SSS 70, Course record 61.
Club membership 650.

Visitors	must contact in advance & be member of recognised golf club or have handicap certificate.
Societies	must contact in advance.
Green Fees	£30 per day; £20 per round (£32/£30 weekends).
Facilities	⊗ ⤢ ⬛ ♀ ♙ ☗ ☖ ℂ Paul Moger.
Leisure	snooker, caddy cars & trolleys for hire.
Location	Sene (1m NE off B2065)
Hotel	★★★★71% The Hythe Imperial Hotel, Princes Pde, HYTHE ☎ (0303) 267441 100 ⇄ ☞

KINGSDOWN
Map 05 TR34

Walmer & Kingsdown ☎ (0304) 373256
This course near Deal has through the years been overshadowed by its neighbours at Deal and Sandwich, yet it is a testing circuit with many undulations. The course is famous as being the one on which, in 1964, Assistant Professional, Roger Game became the first golfer in Britain to hole out in two at two successive holes; the 7th and 8th. The course is situated on top of the cliffs, with fine views.
18 holes, 6437yds, Par 72, SSS 71, Course record 69.
Club membership 600.

Visitors	must contact in advance & have handicap certificate but may not play before noon on weekends & bank holidays.
Societies	must contact in advance & give one month's notice.
Green Fees	£28 per day; £22 per round (£30/£24 weekends & bank holidays).
Facilities	⊗ ⤢ ⬛ ♀ ♙ ☗ ☖ ℂ Ian Coleman.
Location	The Leas (0.5m S off B2057)
Hotel	B Forte Posthouse, Singledge Ln, Whitfield, DOVER ☎ (0304) 821222 67 ⇄ ☞

LAMBERHURST
Map 05 TQ63

Lamberhurst ☎ (0892) 890591
Parkland course crossing river twice. Fine views.
18 holes, 6232yds, Par 72, SSS 70, Course record 65.
Club membership 700.

Visitors	restricted weekend & bank holiday mornings. Handicap certificate required.
Societies	Tue, Wed & Thu only, by arrangement.
Green Fees	£30 per day; £20 per round (£36 weekends & bank holidays after noon).
Facilities	⊗ ⤢ by prior arrangement ⬛ ♀ ♙ ☗ ☖ ℂ Mike Travers.
Leisure	caddy cars, electric trolleys, trolleys.
Location	Church Rd (N side of village on A21)
Hotel	★★★♨70% Spindlewood Country House Hotel & Restaurant, Wallcrouch, WADHURST ☎ (0580) 200430 9 ⇄ ☞

Phoneday - remember from 16 April 1995 all phone codes in the UK will change - see page 4 for details

---

LITTLESTONE
Map 05 TR02

Littlestone ☎ New Romney (0679) 63355
Located in the Romney Marshes, this flattish seaside links course calls for every variety of shot. The 8th, 15th, 16th and 17th are regarded as classics by international golfers. Allowance for wind must always be made. Extensive practice area.
18 holes, 6460yds, Par 71, SSS 72, Course record 65.
Club membership 500.

Visitors	must contact in advance and have a handicap certificate. No visitors after 3pm weekends and bank holidays.
Societies	must contact one year in advance.
Green Fees	£36 per day; £26 per round (£32 per round weekends).
Facilities	⊗ ⤢ ⬛ ♀ ♙ ☗ ☖ ℂ Stephen Watkins.
Location	St Andrew's Rd (N side of village)
Hotel	★★★★71% The Hythe Imperial Hotel, Princes Pde, HYTHE ☎ (0303) 267441 100 ⇄ ☞

Romney Warren ☎ New Romney (0679) 63355 & 62231
A traditional links course, newly developed alongside the 9-hole course at Littlestone.
18 holes, 5126yds, Par 67, SSS 65.
Club membership 350.

Visitors	contact in advance to obtain times.
Societies	contact in advance.
Green Fees	£20 per day; £10 per round (£26/£13 weekends).
Facilities	⊗ ⤢ ⬛ ♀ ♙ ☗ ☖ ℂ Stephen Watkins.
Location	St Andrews Rd (N side of Littlestone)
Hotel	★★★★71% The Hythe Imperial Hotel, Princes Pde, HYTHE ☎ (0303) 267441 100 ⇄ ☞

MAIDSTONE
Map 05 TQ75

Cobtree Manor Park ☎ (0622) 681560
An undulating parkland course with some water hazards.
18 holes, 5716yds, Par 69, SSS 68, Course record 67.
Club membership 550.

Visitors	no restrictions.
Societies	Mon-Fri only, by arrangement.
Green Fees	not confirmed.
Facilities	⊗ ⤢ ⬛ ♀ ♙ ☗ ☖ ℂ Martin Drew.
Location	Chatham Rd, Sandling (on A229 0.25m N of M20 junc 6)
Hotel	★★59% Boxley House Hotel, Boxley Rd, Boxley, MAIDSTONE ☎ (0622) 692269 11 ⇄ ☞ Annexe7 ⇄ ☞

Leeds Castle ☎ (0622) 880467
Situated around Leeds Castle, this is one of the most picturesque courses in Britain. Re-designed in the 1980s by Neil Coles, it is a challenging 9-hole course with the added hazard of the Castle moat. 18-holes may be played on weekdays.
9 holes, 2880yds, Par 34, SSS 34, Course record 32.

Visitors	booking must be made. Bookings taken from 6 days in advance.
Societies	bookings taken up to 2yrs in advance.
Green Fees	£15 per 18 holes; £8.50 per 9 holes (£9.50 per 9 holes weekends in summer).
Facilities	(Inn situated in shop car park) ☖ ☗ ℂ C A Miller. ▶

Leisure	putting green, trolley hire, nets.
Location	On A20, 4m E of Maidstone
Hotel	★★★★60% Tudor Park Hotel, Golf & Country Club, Ashford Rd, Bearstead, MAIDSTONE ☎ (0622) 734334 119 ⇆ ⚑

RAMSGATE — Map 05 TR36

St Augustine's ☎ Thanet (0843) 590333
A comfortably flat course in this famous bracing Championship area of Kent. Neither as long nor as difficult as its lordly neighbours, St Augustine's will nonetheless extend most golfers. Dykes run across the course.
18 holes, 5197yds, Par 69, SSS 65.
Club membership 600.

Visitors	must contact in advance and have a handicap certificate.
Societies	must contact in advance.
Green Fees	£20 per day/round (£22 weekends and bank holidays).
Facilities	⊗ & ⅏ by prior arrangement ⓑ ♏ ♀ ♨ 🖻 ⓵ Derek Scott.
Leisure	caddy cars.
Location	Cottington Rd, Cliffsend
Hotel	★★62% Marina Resort Hotel, Harbour Pde, RAMSGATE ☎ (0843) 588276 59 ⇆ ⚑

ROCHESTER — Map 05 TQ76

Rochester & Cobham Park ☎ Shorne (047482) 3411
A first-rate course of challenging dimensions in undulating parkland. All holes differ and each requires accurate drive placing to derive the best advantage. The clubhouse and course are situated a quarter of a mile from the western end of the M2. The club was formed in 1891.
18 holes, 6440yds, Par 72, SSS 71, Course record 66.
Club membership 700.

Visitors	must contact in advance & have handicap certificate. No visitors weekends until after 4pm.
Societies	Tue & Thu only, by arrangement.
Green Fees	£36 per day; £26 per round (£26 per round weekends after 4pm).
Facilities	⊗ ⅏ ⓑ ♏ ♀ ♨ 🖻 ⓵ Matt Henderson.
Location	Park Pale (2.5m W on A2)
Hotel	★★★★68% Bridgewood Manor Hotel, Bridgewood Roundabout, Maidstone Rd, ROCHESTER ☎ (0634) 201333 100 ⇆ ⚑

SANDWICH — Map 05 TR35

Prince's ☎ (0304) 611118
A 27 hole championship links of the highest calibre built in three loops of nine holes from a modern clubhouse. The course represents all that is best in traditional links golf in the use of depression ridges and broken ground on a predominantly flat surface with as little protection from the wind as possible. The three 18 hole combinations all demand the highest standard of distance judgement.
Dunes: 9 holes, 3343yds, Par 36, SSS 36.
Himalayas: 9 holes, 3163yds, Par 35, SSS 35.
Shore: 9 holes, 3347yds, Par 36, SSS 36.
Club membership 450.

Visitors	must contact in advance and have a handicap certificate.
Societies	must contact in advance.
Green Fees	£36 per day; £31 per round (£46.50/£41 per day; £35.50 per round weekends & bank holidays).
Facilities	⊗ ⅏ ⓑ ♏ ♀ ♨ 🖻 ⓵ ⓵ Chris Evans.
Leisure	snooker, pool table, games room.
Location	Prince's Dr, Sandwich Bay (2m E via toll road)
Hotel	★★62% Marina Resort Hotel, Harbour Pde, RAMSGATE ☎ (0843) 588276 59 ⇆ ⚑

ROYAL ST GEORGE'S See page 119

SEVENOAKS — Map 05 TQ55

Knole Park ☎ (0732) 452150
The course is set in a majestic park with many fine trees and deer running loose. It has a wiry turf seemingly impervious to rain. Certainly a pleasure to play on. Excellent views of Knole House and the North Downs. Outstanding greens.
18 holes, 6249yds, Par 70, SSS 70.
Club membership 850.

Visitors	must have handicap certificate, but may not play at weekends or bank holidays. Must contact in advance.
Societies	must apply in writing one year in advance.
Green Fees	£26 per round.
Facilities	⊗ ⓑ ♏ ♀ ♨ 🖻 ⓵ P E Gill.
Leisure	squash, snooker.
Location	Seal Hollow Rd (SE side of town centre off B2019)
Hotel	★★★66% Royal Oak Hotel, Upper High St, SEVENOAKS ☎ (0732) 451109 21 ⇆ ⚑Annexe16 ⇆ ⚑

SHEERNESS — Map 05 TQ97

Sheerness ☎ (0795) 662585
Marshland/meadowland course, few bunkers, but many ditches and water hazards. Often windy.
18 holes, 6460yds, Par 72, SSS 71, Course record 67.
Club membership 600.

Visitors	with member only at weekends. A handicap certificate is required.
Societies	must apply in writing.
Green Fees	£20 per day; £15 per round.
Facilities	⊗ ⓑ ♏ ♀ ♨ 🖻 ⓵ W Evans.
Location	Power Station Rd (1.5m E off A249)
Hotel	★★★★68% Bridgewood Manor Hotel, Bridgewood Roundabout, Maidstone Rd, ROCHESTER ☎ (0634) 201333 100 ⇆ ⚑

SHOREHAM — Map 05 TQ56

Darenth Valley ☎ Otford (0959) 522944
Easy walking parkland course in beautiful valley. Testing 12th hole, par 4.
18 holes, 6327yds, Par 72, SSS 71.

▶

ROYAL ST. GEORGE'S

SANDWICH ☎(0304) 613090   **Map 05 TR35**

John Ingham writes: Sandwich is one of the most beautiful and unspoiled towns in southern England. Driving to this part of Kent is much like stepping back into history. The big golf course here, Royal St George's, is where Sandy Lyle won the Open Championship in 1985 by one shot from that colourful American, Payne Stewart.

Like the region, the clubhouse is old-fashioned and the seats near the window in the bar seem to have been there forever. The bar staff may know as much about fishing or lifeboats as they know about beer, and make a visit there a delight, providing you are not looking for modern sophistication.

The course itself is the truest links you will find in all England and the Royal & Ancient, in its wisdom, choose Royal St George's for major championships knowing it will find the pedigree player at the end of a week. Close to the sea, overlooking Pegwell Bay, any kind of wind can make this man-size test even tougher. The sweeping rough at the 1st can be daunting, so can the bunkers and the huge sandhills. But there are classic shots here.

Off-sea breezes can turn to incredible gales, and it is possible to find the course virtually unplayable. A smooth swing can be blown inside out and stories of three good woods to reach certain greens, into wind, are commonplace. Often the problem in high winds is simply to stand up and address the ball. Putting, too, can be almost impossible, with the ball blown off the surface and maybe into the sand. Christy O'Connor Jnr put together a 64 here, and no wonder it's the record!

Membership 675

Visitors	must contact in advance and have a handicap certificate. May not play at weekends
Societies	must apply in writing
Green fees	Midweek only £50 (18 holes); day £70 (to be amended during 1995)
Facilities	⊗ ⑤ 🍺 ♀ ♨ 🏠 🍽 caddy cars ((NiallCameron)
Location	1.5m E of town

18 holes, 6903yds, Par 70, SSS 74.
Course record 64 (C. O'Connor Jnr)

WHERE TO STAY AND EAT NEARBY

HOTELS:

CANTERBURY
★★★ 61% Falstaff, St Dunstans St. ☎ (0227) 462138. 24 ⇆ 🍴 English & Continental cuisine

★★★ 60% Chaucer, Ivy Lane ☎(0227) 464427. 42 ⇆ 🍴. English & Continental cuisine

DOVER
Forte Posthouse, Singledge Ln, Whitfield (3m NW jct A2/A256. ☎ (0304) 821222. 67 ⇆ 🍴

RAMSGATE
★★ 62% Marina Resort, Harbour Pde. ☎ Thanet (0843) 588276. 59 ⇆ 🍴 English & Continental cuisine

RESTAURANTS:

CANTERBURY
✕ ❀ Ristorante Tuo e Mio, 16 The Borough. ☎ (0227) 761471 Italian cuisine

ST MARGARET'S AT CLIFFE
✕✕ ❀❀ Wallets Court, West Cliffe ☎ Dover (0304) 852424 English & French cuisine

Visitors must book tees times through professional on
(0959) 522922.
Societies must telephone (0959) 522922 in advance.
Green Fees £11 per round (£15 weekends).
Facilities ⊗ ⑾ ☖ 🍺 ♀ ☂ 🏠 ⚑ ℓ Scott Fotheringham.
Leisure putting greens, practice nets, trolleys.
Location Station Rd (1m E on A225)
Hotel ★★★66% Royal Oak Hotel, Upper High St,
SEVENOAKS
☎ (0732) 451109 21 ⇆ 🐾Annexe16 ⇆ 🐾

SITTINGBOURNE   Map 05 TQ96

The Oast Golf Centre ☎ (0795) 473527
A Par 3 Approach course of 9 holes with 18 tees augmented
by a 17-bay floodlit driving range and a putting green.
9 holes, 1649yds, Par 54, SSS 54.
Visitors no restrictions.
Societies telephone in advance if meals required.
Green Fees £5.50 per 18 holes; £3.50 per 9 holes.
Facilities ⊗ ⑾ by prior arrangement ☖ 🍺 ♀ (all day) 🏠
⚑ ℓ G Nixon.
Leisure putting green, 17 bay driving range.
Location Church Rd, Tonge (2m NE)
Hotel ★★★★68% Bridgewood Manor Hotel,
Bridgewood Roundabout, Maidstone Rd,
ROCHESTER ☎ (0634) 201333 100 ⇆ 🐾

Sittingbourne & Milton Regis ☎ Newington (0795)
842261
A downland course with pleasant vistas. There are a few
uphill climbs, but the course is far from difficult. The 166-
yard, 2nd hole is a testing par 3.
18 holes, 6272yds, Par 71, SSS 70.
Club membership 714.
Visitors may not play at weekends & are restricted Wed.
Societies must apply in writing.
Green Fees £20 per 18 holes; £32 per 36 holes.
Facilities ⊗ ⑾ ☖ 🍺 ♀ ☂ 🏠 ⚑ ℓ John Hearn.
Location Wormdale, Newington (turn off A249 at
Dalaway)
Hotel ★★★★68% Bridgewood Manor Hotel,
Bridgewood Roundabout, Maidstone Rd,
ROCHESTER ☎ (0634) 201333 100 ⇆ 🐾

TENTERDEN   Map 05 TQ83

Tenterden ☎ (0580) 763987 & 762409
Attractive parkland course, last 3 holes are hilly.
18 holes, 6030yds, Par 70, SSS 69.
Club membership 650.
Visitors restricted weekends & bank holidays. Must
contact in advance.
Societies must apply in writing.
Green Fees £20 per day (weekends with member only).
Facilities ⊗ ⑾ by prior arrangement ☖ 🍺 ♀ ☂ 🏠
ℓ Darren Lewis.
Leisure practice grounds, lessons available.
Location Woodchurch Rd (0.75m E on B2067)
Hotel ★★★56% White Lion Hotel, High St,
TENTERDEN ☎ (0580) 765077 15 ⇆ 🐾

TONBRIDGE   Map 05 TQ54

Poultwood ☎ (0732) 364039
With the opening of a 9-hole course in the summer of 1994
there are now two public 'pay and play' parkland courses in
an idyllic woodland setting. The courses are ecologically
designed, offering varied walking, water hazards, natural and
interesting playing opportunities for all standards of golfer.
18 holes, 5569yds, Par 68, SSS 67.
Visitors no restrictions.
Societies must apply in writing.
Green Fees £8.40/£7.70 per round (£12.60/£11.60
weekends).
Facilities ⊗ ⑾ ☖ 🍺 ♀ ☂ 🏠 ⚑ ℓ
Leisure squash.
Location Higham Ln (off A227)
Hotel ★★★61% Rose & Crown Hotel, High St,
TONBRIDGE
☎ (0732) 357966 50rm(49 ⇆ 🐾)

TUNBRIDGE WELLS (ROYAL)   Map 05 TQ53

Nevill ☎ (0892) 525818
Just within Sussex, the county boundary with Kent runs
along the northern perimeter of the course. Open
undulating ground, well-wooded with much heather and
gorse for the first half. The second nine holes slope away
from the clubhouse to a valley where a narrow stream
hazards two holes.
18 holes, 6336yds, Par 71, SSS 70.
Club membership 960.
Visitors must contact in advance.
Societies must apply in writing.
Green Fees not confirmed.
Facilities ⊗ ⑾ by prior arrangement ☖ 🍺 ♀ ☂ 🏠
⚑ ℓ
Location Benhall Mill Rd
Hotel ★★★70% Spa Hotel, Mount Ephraim,
TUNBRIDGE WELLS
☎ (0892) 520331 76 ⇆ 🐾

Tunbridge Wells ☎ (0892) 523034
Somewhat hilly, well-bunkered parkland course with lake;
trees form natural hazards.
9 holes, 4560yds, Par 65, SSS 62.
Club membership 525.
Visitors must be members of an affiliated club and
possess handicap certificate.
Societies apply in writing.
Green Fees not confirmed.
Facilities ⊗ ⑾ ☖ 🍺 ♀ ☂ 🏠 ℓ Keith Smithson.
Location Langton Rd (1m W on A264)
Hotel ★★★70% Spa Hotel, Mount Ephraim,
TUNBRIDGE WELLS
☎ (0892) 520331 76 ⇆ 🐾

WESTGATE ON SEA   Map 05 TR37

Westgate and Birchington ☎ Thanet (0843) 831115
Seaside course.
18 holes, 4926yds, Par 64, SSS 64.
Club membership 310.
Visitors must contact in advance & have handicap
certificate, restricted at weekends.

Societies must contact three months in advance.
Green Fees £15 per day/round (£18 weekends & bank
holidays).
Facilities ⊗ by prior arrangement ⓑ 🍺 (all catering Tue-
Thu only) ♀ ⚲ 🏠 ⓒ Roger Game.
Location 176 Canterbury Rd (E side of town centre off
A28)
Hotel ★★56% Ivyside Hotel, 25 Sea Rd,
WESTGATE ON SEA
☎ (0843) 831082 67rm(65 ⇆ ⌂)

WEST KINGSDOWN   Map 05 TQ56

Woodlands Manor ☎ (0959) 523806
Interesting, undulating parkland course with testing 1st, 9th
and 15th holes.
18 holes, 5858yds, Par 69, SSS 68.
Club membership 550.
Visitors with member only weekend afternoons.
Societies apply in writing.
Green Fees not confirmed.
Facilities ♀ ⚲ 🏠 ⓒ ⌂
Location Woodlands (2m S off A20)
Hotel ★★★★59% Brands Hatch Thistle, BRANDS
HATCH ☎ (0474) 854900 140 ⇆ ⌂

WHITSTABLE   Map 05 TR16

Chestfield (Whitstable) ☎ Chestfield (022779) 4411
Gently undulating parkland course with sea views. The Par 3
3rd is generally played into the wind and the Par 4th has a
difficult lefthand dogleg.
18 holes, 6181yds, Par 70, SSS 70, Course record 64.
Club membership 730.
Visitors must contact in advance & have handicap
certificate but may not play at weekends.
Societies must apply in writing.
Green Fees £28 per day; £10 per round.
Facilities ⊗ ⓑ 🍺 ♀ ⚲ 🏠 ⓒ John Brotherton.
Leisure caddy cars to book.
Location 103 Chestfield Rd (2m SE off A299)
Hotel ★★★60% Chaucer Hotel, Ivy Ln,
CANTERBURY ☎ (0227) 464427 42 ⇆ ⌂

Whitstable & Seasalter ☎ (0227) 272020
Links course.
9 holes, 5276yds, Par 66, SSS 63.
Club membership 300.
Visitors must play with member at weekends.
Societies apply for details
Green Fees £15 per round.
Facilities ⓑ 🍺 ♀ ⚲ 🏠
Location Collingwood Rd (W side of town centre off
B2205)
Hotel ★★★60% Chaucer Hotel, Ivy Ln,
CANTERBURY ☎ (0227) 464427 42 ⇆ ⌂

> If visiting a brand new course, be sure
> to telephone before your visit to
> confirm the course information is
> correct

ACCRINGTON   Map 07 SD72

Accrington & District ☎ (0254) 232734
Moorland course with pleasant views of the Pennines and
surrounding areas.
18 holes, 5969yds, Par 70, SSS 69, Course record 65.
Club membership 600.
Visitors must contact in advance.
Societies contact in advance.
Green Fees £15 per day Mon-Thu (£18 Fri-Sun & bank
holidays).
Facilities ⊗ 川 ⓑ 🍺 ♀ ⚲ 🏠 ⓒ ⌂ Bill Harling.
Location Devon Av, Oswaldtwistle (mid way between
Accrington & Blackburn)
Hotel ★★★65% Dunkenhalgh Hotel, Blackburn Rd,
Clayton le Moors, ACCRINGTON
☎ (0254) 398021 37 ⇆ ⌂Annexe42 ⇆ ⌂

Baxenden & District ☎ (0254) 234555
Moorland course.
9 holes, 5740yds, SSS 68.
Visitors may not play Sat, Sun and bank holidays except
with member.
Societies must contact in advance.
Green Fees not confirmed.
Facilities ♀ ⚲
Location Top o' th' Meadow, Baxenden (1.5m SE off
A680)
Hotel ★★★65% Dunkenhalgh Hotel, Blackburn Rd,
Clayton le Moors, ACCRINGTON
☎ (0254) 398021 37 ⇆ ⌂Annexe42 ⇆ ⌂

Green Haworth ☎ (0254) 237580
Moorland course dominated by quarries and difficult in
windy conditions.
9 holes, 5556yds, Par 68, SSS 67, Course record 67.
Club membership 360.
Visitors may not play Sun, Mar-Oct.
Societies apply in writing. Weekdays only before 5pm.
Green Fees £10 per day (£15 Sat).
Facilities ⊗ 川 ⓑ 🍺 ♀ ⚲
Leisure snooker.
Location Green Haworth (2m S off A680)
Hotel ★★★56% Blackburn Moat House, Preston New
Rd, BLACKBURN ☎ (0254) 264441 98 ⇆ ⌂

BACUP   Map 07 SD82

Bacup ☎ (0706) 873170
Moorland course, predominantly flat except climbs to 1st and
10th holes.
9 holes, 5652yds, Par 68, SSS 67.
Club membership 350.
Visitors no restrictions.
Societies must contact in writing.
Green Fees not confirmed.
Facilities ⊗ 川 ⓑ 🍺 ♀ ⚲
Leisure snooker.
Location Bankside Ln (W side of town off A671)
Hotel ★★★59% Friendly Stop Inn, Keirby Walk,
BURNLEY ☎ (0282) 427611 49 ⇆ ⌂

BARNOLDSWICK   Map 07 SD84

Ghyll ☎ Earby (0282) 842466
Excellent, parkland course with outstanding views, especially
from the 8th tee where you can see the Three Peaks. Testing
3rd hole is an uphill par 4.
9 holes, 5422yds, Par 68, SSS 66, Course record 64.
Club membership 310.

Visitors	may not play Tue mornings, Fri after 4.30pm & Sun.
Societies	must contact in writing.
Green Fees	£14 per day (£18 weekends & bank holidays).
Facilities	⌂
Location	Ghyll Brow (1m NE on B6252)
Hotel	★★★64% Stirk House Hotel, GISBURN ☎ (0200) 445581 36 ⇆ ↾ Annexe12 ⇆

BLACKBURN   Map 07 SD62

Blackburn ☎ (0254) 51122
Parkland course on a high plateau with stream and hills.
Superb views of Lancashire coast and the Pennines.
18 holes, 6147yds, Par 71, SSS 70, Course record 63.
Club membership 800.

Visitors	restricted Tue & weekends.
Societies	must contact in advance.
Green Fees	£19 per day (£22 weekends).
Facilities	⊗ ⑴ by prior arrangement ⌂ ▼ ⚲ ⌂ ⊡ ↾ Alan Rodwell.
Leisure	snooker, large practice area.
Location	Beardwood Brow (1.25m NW of town centre off A677)
Hotel	★★★56% Blackburn Moat House, Preston New Rd, BLACKBURN ☎ (0254) 264441 98 ⇆ ↾

BLACKPOOL   Map 07 SD33

Blackpool North Shore ☎ (0253) 352054
Undulating parkland course.
18 holes, 6400yds, Par 71, SSS 71.
Club membership 900.

Visitors	may not play Thu & Sat. Advisable to contact in advance.
Societies	must contact in advance.
Green Fees	£25 per day (£30 weekends & bank holidays).
Facilities	⚲ ⊡ ↾ ↾ Brendan Ward.
Leisure	snooker.
Location	Devonshire Rd (On A587 N of town centre)
Hotel	★★71% Brabyns Hotel, Shaftesbury Av, North Shore, BLACKPOOL ☎ (0253) 54263 due to change to 354263 22 ⇆ ↾ Annexe3 ⇆ ↾

BURNLEY   Map 07 SD83

Burnley ☎ (0282) 421045
Moorland course with hilly surrounds.
18 holes, 5899yds, Par 69, SSS 69, Course record 65.
Club membership 700.

Visitors	may not play at weekends.
Societies	must contact in advance.
Green Fees	£18 per day (£25 weekends & bank holidays).
Facilities	⊗ ⑴ ⌂ ▼ (no catering Mon or Wed pm) ⚲ ⌂ ⊡ ↾ William Tye.

Leisure	snooker, trolleys.
Location	Glen View (1.5m S off A646)
Hotel	★★★59% Friendly Stop Inn, Keirby Walk, BURNLEY ☎ (0282) 427611 49 ⇆ ↾

Towneley ☎ (0282) 38473
Parkland course, with other sporting facilities.
18 holes, 5812yds, Par 70, SSS 68, Course record 65.
Club membership 300.

Visitors	must contact in advance at weekends.
Societies	must contact in advance.
Green Fees	not confirmed.
Facilities	⊗ (ex Mon) ⑴ by prior arrangement ⌂ (ex Mon) ▼ ⚲ ⌂ ⊡ ↾ ↾
Location	Towneley Park, Todmorden Rd (1m SE of town centre on A671)
Hotel	★★★71% Oaks Hotel, Colne Rd, Reedley, BURNLEY ☎ (0282) 414141 58 ⇆ ↾

CHORLEY   Map 07 SD51

Chorley ☎ (0257) 480263
A splendid moorland course with plenty of fresh air. The
well-sited clubhouse affords some good views of the
Lancashire coast and of Angelzarke, a local beauty spot.
Beware of the short 3rd hole with its menacing out-of-
bounds.
18 holes, 6307yds, Par 71, SSS 70.
Club membership 500.

Visitors	must contact in advance & have handicap certificate. Restricted Sat-Mon.
Societies	must contact in advance.
Green Fees	£25 per day/round.
Facilities	⊗ ⑴ ⌂ (no catering Mon) ▼ ⚲ ⌂ ⊡ ↾
Leisure	snooker, pool table, TV, caddy cars.
Location	Hall o' th' Hill, Heath Charnock (2.5m SE on A673)
Hotel	★★★67% Pines Hotel, CLAYTON-LE-WOODS ☎ (0772) 38551 39 ⇆ ↾

Duxbury Jubilee Park ☎ (0257) 265380
Municipal parkland course.
18 holes, 6390yds, Par 71, SSS 70.
Club membership 225.

Visitors	must book 6 days in advance.
Societies	weekdays only. Must contact in advance.
Green Fees	£6.25 per round (£8.50 weekends & bank holidays).
Facilities	⊗ ⑴ ⌂ ▼ ⚲ ⌂ ⊡ ↾ ↾ David Clarke.
Location	Duxbury Park (2.5m S off A6)
Hotel	B Welcome Lodge, Mill Ln, CHARNOCK RICHARD ☎ (0257) 791746 100 ⇆

Shaw Hill Hotel Golf & Country Club ☎ (0257)
269221
A fine course designed by one of Europe's most
prominent golf architects and offering a considerable
challenge as well as tranquillity and scenic charm. Seven
lakes guard par 5 and long par 4 holes.
18 holes, 6405yds, Par 72, SSS 71, Course record 66.
Club membership 500.

Visitors	denims and trainers not allowed on course or in clubhouse. Jacket and tie required in restaurant.
Societies	must telephone in advance.

Green Fees £30 per round Mon-Thu (£40 Fri-Sun).
Facilities ⊗ (ex Sat) ⊪ ⓑ 🖤 ♀ ⚘ 🏠 ⛳ 🍴
𝄢 David Clark.
Leisure snooker, caddy cars (Etr-Oct).
Location Preston Rd, Whittle-Le-Woods (on A6 1.5m N)
Hotel ★★★65% Shaw Hill Hotel Golf & Country Club, Preston Rd, Whittle-le-Woods, CHORLEY ☎ (0257) 269221 22 ⇄ 🐾

CLITHEROE
Map 07 SD74

Clitheroe ☎ (0200) 22292
One of the best inland courses in the country. Clitheroe is a parkland-type course with water hazards and good scenic views, particularly on towards Longridge, and Pendle Hill. The Club has been the venue for the Lancashire Amateur Championships, and for the 1991 County Championships Tournament.
18 holes, 6326yds, Par 71, SSS 71, Course record 67.
Club membership 720.
Visitors must contact in advance.
Societies must contact in writing.
Green Fees £25 per day (£30 weekends & bank holidays).
Facilities ⊗ ⊪ ⓑ 🖤 ♀ ⚘ 🏠 𝄢 John Twissell.
Leisure trolleys.
Location Whalley Rd, Pendleton (2m S on A671)
Hotel ★★67% Shireburn Arms Hotel, HURST GREEN ☎ (0254) 826518 15 ⇄ 🐾

COLNE
Map 07 SD84

Colne ☎ (0282) 863391
Moorland course.
9 holes, 5961yds, Par 70, SSS 69.
Club membership 300.
Visitors restricted Thu. Must contact in advance.
Societies may not play Thu or weekends. Must contact in advance.
Green Fees £14 per day/round.
Facilities ⊗ & ⊪ by prior arrangement ⓑ 🖤 ♀ ⚘
Leisure snooker.
Location Law Farm, Skipton Old Rd (1m E off A56)
Hotel ★★★64% Stirk House Hotel, GISBURN ☎ (0200) 445581 36 ⇄ 🐾Annexe12 ⇄

DARWEN
Map 07 SD62

Darwen ☎ (0254) 701287
Moorland course.
18 holes, 5752yds, Par 68, SSS 68, Course record 65.
Club membership 600.
Visitors may not play on Sat.
Societies must telephone in advance.
Green Fees £17 per day; £13 per day (£24/£20 weekends).
Facilities ⊗ ⊪ ⓑ 🖤 (no catering Mon) ♀ (ex Mon) ⚘ 🏠 𝄢 Wayne Lennon.
Location Winter Hill (1m NW)
Hotel ★★★62% Whitehall Hotel, Springbank, Whitehall, DARWEN ☎ (0254) 701595 15 ⇄ 🐾

FLEETWOOD
Map 07 SD34

Fleetwood ☎ (0253) 873661 & 773573
Championship length, flat seaside links where the player must always be alert to changes of direction or strength of the wind.
18 holes, 6723yds, Par 72, SSS 72, Course record 64.
Club membership 600.
Visitors may not play on competition days.
Societies must contact in advance. A deposit of £5 per player is required.
Green Fees £20 per day (£25 weekends & bank holidays).
Facilities ⊗ ⊪ ⓑ 🖤 ♀ ⚘ 🏠 𝄢 Clive Thomas Burgess.
Leisure snooker.
Location Princes Way (W side of town centre)
Hotel ★★67% Mains Hall Country House Hotel, Mains Ln, Little Singleton, POULTON-LE-FYLDE ☎ (0253) 885130 9rm(7 ⇄ 🐾)

HARWOOD, GREAT
Map 07 SD73

Great Harwood ☎ Blackburn (0254) 884391
Flat parkland course with fine views of the Pendle region.
9 holes, 6411yds, Par 73, SSS 71, Course record 68.
Club membership 325.
Visitors may not play Tue or competition days.
Societies must contact in writing.
Green Fees £13 per round (£16 weekends & bank holidays).
Facilities ⊪ ⓑ & 🖤 (ex Mon) ♀ (ex Mon) ⚘
Leisure snooker.
Location Harwood Bar, Whallwy Rd (E side of town centre on A680)
Hotel ★★★65% Dunkenhalgh Hotel, Blackburn Rd, Clayton le Moors, ACCRINGTON ☎ (0254) 398021 37 ⇄ 🐾Annexe42 ⇄ 🐾

HASLINGDEN
Map 07 SD72

Rossendale ☎ Rossendale (0706) 831339
Testing, and usually windy meadowland course.
18 holes, 6267yds, Par 72, SSS 70, Course record 68.
Club membership 700.
Visitors must contact professional's shop in advance (0706) 213616. With member only Sat.
Societies must telephone in advance & confirm in writing.
Green Fees £22.50 (£27.50 weekends & bank holidays).
Facilities ⊗ ⊪ ⓑ & 🖤 (ex Mon) ♀ (ex Mon lunchtime) ⚘ 🏠 𝄢 S J Nicholls.
Leisure snooker.
Location Ewood Ln Head (1.5m S off A56)
Hotel ★★★63% Old Mill Hotel, Springwood, RAMSBOTTOM ☎ (0706) 822991 36 ⇄

HEYSHAM
Map 07 SD46

Heysham ☎ Lancaster (0524) 851011
Seaside parkland course, partly wooded. The 15th is a 459 yard Par 4 hole nearly always played into the prevailing south west wind.
18 holes, 6258yds, Par 69, SSS 70, Course record 65.
Club membership 900.

▶

Visitors   no restrictions.
Societies   must contact in writing.
Green Fees   £23 per day; £18 per round (£27 weekends & bank holidays).
Facilities   ⊗ ⅲ ⅂ ⅃ ♀ ⅄ ⌂ ℓ Simon Fletcher.
Leisure   snooker, trolleys.
Location   Trumacar Park, Middleton Rd (0.75m S off A589)
Hotel   ★★60% Clarendon Hotel, Promenade, West End, MORECAMBE ☎ (0524) 410180 31rm(28 ⇄ ↶)

KNOTT END-ON-SEA   Map 07 SD34

Knott End ☎ Blackpool (0253) 810576
Pleasant, undulating parkland course on banks of River Wyre. Open to sea breezes.
18 holes, 5789yds, Par 69, SSS 68.
Club membership 500.
Visitors   must contact one day in advance.
Societies   must contact in writing.
Green Fees   £21 per day (£26 weekends).
Facilities   ⊗ ⅲ ⅂ ♀ ⅄ ⌂ ℓ Paul Walker.
Leisure   snooker.
Location   Wyre-Side (W side of village off B5377)
Hotel   ★★67% Mains Hall Country House Hotel, Mains Ln, Little Singleton, POULTON-LE-FYLDE ☎ (0253) 885130 9rm(7 ⇄ ↶)

LANCASTER   Map 07 SD46

Lancaster Golf & Country Club ☎ (0524) 751247
This course is unusual for parkland golf as it is exposed to the winds coming off the Irish Sea. It is situated on the Lune estuary and has some natural hazards and easy walking. There are however several fine holes among woods near the old clubhouse.
18 holes, 6282yds, Par 71, SSS 71.
Club membership 925.
Visitors   no visitors at weekends. Must contact in advance and have a handicap certificate.
Societies   Mon-Fri only. Must contact in advance. Handicap certificate required.
Green Fees   £28 per day.
Facilities   ⊗ ⅲ ⅂ ⅃ ♀ ⅄ ⌂ ℓ David Sutcliffe.
Leisure   snooker, caddy cars for hire.
Location   Ashton Hall, Ashton-with-Stodday (3m S on A588)
Hotel   ★★★72% Lancaster House Hotel, Green Ln, Ellel, LANCASTER ☎ (0524) 844822 80 ⇄ ↶

Lansil ☎ (0532) 685180
Parkland course.
9 holes, 5608yds, Par 70, SSS 67.
Club membership 375.
Visitors   may not play before 1pm at weekends.
Societies   weekdays only; must contact in writing.
Green Fees   not confirmed.
Facilities   ⊗ ⅲ ⅂ ⅃ (catering eves & weekends only) ♀ (eves & weekends) ⅄
Location   Caton Rd (N side of town centre on A683)
Hotel   B Forte Posthouse, Waterside Park, Caton Rd, LANCASTER ☎ (0524) 65999 115 ⇄ ↶

LANGHO   Map 07 SD73

Mytton Fold Farm Hotel ☎ Blackburn (0254) 240662
A new course opened in Summer 1994. The course has panoramic views across the Ribble Valley and Pendle Hill. Tight fairways and water hazards are designed to make this a challenging course for any golfer.
18 holes, 6217yds, Par 72, SSS 72.
Club membership 300.
Visitors   bookings only, no handicap necessary in 1995, dress code to be observed.
Societies   telephone in advance.
Green Fees   £17.50 per 18 holes.
Facilities   ⊗ ⅲ ⅂ ⅃ ♀ ⅄ ⌂ ⅂ ⅋ ℓ Gary P Cope.
Leisure   snooker.
Location   Whalley Rd
Hotel   ★★★64% Mytton Fold Farm Hotel, Whalley Rd, LANGHO ☎ (0254) 240662 27 ⇄ ↶

LEYLAND   Map 07 SD52

Leyland ☎ (0772) 436457
Parkland course, fairly flat and usually breezy.
18 holes, 6123yds, Par 70, SSS 69.
Club membership 860.
Visitors   restricted weekends & bank holidays. Must contact in advance.
Societies   must contact in advance.
Green Fees   on application.
Facilities   ⊗ ⅲ by prior arrangement ⅂ ⅃ ♀ ⅄ ⌂ ℓ Colin Burgess.
Leisure   caddy cars.
Location   Wigan Rd (E side of town centre on A49)
Hotel   ★★★67% Pines Hotel, CLAYTON-LE-WOODS ☎ (0772) 38551 39 ⇄ ↶

LONGRIDGE   Map 07 SD63

Longridge ☎ (0772) 783291
Moorland course 850 ft high with views of the Ribble Valley, Trough of Bowland, The Fylde and Welsh Mountains.
18 holes, 5970yds, Par 70, SSS 68, Course record 66.
Club membership 600.
Visitors   may not play 8-9.30am, noon-1pm, Sun 11am-12.15pm (winter) & weekends in summer.
Societies   must contact in writing.
Green Fees   £18 Mon-Fri per day (£21 weekends).
Facilities   ⊗ ⅲ by prior arrangement ⅂ ⅃ ♀ ⅄ ⌂ ℓ N S James.
Leisure   snooker.
Location   Fell Barn, Jeffrey Hill (8m NE of Preston off B6243)
Hotel   ★★67% Shireburn Arms Hotel, HURST GREEN ☎ (0254) 826518 15 ⇄ ↶

LYTHAM ST ANNES   Map 07 SD32

Fairhaven ☎ (0253) 736741
A flat, but interesting parkland links course of good standard. There are natural hazards as well as numerous bunkers and players need to produce particularly accurate second shots.
18 holes, 6884yds, Par 74, SSS 73.
Club membership 950.

Visitors	welcome, but may not play before 9am or between noon & 1.30pm.
Societies	must contact in advance.
Green Fees	£35 per day; £25 per round (£30 per round weekends & bank holidays).
Facilities	⊗ ⅢⅢ ☒ ☒ ♀ ☒ ☒ ☒ ☒ Ian Howieson.
Leisure	snooker.
Location	Lytham Hall Park, Ansdell (E side of town centre off B5261)
Hotel	★★★64% Bedford Hotel, 307-311 Clifton Dr South, LYTHAM ST ANNES ☎ (0253) 724636 36 ⇥ ☒

Lytham Green Drive ☎ (0253) 737390
Pleasant parkland course, ideal for holidaymakers.
18 holes, 6175yds, Par 70, SSS 69.
Club membership 780.

Visitors	must contact in advance & have handicap certificate but may not play at weekends.
Societies	must contact in advance.
Green Fees	not confirmed.
Facilities	☒ ☒ ♀ ☒ ☒ ☒ Andrew Lancaster.
Leisure	snooker.
Location	Ballam Rd (E side of town centre off B5259)
Hotel	★★★★54% Clifton Arms, West Beach, Lytham, LYTHAM ST ANNES ☎ (0253) 739898 41 ⇥ ☒

ROYAL LYTHAM ST ANNES See page 127

St Annes Old Links ☎ (0253) 723597
Seaside links, qualifying course for open championship; compact and of very high standard, particularly greens. Windy, very long 5th, 17th and 18th holes. Famous hole: 9th (171 yds), par 3. Excellent club facilities.
18 holes, 6616yds, par 72, SSS 72,Course record 64.
Club membership 950.

Visitors	may not play on Sat or before 9.15am & between noon-2pm. Sundays by prior arrangement only. handicap certificate requested.
Societies	must contact in advance.
Green fees	£28 per day (£35 weekends & bank holidays).
Facilities	⊗ ⅢⅢ ☒ ☒ ♀ ☒ ☒ ☒ G G Hardiman.
Leisure	snooker.
Location	Highbury Rd (N side of town centre)
Hotel	★★★64% Bedford Hotel, 307-311 Clifton Dr South, Lytham St Annes ☎ (0253) 724636 36 ⇥ ☒

MORECAMBE   Map 07 SD46

Morecambe ☎ (0524) 412841
Holiday golf at its most enjoyable. The well-maintained, wind-affected seaside parkland course is not long but full of character. Even so the panoramic views across Morecambe Bay and to the Lake District and Pennines make concentration difficult. The 4th is a testing hole.
18 holes, 5770yds, Par 67, SSS 68.
Club membership 1000.

Visitors	may not play before 9.30am, noon-1.30pm Mon-Sat or before 11.15am Sun. Must have a handicap certificate.
Societies	must contact in advance.
Green Fees	£21 per day; £16 per round (£26/£21 weekends & bank holidays).

Facilities	⊗ ⅢⅢ ☒ ☒ (no catering Mon) ♀ ☒ ☒ ☒ Philip de Valle.
Leisure	snooker.
Location	Bare (N side of town centre on A5105)
Hotel	★★★65% Elms Hotel, Bare Village, MORECAMBE ☎ (0524) 411501 40 ⇥ ☒

NELSON   Map 07 SD83

Marsden Park ☎ (0282) 67525
Hilly, parkland course open to the wind.
18 holes, 5806yds, Par 70, SSS 68, Course record 66.
Club membership 320.

Visitors	must telephone in advance at weekends.
Societies	may not play on Sat. Must contact in writing.
Green Fees	not confirmed.
Facilities	☒ & ☒ (weekends or by prior arrangement) ♀ (weekends or by prior arrangement) ☒ ☒ ☒ Nick Brown.
Location	Nelson Municipal Golf Course, Townhouse Rd (E side of town centre off A56)
Hotel	★★★71% Oaks Hotel, Colne Rd, Reedley, BURNLEY ☎ (0282) 414141 58 ⇥ ☒

Nelson ☎ (0282) 614583
Hilly moorland course, usually windy, with good views. Testing 8th hole, par 4.
18 holes, 5967yds, Par 70, SSS 69.
Club membership 600.

Visitors	may not play Thu afternoons & Sat Apr-Oct.
Societies	must contact in writing.
Green Fees	£20 per day (£24 weekends & bank holidays).
Facilities	⊗ & ⅢⅢ & ☒ (ex Mon & Fri) ☒ ♀ ☒ ☒ ☒ N Sumner.
Leisure	caddy car hire, satellite tv.
Location	King's Causeway, Brierfield (1.5m SE)
Hotel	★★★71% Oaks Hotel, Colne Rd, Reedley, BURNLEY ☎ (0282) 414141 58 ⇥ ☒

ORMSKIRK   Map 07 SD40

Ormskirk ☎ (0695) 72112
A pleasantly secluded, fairly flat, parkland course with much heath and silver birch. Accuracy from the tees will provide an interesting variety of second shots.
18 holes, 6358yds, Par 70, SSS 70.
Club membership 300.

Visitors	restricted Sat. Must contact in advance and have an introduction from own club.
Societies	must contact in writing.
Green Fees	not confirmed.
Facilities	⊗ ⅢⅢ ☒ ☒ (no catering Mon) ♀ ☒ ☒ ☒ Jack Hammond.
Location	Cranes Ln, Lathom (1.5m NE)
Hotel	★★★64% Holland Hall Hotel, 6 Lafford Ln, UPHOLLAND ☎ (0695) 624426 28 ⇥ ☒ Annexe6 ⇥ ☒

For an explanation of symbols and abbreviations, see page 5

PLEASINGTON · Map 07 SD62

Pleasington ☎ Blackburn (0254) 202177
Plunging and rising across lovely moorland turf this
course tests judgement of distance through the air to
greens of widely differing levels. The 11th and 17th are
testing holes.
18 holes, 6417yds, Par 71, SSS 71.
Club membership 700.
Visitors may play Mon & Wed-Fri only.
Societies must contact in advance.
Green Fees £26 (£30 weekends & bank holidays).
Facilities ⊗ ⅢⅢ ⅛ & ▆ by prior arrangement ♀ 👤 🏠
　　　　　 ⅃ Ged Furey.
Leisure snooker.
Location W side of village
Hotel ★★★56% Blackburn Moat House, Preston
　　　　　 New Rd, BLACKBURN
　　　　　 ☎ (0254) 264441 98 ⇆ ♠

POULTON-LE-FYLDE · Map 07 SD33

Poulton-le-Fylde ☎ (0253) 892444
Municipal parkland course, with easy walking.
9 holes, 5958yds, Par 70, SSS 69.
Club membership 300.
Visitors no restrictions.
Societies apply in writing.
Green Fees not confirmed.
Facilities ⊗ ⅢⅢ ▆ ♀ 👤 🏠 ☂⅃ D Spencer.
Leisure heated indoor swimming pool, snooker.
Location Breck Rd (N side of town)
Hotel ★★67% Mains Hall Country House Hotel,
　　　　　 Mains Ln, Little Singleton, POULTON-LE-
　　　　　 FYLDE ☎ (0253) 885130 9rm(7 ⇆ ♠)

PRESTON · Map 07 SD52

Ashton & Lea ☎ (0772) 726480 & 735282
Heathland/parkland course with pond and streams, offering
pleasant walks and some testing holes.
18 holes, 6346yds, Par 71, SSS 70, Course record 65.
Club membership 825.
Visitors must contact in advance, restricted competition
　　　　　 days & members tee times.
Societies weekdays only. Must contact in writing.
Green Fees £20 per day (£24 weekends & bank holidays).
Facilities ⊗ ⅢⅢ ▆ ♀ 👤 🏠 ⅃ M Greenough.
Leisure snooker.
Location Tudor Av, Lea (3m W on A5085)
Hotel B Forte Posthouse, Ringway, PRESTON
　　　　　 ☎ (0772) 259411 121 ⇆ ♠

Fishwick Hall ☎ (0772) 798300
Meadowland course overlooking River Ribble. Natural
hazards.
18 holes, 6092yds, Par 70, SSS 69, Course record 66.
Club membership 700.
Visitors advisable to contact in advance.
Societies must contact in advance.
Green Fees £20 per day (£25 weekends & bank holidays).
Facilities ⊗ ⅢⅢ ⅛ ▆ ♀ 👤 🏠 ⅃ Stuart Bence.
Leisure snooker.
Location Glenluce Dr, Farringdon Park

Hotel B Forte Posthouse, Ringway, PRESTON
　　　　　 ☎ (0772) 259411 121 ⇆ ♠

Ingol ☎ (0772) 734556
Long, high course with natural water hazards.
18 holes, 5868yds, Par 70, SSS 68.
Club membership 800.
Visitors must contact in advance but may not play on
　　　　　 competition days.
Societies must contact in writing.
Green Fees £15 per day (£25 weekends & bank holidays).
Facilities ⊗ ⅢⅢ ⅛ ▆ ♀ 👤 🏠 ⅃ Steve Laycock.
Leisure squash, snooker.
Location Tanterton Hall Rd, Ingol (2m NW junc 32 of
　　　　　 M55 off B5411)
Hotel B Forte Posthouse, Ringway, PRESTON
　　　　　 ☎ (0772) 259411 121 ⇆ ♠

Penwortham ☎ (0772) 744630
A progressive golf club set close to the banks of the
River Ribble. The course has tree-lined fairways,
excellent greens, and provides easy walking. Testing
holes include the 178-yd, par 3 third, the 480-yd, par 5
sixth, and the 398-yd par 4 sixteenth.
18 holes, 5915yds, Par 69, SSS 68.
Club membership 870.
Visitors must contact in advance, restricted daily
　　　　　 after 10am.
Societies Mon & Wed-Fri only. Must contact in
　　　　　 advance.
Green Fees £28 per day; £22 per round (£28 Sun).
Facilities ⊗ ⅢⅢ ⅛ ▆ ♀ 👤 🏠 ⅃ John Wright.
Leisure snooker.
Location Blundell Ln, Penwortham (1.5m W of town
　　　　　 centre off A59)
Hotel ★★★64% Tickled Trout, Preston New Rd,
　　　　　 Samlesbury, PRESTON
　　　　　 ☎ (0772) 877671 72 ⇆ ♠

Preston ☎ (0772) 700011
Pleasant inland golf at this course set in very agreeable
parkland. There is a well-balanced selection of holes,
undulating amongst groups of trees, and not requiring great
length.
18 holes, 6233yds, Par 71, SSS 70, Course record 63.
Club membership 800.
Visitors may play midweek only. Must contact in
　　　　　 advance and have a handicap certificate.
Societies must contact in writing/telephone.
Green Fees £27 per day; £22 per round.
Facilities ⊗ ⅢⅢ ⅛ ▆ (no catering Mons in winter) ♀ 👤
　　　　　 🏠 ⅃ P A Wells.
Leisure snooker.
Location Fulwood Hall Ln, Fulwood (N side of town
　　　　　 centre)
Hotel ★★★70% Broughton Park Hotel & Country
　　　　　 Club, Garstang Rd, Broughton, PRESTON
　　　　　 ☎ (0772) 864087 98 ⇆ ♠

RISHTON · Map 07 SD73

Rishton ☎ Great Harwood (0254) 884442
Undulating moorland course.
9 holes, 6098yds, Par 70, SSS 69, Course record 66.
Club membership 250.

▶

ℛOYAL ℒYTHAM AND ℱT. ℬNNES

LYTHAM ST ANNES ☎ (0253) 724206   Map 07 SD32

John Ingham writes: Venue for many Open Championships, the most famous winner here was amateur Bobby Jones who, in 1926, put together a four-round total of 291 using wooden clubs and the old-fashioned ball. In the last round, when level with Al Watrous with two to play, Jones bunkered his teeshot at the 17th while Watrous hit a perfect drive and then a fine second on to the green. Jones climbed into the bunker, decided a 175-yard shot was needed if he had any chance, and hit a club similar to today's 4-iron. The shot was brilliant and finished, not only on the green, but nearer than his rival. Shaken, Watrous 3-putted, Jones got his four and finished with a perfect par while Watrous, rattled, had taken six. The club placed a plaque by the famous bunker and it's there to this day.

Since that time the course, which runs close to the railway but slightly inland from the sea, has staged other historic Opens. Bob Charles of New Zealand became the only left-hander to win the title while Tony Jacklin, in 1969, signalled the re-awakening of British golf by winning.

This huge links, not far from Blackpool, is not easy. When the wind gets up it can be a nightmare. And not everyone approves a championship course that starts with a par 3 hole and it is, in fact, a rare thing in Britain. Some object to the close proximity of red-bricked houses, and aren't keen on trains that rattle past. Now there is an additional nine-hole course and a driving range.

But it's a test full of history and deserves to be played.

Visitors	weekdays only. Must contact in advance, and have a letter of introduction from their own club with a handicap certificate
Societies	
Green fees	must apply to Secretary £75 per day; £55 per round (both include lunch)
Facilities	⊗ ⅏ (by arrangement) 🍴 🍷 ♀ 🛏 ⚒ 🖼 🎿 (E.Birchenough)
Leisure	snooker
Location	Links Gate (0.5m E of St Annes town)

**18 holes, 6673 yds, Par 71, SSS 73,
Course record 65 (Seve Ballesteros)**

WHERE TO STAY AND EAT NEARBY

HOTELS:

LYTHAM ST ANNES

★★★ 64% Bedford, 307-311 Clifton Drive South. ☎(0253) 724636. 36 ⇌ ℕ English & Continental cuisine

★★★ 66% Chadwick, South Promenade. ☎(0253) 720061. 72 ⇌ ℕ English & French cuisine

★★ 66% New Glendower, North Promenade. ☎(0253) 723241 60 ⇌ ℕ English cuisine

★★ 66% St Ives, 7-9 South Promenade. ☎(0253) 720011. 70 (63 ⇌ ℕ) English & French cuisine

RESTAURANT:

THORNTON

✕ ✕ ⊛The Victorian House, ☎ Blackpool (0253) 860619 French cuisine

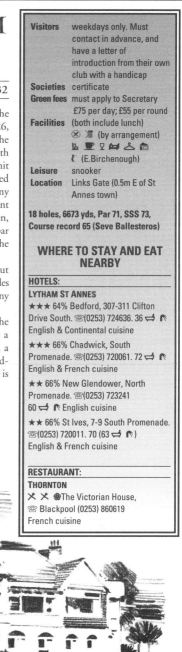

Visitors	must play with member on weekends and bank holidays.
Societies	must contact in advance.
Green Fees	not confirmed.
Facilities	⊗ 🍴 🛍 & 🍺 by prior arrangement ⚲ by arrangement ⛳
Location	Eachill Links, Hawthorn Dr (S side of town off A678)
Hotel	★★★65% Dunkenhalgh Hotel, Blackburn Rd, Clayton le Moors, ACCRINGTON ☎ (0254) 398021 37 ⇔ ☏Annexe42 ⇔ ☏

SILVERDALE   Map 07 SD47

Silverdale ☎ (0524) 701300
Difficult heathland course with rock outcrops. Excellent views.
12 holes, 5417yds, Par 69, SSS 67.
Club membership 500.

Visitors	may only play on Sun in summer if accompanied by a member.
Societies	must contact in writing.
Green Fees	£12 per day (£17 weekends & bank holidays).
Facilities	⛳ 🛍 ☏ S Sumner Roberts.
Location	Red Bridge Ln (opposite Silverdale Station)
Hotel	★62% Wheatsheaf Hotel, BEETHAM ☎ (05395) 62123 6 ⇔ ☏

UPHOLLAND   Map 07 SD50

Beacon Park ☎ (0695) 622700
Undulating/hilly parkland course, designed by Donald Steel, with magnificent view of the Welsh hills and Blackpool Tower. Twenty-four-bay floodlit driving range.
18 holes, 5996yds, Par 72, SSS 69, Course record 68.
Club membership 300.

Visitors	may book 6 days in advance for weekends & bank holidays.
Societies	apply in writing
Green Fees	£5.50 per 18 holes (£7 weekends & bank holidays).
Facilities	⊗ 🍴 🛍 🍺 ⚲ ⛳ ☏🍴 ☏ Ray Peters.
Leisure	24 bay floodlit driving range.
Location	Beacon Ln (S of Ashurst Beacon Hill)
Hotel	★★★64% Holland Hall Hotel, 6 Lafford Ln, UPHOLLAND ☎ (0695) 624426 28 ⇔ ☏Annexe6 ⇔ ☏

Dean Wood ☎ (0695) 622219
This parkland course has a varied terrain - flat front nine, undulating back nine. Beware the par 4, 11th and 17th holes, which has ruined many a card. If there were a prize for the best maintained course in Lancashire, Dean Wood would be a strong contender.
18 holes, 6137yds, Par 71, SSS 70, Course record 66.
Club membership 850.

Visitors	restricted weekends, bank holidays & competition days. Must contact in advance.
Societies	must contact in writing.
Green Fees	not confirmed.
Facilities	⊗ 🍴 🛍 🍺 ⚲ ⛳ ☏🍴 Tony Coop.
Leisure	snooker.

Location	Lafford Ln (0.5m NE off A577)
Hotel	★★★64% Holland Hall Hotel, 6 Lafford Ln, UPHOLLAND ☎ (0695) 624426 28 ⇔ ☏Annexe6 ⇔ ☏

WHALLEY   Map 07 SD73

Whalley ☎ (0254) 822236
Parkland course on Pendle Hill, overlooking the Ribble Valley. Superb views. Ninth hole over pond.
9 holes, 6258mtrs, Par 72, SSS 70.
Club membership 325.

Visitors	restricted Thu 12.30-4pm & Sat Apr-Sep.
Societies	must give 4 weeks notice Apr-Sep.
Green Fees	£15 per day (£20 weekends & bank holidays).
Facilities	⊗ 🍴 🛍 🍺 ⚲ ⛳ ☏ 🍴 ☏ Harry Smith.
Location	Long Leese Barn, Portfield Ln (1m SE off A671)
Hotel	★★★★64% Foxfields Country Hotel & Restaurant, Whalley Rd, BILLINGTON ☎ (0254) 822556 28 ⇔ ☏

WHITWORTH   Map 07 SD81

Lobden ☎ Rochdale (0706) 343228
Moorland course, with hard walking. Windy.
9 holes, 5750yds, Par 70, SSS 68.
Club membership 200.

Visitors	may not play Tue 3pm-7pm, Wed after 4pm or Sat.
Societies	must contact in writing.
Green Fees	£10 per day (£12 weekends & bank holidays).
Facilities	⊗ 🍴 🛍 🍺 (catering by prior arrangement) ⚲ ⛳
Leisure	snooker.
Location	Lobden Moor (E side of town centre off A671)
Hotel	★★61% Midway Hotel, Manchester Rd, Castleton, ROCHDALE ☎ (0706) 32881 24 ⇔ ☏

WILPSHIRE   Map 07 SD63

Wilpshire ☎ Blackburn (0254) 248260
Semi-moorland course. Testing 17th hole (229 yds) par 3. Extensive views of Ribble Valley, the coast and the Yorkshire Dales.
18 holes, 5921yds, Par 69, SSS 68.
Club membership 794.

Visitors	may not play on competition days.
Societies	must contact in writing.
Green Fees	£25 (£30 weekends & bank holidays).
Facilities	⊗ 🍴 🛍 🍺 ⚲ ⛳ ☏ ☏ Walter Slaven.
Leisure	caddy cars.
Hotel	★★★56% Blackburn Moat House, Preston New Rd, BLACKBURN ☎ (0254) 264441 98 ⇔ ☏

> This guide is up-dated annually – make sure you use the up-to-date edition

LEICESTERSHIRE

ASHBY-DE-LA-ZOUCH
Map 08 SK31

Willesley Park ☎ (0530) 414596
Undulating heathland and parkland course with quick draining sandy sub-soil.
18 holes, 6304yds, Par 70, SSS 70.
Club membership 600.
Visitors may not play before 9.30am on weekends & bank holidays. Must contact in advance and have a handicap certificate.
Societies telephone to book, up to a year in advance.
Green Fees £27.50 per day (£32.50 weekends & bank holidays).
Facilities ⛾ 🍴 ⚑
Leisure snooker.
Location Measham Rd (SW side of town centre on A453)
Hotel ★★★ Stanhope Arms Brewers Fayre, Ashby Rd East, BRETBY ☎ (0283) 217954 24 ⇋ ☔

BIRSTALL
Map 04 SK50

Birstall ☎ Leicester (0533) 674322
Parkland course with trees, shrubs, ponds and ditches.
18 holes, 6222yds, Par 70, SSS 70, Course record 62.
Club membership 500.
Visitors with member only Tue & weekends.
Societies apply in writing.
Green Fees £25 per day (weekdays).
Facilities ⊗ 🍴 (during season) 🏌 ⛾ ⚑ 🧺 🍴
⚑ D R Clarke.
Leisure snooker, practice ground.
Location Station Rd (2m N of Leicester on A6)
Hotel ★★★58% Hotel Saint James, Abbey St, LEICESTER ☎ (0533) 510666 72 ⇋ ☔

BOTCHESTON
Map 04 SK40

Leicestershire Forest Golf Centre
☎ Hinckley (0455) 824800
Parkland course with many trees, four Par 4s, but no steep gradients.
18 holes, 6111yds, Par 72, SSS 69, Course record 72.
Club membership 450.
Visitors must contact in advance for weekends.
Societies must telephone in advance.
Green Fees not confirmed.
Facilities ⊗ & 🍴 by prior arrangement 🏌 ⛾ ⚑ 🧺 🍴 ⚑
⚑ Martin Wing.
Leisure driving range.
Location Markfield Ln
Hotel ★★★71% Field Head Hotel, Markfield Ln, MARKFIELD ☎ (0530) 245454 28 ⇋ ☔

COSBY
Map 04 SP59

Cosby ☎ Leicester (0533) 864759
Undulating parkland course with a number of tricky, tight driving holes.
18 holes, 6418yds, Par 71, SSS 71, Course record 66.
Club membership 680.

Visitors restricted weekdays before 4pm. With member only weekends & bank holidays. Advisable to contact in advance and have handicap certificate.
Societies book with secretary.
Green Fees £24 per day; £22 per round.
Facilities ⊗ 🍴 🏌 ⛾ ⚑ 🧺 🍴 ⚑ Martin Wing.
Leisure snooker, practice area.
Location Chapel Ln, Broughton Rd (S side of village)
Hotel B Forte Posthouse, Braunstone Ln East, LEICESTER ☎ (0533) 630500 172 ⇋ ☔

GREETHAM
Map 08 SK91

Greetham Valley ☎ Empingham (0780) 460666 & 460444
Set in 200 acres, including mature woodland and water hazards, Greetham Valley was opened in spring 1992. The complex comprises an 18-hole course and clubhouse, a floodlit 9-hole Par 3 and a 21-bay floodlit driving range.
18 holes, 6656yds, Par 72, SSS 71, Course record 68.
Club membership 650.
Visitors must contact in advance. Par 3 & driving range open to non members any day.
Societies apply in writing.
Green Fees £25 per day, £15 per round (£35/£25 weekends).
Facilities ⊗ 🍴 🏌 ⛾ ⚑ 🧺 🍴 ⚑ Mark Cunningham.
Leisure fishing, caddy cars, putting green, 21 bay range.
Location Off B668 in Greetham
Hotel ★★68% Ram Jam Inn, Great North Rd, STRETTON
☎ (0780) 410776 Annexe7 ⇋ ☔

HINCKLEY
Map 04 SP49

Hinckley ☎ (0455) 615124
Rolling parkland with lake features, and lined fairways.
18 holes, 6517yds, Par 71, SSS 71.
Club membership 1000.
Visitors with member only weekends and bank holidays. Must contact in advance and have a handicap certificate.
Societies apply by letter.
Green Fees £25 per day; £20 per round.
Facilities ⊗ 🍴 🏌 ⛾ ⚑ 🧺 ⚑ Richard Jones.
Leisure snooker, caddys available.
Location Leicester Rd (1.5m NE on A47)
Hotel ★★63% Longshoot Toby Hotel, Watling St, NUNEATON
☎ (0203) 329711 Annexe47 ⇋ ☔

KETTON
Map 04 SK90

Luffenham Heath ☎ Stamford (0780) 720205
This undulating heathland course with low bushes, much gorse and many trees, lies in a conservation area for flora and fauna. From the higher part of the course there is a magnificent view across the Chater Valley.
18 holes, 6250yds, Par 70, SSS 70, Course record 64.
Club membership 555.
Visitors must contact in advance and a handicap certificate required.
Societies must telephone in advance.
Green Fees not confirmed.
Facilities ⊗ & 🍴 by prior arrangement 🏌 ⛾ ⚑ 🧺
⚑ J A Lawrence. ▶

Location	Stamford (1.5m SW on A6121)
Hotel	★★★75% George of Stamford Hotel, St Martins, STAMFORD ☎ (0780) 55171 47 ⇔ ⋒

KIBWORTH   Map 04 SP69

Kibworth ☎ (0533) 792301
Parkland course with easy walking. A brook affects a number of fairways
18 holes, 6282yds, Par 71, SSS 70.
Club membership 700.
Visitors   a handicap certificate is required. With member only weekends.
Societies   must contact in advance.
Green Fees not confirmed.
Facilities   ♀ ♨ 🏠 🏌 ⋔
Leisure   snooker.
Location   Weir Rd, Beauchamp (S side of village)
Hotel   ★★★66% Three Swans Hotel, 21 High St, MARKET HARBOROUGH ☎ (0858) 466644 20 ⇔ ⋒Annexe16 ⇔ ⋒

KIRBY MUXLOE   Map 04 SK50

Kirby Muxloe ☎ Leicester (0533) 393457
Pleasant parkland course with a lake in front of the 17th green and a short 18th.
18 holes, 6303yds, Par 71, SSS 70, Course record 62.
Club membership 700.
Visitors   must contact in advance and a handicap certificate is required. Restricted at weekends.
Societies   must contact in advance.
Green Fees £25 per day; £20 per round (weekends with member only).
Facilities   ⊗ ⫴ 🍴 ♬ ♀ ♨ 🏠 ⋔ Robert Stephenson.
Leisure   snooker, driving range.
Location   Station Rd (S side of village off B5380)
Hotel   ★★★★58% Holiday Inn, St Nicholas Circle, LEICESTER ☎ (0533) 531161 188 ⇔ ⋒

LEICESTER   Map 04 SK50

Humberstone Heights ☎ (0533) 764674
Municipal parkland course with 9 hole pitch and putt.
18 holes, 6300yds, Par 70, SSS 71, Course record 66.
Club membership 500.
Visitors   no restrictions.
Societies   must telephone in advance.
Green Fees £7.40 per round (£8.80 weekends).
Facilities   ⊗ (ex Mon) ⫴ (Sat & Sun only) 🍴 ♬ ♀ ♨ 🏠 🏌 ⋔ Philip Highfield.
Leisure   driving range & pitch & putt course.
Location   Gypsy Ln (2.5m NE of city centre)
Hotel   ★★★59% Leicester Forest Moat House, Hinckley Rd, Leicester Forest East, LEICESTER ☎ (0533) 394661 34 ⇔ ⋒

Leicestershire ☎ (0533) 738825
Pleasantly undulating parkland course.
18 holes, 6312yds, Par 68, SSS 70.
Club membership 750.
Visitors   must contact in advance & have handicap certificate. Restricted Sat & Tue.

Societies   must telephone in advance.
Green Fees £28 per day; £23 per round (£34/£29 weekends & bank holidays).
Facilities   ♀ ♨ 🏠 ⋔ John R Turnbull.
Location   Evington Ln (2m E of city off A6030)
Hotel   ★★★67% Leicestershire Moat House, Wigston Rd, Oadby, LEICESTER ☎ (0533) 719441 57 ⇔ ⋒

Western ☎ (0533) 872339
Pleasant, undulating parkland course with open aspect fairways in two loops of nine holes.Not too difficult but a good test of golf off the back tees.
18 holes, 6561yds, Par 72, SSS 71.
Club membership 400.
Visitors   Booking system in operation phone for details.
Societies   may only play Mon-Thu. Must contact the professional in advance.
Green Fees £6.80 (£8.80 weekends).
Facilities   ⊗ ♀ ♨ 🏠 🏌 ⋔ Bruce Nicholas Whipham.
Leisure   indoor school.
Location   Scudamore Rd, Braunstone Frith (1.5m W of city centre off A47)
Hotel   B Forte Posthouse, Braunstone Ln East, LEICESTER ☎ (0533) 630500 172 ⇔ ⋒

LOUGHBOROUGH   Map 08 SK51

Longcliffe ☎ (0509) 239129
A re-designed course of natural heathland with outcrops of granite forming natural hazards especially on the 1st and 15th. The course is heavily wooded and has much bracken and gorse. There are a number of tight fairways and one blind hole.
18 holes, 6551yds, Par 71, SSS 72.
Club membership 600.
Visitors   must contact in advance & have handicap certificate. With member only at weekends.
Societies   by prior arrangement.
Green Fees £27 per day; £22 per round.
Facilities   ⊗ ⫴ 🍴 ♬ ♀ ♨ 🏠 ⋔ Ian D Bailey.
Location   Snell's Nook Ln, Nanpantan (3m SW off B5350)
Hotel   ★★★63% Friendly Hotel, New Ashby Rd, LOUGHBOROUGH ☎ (0509) 211800

LUTTERWORTH   Map 04 SP58

Lutterworth ☎ (0455) 552532
Hilly course with River Swift running through.
18 holes, 5570yds, Par 67, SSS 67.
Club membership 600.
Visitors   may not play at weekends.
Societies   Mon-Fri; must contact in advance.
Green Fees not confirmed.
Facilities   ⊗ ⫴ 🍴 ♬ ♀ ♨ 🏠 ⋔ Nick Melvin.
Location   Rugby Rd (0.5m S on A426)
Hotel   ★★★63% Denbigh Arms Hotel, High St, LUTTERWORTH ☎ (0455) 553537 31 ⇔ ⋒

> **For an explanation of symbols and abbreviations, see page 5**

MARKET HARBOROUGH   Map 04 SP78

Market Harborough ☎ (0858) 463684
A parkland course situated close to the town. There are wide-ranging views over the surrounding countryside.
9 holes, 6080yds, Par 71, SSS 69.
Club membership 550.
Visitors   must play with member at weekends.
Societies   must telephone (0536) 771771 in advance.
Green Fees £22 per day; £16 per round.
Facilities   ⊗ ⅢⅢ ⅃ ♥ ♀ ㅿ 🏠 ⅋ ℓ Frazer Baxter.
Location   Oxendon Rd (1m S on A508)
Hotel   ★★★66% Three Swans Hotel, 21 High St, MARKET HARBOROUGH
               ☎ (0858) 466644 20 ⊨ ℝAnnexe16 ⊨ ℝ

MELTON MOWBRAY   Map 08 SK71

Melton Mowbray ☎ (0664) 62118
Downland but flat course providing easy walking. Open to the wind.
18 holes, 6222yds, Par 70, SSS 70.
Club membership 650.
Visitors   must contact in advance.
Societies   must contact in advance.
Green Fees £18 per day (£25 weekends).
Facilities   ⊗ ⅢⅢ by prior arrangement ⅃ ♥ ♀ ㅿ 🏠 ⅋
             ℓ Tony Westwood.
Location   Thorpe Arnold (2m NE on A607)
Hotel   ★★65% Sysonby Knoll Hotel, Asfordby Rd, MELTON MOWBRAY
               ☎ (0664) 63563 23 ⊨ ℝAnnexe1 ⊨ ℝ

OADBY   Map 04 SK60

Glen Gorse ☎ Leicester (0533) 714159 & 713748
Fairly flat 18-hole parkland course with some strategically placed mature trees, new saplings and ponds affecting play on 6 holes. Ridge and furrow is a feature of 5 holes.
18 holes, 6603yds, Par 72, SSS 72, Course record 65.
Club membership 700.
Visitors   unrestricted on weekdays, with member only Sat & Sun.
Societies   by prior arrangement.
Green Fees £25 per day; £22 per round.
Facilities   ⊗ ⅢⅢ ⅃ ♥ (no catering Mon) ♀ (ex Mon) ㅿ
             🏠 ⅋ ℓ Bob Larratt.
Leisure   riding, snooker.
Location   Glen Rd (on A6 trunk road between Oadby/Great Glen)
Hotel   ★★★67% Leicestershire Moat House, Wigston Rd, Oadby, LEICESTER
             ☎ (0533) 719441 57 ⊨ ℝ

Oadby ☎ (0533) 700326
Municipal parkland course.
18 holes, 6228yds, Par 71, SSS 69.
Club membership 400.
Visitors   no restrictions.
Societies   must contact in advance.
Green Fees not confirmed.
Facilities   ♀ ㅿ 🏠 ⅋ ℓ
Location   Leicester Rd (West side of town centre off A6)

ROTHLEY   Map 08 SK51

Rothley Park ☎ (0533) 302809
Parkland course in picturesque situation.
18 holes, 6167yds, Par 70, SSS 69.
Club membership 600.
Visitors   restricted Tue, weekends & competitions. Must contact in advance and a handicap certificate required.
Societies   apply in writing.
Green Fees £30 per day; £25 per round.
Facilities   ⊗ ⅢⅢ ⅃ & ♥ by prior arrangement ♀ ㅿ 🏠
             ℓ Andrew Collins.
Location   Westfield Ln (0.75m W on B5328)
Hotel   ★★★70% Rothley Court Hotel, Westfield Ln, ROTHLEY
             ☎ (0533) 374141 15 ⊨ ℝAnnexe21 ⊨ ℝ

SCRAPTOFT   Map 04 SK60

Scraptoft ☎ (0533) 418863
Pleasant, inland country course.
18 holes, 6166yds, Par 69, SSS 69.
Club membership 550.
Visitors   with member only weekends. Handicap certificate required.
Societies   apply in writing.
Green Fees not confirmed.
Facilities   ⊗ ⅢⅢ ⅃ ♥ (no catering Mon) ♀ ㅿ 🏠 ⅋
             ℓ Simon Sherratt.
Location   Beeby Rd (1m NE)
Hotel   ★★★67% Leicestershire Moat House, Wigston Rd, Oadby, LEICESTER
             ☎ (0533) 719441 57 ⊨ ℝ

ULLESTHORPE   Map 04 SP58

Ullesthorpe ☎ Leire (0455) 209023
Parkland course. Many leisure facilities.
18 holes, 6650yds, Par 72, SSS 72.
Club membership 640.
Visitors   may not play weekends. Must contact in advance.
Societies   contact in advance.
Green Fees not confirmed.
Facilities   ⊗ ⅢⅢ ⅃ ♥ ♀ ㅿ 🏠 ⊨ ℓ
Leisure   hard tennis courts, heated indoor swimming pool, snooker, sauna, solarium, gymnasium.
Location   Frolesworth Rd (0.5m N off B577)
Hotel   ★★★63% Denbigh Arms Hotel, High St, LUTTERWORTH ☎ (0455) 553537 31 ⊨ ℝ

WHETSTONE   Map 04 SP59

Whetstone ☎ (0533) 861424
Small and very flat parkland course adjacent to motorway.
18 holes, 5795yds, Par 68, SSS 68, Course record 64.
Club membership 500.
Visitors   limited times at weekends
Societies   must contact in advance.   ▶

Green Fees not confirmed.
Facilities ⊗ & 〗ⅲ (ex weekends) 🏌 (ex Sun) 💺 ♀ 🛆 🏠
  ⎰ David Raitt.
Location Cambridge Rd, Cosby (1m S of village)
Hotel B Forte Posthouse, Braunstone Ln East,
  LEICESTER ☎ (0533) 630500 172 ⇆ ☏

WOODHOUSE EAVES   Map 08 SK51

Charnwood Forest ☎ (0509) 890259
Hilly heathland course with hard walking, but no bunkers.
9 holes, 5960yds, Par 69, SSS 69.
Club membership 336.
Visitors may be restricted Tue.
Societies apply in writing.
Green Fees £20 for 18 holes; £25 (weekends).
Facilities ⊗ 〗ⅲ 🏌 💺 🛆
Location Breakback Ln (0.75m NW off B591)
Hotel ★★★69% Quorn Country Hotel, Charnwood
  House, Leicester Rd, QUORN
  ☎ (0509) 415050 19 ⇆ ☏

Lingdale ☎ (0509) 890703
Parkland course located in Charnwood Forest with some hard walking at some holes. The par 3, (3rd) and par 5, (8th) are testing holes. The 4th and 5th have water hazards.
18 holes, 6556yds, Par 71, SSS 71.
Club membership 609.
Visitors restricted weekends & competition days.
Societies must contact in writing.
Green Fees £18 per day (£20 weekends).
Facilities ⊗ 〗ⅲ 🏌 💺 🛆 🏠 ⎰ Peter Sellears.
Leisure practice ground, pool table.
Location Joe Moore's Ln (1.5m S off B5330)
Hotel ★★★69% Quorn Country Hotel, Charnwood
  House, Leicester Rd, QUORN
  ☎ (0509) 415050 19 ⇆ ☏

• LINCOLNSHIRE •

BELTON   Map 08 SK93

Belton Woods Hotel & Country Club ☎ Grantham (0476) 593200
Two challenging 18-hole courses, a 9-hole Par 3 and a driving range. The Lakes Course has 13 lakes, while The Woodside boasts the third longest hole in Europe at 613 yards. Many leisure facilities.
The Lakes: 18 holes, 6970yds, Par 72, SSS 73.
The Woodside: 18 holes, 6926yds, Par 73, SSS 73.
Spitfire: 9 holes, 1184yds, Par 27.
Club membership 900.
Visitors no advanced booking permitted.
Societies advance booking required.
Green Fees £19.50 per 18 holes; £5 per 9 holes.
Facilities ⊗ 〗ⅲ 🏌 💺 ♀ 🛆 🏠 ⎰ Anthony Roberts.
Leisure hard tennis courts, heated indoor swimming
  pool, squash, snooker, sauna, solarium,
  gymnasium, golf buggies.

Location On A607, 2m N of Grantham
Hotel ★★★★66% Belton Woods Hotel, BELTON
  ☎ (0476) 593200 136 ⇆ ☏

BLANKNEY   Map 08 TF06

Blankney ☎ Metheringham (0526) 320263
Open parkland course with mature trees; fairly flat.
18 holes, 6450yds, Par 71, SSS 71, Course record 66.
Club membership 630.
Visitors restricted at weekends. Must contact in advance.
Societies contact in advance.
Green Fees £25 per day; £15 per round (£30/£20 weekends
  & bank holidays).
Facilities ⊗ 〗ⅲ 🏌 💺 ♀ 🛆 🏠 🛒 ⎰ Graham Bradley.
Leisure squash, snooker.
Location 1m SW on B1188
Hotel ★★★60% Moor Lodge Hotel, Sleaford Rd,
  BRANSTON ☎ (0522) 791366 25 ⇆ ☏

BOSTON   Map 08 TF34

Boston ☎ (0205) 350589 or 362306
Parkland course many water hazards in play on ten holes.
18 holes, 6483yds, Par 72, SSS 71, Course record 70.
Club membership 650.
Visitors welcome except weekends & bank holidays.
  Must contact in advance.
Societies apply two weeks in advance.
Green Fees £20 per day; £15 per round (£30/£20 weekends).
Facilities ⊗ 〗ⅲ 🏌 💺 ♀ 🛆 🏠 🛒 ⎰ Terry Squires.
Location Cowbridge, Horncastle Rd (2m N off B1183)
Hotel ★★60% New England, 49 Wide Bargate,
  BOSTON ☎ (0205) 365255 25 ⇆

BOURNE   Map 08 TF02

Toft Hotel ☎ Witham-on-the-Hill (077833) 616 due to change to (0778) 590616
Parkland course on the verge of the Lincoln Edge. Includes lake and uses contours of the hills to full effect.
18 holes, 6486yds, Par 72, SSS 71, Course record 68.
Club membership 500.
Visitors advisable to book.
Societies apply in advance by telephone.
Green Fees £18 per day (£25 weekends & bank holidays).
Facilities ⊗ 〗ⅲ 🏌 💺 ♀ 🛆 🏠 🛒 🛒 ⎰ Mark Jackson.
Leisure four golf buggies for hire.
Location Toft (15m SE of Spalding,on A6121
  Bourne/Stamford)
Hotel ★★60% Angel Hotel, Market Place, BOURNE
  ☎ (0778) 422346 14 ⇆ ☏

GAINSBOROUGH   Map 08 SK88

Gainsborough ☎ (0427) 613088
Scenic parkland course. Floodlit driving range.
18 holes, 6620yds, Par 73, SSS 72.
Club membership 600.
Visitors welcome weekdays. Must contact in advance.
Societies must telephone in advance.
Green Fees not confirmed.
Facilities ⊗ 〗ⅲ (Tue-Sat) 🏌 💺 ♀ 🛆 🏠
  ⎰ Stephen Cooper.

Leisure	snooker, driving range.
Location	Thonock (1m N off A159)
Hotel	★★65% Hickman-Hill Hotel, Cox's Hill, GAINSBOROUGH ☎ (0427) 613639 8rm(3 ⇥3 ⋒)

GEDNEY HILL   Map 08 TF31

Gedney Hill ☎ Holbeach (0406) 330922 & 330183
Flat parkland course similar to a links course. Made testing by Fen winds and small greens. Also a 10-bay driving range.
18 holes, 5493yds, Par 70, SSS 66, Course record 67.
Club membership 300.

Visitors	no restrictions.
Societies	telephone in advance.
Green Fees	not confirmed.
Facilities	⊗ ⅷ ⅃ ♨ ♀ ♨ ⋒ ⊶ ⋔ David Creek.
Leisure	snooker, 10 bay driving range.
Location	West Drove (5m SE of Spalding)
Hotel	★★63% Queens Hotel, South Brink, WISBECH ☎ (0945) 583933 12 ⇥ ⋒Annexe6 ⇥

GRANTHAM   Map 08 SK93

Belton Park ☎ (0476) 67399
Parkland course, wooded, with water features, deer park and Canadian Geese Reserve. Famous holes: 5th, 12th, 16th and 18th. 27-holes, with three 9-hole combinations.
18 holes, 6420yds, Par 71, SSS 71, Course record 65.
Ancaster: 18 holes, 6252yds, Par 70, SSS 70.
Belmont: 18 holes, 6016yds, Par 69, SSS 69.
Club membership 900.

Visitors	no restrictions.
Societies	apply in writing.
Green Fees	not confirmed.
Facilities	⊗ ⅷ by prior arrangement ♨ ♀ ♨ ⋒ ⊶ ⋔ Brian McKee.
Leisure	two practice fairways.
Location	Belton Ln, Londonthorpe Rd (1.5m NE off A607)
Hotel	★★★62% Angel & Royal Hotel, High St, GRANTHAM ☎ (0476) 65816 30 ⇥ ⋒

Sudbrook Moor ☎ (0400) 50796 & 50876
A testing 9-hole parkland course in open countryside.
9 holes, 4566yds, Par 66, SSS 61, Course record 69.

Visitors	preferable to contact in advance.
Societies	prior application.
Green Fees	£5 per day (£7 weekends and bank holidays).
Facilities	⊗ ♨ ♀ ♨ ⋒ ⊶ ⋔ Tim Hutton.
Location	Charity St, Carlton Scroop
Hotel	★★68% Kings Hotel, North Pde, GRANTHAM ☎ (0476) 590800 22rm(21 ⇥ ⋒)

HORNCASTLE   Map 08 TF26

Horncastle ☎ (0507) 526800
Heathland course with many water hazards and bunkers; very challenging. There is a 25-bay floodlit driving range.
18 holes, 5782yds, Par 70, SSS 70, Course record 71.
Par 3: 9 holes, 4025yds, Par 27, SSS 27.
Club membership 300.

Visitors	no jeans, T-shirts or tracksuits.
Societies	apply in writing.

Green Fees	£15 per day; £10 per round. Par 3 pay as you play £3 per 9 holes.
Facilities	⊗ ⅷ ⅃ ♨ ♀ ♨ ⋒ ⊶ E C Wright.
Leisure	fishing, floodlit driving range.
Location	West Ashby (1.5m N Horncastle)
Hotel	★★★68% Petwood House Hotel, Stixwould Rd, WOODHALL SPA ☎ (0526) 352411 46 ⇥ ⋒

LINCOLN   Map 08 SK97

Canwick Park ☎ (0522) 522166 & 542912
Parkland course. Testing 14th hole (par 3).
18 holes, 6237yds, Par 70, SSS 70.
Club membership 576.

Visitors	restricted at weekends. Must contact in advance.
Societies	must contact 1 month in advance.
Green Fees	£22 per day; £15 per round (£19 weekends & bank holidays).
Facilities	⊗ ⅷ by prior arrangement ♨ ♀ ♨ ⋒ ⊶ ⋔ S Williamson.
Location	Canwick Park, Washingborough Rd (2m SE on B1190)
Hotel	B Forte Posthouse, Eastgate, LINCOLN ☎ (0522) 520341 70 ⇥ ⋒

Carholme ☎ (0522) 23725
Parkland course where prevailing west winds can add interest. Good views.
18 holes, 6114yds, Par 71, SSS 69.
Club membership 700.

Visitors	may not play Sat, Sun & bank holidays. Must contact in advance.
Societies	apply in writing.
Green Fees	£16.50 per day; £12.50 per round (weekdays).
Facilities	♨ ♀ ♨ ⋒ ⊶ ⋔ Gary Leslie.
Location	Carholme Rd (1m W of city centre on A57)
Hotel	★★★★63% The White Hart, Bailgate, LINCOLN ☎ (0522) 526222 48 ⇥

LOUTH   Map 08 TF38

Louth ☎ (0507) 603681
Undulating parkland course, fine views.
18 holes, 6477yds, Par 71, SSS 71.
Club membership 700.

Visitors	must contact in advance and have a handicap certificate.
Societies	must contact in advance.
Green Fees	£20 day; £16 per round (£30/£25 weekends and bank holidays).
Facilities	⊗ ⅷ by prior arrangement ♨ ♀ ♨ ⋒ ⊶ ⋔ A Blundell.
Leisure	squash, caddy cars, trolleys.
Location	Crowtree Ln (SE side of town centre off A157)
Hotel	★★★61% Beaumont Hotel, Victoria Rd, LOUTH ☎ (0507) 605005 17 ⇥ ⋒

MARKET RASEN   Map 08 TF18

Market Rasen & District ☎ (0673) 842416 or 842319
Picturesque, well-wooded heathland course, easy walking, breezy with becks forming natural hazards. Good views of Lincolnshire Wolds.
18 holes, 6043yds, Par 70, SSS 69, Course record 65.
Club membership 550.   ▶

Visitors must play with member at weekends and must contact in advance.
Societies Tue & Fri only; must contact in advance.
Green Fees not confirmed.
Facilities ⊗ ⓑ ▆ ♀ ☋ ⓕ A M Chester.
Location Legsby Rd (2m SE)
Hotel B Forte Posthouse, Eastgate, LINCOLN ☎ (0522) 520341 70 ⇋ 🐾

SKEGNESS   Map 09 TF56

North Shore Hotel & Golf Club ☎ (0754) 763298
A half-links, half-parkland course designed by James Braid in 1910. Easy walking and good sea views.
18 holes, 6134yds, Par 71, SSS 71, Course record 68.
Club membership 400.
Visitors must observe dress rules & must be competent golfers.
Societies telephone in advance.
Green Fees not confirmed.
Facilities ⊗ ⑅ ⓑ ▆ ♀ ☋ ⓕ ⓚ ⓕ
Leisure hard tennis courts, snooker.
Location North Shore Rd (1m N of town centre off A52)
Hotel ★★62% North Shore Hotel, North Shore Rd, SKEGNESS ☎ (0754) 763298 30 ⇋ 🐾Annexe3 ⇋ 🐾

Seacroft ☎ (0754) 763020
A typical seaside links with flattish fairways separated by low ridges and good greens. Easy to walk round. To the east are sandhills leading to the shore. Southward lies 'Gibraltar Point Nature Reserve'.
18 holes, 6501yds, Par 71, SSS 71.
Club membership 620.
Visitors must contact in advance & have handicap certificate but may not play before 9.30am.
Societies contact in advance.
Green Fees £28 per day; £20 per round (£35/£25 weekends & bank holidays).
Facilities ⊗ ⑅ ⓑ ▆ ♀ (ex Tue) ⓕ ⓕ Robin Lawie.
Location Drummond Rd, Seacroft (S side of town centre)
Hotel ★★★59% Crown Hotel, Drummond Rd, Seacroft, SKEGNESS ☎ (0754) 610760 27 ⇋ 🐾

SLEAFORD   Map 08 TF04

Sleaford ☎ South Rauceby (05298) 273
Inland links-type course, moderately wooded and fairly flat.
18 holes, 6443yds, Par 72, SSS 71.
Club membership 650.
Visitors may not play Sun in winter. Must have a handicap certificate.
Societies apply in writing.
Green Fees £18 per round/day (£26 weekends & bank holidays).
Facilities ⊗ ⑅ by prior arrangement ⓑ ▆ ♀ ☋ ⓕ ⓕ James Wilson.
Leisure trolleys for hire.
Location South Rauceby (1m W off A153)
Hotel ★★★62% Angel & Royal Hotel, High St, GRANTHAM ☎ (0476) 65816 30 ⇋ 🐾

SPALDING   Map 08 TF22

Spalding ☎ (0775) 680386 & 680234
A pretty, well laid-out course in a fenland area. The River Glen runs beside the 1st and 2nd holes, and streams, ponds and new tree plantings add to the variety of this well-maintained course.
18 holes, 6450yds, Par 71, SSS 71.
Club membership 750.
Visitors are advised to contact in advance and must have a handicap certificate.
Societies must contact in advance. Societies on Thu all day and Tue pm.
Green Fees £20 per day (£25 weekends & bank holidays).
Facilities ⊗ (ex Tue) ⑅ (ex Tue & Sun) ▆ ♀ ☋ ⓕ ⓕ John Spencer.
Location Surfleet (5m N off A16)
Hotel ★★60% New England, 49 Wide Bargate, BOSTON ☎ (0205) 365255 25 ⇋

STAMFORD   Map 08 TF00

Burghley Park ☎ (0780) 53789
Open parkland course with superb greens, many new trees, ponds and bunkers. Situated in the grounds of Burghley House.
18 holes, 6200yds, Par 70, SSS 70, Course record 64.
Club membership 950.
Visitors with member only weekends. Must contact in advance & have handicap certificate.
Societies apply in writing.
Green Fees £20 per day (half price after noon in winter months & after 5pm in summer).
Facilities ⊗ ⑅ ⓑ ⓑ (Tue-Sun in summer) ▆ ♀ ☋ ⓕ ⓕ Glenn Davies.
Location St Martins (1m S of town on B1081)
Hotel ★★★75% George of Stamford Hotel, St Martins, STAMFORD ☎ (0780) 55171 47 ⇋ 🐾

STOKE ROCHFORD   Map 08 SK92

Stoke Rochford ☎ Great Ponton (047683) 275
Parkland course designed by C. Turner.
18 holes, 6251yds, Par 70, SSS 70, Course record 65.
Club membership 525.
Visitors must contact in advance, restricted to 9am weekdays, 10.30am weekends & bank holidays.
Societies contact one year in advance.
Green Fees not confirmed.
Facilities ⊗ & ⑅ by prior arrangement ⓑ ▆ by prior arrangement ♀ ☋ ⓕ ⓕ Angus Dow.
Leisure snooker.
Location Off A1 5m S of Grantham
Hotel ★★68% Kings Hotel, North Pde, GRANTHAM ☎ (0476) 590800 22rm(21 ⇋ 🐾)

If you know of a golf course that welcomes visitors and is not already in this guide, we should be grateful for information

---

134

SUTTON BRIDGE   Map 09 TF42

Sutton Bridge ☎ Holbeach (0406) 350323
Parkland course.
9 holes, 5850yds, Par 70, SSS 68.
Club membership 350.
Visitors	may not play competition days, weekends & bank holidays. Must contact in advance & have handicap certificate.
Societies	telephone in advance.
Green Fees	not confirmed.
Facilities	⊗ ⅷ ⮜ 🍺 (no catering Mon) ♀ (ex Mon) ⌂ 🏠 ⌐ᵀ🍴 R Wood.
Location	New Rd (E side of village off A17)
Hotel	★★★65% The Duke's Head, Tuesday Market Pl, KING'S LYNN ☎ (0553) 774996 71 ⇆ ⮝

SUTTON ON SEA   Map 09 TF58

Sandilands ☎ (0507) 441432
Flat links course on the sea shore.
18 holes, 5995yds, Par 70, SSS 69.
Club membership 300.
Visitors	no restrictions.
Societies	welcome weekdays only, telephone in advance.
Green Fees	£18 per day; £12 per round (£18 per round weekends & bank holidays).
Facilities	⊗ ⅷ 🍺 ♀ ⌂ 🏠
Leisure	trolleys.
Location	1.5m S off A52
Hotel	★★69% Grange & Links Hotel, Sea Ln, Sandilands, MABLETHORPE ☎ (0507) 441334 23 ⇆ ⮝

TORKSEY   Map 08 SK87

Lincoln ☎ (0427) 718210
A testing inland course with quick-drying sandy subsoil and easy walking.
18 holes, 6438yds, Par 71, SSS 71.
Club membership 700.
Visitors	may not play between noon-1.30pm or on weekends & bank holidays. Must contact in advance and have a handicaps certificate.
Societies	apply by letter.
Green Fees	£23 per day; £18 per round.
Facilities	⊗ & ⅷ by prior arrangement ⮜ 🍺 ♀ ⌂ 🏠 🍴 Ashley Carter.
Location	SW side of village
Hotel	★★★★63% The White Hart, Bailgate, LINCOLN ☎ (0522) 526222 48 ⇆

Millfield ☎ (0427) 718255
There is an unusual set-up at Millfield with a 15 hole 4,201 yard Family course on which anyone can play, as well as a 9-hole Par 3 and an 18-hole course of nearly 6,000 yards. Due to its location in flat Lincolnshire the courses are affected by winds, which change every day.
18 holes, 5974yds, Par 69, SSS 69.
Family 15: 15 holes, 4201yds, Par 56.
Visitors	18 hole; shoes must be worn, no jeans etc. Family 15 hole no restrictions.
Societies	welcome on weekdays.

Green Fees 18 hole: £8 per day, £6 per round. Family 15 £4 all day, Par 3 £2 all day.
Facilities	🍺 ⌂ 🏠 ⮝
Location	Sandfield Farm, Laughterton (on A1133 1m N of A57)
Hotel	★★★★63% The White Hart, Bailgate, LINCOLN ☎ (0522) 526222 48 ⇆

WOODHALL SPA   Map 08 TF16

> **Woodhall Spa** ☎ (0526) 352511
> One of the country's greatest and most beautiful heathland courses, founded in 1905, and originally laid out by Harry Vardon. It provides flat, easy walking amongst heather and tree-lined fairways, and is renowned for its vast bunkers and clubhouse atmosphere.
> *18 holes, 6907yds, Par 73, SSS 73.*
> *Club membership 460.*
> | | |
> |---|---|
> | Visitors | must be a member of a golf club affiliated to the appropriate Golf Union, maximum handicap gentlemen 20-ladies 30, handicap certificate must be produced. |
> | Societies | must book in advance. |
> | Green Fees | £40 per day; £26 per round (£45/£30 weekends & bank holidays). |
> | Facilities | ⊗ ⅷ by prior arrangement ⮜ 🍺 ♀ ⌂ 🏠 🍴 Campbell C Elliott. |
> | Leisure | pitch & putt. |
> | Location | The Broadway (NE side of village off B1191) |
> | Hotel | ★★★68% Petwood House Hotel, Stixwould Rd, WOODHALL SPA ☎ (0526) 352411 46 ⇆ ⮝ |

WOODTHORPE   Map 09 TF48

Woodthorpe Hall ☎ Withern (0507) 450294
Parkland course.
18 holes, 4659yds, Par 64, SSS 63.
Club membership 400.
Visitors	no restrictions.
Societies	apply at least one month prior to visit.
Green Fees	£8 per day.
Facilities	⊗ ⅷ ⮜ 🍺 ♀ ⮝
Leisure	snooker.
Location	8m due W of Sutton-on-Sea
Hotel	★★69% Grange & Links Hotel, Sea Ln, Sandilands, MABLETHORPE ☎ (0507) 441334 23 ⇆ ⮝

Each golf-course entry has a recommended AA-appointed hotel. For a wider choice of places to stay, consult *AA Hotels in Britain and Ireland* and *AA Inspected Bed and Breakfast in Britain and Ireland* available from your local book shop or AA shops

LONDON

Courses within the London Postal District area (ie those that have London Postcodes - W1, SW1 etc) are listed here in postal district order commencing East then North, South and West.
Courses outside the London Postal area, but within Greater London are to be found listed under the county of **Greater London** in the gazetteer (see page 74).

E4 CHINGFORD

Royal Epping Forest ☎ 081-529 2195 & 081-529 5708
Woodland course. 'Red' garments must be worn.
18 holes, 6620yds, Par 72, SSS 70.
Club membership 495.
Visitors   booking system in operation.
Green Fees not confirmed.
Facilities café ⛴ 🏠 ₵
Location   Forest Approach, Chingford (300 yds S of Chingford Station)
Hotel   ★★★68% Woodford Moat House, Oak Hill, WOODFORD GREEN
                 ☎ 081-505 4511 99 ⇆ 🐾

West Essex ☎ 081-529 7558
Testing parkland course within Epping Forest. Notable holes are 8th (par 4), 16th (par 4), 18th (par 5).
18 holes, 6289yds, Par 71, SSS 70.
Club membership 645.
Visitors   must contact in advance & have handicap certificate but may not play on Tue morning, Thu afternoon & weekends.
Societies   must contact in advance.
Green Fees £30 per day; £25 per round.
Facilities ⊗ ℳ by prior arrangement ⓛ 🍺 ♀ ⛴ 🏠
                 ₵ Robert Joyce.
Leisure   snooker, buggies for hire.
Location   Bury Rd, Sewardstonebury (off N Circular Rd at Chingford on M25)
Hotel   ★★59% Roebuck Hotel, North End, BUCKHURST HILL ☎ 081-505 4636 29 ⇆ 🐾

E11 LEYTONSTONE

Wanstead ☎ 081-989 3938
A flat, picturesque parkland course with many trees and shrubs and providing easy walking. The par 3, 16th, involves driving across a lake.
18 holes, 6109yds, Par 69, SSS 69, Course record 61.
Club membership 500.
Visitors   must contact in advance and may only play Mon, Tue & Fri.
Societies   by arrangement.
Green Fees £25 per day.
Facilities ⊗ ℳ ⓛ 🍺 ♀ ⛴ 🏠 ₵ Gary Jacom.
Leisure   fishing.

Location   Overton Dr, Wanstead (from central London A11 NE to Wanstead)
Hotel   ★★★68% Woodford Moat House, Oak Hill, WOODFORD GREEN
                 ☎ 081-505 4511 99 ⇆ 🐾

N2 EAST FINCHLEY

Hampstead ☎ 081-455 0203
Undulating parkland course.
9 holes, 5812yds, Par 68, SSS 68, Course record 65.
Club membership 500.
Visitors   restricted Tue and weekends, phone professional 081-455 7089
Societies   apply in writing.
Green Fees £23 per 18 holes (£30 per 18 holes weekends and bank holidays).
Facilities ⓛ 🍺 ♀ ⛴ 🏠 ₵
Location   Winnington Rd
Hotel   B Forte Posthouse, Haverstock Hill, LONDON
                 ☎ 071-794 8121 140 ⇆ 🐾

N6 HIGHGATE

Highgate ☎ 081-340 1906
Parkland course.
18 holes, 5985yds, Par 69, SSS 69.
Club membership 705.
Visitors   may not play Wed & weekends.
Societies   by arrangement.
Green Fees not confirmed.
Facilities ⊗ ℳ by prior arrangement ⓛ 🍺 ♀ ⛴ 🏠
                 ₵ Robin Turner.
Location   Denewood Rd
Hotel   B Marriott Hotel, 128 King Henry's Rd, LONDON ☎ 071-722 7711 303 ⇆ 🐾

N9 LOWER EDMONTON

Lee Valley Leisure ☎ 081-803 3611
Tricky municipal parkland course with some narrow fairways and the River Lea providing a natural hazard.
18 holes, 4902yds, Par 66, SSS 66, Course record 64.
Visitors   no restrictions.
Societies   small maximum 28 people.
Green Fees £9 per round (£12 weekends & bank holidays).
Facilities ⊗ 🍺 ♀ ⛴ 🏠 ₵ R Gerken.
Leisure   heated indoor swimming pool, squash, snooker, sauna, solarium, gymnasium, 20 bay flood lit range.
Location   Picketts Lock Sports Centre, Edmonton
Hotel   ★★60% Holtwhites Hotel, 92 Chase Side, ENFIELD ☎ 081-363 0124 30rm(28 ⇆ 🐾)

N14 SOUTHGATE

Trent Park ☎ 081-366 7432 & 081-364 4450
Parkland course set in 150 acres of green belt area. Seven holes played across Merryhills brook. Testing holes are 2nd (423 yds) over brook, 190 yds from the tee, and up to plateau green; 7th (463 yds) dog-leg, over brook, par 4.
18 holes, 6008yds, Par 69, SSS 69.
Club membership 950.
Visitors   no restrictions.

Societies	welcome Mon-Fri, must apply in advance.
Green Fees	£10 per round (£12 weekends).
Facilities	⊗ ⌂ ☕ ♀ ⬟ 🏠 ⚑ �llⅬ Tony Sheaff.
Leisure	floodlit golf driving range.
Location	Bramley Rd, Southgate
Hotel	★★★★63% West Lodge Park Hotel, Cockfosters Rd, HADLEY WOOD ☎ 081-440 8311 48 ⇄ 🏠Annexe2 ⇄ 🏠

N20 WHETSTONE

North Middlesex ☎ 081-445 1604
Short parkland course renowned for its tricky greens.
18 holes, 5625yds, Par 69, SSS 66.
Club membership 624.

Visitors	must contact in advance and are advised to have handicap certificate.
Societies	must telephone in advance.
Green Fees	£27.50 per day; £22 per round (£30 per round weekends).
Facilities	⊗ ⌂ ☕ ♀ ⬟ 🏠 ⚑ �llⅬ Steve Roberts.
Location	The Manor House, Friern Barnet Ln, Whetstone
Hotel	★★★68% Edgwarebury Hotel, Barnet Ln, ELSTREE ☎ 081-953 8227 50 ⇄ 🏠

South Herts ☎ 081-445 2035
An open undulating parkland course officially in
Hertfordshire, but now in a London postal area. It is,
perhaps, most famous for the fact that two of the greatest
of all British professionals, Harry Vardon and Dai Rees,
CBE were professionals at the club. The course is testing,
over rolling fairways, especially in the prevailing south-
west wind.
18 holes, 6432yds, Par 72, SSS 71.
Club membership 830.

Visitors	must contact in advance & have handicap certificate.
Societies	Wed-Fri only, must apply in writing.
Green Fees	not confirmed.
Facilities	⬟ 🏠 ⚑ ⅬⅬ
Location	Links Dr, Totteridge
Hotel	B Forte Posthouse, Bignells Corner, SOUTH MIMMS ☎ (0707) 643311 120 ⇄ 🏠

N21 WINCHMORE HILL

Bush Hill Park ☎ 081-360 5738
Pleasant parkland course surrounded by trees.
18 holes, 5809yds, Par 70, SSS 68.
Club membership 700.

Visitors	may not play Wed mornings or weekends & bank holidays.
Societies	by arrangement.
Green Fees	£30 per day; £22 per round.
Facilities	⊗ ⌂ ☕ ♀ (ex Sun) ⬟ ⚑Ⅼ George Low.
Location	Bush Hill, Winchmore Hill
Hotel	★★60% Holtwhites Hotel, 92 Chase Side, ENFIELD ☎ 081-363 0124 30rm(28 ⇄ 🏠)

N22 WOOD GREEN

Muswell Hill ☎ 081-888 1764
Narrow parkland course.
18 holes, 6474yds, Par 71, SSS 71, Course record 65.
Club membership 500.

Visitors	restricted Tue morning, weekends & bank holidays. Must contact in advance.
Societies	by arrangement.
Green Fees	£33 per day; £23 per round.
Facilities	⊗ ⫰ ⌂ ☕ ♀ ⬟ 🏠 ⚑ Ⅼ Ian Roberts.
Leisure	caddy cars, trolleys.
Location	Rhodes Av, Wood Green (off N Circular Rd at Bounds Green)
Hotel	★★★62% Raglan Hall Hotel, 8-12 Queens Ave, Muswell Hill, LONDON ☎ 081-883 9836 46 ⇄ 🏠

NW7 MILL HILL

Finchley ☎ 081-346 2436
Easy walking on wooded parkland course.
18 holes, 6411yds, Par 72, SSS 71.
Club membership 500.

Visitors	can play most weekdays and after mid-day at weekends. Must contact in advance.
Societies	must apply by telephone.
Green Fees	£33 per day; £28 per round (£37 per round weekends and bank holidays).
Facilities	⊗ ⫰ ⌂ ☕ (all catering by arrangement) ♀ ⬟ 🏠 ⚑ Ⅼ
Leisure	caddy cars.
Location	Nether Court, Frith Ln, Mill Hill (Near Mill Hill East Tube Station)
Hotel	★★★68% Edgwarebury Hotel, Barnet Ln, ELSTREE ☎ 081-953 8227 50 ⇄ 🏠

Hendon ☎ 081-346 6023
Easy walking, parkland course with a good variety of trees,
and providing testing golf.
18 holes, 6266yds, Par 70, SSS 70.
Club membership 560.

Visitors	must contact in advance. Restricted weekends & bank holidays.
Societies	must contact in advance.
Green Fees	£30 per day; £25 per round (£35 per round weekends & bank holidays).
Facilities	⊗ ⫰ by prior arrangement ⌂ ☕ ♀ ⬟ 🏠 ⚑ Ⅼ Stuart Murray.
Leisure	trolley hire.
Location	Sanders Ln, Mill Hill (10 mins from junc 2 of M1 southbound)
Hotel	★★★68% Edgwarebury Hotel, Barnet Ln, ELSTREE ☎ 081-953 8227 50 ⇄ 🏠

Mill Hill ☎ 081-959 2339
Undulating parkland course with all holes separated by good
tree and shrub cover.
18 holes, 6247yds, Par 69, SSS 70, Course record 65.
Club membership 550.

Visitors	restricted weekends & bank holidays. Must contact in advance.
Societies	must contact in advance.
Green Fees	not confirmed.
Facilities	⊗ ⫰ (Mon, Wed & Fri) ⌂ ☕ ♀ ⬟ 🏠 ⚑ Ⅼ Alex Daniel.
Leisure	snooker.
Location	100 Barnet Way, Mill Hill (On A1 S bound carriageway)
Hotel	★★★68% Edgwarebury Hotel, Barnet Ln, ELSTREE ☎ 081-953 8227 50 ⇄ 🏠

SE9 ELTHAM

Eltham Warren ☎ 081-850 1166 & 081-850 4477
Parkland course with narrow fairways and small greens. The course is bounded by the A210 on one side and Eltham Park on the other.
9 holes, 5840yds, Par 69, SSS 68, Course record 66.
Club membership 450.
Visitors	may not play at weekends. Must contact in advance and have a handicap certificate.
Societies	must telephone in advance.
Green Fees	£25 per day.
Facilities	⊗ 川 by prior arrangement ⓑ ⬛ ♀ ♨ 🏠 ⓛ Ross Taylor.
Leisure	snooker.
Location	Bexley Rd, Eltham
Hotel	★★★65% Bromley Court Hotel, Bromley Hill, BROMLEY ☎ 081-464 5011 120 ⇔ ⑃

Royal Blackheath ☎ 081-850 1795
A pleasant, parkland course of great character as befits the antiquity of the Club; the clubhouse dates from the 17th century. Many great trees survive and there are two ponds. The 18th requires a pitch to the green over a thick clipped hedge, which also crosses the front of the 1st tee.
18 holes, 6219yds, Par 70, SSS 70.
Club membership 750.
Visitors	must contact in advance but may play mid-week only, handicap certificate is required.
Societies	mid-week only, must apply in writing.
Green Fees	not confirmed.
Facilities	⊗ ⓑ ⬛ ♀ ♨ 🏠 ⑃ ⓛ Ian McGregor.
Leisure	golf museum.
Location	Court Rd
Hotel	★★★65% Bromley Court Hotel, Bromley Hill, BROMLEY ☎ 081-464 5011 120 ⇔ ⑃

SE18 WOOLWICH

Shooters Hill ☎ 081-854 6368
Hilly and wooded parkland course with good view and natural hazards.
18 holes, 5736 yds, Par 69, SSS 68.
Club membership 960.
Visitors	must have handicap certificate.
Societies	Tue & Thu only, by arrangement.
Green Fees	£30 per day; £24 per round.
Facilities	⊗ 川 ⓑ ⬛ ♀ ♨ 🏠 ⓛ Michael Ridge.
Leisure	caddy cars.
Location	Eaglesfield Rd, Shooters Hill (Shooters Hill Rd from Blackheath)
Hotel	B Forte Posthouse, Black Prince Interchange, Southwold Rd, BEXLEY ☎ (0322) 526900 102 ⇔ ⑃

SE21 DULWICH

Dulwich & Sydenham Hill ☎ 081-693 3961
Parkland course overlooking London. Hilly with narrow fairways.
18 holes, 6192yds, Par 69, SSS 69.
Club membership 850.

Visitors	with member only weekends.
Societies	must telephone in advance & confirm in writing.
Green Fees	not confirmed.
Facilities	⊗ ⓑ ⬛ ♀ ♨ 🏠 ⓛ David Baillie.
Location	Grange Ln, College Rd
Hotel	★★★65% Bromley Court Hotel, Bromley Hill, BROMLEY ☎ 081-464 5011 120 ⇔ ⑃

SE22 EAST DULWICH

Aquarius ☎ 081-693 1626
Course laid-out on two levels around and over covered reservoir; hazards include vents and bollards.
9 holes, 5246yds, Par 66, SSS 66.
Club membership 440.
Visitors	must be accompanied by member and have a handicap certificate.
Green Fees	not confirmed.
Facilities	⊗ (Sun only) ⓑ ⬛ ♀ ♨ 🏠 ⓛ Frederick Private.
Location	Marmora Rd, Honor Oak, Off Forest Hill Rd
Hotel	★★★65% Bromley Court Hotel, Bromley Hill, BROMLEY ☎ 081-464 5011 120 ⇔ ⑃

SW15 PUTNEY

Richmond Park ☎ 081-876 1795
Two public parkland courses.
Princes: 36 holes, 5909yds, Par 68, SSS 68.
Dukes: 18 holes, 6068yds, Par 72.
Visitors	welcome but not spectators or caddies.
Societies	must contact in advance.
Green Fees	not confirmed.
Facilities	⊗ 川 ⓑ ⬛ ♀ ♨ 🏠 ⑃ ⓛ Patrick Ryan.
Location	Roehampton Gate, Priory Ln
Hotel	★★★66% Richmond Hill, 146-150 Richmond Hill, RICHMOND ☎ 081-940 2247 & 081-940 5466 124 ⇔ ⑃

SW18 WANDSORTH

Springfield Park ☎ 081-871 2468
Attractive flat parkland course in the middle of London. The longest drive is the 430 yard 3rd to one of the course's superb greens. Well placed bunkers trap the careless shot and the course rewards the accurate player.
9 holes, 2317yds, Par 31, SSS 62, Course record 57.
Club membership 320.
Visitors	welcome other than Sat & Sun up to noon, tee times can be pre booked by telephone.
Societies	telephone or write to the secretary.
Green Fees	18 holes: Mon-Fri £5 before 9am & after 6pm; £6.50 all day (weekends & bank holidays £8.50 from noon onwards).
Facilities	⊗ 川 ⓑ ⬛ ♀ ♨ 🏠 ⑃ ⓛ Patrick Tallack.
Leisure	snooker, putting green,practice nets.
Location	Burntwood Ln, Wandsworth
Hotel	★★★★67% Cannizaro House, West Side, Wimbledon Common, LONDON ☎ 081-879 1464 46 ⇔ ⑃

SW19 WIMBLEDON

> **Royal Wimbledon** ☎ 081-946 2125
> A club steeped in the history of the game, it is also of
> great age, dating back to 1865. Of sand and heather like
> so many of the Surrey courses its 12th hole (par 4) is
> rated as the best on the course.
> *18 holes, 6300yds, Par 70, SSS 70.*
> *Club membership 1050.*
> **Visitors** must be guests of current club member.
> **Societies** welcome Wed-Thu. Must apply in writing.
> **Green Fees** not confirmed.
> **Facilities** ⛛🏠🎺🍴
> **Location** 29 Camp Rd
> **Hotel** ★★★66% Richmond Hill, 146-150
> Richmond Hill, RICHMOND
> ☎ 081-940 2247 & 081-940 5466 124 ➡🐾

Wimbledon Common ☎ 081-946 0294
Quick-drying course on Wimbledon Common. Well wooded,
with long challenging short holes but no bunkers. All players
must wear plain red upper garments.
18 holes, 5438yds, Par 68, SSS 66.
Club membership 250.
Visitors with member only at weekends.
Societies must telephone in advance.
Green Fees £22 per day; £15 per round.
Facilities ⊗ 🏠🍺🍷⛛🎺🍴 J S Jukes.
Leisure snooker.
Location Camp Rd
Hotel ★★★★67% Cannizaro House, West Side,
Wimbledon Common, LONDON
☎ 081-879 1464 46 ➡🐾

Wimbledon Park ☎ 081-946 1250
Easy walking on parkland course. Sheltered lake provides
hazard on 3 holes.
18 holes, 5465yds, Par 66, SSS 66.
Club membership 700.
Visitors restricted weekends & bank holidays. Must
contact in advance and have handicap certificate
or letter of introduction.
Societies must apply in writing.
Green Fees not confirmed.
Facilities ⊗ 🏠🍺🍷⛛🎺🍴 D Wingrove.
Location Home Park Rd, Wimbledon (400 yds from
Wimbledon Park Station)
Hotel ★★★66% Richmond Hill, 146-150 Richmond
Hill, RICHMOND
☎ 081-940 2247 & 081-940 5466 124 ➡🐾

W7 HANWELL

Brent Valley ☎ 081-567 1287
Municipal parkland course with easy walking. The River
Brent winds through the course.
18 holes, 5426yds, Par 67, SSS 66.
Club membership 350.
Visitors no restrictions.
Societies one month's notice required.
Green Fees not confirmed.
Facilities ⊗ (vary with season) 🎺 by prior arrangement 🏠
🍺⛛🍷🎺🍴 Peter Byrne.

Location 138 Church Rd, Hanwell
Hotel ★★★62% Master Robert Hotel, Great West Rd,
HOUNSLOW ☎ 081-570 6261 100 ➡🐾

MERSEYSIDE

BEBINGTON   Map 07 SJ38

Brackenwood ☎ 051-608 3093
Municipal parkland course with easy walking.
18 holes, 6285yds, Par 70, SSS 70.
Club membership 320.
Societies must apply in advance.
Green Fees not confirmed.
Facilities 🏠🍺🍷🎺🍴
Location Brackenwood Park (0.75m N of M53 junc 4 on
B5151)
Hotel ★★63% Bridge Inn, Bolton Rd, Port Sunlight,
BEBINGTON ☎ 051-645 8441 16 ➡🐾

BIRKENHEAD   Map 07 SJ38

Arrowe Park ☎ 051-677 1527
Pleasant municipal parkland course.
18 holes, 6435yds, Par 72, SSS 71.
Club membership 210.
Visitors no restrictions.
Societies must telephone in advance.
Green Fees not confirmed.
Facilities 🏠⛛🎺🍴 Clive Scanlon.
Location Woodchurch (1m from M53 junc 3 on A551)
Hotel ★★★66% Bowler Hat Hotel, 2 Talbot Rd,
Oxton, BIRKENHEAD
☎ 051-652 4931 32 ➡🐾

Prenton ☎ 051-608 1461 & 051-608 1083
Parkland course with easy walking and views of the Welsh
Hills.
18 holes, 5966yds, Par 70, SSS 69.
Club membership 760.
Visitors restricted to yellow course.
Societies welcome Wed & Fri, contact in advance.
Green Fees £23 per day (£25 weekends & bank holidays).
Facilities ⊗ 🎺 by prior arrangement 🏠🍺🍷⛛🏠
🍴 Robin Thompson.
Leisure snooker.
Location Golf Links Rd, Prenton (S side of town centre
off B5151)
Hotel ★★63% Riverhill Hotel, Talbot Rd, Oxton,
BIRKENHEAD ☎ 051-653 3773 16 ➡🐾

Wirral Ladies ☎ 051-652 1255
Heathland course with heather and birch.
18 holes, 4966yds, SSS 70.
Club membership 450.
Visitors may not play over Christmas and Easter
holidays.
Societies must telephone in advance.
Green Fees £25 per day; £20 per round (weekend prices not
supplied). ▶

Facilities ⊗ ⓑ 🍺 ♀ 🛆 🏠 🍴 Philip Chandler.
Location 93 Bidston Rd, Oxton (W side of town centre on B5151)
Hotel ★★★66% Bowler Hat Hotel, 2 Talbot Rd, Oxton, BIRKENHEAD ☎ 051-652 4931 32 ➪ 🅿

BLUNDELLSANDS   Map 07 SJ39

West Lancashire ☎ 051-924 1076
Challenging, traditional links with sandy subsoil overlooking the Mersey Estuary. The course provides excellent golf throughout the year. The four short holes are very fine.
18 holes, 6763yds, Par 72, SSS 73.
Club membership 650.
Visitors may not play on competition days; must have a handicap certificate.
Societies must contact in advance.
Green Fees £33 per day; £22 per round (£40 per day weekends & bank holidays).
Facilities ⊗ (ex Mon) 🍴 by prior arrangement ⓑ 🍺 ♀ 🛆 🏠 🍴 David Lloyd.
Leisure snooker.
Location Hall Rd West (N side of village)
Hotel ★★★64% Blundellsands Hotel, The Serpentine, BLUNDELLSANDS ☎ 051-924 6515 41 ➪ 🅿

BOOTLE   Map 07 SJ39

Bootle ☎ 051-928 1371
Municipal seaside course, with prevailing north-westerly wind. Testing holes: 5th (200 yds) par 3; 7th (415 yds) par 4.
18 holes, 6362yds, Par 70, SSS 70, Course record 64.
Club membership 380.
Visitors no restrictions.
Societies must contact in advance.
Green Fees £3.55 per round (£5.25 weekends & bank holidays).
Facilities ⊗ ⓑ 🍺 ♀ 🛆 🏠 🍴 Alan Bradshaw.
Location Dunnings Bridge Rd (2m NE on A5036)
Hotel ★★★64% Blundellsands Hotel, The Serpentine, BLUNDELLSANDS ☎ 051-924 6515 41 ➪ 🅿

BROMBOROUGH   Map 07 SJ38

Bromborough ☎ 051-334 2155
Parkland course.
18 holes, 6650yds, Par 72, SSS 73.
Club membership 700.
Visitors may not play on Sun, Tue mornings & Sat before 2.30pm.
Societies normal society day Wed ; must telephone in advance.
Green Fees £26 per day (£30 weekends).
Facilities ⊗ ⓑ 🍺 ♀ 🛆 🏠 🍴 Geoff Berry.
Location Raby Hall Rd (0.5m W of Station)
Hotel B Travel Inn, High St, BROMBOROUGH ☎ 051-334 2917 31 ➪ 🅿

CALDY   Map 07 SJ28

Caldy ☎ 051-625 5660
A parkland course situated on the estuary of the River Dee with many of the fairways running parallel to the river. Of Championship length, the course offers excellent golf all year, but is subject to variable winds that noticeably alter the day to day playing of each hole. There are excellent views of North Wales and Snowdonia.
18 holes, 6675yds, Par 72, SSS 73, Course record 68.
Club membership 800.
Visitors may play on weekdays only. Must contact in advance and have an introduction from own club.
Societies must telephone in advance.
Green Fees not confirmed.
Facilities ⊗ 🍴 ⓑ 🍺 ♀ 🛆 🏠 🍴 K Jones.
Leisure snooker.
Location Links Hey Rd (SE side of village)
Hotel ★★61% Parkgate Hotel, Boathouse Ln, PARKGATE ☎ 051-336 5001 27 ➪ 🅿

EASTHAM   Map 07 SJ38

Eastham Lodge ☎ 051-327 3003
A 15-hole parkland course with many trees. Three holes played twice to make 18, but restricted to 15 holes in winter.
18 holes, 5584yds, Par 69, SSS 67.
Club membership 790.
Visitors with member only at weekends.
Societies welcome Mon, Tue & Fri. Must apply in advance.
Green Fees £22 weekdays.
Facilities ⊗ 🍴 by prior arrangement ⓑ 🍺 ♀ 🛆 🏠 🍴 R Boobyers.
Leisure snooker, trolley hire.
Location 117 Ferry Rd (1.5m N)
Hotel B Travel Inn, High St, BROMBOROUGH ☎ 051-334 2917 31 ➪ 🅿

FORMBY   Map 07 SD30

Formby ☎ (07048) 72164
Championship seaside links through sandhills and partly through pine trees.It plays well throughout the year.
18 holes, 6490yds, Par 72, SSS 72.
Club membership 600.
Visitors must contact in advance & have handicap certificate. Restricted play Wed, weekends or bank holidays.
Societies Tues, Thu & Fri only. Must contact in advance.
Green Fees £45 per day/round.
Facilities ⊗ (ex Mon) ⓑ 🍺 ♀ 🛆 🏠 🥪 🍴 C P Harrison.
Location Golf Rd (N side of town)
Hotel ★★★64% Blundellsands Hotel, The Serpentine, BLUNDELLSANDS ☎ 051-924 6515 41 ➪ 🅿

Formby Ladies ☎ (0704) 873493
Seaside links - one of the few independent ladies clubs in the
country. The course has contrasting hard-hitting holes in flat
country and tricky holes in sandhills and woods.
18 holes, 5374yds, Par 71, SSS 71.
Club membership 423.
Visitors	must contact in advance and may not play Thu or before noon Sat & Sun.
Societies	must apply in advance.
Green Fees	not confirmed.
Facilities	🏪 💷 ♀ 🛇 🏠 ℄
Location	Golf Rd (N side of town)
Hotel	★★★64% Blundellsands Hotel, The Serpentine, BLUNDELLSANDS ☎ 051-924 6515 41 ⇥ 🐾

HESWALL   Map 07 SJ28

Heswall ☎ (051342) 1237
A pleasant parkland course in soft undulating country
over-looking the estuary of the River Dee. There are
excellent views of the Welsh hills and coastline, and a
good test of golf. The clubhouse is modern and well-
appointed with good facilities.
18 holes, 6472yds, Par 72, SSS 72, Course record 65.
Club membership 900.
Visitors	must contact in advance & handicap certificate required.
Societies	welcome Wed & Fri only, must apply in advance.
Green Fees	£30 per day/round.
Facilities	⊗ & 🍴 by prior arrangement 🏪 💷 ♀ 🛇 🏠 ℉ ℄ Alan Thompson.
Leisure	snooker, large practice area.
Location	Cottage Ln (1m S off A540)
Hotel	★★61% Parkgate Hotel, Boathouse Ln, PARKGATE ☎ 051-336 5001 27 ⇥ 🐾

HOYLAKE   Map 07 SJ28

Hoylake ☎ 051-632 2956
Flat, generally windy semi-links course. Tricky fairways.
18 holes, 6313yds, Par 70, SSS 70, Course record 67.
Club membership 303.
Societies	must telephone 051-632 4883 M E Down club steward or 051-632 2956 club professional.
Green Fees	£6 per round.
Facilities	⊗ 🍴 🏪 💷 (contact club steward for catering) ♀ (ex Fri) 🛇 🏠 ℉ ℄ Simon Hooton.
Leisure	practice ground no charge.
Location	Carr Ln, Municipal Links (SW side of town off A540)
Hotel	★★★66% Bowler Hat Hotel, 2 Talbot Rd, Oxton, BIRKENHEAD ☎ 051-652 4931 32 ⇥ 🐾

Royal Liverpool ☎ 051-632 3101
A world famous, windswept seaside links course.
18 holes, 6840yds, Par 72, SSS 74, Course record 67.
Club membership 650.
Visitors	must contact in advance & have a handicap certificate. Restricted before 9.30am & between 1-2pm. No play Thu am (ladies day). Limited play weekends.
Societies	must contact in writing.

Green Fees	£55 per day; £40 per round.
Facilities	⊗ 🏪 💷 ♀ 🛇 🏠 ℉ ℄ John Heggarty.
Leisure	snooker.
Location	Meols Dr (SW side of town on A540)
Hotel	★★★66% Bowler Hat Hotel, 2 Talbot Rd, Oxton, BIRKENHEAD ☎ 051-652 4931 32 ⇥ 🐾

HUYTON   Map 07 SJ49

Bowring ☎ 051-489 1901
Flat parkland course.
9 holes, 2796yds, Par 34.
Club membership 80.
Visitors	no restrictions.
Green Fees	£5 per round.
Facilities	🏪 💷 ♀ 🛇 🏠 ℄
Location	Bowring Park, Roby Rd (on A5080 adjacent M62 junc 5)
Hotel	★58% Rockland Hotel, View Rd, RAINHILL ☎ 051-426 4603 10rm(9 ⇥)

Huyton & Prescot ☎ 051-489 3948
An easy walking, parkland course providing excellent golf.
18 holes, 5738yds, Par 68, SSS 68.
Club membership 700.
Visitors	restricted at weekends. Must contact in advance and have an introduction from own club.
Societies	must telephone in advance.
Green Fees	not confirmed.
Facilities	⊗ 🍴 by prior arrangement 🏪 💷 ♀ 🛇 🏠 ℉ ℄ Ronald Pottage.
Leisure	snooker.
Location	Hurst Park, Huyton Ln (1.5m NE off B5199)
Hotel	★58% Rockland Hotel, View Rd, RAINHILL ☎ 051-426 4603 10rm(9 ⇥)

LIVERPOOL   Map 07 SJ39

Allerton Park ☎ 051-428 1046
Parkland course.
18 holes, 5459yds, Par 67, SSS 67, Course record 62.
Club membership 300.
Visitors	no restrictions.
Green Fees	not confirmed.
Facilities	🏪 💷 ♀ 🏠 ℉ ℄
Location	Allerton Manor Golf Estate, Allerton Rd (5.5m SE of city centre off A562 and B5180)
Hotel	★★59% Grange Hotel, Holmfield Rd, Aigburth, LIVERPOOL ☎ 051-427 2950 25 ⇥ 🐾

The Childwall ☎ 051-487 0654
Parkland golf is played here over a testing course, where
accuracy from the tee is well-rewarded. The course is
very popular with visiting societies for the clubhouse has
many amenities. Course designed by James Braid.
18 holes, 6425yds, Par 69, SSS 69, Course record 65.
Club membership 600.
Visitors	must use yellow tees only and have a handicap certificate.
Societies	must telephone in advance.
Green Fees	£22 per day (£31.50 weekends).
Facilities	⊗ 🍴 🏪 💷 ♀ 🛇 🏠 ℉ ℄ Nigel M Parr.

▶

Leisure	snooker.
Location	Naylors Rd, Gateacre (7m E of city centre off B5178)
Hotel	★58% Rockland Hotel, View Rd, RAINHILL ☎ 051-426 4603 10rm(9 ⇆)

Kirkby-Liverpool Municipal ☎ 051-546 5435
Flat, easy course.
Liverpool Municipal Golf Club: 18 holes, 6588yds, Par 72, SSS 71, Course record 70.
Club membership 150.
Visitors must contact in advance.
Societies must contact 1 week in advance.
Green Fees not confirmed.
Facilities ⊗ by prior arrangement ℳ by prior arrangement ⮤ 🍴 ♀ ☖ 🏠 ⛳ 𝆑 Dave Weston.
Location Ingoe Ln, Kirkby (7.5m NE of city centre on A506)
Hotel ★★★★59% Liverpool Moat House Hotel, Paradise St, LIVERPOOL ☎ 051-709 0181 251 ⇆ 𝄞

Lee Park ☎ 051-487 3882
Flat course with ponds in places.
18 holes, 5508mtrs, Par 71, SSS 69.
Club membership 600.
Visitors must dress acceptably.
Societies must contact in advance.
Green Fees £19.50 (£25.50 weekends & bank holidays).
Facilities ⊗ ℳ ⮤ 🍴 ♀ ☖
Leisure snooker.
Location Childwall Valley Rd (7m E of city centre off B5178)
Hotel ★★★★59% Liverpool Moat House Hotel, Paradise St, LIVERPOOL ☎ 051-709 0181 251 ⇆ 𝄞

West Derby ☎ 051-228 1540 & 051-254 1034	

A parkland course always in first-class condition, and so giving easy walking. The fairways are well-wooded. Care must be taken on the first nine holes to avoid the brook which guards many of the greens. A modern well-designed clubhouse with many amenities, overlooks the course.
18 holes, 6333yds, Par 72, SSS 70.
Club membership 550.
Visitors may not play before 9.30am.
Societies may not play on Sat, Sun & bank holidays; must contact in advance.
Green Fees not confirmed.
Facilities ⊗ ℳ ⮤ 🍴 ♀ ☖ 🏠 𝆑 Nick Brace.
Leisure snooker.
Location Yew Tree Ln, West Derby (4.5m E of city centre off A57)
Hotel ★★59% Grange Hotel, Holmfield Rd, Aigburth, LIVERPOOL ☎ 051-427 2950 25 ⇆ 𝄞

Woolton ☎ 051-486 1298
Parkland course providing a good round of golf for all standards.
18 holes, 5706yds, Par 69, SSS 68.
Club membership 650.
Visitors must contact in advance.
Societies must apply in writing.

Green Fees not confirmed.
Facilities ⯐ 🏠 𝆑
Leisure snooker.
Location Speke Rd (7m SE of city centre off A562)
Hotel ★★59% Grange Hotel, Holmfield Rd, Aigburth, LIVERPOOL ☎ 051-427 2950 25 ⇆ 𝄞

NEWTON-LE-WILLOWS   Map 07 SJ59

Haydock Park ☎ (0925) 228525	

A well-wooded parkland course, close to the well-known racecourse, and always in excellent condition. The pleasant undulating fairways offer some very interesting golf and the 6th, 9th, 11th and 13th holes are particularly testing. The clubhouse is very comfortable.
18 holes, 6043yds, Par 70, SSS 69.
Club membership 550.
Visitors must be member of a recognised club. With member only weekends & bank holidays. Must contact in advance.
Societies must apply in writing.
Green Fees £24 per day/round.
Facilities ⊗ ℳ ⮤ 🍴 ♀ ☖ 🏠 𝆑
Leisure snooker.
Location Golborne Park, Newton Ln (0.75m NE off A49)
Hotel B Forte Posthouse, Lodge Ln, Newton-Le-Willows, HAYDOCK ☎ (0942) 717878 136 ⇆ 𝄞

ST HELENS   Map 07 SJ59

Grange Park ☎ (0744) 26318	

A course of Championship length set in plesant country surroundings - playing the course it is hard to believe that industrial St Helens lies so close at hand. The course is a fine test of golf and there are many attractive holes liable to challenge all grades.
18 holes, 6429yds, Par 72, SSS 71, Course record 65.
Club membership 700.
Visitors must contact in advance & have handicap certificate. Play allowed weekdays only.
Societies must apply in writing.
Green Fees £26 per 36 holes; £21 per 27 holes.
Facilities ⊗ ℳ ⮤ 🍴 ♀ ☖ 🏠 ⛳ 𝆑 Paul G Evans.
Leisure snooker.
Location Prescot Rd (1.5m W on A58)
Hotel ★★★★64% Chalon Court, Chalon Way, Linkway West, ST HELENS ☎ (0744) 453444 84 ⇆ 𝄞

Sherdley Park ☎ (0744) 813149
Fairly hilly course with ponds in places.
18 holes, 5941yds, Par 70, SSS 69.
Club membership 160.
Visitors no restrictions.
Green Fees not confirmed.
Facilities ⯐ 🏠 ⛳ 𝆑
Location Sherdley Rd (2m S off A570)
Hotel ★★★★64% Chalon Court, Chalon Way, Linkway West, ST HELENS ☎ (0744) 453444 84 ⇆ 𝄞

THE ROYAL BIRKDALE

SOUTHPORT ☎(0704) 567920   Map 07 SD31

John Ingham writes: There are a few seaside links in the world that can be described as 'great', but Royal Birkdale, with its expanse of towering sandhills and willow scrub, is one of them. There have been some changes since the club was founded in 1889 and they have hosted everything that matters here, including the Open and the Ryder Cup. Some changes have been made even since Arnold Palmer hit that wondrous recovery shot that helped him win an Open in the early sixties, and led to a plaque being erected at the spot from which the divot was taken.

Well bunkered, the sandhills run along the edges of the fairways and make ideal platforms from which to view the Open Championship - played frequently here because the examination is supreme in the United Kingdom.

The links, in a wind, may be too difficult for the weekender. Certainly it found out Dai Rees in 1961 when he was chasing Palmer for the title. In the last round the course struck at the very first hole. Rees had hit his teeshot a might to the left, and then had to wait for the players to hole out on the green ahead, before attempting a powerful shot with a lofted wood from the fairway. The ball smacked into the back of a bunker, and fell back into sand. Rees took an awful seven and Palmer beat him for the trophy - by one shot. The Welshman had stormed back in 31 but his chance to win an Open had gone forever. But Rees still touched his hat to the links, and held it in great respect as, indeed, does Arnold Palmer.

But for the amateur, another problem is simply hitting the ball far enough. If you play this terrific course from the Open Championship back tees, it measures 7080 yards and par 73 takes some getting, even with your handicap allowance!

Membership 800

Visitors	must contact in advance, and have a letter of introduction from their own club with a handicap cetificate
Societies	must apply in writing or by telephone in advance
Green fees	Weekdays £70 per day, £50 per round
Facilities	⅏ (by prior arrangement) 🍴☕️♀🏌🛍📠⛳ ♟ (Richard Bradbeer)
Location	Waterloo Road, Birkdale (1.50m S of town on A565)

18 holes, 6305yds, Par 71, SSS 71, Course record 63 (1991 Open, Jodie Mudd, USA)

WHERE TO STAY AND EAT NEARBY

HOTELS:

SOUTHPORT

★★★ 65% Royal Clifton, Promenade. ☎ (0704) 533771. 107 🛏 ♟ English & French cuisine

★★★ 65% Scarisbrick, Lord St. ☎ (0704) 543000. 77 🛏 ♟ English & French cuisine

★★ 68% Balmoral Lodge, 41 Queens Rd. ☎ (0704) 544298. 15 🛏 ♟

★★★ 65% Stutelea Hotel & Leisure Club, Alexandra Rd. ☎ (0704) 544220 20 🛏 ♟

RESTAURANT:

WRIGHTINGTON

✕ ✕❀ High Moor, Highmoor Ln (jct 27 off M6, take B5239). ☎ Appley Bridge (0257) 252364 English & French cuisine

SOUTHPORT   Map 07 SD31

The Hesketh ☎ (0704) 536897
Hesketh is the senior club in Southport, founded in 1885.
The Championship course comprises much of the
original territory plus a large area of reclaimed land on
the seaward side - essentially 'Links' in character.
18 holes, 6407yds, Par 71, SSS 72, Course record 66.
Club membership 600.

Visitors	must have a handicap certificate. May not play Tue mornings (Ladies) or 12.30-2pm daily.
Societies	welcome.
Green Fees	£35 per day; £25 per round (£40 weekends).
Facilities	⊗ ⅢⅢ 🝙 ☕ (no catering Mon in winter) ♀ ⚑ 🏠 ⛿ 🍴 John Donoghue.
Leisure	snooker.
Location	Cockle Dick's Ln, off Cambridge Rd (1m NE of town centre off A565)
Hotel	★★65% Bold Hotel, Lord St, SOUTHPORT ☎ (0704) 532578 23rm(15 ⇋7 🐾)

Hillside ☎ (0704) 567169
Championship links course with natural hazards open to
strong wind.
18 holes, 6850yds, Par 72, SSS 74.
Club membership 750.

Visitors	must contact in advance. Restricted Tue (am), weekends & bank holidays. Members only between 12-2pm.
Societies	must apply in advance.
Green Fees	£45 per day; £35 per round (£45 per round Sun).
Facilities	⊗ ⅢⅢ by prior arrangement 🝙 ☕ ♀ ⚑ 🏠 🍴 Brian Seddon.
Leisure	snooker, putting green & practice ground.
Location	Hastings Rd, Hillside (2m SW of town centre on A565)
Hotel	★★★65% Royal Clifton Hotel, Promenade, SOUTHPORT ☎ (0704) 533771 107 ⇋ 🐾

Park ☎ (0704) 530133
Very flat municipal parkland course.
18 holes, 6200yds, Par 70, SSS 70.
Club membership 400.

Visitors	restricted weekends, telephone for details.
Green Fees	not confirmed.
Facilities	♀ (members only) 🏠 ⛿
Location	Park Rd (N side of town centre off A565)
Hotel	★★★65% Royal Clifton Hotel, Promenade, SOUTHPORT ☎ (0704) 533771 107 ⇋ 🐾

ROYAL BIRKDALE See page 143

Southport & Ainsdale ☎ (0704) 578000
'S and A', as it is known in the north is another of the
fine championship courses for which this part of the
country is famed. This club has staged many important
events and offers golf of the highest order.
18 holes, 6603yds, Par 72, SSS 73.
Club membership 815.

Visitors	welcome except Thu am, weekends & bank holidays. Must contact club in advance & have handicap certificate.
Societies	must apply in advance.
Green fees	£40 per day; £30 per round (£45 weekends & bank holidays).
Facilities	⊗ ⅢⅢ by prior arrangement 🝙 ☕ ♀ ⚑ 🏠 ⛿ 🍴
Leisure	snooker.
Location	Bradshaws Ln, Ainsdale (3m S off A565)
Hotel	★★★65% Royal Clifton Hotel, Promenade, SOUTHPORT ☎ (0704) 533771 107 ⇋ 🐾

Southport Municipal ☎ (0704) 535286
Municipal seaside links course. Played over by Alt Golf Club.
18 holes, 6400yds, par 70, SSS 69, course record 66.
Club membership 750.

Visitors	no restrictions.
Societies	must telephone 6 days in advance.
Green fees	£5.50 per round (£7.50 weekends & bank holidays).
Facilities	⊗ ⅢⅢ 🝙 ☕ (catering is seasonal) ♀ ⚑ 🏠 ⛿ 🍴 Bill Fletcher.
Leisure	snooker.
Location	Park Rd West (N side of town centre off A565)
Hotel	★★★65% Royal Clifton Hotel, Promenade, SOUTHPORT ☎ (0704) 533771 107 ⇋ 🐾

Southport Old Links ☎ (0704) 28207
Seaside course with tree-lined fairways and easy walking.
One of the oldest courses in Southport, Henry Vardon won
the 'Leeds Cup' here in 1922.
9 holes, 6378yds, Par 72, SSS 71.
Club membership 400.

STUTELEA HOTEL
& *Leisure Club* AA ★★★
ALEXANDRA ROAD, SOUTHPORT PR9 0NB
TEL: FAX:
01704 544220   01704 500232

20 deluxe bedrooms (single to family suites) all with
private bathroom, some with balconies overlooking
gardens.
8 apartments (studio to 2 bedroom) all with private
bathroom and fitted kitchen.
All accommodation has colour TV, radio, direct dial
telephone, hair dryer, trouser press and tea/coffee
making facilities.
Heated indoor swimming pool, jacuzzi, Scandinavian
sauna, steam room, 2 solaria, gymnasium, games
room. Gardens and car park. 2 licensed bars,
restaurant, lounge with library, lift.

Visitors except Wed, Sun & bank holidays. Must contact in advance & have handicap certificate.
Societies welcome except Wed & Sun & bank holidays, must apply in advance.
Green fees £25 per day; £18 per round (£25 per round weekends).
Facilities ⌂ ♥ ♀ ⚒ ⚑ ⌔ P Atkiss.
Location Moss Ln, Churchtown (NW side of town centre off A5267)
Hotel ★★65% Bold Hotel, Lord St, SOUTHPORT
☎ (0704) 532578 23rm(15 ⇄7 ⋔)

WALLASEY
Map 07 SJ29

Bidston ☎ 051-638 3412
Parkland course, with westerly winds.
18 holes, 5827yds, Par 70, SSS 71, Course record 66.
Club membership 650.
Visitors must contact in advance, restricted weekends.
Societies must apply in writing.
Green Fees £25 per day.
Facilities ⊗ ⚒ by prior arrangement ⌂ ♥ ♀ ⚒ ⚑
⌔ R J Law.
Leisure snooker.
Location Bidston Link Rd (0.5m W of M53 junc 1 entrance off A551)
Hotel ★★★66% Bowler Hat Hotel, 2 Talbot Rd, Oxton, BIRKENHEAD
☎ 051-652 4931 32 ⇄ ⋔

Leasowe ☎ 051-677 5852
Rather flat, semi-links, seaside course.
18 holes, 6204yds, Par 71, SSS 71.
Club membership 580.
Visitors may not play before 9.30am or 12.30-2pm from the 1st tee.
Societies must contact in advance by telephone.
Green Fees £18 per day (£22 weekends & bank holidays).
Facilities ⊗ ⚒ by prior arrangement ⌂ ♥ ♀ (ex Sun) ⚒
⚑ ⎁ ⌔ Neil Sweeney.
Leisure caddy cars, practice ground.
Location Moreton (2m W on A551)
Hotel ★★★66% Bowler Hat Hotel, 2 Talbot Rd, Oxton, BIRKENHEAD
☎ 051-652 4931 32 ⇄ ⋔

Wallasey ☎ 051-691 1024
A well-established sporting links, adjacent to the Irish Sea, with huge sandhills and many classic holes where the player's skills are often combined with good fortune. Large, firm greens and fine views but not for the faint-hearted.
18 holes, 6605yds, Par 72, SSS 73.
Club membership 700.
Visitors must be member of a recognised club & have handicap certificate. Must contact in advance.
Societies must apply in writing.
Green Fees £31.50 per day; £26.50 per round (£37/£31.50 weekends & bank holidays).
Facilities ⊗ ⌂ ♥ ♀ ⚒ ⚑ ⌔ Mike Adams.
Location Bayswater Rd (N side of town centre off A554)

Hotel ★★★66% Bowler Hat Hotel, 2 Talbot Rd, Oxton, BIRKENHEAD
☎ 051-652 4931 32 ⇄ ⋔

Warren ☎ 051-639 8323
Short, undulating links course with first-class greens and prevailing winds off the sea.
9 holes, 5854yds, Par 72, SSS 68.
Club membership 150.
Visitors except Sun until 10.30.am.
Green Fees not confirmed.
Facilities ⚑ ⎁ ⌔ Ken Lamb.
Location Grove Rd (N side of town centre off A554)
Hotel ★★★66% Bowler Hat Hotel, 2 Talbot Rd, Oxton, BIRKENHEAD
☎ 051-652 4931 32 ⇄ ⋔

NORFOLK

BARNHAM BROOM
Map 05 TG00

Barnham Broom Golf and Country Club
☎ (0603) 759393
Attractive river valley courses with modern hotel and leisure complex.
Hill Course: 18 holes, 6628yds, Par 72, SSS 72.
Valley Course: 18 holes, 6470yds, Par 71, SSS 71.
Club membership 550.
▶

AA
★ ★ ★

BARNHAM BROOM HOTEL

GOLF, CONFERENCE AND LEISURE
Barnham Broom, Norwich NR9 4DD
Tel: (0603) 759393 Fax: (0603) 758224
After April Area Code will be (01603)

In a beautiful valley, this modern hotel and leisure complex has 52 bedrooms all with private bathrooms; a spacious lounge with open log fire; two bars; and a host of leisure facilities including two 18 hole championship golf courses (one par 71, one par 72), practice holes and putting green areas.

Inside the leisure centre are a heated indoor swimming pool; sauna; solarium; steam room; a beauty and hairdressing salon and a fully equipped gymnasium. Other sports facilities include four squash courts, 3 all-weather tennis courts and a full size snooker table.

The complex also contains a spacious and comprehensively equipped conference centre.

Prices include full English breakfast.
Children charged for meals as taken.
Host: Richard Bond.

Access: From London and the South via A11; from Midlands and the North via A47. 10 miles west of Norwich. Norwich Airport 10 miles.

Visitors	must contact in advance. With member only at weekends.
Societies	must apply in writing.
Green Fees	£30 per day; £20 per round.
Facilities	⊗ �🏛 🏌 ⬛ ♀ 🔥 🏠 ⛳ 🏓 ⛾ Stephen Beckham.
Leisure	hard tennis courts, heated indoor swimming pool, squash, snooker, sauna, solarium, gymnasium, hairdressing salon, beautician, jacuzzi.
Location	Honingham Rd (1m N, S of A47)
Hotel	★★★66% Barnham Broom Hotel Conference & Leisure, Centre, BARNHAM BROOM ☎ (0603) 759393 52 ⇔ ⛾ *See advertisement on page 145*

BAWBURGH — Map 05 TG10

Bawburgh ☎ (0603) 746390
An open-links. Driving range available.
18 holes, 6066yds, Par 70, SSS 69.
Club membership 750.

Visitors	must contact in advance.
Societies	must contact in advance.
Green Fees	on application.
Facilities	⊗ 🏌 ⬛ ♀ 🏠 ⛾ Chris Potter.
Leisure	covered floodlit driving range.
Location	Norwich Golf Centre, Long Ln
Hotel	★★★69% Park Farm Hotel, HETHERSETT ☎ (0603) 810264 6 ⇔ ⛾Annexe32 ⇔ ⛾

BRANCASTER — Map 09 TF74

Royal West Norfolk ☎ (0485) 210087
If you want to see what golf courses were like years ago, then go to the Royal West Norfolk where tradition exudes from both clubhouse and course. Close by the sea, the links are laid out in the grand manner and are characterised by sleepered greens, superb cross-bunkering and salt marshes.
18 holes, 6428yds, Par 71, SSS 71, Course record 66.
Club membership 767.

Visitors	must contact in advance and may only play after 10am at weekends with permission.
Societies	must contact Secretary in advance.
Green Fees	£32 per day (£42.50 weekends).
Facilities	⊗ 🏌 ⬛ ♀ 🏠 ⛳ ⛾
Leisure	practice ground.
Hotel	★★70% Titchwell Manor Hotel, TITCHWELL ☎ (0485) 210221 11rm(7 ⇔ ⛾)Annexe4 ⇔ ⛾

CROMER — Map 09 TG24

Royal Cromer ☎ (0263) 512884
Seaside course set out on cliff edge, hilly and subject to wind.
18 holes, 6508yds, Par 72, SSS 71.
Club membership 700.

Visitors	must contact in advance & have handicap certificate.
Societies	by arrangement.
Green Fees	£25 per day (£30 weekends & bank holidays).
Facilities	⊗ �🏛 by prior arrangement 🏌 ⬛ ♀ 🏠 ⛾ Robin Page.

Leisure	practice ground.
Location	145 Overstrand Rd (1m E on B1159)
Hotel	★★68% Red Lion, Brooke St, CROMER ☎ (0263) 514964 12 ⇔ ⛾

DENVER — Map 05 TF60

Ryston Park ☎ Downham Market (0366) 383834
Parkland course.
9 holes, 3146yds, Par 35, SSS 70, Course record 66.
Club membership 320.

Visitors	may not play weekends or bank holidays.
Societies	Mon-Fri only, must telephone in advance.
Green Fees	£20 per day.
Facilities	⊗ �🏛 (ex Mon) 🏌 ⬛ ♀ 🏠
Location	0.5m S on A10
Hotel	★★64% Castle Hotel, High St, DOWNHAM MARKET ☎ (0366) 384311 12rm(9 ⇔ ⛾)

DISS — Map 05 TM18

Diss ☎ (0379) 642847
Commonland course with natural hazards.
18 holes, 6238yds, Par 73, SSS 70.
Club membership 650.

Visitors	must contact in advance but may not play weekends & bank holidays.
Societies	by arrangement.
Green Fees	£20 per day.
Facilities	⊗ �🏛 🏌 ⬛ ♀ 🏠 ⛾
Location	Stuston (1.5m SE on B1118)
Hotel	★★62% Scole Inn, SCOLE ☎ (0379) 740481 12 ⇔ ⛾Annexe11 ⇔ ⛾

EAST DEREHAM — Map 09 TF91

Dereham ☎ Dereham (0362) 695900
Parkland course.
9 holes, 6225yds, Par 71, SSS 70, Course record 66.
Club membership 520.

Visitors	must contact in advance and have a handicap certificate; must play with member at weekends.
Societies	must contact in advance.
Green Fees	£16 per day.
Facilities	⊗ �🏛 & 🏌 (ex Mon) ⬛ ♀ (ex Sun) 🏠 ⛳ ⛾ G Kitley.
Location	Quebec Rd (N side of town centre off B1110)
Hotel	★★63% King's Head Hotel, Norwich St, DEREHAM ☎ (0362) 693842 & 693283 10rm(4 ⇔2 ⛾)Annexe5 ⇔ ⛾

FAKENHAM — Map 09 TF92

Fakenham ☎ (0328) 820316 & 862867
A well-wooded 9-hole course.
9 holes, 6000yds, Par 71, SSS 69, Course record 67.
Club membership 520.

Visitors	any time with member, restricted until after noon weekends and bank holidays.
Societies	apply in writing.
Green Fees	£14 per day (£18 weekends & bank holidays).
Facilities	⊗ �🏛 🏌 ⬛ ♀ 🏠 ⛾ J Westwood.
Leisure	hard tennis courts, squash.

Location	Gallow Sports Centre, The Race Course
Hotel	★★56% Crown Hotel & Restaurant, The Buttlands, WELLS-NEXT-THE-SEA ☎ (0328) 710209 15rm(5 ⇌5 ⋫)

GORLESTON-ON-SEA   Map 05 TG50

Gorleston ☎ Great Yarmouth (0493) 661911
Seaside course.
18 holes, 6400yds, Par 71, SSS 71, Course record 68.
Club membership 900.

Visitors	must have handicap certificate.
Societies	must contact in advance.
Green Fees	£20 per day (£25 weekends).
Facilities	⊗ ⫫ ⓛ ♥ ♀ ♨ ⌂ ⋏ Nick Brown.
Leisure	snooker.
Location	Warren Rd (S side of town centre)
Hotel	★★★69% Cliff Hotel, Gorleston, GREAT YARMOUTH ☎ (0493) 662179 39 ⇌ ⋫

HUNSTANTON   Map 09 TF64

Hunstanton ☎ (0485) 532811
A championship links course set among some of the most natural golfing country in East Anglia. Known for its fast and true greens. The wind is usually a factor in play and it is a real test to play to handicap.
18 holes, 6670yds, Par 72, SSS 72, Course record 65.
Club membership 670.

Visitors	must contact in advance and be a club member with current handicap certificate. Restricted at weekends & may not play bank holiday weekends.
Societies	advisable to apply in writing.
Green Fees	£32 per day (£38 weekends). Reduced fees Nov-Feb.
Facilities	⊗ (ex Mon) ⫫ by prior arrangement ⓛ ♥ ♀ ♨ ⌂ ⋏ John Carter.
Leisure	buggies, trolleys.
Location	2m N off A149
Hotel	★★69% Caley Hall Motel, Old Hunstanton Rd, HUNSTANTON ☎ (0485) 533486 Annexe29rm(27 ⇌)
Additional hotel	★★61% The Lodge Hotel, Old Hunstanton Rd, HUNSTANTON ☎ (0485) 532896 16 ⇌ ⋫

KING'S LYNN   Map 09 TF62

Eagles ☎ (0553) 827147 & 829777
Parkland course with plenty of water hazards and bunkers. Also Par-3 course and floodlit, covered driving range.
9 holes, 4284yds, Par 64, SSS 61.
Club membership 350.

Visitors	no restrictions.
Societies	telephone in advance.
Green Fees	£12 per 18 holes, £6 per 9 holes (£14/£7 weekends and bank holidays). Par 3 £4 per 18 holes, £2.50 per 9 holes.
Facilities	⊗ ⫫ by prior arrangement ⓛ ♥ ♀ ♨ ⌂ ⋏ ⋏
Leisure	par 3 course, floodlit driving range.
Location	39 School Rd, Tilney All Saints
Hotel	★★★65% The Duke's Head, Tuesday Market Pl, KING'S LYNN ☎ (0553) 774996 71 ⇌ ⋫

King's Lynn ☎ (0553) 631654
Challenging, wooded parkland course.
18 holes, 6646yds, Par 72, SSS 72, Course record 64.
Club membership 945.

Visitors	must contact in advance and have handicap certificate.
Societies	by arrangement.
Green Fees	£30 per day/round (£38 weekends).
Facilities	⊗ ⫫ by prior arrangement ⓛ ♥ ♀ ♨ ⌂ ⋏ Chris Hanlon.
Leisure	snooker.
Location	Castle Rising (4m NE off A148)
Hotel	★★★65% The Duke's Head, Tuesday Market Pl, KING'S LYNN ☎ (0553) 774996 71 ⇌ ⋫

MIDDLETON   Map 09 TF61

Middleton Hall ☎ King's Lynn (0553) 841800
The 9-hole King's course (played off 18 tees) is a pleasant parkland course constructed with conservation in mind around numerous mature trees, pond and reservoir. Additional Par 3 pitch and putt course.
9 holes, 5570yds, Par 68, SSS 67, Course record 69.
Club membership 300.

Visitors	no restrictions.
Societies	must contact in advance.
Green Fees	£12 per day (£14 weekends).
Facilities	⊗ ⫫ ⓛ ♥ ♀ ♨ ⌂ ⋏ ⋏ Fraser Scott.
Leisure	covered driving range.
Location	4m from King's Lynn off A47
Hotel	★★★66% Butterfly Hotel, Beveridge Way, Hardwick Narrows, KING'S LYNN ☎ (0553) 771707 50 ⇌ ⋫

MUNDESLEY   Map 09 TG33

Mundesley ☎ (0263) 720279
Seaside course, good views, windy.
9 holes, 5410yds, Par 68, SSS 66.
Club membership 400.

Visitors	restricted Wed & weekends. Must contact in advance.
Societies	must contact one month in advance.
Green Fees	not confirmed.
Facilities	⊗ ⫫ & ⓛ (ex Thu) ♥ ♀ ♨ ⌂ ⋏ T G Symmons.
Location	Links Rd (W side of village off B1159)
Hotel	★★68% Red Lion, Brooke St, CROMER ☎ (0263) 514964 12 ⇌ ⋫

NORWICH   Map 05 TG20

Eaton ☎ (0603) 51686
An undulating, tree-lined parkland course with excellent trees.
18 holes, 6135yds, Par 70, SSS 69, Course record 64.
Club membership 1000.

Visitors	restricted before 11.30am weekends, must contact in advance & have handicap certificate.
Societies	by arrangement.
Green Fees	£28 per day; £15 per round (£35/£20 weekends).
Facilities	⊗ ⫫ by prior arrangement ⓛ ♥ ♀ ♨ ⌂ ⋏ Nigel Bundy.
Location	Newmarket Rd (2.5m SW of city centre off A11)

▶

Hotel   ★★62% Arlington Hotel, 10 Arlington Ln, Newmarket Rd, NORWICH ☎ (0603) 617841 44 ⇥

Royal Norwich ☎ (0603) 429928
Undulating heathland course.
18 holes, 6603yds, Par 72, SSS 72, Course record 66.
Club membership 750.
Visitors   must contact in advance & have handicap certificate but may not play at weekends & bank holidays.
Societies   must contact in advance.
Green Fees £28 per day.
Facilities   ⊗ (ex Sun) ⊁ (Tue & Thu summer only) ⓑ ☕ ♀ ♨ 🏠 ⚐ ⚘ Gary Potter.
Leisure   practice grounds.
Location   Drayton High Rd, Hellesdon (2.5m NW of city centre on A1067)
Hotel   ★★★66% Hotel Norwich, 121-131 Boundary Rd, NORWICH ☎ (0603) 787260 108 ⇥ 🐾

Sprowston Park ☎ (0603) 410657
A Pay & Play course set in 100 acres of parkland. A very tight course, so accuracy is required for good golf. The facilities include a 27-bay driving range, a practice area and tuition from a team of professionals.
18 holes, 5982yds, Par 70, SSS 70, Course record 64.
Club membership 620.
Visitors   restricted Sat & Sun 8-10.30am.
Societies   must book in advance.
Green Fees £12 per round (£15 Sat,Sun & bank holidays).
Facilities   ⊗ ⊁ by prior arrangement ⓑ ☕ ♀ ♨ 🏠 ⚐ ⚘ P J Grice.
Leisure   heated indoor swimming pool, sauna, solarium, gymnasium, tuition.
Location   Wroxham Rd (4m NE from city centre on A1151)
Hotel   ★★★★67% Sprowston Manor, Wroxham Road, Sprowston, NORWICH ☎ (0603) 410871 97 ⇥ 🐾

SHERINGHAM   Map 09 TG14

Sheringham ☎ (0263) 823488
Splendid cliff-top links with gorse, good 'seaside turf' and plenty of space. Straight driving is essential for a low score. The course is close to the shore and can be very windswept, but offers magnificent views.
18 holes, 6464yds, Par 70, SSS 71, Course record 68.
Club membership 700.
Visitors   must contact in advance & have handicap certificate.
Societies   must apply in writing.
Green Fees £28 per day (£33 weekends & bank holidays).
Facilities   ⊗ ⊁ ⓑ ☕ (all catering by prior arrangement) ♀ ♨ 🏠 🛏 ⚘ R H Emery.
Location   Weybourne Rd (W side of town centre on A149)
Hotel   ★★65% Beaumaris Hotel, South St, SHERINGHAM ☎ (0263) 822370 24rm(17 ⇥5 🐾)

For an explanation of symbols and abbreviations, see page 5

SWAFFHAM   Map 05 TF80

Swaffham ☎ (0760) 721611
Heathland course.
9 holes, 6252yds, Par 72, SSS 70.
Club membership 510.
Visitors   must contact in advance. With member only at weekends.
Societies   must contact one month in advance.
Green Fees £18 per day/round.
Facilities   ⊗ ⊁ (ex Mon & Tue) ⓑ ☕ ♀ ♨ 🏠 ⚘ Peter Field.
Location   Cley Rd (1.5m SW)
Hotel   ★★★60% George Hotel, Station Rd, SWAFFHAM ☎ (0760) 721238 27rm(24 ⇥1 🐾)

THETFORD   Map 05 TL88

Feltwell ☎ (0842) 827762 & 827644
In spite of being an inland links, this 9-hole course is still open and windy.
9 holes, 6175yds, Par 70, SSS 69.
Club membership 400.
Visitors   dress restriction, no jeans,tracksuits or collarless shirts, golf shoes to be worn.
Societies   apply in writing or telephone in advance.
Green Fees £12 (£20 weekends & bank holidays).
Facilities   ⊗ ⊁ ⓑ ☕ (no catering Mon) ♀ (closed Mon) ♨ ⚘
Leisure   trolleys for hire.
Location   Thor Ave, Feltwell
Hotel   ★★★62% Bell Hotel, King St, THETFORD ☎ (0842) 754455 47 ⇥ 🐾

Thetford ☎ (0842) 752169
This is a course with a good pedigree. It was laid-out by a fine golfer, C.H. Mayo, later altered by James Braid and then again altered by another famous course designer, Mackenzie Ross. It is a testing heathland course with a particularly stiff finish.
18 holes, 6879yds, Par 72, SSS 73.
Club membership 700.
Visitors   must contact in advance & have handicap certificate. With member only at weekends.
Societies   must contact in advance.
Green Fees £26 per day/round (weekdays).
Facilities   ⊗ ⊁ by prior arrangement ⓑ ☕ ♀ ♨ 🏠 ⚘ Norman Arthur.
Location   Brandon Rd (0.75m W on B1107)
Hotel   ★★★62% Bell Hotel, King St, THETFORD ☎ (0842) 754455 47 ⇥ 🐾

WATTON   Map 05 TF90

Richmond Park ☎ (0953) 881803
Meadowland course dotted with newly planted trees and set on either side of the Little Wissey River.
18 holes, 6300yds, Par 71, SSS 70.
Club membership 500.
Visitors   handicap certificates are required for Sat & Sun mornings.
Societies   apply in writing.
Green Fees £20 per day; £15 per round (£20 weekends).

Facilities ⊗ 〗𝄞 🛢 ♌ ♉ ☖ ☖ 𝄢 Alan Hemsley.
Leisure gymnasium.
Location Saham Rd
Hotel ★★★60% George Hotel, Station Rd,
SWAFFHAM
☎ (0760) 721238 27rm(24 ⇆1 ⋒)

WEST RUNTON   Map 09 TG14

Links Country Park Hotel & Golf Club ☎ (0263) 837691
Parkland course 500 yds from the sea, with superb views
overlooking West Runton. The hotel offers extensive leisure
facilities.
9 holes, 4814yds, Par 66, SSS 64.
Club membership 250.
Visitors must have a handicap certificate.
Societies must telephone in advance.
Green Fees not confirmed.
Facilities ⊗ 〗𝄞 🛢 ♌ ♉ ☖ ☖ 𝄞 𝄢 𝄢 𝄢 Mike Jubb.
Leisure hard tennis courts, heated indoor swimming
pool, riding, sauna, solarium.
Location S side of village off A149
Hotel ★★70% Dormy House Hotel, Cromer Rd,
WEST RUNTON ☎ (0263) 837537 16 ⇆ ⋒

YARMOUTH, GREAT   Map 05 TG50

Great Yarmouth & Caister ☎ (0493) 728699
This great old club, which celebrated its centenary in
1982, has played its part in the development of the game.
It is a fine old-fashioned links where not many golfers
have bettered the SSS in competitions. The 468-yard 8th
(par 4), is a testing hole.
18 holes, 6330yds, Par 70, SSS 70, Course record 67.
Club membership 775.
Visitors restricted weekdays until 9am, Sat except
10.30-12.30 and Sun until 11.30 Must have
an introduction from own club.
Societies must apply in writing.
Green Fees £23.50 (£28 weekends).
Facilities ⊗ 〗𝄞 🛢 ♌ ♉ ☖ ☖ 𝄞 𝄢 Robert Foster.
Leisure riding, snooker.
Location Beach House, Caister on Sea (0.5m N off
A149)
Hotel ★★★63% Imperial Hotel, North Dr,
GREAT YARMOUTH
☎ (0493) 851113 39 ⇆ ⋒

NORTH YORKSHIRE

ALDWARK   Map 08 SE46

Aldwark Manor ☎ Tollerton (0347) 838353
An easy walking, scenic 18-hole parkland course with holes
both sides of the River Ure. The course surrounds the
Victorian Aldwark Manor Golf Hotel.
18 holes, 6171yds, Par 71, SSS 69, Course record 69.
Club membership 500.

Visitors must contact in advance, restricted weekends.
Societies must telephone in advance.
Green Fees £20 per day; £16 per round (£24/£20 weekends
& bank holidays).
Facilities ⊗ 〗𝄞 🛢 ♌ ♉ ☖ 𝄞 𝄢 𝄢 Gary M Platt.
Leisure fishing.
Location 5m SE of Boroughbridge off A1
Hotel ★★★⚑70% Aldwark Manor Hotel,
ALDWARK
☎ (0347) 838146 17 ⇆ ⋒Annexe3 ⇆ ⋒

BEDALE   Map 08 SE28

Bedale ☎ (0677) 422451
Secluded parkland course with many trees.
18 holes, 6565yds, Par 69, SSS 68.
Club membership 800.
Visitors must contact in advance.
Societies must apply in advance.
Green Fees £18 per day/round (£28 weekends & bank
holidays).
Facilities ⊗ 〗𝄞 🛢 ♌ ♉ ☖ 𝄢
Location Leyburn Rd (N side of town on A684)
Hotel ★★62% Motel Leeming, Great North Rd,
BEDALE ☎ (0677) 422122 40 ⇆ ⋒

BENTHAM   Map 07 SD66

Bentham ☎ (05242) 62455
Moorland course with glorious views.
9 holes, 5760yds, Par 70, SSS 69, Course record 69.
Club membership 480.   ▶

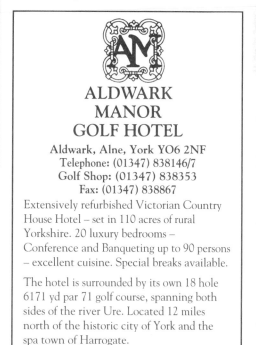

ALDWARK MANOR GOLF HOTEL

Aldwark, Alne, York YO6 2NF
Telephone: (01347) 838146/7
Golf Shop: (01347) 838353
Fax: (01347) 838867

Extensively refurbished Victorian Country
House Hotel – set in 110 acres of rural
Yorkshire. 20 luxury bedrooms –
Conference and Banqueting up to 90 persons
– excellent cuisine. Special breaks available.

The hotel is surrounded by its own 18 hole
6171 yd par 71 golf course, spanning both
sides of the river Ure. Located 12 miles
north of the historic city of York and the
spa town of Harrogate.

Visitors	no restrictions.
Societies	must apply in advance.
Green Fees	not confirmed.
Facilities	♨ ♀ ⚐
Location	Robin Ln (N side of High Bentham)
Hotel	★★67% The Traddock, AUSTWICK ☎ (05242) 51224 12rm(11 ⇌ ♠)

CATTERICK GARRISON   Map 08 SE29

Catterick Garrison ☎ Richmond (0748) 833268
Scenic parkland/moorland course of Championship standard, with good views of the Pennines and Cleveland hills. Testing 1st and 3rd holes.
18 holes, 6331yds, Par 71, SSS 70.
Club membership 750.

Visitors	must contact in advance and have a handicap certificate.
Societies	must contact in writing.
Green Fees	not confirmed.
Facilities	⚐ 🏠 ⚑ ⚔
Location	Leyburn Rd (1m W)
Hotel	★★58% Bridge House Hotel, CATTERICK BRIDGE ☎ (0748) 818331 16rm(4 ⇌9 ♠)

COPMANTHORPE   Map 08 SE54

Pike Hills ☎ York (0904) 706566
Parkland course surrounding nature reserve. Level terrain.
18 holes, 6121yds, Par 71, SSS 69.
Club membership 800.

Visitors	with member only weekends & bank holidays. Must contact in advance.
Societies	must apply in advance.
Green Fees	not confirmed.
Facilities	⊗ ⫴ ⅃ ♨ ♀ ⚐ 🏠 ⚑ ⚔
Location	Tadcaster Rd (3m SW of York on A64)
Hotel	★★★★64% Swallow Hotel, Tadcaster Rd, YORK ☎ (0904) 701000 113 ⇌ ♠

EASINGWOLD   Map 08 SE56

Easingwold ☎ (0347) 821964
Parkland course with easy walking. Trees are a major feature and on six holes water hazards come into play.
18 holes, 6285yds, Par 72, SSS 70, Course record 65.
Club membership 575.

Visitors	with member only weekends & bank holidays (winter). Must contact in advance.
Societies	must apply in advance.
Green Fees	£23 per day (£28 weekends).
Facilities	⊗ & ⫴ by prior arrangement ⅃ & ♨ (limited Mon) ♀ (ex Sun) ⚐ 🏠 ⚑ ⚔ John Hughes.
Leisure	pool table.
Location	Stillington Rd (1m S)
Hotel	★★62% George Hotel, Market Place, EASINGWOLD ☎ (0347) 821698 14 ⇌ ♠

For an explanation of symbols and
abbreviations, see page 5

FILEY   Map 08 TA18

Filey ☎ Scarborough (0723) 513293
Parkland course with good views, windy. Stream runs through course. Testing 9th and 13th holes.
18 holes, 6104yds, Par 70, SSS 69.
Club membership 950.

Visitors	except bank holidays & special competition days. Must contact in advance.
Societies	must apply in advance.
Green Fees	£20 per day (£25 weekends).
Facilities	⊗ ⫴ ⅃ ♨ ♀ ⚐ 🏠 ⚔ D England.
Leisure	snooker, caddy cars & trolleys for hire.
Location	West Av (0.5m S)
Hotel	★65% Sea Brink Hotel, The Beach, FILEY ☎ (0723) 513257 11 ⇌ ♠

GANTON   Map 08 SE97

Ganton ☎ Sherburn (0944) 70329
Championship course, heathland, gorse-lined fairways and heavily bunkered; variable winds.
18 holes, 6720yds, Par 73, SSS 74.
Club membership 580.

Visitors	must contact in advance and may not play at weekends.
Societies	must apply in advance.
Green Fees	not confirmed.
Facilities	⊗ & ⫴ by prior arrangement ⅃ ♨ ♀ ⚐ 🏠 ⚔
Location	0.25m NW off A64
Hotel	★★65% East Ayton Lodge Country House, Moor Ln, Forge Valley, EAST AYTON ☎ (0723) 864227 11 ⇌ ♠Annexe6 ⇌ ♠

HARROGATE   Map 08 SE35

Harrogate ☎ (0423) 862999
One of Yorkshire's oldest and best courses was designed in 1897 by 'Sandy' Herd. A perfect example of golf architecture, its greens and fairways offer an interesting but fair challenge. The undulating parkland course once formed part of the ancient Forest of Knaresborough. Excellent clubhouse.
18 holes, 6241yds, Par 69, SSS 70, Course record 66.
Club membership 750.

Visitors	must contact in advance & have a handicap certificate.
Societies	must contact in writing or intially by telephone.
Green Fees	£30 per day; £26 per round (£40 day/round weekends & bank holidays).
Facilities	⊗ & ⫴ by prior arrangement ⅃ ♨ ♀ ⚐ 🏠 ⚑ ⚔ P Johnson.
Leisure	snooker.
Location	Forest Ln Head, Starbeck (2.25m N on A59)
Hotel	★★★69% Balmoral Hotel & Restaurant, Franklin Mount, HARROGATE ☎ (0423) 508208 20 ⇌ ♠

Oakdale ☎ (0423) 567162
A pleasant, undulating parkland course which provides a good test of golf for the low handicap player without intimidating the less proficient. A special feature is an attractive stream which comes in to play on four holes. Excellent views from the clubhouse which has good facilities.
18 holes, 6456yds, Par 71, SSS 71.
Club membership 850.
Visitors	except 8-9.30am & 12.30-1.30pm. Contact in advance.
Societies	must apply at least one month in advance.
Green Fees	£30 per day; £25 per round (£30 per round weekends and bank holidays).
Facilities	⊗ ⅋ ┗ ♥ ♀ ☇ ☎ ⚐ ℓ Clive Dell.
Leisure	snooker.
Location	Oakdale (N side of town centre off A61)
Hotel	★★★65% Grants Hotel, 3-13 Swan Rd, HARROGATE ☎ (0423) 560666 42 ⇆ ↾

Rudding Park ☎ (0423) 872228
Due to open in Spring 1995, Rudding Park has been designed by Hawtree of Oxford as a parkland course with 5 water features to be operated on a Pay and Play basis.
18 holes, 6807yds, Par 72.
Visitors	handicap certificate required and dress code must be observed.
Societies	apply by telephone in advance.
Green Fees	to be confirmed.
Facilities	catering to be confirmed ♀ ☇ ☎ ⚐ ℓ to be appointed.
Leisure	heated outdoor swimming pool.
Location	Follifoot
Hotel	★★★64% Studley Hotel, Swan Rd, HARROGATE ☎ (0423) 560425 36 ⇆ ↾

KIRKBYMOORSIDE Map 08 SE68

Kirkbymoorside ☎ (0751) 31525
Hilly parkland course with narrow fairways, gorse and hawthorn bushes. Beautiful views.
18 holes, 6000yds, Par 69, SSS 69, Course record 67.
Club membership 600.
Visitors	must contact in advance.
Societies	must apply in advance.
Green Fees	not confirmed.
Facilities	⊗ ⅋ ┗ ♥ ♀ ☇
Location	Manor Vale (N side of village)
Hotel	★★♨69% Appleton Hall Country House Hotel, APPLETON-LE-MOORS ☎ (0751) 417227 417452 10 ⇆ ↾

KNARESBOROUGH Map 08 SE35

Knaresborough ☎ Harrogate (0423) 862690
Undulating parkland course with mature trees.
18 holes, 6481yds, Par 70, SSS 71.
Club membership 792.
Visitors	must contact in advance, restricted Tue & weekends. With member only on bank holiday weekends.
Societies	must contact at least 2 weeks in advance.
Green Fees	£24 per day; £18 per round (£29/£24 weekends).
Facilities	⊗ ⅋ ┗ ♥ ♀ ☇ ☎ ℓ Gary J Vickers.

Leisure	practice ground.
Location	Boroughbridge Rd (1.25 N on A6055)
Hotel	★★★69% Dower House Hotel, Bond End, KNARESBOROUGH ☎ (0423) 863302 28 ⇆ ↾Annexe4 ⇆ ↾

MALTON Map 08 SE77

Malton & Norton ☎ (0653) 693882
Parkland course with panoramic views of the moors. Very testing 1st hole (564 yds dog-leg, left).
Welham: 18 holes, 6426yds, Par 72, SSS 71.
Park: 18 holes, 6242yds, Par 72, SSS 70.
Derwent: 18 holes, 6286yds, Par 72, SSS 70.
Club membership 750.
Visitors	must contact in advance.
Societies	must apply in writing.
Green Fees	£20 per day/round (£25 weekends & bank holidays).
Facilities	⊗ ⅋ ┗ ♥ ♀ ☇ ☎ ⚐ ℓ S I Robinson.
Location	Welham Park, Norton (1m S)
Hotel	★★★♨70% Burythorpe House, Burythorpe, MALTON ☎ (065385) 200 10 ⇆ ↾

MASHAM Map 08 SE28

Masham ☎ Ripon (0765) 689379
Flat parkland course crossed by River Burn, which comes into play on two holes.
9 holes, 5244yds, Par 66, SSS 66.
Club membership 302.
Visitors	must play with member at weekends & bank holidays.
Societies	must contact the secretary in advance.
Green Fees	not confirmed.
Facilities	⊗ ┗ ♥ ♀ ☇
Location	Burnholme, Swinton Rd (1m SW off A6108)
Hotel	★★♨70% Jervaulx Hall Hotel, MASHAM ☎ (0677) 60235 10 ⇆ ↾

PANNAL Map 08 SE35

Pannal ☎ Harrogate (0423) 872628
Fine championship course. Moorland turf but well-wooded with trees closely involved with play.
18 holes, 6659yds, Par 72, SSS 72.
Club membership 790.
Visitors	must contact in advance.
Societies	must apply several months in advance.
Green Fees	£36 per day; £29 per round (£36 per round weekends).
Facilities	⊗ & ⅋ by prior arrangement ┗ ♥ ♀ ☇ ☎ ⚐ ℓ Murray Burgess.
Location	Follifoot Rd (E side of village off A61)
Hotel	★★★★55% The Majestic, Ripon Rd, HARROGATE ☎ (0423) 568972 156 ⇆ ↾

Use the **AA** *Hotels* or *Bed and Breakfast* guides to extend your choice of accommodation

RAVENSCAR   Map 08 NZ90

Raven Hall Hotel Golf Course ☎ (0723) 870353
Opened by the Earl of Cranbrook in 1898, this 9-hole clifftop
course is sloping and with good quality small greens. For
1994 new bunkers were created. Because of its clifftop
position it is subject to strong winds which make it great fun
to play, especially the 6th hole.
9 holes, 1894yds, Par 32, SSS 32.
Club membership 120.

Visitors	spikes essential, no jeans/T shirts, busy at weekends.
Societies	telephone in advance.
Green Fees	£10 per day (£15 weekends).
Facilities	⊗ 〗 ⅃ ⬛ ♀ ⅊ ✿ ⨝
Leisure	hard tennis courts, heated indoor plus outdoor swimming pool, snooker, sauna, croquet, putting.
Location	Situated on cliff top
Hotel	★★★61% Raven Hall Hotel, RAVENSCAR ☎ (0723) 870353 53 ⇌ ╠

RICHMOND   Map 07 NZ10

Richmond ☎ (0748) 825319
Parkland course.
18 holes, 5769yds, Par 70, SSS 68, Course record 64.
Club membership 600.

Visitors	may not play before 11.30am on Sun.
Societies	must contact in writing.
Green Fees	£16 per day (£25 weekends).
Facilities	⊗ 〗 ⅃ ⬛ ♀ ⬥ 🏠 ⅊ ⅃ Paul Jackson.
Location	Bend Hagg (0.75m N)
Hotel	★★67% King's Head Hotel, Market Place, RICHMOND ☎ (0748) 850220 24 ⇌ ╠Annexe4 ⇌ ╠

RIPON   Map 08 SE37

Ripon City ☎ (0765) 603640
Hard-walking on undulating parkland course; two testing par
3's at 5th and 7th.
18 holes, 6067yds, Par 71, SSS 69, Course record 65.
Club membership 625.

Visitors	must contact in advance & have handicap certificate.
Societies	must contact in writing.
Green Fees	£18 per day (£25 weekends & bank holidays).
Facilities	⊗ & ⅃ (ex Mon) ⬛ ♀ (times vary) ⬥ 🏠 ⅃
Location	Palace Rd (1m NW on A6108)
Hotel	★★★67% Ripon Spa Hotel, Park St, RIPON ☎ (0765) 602172 40 ⇌ ╠

SCARBOROUGH   Map 08 TA08

Scarborough North Cliff ☎ (0723) 360786
Seaside parkland course begining on cliff top overlooking
bay and castle. Good views.
18 holes, 6425yds, Par 71, SSS 71, Course record 66.
Club membership 860.

Visitors	must be member of a club with handicap certificate.
Societies	Mon-Fri, must apply in writing.

Green Fees £23 per day/round (£28 weekends & bank
holidays).

Facilities	⊗ 〗 ⅃ ⬛ ♀ ⬥ 🏠 ⅊ ⅃ S N Deller.
Leisure	electric caddy car hire.
Location	North Cliff Av (2m N of town centre off A165)
Hotel	★★★63% Esplanade Hotel, Belmont Rd, SCARBOROUGH ☎ (0723) 360382 73 ⇌ ╠

Scarborough South Cliff ☎ (0723) 374737
Parkland/seaside course designed by Dr Mackenzie.
18 holes, 6039yds, Par 70, SSS 69.
Club membership 700.

Visitors	contact in advance may not play before 9.30am Mon-Fri, 10am Sat and 10.30am Sun.
Societies	must contact Secretary in advance.
Green Fees	not confirmed.
Facilities	⊗ 〗 ⅃ ⬛ ♀ ⬥ 🏠
Location	Deepdale Av (1m S on A165)
Hotel	★★65% Bradley Court, 7-9 Filey Rd, South Cliff, SCARBOROUGH ☎ (0723) 360476 40 ⇌ ╠

SELBY   Map 08 SE63

Selby ☎ (0757) 228622
Mainly flat, links-type course; prevailing SW wind. Testing
holes including the 3rd, 7th and 16th.
18 holes, 6246yds, Par 70, SSS 70.
Club membership 780.

Visitors	restricted 11am-1pm (Nov-Mar). With member only weekends. Must contact in advance and have a handicap certificate.
Societies	welcome Wed-Fri, must apply in advance.
Green Fees	£24 per day; £22 per round.
Facilities	⊗ 〗 ⅃ ⬛ ♀ ⬥ 🏠 ⅊ ⅃ C A C Smith.
Leisure	snooker.
Location	Brayton Barff
Hotel	★★★★68% Monk Fryston Hall, MONK FRYSTON ☎ (0977) 682369 28 ⇌ ╠

SETTLE   Map 07 SD86

Settle ☎ (0729) 825288
Picturesque parkland course.
9 holes, 4596yds, Par 64, SSS 62.
Club membership 278.

Visitors	restricted on Sun.
Societies	apply in writing.
Green Fees	not confirmed.
Facilities	♀ ⬥
Location	Buckhaw Brow, Giggleswick (1m N on A65)
Hotel	★★★63% Falcon Manor Hotel, Skipton Rd, SETTLE ☎ (0729) 823814 15 ⇌ ╠Annexe5 ⇌ ╠

SKIPTON   Map 07 SD95

Skipton ☎ (0756) 795657 & 793922
Undulating parkland course with some water hazards and
panoramic views.
18 holes, 5771yds, Par 70, SSS 69.
Club membership 750.

Visitors	except competition days. Must contact in advance.
Societies	must apply in writing.

Green Fees £20 per day (£25 Sun & bank holidays).
Facilities ⊗ 🍴 ⅃ 🏌 ♀ ⅄ 🏠 ⅂ ⅃ Peter Robinson.
Leisure snooker, practice ground.
Location Off North West By-Pass (1m N on A65)
Hotel ★★★82% Devonshire Arms Country House
Hotel, BOLTON ABBEY
☎ (0756) 710441 40 ⌣ ⅃

STOCKTON-ON-THE-FOREST   Map 08 SE65

Forest Park ☎ York (0904) 400425
A parkland/meadowland course, opened in 1991, with natural
features including a stream and mature and new trees.
Old Foss Course: 18 holes, 6600yds, Par 71, SSS 72.
The West Course: 9 holes, 6372yds, Par 70, SSS 70.
Club membership 650.
Visitors welcome, subject to tee availability. Advisable
to contact club in advance.
Societies by prior arrangement.
Green Fees £20 per day; £14.50 per round (£25/£20
weekends & bank holidays).
Facilities ⊗ 🍴 by prior arrangement ⅃ 🏌 ♀ ⅄ 🏠
Leisure driving range.
Location 1.5m from end of A64, York bypass
Hotel ★★★68% York Pavilion Hotel, 45 Main St,
Fulford, YORK
☎ (0904) 622099 13 ⌣ ⅃ Annexe10 ⌣ ⅃

TADCASTER   Map 08 SE44

Cocksford ☎ (0937) 834253
An attractive Par 70 parkland course that is testing but non-
strenuous.
18 holes, 5518yds, Par 70, SSS 68.
Club membership 500.
Visitors must contact club in advance.
Societies must contact in advance.
Green Fees £16 (£21 weekends & bank holidays).
Facilities ⊗ 🍴 ⅃ 🏌 ♀ ⅄ 🏠 ⅂ ⌣
⅃ Graham Thompson.
Leisure outdoor swimming pool.
Location Cocksford, Stutton (between York & Leeds,
A162 from Tadcaster)
Hotel ★★★(red)⅃⅃ Bilbrough Manor Country House
Hotel, BILBROUGH
☎ (0937) 834002 17 ⌣ ⅃

THIRSK   Map 08 SE48

Thirsk & Northallerton ☎ (0845) 522170
The course has good views of the nearby Hambleton Hills.
Testing course, mainly flat land.
9 holes, 6257yds, Par 72, SSS 70, Course record 69.
Club membership 389.
Visitors must be a member of recognised golf club &
cannot play before 9.30am. With member only
Sun. Must contact in advance and have an
introduction from own club.
Societies must apply in writing.
Green Fees not confirmed.
Facilities ⊗ by prior arrangement 🍴 by prior arrangement
⅃ 🏌 ♀ ⅄ 🏠 ⅂ ⅃ Andrew Wright.
Location Thornton-le-Street (2m N on A168)
Hotel ★★61% Three Tuns Hotel, Market Place,
THIRSK ☎ (0845) 523124 11 ⌣ ⅃

WHITBY   Map 08 NZ81

Whitby ☎ (0947) 602768
Seaside course on cliff top. Good views and fresh sea breeze.
18 holes, 6134yds, Par 69, SSS 70.
Club membership 950.
Visitors may not play on competition days.
Societies must contact in writing.
Green Fees £17.50 per day/round (£25 weekends and bank
holidays).
Facilities ⊗ 🍴 ⅃ 🏌 (no catering Mon) ♀ ⅄ 🏠 ⅂
⅃ Brian English.
Leisure snooker.
Location Low Straggleton, Sandsend Rd (1.5m NW on A174)
Hotel ★★67% White House Hotel, Upgang Lane,
West Cliff, WHITBY
☎ (0947) 600469 12rm(7 ⌣ 4 ⅃)

YORK   Map 08 SE65

Fulford ☎ (0904) 413579
A flat, parkland/moorland course well-known for the
superb quality of its turf, particularly the greens, and now
famous as the venue for some of the best golf
tournaments in the British Isles.
18 holes, 6775yds, Par 72, SSS 72, Course record 62.
Club membership 600.
Visitors must contact in advance and have a
handicap certificate.
Societies must contact in writing.
Green Fees £30 per day; £20 per round (£35 weekends
& bank holidays).
Facilities ⊗ 🍴 ⅃ 🏌 ♀ ⅄ 🏠 ⅂ ⅃ Bryan Hessay.
Leisure snooker.
Location Heslington Ln (2m SE)
Hotel ★★★★64% Swallow Hotel, Tadcaster Rd,
YORK ☎ (0904) 701000 113 ⌣ ⅃
See advertisement on page 154.

Heworth ☎ (0904) 422389
11-hole parkland course, easy walking. Holes 3 to 9 played
twice from different tees.
11 holes, 6141yds, Par 70, SSS 69.
Club membership 460.
Visitors advisable to contact in advance but may not play
on Sun mornings in winter.
Societies must contact the secretary in writing.
Green Fees £14 per day; £10 per round (£17/£14 weekends
& bank holidays).
Facilities ⊗ 🍴 by prior arrangement ⅃ 🏌 (no catering
Mon) ♀ 🏠 ⅂ ⅃ Gregg Roberts.
Location Muncaster House, Muncastergate (1.5m NE of
city centre on A1036)
Hotel ★★★68% Dean Court Hotel, Duncombe Place,
YORK ☎ (0904) 625082 40 ⌣ ⅃

Swallow Hall ☎ (0904) 448219 & 448889
A small 18-hole, Par 3 course with 2 par 4s. Attached to a
caravan park.
18 holes, 3092yds.
Club membership 100.
Visitors no restrictions.
Societies must telephone in advance.
Green Fees £7 per 18 holes; £3.50 per 9 holes (£8-£4
weekends). ▶

GOLFERS YORK

Play Your Best Shot

Take a Breakaway to York and stay at the
Four Star Swallow Hotel and Leisure Club
overlooking the racecourse of this
beautiful and historic city.

Swallow Breakaway guests receive 2 nights
accommodation, full breakfast each day, 3 course
dinner on both evenings, and one lunch.

Championship Fulford, Country, Municipal
and Pay as you Play, all nearby. Nine hole
putting green and golf practice net in the
hotel grounds. The Swallow Leisure Club
and York City provide captivating
alternatives for your non-playing partner.
Simply the best of both worlds – Golf and
Tourism at their best!!

Telephone Now for your personal copy of
the brochure on York (01904) 701000 or
Fax (01904) 702308

**SWALLOW
HOTEL**
Y O R K
★★★★

Facilities	♨ ♿ ⛳ 🏨
Location	Crockey Hill
Hotel	★★★68% York Pavilion Hotel, 45 Main St, Fulford, YORK ☎ (0904) 622099 13 ⇔ ℟Annexe10 ⇔ ℟

York ☎ (0904) 491840
A pleasant, well-designed, heathland course with easy walking. The course is of good length but being flat the going does not tire. There are two testing pond holes.
18 holes, 6285yds, Par 70, SSS 70, Course record 65.
Club membership 700.

Visitors	not before 9am & not between 12-1.30pm. With member only weekends. Must contact in advance.
Societies	must apply in advance.
Green Fees	£26 per day/£20 per round (£32 weekends & bank holidays).
Facilities	⊗ ⅶ ⅃ ♨ (catering limited Fri) ♀ ⚐ 🏨 ℓ A B Mason.
Location	Lords Moor Ln, Strensall (6m NE, E of Strensall village)
Hotel	★★★68% Dean Court Hotel, Duncombe Place, YORK ☎ (0904) 625082 40 ⇔ ℟

> If visiting a brand new course, be sure
> to telephone before your visit to
> confirm the course information is
> correct

NORTHAMPTONSHIRE

CHACOMBE　　　　　Map 04 SP44

Cherwell Edge ☎ (0295) 711591
Parkland course open since 1980.
18 holes, 5800yds, Par 70, SSS 68, Course record 67.
Club membership 650.

Visitors	no restrictions but golf shoes to be worn (can be hired) and tidy appearance expected.
Societies	must apply by telephone.
Green Fees	£9.50 per round (£13 weekends).
Facilities	⊗ ⅶ ⅃ ♨ ♀ ⚐ 🏨 ⛳ ℓ Richard Jefferies.
Leisure	caddy cars reservations 4 days ahead.
Location	0.5m S off B4525
Hotel	★★★63% Whately Hall Hotel, Banbury Cross, BANBURY ☎ (0295) 263451 74 ⇔ ℟

COLD ASHBY　　　　　Map 04 SP67

Cold Ashby ☎ Northampton (0604) 740099 & 740548
Undulating parkland course, nicely matured, with superb views.
18 holes, 6020yds, Par 70, SSS 69.
Club membership 600.

Visitors	restricted weekends before 2pm.
Societies	by arrangement.
Green Fees	£20 per day; £14 per round (£16 per round weekends & bank holidays).
Facilities	⊗ ⅶ ⅃ ♨ ♀ ⚐ 🏨 ⛳ ℓ Shane Rose.
Location	Stanford Rd (1m W)
Hotel	B Forte Posthouse, CRICK ☎ (0788) 822101 88 ⇔ ℟

COLLINGTREE　　　　　Map 04 SP75

Collingtree Park ☎ (0604) 700000
Superb 18-hole resort course designed by former U.S.
and British Open champion Johnny Miller. Stunning
island green at the 18th hole. Green fee includes buggy
cart and range balls. The Golf Academy includes a
driving range, practice holes, indoor video teaching
room, golf custom-fit centre.
18 holes, 6692yds, Par 72, SSS 72.

Visitors	must contact in advance & have handicap certificate.
Societies	contact in advance.
Green Fees	£20 per round (£30 weekends).
Facilities	⊗ ⅶ ⅃ ♨ ♀ ⚐ 🏨 ⛳ ℓ
Leisure	buggies, trolleys.
Location	Windingbrook Ln (M1-junc 15 on A508 to Northampton)
Hotel	★★★★63% Swallow Hotel, Eagle Dr, NORTHAMPTON ☎ (0604) 768700 122 ⇔ ℟

CORBY　　　　　Map 04 SP88

Corby Public ☎ (0536) 260756
Municipal course laid out on made-up quarry ground and
open to prevailing wind. Wet in winter.
18 holes, 6677yds, Par 72, SSS 72.
Club membership 650.

Visitors	no restrictions.
Societies	must apply in writing.
Green Fees	not confirmed.
Facilities	⊗ ⅷ by prior arrangement ⅂ ⍐ ♀ ⌂ ⌂ ⌁ ⌁ Gary Brown.
Location	Stamford Rd, Weldon (4m NE on A43)
Hotel	★★★62% The Talbot, New St, OUNDLE ☎ (0832) 273621 40 ⇄ ⌁

DAVENTRY Map 04 SP56

Daventry & District ☎ (0327) 702829
A hilly course with hard walking.
18 holes, 5555yds, Par 69, SSS 67, Course record 68.
Club membership 300.

Visitors	restricted Sun mornings & weekends (Oct-Mar).
Societies	contact the club professional.
Green Fees	not confirmed.
Facilities	⊗ (weekends only) ⅂ & ⍐ by prior arrangement ♀ ⌂ ⌂ ⌁ ⌁ Michael Higgins.
Location	Norton Rd (1m NE)
Hotel	★★★69% Daventry Resort Hotel, Ashby Rd (A361), DAVENTRY ☎ (0327) 301777 138 ⇄ ⌁

FARTHINGSTONE Map 04 SP65

Farthingstone Hotel & Golf Course ☎ Preston Capes (0327) 361291
Pleasant rambling course with open aspect and widespread views.
18 holes, 6248yds, Par 71, SSS 71.
Club membership 500.

Visitors	must contact in advance.
Societies	must contact in advance.
Green Fees	£7.50 per round (£12.50 weekends).
Facilities	⊗ ⅷ ⅂ ⍐ ♀ ⌂ ⌂ ⌁
Leisure	squash, snooker, caddy cars, pool table.
Location	1m W
Hotel	★★62% Globe Hotel, High St, WEEDON ☎ (0327) 40336 17 ⇄ ⌁

HELLIDON Map 04 SP55

Hellidon Lakes Hotel & Country Club ☎ Byfield (0327) 62550
Spectacular parkland course designed by David Snell.
18 holes, 6691yds, Par 72, SSS 72.
Club membership 500.

Visitors	must contact in advance & have handicap certificate at weekends.
Societies	must telephone in advance.
Green Fees	not confirmed.
Facilities	⊗ ⅷ ⅂ ⍐ ♀ ⌂ ⌂ ⌁ ⌁ John Kennedy.
Leisure	hard tennis courts, heated indoor swimming pool, fishing, riding, sauna, solarium, gymnasium.
Hotel	★★★★66% Hellidon Lakes Hotel & Country Club, HELLIDON ☎ (0327) 62550 25 ⇄ ⌁ *See advertisement on page 195.*

KETTERING Map 04 SP87

Kettering ☎ (0536) 512074 & 511104
A very pleasant, mainly flat meadowland course with easy walking.
18 holes, 6035yds, Par 69, SSS 69, Course record 65.
Club membership 700.

Visitors	with member only weekends & bank holidays.
Societies	by arrangement.
Green Fees	£22 per day/round.
Facilities	⊗ ⅷ ⅂ ⍐ ♀ ⌂ ⌂ ⌁ ⌁ Kevin Theobald.
Location	Headlands (S side of town centre)
Hotel	★★★★67% Kettering Park Hotel, Kettering Parkway, KETTERING ☎ (0536) 416666 88 ⇄ ⌁

NORTHAMPTON Map 04 SP76

Delapre Golf Complex ☎ (0604) 764036
Rolling parkland course, part of municipal golf complex, which includes two 9-hole, par 3 courses, pitch-and-putt and 33 bay driving-range.
Main Course: 18 holes, 6356yds, Par 70, SSS 70, Course record 66.
Hardingstone: 9 holes, 2146yds, Par 32, SSS 32.
Club membership 1000.

Visitors	must pre-book and pay in advance.
Societies	must book and pay full green fees 2 weeks in advance.
Green Fees	£7.30 per 18 holes (£9.50 weekends); £5 per 9 holes (£6 weekends).
Facilities	⊗ ⅷ ⅂ ⍐ ♀ ⌂ ⌂ ⌁ ⌁ John Corby.
Leisure	pitch & putt, driving range, Par 3.
Location	Eagle Dr, Nene Valley Way (2m SE)
Hotel	★★★63% Westone Moat House, Ashley Way, Weston Favell, NORTHAMPTON ☎ (0604) 406262 31 ⇄ ⌁Annexe35 ⇄ ⌁

Kingsthorpe ☎ (0604) 710610
A compact, undulating parkland course set within the town boundary. Not a long course but testing enough to attract a competitive membership that boasts several County players.
18 holes, 6006yds, Par 69, SSS 69.
Club membership 650.

Visitors	must contact in advance and have handicap certificate. With member only weekends & bank holidays.
Societies	by arrangement.
Green Fees	£22 per day/round.
Facilities	⊗ ⅷ by prior arrangement ⅂ ⍐ ♀ ⌂ ⌂ ⌁ Paul Armstrong.
Location	Kingsley Rd (N side of town centre on A5095)
Hotel	★★★63% Westone Moat House, Ashley Way, Weston Favell, NORTHAMPTON ☎ (0604) 406262 31 ⇄ ⌁Annexe35 ⇄ ⌁

Northampton ☎ (0604) 845155
New parkland course with water in play on three holes.
18 holes, 6534yds, Par 72, SSS 71.
Club membership 965.

Visitors	must have handicap certificate. Members only club.
Societies	by arrangement.
Green Fees	£25 per day.
Facilities	⊗ ⅷ ⅂ ⍐ ♀ ⌂ ⌁ Mark Chamberlain. ▶

Location Harlestone (NW of town centre on A428)
Hotel ★★★65% Northampton Moat House, Silver Street, Town Centre, NORTHAMPTON
☎ (0604) 22441 142 ⇄ ☞

Northamptonshire County ☎ (0604) 843025
Undulating heathland/woodland course with gorse, heather and fine pine woods.
18 holes, 6503yds, Par 70, SSS 71.
Club membership 850.
Visitors restricted weekends. Must contact in advance and have a handicap certificate.
Societies Wed & Thu only, must contact in advance.
Green Fees £35 day summer; £25 winter.
Facilities ⊗ ⵗ ﻝ ♥ ♀ 스 ☎ ᐦ Tim Rouse.
Leisure practice range.
Location Sandy Ln, Church Brampton (4m NW of town centre off A50)
Hotel ★★★63% Westone Moat House, Ashley Way, Weston Favell, NORTHAMPTON
☎ (0604) 406262 31 ⇄ ☞Annexe35 ⇄ ☞

OUNDLE   Map 04 TL08

Oundle ☎ (0832) 273267
Undulating parkland course, shortish but difficult. A small brook affects some of the approaches to the greens.
18 holes, 5549yds, Par 70, SSS 67.
Club membership 630.
Visitors may not play before 10.30am weekends unless with member.
Societies must apply in writing.
Green Fees £20 per day (£30 weekends).
Facilities ⊗ ⵗ ﻝ ♥ ♀ 스 ☎ ᐦ Richard Keys.
Location Benefield Rd (1m W on A427)
Hotel ★★★62% The Talbot, New St, OUNDLE
☎ (0832) 273621 40 ⇄ ☞

STAVERTON   Map 04 SP56

Staverton Park ☎ Daventry (0327) 705911
Open course, fairly testing with good views.
18 holes, 6204yds, Par 71, SSS 71.
Club membership 400.
Visitors restricted weekends. Must contact in advance.
Societies by arrangement.
Green Fees £17.50 per round (£22.50 weekends).
Facilities ⊗ ⵗ ﻝ ♥ ♀ 스 ☎ ᛜ ⟿ ᐦ Richard Mudge.
Leisure sauna, gymnasium, driving range/putting greens, caddy cars.
Location 0.75m NE of Staverton on A425
Hotel ★★★69% Daventry Resort Hotel, Ashby Rd (A361), DAVENTRY
☎ (0327) 301777 138 ⇄ ☞

WELLINGBOROUGH   Map 04 SP86

Rushden ☎ Rushden (0933) 312581
Parkland course with brook running through the middle.
10 holes, 6335yds, Par 71, SSS 70, Course record 69.
Club membership 400.
Visitors may not play Wed afternoon. With member only weekends.
Societies must apply in writing.
Green Fees not confirmed.

Facilities ⊗ & ⵗ ﻝ ♥ ♀ (ex Mon) 스
Location Kimbolton Rd, Chelveston (2m E of Higham Ferrers on A45)
Hotel ★★★63% Hind Hotel, Sheep St, WELLINGBOROUGH
☎ (0933) 222827 34 ⇄ ☞

Wellingborough ☎ (0933) 677234
An undulating parkland course with many trees. The 514-yd, 14th is a testing hole. The clubhouse is a stately home.
18 holes, 6620yds, Par 72, SSS 72, Course record 68.
Club membership 850.
Visitors must contact in advance & have handicap certificate, but may not play at weekends & bank holidays.
Societies must apply in writing.
Green Fees £27 per day; £22 per round.
Facilities ⊗ ⵗ ﻝ ♥ ♀ 스 ☎ ᐦ David Clifford.
Leisure outdoor swimming pool, snooker, caddy cars.
Location Gt Harrowden Hall (2m N on A509)
Hotel ★★★63% Hind Hotel, Sheep St, WELLINGBOROUGH
☎ (0933) 222827 34 ⇄ ☞

◆ NORTHUMBERLAND ◆

ALLENDALE   Map 12 NY85

Allendale ☎ 091-267 5875
A newly built parkland course set 1000 feet above sea level with superb views. The course is two 9-hole loops on fairly hilly terrain. The club has recently moved to this new course having been at their previous ground for 69 years.
9 holes, 5044yds, Par 66, SSS 63.
Club membership 180.
Visitors restricted Sun mornings & Aug bank holiday till 4pm.
Societies contact 2-3 weeks in advance.
Green Fees £5 per day (£7 weekends & bank holidays).
Facilities ♥ 스 ☎
Leisure riding.
Location High Studdon Allenheads Rd (1.5m S on B6295)
Hotel ★★64% County Hotel, Priestpopple, HEXHAM ☎ (0434) 602030 9 ⇄ ☞

ALNMOUTH   Map 12 NU21

Alnmouth ☎ (0665) 830231
Coastal course with pleasant views.
18 holes, 6500yds, Par 71, SSS 71, Course record 65.
Club membership 850.
Visitors may not play Wed, Fri, weekends & bank holidays. Must contact in advance.
Societies by arrangement.
Green Fees £25 per day.
Facilities ⊗ ⵗ ﻝ ♥ ♀ 스 ☎ ⟿
Location Foxton Hall (1m NE)
Hotel ★★★59% White Swan Hotel, Bondgate Within, ALNWICK ☎ (0665) 602109 43 ⇄ ☞

Alnmouth Village ☎ (0665) 830370
Seaside course with part coastal view.
9 holes, 6078yds, Par 70, SSS 70.
Club membership 480.

Visitors	no restrictions.
Societies	must contact in advance.
Facilities	♀⅃
Location	Marine Rd (E side of village)
Hotel	★★★59% White Swan Hotel, Bondgate Within, ALNWICK ☎ (0665) 602109 43 ⇌ ♞

ALNWICK
Map 12 NU11

Alnwick ☎ (0665) 602632
Parkland course offering a fair test of golfing skills.
9 holes, 5387yds, Par 66, SSS 66.
Club membership 402.

Visitors	may not play on competition days.
Societies	must contact in advance.
Green Fees	£15 per day; £10 per round (£20 per day; £15 per round weekends & bank holidays).
Facilities	⊗ ⅃ ♥ ♀⅃
Location	Swansfield Park (S side of town)
Hotel	★★★59% White Swan Hotel, Bondgate Within, ALNWICK ☎ (0665) 602109 43 ⇌ ♞

BAMBURGH
Map 12 NU13

Bamburgh Castle ☎ (0668) 214378
This is not a long, links course, but there are those who have played golf all over the world who say that for sheer breathtaking beauty this northern seaside gem cannot be bettered. And the course itself is the greatest fun to play. Magnificent views of Farne Island, Lindisfarne and Holy Island.
18 holes, 5621yds, Par 68, SSS 67, Course record 63.
Club membership 650.

Visitors	with member only bank holidays & competition days. Must contact in advance & have handicap certificate.
Societies	apply in writing.
Green Fees	£30 per day; £25 per round (£35/£30 weekends).
Facilities	⊗ ⅃ ♥ ♥ (no catering Tue) ♀⅃ 🎒
Leisure	buggies.
Location	6m E of A1 via B1341 or B1342
Hotel	★★69% Lord Crewe Arms, Front St, BAMBURGH ☎ (0668) 214243 25rm(20 ⇌ ♞)
Additional hotel	★★60% Victoria Hotel, Front St, BAMBURGH ☎ (0668) 214431 24rm(16 ⇌1 ♞)

BEDLINGTON
Map 12 NZ28

Bedlingtonshire ☎ (0670) 822087
Meadowland/parkland course with easy walking. Under certain conditions the wind can be a distinct hazard.
18 holes, 6813yds, Par 73, SSS 73.
Club membership 950.

Visitors	must contact in advance.
Societies	apply in advance to the Professional.
Green Fees	£16 per day (£19 weekends).
Facilities	⊗ ⅃ by prior arrangement ♥ ♥ ♀⅃ 🎒 ⅄ ꙿ Marcus Webb.
Location	Acorn Bank (1m SW on A1068)
Hotel	★★★★55% Holiday Inn, Great North Rd, SEATON BURN ☎ 091-236 5432 150 ⇌ ♞

BELFORD
Map 12 NU13

Belford ☎ (0668) 213433
On the east coast, this course is often affected by crosswinds especially the 4th - the compensation is spectacular views of Holy Island. A number of other holes are affected by mature trees.
9 holes, 3152yds, Par 72, SSS 70, Course record 74.
Club membership 280.

Visitors	weekdays and after 10am at weekends.
Societies	apply in advance by telephone or in writing.
Green Fees	£16 per day; £13 per 18 holes; £9 per 9 holes (£20/£15/£10 weekends and bank holidays).
Facilities	⊗ ⅃ (restricted in winter) ♥ ♥ ♀⅃ 🎒 ꙿ
Leisure	floodlit driving range, one caddy car.
Location	South Rd (off A1 between Alnwick & Berwick on Tweed)
Hotel	★★★64% Blue Bell Hotel, Market Place, BELFORD ☎ (0668) 213543 17 ⇌ ♞

AA

ETB
✹✹✹
Approved

VICTORIA HOTEL

Bamburgh, Northumberland NE69 7BP
Tel: Bamburgh (0166 84) 431

Stay on Northumbria's enchanted shore, amid castles, magnificent beaches and tiny fishing villages – absolutely unspoilt and a paradise for walkers, golfers and lovers of wildlife. Nine first class golf courses, playable all year, lie within a few miles radius.
The famous old Victoria Hotel, in the centre of Bamburgh, Northumbria's ancient capital, offers great comfort, good food, a wonderful atmosphere and excellent value. 24 rooms, most with private bath, all with colour television, direct-dial telephone and tea/coffee facilities.

BELLINGHAM   Map 12 NY88

Bellingham ☎ (0434) 220530
9-hole downland course with natural hazards and 18 tees.
9 holes, 5245yds, Par 67, SSS 66.
Club membership 340.

Visitors	must adhere to start sheet weekdays & Sat, no play on Sun until after 5pm.
Societies	must contact in advance.
Green Fees	£10 per day (£15 per day weekends).
Facilities	⊗ ⅷ ⅃ ▼ (catering Apr-Oct by prior arrangement) ♀ ⅍
Leisure	practice ground.
Location	Boggle Hole (N side of village on B6320)
Hotel	★★66% Riverdale Hall Hotel, BELLINGHAM ☎ (0434) 220254 20 ⇆ ⋔

BERWICK-UPON-TWEED   Map 12 NT95

Berwick-upon-Tweed (Goswick) ☎ (0289) 387256
Natural seaside links course, with undulating fairways, elevated tees and good greens.
18 holes, 6425yds, Par 72, SSS 71, Course record 64.
Club membership 580.

Visitors	may only play between 10am-noon & after 2pm weekends. Must contact professional tel: (0289) 387380
Societies	party of 8 or more by arrangement.
Green Fees	£24 per day; £18 per round (£32/£24 weekends).
Facilities	⊗ ⅷ ⅃ ▼ ♀ ⅍ 🛅 ⅌ ⅃ Paul Terras.
Leisure	buggies/electric carts/trolleys for hire.
Location	Goswick (6m S off A1)
Hotel	★★★⅋66% Tillmouth Park Hotel, CORNHILL-ON-TWEED ☎ (0890) 882255 12 ⇆ ⋔ Annexe2 ⇆ ⋔

Magdalene Fields ☎ (0289) 306384
Seaside course with natural hazards formed by sea bays. Last 9 holes open to winds. Testing 18th hole over bay (par 3).
18 holes, 6526yds, Par 72, SSS 71, Course record 69.
Club membership 450.

Visitors	must contact in advance. Must possess individual sets of clubs.
Societies	must contact in advance.
Green Fees	£18 per day; £14 per round (£20/£16 weekends).
Facilities	⊗ ⅷ ⅃ ▼ (catering by arrangement) ♀ ⅍
Location	Magdalene Fields (E side of town centre)
Hotel	★★★⅋66% Tillmouth Park Hotel, CORNHILL-ON-TWEED ☎ (0890) 882255 12 ⇆ ⋔ Annexe2 ⇆ ⋔

BLYTH   Map 12 NZ38

Blyth ☎ (0670) 367728
Course built over old colliery. Parkland with water hazards.
18 holes, 6300yds, Par 72, SSS 71.
Club membership 815.

Visitors	with member only after 3pm & at weekends.
Societies	apply in writing.
Green Fees	£18 per day; £16 per round.
Facilities	⊗ ⅷ by prior arrangement ⅃ ▼ ♀ ⅍ 🛅 ⅃ P Chapman.
Leisure	pool table.

Location	New Delaval (6m N of Whitley Bay)
Hotel	★★★64% Windsor Hotel, South Pde, WHITLEY BAY ☎ 091-251 8888 64 ⇆ ⋔

CRAMLINGTON   Map 12 NZ27

Arcot Hall ☎ 091-236 2794
A wooded parkland course, reasonably flat.
18 holes, 6389yds, Par 70, SSS 70, Course record 65.
Club membership 700.

Visitors	with member only weekends & bank holidays. Must be member of a Golf Club or have handicap certificate.
Societies	welcome midweek only, contact in advance.
Green Fees	£25 (£28 weekends).
Facilities	⊗ ⅷ ⅃ ▼ ♀ ⅍ 🛅 ⅌ ⅃ Graham Cant.
Leisure	snooker, trolleys.
Location	2m SW off A1
Hotel	★★★★55% Holiday Inn, Great North Rd, SEATON BURN ☎ 091-236 5432 150 ⇆ ⋔

EMBLETON   Map 12 NU22

Dunstanburgh Castle ☎ (0665) 576562
Rolling links designed by James Braid, with castle and bird sanctuary either side. Superb views.
18 holes, 6039yds, Par 70, SSS 69.
Club membership 380.

Visitors	no restrictions.
Societies	contact in advance.
Green Fees	£12.50 per day (£18.50 per day; £16 per round weekends & bank holidays).
Facilities	⊗ ⅷ ⅃ ▼ ♀ ⅍ 🛅 ⅌
Location	0.5m E
Hotel	★★72% Beach House Hotel, Sea Front, SEAHOUSES ☎ (0665) 720337 14 ⇆ ⋔

HEXHAM   Map 12 NY96

Hexham ☎ (0434) 603072
A very pretty undulating parkland course with interesting natural contours. From parts of the course, particularly the elevated 6th tee, there are the most exquisite views of the valley below. As good a parkland course as any in the North of England.
18 holes, 6000yds, Par 70, SSS 68.
Club membership 700.

Visitors	advance booking advisable.
Societies	welcome weekdays, contact in advance.
Green Fees	£26 per day; £20 per round (£33/£26 weekends & bank holidays).
Facilities	⊗ ⅷ ⅃ ▼ ♀ ⅍ 🛅 ⅌ ⅃ Martin W Forster.
Leisure	squash, snooker.
Location	Spital Park (1m NW on B6531)
Hotel	★★★63% Beaumont Hotel, Beaumont St, HEXHAM ☎ (0434) 602331 23 ⇆ ⋔

If you know of a golf course that welcomes visitors and is not already in this guide, we should be grateful for information

---

158

Tynedale ☎ (0434) 608154
Flat, easy moorland course. Bounded by river and railway.
9 holes, 5643yds, Par 69, SSS 67.
Club membership 392.

Visitors	may not play Sun mornings.
Societies	must contact in advance.
Green Fees	£10 (£12 weekends & bank holidays).
Facilities	⊗ ⅲ (Sun only) ⬛ ♥ ♀ ♨ ⌂ ⛳ ♛ Claire Brown.
Leisure	pool table.
Location	Tyne Green (N side of town)
Hotel	★★★63% Beaumont Hotel, Beaumont St, HEXHAM ☎ (0434) 602331 23 ⇔ ♗

MORPETH Map 12 NZ28

Morpeth ☎ (0670) 519980 & 504942
Parkland course with views of the Cheviots.
18 holes, 6206yds, Par 72, SSS 70, Course record 67.
Club membership 700.

Visitors	restricted weekends & bank holidays. Must contact in advance and have a handicap certificate.
Societies	apply in writing.
Green Fees	not confirmed.
Facilities	⊗ ⅲ ⬛ ♥ ♀ ♨ ⌂ ♛ Martin Jackson.
Leisure	snooker.
Location	The Common (S side of town centre on A197)
Hotel	★★★★♨75% Linden Hall Hotel and Health Spa, LONGHORSLEY ☎ (0670) 516611 50 ⇔ ♗

NEWBIGGIN-BY-THE-SEA Map 12 NZ38

Newbiggin-by-the-Sea ☎ (0670) 817344
Seaside-links course.
18 holes, 6452yds, Par 72, SSS 71, Course record 67.
Club membership 500.

Visitors	must contact in advance and may not play before 10am or on competition days.
Societies	must apply in writing.
Green Fees	£12 per day/round (£17 weekends).
Facilities	⊗ & ⅲ by prior arrangement ⬛ ♥ ♀ ♨ ⌂ ⛳ ♛ David J Fletcher.
Leisure	snooker.
Location	Prospect Place (N side of town)
Hotel	★★★★♨75% Linden Hall Hotel and Health Spa, LONGHORSLEY ☎ (0670) 516611 50 ⇔ ♗

PONTELAND Map 12 NZ17

Ponteland ☎ (0661) 822689
Open parkland course offering testing golf and good views.
18 holes, 6524yds, Par 72, SSS 71, Course record 66.
Club membership 720.

Visitors	with member only Fri, weekends & bank holidays.
Societies	welcome Tue & Thu only. Must contact in advance.
Green Fees	£22.50 per day/round.
Facilities	⊗ ⅲ (ex Mon) ⬛ ♥ ♀ ♨ ⌂ ♛ Alan Crosby.
Leisure	caddy cars.
Location	53 Bell Villas (0.5m E on A696)

Hotel ★★★64% Airport Moat House Hotel, Woolsington, NEWCASTLE UPON TYNE AIRPORT ☎ (0661) 824911 100 ⇔ ♗

PRUDHOE Map 12 NZ06

Prudhoe ☎ (0661) 832466
Parkland course with natural hazards and easy walking along undulating fairways.
18 holes, 5812yds, Par 69, SSS 68, Course record 63.
Club membership 700.

Visitors	must contact in advance. Weekends after 4.30pm
Societies	must contact in writing.
Green Fees	£20 per day (£25 weekends).
Facilities	⊗ ⬛ ♥ ♀ ♨ ⌂ ♛ John Crawford.
Location	Eastwood Park (E side of town centre off A695)
Hotel	★★64% County Hotel, Priestpopple, HEXHAM ☎ (0434) 602030 9 ⇔ ♗

ROTHBURY Map 12 NU00

Rothbury ☎ (0669) 20718 & 21271
Very flat parkland course alongside the River Coquet.
9 holes, 2788yds, Par 68, SSS 67, Course record 65.
Club membership 400.

Visitors	may play at weekends by arrangement only.
Societies	may not play at weekends. Must contact in advance.
Green Fees	£11 per day (£16 weekends).
Facilities	⬛ ♥ (ex Mon) ♀ (ex Mon) ♨
Location	Old Race Course (S side of town off B6342)
Hotel	★★★59% White Swan Hotel, Bondgate Within, ALNWICK ☎ (0665) 602109 43 ⇔ ♗

SEAHOUSES Map 12 NU23

Seahouses ☎ Alnwick (0665) 720794
Typical links course with many hazards, including the famous 10th, 'Logans Loch', water hole.
18 holes, 5462yds, Par 67, SSS 67, Course record 67.
Club membership 550.

Visitors	must contact in advance for weekends.
Societies	apply in writing.
Green Fees	£15 per day (£20 weekends & bank holidays).
Facilities	⊗ ⅲ ⬛ ♥ (no catering Tue unless by prior arrangement) ♀ (ex Tue) ♨ ⌂
Location	Beadnell Rd (S side of village on B1340)
Hotel	★★70% Olde Ship Hotel, SEAHOUSES ☎ (0665) 720200 12 ⇔ ♗Annexe3 ⇔ ♗

STOCKSFIELD Map 12 NZ06

Stocksfield ☎ (0661) 843041
Challenging course: parkland (9 holes), woodland (9 holes).
18 holes, 5594yds, Par 68, SSS 68.
Club membership 700.

Visitors	welcome except weekends until 4pm. Must contact in advance.
Societies	must contact in advance.
Green Fees	£20 per day; £15 per round (£20 per round weekends & bank holidays).
Facilities	⬛ ♥ ♀ ♨ ⌂ ⛳ ♛ Steven McKenna.
Location	New Ridley Rd (2.5m SE off A695)

▶

Hotel   ★★★63% Beaumont Hotel, Beaumont St,
HEXHAM ☎ (0434) 602331 23 ⇌ ℝ

WARKWORTH   Map 12 NU20

Warkworth ☎ (0665) 711596
Seaside links course, with good views and alternative tees for
the back nine.
*9 holes, 5817yds, Par 70, SSS 68, Course record 66 or 58
holes.*
Club membership 440.
Visitors   welcome except Tue & Sat.
Societies   apply in writing.
Green Fees   £12 per day (£20 weekends & bank holidays).
Facilities   Ꮭ ♥ ♀ ⚘
Leisure   caddy cars.
Location   The Links (0.5m E of village off A1068)
Hotel   ★★★59% White Swan Hotel, Bondgate Within,
ALNWICK ☎ (0665) 602109 43 ⇌ ℝ

WOOLER   Map 12 NT92

Wooler ☎ (0668) 281956
Hilltop, moorland course with spectacular views over the
Glendale valley. Nine greens played from 18 tees. A very
challenging course when windy with one Par 5 of 580 yards.
The course is much under used during the week so is always
available. Honesty box payment of green fees and no waiting.
9 holes, 6372yds, Par 72, SSS 71, Course record 69.
Club membership 300.
Visitors   course closed for major club competitions
otherwise no restrictions.
Societies   by prior arrangement with secretary.
Green Fees   £10 (£15 weekends & bankholidays).
Facilities   all catering by prior arrangement ♀ ⚘
Leisure   trolleys,golf car hire for disabled.
Location   Dod Law, Doddington (at Doddington on B6525
Wooler/Berwick Rd)
Hotel   ★★59% Tankerville Arms Hotel, Cottage Rd,
WOOLER ☎ (0668) 81581 17 ⇌ ℝ

NOTTINGHAMSHIRE

EAST LEAKE   Map 08 SK52

Rushcliffe ☎ (0509) 852959
Hilly, tree-lined and picturesque parkland course.
18 holes, 6020yds, Par 70, SSS 68, Course record 65.
Club membership 700.
Visitors   restricted weekends & bank holidays 9.30-11am
& 3-4.30pm.
Societies   must apply in advance.
Green Fees   £21 per day (£25 weekends).
Facilities   ⊗ ℳ Ꮭ ♥ ♀ ⚘ 🏠 ℓ Tim Smart.
Leisure   snooker.
Location   Stocking Ln (1m N)
Hotel   ★★★60% Yew Lodge, 33 Packington Hill,
Kegworth, EAST MIDLANDS AIRPORT
☎ (0509) 672518 54 ⇌ ℝ

KEYWORTH   Map 08 SK63

Stanton on the Wolds ☎ Nottingham (0602) 372006
Parkland course, fairly flat with stream running through four
holes.
18 holes, 6437yds, Par 73, SSS 71.
Club membership 900.
Visitors   restricted Tue & competition days. Must contact
in advance & have handicap certificate.
Societies   must apply in Oct
Green Fees   not confirmed.
Facilities   ⊗ ℳ Ꮭ ♥ ♀ ⚘ 🏠 ℓ
Location   E side of village
Hotel   ★★65% Rufford Hotel, 53 Melton Road,West
Bridgford, NOTTINGHAM
☎ (0602) 814202 35 ℝ

KIRKBY IN ASHFIELD   Map 08 SK55

Notts ☎ Mansfield (0623) 753225
Undulating heathland Championship course.
18 holes, 7020yds, Par 72, SSS 74, Course record 66.
Club membership 500.
Visitors   must contact in advance & have handicap
certificate. With member only weekends &
bank holidays.
Societies   must apply in advance.
Green Fees   £42 per day; £33 per round.
Facilities   ⊗ ℳ Ꮭ ♥ ♀ ⚘ 🏠 ℸ ℓ Brian Waites.
Leisure   driving range.
Location   Hollinwell (1.5m SE off A611)
Hotel   ★★★★62% Swallow Hotel, Carter Ln East,
SOUTH NORMANTON
☎ (0773) 812000 161 ⇌ ℝ

MANSFIELD   Map 08 SK56

Sherwood Forest ☎ (0623) 26689
As the name suggests, the Forest is the main feature of
this natural heathland course with its heather, silver birch
and pine trees. The homeward nine holes are particularly
testing. The 11th and 14th are notable par 4 holes on this
well-bunkered course designed by the great James Braid.
18 holes, 6714yds, Par 71, SSS 73.
Club membership 758.
Visitors   allowed Mon, Thu & Fri only. Must contact
in advance and have a handicap certificate.
Societies   welcome Mon, Thu & Fri, must apply in
advance.
Green Fees   £35 per day; £30 per round.
Facilities   ⊗ ℳ Ꮭ ♥ ♀ ⚘ 🏠 ℓ Ken Hall.
Location   Eakring Rd (2.5m E)
Hotel   ★★64% Pine Lodge Hotel, 281-283
Nottingham Rd, MANSFIELD
☎ (0623) 22308 20rm(19 ⇌ ℝ)

MANSFIELD WOODHOUSE   Map 08 SK56

Mansfield Woodhouse ☎ Mansfield (0623) 23521
Easy walking on heathland.
9 holes, 2446yds, Par 68, SSS 64 or 2446yds, Par 68, SSS 64.
Club membership 130.
Visitors   no restrictions.
Societies   must contact by telephone.

Green Fees not confirmed.
Facilities ⊗ ⊾ ☕ ♀ ⌂ ⛳ ℓ Leslie Highfield.
Location Leeming Ln North (N side of town centre off A60)
Hotel ★★64% Pine Lodge Hotel, 281-283 Nottingham Rd, MANSFIELD
☎ (0623) 22308 20rm(19 ⇌ ↱)

NEWARK-ON-TRENT Map 08 SK75

Newark ☎ (0636) 626282
Wooded, parkland course in secluded situation with easy walking.
18 holes, 6421yds, Par 71, SSS 71.
Club membership 650.
Visitors must contact in advance and have handicap certificate.
Societies must apply in writing.
Green Fees on application.
Facilities ⊗)Ⅲ ⊾ ☕ ♀ △ ⌂ ℓ Tony Bennett.
Leisure snooker.
Location Coddington (4m E on A17)
Hotel ★★69% Grange Hotel, 73 London Rd, NEWARK
☎ (0636) 703399 10 ⇌ ↱Annexe5 ⇌ ↱

NOTTINGHAM Map 08 SK53

Beeston Fields ☎ (0602) 257062
Parkland course with sandy subsoil and wide, tree-lined fairways. The par 3, 14th has elevated tee and small bunker-guarded green.
18 holes, 6414yds, Par 71, SSS 71, Course record 68.
Club membership 750.
Visitors must contact in advance and have a handicap certificate.
Societies must apply in advance.
Green Fees not confirmed.
Facilities ⊗)Ⅲ ⊾ ☕ ♀ △ ⌂ ⛳ ℓ Alun Wardle.
Leisure snooker.
Location Beeston (4m SW off A52)
Hotel B Forte Posthouse, Bostocks Ln, SANDIACRE
☎ (0602) 397800 91 ⇌ ↱

Bramcote Hills ☎ (0602) 281880
A Pay and Play, 18-hole Par 3 course with challenging greens.
18 holes, 1500yds, Par 54.
Visitors no restrictions
Societies telephone in advance.
Green Fees not confirmed.
Facilities ☕ ⌂ ⛳
Location Thoresby Rd, Derby Rd, Bramcote (off A52 Derby rd)
Hotel ★★67% Priory Hotel, Derby Rd, Wollaton Vale, NOTTINGHAM ☎ (0602) 221691 31 ⇌ ↱

Bulwell Forest ☎ (0602) 770576
Municipal heathland course with many natural hazards. Very tight fairways and subject to wind.
18 holes, 5606yds, Par 68, SSS 67, Course record 62.
Club membership 450.
Visitors restricted weekends. Must contact in advance.
Societies must apply in writing.
Green Fees not confirmed.
Facilities ⊗ ⊾ ☕ ♀ △ ⌂ ⛳ ℓ C D Hall.
Location Hucknall Rd, Bulwell (4m NW of city centre on A611)
Hotel ★★★70% Nottingham Moat House, Mansfield Rd, NOTTINGHAM
☎ (0602) 602621 172 ⇌ ↱

Chilwell Manor ☎ (0602) 258958
Flat parkland course.
18 holes, 6379yds, Par 70, SSS 70.
Club membership 750.
Visitors with member only weekends. Must contact in advance and have a handicap certificate.
Societies welcome Mon, must apply in advance.
Green Fees £18.
Facilities catering by prior arrangement △ ⌂ ℓ
Location Meadow Ln, Chilwell (4m SW on A6005)
Hotel ★★62% Europa Hotel, 20 Derby Rd, LONG EATON ☎ (0602) 728481 15 ⇌ ↱

Edwalton Municipal ☎ (0602) 234775 & 231987
Gently sloping, 9-hole parkland course. Also 9-hole Par 3 and large practice ground.
9 holes, 3372yds, Par 72, SSS 72, Course record 71.
Club membership 900.
Visitors booking system in operation.
Societies prior booking necessary.
Green Fees £4.30.
Facilities ⊗)Ⅲ by prior arrangement ⊾ ☕ ♀ △ ⌂ ⛳ ℓ John Staples.
Leisure par 3 course.
Location Wellin Ln, Edwalton (S of Nottingham, off A606)
Hotel ★★★64% Swans Hotel & Restaurant, 84-90 Radcliffe Rd, West Bridgford, NOTTINGHAM
☎ (0602) 814042 31 ⇌ ↱

Mapperley ☎ (0602) 265611
Hilly meadowland course but with easy walking.
18 holes, 6283yds, Par 71, SSS 70.
Club membership 650.
Visitors must be member of recognised club and have a handicap certificate.
Societies must apply in writing and pay a deposit.
Green Fees £17 (£19 weekends and bank holidays).
Facilities ⊗)Ⅲ by prior arrangement ⊾ ☕ ♀ △ ⌂ ⛳ ℓ Paul Richmond.
Leisure pool table.
Location Central Av, Mapperley Plains (3m NE of city centre off B684)
Hotel B Forte Crest, Saint James's St, NOTTINGHAM ☎ (0602) 470131 130 ⇌

Nottingham City ☎ (0602) 278021 & 276916
A pleasant municipal parkland course on the city outskirts.
18 holes, 6218yds, Par 69, SSS 70, Course record 64.
Club membership 425.
Visitors restricted Sat 7am-3pm.
Societies welcome except weekends.
Green Fees not confirmed.
Facilities ⊗)Ⅲ by prior arrangement ⊾ ☕ ♀ △ ⌂ ⛳ ℓ Cyril Jepson.
Location Bulwell Hall Park (4m NW of city centre off A6002)
Hotel ★★★70% Nottingham Moat House, Mansfield Rd, NOTTINGHAM
☎ (0602) 602621 172 ⇌ ↱

Wollaton Park ☎ (0602) 787574
A pleasant, fairly level course set in a park close to the centre of Nottingham, with red and fallow deer herds. The fairways are tree-lined. The 502-yd dog-leg 15th is a notable hole. The stately home - Wollaton Hall - is situated in the park.
18 holes, 6494yds, Par 71, SSS 71, Course record 65.
Club membership 770.

Visitors	by arrangement with the professional.
Societies	welcome Tue & Fri, must apply in advance.
Green Fees	£35 per 36 holes; £22 per 18 holes.
Facilities	⊗ ⅢⅠ ⅃⅃ 💺 ♀ 🛆 🖬 ✆ John Lower.
Leisure	snooker, pitch & putt, practice putting area.
Location	Wollaton Park (2.5m W of city centre off A52)
Hotel	★★★64% Swans Hotel & Restaurant, 84-90 Radcliffe Rd, West Bridgford, NOTTINGHAM ☎ (0602) 814042 31 ⇥ 🕅

OXTON

Map 08 SK65

Oakmere Park ☎ Nottingham (0602) 653545
Set in rolling parkland in the heart of picturesque Robin Hood country. The par 4 (16th) and par 5 (1st) are notable. Thirty-bay floodlit driving range.
North Course: 18 holes, 6617mtrs, Par 72, SSS 72.
South Course: 9 holes, 3216mtrs, Par 37, SSS 37.
Club membership 450.

Visitors	correct golf attire required, please book for weekends.
Societies	please apply in writing or telephone.
Green Fees	North £16 per round (£20 weekends); South £6 per round (£8 weekends).
Facilities	⊗ ⅢⅠ ⅃⅃ 💺 ♀ 🛆 🖬 ✆⅂ Stephen Meade.
Leisure	30 bay floodlit driving range,caddy cars.
Location	Oaks Ln (1m NW off A6097)
Hotel	★★★65% Saracen's Head Hotel, Market Place, SOUTHWELL ☎ (0636) 812701 27 ⇥ 🕅

RADCLIFFE-ON-TRENT

Map 08 SK63

Radcliffe-on-Trent ☎ (0602) 333000
Fairly flat, parkland course with three good finishing holes: 16th (427 yds) par 4; 17th (180 yds) through spinney, par 3; 18th (331 yds) dog-leg par 4. Excellent views.
18 holes, 6423yds, Par 70, SSS 71.
Club membership 650.

Visitors	restricted Tue (Ladies Day).
Societies	welcome Wed. Must contact in advance.
Green Fees	£21 per day (£26 weekends & bank holidays).
Facilities	⊗ ⅢⅠ ⅃⅃ 💺 ♀ 🛆 🖬 ✆ Robert Ellis.
Leisure	trolleys.
Location	Drewberry Ln, Cropwell Rd (1m SE off A52)
Hotel	★★★64% Swans Hotel & Restaurant, 84-90 Radcliffe Rd, West Bridgford, NOTTINGHAM ☎ (0602) 814042 31 ⇥ 🕅

RETFORD

Map 08 SK78

Retford ☎ (0777) 703733
A wooded, parkland course.
18 holes, 6301yds, Par 71, SSS 70, Course record 71.
Club membership 722.

Visitors	advisable to contact in advance, welcome except before 11am on Tue, and with member only at weekends and holidays.
Societies	apply in writing or telephone.
Green Fees	not confirmed.
Facilities	⊗ ⅢⅠ ⅃⅃ 💺 ♀ 🛆 🖬 ✆ Stuart Betteridge.
Location	Brecks Rd, Ordsall (1.5m S A620, between Worksop & Gainsborough)
Hotel	★★★66% West Retford Hotel, 24 North Rd, RETFORD ☎ (0777) 706333 Annexe60 ⇥ 🕅

RUDDINGTON

Map 08 SK53

Ruddington Grange ☎ Nottingham (0602) 846141
Undulating parkland course with water hazards on 12 holes.
18 holes, 6490yds, Par 72, SSS 72.
Club membership 650.

Visitors	a handicap certificate is required, contact in advance if possible. Play may be restricted Sat & Wed mornings.
Societies	must contact in advance.
Green Fees	£15 per day (£20 weekends).
Facilities	⊗ by prior arrangement ⅢⅠ ⅃⅃ 💺 ♀ 🛆 🖬 ✆ Richard Daibell.
Location	Wilford Rd (5m S of Nottingham, A60 to Ruddington)
Hotel	★★★64% Swans Hotel & Restaurant, 84-90 Radcliffe Rd, West Bridgford, NOTTINGHAM ☎ (0602) 814042 31 ⇥ 🕅

SERLBY

Map 08 SK68

Serlby Park ☎ (0777) 818268
Parkland course.
9 holes, 5325yds, Par 66, SSS 66.
Club membership 300.

Visitors	must be accompanied by member.
Green Fees	not confirmed.
Facilities	♀ (weekends) 🛆 🖬
Location	E side of village off A638
Hotel	★★★63% Charnwood Hotel, Sheffield Rd, BLYTH ☎ (0909) 591610 20 ⇥ 🕅

SUTTON IN ASHFIELD

Map 08 SK45

Coxmoor ☎ Mansfield (0623) 557359
Undulating moorland/heathland course with easy walking and excellent views. The clubhouse is modern with a well-equipped games room. The course lies adjacent to Forestry Commission land over which there are several footpaths and extensive views.
18 holes, 6251yds, Par 73, SSS 70.
Club membership 600.

Visitors	restricted weekends & bank holidays. Must contact in advance.
Societies	must apply in advance.
Green Fees	£27 per day.
Facilities	⊗ ⅢⅠ ⅃⅃ 💺 ♀ 🛆 🖬 ✆ David Ridley.
Leisure	snooker.
Location	Coxmoor Rd (2m SE off A611)
Hotel	★★★★62% Swallow Hotel, Carter Ln East, SOUTH NORMANTON ☎ (0773) 812000 161 ⇥ 🕅

WORKSOP

Map 08 SK57

Kilton Forest ☎ (0909) 472488 & 486563
Slightly undulating, parkland course on the north edge of
Sherwood Forest. Includes three ponds.
18 holes, 6569yds, Par 72, SSS 72, Course record 68.
Club membership 450.
Visitors must contact in advance, restricted Sun.
Societies must contact in writing.
Green Fees £5.90 (£8.15 weekends & bank holidays).
Facilities ⊗ ⟩⊪ ⓑ ♥ ♀ ♨ 🖻 ⑂ ⑁ Peter W Foster.
Leisure bowling green.
Location Blyth Rd (1m NE of town centre on B6045)
Hotel ★★72% Lion Hotel, 112 Bridge St,
WORKSOP ☎ (0909) 477925 30 ⇆ 🅽

Lindrick ☎ (0909) 475282
Heathland course with some trees and masses of gorse.
18 holes, 6612yds, Par 71, SSS 72.
Club membership 500.
Visitors must contact in advance. Restricted Tue &
weekends.
Societies welcome except Tue (am) & weekends by
prior arrangement with the Secretary.
Green Fees £40 per day/round (£45 weekends); £25 per
day/round winter.
Facilities ⊗ ⟩⊪ ⓑ ♥ ♀ ♨ 🖻 ⑁ Peter Cowen.
Leisure snooker, practice grounds.
Location Lindrick Common (4m NW on A57)
Hotel ★★72% Lion Hotel, 112 Bridge St,
WORKSOP ☎ (0909) 477925 30 ⇆ 🅽

Worksop ☎ (0909) 472696
Adjacent to Clumber Park this course has a heathland-type
terrain, with gorse, broom, oak and birch trees. Fast, true
greens, dry all year round.
18 holes, 6651yds, Par 72, SSS 73.
Club membership 500.
Visitors by arrangement with professional (0909) 477732
Societies must apply in advance.
Green Fees not confirmed.
Facilities ⊗ ⟩⊪ ⓑ ♥ ♀ ♨ 🖻 ⑁ J R King.
Leisure snooker.
Location Windmill Ln (1.75m S off A620)
Hotel ★★★70% Clumber Park Hotel, Clumber Park,
WORKSOP ☎ (0623) 835333 48 ⇆ 🅽

OXFORDSHIRE

ABINGDON

Map 04 SU49

Drayton Park ☎ (0235) 550607
Set in the heart of the Oxfordshire countryside, an 18-hole
parkland course designed by Hawtree. Five lakes and sand
based greens.
18 holes, 6500yds, Par 67, SSS 68, Course record 67.
Club membership 500.

Visitors may phone to book, must have golf shoes, no
jeans or tracksuits.
Societies contact in advance.
Green Fees not confirmed.
Facilities ⊗ ⟩⊪ by prior arrangement ⓑ ♥ ♀ ♨ 🖻
⑁ Dinah Masey,Tony Williams.
Leisure 21 bay driving range,9 hole par 3 course.
Location Steventon Rd, Drayton Village (between Oxford
& Newbury,off A34 at Didcot)
Hotel ★★★59% The Upper Reaches, Thames St,
ABINGDON ☎ (0235) 522311 25 ⇆ 🅽

BURFORD

Map 04 SP21

Burford ☎ (099382) 2583
Created out of open-farmland, this parkland course has high
quality fairways and greens.
18 holes, 6405yds, Par 71, SSS 71.
Club membership 800.
Visitors must contact in advance. No visitors Tue (Ladies
Day), & weekends.
Societies by contact in advance.
Green Fees £25 per day.
Facilities ⊗ ⟩⊪ ⓑ ♥ ♀ ♨ 🖻 ⑁ ⑂ Norman Allen.
Location Swindon Rd (0.5m S off A361)
Hotel ★★67% Golden Pheasant Hotel, High St,
BURFORD ☎ (099382) 3223 & 3417 12 ⇆ 🅽

CHESTERTON

Map 04 SP52

Chesterton Golf & Country Club ☎ Bicester (0869)
242023 & 241204
Laid out all over one-time farmland. Well-bunkered, and water
hazards increase the difficulty of the course.
18 holes, 6230yds, Par 71, SSS 70, Course record 68.
Club membership 650.
Visitors must pre-book for weekends & bank holidays.
Societies must contact in advance.
Green Fees £15 per day; £12 per round (£24/£18 weekends
& bank holidays).
Facilities ⊗ (ex Mon) ⟩⊪ by prior arrangement ⓑ ♥ ♀ ♨
🖻 ⑁ J W Wilkshire.
Leisure snooker.
Location 0.5m W on A4095
Hotel ★★68% Jersey Arms Hotel, MIDDLETON
STONEY
☎ (086989) 234 & 505 6 ⇆Annexe10 ⇆

CHIPPING NORTON

Map 04 SP32

Chipping Norton ☎ (0608) 642383
Pleasant downland course open to winds.
18 holes, 6280yds, Par 71, SSS 70.
Club membership 850.
Visitors with member only at weekends. Must contact in
advance.
Societies must apply in writing.
Green Fees £22 per day/round, £15 after 2pm. Oct-Mar £15
per day.
Facilities ⊗ ⟩⊪ ⓑ ♥ ♀ ♨ 🖻 ⑁ ⑂ Bob Gould.
Location Southcombe (1.5m E on A44)
Hotel ★★64% The White Hart Hotel, 16 High St,
CHIPPING NORTON
☎ (0608) 642572 16 ⇆ 🅽Annexe4 ⇆

FRILFORD   Map 04 SU49

Frilford Heath ☎ (0865) 390864
Two 18-hole heathland courses. Both the Red and the
Green courses are of outstanding interest and beauty.
Heather, pine, birch and, in particular, a mass of
flowering gorse enhance the terrain. The greens are
extensive.
*Red Course: 18 holes, 6768yds, Par 73, SSS 73, Course
record 67.*
*Green Course: 18 holes, 6006yds, Par 69, SSS 69,
Course record 65.*
Club membership 1400.
Visitors   restricted weekends & bank holidays.
Societies   Mon, Wed & Fri only.
Green Fees   £42 per day (£52 weekends).
Facilities   ⊗ ⅏ by prior arrangement 💪 ♀ ⌂ 🏠 ⚲
                  ⚑ Derek Craik.
Leisure   caddy cars available.
Location   Abingdon (1m N off A338)
Hotel   ★★★63% Abingdon Lodge Hotel,
                  Marcham Rd, ABINGDON
                  ☎ (0235) 553456 63 ⇄ 📮

HENLEY-ON-THAMES   Map 04 SU78

Aspect Park ☎ (0491) 577562 & 578306
Parkland course. 18-hole course due to open Summer 1995.
9 holes, 5626yds, Par 68, SSS 66, Course record 69.
Club membership 500.
Visitors   must contact in advance, handicap certificate
                  required weekend am.
Societies   must contact in advance.
Green Fees   not confirmed.
Facilities   ⊗ ⅏ 💪 ♀ ⌂ 🏠 ⚲ ⚑ Roger Frost.
Location   Remenham Hill
Hotel   ★★★65% Red Lion Hotel, Hart St, HENLEY-
                  ON-THAMES
                  ☎ (0491) 572161 26rm(23 ⇄ 📮)

Badgemore Park ☎ (0491) 572206
Parkland course with many trees and easy walking. The 13th
is a very difficult par 3 hole played over a valley to a narrow
green.
18 holes, 6112yds, Par 69, SSS 69.
Club membership 880.
Visitors   must contact in advance & have handicap
                  certificate.
Societies   must apply in writing.
Green Fees   £27 per day (£30 weekends).
Facilities   ⊗ 💪 ♀ ⌂ 🏠 ⚑ Jonathon Dunn.
Leisure   squash.
Location   1m W
Hotel   ★★★65% Red Lion Hotel, Hart St, HENLEY-
                  ON-THAMES
                  ☎ (0491) 572161 26rm(23 ⇄ 📮)

Henley ☎ (0491) 575742
Undulating parkland course. 6th hole, blind (par 4), with
steep hill.
18 holes, 6130yds, Par 69, SSS 69, Course record 5.
Club membership 830.
Visitors   must contact in advance & have handicap
                  certificate & can play Mon-Fri, except bank
                  holidays.

Societies   must contact in advance.
Green Fees   £30 per day (weekdays only).
Facilities   ⊗ ⅏ 💪 ♀ ⌂ 🏠 ⚑ Mark Howell.
Location   Harpsden (1.25m S off A4155)
Hotel   ★★★65% Red Lion Hotel, Hart St, HENLEY-
                  ON-THAMES
                  ☎ (0491) 572161 26rm(23 ⇄ 📮)

NUFFIELD   Map 04 SU68

Huntercombe ☎ (0491) 641207
This heathland/woodland course overlooks the
Oxfordshire plain and has many attractive and interesting
fairways and greens. Walking is easy after the 3rd which
is a notable hole. The course is subject to wind and grass
pot bunkers are interesting hazards.
18 holes, 6301yds, Par 70, SSS 70, Course record 63.
Club membership 900.
Visitors   must contact in advance and have a
                  handicap certificate.
Societies   must contact in advance.
Green Fees   £32 per day (£32 per round weekends).
Facilities   ⊗ ⅏ 💪 💪 ♀ ⌂ 🏠 ⚑ John B Draycott.
Location   N off A423
Hotel   ★★★65% Shillingford Bridge Hotel,
                  Shillingford, WALLINGFORD
                  ☎ (086732) 8567 due to change to (0865)
                  858567 34 ⇄ 📮Annexe8 ⇄ 📮

OXFORD   Map 04 SP50

North Oxford ☎ (0865) 54415
Gently undulating parkland course.
18 holes, 5736yds, Par 67, SSS 67.
Club membership 650.
Visitors   must contact in advance, at weekends & bank
                  holidays may only play after 4pm.
Societies   must contact in advance.
Green Fees   £25 per round.
Facilities   ⊗ ⅏ by prior arrangement 💪 💪 ♀ ⌂ 🏠
                  ⚑ Robert Harris.
Location   Banbury Rd (3m N of city centre on A423)
Hotel   ★★★62% Oxford Moat House, Godstow Rd,
                  Wolvercote Rbt, OXFORD
                  ☎ (0865) 59933 155 ⇄

Southfield ☎ (0865) 242158
Home of the City, University and Ladies Clubs, and well-
known to graduates throughout the world. A challenging
course, in varied parkland setting, providing a real test
for players.
18 holes, 5973yds, Par 69, SSS 69.
Club membership 850.
Visitors   with member only at weekends.
Societies   must apply in writing.
Green Fees   £24 per day (weekdays).
Facilities   ⊗ ⅏ by prior arrangement 💪 💪 ♀ ⌂ 🏠
                  ⚑ Tony Rees.
Location   Hill Top Rd (1.5m SE of city centre off
                  B480)
Hotel   ★★★65% Eastgate Hotel, The High,
                  Merton St, OXFORD
                  ☎ (0865) 248244 43 ⇄ 📮

SHRIVENHAM
Map 04 SU28

Shrivenham Park ☎ (0793) 783853
Parkland course with easy walking. The par 4, 17th is a difficult dog-leg.
18 holes, 5527yds, Par 68.
Club membership 300.
Visitors no restrictions.
Societies must apply in advance.
Green Fees not confirmed.
Facilities ⊗ 🍽 🛍 💺 ♀ ⚲ 🍴 ♣ Simmon Jerreries.
Location Pennyhooks (0.5m NE of town centre)
Hotel B Forte Crest, Oxford Rd, Stratton St Margaret, SWINDON ☎ (0793) 831333 91 ⇄ 🛏

TADMARTON
Map 04 SP33

Tadmarton Heath ☎ Hook Norton (0608) 737278
A mixture of heath and sandy land, the course, which is open to strong winds, incorporates the site of an old Roman encampment. The clubhouse is an old farm building with a 'holy well' from which the greens are watered. The 7th is a testing hole over water.
18 holes, 5682yds, Par 69, SSS 68, Course record 63.
Club membership 600.
Visitors with member only at weekends.
Societies by arrangement.
Green Fees £15/£26 per day; £16 after 2.30pm.
Facilities ⊗ 🍽 🛍 💺 ♀ ⚲ 🍴 ♣ Les Bond.
Leisure fishing.
Location 1m SW of Lower Tadmarton off B4035
Hotel ★★61% Olde School Hotel, Church St, BLOXHAM ☎ (0295) 720369 11 ⇄ 🛏Annexe27 ⇄ 🛏

SHROPSHIRE

BRIDGNORTH
Map 07 SO79

Bridgnorth ☎ (0746) 763315
A pleasant course laid-out on parkland on the bank of the River Severn.
18 holes, 6673yds, Par 73, SSS 72, Course record 65.
Club membership 725.
Visitors must contact in advance but may not play on Wed. Restricted weekends.
Societies must contact in writing.
Green Fees £24 per day; £18 per round (£30/£24 weekends).
Facilities ⊗ 🍽 🛍 💺 (no catering Mon) ♀ (ex Mon) ⚲ 🍴 ♣ Paul Hinton.
Leisure fishing.
Location Stanley Ln (1m N off B4373)
Hotel ★★60% Falcon Hotel, Saint John St, Lowtown, BRIDGNORTH ☎ (0746) 763134 15rm(5 ⇄7 🛏)

CHURCH STRETTON
Map 07 SO49

Church Stretton ☎ (0694) 722281
Hillside course constructed by James Braid on the lower slopes of the Long Mynd.
18 holes, 5008yds, Par 66, SSS 65, Course record 62.
Club membership 500.
Visitors may not play before 10.30am at weekends & bank holidays. Must contact in advance & have handicap certificate.
Societies must contact in advance.
Green Fees £12 per day (£18 weekends).
Facilities ⊗ 🍽 by prior arrangement 🛍 💺 ♀ ⚲ 🍴 ♣ D Aidey.
Location Trevor Hill (NW side of village off B4370)
Hotel ★★71% Mynd House Hotel, Little Stretton, CHURCH STRETTON ☎ (0694) 722212 8 ⇄ 🛏

LILLESHALL
Map 07 SJ71

Lilleshall Hall ☎ Telford (0952) 603840
Heavily-wooded parkland course. Easy walking.
18 holes, 5906yds, Par 68, SSS 68.
Club membership 650.
Visitors must contact in advance and play with member at weekends.
Societies must apply in writing by Dec for the following year.
Green Fees not confirmed.
Facilities ⊗ 🛍 💺 ♀ ⚲ 🍴 ♣
Location 3m SE
Hotel ★★65% Royal Victoria Hotel, St Mary's St, NEWPORT ☎ (0952) 820331 24rm(16 ⇄7 🛏)

LUDLOW
Map 07 SO57

Ludlow ☎ Bromfield (058477) 285
A long-established parkland course in the middle of the racecourse. Very flat, quick drying, with broom and gorse-lined fairways.
18 holes, 6193yds, Par 70, SSS 70.
Club membership 650.
Visitors must play with member at weekends in winter. Must contact in advance and have a handicap certificate.
Societies must contact in writing.
Green Fees £18 per day (£24 weekends).
Facilities ⊗ 🍽 🛍 💺 ♀ ⚲ 🍴 ♣ Russell Price.
Location Bromfield (2m N off A49)
Hotel ★★★70% The Feathers at Ludlow, Bull Ring, LUDLOW ☎ (0584) 875261 40 ⇄ 🛏

MARKET DRAYTON
Map 07 SJ63

Market Drayton ☎ (0630) 652266
Parkland course in quiet, picturesque surroundings providing a good test of golf. Bungalow on course is made available for golfing holidays.
18 holes, 6400yds, Par 71, SSS 70, Course record 69.
Club membership 550.
Visitors may not play on Sun; must play with member on Sat. Must contact in advance.
Societies must contact in advance. ▶

Green Fees £20 per day.
Facilities ⊗ 〨 🏌 🍺 ♀ 🏌 🏠 ⧸ Russel Clewes.
Location Sutton (1m SW)
Hotel ★★★♨70% Goldstone Hall, Goldstone,
MARKET DRAYTON
☎ (063086) 202 & 487 8 ⇌ 🕈

MEOLE BRACE
Map 07 SJ41

Meole Brace ☎ (0743) 364050
Pleasant municipal course.
12 holes, 3066yds, Par 43, SSS 42.
Visitors no restrictions.
Green Fees not confirmed.
Facilities 🏌 🏠 ⧸ ⧸
Location NE side of village off A49
Hotel ★★★62% Lion Hotel, Wyle Cop,
SHREWSBURY ☎ (0743) 353107 59 ⇌ 🕈

OSWESTRY
Map 07 SJ22

Mile End ☎ (0691) 670580 & 671246
Opened in 1992, a gently undulating 9-hole parkland-type
course. Well-spaced holes in 70 acres.
9 holes, 6130yds, Par 70, SSS 69.
Club membership 310.
Visitors must have handicap certificate or proof of
membership to bona fide Club.
Societies must contact in advance.
Green Fees £14 per day; £10 per round (£18/£14 weekends
& bank holidays).
Facilities ⊗ 🏌 🍺 ♀ 🏌 🏠 ⧸ Scott Carpenter.
Leisure floodlit driving range.
Location Mile End
Hotel ★★★67% Wynnstay Hotel, Church St,
OSWESTRY ☎ (0691) 655261 27 ⇌ 🕈

Oswestry ☎ (0691) 610535
Parkland course laid-out on undulating ground.
18 holes, 6024yds, Par 70, SSS 69.
Club membership 700.
Visitors must be a member of a recognised Golf Club.
Must contact in advance.
Societies Wed & Fri only. Must contact in advance.
Green Fees not confirmed.
Facilities ⊗ 〨 🏌 🍺 ♀ 🏌 🏠 ⧸ David Skelton.
Leisure snooker.
Location Aston Park (2m SE on A5)
Hotel ★★★67% Wynnstay Hotel, Church St,
OSWESTRY ☎ (0691) 655261 27 ⇌ 🕈

PANT
Map 07 SJ22

Llanymynech ☎ Llanymynech (0691) 830983
Upland course on the site of an early Iron Age/Roman hillfort
with far-reaching views. The 4th fairway crosses the Welsh
border.
18 holes, 6114yds, Par 70, SSS 69.
Club membership 700.
Visitors must contact in advance & must play with
member after 4.30pm.
Societies must contact in writing.
Green Fees £19 per day; £14 per round (£24/£20 weekends
& bank holidays).

Facilities ⊗ 〨 🏌 🍺 ♀ 🏌 🏠 ⧸ ⧸ Andrew P Griffiths.
Leisure caddy cars for hire.
Location 0.5m SW off A483
Hotel ★★★67% Wynnstay Hotel, Church St,
OSWESTRY ☎ (0691) 655261 27 ⇌ 🕈

SHIFNAL
Map 07 SJ70

Shifnal ☎ Telford (0952) 460330
Well-wooded parkland course. Walking is easy and an
attractive country mansion serves as the clubhouse.
18 holes, 6468yds, Par 71, SSS 71, Course record 65.
Club membership 560.
Visitors must play with member on weekends & bank
holidays.
Societies must contact in advance.
Green Fees £30 per day; £22 per round.
Facilities ⊗ 〨 🏌 🍺 ♀ 🏌 🏠 ⧸ Justin Flanagan.
Leisure snooker.
Location Decker Hill (1m N off B4379)
Hotel ★★★★63% Park House Hotel, Silvermere Park,
Park St, SHIFNAL
☎ (0952) 460128 38 ⇌ 🕈Annexe16 ⇌ 🕈

SHREWSBURY
Map 07 SJ41

Shrewsbury ☎ (0743) 872976
Parkland course. First nine flat, second undulating with good
views.
18 holes, 6300yds, Par 70, SSS 70.
Club membership 872.
Visitors may only play between 10am-noon and after
2.15pm at weekends. Must contact in advance
and have a handicap certificate.
Societies must contact in writing.
Green Fees £20 per day; £15 per round (£25 per round/day
weekends and bank holidays).
Facilities ⊗ 〨 🏌 🍺 ♀ 🏌 🏠 ⧸ Peter Seal.
Leisure snooker.
Location Condover (4m S off A49)
Hotel ★★★68% Prince Rupert Hotel, Butcher Row,
SHREWSBURY ☎ (0743) 236000 65 ⇌

TELFORD
Map 07 SJ60

The Shropshire ☎ (0952) 677866
Pay and Play, 3 loops of 9-holes. Also tuition hole, practice
green, 12 hole pitch and putt and 18-hole contoured putting
green.
Blue: 9 holes, 3286yds, Par 35, SSS 35.
Silver: 9 holes, 3303yds, Par 36, SSS 36.
Gold: 9 holes, 3334yds, Par 36, SSS 36.
Club membership 250.
Visitors must book 7 days in advance.
Societies must book in advance.
Green Fees £10 (£17 weekends).
Facilities ⊗ 〨 🏌 🍺 ♀ 🏌 🏠 ⧸ ⧸ Kevin Craggs.
Leisure fishing, riding, snooker, caddy cars, archery,
pitch & putt.
Location Muxton Grange, Muxton
Hotel ★★★69% Holiday Inn, St Quentin Gate,
TELFORD ☎ (0952) 292500 100 ⇌ 🕈

Telford Hotel Golf & Country Club ☎ (0952) 585642
Rolling parkland course with easy walking. Three lakes and
large sand traps are hazards to the fine greens.
18 holes, 6766yds, Par 72, SSS 72.
Club membership 625.

Visitors	must have a handicap certificate or be member of recognised Golf Club. Must contact in advance.
Societies	must contact by telephone or post
Green Fees	not confirmed.
Facilities	⊗ ⑪ ⓛ ⚑ ♀ ⚒ 🏠 ⛳ 🛏 ¶ Graham Farr.
Leisure	heated indoor swimming pool, squash, snooker, sauna, solarium, gymnasium, 9 hole par 3 course, driving range.
Location	Sutton Hill (4m S of town centre off A442)
Hotel	★★★68% Telford Hotel Golf & Country Club, Great Hay Dr, Sutton Hill, TELFORD ☎ (0952) 585642 86 ⇆ ⌑

WELLINGTON   Map 07 SJ61

Wrekin ☎ Telford (0952) 244032
Downland course with some hard walking but rewarding views.
18 holes, 5699yds, Par 66, SSS 67.
Club membership 700.

Visitors	must contact in advance.
Societies	must telephone in advance.
Green Fees	£18 per day (£25 weekends).
Facilities	⊗ ⑪ ⓛ ⚑ (no catering Mon) ♀ ⚒ 🏠 ¶ K Housden.
Leisure	electric trolleys & others for hire.
Location	Ercall Woods (1.25m S off B5061)
Hotel	★★★67% Buckatree Hall Hotel, The Wrekin, Wellington, TELFORD ☎ (0952) 641821 64 ⇆ ⌑

WESTON-UNDER-REDCASTLE   Map 07 SJ52

Hawkstone Park Hotel ☎ (0939) 200611
In a beautiful setting, with natural hazards and good
views, Hawkstone Course has been established for over
50 years and enjoys a superb setting. A new course, the
Windmill, is being developed.
See advertisement Inside Front Cover.
18 holes, 6465yds, Par 72, SSS 70.
Club membership 450.

Visitors	must contact in advance.
Green Fees	not confirmed.
Facilities	⚒ 🏠 ⛳ ¶
Location	N side of village 0.75m E of A49
Hotel	★★65% Bear Hotel, HODNET ☎ (063084) 214 & 788 6 ⇆ ⌑

WHITCHURCH   Map 07 SJ54

Hill Valley ☎ (0948) 663584
This parkland course opened in 1975, and its Main Course
was designed to championship standard by Peter Alliss and
Dave Thomas. The hilly terrain is enhanced by many
glorious views. There are natural water hazards on seven
holes. Also 9-hole Northern Course and par 3 course.
Championship: 18 holes, 6517yds, Par 72, SSS 71,
Course record 64.
Northern: 18 holes, 6050yds, Par 72, SSS 69.
Club membership 600.

Visitors	must contact in advance. Restricted Sun.
Societies	must contact in advance; a deposit will be required.
Green Fees	Championship: £19 (£25 weekends); Northern £6 (£9 weekends).
Facilities	⊗ ⑪ ⓛ ⚑ ♀ ⚒ 🏠 ⛳ 🛏 ¶ A R Minshall.
Leisure	hard tennis courts, snooker, caddy cars, trolleys.
Location	Terrick Rd (1m N)
Hotel	★★★63% Terrick Hall Country Hotel, Hill Valley, WHITCHURCH ☎ (0948) 663031 10 ⇆ ⌑Annexe7 ⇆ ⌑

WORFIELD   Map 07 SO79

Worfield ☎ (07464) 372 & 541
Opened in 1991, this undulating course with good-sized
greens, well placed bunkers and 2 lakes, rated highly in a golf
magazine survey.
18 holes, 6798yds, Par 73, SSS 73, Course record 73.
Club membership 300.

Visitors	must contact in advance, weekends only after 10am.
Societies	contact in advance and confirm in writing with deposit.
Green Fees	£20 per day; £15 per round (£25/£20 weekends).
Facilities	⊗ ⑪ ⓛ ⚑ ♀ ⚒ 🏠 ¶ Steve Russell.
Leisure	practice range, putting green, buggies.
Location	3m W of Bridgenorth, off A454
Hotel	★★★★74% Old Vicarage Hotel, WORFIELD ☎ (07464) 497 10 ⇆ ⌑Annexe4 ⇆ ⌑

SOMERSET

BURNHAM-ON-SEA   Map 03 ST34

Brean ☎ Brean Down (0278) 751570
Level and open moorland course with water hazards.
Facilities of 'Brean Leisure Park' adjoining.
18 holes, 5714yds, Par 69, SSS 68.
Club membership 550.

Visitors	may not play on Sat & Sun before 1pm. Must have a handicap certificate.
Societies	weekdays only. Must contact in advance.
Green Fees	£18 per day; £12 per round (£15 per round weekends).
Facilities	⊗ ⑪ ⓛ ⚑ ♀ ⚒ 🏠 ⛳ 🛏 ¶
Leisure	outdoor and indoor heated swimming pools, fishing, riding, sauna.
Location	Coast Rd, Brean (6m N on coast rd)
Hotel	★★63% Royal Clarence Hotel, 31 The Esplanade, BURNHAM-ON-SEA ☎ (0278) 783138 19rm(18 ⇆ ⌑)

> **For an explanation of symbols and abbreviations, see page 5**

BURNHAM and BERROW GOLF CLUB

Championship links course with panoramic views of the Somerset hills and the Devon coast line sweeping across the reed beds and the Bristol Channel with the islands of Steepholm and Flatholm standing out against the background of the Welsh coast line.

18 holes. 6447 yards. Par 71, SSS 72, course record 66
9 hole course. 6332 yards. Par 72, SSS 70.

St Christophers Way, Burnham-on-Sea, Somerset TA8 2PE
Telephone: 01278 785760
Secretary: Mrs E L Sloman

Burnham & Berrow ☎ (0278) 783137
Links championship course with large sandhills.
Championship: 18 holes, 6447yds, Par 71, SSS 72, Course record 66.
9 Hole: 9 holes, 6332yds, Par 72, SSS 70.
Club membership 940.

Visitors	must contact in advance & have handicap certificate (22 or under gentlemen, 30 or under ladies) to play on the Championship course.
Societies	must apply in advance.
Green Fees	£30 per day (£40 weekends & bank holidays); 9 hole day.
Facilities	⊗ ⊪ by prior arrangement ⅃ ▥ ♀ ♨ 🖻 ⑂ ⋒ᶜ Mark Crowther-Smith.
Location	St Christopher's Way (N side of town off B3140)
Hotel	★★63% Royal Clarence Hotel, 31 The Esplanade, BURNHAM-ON-SEA ☎ (0278) 783138 19rm(18 ➪ ♠)

CHARD   Map 03 ST30

Windwhistle Golf, Squash & Country Club
☎ (0460) 30231
Parkland course at 735 ft above sea level with outstanding views over the Somerset Levels to the Bristol Channel and South Wales.
East/West Course: 18 holes, 6500yds, Par 73, SSS 71.
Club membership 600.
Visitors must contact in advance.

Societies   by prior arrangement.
Green Fees   not confirmed.
Facilities   ⊗ ⊪ ⅃ (catering by arrangement) ▥ ♀ ♨ 🖻
Leisure   squash.
Location   Cricket St Thomas (3m E on A30)
Hotel   ★★65% Shrubbery Hotel, ILMINSTER ☎ (0460) 52108 14 ➪ ♠

ENMORE   Map 03 ST23

Enmore Park ☎ Bridgwater (0278) 671481 & 671519
Hilly, parkland course with water features on foothills of Quantocks. Wooded countryside and views of Quantocks and Mendips. 1st and 10th are testing holes.
18 holes, 6241yds, Par 71, SSS 71, Course record 65.
Club membership 800.

Visitors	restricted competition days & weekends.
Societies	must apply in writing.
Green Fees	£25 per day; £18 per round (£25 weekends).
Facilities	⊗ ⊪ ⅃ ▥ (restricted catering Mon/Wed) ♀ ♨ 🖻 ⑂
Leisure	large practice area, buggy for hire.
Location	1m E
Hotel	★★★71% Walnut Tree Inn, North Petherton, BRIDGWATER ☎ (0278) 662255 28 ➪

GURNEY SLADE   Map 03 ST64

Mendip ☎ Oakhill (0749) 840570
Undulating downland course offering an interesting test of golf on superb fairways.
18 holes, 6330yds, Par 71, SSS 70.
Club membership 780.

Visitors	must contact in advance and have handicap certificate weekends.
Societies	must apply in advance.
Green Fees	£25 per day; £20 per round (£30 weekends & bank holidays).
Facilities	⊗ ⊪ ⅃ ▥ ♀ ♨ 🖻 ⑂ ⋒ᶜ Ron Lee.
Location	1.5m S off A37
Hotel	★★★68% Centurion Hotel, Charlton Ln, MIDSOMER NORTON ☎ (0761) 417711 44 ➪ ♠

LANGPORT   Map 03 ST42

Long Sutton ☎ Long Sutton (0458) 241017
Gentle, undulating, Pay and Play course.
18 holes, 6368yds, Par 71, SSS 70.
Club membership 500.

Visitors	advisable to book at weekends.
Societies	contact in advance.
Green Fees	£18 per day; £12 per round (£24/£16 weekends).
Facilities	⅃ ▥ ♀ ♨ 🖻 ⑂ ⋒ᶜ Stewart Adwick.
Leisure	driving range.
Location	Long Load (5m NW of Yeovil off A372)
Hotel	★★★68% The Hollies, Bower Hinton, MARTOCK ☎ (0935) 822232 Annexe15 ➪ ♠

Phoneday - remember from 16 April 1995 all phone codes in the UK will change - see page 4 for details

MINEHEAD   Map 03 SS94

Minehead & West Somerset ☎ (0643) 702057
Flat seaside links, very exposed to wind, with good turf
set on a shingle bank. The last five holes adjacent to the
beach are testing. The 215-yard 18th is wedged between
the beach and the club buildings and provides a good
finish.
18 holes, 6228yds, Par 71, SSS 71.
Club membership 543.
Visitors   no restrictions.
Societies   must contact in writing.
Green Fees £19.50 (£23 weekends & bank holidays).
Facilities   ⊗ ⅊ ⅃ ⅄ ⚑ ☇ ☕ ⚐ ⎵ { Ian Read.
Location   The Warren (E side of town centre)
Hotel   ★★★67% Northfield Hotel, Northfield Rd,
           MINEHEAD ☎ (0643) 705155 24 ⇆ ☏

TAUNTON   Map 03 ST22

Taunton & Pickeridge ☎ (0823) 421537
Downland course with extensive views.
18 holes, 5927yds, Par 69, SSS 68, Course record 63.
Club membership 600.
Visitors   must have a handicap certificate Must contact in
           advance and have an introduction from own
           club.
Societies   must telephone in advance.
Green Fees not confirmed.
Facilities   ⊗ ⅊ ⅃ ⅄ ⚑ ☇ ⚐ {
Leisure   snooker.
Location   Corfe (4m S off B3170)
Hotel   ★★★59% County Hotel, East St, TAUNTON
           ☎ (0823) 337651 66 ⇆ ☏

Taunton Vale ☎ West Monkton (0823) 412220 & 412880
An 18 hole and a 9 hole golf course in a parkland complex
occupying 156 acres in the Vale of Taunton. Complex
includes a floodlit driving range.
Charlton: 18 holes, 6072yds, Par 70, SSS 69.
Durston: 9 holes, 2004yds, Par 32, SSS 60.
Club membership 700.
Visitors   dress code is applied.
Societies   must telephone in advance.
Green Fees 18 holes: £20 per day; £14 per round
           (£25/£17.50 weekends). 9 holes: £10 per day; £7
           per round (£13/£8.75 weekends).
Facilities   ⊗ ⅃ ⅄ ⚑ ☇ ⚐ ⎵ { Martin Keitch.
Leisure   floodlit driving range.
Location   Creech Heathfield
Hotel   ★★★59% County Hotel, East St, TAUNTON
           ☎ (0823) 337651 66 ⇆ ☏

Vivary Park Municipal ☎ (0823) 333875
A parkland course, tight and narrow with ponds.
18 holes, 4620yds, Par 63, SSS 63.
Visitors   must contact in advance.
Societies   apply in writing.
Green Fees not confirmed.
Facilities   ⅄ ⚑ ⚐ ⎵ {
Leisure   snooker.
Location   Fons George (S side of town centre off A38)
Hotel   ★★65% Falcon Hotel, Henlade, TAUNTON
           ☎ (0823) 442502 11 ⇆ ☏

WEDMORE   Map 03 ST44

Isle of Wedmore ☎ (0934) 712452 & 713649
Gentle undulating course designed to maintain natural
environment. Existing woodland and hedgerow enhanced by
new planting. Magnificent panoramic views of Cheddar
Valley and Glastonbury Tor.
18 holes, 5732yds, Par 70, SSS 69, Course record 74.
Club membership 500.
Visitors   no restrictions.
Societies   contact in advance.
Green Fees £15 per day; £12 per round (£18/£15 weekends).
Facilities   ⊗ ⅊ ⅃ ⅄ ⚑ ☇ ⚐ ⎵ { Graham Coombe.
Location   Lineage (off B3139 between Wells & Burnham-
           on-Sea)
Hotel   ★★★66% Swan Hotel, Sadler St, WELLS
           ☎ (0749) 678877 38 ⇆ ☏

WELLS   Map 03 ST54

Wells (Somerset) ☎ (0749) 675005
Beautiful wooded course with wonderful views. The
prevailing SW wind complicates the 448-yd, 3rd.
18 holes, 6014yds, Par 70, SSS 69, Course record 66.
Club membership 800.
Visitors   must contact in advance & have handicap
           certificate weekends. Tee times restricted.
Societies   must apply in writing.
Green Fees £19 per day; £16 per round (£23/£20 weekends
           & public holidays).
Facilities   ⊗ ⅊ ⅃ ⅄ ⚑ ☇ ⚐ ⎵ { Adrian Bishop.   ▶

SWAN HOTEL
WELLS - SOMERSET
TEL. (01749) 678877

A 15th-century coaching Inn with 10
original four-poster beds and log fires.

Golfing Breaks available:-

5 nights commencing
19th June – 10th July – 21st August

Tee off times arranged and
Golf Societies welcome.

With a superb view of the West Front of
Wells Cathedral it's just the place if you
wish to tour the West Country.

Please write or telephone the Manager
for further details.

A MEMBER OF
BEST WESTERN HOTELS
AA ★ ★ ★

Location East Horrington Rd (1.5m E off B3139)
Hotel ★★★66% Swan Hotel, Sadler St, WELLS
☎ (0749) 678877 38 ⇌ ſ҃

YEOVIL
Map 03 ST51

Yeovil ☎ (0935) 75949 & 22965
The opener lies by the River Yeo before the gentle climb to high downs with good views. The outstanding 14th and 15th holes present a challenge, being below the player with a deep railway cutting on the left of the green.
Old: 18 holes, 6144yds, Par 72, SSS 70, Course record 64.
New: 9 holes, 5016yds, Par 68, SSS 66.
Club membership 720.
Visitors must contact in advance. Handicap certificate required on 18 hole at all times & on 9 hole at weekends.
Societies Mon, Wed & Fri only, must contact in advance.
Green Fees not confirmed.
Facilities ⊗ ᗰ ᗷ ⚑ ♀ ᗢ ⛿ ↑ �ᵞ Geoff Kite.
Leisure snooker.
Location Sherborne Rd (1m E on A30)
Hotel ★★★60% The Manor Hotel, Hendford, YEOVIL
☎ (0935) 23116 20 ⇌ ſ҃Annexe21 ⇌ ſ҃

● SOUTH YORKSHIRE ●

BARNSLEY
Map 08 SE30

Barnsley ☎ (0226) 382856
Undulating municipal parkland course with easy walking apart from last 4 holes. Testing 8th and 18th holes.
18 holes, 6042yds, Par 69, SSS 69, Course record 64.
Club membership 450.
Visitors no restrictions.
Societies by arrangement.
Green Fees not confirmed.
Facilities ⊗ by prior arrangement ᗷ ⚑ ♀ ᗢ ⛿ ↑ �ᵞ Mike Melling.
Location Wakefield Rd, Staincross (3m N on A61)
Hotel ★★★68% Ardsley Moat House, Doncaster Rd, Ardsley, BARNSLEY
☎ (0226) 289401 73 ⇌ ſ҃

BAWTRY
Map 08 SK69

Austerfield Park ☎ Doncaster (0302) 710841 & 710850
Long moorland course with postage stamp 8th and testing 618-yd 7th. Driving range attached.
18 holes, 6854yds, Par 73, SSS 73, Course record 72.
Club membership 450.
Visitors no restrictions.
Societies must apply in writing.
Green Fees £17 per day; £13 per round (£21/£17 weekends).
Facilities ⊗ ᗰ ᗷ ⚑ ♀ ᗢ ⛿ ↑

Leisure bowling green (flat), driving range.
Location Cross Ln, Austerfield (2m NE on A614)
Hotel ★★65% Falcon Hotel, Henlade, TAUNTON
☎ (0823) 442502 11 ⇌ ſ҃

CONISBROUGH
Map 08 SK59

Crookhill Park Municipal ☎ Rotherham (0709) 862979
A rolling parkland course.
18 holes, 5839yds, Par 70, SSS 68.
Club membership 500.
Visitors restricted weekends before 9am. Must contact in advance.
Societies by arrangement.
Green Fees not confirmed.
Facilities ᗷ ⚑ ♀ ᗢ ⛿ ↑ �ᵞ Richard Swaine.
Leisure pool table.
Location Carr Ln (1.5m SE on B6094)
Hotel ★★★61% Danum Swallow Hotel, High St, DONCASTER ☎ (0302) 342261 66 ⇌ ſ҃

DONCASTER
Map 08 SE50

Doncaster ☎ (0302) 868316
Pleasant undulating heathland course with wooded surroundings. Quick drying, ideal autumn, winter and spring.
18 holes, 6220yds, Par 69, SSS 70.
Club membership 600.
Visitors may not play before 11am weekends & bank holidays.
Societies must contact in advance.
Green Fees £24 per day; £20 per round (£30/£25 weekends & bank holidays).
Facilities ⊗ ᗰ ᗷ ⚑ ♀ ᗢ ⛿ ↑ ﹐covᵞ Graham Bailey.
Location 278 Bawtry Rd, Bessacarr (5m SE on A638)
Hotel ★★★64% Mount Pleasant Hotel, Great North Rd, ROSSINGTON
☎ (0302) 868696 & 868219 32 ⇌ ſ҃

Doncaster Town Moor ☎ (0302) 535286 & 533167
Easy walking, but testing, heathland course with good true greens. Friendly club. Notable hole is 11th (par 4), 464 yds. Situated in centre of racecourse.
18 holes, 6094yds, Par 69, SSS 69, Course record 67.
Club membership 520.
Visitors may not play on Sun morning.
Societies must contact in advance.
Green Fees £16/£14 per day/round (£18/£16 weekends & bank holidays).
Facilities ⊗ ᗰ by prior arrangement ᗷ ⚑ ♀ ᗢ ᗢ ⛿ covᵞ Steven C Poole.
Leisure pool table.
Location Bawtry Rd, Belle Vue (1.5m E,at racecourse,on A638)
Hotel ★★★61% Danum Swallow Hotel, High St, DONCASTER ☎ (0302) 342261 66 ⇌ ſ҃

Owston Park ☎ (0302) 330821
A flat course surrounded by woodland. A lot of mature trees and a few ditches in play. A practice putting green and chipping area.
9 holes, 3042yds, Par 36, SSS 71.
Visitors no restrictions.
Societies contact in advance.
Green Fees £6.50 per 18 holes mid week; £3.75 per 9 holes.

Facilities 🏌 ⛳ 🏠 ⛳🍴 ⛳ Mike Parker.
Location Owston Hall, nr Carcroft (6m N of Doncaster off A19)
Hotel ★★★61% Danum Swallow Hotel, High St, DONCASTER ☎ (0302) 342261 66 ⇔ 🐾

Wheatley ☎ (0302) 831655
Fairly flat well-bunkered, lake-holed, parkland course.
18 holes, 6169yds, Par 70, SSS 69.
Club membership 600.
Visitors must contact in advance and have an introduction from own club.
Societies must contact in advance.
Green Fees not confirmed.
Facilities ⊗ ⏬ 🃏 🏌 ♀ ⛳ 🏠 ⛳ T C Parkinson.
Location Armthorpe Rd (NE side of town centre off A18)
Hotel ★★★62% Grand St Leger, Bennetthorpe, DONCASTER ☎ (0302) 364111 21 ⇔ 🐾

HICKLETON — Map 08 SE40

Hickleton ☎ Rotherham (0709) 896081
Undulating parkland course with stream running through; designed by Neil Coles and Brian Huggett.
18 holes, 6403yds, Par 71, SSS 71.
Club membership 600.
Visitors restricted weekends after 2.30pm. Must contact in advance.
Societies must contact in advance on (0709) 888436.
Green Fees £18 per day/round (£20 weekends; £25 bank holidays).
Facilities ⊗ ⏬ 🃏 & 🏌 by prior arrangement ♀ ⛳ 🏠 ⛳ Paul Shepherd.
Location 0.5m W on B6411
Hotel ★★★61% Danum Swallow Hotel, High St, DONCASTER ☎ (0302) 342261 66 ⇔ 🐾

HIGH GREEN — Map 08 SK39

Tankersley Park ☎ Sheffield (0742) 468247
Akin to an inland links, this parkland course is hilly, windy and has good views.
18 holes, 6212yds, Par 69, SSS 71, Course record 65.
Club membership 500.
Visitors With member only at weekends. Must contact in advance.
Societies must apply in writing.
Green Fees £22 per day; £17 per round.
Facilities ⊗ ⏬ by prior arrangement 🃏 🏌 ♀ ⛳ 🏠 ⛳ Ian Kirk.
Location 1m NE
Hotel ★★★67% Tankersley Manor, Church Ln, TANKERSLEY ☎ (0226) 744700 20 ⇔ 🐾

RAWMARSH — Map 08 SK49

Wath ☎ (0709) 872149
Parkland course, not easy in spite of its length; 17th hole (par 3) is a difficult 244yds with narrow driving area.
18 holes, 5857yds, Par 68, SSS 68, Course record 66.
Club membership 550.
Visitors must play with member at weekends. Must contact in advance and have a handicap certificate.
Societies must contact in writing.

Green Fees £16 per day/round.
Facilities ⊗ ⏬ 🃏 🏌 ♀ ⛳ 🏠 ⛳ Chris Bassett.
Location Abdy Ln (2.5m N off A633)
Hotel ★★66% Brentwood Hotel, Moorgate Rd, ROTHERHAM ☎ (0709) 382772 33 ⇔ 🐾Annexe10 ⇔ 🐾

ROTHERHAM — Map 08 SK49

Grange Park ☎ (0709) 559497
Parkland/meadowland course, with panoramic views especially from the back nine. The golf is testing, particularly at the 1st, 4th and 18th holes (par 4), and 8th, 12th and 15th (par 5).
18 holes, 6461yds, Par 71, SSS 70.
Club membership 325.
Visitors no restrictions.
Societies apply in writing.
Green Fees not confirmed.
Facilities ⊗ ⏬ 🃏 🏌 ♀ ⛳ 🏠 ⛳ Eric Clark.
Location Upper Wortley Rd (3m NW off A629)
Hotel ★★66% Brentwood Hotel, Moorgate Rd, ROTHERHAM ☎ (0709) 382772 33 ⇔ 🐾Annexe10 ⇔ 🐾

Phoenix ☎ (0709) 363864 & 370759
Undulating meadowland course with variable wind.
18 holes, 6145yds, Par 71, SSS 69.
Club membership 750.
Visitors no restrictions.
Societies must apply in writing.
Green Fees £21 per day (£28 weekends & bank holidays).
Facilities ⊗ ⏬ 🃏 🏌 (all catering by prior arrangement) ♀ ⛳ 🏠 ⛳ Andrew Limb.
Leisure hard tennis courts, squash, fishing, snooker, gymnasium, caddy cars.
Location Pavilion Ln, Brinsworth (SW side of town centre off A630)
Hotel ★★66% Brentwood Hotel, Moorgate Rd, ROTHERHAM ☎ (0709) 382772 33 ⇔ 🐾Annexe10 ⇔ 🐾

Rotherham Golf Club Ltd ☎ (0709) 850812 & 850466
Parkland course with easy walking along tree-lined fairways.
18 holes, 6324yds, Par 70, SSS 70.
Club membership 440.
Visitors must contact in advance. Restricted weekends & bank holidays.
Societies must contact in advance.
Green Fees £26.50 per day (£31.50 weekends & bank holidays).
Facilities ⊗ ⏬ by prior arrangement 🃏 🏌 ♀ ⛳ 🏠 ⛳
Leisure snooker.
Location Thrybergh Park, Thrybergh (3.5m E on A630)
Hotel ★★66% Brentwood Hotel, Moorgate Rd, ROTHERHAM ☎ (0709) 382772 33 ⇔ 🐾Annexe10 ⇔ 🐾

Sitwell Park ☎ (0709) 541046
Parkland course with easy walking.
18 holes, 5914yds, Par 69, SSS 68.
Club membership 500.
Visitors must contact in advance, restricted weekends.
Societies must contact in advance.
Green Fees £29 per day; £24 per round (£33/£29 weekends & bank holidays). ▶

Facilities ⊗ ⅷ by prior arrangement ⓑ ♨ ♀ ⚘ 🏠
ⓛ Nic Taylor.
Leisure snooker, caddy cars.
Location Shrogs Wood Rd
Hotel ★★66% Brentwood Hotel, Moorgate Rd,
ROTHERHAM
☎ (0709) 382772 33 ⇌ ⓡAnnexe10 ⇌ ⓡ

SHEFFIELD   Map 08 SK38

Abbeydale ☎ (0742) 360763
Parkland course, well-kept and wooded. Testing hole: 12th,
par 3.
18 holes, 6419yds, Par 72, SSS 71.
Club membership 750.
Visitors restricted Wed 10am-1.30pm.
Societies must apply in writing.
Green Fees £28 per day (£32 weekends & bank holidays).
Facilities ⊗ ⅷ ⓑ ♨ ♀ ⚘ 🏠 ⓛ
Leisure snooker.
Location Twentywell Ln, Dore (4m SW of city centre off
A621)
Hotel B Forte Posthouse, Manchester Rd, Broomhill,
SHEFFIELD ☎ (0742) 670067 135 ⇌ ⓡ

Beauchief Municipal ☎ (0742) 367274
Municipal course with natural water hazards. The rolling land
looks west to the Pennines and a 12th-century abbey adorns
the course.
18 holes, 5452yds, Par 67, SSS 66, Course record 65.
Club membership 450.
Visitors no restrictions.
Societies weekdays only, must apply in writing.
Green Fees not confirmed.
Facilities ⊗ ⅷ by prior arrangement ⓑ ♨ ♀ ⚘ 🏠 ⓣ
ⓛ Brian English.
Location Abbey Ln (4m SW of city centre off A621)
Hotel ★★★70% Beauchief Hotel, 161 Abbeydale Rd
South, SHEFFIELD
☎ (0742) 620500 41 ⇌ ⓡ

Birley Wood ☎ (0742) 647262
Undulating meadowland course with well-varied features,
easy walking and good views. Practice range and green.
18 holes, 5100yds, Par 66, SSS 64.
Club membership 300.
Visitors no restrictions.
Societies apply in advance by phoning (0742) 431253.
Green Fees £7.25 until noon, £6.95 noon-4.45pm & £7.50
until twilight (£7.50 weekends).
Facilities (pub on site, food served) ⚘ ⓣ ⓛ Peter Ball.
Leisure coaching courses.
Location Birley Ln (4.5m SE of city centre off A621)
Hotel ★★★65% Mosborough Hall Hotel, High St,
Mosborough, SHEFFIELD
☎ (0742) 484353 23 ⇌ ⓡ

Concord Park ☎ (0742) 456806
Hilly municipal parkland course with some fairways wood-
flanked, good views, often windy. Eight par 3 holes.
18 holes, 4321yds, Par 65, SSS 62.
Club membership 170.
Visitors no restrictions.
Green Fees £6.20.
Facilities ⚘

Location Shiregreen Ln (3.5m N of city centre on B6086
off A6135)
Hotel B Forte Posthouse, Manchester Rd, Broomhill,
SHEFFIELD ☎ (0742) 670067 135 ⇌ ⓡ

Dore & Totley ☎ (0742) 360492
Flat parkland course.
18 holes, 6265yds, Par 70, SSS 70.
Club membership 580.
Visitors must contact in advance a handicap certificate
may be requested, may not play 9.30am-noon &
after 2.30pm.
Societies must apply in writing.
Green Fees not confirmed.
Facilities ⊗ ⅷ ⓑ ♨ ♀ ⚘ 🏠 ⓛ Neil Cheetham.
Leisure snooker.
Location Bradway Rd, Bradway (7m S of city centre on
B6054 off A61)
Hotel B Forte Posthouse, Manchester Rd, Broomhill,
SHEFFIELD ☎ (0742) 670067 135 ⇌ ⓡ

Hallamshire Golf Club Ltd ☎ (0742) 302153
Situated on a shelf of land at a height of 850 ft.
Magnificent views to the west. Moorland turf, long
carries over ravine. Good natural drainage.
18 holes, 6396yds, Par 71, SSS 71, Course record 68.
Club membership 550.
Visitors no restrictions.
Societies by arrangement.
Green Fees £27 per day (£34 weekends).
Facilities ⊗ ⅷ by prior arrangement ⓑ ♨ ♀ ⚘ 🏠
ⓣ ⓛ G R Tickell.
Leisure caddy carts for hire.
Location Redmires Rd, Sandygate
Hotel B Forte Posthouse, Manchester Rd,
Broomhill, SHEFFIELD
☎ (0742) 670067 135 ⇌ ⓡ

Hillsborough ☎ (0742) 343608 & 349151
Beautiful moorland/woodland course 500 ft above sea-level,
reasonable walking.
18 holes, 6216yards, Par 71, SSS 70.
Club membership 700.
Visitors restricted weekends. Advance booking
advisable.
Societies must apply in writing.
Green Fees not confirmed.
Facilities ⊗ ⅷ by prior arrangement ⓑ ♨ ♀ ⚘ 🏠
ⓛ Graham Walker.
Leisure snooker.
Location Worrall Rd (3m NW of city centre off A616)
Hotel ★★★58% Rutland Hotel, 452 Glossop Rd,
Broomhill, SHEFFIELD ☎ (0742) 664411
73rm(68 ⇌1 ⓡ)Annexe17 ⇌ ⓡ

Lees Hall ☎ (0742) 554402
Parkland/meadowland course with panoramic view of city.
18 holes, 6137yds, Par 71, SSS 69, Course record 63.
Club membership 725.
Visitors restricted Wed.
Societies must apply in writing.
Green Fees not confirmed.
Facilities ⊗ & ⅷ (ex Tue) ⓑ by prior arrangement (ex
Tue) ♨ ♀ ⚘ 🏠 ⓛ J R Wilkinson.
Leisure snooker.

Location Hemsworth Rd, Norton (3.5m S of city centre off A6102)
Hotel B Forte Posthouse, Manchester Rd, Broomhill, SHEFFIELD ☎ (0742) 670067 135 ⊨ ໂ

Tinsley Park Municipal Golf ☎ (0742) 42237
Undulating meadowland course with plenty of trees and rough.
18 holes, 6064yds, Par 71, SSS 69.
Club membership 420.
Visitors no restrictions.
Societies apply in writing to Sheffield City Council, Recreation Dept., Meersbrook Park, Sheffield.
Green Fees £7.50 per round.
Facilities ⊗ & ⅋ by prior arrangement ⅄ ☕ ♀ (ex Mon) ⌂ 🛱 ⚓ ໂ A P Highfield.
Location High Hazels Park (4m E of city centre off A630)
Hotel ★★★65% Mosborough Hall Hotel, High St, Mosborough, SHEFFIELD ☎ (0742) 484353 23 ⊨ ໂ

SILKSTONE
Map 08 SE20

Silkstone ☎ Barnsley (0226) 790328
Parkland/downland course, fine views over the Pennines. Testing golf.
18 holes, 6078yds, Par 70, SSS 70.
Club membership 600.
Visitors with member only at weekends.
Societies apply in writing.
Green Fees £23 per day.
Facilities ⊗ ⅋ by prior arrangement ⌂ ☕ ♀ ⌂ 🛱 ໂ Kevin Guy.
Leisure snooker.
Location Field Head, Elmhurst Ln (1m E off A628)
Hotel ★★★68% Ardsley Moat House, Doncaster Rd, Ardsley, BARNSLEY ☎ (0226) 289401 73 ⊨ ໂ

STOCKSBRIDGE
Map 08 SK29

Stocksbridge & District ☎ Sheffield (0742) 882003
Hilly moorland course.
18 holes, 5200yds, Par 65, SSS 65, Course record 62.
Club membership 450.
Visitors no restrictions.
Societies apply to secretary.
Green Fees £15 per day (£24 weekends & bank holidays).
Facilities ⊗ ⅋ ⌂ ☕ ♀ ⌂
Location 30 Royd Ln, Townend (S side of town centre)
Hotel B Forte Posthouse, Manchester Rd, Broomhill, SHEFFIELD ☎ (0742) 670067 135 ⊨ ໂ

THORNE
Map 08 SE61

Thorne ☎ (0405) 812084 & 815173
Picturesque parkland course with 6000 newly planted trees.
18 holes, 5366yds, Par 68, SSS 65.
Club membership 300.
Visitors no restrictions.
Societies apply in writing or phone.
Green Fees £8 per round (£9 weekends & bank holidays).
Facilities ⊗ ⌂ ☕ ♀ ⌂ 🛱 ⚓ ໂ Richard Highfield.
Location Kirton Ln (14m SE of Pontefract off of M18)
Hotel ★★67% Belmont Hotel, Horsefair Green, THORNE ☎ (0405) 812320 23 ⊨ ໂ

WORTLEY
Map 08 SK39

Wortley ☎ Sheffield (0742) 885294
Well-wooded, undulating parkland course sheltered from prevailing wind.
18 holes, 6037yds, Par 68, SSS 69.
Club membership 440.
Visitors may not play before 9am (10am on Tue and weekends). Must contact in advance and have a handicap certificate.
Societies Wed & Fri only, by arrangement. Apply in writing.
Green Fees £21 per day/round (£25 weekends & bank holidays).
Facilities ⊗ by prior arrangement ⅋ (ex Mon) ⌂ ☕ ♀ ⌂ 🛱 ⚓ ໂ J Tilson.
Location Hermit Hill Ln (0.5m NE of village off A629)
Hotel B Forte Posthouse, Manchester Rd, Broomhill, SHEFFIELD ☎ (0742) 670067 135 ⊨ ໂ

STAFFORDSHIRE

BARLASTON
Map 07 SJ83

Barlaston ☎ Stoke-on-Trent (0782) 372795
Picturesque meadowland course designed by Peter Alliss.
18 holes, 5800yds, Par 69, SSS 68.
Club membership 600.
Visitors may not play before 10am weekends and bank holidays.
Societies telephone or apply in writing.
Green Fees £18 (£22.50 weekends).
Facilities ⊗ ⅋ ⌂ ☕ ♀ ⌂ 🛱 ໂ Ian Rogers.
Location Meaford Rd
Hotel ★★★65% Stone House Hotel, STONE ☎ (0785) 815531 47 ⊨ ໂ

BROCTON
Map 07 SJ91

Brocton Hall ☎ (0785) 661901
Parkland course with gentle slopes in places, easy walking.
18 holes, 6095yds, Par 69, SSS 69.
Club membership 750.
Visitors not competition days. Must contact in advance.
Societies must apply in advance.
Green Fees £25 per day (£30 weekends & bank holidays).
Facilities ⊗ ⅋ by prior arrangement ⌂ ☕ ♀ ⌂ 🛱 ໂ R G Johnson.
Leisure snooker.
Location NW side of village off A34
Hotel ★★★63% Garth Hotel, Wolverhampton Rd, Moss Pit, STAFFORD ☎ (0785) 56124 60 ⊨ ໂ

> Entries with a shaded background identify courses that are considered to be particularly interesting

BURTON-UPON-TRENT　　　　　　Map 07 SK22

Branston ☎ (0283) 43207
Parkland course, adjacent to River Trent, on undulating ground with natural water hazards.
18 holes, 6541yds, Par 72, SSS 71.
Club membership 700.
Visitors	must contact in advance. With member only weekends.
Societies	must apply in writing.
Green Fees	not confirmed.
Facilities	⊗ 〗 by prior arrangement ᒐ 🍺 ♀ 스 🏠 ⛳ ⎰ Steve Warner.
Location	Burton Rd, Branston (1.5m SW on A5121)
Hotel	★★★62% Riverside Hotel, Riverside Dr, Branston, BURTON UPON TRENT ☎ (0283) 511234 22 ⇆ ℞

Burton-upon-Trent ☎ (0283) 44551
Undulating parkland course with trees a major feature. There are testing par 3s at 10th and 12th. The 18th has a lake around its green.
18 holes, 6579yds, Par 71, SSS 71, Course record 65.
Club membership 600.
Visitors	must contact in advance and have a handicap certificate or play with member.
Societies	must contact in writing for parties of 16 & over.
Green Fees	£25 per day; £20 per round (£30 per day; £25 per round weekends & bank holidays).
Facilities	⊗ & 〗 by prior arrangement & ᒐ (ex Mon) 🍺 ♀ 스 🏠 ⛳ ⎰ Gary Stafford.
Leisure	snooker.
Location	43 Ashby Rd East (3m E on A50)
Hotel	★★★62% Riverside Hotel, Riverside Dr, Branston, BURTON UPON TRENT ☎ (0283) 511234 22 ⇆ ℞

Craythorne ☎ (0283) 64329
A relatively short parkland course but the tight fairways make it challenging. Major renovations were commenced during 1994.
18 holes, 5255yds, Par 68, SSS 67.
Club membership 500.
Visitors	starting times available by phone.
Societies	apply in writing or telephone for details.
Green Fees	£16 per round (£20 weekends).
Facilities	⊗ 〗 ᒐ 🍺 ♀ 스 🏠 ⛳ ⎰ Steve Hadfield.
Location	Craythorne Rd, Stretton (off A38 through Stretton village)
Hotel	★★★62% Riverside Hotel, Riverside Dr, Branston, BURTON UPON TRENT ☎ (0283) 511234 22 ⇆ ℞

CANNOCK　　　　　　　　　　Map 07 SJ91

Cannock Park ☎ (0543) 578850
Part of a large leisure centre, this parkland-type course plays alongside Cannock Chase. Good drainage, open most of year.
18 holes, 4826yds, Par 66, SSS 65.
Club membership 250.
Visitors	no restrictions.
Societies	weekdays only, apply in writing.
Green Fees	£6 per round (£7.50 weekends).
Facilities	⊗ ᒐ 🍺 ♀ 스 🏠 ⛳ ⎰ David Dunk.
Leisure	heated indoor swimming pool, sauna, solarium, gymnasium.

Location	Stafford Rd (4m S of Brocton)
Hotel	★★★68% Roman Way Hotel, Watling St, Hatherton, CANNOCK ☎ (0543) 572121 56 ⇆ ℞

ENVILLE　　　　　　　　　　Map 07 SO88

Enville ☎ Kinver (0384) 872074
Easy walking on two fairly flat parkland/moorland courses - the 'Highgate' and the 'Lodge'.
Highgate: 18 holes, 6556yds, Par 72, SSS 72.
Lodge: 18 holes, 6217yds, Par 70, SSS 70.
Club membership 900.
Visitors	must play with member at weekends. Must contact in advance and have a handicap certificate.
Societies	must contact in writing.
Green Fees	weekdays £22 per round; £26.50 per 27 holes; £32 per 36 holes.
Facilities	⊗ 〗 ᒐ 🍺 ♀ 스 🏠 ⎰ Sean Power.
Leisure	snooker, caddy car available for booking.
Location	Highgate Common (2m NE)
Hotel	★★64% Talbot Hotel, High St, STOURBRIDGE ☎ (0384) 394350 25 ⇆ ℞

GOLDENHILL　　　　　　　　Map 07 SJ85

Goldenhill ☎ Stoke-on-Trent (0782) 784715
Rolling parkland course with water features on six of the back nine holes.
18 holes, 5957yds, Par 71, SSS 68.
Club membership 400.
Visitors	contact in advance for weekend play.
Societies	must apply in writing.
Green Fees	£5.50 per round (£6.50 weekends).
Facilities	⊗ 〗 by prior arrangement ᒐ 🍺 ♀ 스 🏠 ⛳ ⎰ Tony Clingan.
Location	Mobberley Rd (on A50, 4m N of Stoke)
Hotel	★★★66% Manor House Hotel, Audley Rd, ALSAGER ☎ (0270) 884000 57 ⇆ ℞

HAZELSLADE　　　　　　　　Map 07 SK01

Beau Desert ☎ Hednesford (0543) 422626
Woodland course.
18 holes, 6300yds, Par 70, SSS 71.
Club membership 500.
Visitors	restricted weekends.
Societies	apply in writing.
Green Fees	£30 per day (£45 weekends).
Facilities	⊗ 〗 ᒐ 🍺 ♀ 스 🏠 ⎰ Barry Stevens.
Location	0.5m NE of village
Hotel	★★★68% Roman Way Hotel, Watling St, Hatherton, CANNOCK ☎ (0543) 572121 56 ⇆ ℞

HIMLEY　　　　　　　　　　Map 07 SO89

Himley Hall Golf Centre ☎ Wolverhampton (0902) 895207
Parkland course set in grounds of Himley Hall Park, with lovely views. Large practice area including a pitch-and-putt.
9 holes, 3125yds, Par 36, SSS 35.
Club membership 200.

Visitors   restricted weekends.
Green Fees £6 per round (£6.50 weekends) (18 holes).
Facilities ⊗ ᵇ ▦ 📷
Leisure   putting green, 9 hole pitch & putt.
Location   Log Cabin, Himley Hall Park (0.5m E on B4176)
Hotel   ★★★62% Himley Country Club & Hotel,
                School Rd, HIMLEY
                ☎ (0902) 896716 76 ⇌ ℟

LEEK   Map 07 SJ95

Leek ☎ (0538) 384779
Undulating, challenging moorland course.
18 holes, 6240yds, Par 70, SSS 70, Course record 63.
Club membership 750.
Visitors   must contact in advance & have handicap
                certificate, restricted before 3pm.
Societies   must apply in advance.
Green Fees £24 per day (£30 weekends & bank holidays).
Facilities ⊗ ▦ ᵇ ▦ ♀ ⚲ 📷 ℓ Peter A Stubbs.
Leisure   snooker.
Location   Birchall (0.75m S on A520)
Hotel   ★★66% Bank End Farm Motel, Leek Old Rd,
                Longsdon ☎ (0538) 383638 10rm(9 ⇌ ℟)

Westwood (Leek) ☎ (0538) 398385
A challenging moorland/parkland course.
18 holes, 6156yds, Par 69, SSS 69, Course record 62.
Visitors   no visitors on Sun.
Societies   book inadvance Mon-Fri.
Green Fees £18 per day.
Facilities ⊗ ▦ ᵇ ▦ ♀ ⚲ 📷 ℓ Colin Smith.
Location   Wallbridge, Newcastle Rd
Hotel   ★★66% Bank End Farm Motel, Leek Old Rd,
                Longsdon ☎ (0538) 383638 10rm(9 ⇌ ℟)

LICHFIELD   Map 07 SK10

Seedy Mill ☎ (0543) 417333
New, gently-rolling parkland course in picturesque rural
setting. Lakes and streams are abundant, and there are four
challenging Par 3s. Well contoured green, good bunkering.
Also a superb 9-hole Par 3 course.
18 holes, 6305yds, Par 72, SSS 70.
Club membership 1100.
Visitors   must contact in advance & play to max. offical
                handicap standard (28 men, 36 ladies).
Societies   must contact in advance.
Green Fees £13-£20 per round.
Facilities ⊗ ▦ ᵇ ▦ ♀ ⚲ 📷 ℟ ℓ Andrew Bolton.
Leisure   9 hole par 3 course, caddy cars.
Location   Elmhurst (at Elmhurst, 1.5m N of Lichfield, off
                A515)
Hotel   ★★★63% Little Barrow Hotel, Beacon St,
                LICHFIELD ☎ (0543) 414500 24 ⇌ ℟

Whittington Heath ☎ (0543) 432317
18 magnificent holes winding their way through heathland
and trees, presenting a good test for the serious golfer.
Leaving the fairway can be severely punished. The dog-
legs are most tempting, inviting the golfer to chance his
arm. Local knowledge is a definite advantage. Clear
views of the famous three spires of Lichfield Cathedral.
18 holes, 6547yds, Par 70, SSS 71.
Club membership 600.

Visitors   must have handicap certificate or EGU card,
                restricted weekends. Must contact in
                advance.
Societies   welcome Wed & Thu, must apply in writing.
Green Fees £32 per day.
Facilities ⊗ ▦ ᵇ ▦ ♀ ⚲ 📷 ℟ ℓ Adrian Sadler.
Leisure   snooker, trolleys.
Location   Tamworth Rd (2.5m SE on A51)
Hotel   ★★★63% Little Barrow Hotel, Beacon St,
                LICHFIELD ☎ (0543) 414500 24 ⇌ ℟

NEWCASTLE-UNDER-LYME   Map 07 SJ84

Newcastle Municipal ☎ (0782) 627596
Open course on the side of a hill without mature trees.
18 holes, 6367yds, Par 72, SSS 70, Course record 68.
Club membership 273.
Visitors   must contact in advance.
Green Fees not confirmed.
Facilities ⊗ ᵇ ▦ ♀ 📷 ℟ ℓ Mark Shryane.
Location   Keele Rd (2m W on A525)
Hotel   B Forte Posthouse, Clayton Rd, NEWCASTLE-
                UNDER-LYME ☎ (0782) 717171 119 ⇌ ℟

Newcastle-Under-Lyme ☎ (0782) 618526 & 617006
Parkland course.
18 holes, 6229yds, Par 72, SSS 71.
Club membership 600.
Visitors   must contact in advance & have handicap
                certificate. With member only weekends.
Societies   welcome Wed & Thu (pm). Phone (0782)
                617006 in advance.
Green Fees not confirmed.
Facilities ♀ ⚲ 📷 ℓ Paul Symonds.
Leisure   snooker.
Location   Whitmore Rd (1m SW on A53)
Hotel   ★★60% The Borough Arms Hotel, King St,
                NEWCASTLE-UNDER-LYME
                ☎ (0782) 629421 30 ⇌ ℟Annexe15 ⇌ ℟

Wolstanton ☎ (0782) 622413
Meadowland/parkland course in an urban area.
18 holes, 5807yds, Par 68, SSS 68.
Club membership 690.
Visitors   with member only at weekends & bank holidays.
Societies   must apply in advance.
Green Fees £18 (weekdays).
Facilities ⊗ ▦ & ᵇ by prior arrangement ▦ ♀ ⚲ 📷
Leisure   snooker, caddy cars.
Location   Dimsdale Old Hall, Hassam Pde, Wolstanton
                (Turn off A34 at The Sportsman Inn)
Hotel   B Forte Posthouse, Clayton Rd, NEWCASTLE-
                UNDER-LYME ☎ (0782) 717171 119 ⇌ ℟

ONNELEY   Map 07 SJ74

Onneley ☎ Stoke-on-Trent (0782) 750577
A tight, picturesque, hillside parkland course.
9 holes, 5584yds, Par 70, SSS 67, Course record 65.
Club membership 400.
Visitors   restricted weekends & bank holidays.
Societies   must apply in writing.
Green Fees £15 per round.
Facilities ⊗ (Tue-Thu) ᵇ ▦ ♀ ⚲   ▶

Location   2m from Woore on A525
Hotel   ★★68% Wheatsheaf Inn at Onneley, Barhill Rd,
            ONNELEY ☎ (0782) 751581 5 🐾

PATTINGHAM   Map 07 SO89

Patshull Park Hotel Golf & Country Club ☎
Wolverhampton (0902) 700100
Picturesque course set in 280 acres of glorious Capability Brown
landscaped parkland. Designed by John Jacobs, the course
meanders alongside trout fishing lakes. Many leisure facilities.
18 holes, 6412yds, Par 72, SSS 71, Course record 63.
Club membership 500.
Visitors   must contact in advance & have handicap certificate.
Societies   must arrange in advance.
Green Fees   £20 per round (£25 weekends); Nov-Mar £15
             (£20 weekends).
Facilities   ⊗ 川 ﾚ ♥ ♀ ≙ 📾 🍴 ⍾ (David Thorp.
Leisure   hard tennis courts, heated indoor swimming
             pool, fishing, snooker, sauna, solarium,
             gymnasium, buggies, driving range.
Location   Off A464
Hotel   ★★★61% Patshull Park Hotel Golf & Country
             Club, Patshull, PATTINGHAM
             ☎ (0902) 700100 48 ⇄ 🐾

PERTON   Map 07 SO89

Perton Park ☎ Wolverhampton (0902) 380103 & 380073
Flat meadowland course set in open countryside.
18 holes, 7007yds, Par 73, SSS 72.
Club membership 400.
Visitors   only wide wheel trolleys, no jeans & shirt must
             have collars.
Societies   welcome anytime, phone for further information.
Green Fees   £5 per round, £6 Fri (£12 weekends & bank
             holidays).
Facilities   ⊗ 川 ﾚ ♥ ♀ ≙ 🍴 (Robert Franklin.
Leisure   snooker, buggies, trolleys, putting green.
Location   Wrottesley Park Rd (6m W of Wolverhampton,
             on A454)
Hotel   ★★68% Ely House Hotel, 53 Tettenhall Rd,
             WOLVERHAMPTON
             ☎ (0902) 311311 18 ⇄ 🐾

STAFFORD   Map 07 SJ92

Stafford Castle ☎ (0785) 223821
Parkland type course.
9 holes, 6382yds, Par 71, SSS 70.
Club membership 400.
Visitors   restricted weekends (am).
Societies   welcome Mon-Fri, must apply in advance.
Green Fees   not confirmed.
Facilities   ⊗ 川 ﾚ ♥ ♀ ≙ 📾
Location   Newport Rd (SW side of town centre off A518)
Hotel   ★★★64% Tillington Hall Hotel, Eccleshall Rd,
             STAFFORD ☎ (0785) 53531 90 ⇄ 🐾

STOKE-ON-TRENT   Map 07 SJ84

Burslem ☎ (0782) 837006
On the outskirts of Tunstall, a moorland course with hard
walking.

9 holes, 5354yds, Par 66, SSS 66.
Club membership 250.
Visitors   except Sun & with member only Sat & bank
             holidays.
Societies   must telephone in advance.
Green Fees   £15 per day.
Facilities   ≙
Location   Wood Farm, High Ln, Tunstall (4m N of city
             centre on B5049)
Hotel   ★★★62% George Hotel, Swan Square,
             Burslem, STOKE-ON-TRENT
             ☎ (0782) 577544 30 ⇄ 🐾

Greenway Hall ☎ (0782) 503158
Moorland course with fine views of the Pennines.
18 holes, 5678yds, Par 67, SSS 67, Course record 65.
Club membership 400.
Visitors   may play weekdays only.
Societies   must telephone in advance.
Green Fees   £14 per round.
Facilities   ♀ ≙
Location   Stanley Rd, Stockton Brook (5m NE off A53)
Hotel   ★★★62% George Hotel, Swan Square,
             Burslem, STOKE-ON-TRENT
             ☎ (0782) 577544 30 ⇄ 🐾

Trentham ☎ (0782) 658109
Parkland course. The par 3, 4th is a testing hole reached over
a copse of trees.
18 holes, 6644yds, Par 72, SSS 72.
Club membership 680.
Visitors   must have handicap certificate. May not play Sat
             & Sun mornings.
Societies   must apply in writing.
Green Fees   £20 (£35 Sun afternoons & bank holidays).
Facilities   ⊗ 川 by prior arrangement ﾚ ♥ ♀ ≙ 📾 🍴
             (Mark Budz.
Leisure   squash, snooker, caddy car.
Location   14 Barlaston Old Rd, Trentham (3m S off
             A5035)
Hotel   ★★★61% Haydon House Hotel, 1-13 Haydon
             St, Basford, STOKE-ON-TRENT
             ☎ (0782) 711311 18 ⇄ 🐾Annexe14 ⇄ 🐾

Trentham Park ☎ (0782) 658800
Fine woodland course.
18 holes, 6403yds, Par 71, SSS 71, Course record 67.
Club membership 640.
Visitors   restricted competition days.
Societies   welcome Wed & Fri, must apply in advance.
Green Fees   not confirmed.
Facilities   ⊗ 川 ﾚ ♥ ♀ ≙ 📾 (Jim McLeod.
Leisure   snooker.
Location   Trentham Park (3m SW off A34)
Hotel   B Forte Posthouse, Clayton Rd, NEWCASTLE-
             UNDER-LYME ☎ (0782) 717171 119 ⇄ 🐾

STONE   Map 07 SJ93

Meadow Vale ☎ (0785) 760900
Opened in 1992, a gently undulating meadowland course with
streams and ponds as features.
18 holes, 6500yds, Par 72, SSS 72.
Club membership 300.

Visitors must contact in advance, with member only weekends am.
Societies contact in advance.
Green Fees not confirmed.
Facilities ⊗ ⽱ ⓫ 🍴 ♀ ⅄ 🏠 ⌑ Stephen R Bassil.
Location Cold Norton
Hotel ★★★65% Stone House Hotel, STONE
☎ (0785) 815531 47 ⇄ 🎀

Stone ☎ (0785) 813103
9-hole parkland course with easy walking and 18 different tees.
9 holes, 6299yds, Par 71, SSS 70, Course record 69.
Club membership 350.
Visitors with member only weekends & bank holidays.
Societies must apply in writing.
Green Fees £15 per day or round.
Facilities ⊗ ⽱ ⓫ ♀ ⅄
Leisure snooker.
Location Filleybrooks (0.5m W on A34)
Hotel ★★★65% Stone House Hotel, STONE
☎ (0785) 815531 47 ⇄ 🎀

TAMWORTH   Map 07 SK20

Drayton Park ☎ (0827) 251139
Parkland course designed by James Braid. Club established since 1897.
18 holes, 6214yds, Par 71, SSS 71, Course record 62.
Club membership 450.
Visitors restricted weekends. Must contact in advance.
Societies must apply in writing.
Green Fees £27 per day/round.
Facilities ⊗ ⽱ ⓫ 🍴 ♀ ⅄ 🏠 ⌑ M W Passmore.
Leisure snooker.
Location Drayton Park (2m S on A4091, next to Drayton Manor Leisure
Hotel ★★★★72% The Belfry, Lichfield Rd,
WISHAW ☎ (0675) 470301 219 ⇄ 🎀

Tamworth Municipal ☎ (0827) 53850
First-class municipal, parkland course and a good test of golf.
18 holes, 6083mtrs, Par 73, SSS 72.
Club membership 700.
Visitors no restrictions.
Societies must contact in advance.
Green Fees £7.80 per 18 holes.
Facilities ⓫ ⓫ 🍴 ♀ ⅄ 🏠 ⌑ Barry Jones.
Leisure snooker, buggies, caddy cars, practice area.
Location Eagle Dr (2.5m E off B5000)
Hotel ★★61% Angel Croft Hotel, Beacon St,
LICHFIELD ☎ (0543) 258737
11rm(3 ⇄6 🎀)Annexe8 ⇄ 🎀

UTTOXETER   Map 07 SK03

Uttoxeter ☎ (0889) 564884
Downland course with open aspect.
18 holes, 5468yds, Par 68, SSS 68.
Club membership 750.
Visitors restricted weekends.
Societies must apply in advance.
Green Fees £20 per day; £13 per round (£17 per round weekends & bank holidays).
Facilities ⊗ ⽱ ⓫ 🍴 ♀ ⅄ 🏠 ⌑ John Pearsall.

Leisure pool table.
Location Wood Ln (1m SE off B5017)
Hotel ★★64% Bank House Hotel, Church St,
UTTOXETER ☎ (0889) 566922 16 ⇄ 🎀

WESTON   Map 07 SJ92

Ingestre Park ☎ (0889) 270845
Parkland course set in the grounds of Ingestre Hall, former home of the Earl of Shrewsbury, with mature trees and pleasant views.
18 holes, 6334yds, Par 70, SSS 70, Course record 67.
Club membership 750.
Visitors with member only weekends & bank holidays. Handicap certificate required to play before 3pm weekdays.
Societies must apply in advance.
Green Fees £20 per round.
Facilities ⊗ ⽱ ⓫ 🍴 ♀ ⅄ 🏠 ⌑ Danny Scullion.
Leisure snooker.
Location 2m SE off A51
Hotel ★★★64% Tillington Hall Hotel, Eccleshall Rd,
STAFFORD ☎ (0785) 53531 90 ⇄ 🎀

WHISTON   Map 07 SK04

Whiston Hall ☎ (0538) 266260
A challenging 18-hole course in scenic countryside and incorporating many natural obstacles.
18 holes, 5741yds, Par 71, SSS 68.
Club membership 235.
Visitors reasonable dress on the course. Must telephone in advance at weekends.
Societies contact in advance.
Green Fees £16 per day; £10 per round (£22/£14 weekends & bank holidays).
Facilities ⊗ & ⓫ (wknds plus wkdays in summer) 🍴 ♀ (wknds;daily summer) ⅄
Leisure fishing, snooker.
Location Whiston Hall (off A52, 3m NE of Cheadle)
Hotel ★★★62% George Hotel, Swan Square, Burslem, STOKE-ON-TRENT
☎ (0782) 577544 30 ⇄ 🎀

SUFFOLK

ALDEBURGH   Map 05 TM45

Aldeburgh ☎ (0728) 452890
A most enjoyable and not unduly difficult seaside course; ideal for golfing holidaymakers. A bracing and fairly open terrain with some trees and heathland.
18 holes, 6330yds, Par 68, SSS 71, Course record 65.
River Course: 9 holes, 2114yds, Par 32, SSS 32.
Club membership 815.
Visitors must contact in advance & have handicap certificate for 18 hole course.
Societies must contact in advance. ▶

WENTWORTH
HOTEL ★★★
Aldeburgh, Suffolk
Tel: (01728) 452312 Fax: (01728) 454343

The Hotel has the comfort and style of a Country House. Two comfortable lounges, with open fires and antique furniture, provide ample space to relax. Each individually decorated bedroom, many with sea views, is equipped with a colour television, radio, hairdryer and optional tea making facilities. The Restaurant serves a variety of fresh produce whilst a light lunch can be chosen from the Bar menu, eaten outside in the sunken terrace garden. Aldeburgh is timeless and unhurried. There are quality shops, two excellent golf courses within a short distance from the hotel, long walks and some of the best birdwatching at Minsmere Bird reserve. Music and the Arts can be heard at the Internationally famous Snape Malting Concert hall. Lastly, there are miles of beach to sit upon and watch the sea!

Green Fees	£30 per day; £20 after noon (£36/25 weekends & bank holidays).
Facilities	⊗ by prior arrangement ⊾ ▀ ♀ ⚥ 🖻 ☂ ⎛ K R Preston.
Location	Saxmundham Rd (1m W on A1094)
Hotel	★★★68% Wentworth Hotel, Wentworth Rd, ALDEBURGH ☎ (0728) 452312 31rm(24 ⇋4 🏠)

BECCLES   Map 05 TM49

Wood Valley ☎ (0502) 712244
Heathland course with natural hazards and particularly exposed to wind.
9 holes, 2779yds, Par 68, SSS 67.
Club membership 200.
Visitors   must play with member on Sun.
Societies   must contact in advance.
Green Fees £11 (£13 weekends and bank holidays).
Facilities   ⊗ by prior arrangement ⊾ ▀ ♀ ⚥ 🖻
Leisure   caddy cars.
Location   The Common (NE side of town)
Hotel   ★★61% Waveney House Hotel, Puddingmoor, BECCLES
                 ☎ (0502) 712270 & 712817 13rm(7 ⇋4 🏠)

Use the AA *Hotels* or *Bed and Breakfast* guides to extend your choice of accommodation

BUNGAY   Map 05 TM38

Bungay & Waveney Valley ☎ (0986) 892337
Heathland course partly comprising Neolithic stone workings, easy walking.
18 holes, 6063yds, Par 69, SSS 69.
Club membership 756.
Visitors   must contact in advance. With member only weekends & bank holidays.
Societies   must contact in advance.
Green Fees £18 per day.
Facilities   ⊗ & ▥ (ex Mon) ⊾ ▀ ♀ ⚥ 🖻 ☂ ⎛ Nigel Whyte.
Leisure   large practice area.
Location   Outney Common (0.5m NW on A143)
Hotel   ★★61% Waveney House Hotel, Puddingmoor, BECCLES
                 ☎ (0502) 712270 & 712817 13rm(7 ⇋4 🏠)

BURY ST EDMUNDS   Map 05 TL86

Bury St Edmunds ☎ (0284) 755979
Undulating parkland course with easy walking and attractive short holes.
18 holes, 6615yds, Par 72, SSS 72, Course record 69 or 9 holes, 2332yds, Par 31, SSS 31.
Club membership 830.
Visitors   with member only at weekends.
Societies   must apply in writing.
Green Fees not confirmed.
Facilities   ⊗ ▥ (summer) ⊾ ▀ ♀ ⚥ 🖻 ☂ ⎛ Mark Jillings.
Leisure   snooker.
Location   Tuthill (2m NW on B1106 off A45)
Hotel   ★★★73% Angel Hotel, Angel Hill, BURY ST EDMUNDS ☎ (0284) 753926 42 ⇋ 🏠

Fornham Park ☎ (0284) 706777
Flat parkland course with many water hazards. Also country club facilities.
18 holes, 6209yds, Par 71, SSS 70, Course record 67.
Club membership 300.
Visitors   no restrictions, but must book a tee time.
Societies   by arrangement.
Green Fees £12 per day; £8 per round (£15/£10 weekends & bank holidays).
Facilities   ⊗ ▥ ⊾ ▀ ♀ ⚥ 🖻 ☂ ⎛ Sean Clark.
Location   St John's Hill Plantation, The Street, Fornham All Saints (2m N off A134)
Hotel   ★★★♣♣70% Ravenwood Hall Hotel, Rougham, BURY ST EDMUNDS
                 ☎ (0359) 270345 7 ⇋Annexe7 ⇋

CRETINGHAM   Map 05 TM26

Cretingham ☎ Earl Soham (0728) 685275
Parkland course.
9 holes, 2120yds, Par 62, SSS 59, Course record 61.
Club membership 360.
Visitors   no restrictions.
Societies   must telephone in advance.
Green Fees £7 per day (£10 weekends & bank holidays).
Facilities   ⊾ ▀ ♀ ⚥ 🖻 ☂ ⎛ Colin Jenkins.

Leisure hard tennis courts, outdoor swimming pool, snooker, practice range, table tennis, pool table.
Location 2m from A1120 at Earl Soham
Hotel ★★67% Crown Hotel, Market Hill, FRAMLINGHAM ☎ (0728) 723521 14 ⇌

FELIXSTOWE   Map 05 TM33

Felixstowe Ferry ☎ (0394) 286834
Seaside links course, pleasant views, easy walking. Testing 491-yd, 7th hole.
18 holes, 6324yds, Par 72, SSS 70, Course record 66.
Club membership 800.
Visitors may not play before 9am. A handicap certificate required
Societies must contact in advance.
Green Fees £21 (£25 weekends).
Facilities ⊗ ⫾ by prior arrangement ⓑ 🍽 ♀ 🛆 🖾 🛒 ℓ Ian MacPherson.
Location Ferry Rd (NE side of town centre)
Hotel ★★★66% Orwell Moat House Hotel, Hamilton Rd, FELIXSTOWE ☎ (0394) 285511 58 ⇌ ℝ

FLEMPTON   Map 05 TL86

Flempton ☎ Bury St Edmunds (0284) 728291
Breckland course.
9 holes, 6080yds, Par 70, SSS 70.
Club membership 300.
Visitors must have handicap certificate. With member only weekends & bank holidays.
Societies must apply in writing.
Green Fees £24 per day; £18.50 per round.
Facilities ⊗ ⫾ ⓑ 🍽 ♀ 🛆 🖾 ℓ
Location 0.5m W on A1101
Hotel ★★66% Suffolk Hotel, 38 The Buttermarket, BURY ST EDMUNDS ☎ (0284) 753995 33 ⇌ ℝ

HALESWORTH   Map 05 TM37

St Helena ☎ (0986) 875567
A 27-hole professionally designed parkland complex of three 9-hole courses, giving 6 playing options of 3 x 18-hole Par 72 and 3 x Par 36 9-hole.
Saint: 9 holes, 3277yds, Par 36, SSS 36.
Helena: 9 holes, 3303yds, Par 36, SSS 36.
Halesworth: 9 holes, 3059yds, Par 36, SSS 36.
Club membership 460.
Visitors a certified handicap certificate is required for Saint and Helena courses, proprietory golf wear and shoes must be worn.
Societies apply in advance.
Green Fees £14.20 per 18 holes; £7.10 per 9 holes (£17 & £8.50 weekends & bank holidays).
Facilities ⊗ ⫾ ⓑ 🍽 ♀ 🛆 🖾 ✧ ℓ Philip Heil.
Leisure riding, floodlit covered driving range.
Location Bramfield Rd (9m W of Southwold)
Hotel ★★★68% Swan Hotel, Market Place, SOUTHWOLD ☎ (0502) 722186 27 ⇌ ℝAnnexe18 ⇌

HAVERHILL   Map 05 TL64

Haverhill ☎ (0440) 61951
Parkland course with small river running through three fairways.
9 holes, 5707yds, Par 68, SSS 67, Course record 67.
Club membership 445.
Visitors may not play on bank holidays before 1pm.
Societies must contact in advance.
Green Fees not confirmed.
Facilities ⓑ 🍽 ♀ 🛆 🖾 ✧ ℓ Simon Mayfield.
Location Coupals Rd (1m SE off A604)
Hotel ★69% The Clare Hotel, Nethergate St, CLARE ☎ (0787) 277449 5rm(3 ℝ)

HINTLESHAM   Map 05 TM04

Hintlesham Hall ☎ (0473) 652761
Magnificent new championship length course blending harmoniously with the ancient parkland surrounding this exclusive hotel. The 6630yd parkland course was designed by Hawtree and Son, one of the oldest established firms of golf course architects in the world. The course is fair but challenging for low and high handicappers alike. Hotel offers beautiful accommodation, excellent cuisine and many facilities.
18 holes, 6630yds, Par 72, SSS 72, Course record 67.
Club membership 300.
Visitors must contact in advance.
Societies must telephone in advance.
Green Fees £45 per day; £26 per round (£75/£45 weekends).
Facilities ⊗ ⫾ ⓑ 🍽 ♀ 🛆 🖾 ✧ ℓ Alastair Spink.
Leisure hard tennis courts, heated outdoor swimming pool, fishing, snooker, sauna, solarium, gymnasium, croquet.
Location In village on A1071
Hotel ★★★★(red)⛊ Hintlesham Hall Hotel, HINTLESHAM ☎ (0473) 652334 & 652268 33 ⇌ ℝ

IPSWICH   Map 05 TM14

Ipswich ☎ (0473) 728941
Many golfers are suprised when they hear that Ipswich has, at Purdis Heath, a first-class golf course. In some ways it resembles some of Surrey's better courses; a beautiful heathland/parkland course with two lakes and easy walking.
18 holes, 6405yds, Par 71, SSS 71 or 9 holes, 1930yds, Par 31, SSS 59.
Club membership 850.
Visitors must contact in advance & have a handicap certificate for 18 hole courses.
Societies must contact in advance.
Green Fees not confirmed.
Facilities ♀ 🛆 🖾 ℓ
Location Purdis Heath (E side of town centre off A1156)
Hotel ★★★70% Marlborough Hotel, Henley Rd, IPSWICH ☎ (0473) 257677 22 ⇌ ℝ

Rushmere ☎ (0473) 725648
Heathland course with gorse and prevailing winds. Testing
5th hole - dog leg, 419 yards (par 4).
18 holes, 6287yds, Par 70, SSS 70.
Club membership 800.
Visitors   restricted weekends & bank holidays. Must have
a handicap certificate.
Societies   by arrangement.
Green Fees £18 per day.
Facilities ⊗ 〉☰ by prior arrangement ⓑ 💻 ♀ ⚲ 🏠 ⚑
    ⓕ N T J McNeill.
Location   Rushmere Heath (2m E off A12)
Hotel   ★★★70% Marlborough Hotel, Henley Rd,
IPSWICH ☎ (0473) 257677 22 ⇥ ⓕ

LOWESTOFT   Map 05 TM59

Rookery Park ☎ (0502) 560380
Parkland course with a 9-hole, Par 3 adjacent.
18 holes, 6385yds, Par 72, SSS 72.
Club membership 1000.
Visitors   must have handicap certificate.
Societies   by arrangement.
Green Fees not confirmed.
Facilities ⊗ (ex Sat) 〉☰ (Wed-Fri only) ⓑ 💻 ♀ ⚲ 🏠 ⚑ ⓕ
Leisure   snooker.
Location   Carlton Colville (3.5m SW on A146)
Hotel   ★★62% Broadlands Hotel, Bridge Rd, Oulton
Broad, LOWESTOFT
☎ (0502) 516031 52 ⇥

NEWMARKET   Map 05 TL66

Links ☎ (0638) 663000
Gently undulating parkland.
18 holes, 6424yds, Par 72, SSS 71, Course record 66.
Club membership 700.
Visitors   must have handicap certificate, restricted Sun
after 11.30am.
Societies   must contact in advance.
Green Fees £24 per day/round (£28 weekends & bank
holidays).
Facilities ⊗ 〉☰ ⓑ 💻 ♀ ⚲ 🏠 ⓕ John Sharkey.
Location   Cambridge Rd (1m SW on A1034)
Hotel   ★★★66% Newmarket Moat House, Moulton
Rd, NEWMARKET
☎ (0638) 667171 47 ⇥ ⓕ

NEWTON   Map 05 TL94

Newton Green ☎ Newton Green (0787) 77217
Flat, commonland course.
9 holes, 5488yds, Par 68, SSS 67.
Club membership 450.
Visitors   must contact in advance but may not play on
Tue, weekends & bank holidays.
Green Fees not confirmed.
Facilities ⊗ 〉☰ ⓑ 💻 ♀ ⚲ 🏠 ⓕ Tim Cooper.
Location   Sudbury Rd (W side of village on A134)
Hotel   ★★★64% Bull Hotel, Hall St, LONG
MELFORD ☎ (0787) 378494 25 ⇥ ⓕ

SOUTHWOLD   Map 05 TM57

Southwold ☎ (0502) 723234
Commonland course with 4-acre practice ground and
panoramic views of the sea.
9 holes, 3004yds, Par 70, SSS 69.
Club membership 450.
Visitors   restricted Sun, bank holidays & competition
days. Must contact in advance.
Societies   must apply in writing.
Green Fees £14 per day (£18 weekends and bank holidays).
Facilities ⊗ ⓑ 💻 ♀ ⚲ 🏠 ⓕ Brian Allen.
Location   The Common (0.5m W off A1095)
Hotel   ★★★68% Swan Hotel, Market Place,
SOUTHWOLD
☎ (0502) 722186 27 ⇥ ⓕ Annexe18 ⇥

STOWMARKET   Map 05 TM05

Stowmarket ☎ Rattlesden (0449) 736473 & 736392
Parkland course.
18 holes, 6101yds, Par 69, SSS 69.
Club membership 600.
Visitors   must contact in advance & have handicap
certificate, but cannot play Wed mornings.
Societies   Thu & Fri only, by arrangement.
Green Fees not confirmed.
Facilities ⊗ 〉☰ ⓑ 💻 (no catering Mon) ♀ ⚲ 🏠
    ⓕ C Aldred.
Location   Lower Rd, Onehouse (2.5m SW off B115)
Hotel   ★★59% Cedars Hotel, Needham Rd,
STOWMARKET ☎ (0449) 612668 24 ⇥ ⓕ

THORPENESS   Map 05 TM45

Thorpeness ☎ Aldeburgh (0728) 452176
The holes of this moorland course are pleasantly varied
with several quite difficult par 4's. Natural hazards
abound. The 15th, with its sharp left dog-leg, is one of
the best holes. Designed by James Braid.
18 holes, 6241yds, Par 69, SSS 71.
Club membership 390.
Visitors   must book in advance.
Societies   by arrangement.
Green Fees not confirmed.
Facilities ♀ ⚲ 🏠 ⚑ ⓕ Mike Grantham.
Leisure   snooker, practice range.
Location   W side of village off B1353
Hotel   ★65% White Horse Hotel, Station Rd,
LEISTON ☎ (0728) 830694 10rm(1 ⇥ 7
ⓕ)Annexe3 ⓕ

WALDRINGFIELD   Map 05 TM24

Waldringfield Heath ☎ (047336) 768
Easy walking heathland course with long drives on 1st, 5th
(586yds) and 10th tees.
18 holes, 6153yds, Par 71, SSS 69.
Club membership 660.
Visitors   welcome Mon-Fri, weekends & bank holidays
after noon.
Societies   advance booking required.
Green Fees not confirmed.
Facilities ⊗ (Mon-Fri) ⓑ 💻 ♀ ⚲ 🏠 ⓕ Tony Dobson.

Location Newbourne Rd (3m NE of Ipswich off old A12)
Hotel ★★★♨73% Seckford Hall Hotel,
WOODBRIDGE
☎ (0394) 385678 23 ➪ ☎Annexe10 ➪ ☏

WITNESHAM   Map 05 TM15

Fynn Valley ☎ (0473) 785267 & 785463
Undulating parkland course plus Par-3 nine-hole and driving range.
18 holes, 5580yds, Par 69, SSS 67, Course record 62.
Club membership 650.
Visitors ladies priority on Wed am, members only Sun until noon.
Societies must apply in advance.
Green Fees £15 per day; £10 per 9 holes; £13.50 per 18 holes.
Facilities ⊗ ℳ (ex Sun) ⛳ 🏌 ♀ ⚐ 🏠 ⛵ ⚑ Robin Mann.
Leisure floodlit driving range, Par 3 course.
Location 2m N of Ipswich on B1077
Hotel ★★★70% Marlborough Hotel, Henley Rd,
IPSWICH ☎ (0473) 257677 22 ➪ ☏

WOODBRIDGE   Map 05 TM24

Ufford Park Hotel Golf & Leisure ☎ (0394) 382836
A challenging new course opened in autumn 1991. The 18-hole Par 70 course is set in ancient parkland has many natural features including 11 water hazards retaind from the original parkland. There is also an extensive hotel and leisure complex beside the course.
18 holes, 6300yds, Par 70, SSS 70.
Club membership 250.
Visitors no restrictions.
Societies must telephone in advance.
Green Fees £15 per round (£18 weekends & bank holidays).
Facilities ⊗ ℳ ⛳ 🏌 ♀ ⚐ 🏠 ⛵ ⚑ Stuart Robertson.
Leisure heated indoor swimming pool, fishing, riding, sauna, solarium, gymnasium, spa bath, table tennis, buggies.
Location Yarmouth Rd, Ufford
Hotel ★★★68% Ufford Park Hotel Golf & Leisure, Yarmouth Rd, Ufford, WOODBRIDGE
☎ (0394) 383555 25 ➪ ☏

Woodbridge ☎ (0394) 382038
A beautiful course, one of the best in East Anglia. It is situated on high ground and in different seasons present golfers with a great variety of colour. Some say that of the many good holes the 14th is the best.
18 holes, 6314yds, Par 70, SSS 70, Course record 64.
Course number 2: 9 holes, 2243yds, Par 62, SSS 62.
Club membership 900.
Visitors must play with member at weekends & bank holidays. Must contact in advance and handicap certificate required for 18 hole course.
Societies must contact in writing up to 1 year in advance.
Green Fees £26 per day/round (18 hole); £12 (9 hole).
Facilities ⊗ ℳ ⛳ 🏌 ♀ ⚐ 🏠 ⚑ Leslie Jones.
Location Bromeswell Heath (2.5m NE off A1152)
Hotel ★★★♨73% Seckford Hall Hotel, WOODBRIDGE ☎ (0394) 385678 23 ➪ ☎Annexe10 ➪ ☏

UFFORD *park*

Hotel Golf & Leisure

★★★

Visit Suffolk's premier complex, open to non-residents for meals, drinks and all manner of business and leisure activity.

- 27 double/twin bedrooms, all en suite
- 10 bedrooms in our Golfing Lodge
- Leisure club with luxury indoor swimming pool (membership available)
- 18 hole, par 70 golf course in parkland setting 2 tier, 18 hole putting green. 9 bay driving nets
- Cedar Restaurant open to non residents
- Conference/function facilities for up to 150
- Personalised wedding arrangements
- Two night Getaway Breaks from £99 per person
- Our main bar is open to the public, bar meals available for lunch & dinner 7 days a week.

For further details contact Stephen Thurlow or Carolyne Butler

UFFORD PARK HOTEL GOLF & LEISURE
Yarmouth Road • Ufford
Woodbridge • Suffolk IP12 1QW
Telephone (01394) 383555

WORLINGTON   Map 05 TL67

Royal Worlington & Newmarket ☎ (0638) 712216
Inland 'links' course. Favourite 9-hole course of many golf writers.
9 holes, 3105yds, Par 35, SSS 70.
Club membership 325.
Visitors with member only at weekends. Must contact in advance and have a handicap certificate.
Societies must apply in writing.
Green Fees not confirmed.
Facilities ⊗ by prior arrangement ⛳ 🏌 ♀ ⚐ 🏠 ⛵ ⚑ Malcolm Hawkins.
Location 0.5m SE
Hotel ★★★63% Riverside Hotel, Mill St, MILDENHALL ☎ (0638) 717274 21 ➪ ☏

SURREY

ADDLESTONE   Map 04 TQ06

New Zealand ☎ (0932) 345049
Heathland course set in trees and heather.
18 holes, 6012yds, Par 68, SSS 69.
Club membership 320.
▶

Visitors   must contact in advance.
Societies contact in advance.
Green Fees £45 per day; £35 per round (£55 weekends).
Facilities ⊗ ⓑ ♥ ♀ ⚲ 🏠 ⛳ 🍴 Vic Elvidge.
Location Woodham Ln (1.5m W of Weybridge)
Hotel   ★★★63% Ship Thistle, Monument Green,
             WEYBRIDGE ☎ (0932) 848364 39 ⇌ 🐾

ASHFORD   Map 04 TQ07

Ashford Manor ☎ (0784) 252049
Parkland course, looks easy but is difficult.
18 holes, 6343yds, Par 70, SSS 70.
Club membership 600.
Visitors   must contact in advance and have an
            introduction from own club.
Societies must contact in advance.
Green Fees not confirmed.
Facilities ⚲ 🏠 ⛳ 🍴
Location Fordbridge Rd (2m E of Staines via A308
            Staines by-pass)
Hotel   ★★★58% Thames Lodge Hotel, Thames St,
            STAINES ☎ (0784) 464433 44 ⇌ 🐾

BANSTEAD   Map 04 TQ25

Banstead Downs ☎ 081-642 2284
Downland course with narrow fairways and hawthorns.
18 holes, 6169yds, Par 69, SSS 69.
Club membership 542.
Visitors   must have handicap certificate. With member
            only weekends.
Societies welcome.
Green Fees not confirmed.
Facilities ⊗ ⓑ ♥ ♀ 🏠 🍴
Location Burdon Ln, Belmont, Sutton (1.5m N on A217)
Hotel   ★★63% Heathside Hotel, Brighton Rd,
            BURGH HEATH ☎ (0737) 353355 73 ⇌ 🐾

Cuddington ☎ 081-393 0952
Parkland course with easy walking and good views.
18 holes, 6394yds, Par 70, SSS 70, Course record 61.
Club membership 790.
Visitors   must contact in advance and have a handicap
            certificate or letter of introduction.
Societies welcome Thu, must apply in advance.
Green Fees £30 per day/round (£35 weekends after 4pm).
Facilities ⊗ 🍽 by prior arrangement ⓑ ♥ ♀ 🏠
            🍴 James Morgan.
Location Banstead Rd (N of Banstead station on A2022)
Hotel   ★★63% Heathside Hotel, Brighton Rd,
            BURGH HEATH ☎ (0737) 353355 73 ⇌ 🐾

BRAMLEY   Map 04 TQ04

Bramley ☎ Guildford (0483) 892696
Downland course, fine views from top.
18 holes, 5966yds, Par 69, SSS 69, Course record 65.
Club membership 780.
Visitors   must play with member at weekends & bank
            holidays. Must contact in advance.
Societies must telephone in advance.
Green Fees £30 per day; £25 per round.
Facilities ⊗ 🍽 ⓑ ♥ ♀ 🏠 ⛳ 🍴 Gary Peddie.

Leisure   driving range.
Location 0.5m N on A281
Hotel   B Forte Crest, Egerton Rd, GUILDFORD
            ☎ (0483) 574444 111 ⇌ 🐾

BROOKWOOD   Map 04 SU95

West Hill ☎ (0483) 474365
Worplesdon's next-door neighbour and a comparably
great heath-and-heather course. Slightly tighter than
Worplesdon with more opportunities for getting into
trouble - but a most interesting and challenging course
with wonderful greens. Water also provides natural
hazards. The 15th is a testing par 3.
18 holes, 6368yds, Par 69, SSS 70, Course record 66.
Club membership 568.
Visitors   must contact in advance & have handicap
            certificate, may not play weekends & bank
            holidays.
Societies must apply in writing.
Green Fees £42 per day; £32 per round.
Facilities ⊗ & 🍽 by prior arrangement ⓑ ♥ ♀ ⚲ 🏠
            ⛳ 🍴 John C Clements.
Leisure   practice golf range & putting green.
Location Bagshot Rd (E side of village on A332)
Hotel   ★★★★(red)♨♨ Pennyhill Park Hotel,
            London Rd, BAGSHOT
            ☎ (0276) 471774 22 ⇌ 🐾Annexe54 ⇌ 🐾

CAMBERLEY   Map 04 SU86

Camberley Heath ☎ (0276) 23258
One of the great 'heath and heather' courses so
frequently associated with Surrey. Several very good
short holes - especially the 8th. The 10th is a difficult and
interesting par 4, as also is the 17th, where the drive must
be held well to the left as perdition lurks on the right.
Course architect Harry Colt.
18 holes, 6337yds, Par 72, SSS 70.
Club membership 600.
Visitors   may not play at weekends. Must contact in
            advance and have a handicap certificate.
Societies must apply in advance.
Green Fees £50 per day; £30 per round.
Facilities ⊗ ⓑ ♥ ♀ ⚲ 🏠 ⛳ 🍴 Gary Smith.
Leisure   caddy cars.
Location Golf Dr (1.25m SE of town centre off A325)
Hotel   ★★★★(red)♨♨ Pennyhill Park Hotel,
            London Rd, BAGSHOT
            ☎ (0276) 471774 22 ⇌ 🐾Annexe54 ⇌ 🐾

CHERTSEY   Map 04 TQ06

Barrow Hills ☎ (0256) 72037
Parkland course with natural hazards.
18 holes, 3090yds, Par 56, SSS 53, Course record 58.
Club membership 235.
Visitors   restricted at weekends & bank holidays in the
            afternoons. Must be accompanied by member.
Green Fees not confirmed.
Facilities ♥
Location Longcross (3m W on B386)
Hotel   ★★★58% Thames Lodge Hotel, Thames St,
            STAINES ☎ (0784) 464433 44 ⇌ 🐾

Laleham ☎ (0932) 564211
Well-bunkered parkland/meadowland course.
18 holes, 6210yds, Par 70, SSS 70, Course record 65.
Club membership 600.

Visitors	must contact in advance. Members guests only at weekends. Discount for members of recognised golf club with CONGU or USGA handicap certificate.
Societies	must contact in writing.
Green Fees	£25 per day; £16.50 per round.
Facilities	⊗ ⅏ by prior arrangement ⌂ ☕ ♀ ⚐ 📷 🍴 Hogan Stott.
Leisure	snooker.
Location	Laleham Reach (1.5m N)
Hotel	★★★58% Thames Lodge Hotel, Thames St, STAINES ☎ (0784) 464433 44 ⇆ 🐾

CHIPSTEAD   Map 04 TQ25

Chipstead ☎ Downland (0737) 555781
Hilly parkland course, hard walking, good views. Testing 18th hole.
18 holes, 5454yds, Par 67, SSS 67.
Club membership 650.

Visitors	restricted weekends.
Societies	must apply in advance.
Green Fees	£25 per day (£20 after 2pm).
Facilities	⌂ ☕ (no catering Mon) ♀ ⚐ 📷 🍴
Location	How Ln (0.5m N of village)
Hotel	★★★★59% Selsdon Park Hotel, Sanderstead, CROYDON ☎ 081-657 8811 170 ⇆ 🐾

COBHAM   Map 04 TQ16

Silvermere ☎ (0932) 866007
Parkland course with many very tight holes through woodland, 17th has 170-yd carry over the lake. Driving range.
18 holes, 6333yds, Par 71, SSS 71.
Club membership 850.

Visitors	may not play at weekends until 1pm. Must contact in advance.
Societies	must contact by telephone.
Green Fees	not confirmed.
Facilities	⊗ ⅏ ⌂ ☕ ♀ ⚐ 📷 🍴 Doug McClelland.
Leisure	fishing, 34 bay driving range.
Location	Redhill Rd (2.25m NW off A245)
Hotel	★★★68% Woodlands Park Hotel, Woodlands Ln, STOKE D'ABERNON ☎ (0372) 843933 58 ⇆ 🐾

CRANLEIGH   Map 04 TQ03

Fernfell Golf & Country Club ☎ (0483) 268855
Scenic woodland/parkland course at the base of the Surrey hills, easy walking. Clubhouse in 400-year-old barn.
18 holes, 5071yds, Par 68, SSS 67, Course record 68.
Club membership 1000.

Visitors	may not play at weekends. Must contact in advance.
Societies	must contact in advance.
Green Fees	not confirmed.
Facilities	⊗ ⅏ ⌂ ☕ ♀ ⚐ 📷 🍴 Trevor Longmuir.
Leisure	hard tennis courts, heated outdoor swimming pool, snooker, sauna.
Location	Barhatch Ln (1m N)

Hotel	★★65% Gatton Manor Hotel Golf & Country Club, Standon Ln, OCKLEY ☎ (0306) 627555 10 ⇆ 🐾

DORKING   Map 04 TQ14

Betchworth Park ☎ (0306) 882052
Parkland course, with hard walking on southern ridge of Boxhill.
18 holes, 6266yds, Par 69, SSS 70, Course record 65.
Club membership 715.

Visitors	restricted Tue & Wed (am), Fri & weekends. Must contact in advance.
Societies	welcome Mon and Thu, must apply in advance.
Green Fees	weekday £31 per day; £25 per round (Sun pm £43).
Facilities	⊗ by prior arrangement ⌂ ☕ ♀ ⚐ 📷 🍴
Location	Reigate Rd (1m E on A25)
Hotel	★★★57% The White Horse, High St, DORKING ☎ (0306) 881138 36 ⇆ 🐾Annexe32 ⇆ 🐾

Dorking ☎ (0306) 889786
Undulating parkland course, easy slopes, wind-sheltered.
Testing holes: 5th 'Tom's Puddle' (par 4); 7th 'Rest and Be Thankful' (par 4); 9th 'Double Decker' (par 4).
9 holes, 5163yds, Par 66, SSS 65, Course record 65.
Club membership 425.

Visitors	with member only weekends & bank holidays.
Societies	must apply in writing.
Green Fees	£20 per day; £16 per 18 holes.
Facilities	⊗ ⅏ by prior arrangement ⌂ ☕ ♀ ⚐ 📷 ⛳ 🍴 Paul Napier.
Leisure	trolleys from professional.
Location	Chart Park (1m S on A24)
Hotel	★★★★62% The Burford Bridge, Burford Bridge, Box Hill, DORKING ☎ (0306) 884561 48 ⇆ 🐾

EAST HORSLEY   Map 04 TQ05

Drift ☎ (0483) 284641
Woodland course with sheltered fairways and many ponds.
18 holes, 6425yds, Par 71, SSS 69.
Club membership 800.

Visitors	must contact in advance. With member only weekends & bank holidays.
Societies	must apply in writing.
Green Fees	£30 per day (£20 after noon, £15 after 3pm).
Facilities	⊗ ⅏ ⌂ ☕ ♀ ⚐ 📷 🍴 Joe Hagen.
Location	1.5m N off B2039
Hotel	★★★63% Thatchers Resort Hotel, Epsom Rd, EAST HORSLEY ☎ (0483) 284291 36 ⇆ 🐾Annexe23 ⇆ 🐾 *See advertisement on page 184*

EFFINGHAM   Map 04 TQ15

Effingham ☎ Bookham (0372) 452203
Easy-walking downland course laid out on 27-acres with tree-lined fairways. It is one of the longest of the Surrey courses with wide subtle greens that provide a provocative but by no means exhausting challenge. Fine views.
18 holes, 6488yds, Par 71, SSS 71, Course record 63.
Club membership 960. ▶

Thatchers Resort Hotel

Epsom Road, East Horsley, Surrey KT24 6TB
Tel: 01483 284291 Fax: 01483 284222

Well known for its Restaurant and imaginative menu. The Hotel is set in the beautiful Surrey countryside, and visitors will find plenty of opportunities for leisure activities and sightseeing. An outdoor swimming pool is open from May to September with some of the bedrooms having poolside views, separate to the main house.

Nearest Golf Course "The Drift Golf Course"

Visitors	must contact in advance. With member only weekends & bank holidays.
Societies	must apply in advance.
Green Fees	£35 per day, £27.50 after 2pm.
Facilities	⊗ ∭ by prior arrangement ⅃ ♥ ♀ ⚲ 🏠 ⛳ ⚑ Steve Hoatson.
Leisure	hard and grass tennis courts, squash, snooker, caddy cars.
Location	Guildford Rd (W side of village on A246)
Hotel	★★★63% Thatchers Resort Hotel, Epsom Rd, EAST HORSLEY ☎ (0483) 284291 36 ⇄ ⁍Annexe23 ⇄ ⁍

ENTON GREEN   Map 04 SU94

West Surrey ☎ Godalming (0483) 421275
A good parkland-type course in rolling, well-wooded setting. Some fairways are tight with straight driving at a premium. The 17th is a testing hole with a long hill walk.
18 holes, 6300yds, Par 71, SSS 70.
Club membership 700.

Visitors	must be member of recognised club with handicap certificate & contact in advance.
Societies	must apply in writing.
Green Fees	£33 per day; £24.50 per round (£43 per day/round weekends & bank holidays).
Facilities	⊗ ∭ ⅃ ♥ ♀ ⚲ 🏠 ⚑ John Hoskison.
Leisure	snooker.
Location	S side of village
Hotel	★★★61% Bush Hotel, The Borough, FARNHAM ☎ (0252) 715237 66 ⇄ ⁍

EPSOM   Map 04 TQ26

Epsom ☎ (03727) 21666
Downland course.
18 holes, 5701yds, Par 69, SSS 68.
Club membership 900.

Visitors	restricted to after midday weekends & bank holidays.
Societies	must contact in advance.
Green Fees	£24 per day; £16 per round (£18 weekends & bank holidays).
Facilities	⊗ ∭ by prior arrangement ⅃ ♥ ♀ ⚲ 🏠 ⚑ Ron Goudie.
Leisure	snooker.
Location	Longdown Ln South, Epsom Downs (SE side of town centre on B288)
Hotel	★★63% Heathside Hotel, Brighton Rd, BURGH HEATH ☎ (0737) 353355 73 ⇄ ⁍

Horton Park Country Club ☎ 081-394 2626
Parkland course.
18 holes, 5208yds, Par 69, SSS 65.
Club membership 554.

Visitors	must book for weekends.
Societies	must telephone in advance.
Green Fees	£11 per round (£13 weekends & bank holidays).
Facilities	⊗ ∭ ⅃ ♥ ♀ ⚲ 🏠 ⚑ Gary Clements.
Leisure	golf carts, driving range, putting green.
Location	Hook Rd
Hotel	★★63% Heathside Hotel, Brighton Rd, BURGH HEATH ☎ (0737) 353355 73 ⇄ ⁍

ESHER   Map 04 TQ16

Moore Place ☎ (0372) 463533
Public course on attractive, undulating parkland laid out some 60 years ago by Harry Vardon. Examples of most of the trees that will survive in the UK are to be found on the course. Testing short holes at 4th, 5th and 7th.
9 holes, 2093yds, Par 32, SSS 30, Course record 25.
Club membership 150.

Visitors	no restrictions.
Societies	must contact in advance.
Green Fees	£5.40 (£7.25 weekends & bank holidays).
Facilities	⊗ ∭ ⅃ ♥ ♀ ⚲ 🏠 ⚑ David Allen.
Location	Portsmouth Rd (SW side of town centre on A244)
Hotel	★★★63% Ship Thistle, Monument Green, WEYBRIDGE ☎ (0932) 848364 39 ⇄ ⁍

Sandown Golf Centre ☎ (0372) 463340
Flat parkland course in middle of racecourse. Additional facilities include a driving range, and a pitch-and-putt course.
New Course: 9 holes, 2828yds, Par 35, SSS 34, Course record 68.
Par 3: 9 holes, 1193yds, Par 27.
Club membership 650.

Visitors	restricted weekends & bank holidays.
Societies	must apply in writing.
Green Fees	£5.25 per 9 holes (£7 weekends); Par 3 course £3.50 (£4.50 weekends).
Facilities	⊗ ⅃ ♥ ♀ ⚲ 🏠 ⚑ Neal Bedward.
Leisure	par 3, pitch & putt, floodlit range.
Location	Sandown Park, More Ln (1m NW off A307)
Hotel	★★63% Haven Hotel, Portsmouth Rd, ESHER ☎ 081-398 0023 16 ⇄ ⁍Annexe4 ⇄ ⁍

Thames Ditton & Esher ☎ 081-398 1551
Commonland course. There is a public right of way across the course.
18 holes, 5190yds, Par 66, SSS 65.
Club membership 400.

Visitors	may not play on Sun mornings.
Societies	must contact in advance.
Green Fees	not confirmed.
Facilities	⊗ & ⅲ by prior arrangement ⌂ 🍷 ♀ ⅄ 🏠 ♪ 🥂 Rodney Hutton.
Location	Marquis of Granby, Portsmouth Rd (1m NE on A307)
Hotel	★★63% Haven Hotel, Portsmouth Rd, ESHER ☎ 081-398 0023 16 ⇆ ♪Annexe4 ⇆ ♪

FARNHAM   Map 04 SU84

Farnham ☎ (0252) 782109
A mixture of meadowland and heath with quick drying sandy subsoil. Several of the earlier holes have interesting features, the finishing holes rather less.
18 holes, 6325yds, Par 72, SSS 70, Course record 67.
Club membership 750.

Visitors	must be member of recognised club & have handicap certificate. With member only weekends.
Societies	must apply in writing one year in advance.
Green Fees	£30 per day; £25 per round.
Facilities	⊗ ⅲ by prior arrangement ⌂ 🍷 ♀ ⅄ 🏠 ♪ 🥂 Grahame Cowlishaw.
Location	The Sands (3m E off A31)
Hotel	★★★61% Bush Hotel, The Borough, FARNHAM ☎ (0252) 715237 66 ⇆ ♪

Farnham Park ☎ (0252) 715216
Municipal parkland course in Farnham Park.
9 holes, 1163yds, Par 27.

Visitors	must contact in advance for weekends and bank holidays.
Societies	must apply in advance.
Green Fees	£3.50 per round (£4.40 weekends & bank holidays).
Facilities	⌂ 🍷 ♀ 🏠 ♪ 🥂 Peter Chapman.
Location	Folly Hill, Farnham Park (N side of town centre on A287)
Hotel	★★★61% Bush Hotel, The Borough, FARNHAM ☎ (0252) 715237 66 ⇆ ♪

GODALMING   Map 04 SU94

Broadwater Park ☎ (0483) 429955
A Par-3 public course with floodlit driving range.
9 holes, 1323yds, Par 54.
Club membership 200.

Visitors	welcome except Sat am when competitions in progress.
Societies	apply in writing.
Green Fees	not confirmed.
Facilities	⌂ 🍷 ♀ 🏠 ♪ 🥂 Kevin D Milton.
Leisure	16 bay covered driving range.
Location	Guildford Rd, Farncombe (4m SW of Guildford)
Hotel	★★64% Inn on the Lake, Ockford Rd, GODALMING ☎ (0483) 415575 20rm(17 ⇆ ♪)

> This guide is up-dated annually –
> make sure you use the up-to-date
> edition

GUILDFORD   Map 04 SU94

Guildford ☎ (0483) 63941
A downland course but with some trees and much scrub. The holes provide an interesting variety of play, an invigorating experience.
18 holes, 6090yds, Par 69, SSS 70.
Club membership 700.

Visitors	must contact in advance. With member only weekends & bank holidays.
Societies	welcome Mon-Fri. Must apply in advance.
Green Fees	£35 per day; £25 per round.
Facilities	⊗ ⅲ ⌂ 🍷 ♀ ⅄ 🏠 ♪ 🥂 P G Hollington.
Leisure	snooker.
Location	High Path Rd, Merrow (E side of town centre off A246)
Hotel	B Forte Crest, Egerton Rd, GUILDFORD ☎ (0483) 574444 111 ⇆ ♪

Milford ☎ (0483) 419200
A Peter Alliss/Clive Clark designed course opened summer 1993. The design has cleverly incorporated a demanding course within an existing woodland and meadow area.
18 holes, 5916yds, Par 69, SSS 68.
Club membership 750.

Visitors	advisable to book in advance.
Societies	contact in advance.
Green Fees	£35 per round (£45 weekends).
Facilities	⊗ ⅲ ⌂ 🍷 ♀ ⅄ 🏠 🥂 Grant Clough.
Leisure	trolleys and caddies for hire.
Location	Milford (6m SW, leave A3 Milford then A3100 to Enton)
Hotel	★★64% Inn on the Lake, Ockford Rd, GODALMING ☎ (0483) 415575 20rm(17 ⇆ ♪)

HINDHEAD   Map 04 SU83

Hindhead ☎ (0428) 604614
A good example of a Surrey heath-and-heather course, and most picturesque. Players must be prepared for some hard walking. The first nine fairways follow narrow valleys requiring straight hitting; the second nine are much less restricted.
18 holes, 6373yds, Par 70, SSS 70, Course record 65.
Club membership 850.

Visitors	must contact in advance and have a handicap certificate.
Societies	Wed & Thu only
Green Fees	£35 per day, £27 after 2pm (£42/32 weekends).
Facilities	⊗ ⅲ ⌂ 🍷 ♀ ⅄ 🏠 ♪ 🥂 Neil Ogilvy.
Leisure	snooker.
Location	Churt Rd (1.5m NW on A287)
Hotel	★★★72% Lythe Hill Hotel, Petworth Rd, HASLEMERE ☎ (0428) 651251 40 ⇆ ♪

KINGSWOOD   Map 04 TQ25

Kingswood ☎ Mogador (0737) 832188
Flat parkland course, easy walking.
18 holes, 6855yds, Par 72, SSS 73.
Club membership 630.

▶

Visitors restricted before noon weekends.
Societies must apply in advance.
Green Fees £45 per day; £30 per round weekdays.
Facilities ⊗ & ⫿⫿ by prior arrangement ⬚ ⬚ ♀ ⤳ ⬚ ⫟ ⫯ Martin Platts.
Leisure squash, snooker, buggies £20 per round/£30 per day.
Location Sandy Ln (5m S of village off A217)
Hotel ★★63% Heathside Hotel, Brighton Rd, BURGH HEATH ☎ (0737) 353355 73 ⇄ ☏

LEATHERHEAD   Map 04 TQ15

Leatherhead ☎ Oxshott (037284) 3966
Parkland course with numerous ditches and only two hills, so walking is easy.
18 holes, 6157yds, Par 71, SSS 69.
Club membership 600.
Visitors restricted Sat & Sun (am). Must contact in advance.
Societies must apply in advance.
Green Fees £25 per round (£35 weekend afternoons).
Facilities ⊗ ⬚ ⬚ ♀ ⤳ ⬚ ⫟ ⫯ Richard Hurst.
Leisure sauna, practice ground, putting green.
Location Kingston Rd (0.25m from junct 9 of M25, on A243)
Hotel ★★★68% Woodlands Park Hotel, Woodlands Ln, STOKE D'ABERNON ☎ (0372) 843933 58 ⇄ ☏

Tyrrells Wood ☎ (0372) 376025
Parkland course with easy walking. Snooker.
18 holes, 6234yds, Par 71, SSS 70.
Club membership 750.
Visitors must contact in advance & play Yellow tee markers only. Handicap certificate required. Restricted weekends.
Societies must apply in writing.
Green Fees £48 per day; £32 per round (weekend Sun pm only £42).
Facilities ⊗ ⫿⫿ ⬚ ⬚ ♀ ⤳ ⬚ ⫟ ⫯ Max Taylor.
Leisure snooker.
Location 1.25m S on A244
Hotel ★★★★62% The Burford Bridge, Burford Bridge, Box Hill, DORKING ☎ (0306) 884561 48 ⇄ ☏

LIMPSFIELD   Map 05 TQ45

Limpsfield Chart ☎ (0883) 722106
Tight heathland course set in National Trust land.
9 holes, 5718yds, Par 70, SSS 68, Course record 64.
Club membership 350.
Visitors with member only or by appointment weekends & not before 3.30pm Thu (Ladies Day).
Societies must apply in advance.
Green Fees £18 per day (£20 weekends & bank holidays).
Facilities ⊗ & ⫿⫿ by prior arrangement ⬚ ⬚ ♀ ⤳
Location Westerham Rd (1m E on A25)
Hotel ★★★65% Kings Arms Hotel, Market Square, WESTERHAM ☎ (0959) 562990 16 ⇄ ☏

LINGFIELD   Map 05 TQ34

Lingfield Park ☎ (0342) 834602
Difficult and challenging, tree-lined parkland course set in 210 acres of beautiful Surrey countryside. Driving range.
18 holes, 6473yds, Par 71, SSS 72.
Club membership 700.
Visitors must be accompanied by member on Sat & Sun.
Societies must telephone in advance; Mon-Fri only.
Green Fees £30 per day; £20 per round.
Facilities ⊗ ⫿⫿ by prior arrangement ⬚ ⬚ ♀ ⤳ ⬚ ⫟ ⫯ Christopher Morley.
Leisure driving range, caddy cars, trolleys.
Location Racecourse Rd (entrance next to Lingfield race course)
Hotel ★★★65% Woodbury House Hotel, Lewes Rd, EAST GRINSTEAD ☎ (0342) 313657 13 ⇄ ☏Annexe1 ☏

OCKLEY   Map 04 TQ14

Gatton Manor Hotel Golf & Country Club ☎ (0306) 627555
Undulating course through woods and over many challenging water holes.
18 holes, 6145yds, Par 72, SSS 69.
Club membership 300.
Visitors must give 2 weeks prior notice. Restricted Sun (am).
Societies must apply in advance.
Green Fees £30 per day; £18 per round;(£50/£25 weekends). Daily reductions after 4pm.

Gatton Manor Hotel
Golf and Country Club ★★
Ockley, Nr. Dorking RH5 5PQ
Tel: Oakwood Hill (01306) 627555/6
Fax: (01306) 627713

Gatton Manor Hotel, Golf & Country Club is an 18th Century manor house set within its own 18-hole championship length golf course and offering 14 well appointed en-suite bedrooms, with an à la carte restaurant serving both English and Continental cuisine. Adjacent to the restaurant is a large bar with a superb selection of wines and spirits.
The hotel also offers two tastefully decorated conference suites available with all the latest equipment. Other outdoor facilities include tennis, fishing and bowls.

Facilities ⊗ ⅏ 🛍 💺 ⚑ 🏌 ️ ♿ Rae Sargent.
Leisure grass tennis courts, fishing, bowls, driving range, putting green.
Location 1.5m SW off A29
Hotel ★★65% Gatton Manor Hotel Golf & Country Club, Standon Ln, OCKLEY
☎ (0306) 627555 10 ⇆ ꞁ

OTTERSHAW
Map 04 TQ06

Foxhills ☎ (0932) 872050
A pair of parkland courses designed in the grand manner and with American course-design in mind. One course is tree-lined, the other, as well as trees, has massive bunkers and artificial lakes which contribute to the interest. Both courses offer testing golf and they finish on the same long 'double green'. Par 3 'Manor' course also available.
Chertsey: 18 holes, 6658yds, Par 73, SSS 72, Course record 65.
Longcross: 18 holes, 6406yds, Par 72, SSS 71.
Manor: 9 holes, 1300yds, Par 27.
Club membership 1100.
Visitors restricted before noon weekends.
Societies welcome Mon-Fri, must apply in advance.
Green Fees £45 per 18 holes; £65 per 36 holes (£55 per 18 holes weekends).
Facilities ⊗ ⅏ 🛍 💺 ⚑ 🏌 ️ ♿ A Goode.
Leisure hard tennis courts, outdoor and indoor heated swimming pools, squash, snooker, sauna, solarium, gymnasium, clay shoot, croquet lawn, archery, boule.
Location Stonehill Rd (1m NW)
Hotel O Foxhills, OTTERSHAW
☎ (0932) 872050 16 ⇆ ꞁ

PIRBRIGHT
Map 04 SU95

Goal Farm ☎ (0483) 473183 & 473205
Beautiful lanscaped parkland 'Pay and Play' course with excellent greens.
9 holes, 1273yds, Par 54, SSS 48.
Club membership 400.
Visitors may not play on Sat & Thu mornings.
Green Fees not confirmed.
Facilities ⚑ 🏌
Location Gole Rd (1.5m NW on B3012)
Hotel B Forte Crest, Lynchford Rd, FARNBOROUGH ☎ (0252) 545051 110 ⇆ ꞁ

PUTTENHAM
Map 04 SU94

Puttenham ☎ Guildford (0483) 810498
Picturesque tree-lined heathland course offering testing golf, easy walking.
18 holes, 6214yds, Par 71, SSS 70.
Club membership 650.
Visitors with member only weekends. Must contact in advance.
Societies must apply in advance.
Green Fees £27 per day; £21 per round.
Facilities ⊗ ⅏ 🛍 💺 ⚑ 🏌 Gary Simmons.
Location 1m SE on B3000
Hotel ★★★61% Bush Hotel, The Borough, FARNHAM ☎ (0252) 715237 66 ⇆ ꞁ

REDHILL
Map 04 TQ25

Redhill & Reigate ☎ Reigate (0737) 240777
Parkland course.
18 holes, 5238yds, Par 67, SSS 66.
Club membership 600.
Visitors may not play before 11am weekends or after 2pm Sun (Jun-Sep). Must contact in advance.
Societies must apply in writing.
Green Fees not confirmed.
Facilities ⊗ ⅏ by prior arrangement 🛍 💺 ⚑ 🏌 ️ ꞁ Barry Davies.
Location Clarence Rd, Pendelton Rd (1m S on A23)
Hotel ★★★65% Reigate Manor Hotel, Reigate Hill, REIGATE ☎ (0737) 240125 51 ⇆ ꞁ

REIGATE
Map 04 TQ25

Reigate Heath ☎ (0737) 242610 & 226793
Heathland course.
9 holes, 5658yds, Par 67, SSS 67, Course record 67.
Club membership 565.
Visitors with member only weekends & bank holidays. Must contact in advance.
Societies must apply in writing.
Green Fees £28 per day; £20 per round.
Facilities ⊗ ⅏ 🛍 💺 (no catering on Mon) 💺 ⚑ 🏌 ꞁ George Gow.
Location 1.5m W off A25
Hotel ★★★65% Reigate Manor Hotel, Reigate Hill, REIGATE ☎ (0737) 240125 51 ⇆ ꞁ

RIPLEY
Map 04 TQ05

Wisley ☎ (0483) 211022
A 27-hole course designed by Robert Trent Jones Jnr, and the first that this well-known American golf architect has designed in the UK. Penncross Bent grasses have been used to provide a superb playing surface.
The Church: 9 holes, 3355yds, Par 36, SSS 73.
The Mill: 9 holes, 3473yds, Par 36, SSS 73.
The Garden: 9 holes, 3385yds, Par 36, SSS 73.
Club membership 510.
Visitors may only play with member.
Green Fees £35 (£17.50 per 9 holes).
Facilities ⊗ ⅏ 🛍 💺 (with member only) 💺 ⚑ 🏌 ️ ꞁ Bill Reid.
Leisure fishing, snooker, sauna.
Hotel ★★★63% Thatchers Resort Hotel, Epsom Rd, EAST HORSLEY
☎ (0483) 284291 36 ⇆ ꞁ Annexe23 ⇆ ꞁ

TANDRIDGE
Map 05 TQ35

Tandridge ☎ Oxted (0883) 712274
Rolling parkland, Colt designed course; good views.
18 holes, 6250yds, Par 70, SSS 70.
Club membership 750.
Visitors must contact in advance & have handicap certificate. Visitors welcome Mon,Wed,Thu also evening green fees after 5pm Mon-Thu.
Societies must apply in advance.
Green Fees not confirmed.
Facilities ⊗ 🛍 💺 ⚑ 🏌 ️ ꞁ ▶

Location   2m SE junc 6 M25, 1.5m E of Godstone on A25
Hotel   ★★★74% Nutfield Priory, NUTFIELD
           ☎ (0737) 822066 52 ⇆ ⚲

TILFORD   Map 04 SU84

Hankley Common ☎ Frensham (0252) 792493
A natural heathland course subject to wind. Greens are
first rate. The 18th, a long par 4, is most challenging, the
green being beyond a deep chasm which traps any but the
perfect second shot. The 7th is a spectacular one-shotter.
18 holes, 6418yds, Par 71, SSS 71.
Club membership 700.
Visitors   handicap certificate required, restricted to
             afternoons at weekends.
Societies   apply in writing.
Green Fees   £35 per day; £28 per round (£35 weekends
             and bank holidays).
Facilities   ⊗ ⓛ ♥ ♀ ⚘ ☎ ⚲ Peter Stow.
Location   0.75m SE
Hotel   ★★★61% Bush Hotel, The Borough.
             FARNHAM ☎ (0252) 715237 66 ⇆ ⚲

VIRGINIA WATER   Map 04 TQ06

WENTWORTH See page 189

WALTON-ON-THAMES   Map 04 TQ16

Burhill ☎ (0932) 227345
A relatively short and easy parkland course with some
truly magnificent trees. The 18th is a splendid par 4
requiring a well-placed drive and a long firm second.
This course is always in immaculate condition.
18 holes, 6224yds, Par 69, SSS 70.
Club membership 1100.
Visitors   may not play Fri-Sun unless introduced by
             member. Must contact in advance & have
             handicap certificate.
Societies   Wed & Thu only, apply in writing.
Green Fees   on application.
Facilities   ⊗ ⓛ ♥ ♀ ⚘ ☎ ⚲ Lee Johnson.
Leisure   squash, badminton.
Location   Burwood Rd (2m S)
Hotel   ★★★63% Ship Thistle, Monument Green,
             WEYBRIDGE ☎ (0932) 848364 39 ⇆ ⚲

WALTON-ON-THE-HILL   Map 04 TQ25

WALTON HEATH See page 191

WEST BYFLEET   Map 04 TQ06

West Byfleet ☎ Byfleet (0932) 343433
An attractive course set against a background of
woodland and gorse. The 13th is the famous 'pond' shot
with a water hazard and two bunkers fronting the green.
No less than six holes of 420 yards or more.
18 holes, 6211yds, Par 70, SSS 70.
Club membership 650.

Visitors   with member only weekends. Restricted Thu
             (Ladies Day).
Societies   must apply in writing.
Green Fees   £33 per day; £27 per round.
Facilities   ⊗ ⓜ ⓛ ♥ ♀ ⚘ ☎ ⚲ David Regan.
Leisure   snooker.
Location   Sheerwater Rd (W side of village on A245)
Hotel   ★★★63% Thatchers Resort Hotel, Epsom
             Rd, EAST HORSLEY
             ☎ (0483) 284291 36 ⇆ ⚲Annexe23 ⇆ ⚲

WEST END   Map 04 SU96

Windlemere ☎ (0276) 858727
A parkland course, undulating in parts with natural water
hazards. There is also a floodlit driving range.
9 holes, 2673yds, Par 34, Course record 30.
Visitors   no restrictions.
Societies   advisable to contact in advance.
Green Fees   18 holes £13 (£16 weekends); 9 holes £7.50 (£9
             weekends).
Facilities   ⓛ ♥ ♀ ⚘ ☎ ⚙
             ⚲ David Thomas & Alistair Kelso.
Leisure   12 bay driving range.
Location   Windlesham Rd (N side of village off A319)
Hotel   ★★★★(red)♣♣ Pennyhill Park Hotel, London
             Rd, BAGSHOT
             ☎ (0276) 471774 22 ⇆ ⚲Annexe54 ⇆ ⚲

WEYBRIDGE   Map 04 TQ06

St George's Hill ☎ (0932) 842406
Comparable and similar to Wentworth, a feature of this
course is the number of long and difficult par 4s. To
score well it is necessary to place the drive - and long
driving pays handsomely. Walking is hard on this
undulating, heavily wooded course with plentiful heather
and rhododendrons.
A+B Course: 18 holes, 6569yds, Par 70, SSS 71.
A+C Course: 18 holes, 6097yds, Par 70, SSS 69.
B+C Course: 18 holes, 6210yds, Par 70, SSS 70.
Club membership 600.
Visitors   must contact in advance and have a
             handicap certificate.
Societies   must contact in advance.
Green Fees   not confirmed.
Facilities   ⊗ ⓜ by prior arrangement ♥ ♀ ⚘ ☎
             ⚲ A C Rattue.
Location   2m S off B374
Hotel   ★★★63% Ship Thistle, Monument Green,
             WEYBRIDGE ☎ (0932) 848364 39 ⇆ ⚲

WOKING   Map 04 TQ05

Hoebridge Golf Centre ☎ (0483) 722611 & 720256
Three public courses set in parkland on Surrey sand belt. 24-
bay floodlit driving range.
Main Course: 18 holes, 6536yds, Par 72, SSS 71.
Shey Course: 9 holes, 2294yds, Par 33, SSS 32.
Maybury: 18 holes, 2230yds, Par 54.
Club membership 400.
Visitors   welcome every day, course and reservation desk
             open dawn to dusk.   ▶

WENTWORTH CLUB

VIRGINIA WATER   Map O4 TQO6
☎ WENTWORTH (0344) 842201

John Ingham writes: Among the really famous inland courses in England you have to name Wentworth. The challenge, in terms of sheer yards, is enormous. But the qualities go beyond this, and include the atmosphere, the heathland, the silver birch and fairway-side homes.

The West Course is the one every visitor wishes to play. You can't possibly name the best hole. Bernard Gallacher, the course professional, has his view, but you may select the 7th where the drive rolls downhill and the second shot has to be played high up to a stepped green. The closing holes really sort out the best of them too.

The clubhouse offers Country Club facilities not typical of many British golf courses. The pro shop resembles a plush city store; evening hospitality events are frequent and society meetings here are catered for as at few other centres for sport, and it's all done in five-star style. Probably it is during the World Match-Play championship when Wentworth can be seen at its best. The tents are up, the superstars pile in and out of huge cars and the air is one of luxury and opulence.

One of the attractions of Wentworth is that the great players, including Ben Hogan and Sam Snead, have played here. Gary Player has won marvellously at Wentworth, beating Tony Lema after being seven down in the 36-hole match! Great competitors from the past have stamped their mark here. Arnold Palmer, back in the 1960s, beat Neil Coles in the Match-Play final but then, a generation later, faced young Seve Ballesteros. The Spaniard saved his bacon by pitching in for an eagle three at the last against Palmer, to take the clash into extra holes, where he won.

Membership 2200

Visitors weekdays only. Must contact in advance, and have a letter of introduction from their own club or a current handicap certificate

Societies apply in advance (handicap restrictions)

Green fees (per round) West Course £80; East Course £60; Edinburgh Course £60

Facilities ⊗ ⅢⅡ ⅃ ♨ ♀ (all day) breakfast from 7am, (private rooms) ⚓ ▣ ☏ ♟ (Bernard Gallacher) driving range, caddy hire

Leisure tennis (hardcourt & grass), outdoor-heated swimming pool, gymnasium, snooker

Location Wentworth Drive (W side of Virginia Water, at junction of A30 and A329)

54 holes. West Course: 18 holes, 6945yds, Par 73, SSS 74, Course record 63 (Wayne Riley) East Course: 18 holes, 6176yds, Par 68, SSS 70, Course record 62 Edinburgh: 18 holes, 6979yds, Par 72, SSS 73, Course record 68

WHERE TO STAY AND EAT NEARBY

HOTELS:
ASCOT
★★★★ 62% The Berystede, Bagshot Rd, Sunninghill. ☎ (0344) 23311 91 ⇦ ♠ European cuisine

★★71% Highclere, 19 Kings Road, Sunninghill. ☎ (0344) 25220. 12 ⇦ ♠ European cuisine

BAGSHOT
★★★★(red)❀❀❀ ♨♨ 76% Pennyhill Park, London Rd. ☎ (0276) 471774 22 ⇦ ♠ Annexe 54 ⇦ ♠ . English & French cuisine

RESTAURANTS:
BRAY
✗✗✗✗❀❀❀❀ The Waterside, River Cottage, Ferry Rd. ☎ Maidenhead (0628) 20691. French cuisine

EGHAM
✗✗❀❀ La Bonne Franquette, 5 High St. ☎ (0784) 439494. French cuisine

Societies   Mon-Fri only, contact Valerie Statham for reservations.
Green Fees   Main: £13. Shey: £7. Maybury: £6 prices are per round.
Facilities   ⊗ ⅲ ᴸ ▣ ♀ ♁ ⌂ ⛳ ℂ Tim Powell.
Leisure   snooker, 24 bay floodlit golf range.
Location   Old Woking Rd, Old Woking (1m SE of Woking Rd)
Hotel   ★★★★(red)♨♨ Pennyhill Park Hotel, London Rd, BAGSHOT
                 ☎ (0276) 471774 22 ⇄ ℂAnnexe54 ⇄ ℂ

Pyrford ☎ Guildford (0483) 723555 & 751070
Opened in September 1993 this inland links style course was designed by Peter Alliss and Clive Clark. Set between Surrey woodlands, the fairways weave between 23 acres of water courses while the greens and tees are connected by rustic bridges. The signature hole is the Par 5 9th at 595 yards, with a dogleg and final approach over water and a sand shelf.
18 holes, 6201yds, Par 72.
Club membership 650.
Visitors   must contact in advance to book tee time. Corporate and societies welcome tel: (0483) 772223
Societies   must contact in advance.
Green Fees   £35 per 18 holes (£30 bank holidays and weekends).Inclusive meal deals available.
Facilities   ⊗ ⅲ ᴸ ▣ ♀ ♁ ⌂ ⛳ ℂ Jeremy Bennett.
Leisure   practice grounds,buggies/power trolleys.
Location   Warren Ln, Pyrford (off A3 Ripley to Pyrford)
Hotel   ★★★★(red)♨♨ Pennyhill Park Hotel, London Rd, BAGSHOT
                 ☎ (0276) 471774 22 ⇄ ℂAnnexe54 ⇄ ℂ

> *Worplesdon* ☎ (0483) 472277
> The scene of the celebrated mixed-foursomes competition. Accurate driving is essential on this heathland course. The short 10th across a lake from tee to green is a notable hole, and the 18th provides a wonderfully challenging par-4 finish.
> *18 holes, 6440yds, Par 71, SSS 71, Course record 64.*
> *Club membership 590.*
> **Visitors**   must play with member at weekends & bank holidays. Must contact in advance and have a handicap certificate.
> **Societies**   must contact in writing.
> **Green Fees** not confirmed.
> **Facilities** ♁ ⌂ ⛳ ℂ J Christine.
> **Location**   Heath House Rd (3.5m SW off B380)
> **Hotel**   ★★★★(red)♨♨ Pennyhill Park Hotel, London Rd, BAGSHOT
>   ☎ (0276) 471774 22 ⇄ ℂAnnexe54 ⇄ ℂ

WOLDINGHAM   Map 05 TQ35

North Downs ☎ (0883) 652057
Downland course, 850 ft above sea-level, with several testing holes.
18 holes, 5843yds, Par 69, SSS 68.
Club membership 700.
Visitors   must play with member at weekends and bank holidays. Must contact in advance and have a handicap certificate.
Societies   must contact in writing.
Green Fees   not confirmed.

Facilities   ⊗ ⅲ ᴸ ▣ ♀ ♁ ⌂ ℂ
Location   Northdown Rd (0.75m S)
Hotel   ★★★65% Kings Arms Hotel, Market Square, WESTERHAM ☎ (0959) 562990 16 ⇄ ℂ

TYNE & WEAR

BACKWORTH   Map 12 NZ37

Backworth ☎ 091-268 1048
Parkland course with easy walking, natural hazards and good scenery.
9 holes, 5930yds, Par 71, SSS 69.
Club membership 500.
Visitors   may not play Sat or Tue & Thu after 5pm & Sun mornings.
Societies   must contact in writing.
Green Fees   £12 per round (£15 weekends & bank holidays).
Facilities   ᴸ ▣ ♀ ♁
Leisure   archery, bowls, cricket, football.
Location   The Hall (W side of town on B1322)
Hotel   ★★★★55% Holiday Inn, Great North Rd, SEATON BURN ☎ 091-236 5432 150 ⇄ ℂ

BIRTLEY   Map 12 NZ25

Birtley ☎ 091-410 2207
Parkland course.
9 holes, 5660yds, Par 66, SSS 67, Course record 63.
Club membership 270.
Visitors   must play with member at weekends.
Societies   apply in writing, must contact 1 month in advance in summer.
Green Fees   not confirmed.
Facilities   ⅲ by prior arrangement ᴸ ▣ ♀ ♁
Location   Portobello Rd
Hotel   B Forte Posthouse, Emerson District 5, WASHINGTON ☎ 091-416 2264 138 ⇄ ℂ

BOLDON   Map 12 NZ36

Boldon ☎ 091-536 5360 & 091-536 4182
Parkland links course, easy walking, distant sea views, windy.
18 holes, 6362yds, Par 72, SSS 70, Course record 67.
Club membership 700.
Visitors   may not play after 3.30pm at weekends & bank holidays. Must contact in advance.
Societies   must contact in advance.
Green Fees   not confirmed.
Facilities   ⊗ ⅲ ᴸ ▣ ♀ ♁ ⌂ ⛳ ℂ
Leisure   snooker.
Location   Dipe Ln, East Boldon (S side of village off A184)
Hotel   ★★★65% Friendly Hotel, Witney Way, Boldon Business Park, BOLDON
                 ☎ 091-519 1999 84 ⇄ ℂ

WALTON HEATH

WALTON-ON-THE-HILL
☎ TADWORTH (0737) 812380

Map O4 TQ25

John Ingham writes: Several historic names are etched on the Honours Board at Walton Heath, almost 700 feet above sea level. The rare atmosphere here is justified because these Surrey courses can claim to be the toughest inland examination in Britain. Walton Heath is famous for staging the Ryder Cup and the European Open Championship but older players will remember it best for the Match-Play Championship battles that involved Sir Henry Cotton and Dai Rees as well as huge money matches that brought names such as Bobby Locke and Fred Daly to public prominence.

Once owned by the News of the World newspaper, MP's, Lords and significant members of the press would be invited down to Walton Heath by Sir Emsley Carr, who was one of the first to employ a lady as Secretary and manager of a well-known championship venue.

The courses were designed in 1903 by Herbert Fowler , who used natural hollows and channels for drainage, so the fairways equal the best on any seaside links and quickly dry out, even after a severe storm.

Erratic shots, wide of the prepared surface, are wickedly punished and weekend players are tormented in awful fashion. Nobody escapes undamaged from the gorse and bracken but it is the heather, with those tough stems, that really snarl up any attempt at an over-ambitious recovery shot. So be advised - if you're caught off the fairway, don't attempt anything fancy. Play back on the shortest route to comparative security.

While the Old Course is most frequently played by visitors, the New Course is very challenging and requires all the subtle shots required if you are to get the ball near the hole. And, in the clubhouse, they serve a spectacular lunch.

Membership 900

Visitors	weekdays only. Must contact in advance and have a handicap certificate
Societies	telephone in advance or apply in writing
Green fees	Weekdays only -per day: £57 before 11.30, £47 after 11.30
Facilities	⊗ 🍽 (3.30-7pm) ☘ ⛳ 🏠 🏌 ♟ (Ken Macpherson)
Location	Deans Lane (SE side of village, off B2032)

36 holes. Old Course: 18 holes, 6801yds, Par 72, SSS 73, Course record 65 (Peter Townsend). New Course: 18 holes, 6609 yds, Par 72, SSS 72, Course record 64 (Clive Clark)

WHERE TO STAY AND EAT NEARBY

HOTELS:
BURGH HEATH
★★ 60% Heathside, Brighton Rd. ☎ (0737) 353355. 73 ⇄ ↾
English & French cuisine

DORKING
★★★★ 62% The Burford Bridge, Burford Bridge, Box Hill (2m NE A24) ☎ (0306) 884561. 48 ⇄ ↾

REIGATE
★★★ 65% Reigate Manor, Reigate Hill. ☎ (0737) 240125. 51 ⇄ ↾
English & French cuisine

STOKE D'ABERNON
★★★✦ 68% Woodlands Park, Woodlands Ln. ☎ Oxshott (0372) 843933. 59(58 ⇄ ↾).
English & French cuisine

RESTAURANTS:
DORKING
✕✕✦✦ Partners West Street, 2-4 West St. ☎ (0306) 882826. French cuisine

SUTTON
✕✦Partners Brasserie, 23 Stonecot Hill. ☎ 081-644 7743. English & French cuisine

CHOPWELL
Map 12 NZ15

Garesfield ☎ (0207) 561278
Undulating parkland course with good views and picturesque woodland surroundings.
18 holes, 6603yds, Par 72, SSS 72.
Club membership 720.
Visitors weekends after 4pm only, unless with member. Must contact in advance.
Societies must contact in advance.
Green Fees not confirmed.
Facilities ⊗ & ⅏ by prior arrangement ᠘ ♨ ♀ ♫ ⌂
Location 0.5m N
Hotel ★★★62% Swallow Hotel, Newgate Arcade, NEWCASTLE UPON TYNE ☎ 091-232 5025 93 ➪ ⋔

FELLING
Map 12 NZ26

Heworth ☎ (0632) 692137
Fairly flat, parkland course.
18 holes, 6437yds, Par 71, SSS 71, Course record 69.
Club membership 500.
Visitors may not play Sat & before 10am Sun.
Societies must apply in writing.
Green Fees not confirmed.
Facilities ⊗ & ⅏ by prior arrangement ᠘ ♨ ♀ ♫
Location Gingling Gate, Heworth (On A195, 0.5m NW of junc with A1(M))
Hotel B Forte Posthouse, Emerson District 5, WASHINGTON ☎ 091-416 2264 138 ➪ ⋔

GATESHEAD
Map 12 NZ26

Ravensworth ☎ 091-487 6014
Moorland/parkland course 600 ft above sea-level with fine views. Testing 13th hole (par 3).
18 holes, 5872yds, Par 68, SSS 68.
Club membership 600.
Visitors no restrictions.
Societies must contact in advance.
Green Fees not confirmed.
Facilities ⊗ ⅏ ᠘ ♨ (lunch/dinner by prior arrangement ex Mon) ♀ ♫ ⌂ ⅂ David Race.
Location Moss Heaps, Wrekenton (3m SE off A6127)
Hotel ★★★66% Swallow Hotel, High West St, GATESHEAD ☎ 091-477 1105 103 ➪ ⋔

GOSFORTH
Map 12 NZ26

Gosforth ☎ 091-285 3495
Parkland course with natural water hazards, easy walking.
18 holes, 6043yds, Par 69, SSS 69.
Club membership 500.
Visitors may not play on Tue (Ladies Day).
Societies must contact in advance.
Green Fees £18 per day.
Facilities ⊗ ⅏ ᠘ ♨ (all catering by prior arrangement) ♀ ♫ ⌂ ⅂ G Garland.
Location Broadway East (N side of town centre off A6125)
Hotel ★★★★67% Swallow Gosforth Park Hotel, High Gosforth Park, Gosforth, NEWCASTLE UPON TYNE ☎ 091-236 4111 178 ➪ ⋔

Gosforth Park ☎ 091-236 4480
A flat, tree-lined parkland course with a burn running through many holes. There is also a 30-bay covered floodlit driving range and a 9-hole pitch-putt.
18 holes, 6100yds, Par 71, SSS 70.
Club membership 650.
Visitors must contact in advance.
Societies must apply in writing.
Green Fees £12 (£14 weekends).
Facilities ⊗ ⅏ by prior arrangement ᠘ ♨ ♀ ♫ ⌂ ⅂ ⅂ Brian Rumney.
Leisure floodlit driving range, pitch & putt.
Location Parklands Golf Club, High Gosforth Park (2m N on B1318 off A6125)
Hotel ★★★★67% Swallow Gosforth Park Hotel, High Gosforth Park, Gosforth, NEWCASTLE UPON TYNE ☎ 091-236 4111 178 ➪ ⋔

HOUGHTON-LE-SPRING
Map 12 NZ35

Houghton-le-Spring ☎ 091-584 1198
Hilly, downland course with natural slope hazards.
18 holes, 6416yds, Par 72, SSS 71.
Club membership 600.
Visitors may not play on Sun/competition days.
Societies must contact secretary in advance.
Green Fees not confirmed.
Facilities ⊗ (ex Thu) ⅏ (ex Wed & Thu) ᠘ ♨ ♀ ♫ ⌂ ⅂ ⅂ Stephen Bradbury.
Location Copt Hill (0.5m E on B1404)
Hotel ★★59% Chilton Lodge Country Pub & Motel, Black Boy Rd, Chilton Moor, Fencehouses, HOUGHTON-LE-SPRING ☎ 091-385 2694 18 ➪ ⋔

NEWCASTLE UPON TYNE
Map 12 NZ26

City of Newcastle ☎ 091-285 1775
A well-manicured parkland course in the Newcastle suburbs, subject to wind.
18 holes, 6508yds, Par 72, SSS 71, Course record 67.
Club membership 570.
Visitors no restrictions.
Societies by arrangement.
Green Fees £19 per day (£22 weekends & bank holidays).
Facilities ⊗ ⅏ ᠘ ♨ ♀ ♫ ⌂ ⅂ Anthony J Matthew.
Leisure snooker.
Location Three Mile Bridge (3m N on A1)
Hotel ★★★64% Airport Moat House Hotel, Woolsington, NEWCASTLE UPON TYNE AIRPORT ☎ (0661) 824911 100 ➪ ⋔

Newcastle United ☎ 091-286 4693
Moorland course with natural hazards.
18 holes, 6484yds, Par 72, SSS 71, Course record 68.
Club membership 500.
Visitors must play with member at weekends.
Societies must contact in writing.
Green Fees not confirmed.
Facilities ⊗ ⅏ ᠘ ♨ ♀ ♫ ⌂
Location Ponteland Rd, Cowgate (1.25m NW of city centre off A6127)

Hotel ★★★62% Imperial Swallow Hotel, Jesmond Rd, NEWCASTLE UPON TYNE
☎ 091-281 5511 125 ⇄ ⁅

Northumberland ☎ 091-236 2498
Many golf courses have been sited inside racecourses, although not so many survive today. One which does is the Northumberland Club's course at High Gosforth Park. Naturally the course is flat but there are plenty of mounds and other hazards to make it a fine test of golf. It should be said that not all the holes are within the confines of the racecourse, but both inside and out there are some good holes. This is a Championship course.
18 holes, 6629yds, Par 72, SSS 72.
Club membership 550.
Visitors may not play at weekends or competition days. Must contact in advance and have handicap certificate.
Societies must apply in writing.
Green Fees £35 per day; £30 per round.
Facilities ♀⚐
Location High Gosforth Park (4m N of city centre off A1)
Hotel ★★★★67% Swallow Gosforth Park Hotel, High Gosforth Park, Gosforth, NEWCASTLE UPON TYNE ☎ 091-236 4111 178 ⇄ ⁅

Parklands ☎ 091-236 4867 & 091-236 4480
Parklands course is set in pleasant parkland with challenging shots around and sometimes over attractive water hazards. The first 9 holes are easier but the second 9 test even the most experienced golfer.
18 holes, 6060yds, Par 71, SSS 69.
Club membership 750.
Visitors a daily start sheet operates with bookings taken from 4.30pm the previous day during weekdays, and from 8am Fri & Sat for weekends.
Societies by prior arrangement with club secretary.
Green Fees £13 per 18 holes (£15 weekends & bank holidays).
Facilities ⊗ � by prior arrangement ⓑ ⚑ ♀⚐ ⌂ ⁅ Brian Rumney.
Leisure two tier 45 bay floodlit driving range.
Location High Gosforth Park (3m N, at the end A1 Western by Pass)
Hotel ★★★★67% Swallow Gosforth Park Hotel, High Gosforth Park, Gosforth, NEWCASTLE UPON TYNE ☎ 091-236 4111 178 ⇄ ⁅

Westerhope ☎ 091-286 9125
Attractive parkland course with tree-lined fairways, and easy walking. Good open views towards the airport.
18 holes, 6468yds, Par 72, SSS 71.
Club membership 778.
Visitors with member only at weekends.
Societies must apply in writing.
Green Fees not confirmed.
Facilities ⊗ ⍩ ⓑ ⚑ ♀⚐ ⌂ ⁅ Nigel Brown.
Location Bowerbank, Whorlton Grange, Westerhope (4.5m NW of city centre off B6324)
Hotel ★★★★67% Swallow Gosforth Park Hotel, High Gosforth Park, Gosforth, NEWCASTLE UPON TYNE ☎ 091-236 4111 178 ⇄ ⁅

RYTON Map 12 NZ16

Ryton ☎ 091-413 3737
Parkland course.
18 holes, 5968yds, Par 70, SSS 68.
Club membership 400.
Visitors with member only at weekends.
Societies apply in writing to secretary.
Green Fees £18 per day; £12 per round (£16 per round weekends & bank holidays).
Facilities ⊗ by prior arrangement ⍩ ⓑ ⚑ ♀⚐
Location Clara Vale (NW side of town off A695)
Hotel ★★★70% Gibside Arms Hotel, Front St, WHICKHAM ☎ 091-488 9292 45 ⇄ ⁅

Tyneside ☎ 091-413 2742
Open parkland course, not heavily bunkered. Water hazard, hilly, practice area.
18 holes, 6042yds, Par 70, SSS 69, Course record 65.
Club membership 900.
Visitors must have a handicap certificate. Must contact in advance to play at weekends.
Societies must apply in writing.
Green Fees £22 per day; £18 per round (£28 per round weekends).
Facilities ⊗ ⍩ ⓑ ⚑ ♀⚐ ⌂ ⁅ Malcolm Gunn.
Location Westfield Ln (NW side of town off A695)
Hotel ★★★70% Gibside Arms Hotel, Front St, WHICKHAM ☎ 091-488 9292 45 ⇄ ⁅

SOUTH SHIELDS Map 12 NZ36

South Shields ☎ 091-456 0475
A slightly undulating downland course on a limestone base ensuring good conditions underfoot. Open to strong winds, the course is testing but fair. There are fine views of the coastline.
18 holes, 6264yds, Par 71, SSS 70.
Club membership 800.
Visitors must contact in advance and have a letter of introduction.
Societies by arrangement.
Green Fees £20 per day (£25 weekends & bank holidays).
Facilities ⊗ ⍩ ⓑ ⚑ ♀⚐ ⌂ ⁅ Gary Parsons.
Leisure caddy cars, pool table.
Location Cleadon Hills (SE side of town centre off A1300)
Hotel ★★★60% Sea Hotel, Sea Rd, SOUTH SHIELDS ☎ 091-427 0999 33 ⇄ ⁅

Whitburn ☎ 091-529 2144 & 091-529 4944
Parkland course.
18 holes, 5773yds, Par 69, SSS 68.
Club membership 650.
Visitors restricted weekends, Tue & competition days.
Societies must apply in writing.
Green Fees £15 per day (£20 weekends & bank holidays).
Facilities ⊗ ⍩ ⓑ ⚑ ♀⚐ ⌂ ⁅ David Stephenson.
Leisure snooker.
Location Lizard Ln (2.5m SE off A183)
Hotel ★★★60% Swallow Hotel, Queen's Pde, Seaburn, SUNDERLAND ☎ 091-529 2041 66 ⇄ ⁅

SUNDERLAND   Map 12 NZ35

Wearside ☎ 091-534 2518
Open, undulating parkland course rolling down to the
River Wear and beneath the shadow of the famous
Penshaw Monument built on the lines of an Athenian
temple it is a well-known landmark. Two ravines cross
the course presenting a variety of challenging holes.
18 holes, 6373yds, Par 71, SSS 74, Course record 64.
Club membership 729.
Visitors   may not play before 9.30am & after 4pm.
                  Must have an introduction from own club.
Societies   must apply in writing.
Green Fees   not confirmed.
Facilities   ⊗ ≡ by prior arrangement 🛍 ☕ ♀ 🛅 🏠
                  ♺ Steven Wynn.
Location   Coxgreen (3.5m W off A183)
Hotel   ★★★★60% Swallow Hotel, Queen's Pde,
                  Seaburn, SUNDERLAND
                  ☎ 091-529 2041 66 ⇆ ☎

TYNEMOUTH   Map 12 NZ36

Tynemouth ☎ 091-257 4578
Well-drained parkland/downland course, easy walking.
18 holes, 6082yds, Par 70, SSS 69.
Club membership 824.
Visitors   must play with member weekends & bank
                  holidays.
Societies   must contact in writing.
Green Fees   not confirmed.
Facilities   ⊗ 🛍 ☕ ♀ 🛅 🏠 ♺ J P McKenna.
Location   Spital Dene (0.5m W)
Hotel   ★★★58% Park Hotel, Grand Pde,
                  TYNEMOUTH
                  ☎ 091-257 1406 49rm(43 ⇆ ☎)

WALLSEND   Map 12 NZ26

Wallsend ☎ 091-262 1973
Parkland course.
18 holes, 6608yds, Par 72, SSS 72, Course record 68.
Club membership 750.
Visitors   may not play before 12.30pm weekends.
Societies   must apply in writing.
Green Fees   £10.50 per round (£12.50 weekends & bank
                  holidays).
Facilities   🛍 ☕ ♀ 🛅 🏠 ♺ Ken Phillips.
Location   Rheydt Av, Bigges Main (NW side of town
                  centre off A193)
Hotel   ★★★60% Newcastle Moat House, Coast Rd,
                  WALLSEND
                  ☎ 091-262 8989 & 091-262 7044 147 ⇆ ☎

WASHINGTON   Map 12 NZ25

Washington Moat House ☎ 091-417 2626
Championship-standard course. Also a 9-hole (par 3) course,
putting green and 21-bay floodlit driving range. 'Bunkers
Bar' at the 10th tee is one of the few 'spike' bars in the
country.
18 holes, 6267yds, Par 73, SSS 71.
Club membership 650.

INTERNATIONAL HOTELIERS

ⱳashingtonˀ Moaᴛ House˞

★ 106 en-suite Bedrooms
★ Luxurious Leisure Club with Pool,
   Sauna, Sunbed, Gymnasium,
   Jacuzzi and Squash.
★ 18 Hole Golf Course, 9 Hole Par 3
   Course and 21 Bay Floodlit Driving
   Range.
★ Restaurant – offering extensive
   Carvery and à La Carte Menus.
★ Abrahams Cocktail Bar.
★ Bunkers Sportsmans Bar.
★ Conference and Banqueting facilities
   for up to 200.
★ Special rates available for golfing
   weekends or Society days.

Washington
(0191) 4172626

Stone Cellar Road, High Usworth, District 12
Washington, Tyne & Wear NE37 1PH

Visitors   must contact in advance. May not play before
                  10am or between noon & 2pm at weekends.
Societies   must apply in writing.
Green Fees   £16 per round (£23 weekends).
Facilities   ⊗ ≡ 🛍 ☕ ♀ 🛅 🏠 ⛳ 🏌 ♺ Warren Marshall.
Leisure   heated indoor swimming pool, squash, sauna,
                  solarium, gymnasium, 21 bay floodlit driving
                  range.
Location   Stone Cellar Rd, High Usworth
Hotel   ★★★65% Washington Moat House, Stone
                  Cellar Rd, District 12, High Usworth,
                  WASHINGTON ☎ 091-417 2626 105 ⇆ ☎

WHICKHAM   Map 12 NZ26

Whickham ☎ 091-488 7309
Parkland course, some uphill walking, fine views.
18 holes, 6129yds, Par 68, SSS 69, Course record 61.
Club membership 600.
Visitors   must have an introduction from own club.
Societies   by arrangement.
Green Fees   not confirmed.
Facilities   ⊗ & ≡ by prior arrangement 🛍 ☕ ♀ 🛅 🏠
Leisure   snooker.
Location   Hollinside Park (1.5m S)
Hotel   ★★★66% Swallow Hotel, High West St,
                  GATESHEAD ☎ 091-477 1105 103 ⇆ ☎

For an explanation of symbols and
abbreviations, see page 5

WHITLEY BAY   Map 12 NZ37

Whitley Bay ☎ 091-252 0180
Downland course close to the sea. A stream runs through the
undulating terrain.
18 holes, 6617yds, Par 71, SSS 72, Course record 66.
Club membership 700.
Visitors with member only at weekends & bank holidays.
Societies Mon-Fri, by arrangement.
Green Fees £25 per day; £18 per round.
Facilities ⊗ ⅏ ⅃ ⚑ (no catering Mon) ⚑ ⚑ ⚑
⚑ Gary Shipley.
Location Claremont Rd (NW side of town centre off
A1148)
Hotel ★★59% Holmedale Hotel, 106 Park Av,
WHITLEY BAY
☎ 091-251 3903 & 091-253 1162 18 ⇔ ⚑

W A R W I C K S H I R E

ATHERSTONE   Map 04 SP39

Atherstone ☎ (0827) 713110
Parkland course, established in 1894 and laid out on hilly
ground.
18 holes, 6235yds, Par 73, SSS 70.
Club membership 350.
Visitors handicap certificate required. With member only
weekends (ex Sun) & bank holidays.
Societies weekdays only, by prior arrangement with
secretary. Handicap certificates are required.
Green Fees £17 per day/round (£22 bank holidays).
Facilities ⊗ ⅏ ⅃ ⚑ ⚑ ⚑ ⚑
Location The Outwoods, Coleshill Rd (0.5m S on B4116)
Hotel ★★66% Old Red Lion Hotel, Long St,
ATHERSTONE ☎ (0827) 713156 22 ⇔ ⚑

BIDFORD-ON-AVON   Map 04 SP15

Bidford Grange ☎ (0789) 490319
Designed by Howard Swan & Paul Tillman, this very long,
championship standard course is built to represent a links course and
is fully irrigated. There are water hazards on the first 7 holes, and
particularly challenging holes on the 16th (223yds,par 3), 8th (600yds,
par 5),and an uphill par 4 at the 13th.
18 holes, 7233yds, Par 72, SSS 74.
Club membership 500.

Visitors no restrictions.
Societies apply in writing or phone, minimum 12,
maximum 36.
Green Fees £25 per day; £16 per 18 holes.
Facilities ⅃ ⚑ ⚑ ⚑ ⚑
Leisure fishing.
Location Stratford Rd (4m W of Stratford upon Avon,
B439)
Hotel ★★★75% Salford Hall Hotel, ABBOTS
SALFORD
☎ (0386) 871300 14 ⇔ ⚑Annexe19 ⇔ ⚑

BRANDON   Map 04 SP47

City of Coventry-Brandon Wood ☎ Coventry (0203)
543141
Municipal parkland course surrounded by fields and bounded
by River Avon on east side. Floodlit driving range.
18 holes, 6610yds, Par 72, SSS 72, Course record 68.
Club membership 580.
Visitors telephone for details.
Societies telephone in advance.
Green Fees £8.25 per round (£10.85 weekends).
Facilities catering by arrangement ⚑ ⚑ ⚑
⚑ Chris Gledhill.
Leisure driving range, floodlit bays.
Location Brandon Ln (1m W)
Hotel ★★★61% The Brandon Hall, Main St,
BRANDON ☎ (0203) 542571 60 ⇔ ⚑

COLESHILL   Map 04 SP28

Maxstoke Park ☎ (0675) 464915
Parkland course with easy walking. Numerous trees and a
lake form natural hazards.
18 holes, 6442yds, Par 71, SSS 71.
Club membership 600.
Visitors with member only at weekends & bank holidays.
Societies must telephone in advance.
Green Fees £25 per round.
Facilities ⊗ ⅃ ⚑ ⚑ ⚑ ⚑ Neil McEwan.
Location Castle Ln (2m E)
Hotel ★★63% Coleshill Hotel, 152 High St,
COLESHILL
☎ (0675) 465527 15 ⇔ ⚑Annexe8 ⇔ ⚑

KENILWORTH   Map 04 SP27

Kenilworth ☎ (0926) 58517
Parkland course in open hilly situation. Club founded in
1887.
18 holes, 6413yds, Par 73, SSS 71, Course record 67.
Club membership 725.

▶

Where golf is just the beginning . . .

Nestling into 240 acres of Warwickshire and Northamptonshire countryside, close to the M1 and
M40 motorways, Hellidon offers the ultimate in leisure facilities but with that personal touch that
only a small, luxury hotel can offer.
Spectacular 18-hole, 6,700 yard championship golf course designed to provide a challenge to both
experienced and novice golfers alike. Company and society golfing days. Golfing breaks.
Residential golf tuition. Golf tuition. Golf and leisure memberships. Weekend and midweek
breaks. Luxury weekends. Conferences and incentives. Corporate entertainment. Wedding
receptions. Special celebrations. 9 more holes opening Summer '94.

Hellidon Lakes
HOTEL & COUNTRY CLUB

★★★★ ⚙ 66%

The Hellidon Lakes Hotel & Country Club, Hellidon, Daventry, Northants NN11 6LN
Tel: (01327) 62550 Fax: (01327) 62559   *See gazetteer under Northamptonshire*

Visitors welcome except competition days. Must contact in advance.
Societies apply in writing.
Green Fees £26 per day/round (£37 weekends).
Facilities ⊗ 〗ⓑ 🖫 ♀ ⚘ 🖾 ⌁ 𝄞 Steven Yates.
Leisure snooker.
Location Crew Ln (0.5m NE)
Hotel ★★64% Clarendon House Hotel, Old High St, KENILWORTH ☎ (0926) 57668 31 ⇆ 🏌

LEA MARSTON   Map 04 SP29

Lea Marston Hotel & Leisure Complex ☎ Curdworth (0675) 470707
Par 3, 'pay-and-play' course, with water hazards, out of bounds, and large bunkers. The venue for the past two years of the Midlands Professional Par 3 Competition. Golf driving range.
9 holes, 783yds, Par 27.
Visitors no restrictions.
Societies must telephone in advance.
Green Fees not confirmed.
Facilities ⊗ 〗ⓑ 🖫 ♀ 🖾 ⌁ 🏊
   𝄞 Andrew Jinks & Neil McEwan.
Leisure hard tennis courts, sauna, solarium, gymnasium.
Location Haunch Ln
Hotel ★★★68% Lea Marston Hotel & Leisure Complex, Haunch Ln, LEA MARSTON ☎ (0675) 470468 22 ⇆ 🏌

LEAMINGTON SPA   Map 04 SP36

Leamington & County ☎ (0926) 425961
Undulating parkland course with extensive views.
18 holes, 6424yds, Par 71, SSS 71.
Club membership 700.
Visitors no restrictions.
Societies telephone in advance.
Green Fees £30 per day; £25 per round (£80/£40 weekends).
Facilities ⊗ 〗ⓑ 🖫 ♀ ⚘ 🖾 𝄞 Iain Grant.
Leisure snooker.
Location Golf Ln, Whitnash (S side of town centre)
Hotel ★★★59% Manor House Hotel, Avenue Rd, LEAMINGTON SPA ☎ (0926) 423251 53 ⇆ 🏌

Newbold Comyn ☎ (0926) 421157
Municipal parkland course with hilly front nine. The par 4, 9th is a 467-yd testing hole.
18 holes, 6315yds, Par 70, SSS 70, Course record 69.
Club membership 420.
Visitors no restrictions.
Societies apply to professional.
Green Fees £9 per round.
Facilities ⚘ 🖾 ⌁ 𝄞 Don Knight.
Leisure heated indoor swimming pool, gymnasium.
Location Newbold Ter East (0.75m E of town centre off B4099)
Hotel ★★★59% Manor House Hotel, Avenue Rd, LEAMINGTON SPA ☎ (0926) 423251 53 ⇆ 🏌

LEEK WOOTON   Map 04 SP26

The Warwickshire ☎ (0926) 409409
Opened in 1993, this is an unusual championship standard course. Designed by Karl Litten, the 36 holes are laid out as four interchangeable loops of 9 holes to create six contrasting yet superb courses in a parkland and woodland setting.
South East: 18 holes, 6977yds, Par 72, SSS 73.
North West: 18 holes, 7178yds, Par 72, SSS 74.
Par 3: 9 holes, 1133yds, Par 27.
Club membership 750.
Visitors valid handicap certificate required.
Societies apply by telephone or letter.
Green Fees £35 per 18 holes; £4 per 9 holes.
Facilities ⊗ 〗ⓑ 🖫 ♀ ⚘ 🖾 𝄞 𝄞 Steve Hutchinson.
Leisure caddy cars, trolleys, driving range.
Location Off A46
Hotel ★★58% Warwick Arms Hotel, High St, WARWICK ☎ (0926) 492759 35 ⇆ 🏌

NUNEATON   Map 04 SP39

Nuneaton ☎ (0203) 347810
Undulating moorland and woodland course.
18 holes, 6429yds, Par 71, SSS 71.
Club membership 675.
Visitors with member only at weekends.
Societies apply in writing.
Green Fees not confirmed.
Facilities ⚘ 🖾 𝄞 Graham Davison.
Leisure snooker.
Location Golf Dr, Whitestone (2m SE off B4114)
Hotel ★★63% Longshoot Toby Hotel, Watling St, NUNEATON ☎ (0203) 329711 Annexe47 ⇆ 🏌

Purley Chase ☎ Chapel End (0203) 393118
Meadowland course with tricky water hazards on eight holes and undulating greens. 13-bay driving range.
18 holes, 6772yds, Par 72, SSS 72.
Club membership 700.
Visitors welcome except mornings at weekend & competition days.
Societies by prior arrangement at least 3 weeks in advance.
Green Fees not confirmed.
Facilities ⊗ 〗 (Fri & Sat) ⓑ 🖫 ♀ ⚘ 🖾
   𝄞 David Llewelyn.
Leisure fishing, 13 bay driving range.
Location Ridge Ln (2m NW off B4114)
Hotel ★★63% Longshoot Toby Hotel, Watling St, NUNEATON ☎ (0203) 329711 Annexe47 ⇆ 🏌

RUGBY   Map 04 SP57

Rugby ☎ (0788) 542306
Parkland course with brook running through the middle and crossed by a viaduct.
18 holes, 5457yds, Par 68, SSS 67, Course record 62.
Club membership 550.
Visitors weekends & bank holidays with member only.
Societies apply in writing.
Green Fees £20 per day.

WHITEFIELDS

AA ★★★

HOTEL & GOLF COMPLEX

A modern hotel and golf complex with restaurant and conference facilities situated in an ideal position on the A45. **Newly** constructed 6433 yard, par 71, 18 hole golf course. **Delight** in the varied landscape with several water features and newly planted trees. **Rest** in comfort in one of the 15 en suite twin/double bedrooms with full facilities. **Relax** after a round of golf in Spikes Bar or **unwind** in friendly surroundings of the 19th Hole Lounge, Bar or Conservatory. **Enjoy** a good satisfying meal in the comfortable 19th Hole Restaurant with an excellent choice of well prepared good value for money food. Snacks available during the day from Spikes Bar. **Spacious** conference room ideal for business meetings or seminars. **Large** car park.

**Whitefields Hotel & Golf Complex,
Coventry Road, Thurlaston, Warks CV23 9JR
Telephone: 01788 521800
Fax: 01788 521695**

Facilities	⊗ ⑴ ᴸ ♨ ♀ ⌖ 🏠 ⚐ ⟨ Andy Peach.
Leisure	snooker, caddy carts for hire.
Location	Clifton Rd (1m NE on B5414)
Hotel	★★★60% Grosvenor Hotel, Clifton Rd, RUGBY ☎ (0788) 535686 21 ⇌ 🛉
Additional hotel	★★★66% Whitefields Hotel & Golf Complex, Coventry Rd, Thurlaston, RUGBY ☎ (0788) 521800

STONELEIGH
Map 04 SP37

Stoneleigh Deer Park ☎ Coventry (0203) 639991
Parkland course in old deer park with many mature trees. The River Avon meanders through the course and comes into play on 4 holes. Also 9-hole course.
Tantara: 18 holes, 6083yds, Par 71, SSS 69.
Avon: 9 holes, 1251yds, Par 27.
Club membership 900.

Visitors	must contact in advance, no visitors at weekends except by prior arrangement.
Societies	by prior arrangement.
Green Fees	not confirmed.
Facilities	⊗ ⑴ ᴸ ♨ ♀ ⌖ 🏠 ⟨ Sid Mouland.
Location	The Old Deer Park, Coventry Rd (3m NE of Kenilworth)
Hotel	★★★64% De Montfort Hotel, The Square, KENILWORTH ☎ (0926) 55944 96 ⇌ 🛉

For an explanation of symbols and abbreviations, see page 5

STRATFORD-UPON-AVON
Map 04 SP25

Stratford Oaks ☎ (0789) 731571
American styled, parkland course designed by Howard Swan.
18 holes, 6100yds, Par 71, SSS 69, Course record 66.
Club membership 600.

Visitors	no restrictions.
Societies	telephone in advance.
Green Fees	£15 per round (£22.50 weekends).
Facilities	⊗ ⑴ ᴸ ♨ ♀ ⌖ 🏠 ⚐ ⟨ Fraser Leek.
Location	Bearley Rd, Snitterfield (4m N of Stratford-upon-Avon)
Hotel	★★★74% Windmill Park Hotel & Leisure Club, Warwick Rd, STRATFORD-UPON-AVON ☎ (0789) 731173 100 ⇌

Stratford-upon-Avon ☎ (0789) 205749
Beautiful parkland course. The par 3, 16th is tricky and the par 5, 17th and 18th, provide a tough end.
18 holes, 6309yds, Par 72, SSS 70, Course record 64.
Club membership 750.

Visitors	restricted on Wed. Must contact in advance.
Societies	must telephone in advance.
Green Fees	not confirmed.
Facilities	⊗ ⑴ ᴸ ♨ ♀ ⌖ 🏠 ⚐ ⟨ N D Powell.
Location	Tiddington Rd (0.75m E on B4086)
Hotel	★★★63% Alveston Manor Hotel, Clopton Bridge, STRATFORD-UPON-AVON ☎ (0789) 204581 108 ⇌ 🛉

Welcombe Hotel ☎ (0789) 295252
Wooded parkland course of great character and boasting superb views of the River Avon, Stratford and the Cotswolds. Set within the hotel's 157-acre estate, it has two lakes and water features.
18 holes, 6217yds, Par 70, SSS 70, Course record 67.
Club membership 400.

Visitors	welcome except before 11am weekends. Must contact in advance.
Societies	booking via Hotel.
Green Fees	£35 per day (£40 weekends & bank holidays).
Facilities	⊗ ⑴ ᴸ ♨ ♀ ⌖ 🏠 ⚐ 🍽
Leisure	hard tennis courts, fishing, snooker, putting green, trolleys for hire.
Location	Warwick Rd (1.5m NE off A46)
Hotel	★★★★70% Welcombe Hotel and Golf Course, Warwick Rd, STRATFORD-UPON-AVON ☎ (0789) 295252 76 ⇌ 🛉

See advetisement on page 198

TANWORTH-IN-ARDEN
Map 04 SP17

Ladbrook Park ☎ (0564) 742264
Parkland course lined with trees.
18 holes, 6427yds, Par 71, SSS 71, Course record 65.
Club membership 750.

Visitors	with member only weekends. Must contact in advance & have handicap certificate.
Societies	telephone in advance.
Green Fees	£20/£25 per day/round.
Facilities	⊗ ⑴ ᴸ ♨ ♀ ⌖ 🏠 ⟨ Steve Harrison.
Leisure	snooker.
Location	Poolhead Ln (1m NW)
Hotel	★★★(red)🏨 Nuthurst Grange Country House Hotel, Nuthurst Grange Ln, HOCKLEY HEATH ☎ (0564) 783972 15 ⇌ 🛉

WELCOMBE
★★★★
HOTEL & GOLF COURSE
STRATFORD-UPON-AVON
Warwickshire
Fax:(01789) 414666
Telephone: (01789) 295252   Telex: 31347

The Welcombe, a Jacobean-style luxury hotel, is situated within a 157 acre parkland estate with its own 18-hole Par 70 Golf Course, just 1½ miles from the centre of Stratford-upon-Avon. The club house facilities include a bar with pub style menu, professional shop and changing facilities and is a short walk away from the luxury of this superb hotel.

**Special golfing packages throughout the year –
Rates and brochure on request.**

ORIENT-EXPRESS HOTELS

WARWICK   Map 04 SP26

Warwick ☎ (0926) 494316
Parkland course with easy walking. Driving range with floodlit bays.
9 holes, 2682yds, Par 34, SSS 66, Course record 67.
Club membership 150.
Visitors   welcome except Sun mornings and racedays.
Green Fees not confirmed.
Facilities   🦅♀♨🏠🏌️♂🍴 John Nixon.
Leisure   snooker, floodlit driving range.
Location   The Racecourse (W side of town centre)
Hotel   ★★64% Lord Leycester Hotel, Jury St,
WARWICK ☎ (0926) 491481 52 ⇄ 🐾

WEST MIDLANDS

ALDRIDGE   Map 07 SK00

Druids Heath ☎ (0922) 55595
Testing, undulating heathland course.
18 holes, 6914yds, Par 72, SSS 73.
Club membership 635.
Visitors   must contact in advance & have handicap certificate. Weekend play permitted after 2pm.
Societies   must contact in advance.

Green Fees £25 per day (£32 weekends).
Facilities   ⊗🦅♨♀♨🏠🍴 Mark P Daubney.
Location   Stonnall Rd (NE side of town centre off A454)
Hotel   ★★★66% Fairlawns Hotel, 178 Little Aston Road,Aldridge, WALSALL
☎ (0922) 55122 35 ⇄ 🐾

BIRMINGHAM   Map 07 SP08

Brandhall ☎ 021-552 2195
Private golf club on municipal parkland course, easy walking, good hazards. Testing holes: 1st-502 yds (par 5); 10th-455 yds dog-leg (par 5).
18 holes, 5734yds, Par 70.
Club membership 300.
Visitors   restricted weekends. Must contact in advance.
Societies   by arrangement.
Green Fees not confirmed.
Facilities   ⊗ (ex Tue) 🍴 by prior arrangement ♨ (ex Tue)
♀ (players only) 🏠🏌️♂🍴 G Mercer.
Location   Heron Rd, Oldbury, Warley (5.5m W of city centre off A4123)
Hotel   B Forte Posthouse, Chapel Ln, GREAT BARR
☎ 021-357 7444 192 ⇄ 🐾
Additional hotel   QQ Robin Hood Lodge Hotel, 142 Robin Hood Ln, Hall Green, BIRMINGHAM
☎ 021-778 5307 7rm(1 ⇄ 2 🐾)

Cocks Moors Woods Municipal ☎ 021-444 3584
Tree-lined, parkland course.
18 holes, 5888yds, Par 69, SSS 68.
Club membership 250.

Visitors   no restrictions.
Societies   must contact in advance.
Green Fees not confirmed.
Facilities   ⚑ 🏨 ⛳
Location   Alcester Rd South, Kings Heath (5m S of city centre on A435)
Hotel   B Forte Crest, Smallbrook Queensway, BIRMINGHAM ☎ 021-643 8171 253 ⊨ ⋔

Edgbaston ☎ 021-454 1736
Parkland course in lovely country.
18 holes, 6118yds, Par 69, SSS 69.
Club membership 880.
Visitors   must contact in advance and have handicap certificate.
Societies   must apply in writing.
Green Fees £35 per day (£45 weekends & bank holidays); winter £27.50/£37.50.
Facilities   ⊗ ⽥ by prior arrangement 🏌 ⛳ ♀ ⚑ 🏨 ⛳
     ⛳ Andrew H Bownes.
Leisure   snooker, caddy cars.
Location   Church Rd, Edgbaston (1m S of city centre on B4217 off A38)
Hotel   ★★★★61% Plough & Harrow, Hagley Rd, Edgbaston, BIRMINGHAM
     ☎ 021-454 4111 44 ⊨ ⋔

Great Barr ☎ 021-358 4376
Parkland course with easy walking. Pleasant views of Barr Beacon National Park.
18 holes, 6545yds, Par 73, SSS 72.
Club membership 600.
Visitors   restricted at weekends.
Societies   must contact in writing.
Green Fees not confirmed.
Facilities   ⊗ & ⽥ by prior arrangement 🏌 ⛳ ♀ ⚑ 🏨 ⛳ ⛳
Leisure   snooker.
Location   Chapel Ln, Great Barr (6m N of city centre off A 34)
Hotel   B Forte Posthouse, Chapel Ln, GREAT BARR
     ☎ 021-357 7444 192 ⊨ ⋔

Handsworth ☎ 021-554 0599 & 021-554 3387
Undulating parkland course with some tight fairways but subject to wind.
18 holes, 6267yds, Par 70, SSS 70.
Club membership 820.
Visitors   restricted weekends, bank holidays & Xmas. Must contact in advance and have a handicap certificate.
Societies   Mon-Fri only, must apply in writing.
Green Fees £30 per day Mon-Fri.
Facilities   ⊗ ⽥ & 🏌 (ex Mon) ⛳ ♀ ⚑ 🏨
     ⛳ Lee Bashford.
Leisure   squash, fishing, snooker, bowling green.
Location   Sunningdale Close, Handsworth Wood (3.5m NW of city centre off A4040)
Hotel   ★★★63% West Bromwich Moat House, Birmingham Rd, WEST BROMWICH
     ☎ 021-553 6111 180 ⊨ ⋔

Harborne ☎ 021-427 3058
Parkland course in hilly situation, with brook running through.
18 holes, 6235yds, Par 70, SSS 70, Course record 65.
Club membership 616.

Visitors   must contact in advance & have a handicap certificate; may not play weekends, bank holidays or 27 Dec-1 Jan.
Societies   must telephone in advance.
Green Fees £35 per day; £30 per round.
Facilities   ⊗ ⽥ 🏌 ⛳ (no catering weekends) ♀ ⚑ 🏨 ⛳
     ⛳ Alan Quarterman.
Leisure   snooker.
Location   40 Tennal Rd, Harborne (3.5 m SW of city centre off A4040)
Hotel   ★★★★61% Plough & Harrow, Hagley Rd, Edgbaston, BIRMINGHAM
     ☎ 021-454 4111 44 ⊨ ⋔

Harborne Church Farm ☎ 021-427 1204
Parkland course with water hazards and easy walking. Some holes might prove difficult.
9 holes, 2457yds, Par 66, SSS 63, Course record 63.
Club membership 250.
Visitors   no restrictions.
Societies   must telephone in advance.
Green Fees £6 per round (18 holes); £3 (9 holes).
Facilities   ⊗ ⽥ ⛳ ⚑ 🏨 ⛳ ⛳ Mark J Hampton.
Location   Vicarage Rd, Harborne (3.5m SW of city centre off A4040)
Hotel   ★★★62% Apollo, 243-247 Hagley Rd, Edgbaston, BIRMINGHAM
     ☎ 021-455 0271 126 ⊨ ⋔

Hatchford Brook ☎ 021-743 9821
Fairly flat, municipal parkland course.
18 holes, 6202yds, Par 69, SSS 70, Course record 65.
Club membership 400.   ▶

Robin Hood Lodge Hotel

142 Robin Hood Lane, Hall Green
Birmingham B28 0JX
Telephone: 0121 778 5307

Small, licensed, family run hotel situated in a delightful, quiet residential suburb of Birmingham just 15 minutes from city centre and the NEC. Some rooms en suite, all with hospitality trays, colour TV, clock radio and hair dryer. Evening meals available. Ample car parking. Birmingham International and main line station only 7 miles also golf courses and leisure complexes within easy reach.

Visitors   no restrictions.
Green Fees £7.60 per 18 holes.
Facilities ⊗ ⓑ 🍺 🐍 🏠 ⛳ ⚑ Paul Smith.
Location   Coventry Rd, Sheldon (6m E of city centre on A45)
Hotel   B Forte Posthouse, Coventry Rd, Elmdon,
         ☎ 021-782 8141 136 ⇔ 🐾

Hilltop ☎ 021-554 4463
Testing and hilly municipal parkland course.
18 holes, 6254yds, Par 71, SSS 70.
Club membership 400.
Visitors   no restrictions but booking recommended.
Societies telephone in advance.
Green Fees £7.80 per 18 holes, £4.70 per 9 holes.
Facilities ⊗ Ⅲ 🍺 🐍 🏠 ⛳ ⚑ Kevin Highfield.
Location   Park Ln, Handsworth (3.5m N of city centre off
         A4040)
Hotel   ★★★63% West Bromwich Moat House,
         Birmingham Rd, WEST BROMWICH
         ☎ 021-553 6111 180 ⇔ 🐾

Moseley ☎ 021-444 2115
Parkland course with a lake, pond and stream to provide
natural hazards. The par-3, 5th goes through a cutting in
woodland to a tree and garden-lined amphitheatre, and the
par-4, 6th entails a drive over a lake to a dog-leg fairway.
18 holes, 6285yds, Par 70, SSS 70, Course record 64.
Club membership 600.
Visitors   may not play at weekends.
Societies welcome.
Green Fees £34 per round.
Facilities ⊗ Ⅲ by prior arrangement ⓑ 🍺 ♀ 🐍 🏠
         ⚑ Gary Edge.
Location   Springfield Rd, Kings Heath (4m S of city centre
         on B4146 off A435)
Hotel   ★★65% Norwood Hotel, 87-89 Bunbury Rd,
         Northfield, BIRMINGHAM
         ☎ 021-411 2202 15 ⇔ 🐾

Rose Hill ☎ 021-453 3159
Hilly municipal course overlooking the city.
18 holes, 6010yds, Par 69, SSS 69, Course record 64.
Club membership 300.
Visitors   may not play between 9 & 10.30am weekends.
Societies must contact in advance.
Green Fees not confirmed.
Facilities ⊗ 🍺 🐍 🏠 ⛳ ⚑ Mike March.
Location   Rosehill, Rednal (10m SW of city centre on
         B4096)
Hotel   ★★65% Norwood Hotel, 87-89 Bunbury Rd,
         Northfield, BIRMINGHAM
         ☎ 021-411 2202 15 ⇔ 🐾

Warley ☎ 021-429 2440
Municipal parkland course in Warley Woods.
9 holes, 2606yds, Par 33, SSS 64, Course record 62.
Club membership 150.
Visitors   no restrictions.
Green Fees not confirmed.
Facilities ⊗ ⓑ 🍺 🐍 🏠 ⛳ ⚑ David Owen.
Location   Lightswood Hill, Bearwood (4m W of city
         centre off A456)
Hotel   ★★★62% Apollo, 243-247 Hagley Rd,
         Edgbaston, BIRMINGHAM
         ☎ 021-455 0271 126 ⇔ 🐾

COVENTRY   Map 04 SP37

Ansty Golf Centre ☎ (0203) 621341 & 621305
18-hole Pay and Play course of two 9-hole loops. Membership
competitions for handicaps. Driving range and putting green.
18 holes, 5793yds, Par 71, SSS 69.
Visitors   no restrictions.
Societies welcome.
Green Fees £9 per 18 holes; £4.50 per 9 holes (£11/£6
         weekends).
Facilities Ⅲ ⓑ 🍺 ♀ 🐍 🏠 ⛳ ⚑ Warwick Stevens.
Leisure   18 bay range & putting green.
Location   Brinklow Rd, Ansty (3m from city centre via
         A4600)
Hotel   ★★★70% Ansty Hall, ANSTY
         ☎ (0203) 612222 25 ⇔ 🐾 Annexe6 ⇔ 🐾

Coventry ☎ (0203) 414152
The scene of several major professional events, this
undulating parkland course has a great deal of quality.
More than that, it usually plays its length, and thus
scoring is never easy, as many professionals have found
to their cost.
18 holes, 6613yds, Par 73, SSS 72, Course record 62.
Club membership 760.
Visitors   must contact in advance & have handicap
         certificate, but may not play at weekends.
Societies by arrangement.
Green Fees £30 (weekdays).
Facilities ⊗ Ⅲ by prior arrangement ⓑ 🍺 ♀ 🐍 🏠
         ⚑ Philip Weaver.
Leisure   snooker.
Location   Finham Park (3m S of city centre on A444)
Hotel   ★★★62% Hylands Hotel, Warwick Rd,
         COVENTRY ☎ (0203) 501600 55 ⇔ 🐾

Coventry Hearsall ☎ (0203) 713470
Parkland course with fairly easy walking. A brook provides
an interesting hazard.
18 holes, 5603yds, Par 70, SSS 67.
Club membership 600.
Visitors   with member only at weekends.
Societies by arrangement.
Green Fees not confirmed.
Facilities ⊗ Ⅲ ⓑ 🐍 🏠 ⚑ Jason Sawyer.
Location   Beechwood Av (1.5m SW of city centre off A429)
Hotel   ★★★62% Hylands Hotel, Warwick Rd,
         COVENTRY ☎ (0203) 501600 55 ⇔ 🐾

The Grange ☎ (0203) 451465
Flat parkland course with very tight out of bounds on a
number of holes, and a river which affects play on five of
them. Well-bunkered, with plenty of trees.
9 holes, 6002yds, Par 72, SSS 69.
Club membership 300.
Visitors   may not play after 2pm weekdays or before noon
         on Sun.
Societies must contact in advance.
Green Fees not confirmed.
Facilities ♀ 🐍
Location   Copsewood, Binley Rd (2m E of city centre on
         A428)
Hotel   ★★★61% The Chace Hotel, London Rd, Toll
         Bar End, COVENTRY
         ☎ (0203) 303398 67 ⇔ 🐾

Windmill Village ☎ (0203) 404040 & 407241
An 18-hole course over rolling parkland with lakes and
ponds. Other leisure facilities available.
18 holes, 5129yds, Par 70, SSS 67.
Club membership 500.

Visitors	welcome except before noon at weekends. Must contact in advance.
Societies	telephone and confirm in writing.
Green Fees	£10.95 per round (£15 weekends).
Facilities	⊗ ⊤ ⅃ ⌐ ⚑ ♀ △ ⇔ ⌁ Robert Hunter.
Leisure	heated indoor swimming pool, fishing, snooker, sauna, solarium, gymnasium, buggies, trolleys, bowling green.
Location	Birmingham Rd, Allesley (off A45 W of Coventry)
Hotel	★★★70% Brooklands Grange Hotel & Restaurant, Holyhead Rd, COVENTRY ☎ (0203) 601601 30 ⇔ ⌁

DUDLEY Map 07 SO99

Dudley ☎ (0384) 233877
Exposed and very hilly parkland course.
18 holes, 5704yds, Par 69, SSS 68.
Club membership 350.

Visitors	may not play at weekends.
Societies	must contact in advance.
Green Fees	£18 per day.
Facilities	⊗ ⌐ ⚑ (am only) ♀ △ ⇔ ⌁ Paul Taylor.
Leisure	snooker, trolleys.
Location	Turner's Hill, Rowley Regis, Warley (2m S of town centre off B4171)
Hotel	★★60% Station Hotel, Birmingham Rd, DUDLEY ☎ (0384) 253418 38 ⇔ ⌁

Swindon ☎ Wombourne (0902) 897031
Attractive undulating woodland/parkland course, with
spectacular views.
Old Course: 18 holes, 6042yds, Par 71, SSS 69.
New Course: 9 holes, 1135yds, Par 27.
Club membership 700.

Visitors	cannot bring narrow wheel trolleys.
Societies	Mon-Fri only, telephone in advance.
Green Fees	£15 per round (£25 weekends & bank holidays).
Facilities	⊗ ⊤ ⅃ ⌐ ⚑ ♀ △ ⇔
Leisure	fishing, snooker, buggies, trolleys.
Location	Bridgnorth Rd, Swindon
Hotel	★★60% Station Hotel, Birmingham Rd, DUDLEY ☎ (0384) 253418 38 ⇔ ⌁

HALESOWEN Map 07 SO98

Halesowen ☎ 021-501 3606
Parkland course in convenient position.
18 holes, 5754yds, Par 69, SSS 68, Course record 65.
Club membership 600.

Visitors	may not play weekends.
Societies	must apply in writing.
Green Fees	£23 per day; £16 per round.
Facilities	⊗ ⊤ ⅃ ⌐ ⚑ ♀ △ ⇔ ⌁ ⌁ Steve Fanning.
Leisure	snooker.
Location	The Leasowes (1m E)
Hotel	★★★62% Apollo, 243-247 Hagley Rd, Edgbaston, BIRMINGHAM ☎ 021-455 0271 126 ⇔ ⌁

KNOWLE Map 07 SP17

Copt Heath ☎ (0564) 772650
Parkland course designed by H. Vardon.
18 holes, 6500yds, Par 71, SSS 71.
Club membership 700.

Visitors	must contact in advance & use yellow tees only. With member only weekends & bank holidays.
Societies	by arrangement.
Green Fees	£40 per day; £35 per round.
Facilities	⊗ ⊤ ⅃ ⌐ ⚑ ♀ △ ⇔ ⌁ B J Barton.
Leisure	buggy hire by prior arrangement.
Location	1220 Warwick Rd (On A41 0.25m S of junc 5 of M42)
Hotel	★★★63% St John's Swallow Hotel, 651 Warwick Rd, SOLIHULL ☎ 021-711 3000 177 ⇔ ⌁

MERIDEN Map 04 SP28

Forest of Arden Hotel Golf and Country Club ☎ Meridan
(0676) 22335
Two parkland courses, set within the grounds of Packington
Park, with extensive water hazards and offering a fine test of
golf. On-site hotel with many leisure facilities.
*Arden Course: 18 holes, 6472yds, Par 72, SSS 71, Course
record 64.*
Aylesford Course: 18 holes, 6258yds, Par 72, SSS 69.
Club membership 800.

Visitors	must have handicap certificate, but may not play weekends (unless hotel resident). Must contact in advance.
Societies	by arrangement.
Green Fees	Arden Course: £50. Aylesford £24 (reduction for residents).
Facilities	⊗ ⊤ ⅃ ⌐ ⚑ ♀ △ ⇔ ⌁ ⚑ ⌁ Mike Tarn.
Leisure	hard tennis courts, heated indoor swimming pool, squash, fishing, snooker, sauna, solarium, gymnasium, steam room, beauty salon.
Location	Shepherd's Ln (1m SW on B4102)
Hotel	★★★★68% Forest of Arden Hotel, Golf & Country Club, Maxstoke Ln, MERIDEN ☎ (0676) 22335 152 ⇔ ⌁

North Warwickshire ☎ (0676) 22259
Parkland course with easy walking.
9 holes, 3186yds, Par 72, SSS 70, Course record 65.
Club membership 425.

Visitors	restricted Thu, weekends & bank holidays. Must contact in advance.
Societies	must apply in writing.
Green Fees	£18 per round.
Facilities	⊗ ⌐ ⚑ ♀ △ ⇔ ⌁ Simon Edwin.
Location	Hampton Ln (1m SW on B4102)
Hotel	★★★68% De Vere Manor Hotel, Main Rd, MERIDEN ☎ (0676) 522735 74 ⇔ ⌁

SEDGLEY Map 07 SO99

Sedgley Golf Centre ☎ (0902) 880503
Public Pay and Play course. Undulating contours and mature
trees with extensive views over surrounding countryside.
9 holes, 3147yds, Par 72, SSS 71.
Club membership 150. ▶

Visitors booking advisable for weekends.
Societies telephone in advance.
Green Fees £6 per 18 holes (£6.50 weekends & bank holidays); £4 per 9 holes (£6 weekends & bank holidays).
Facilities ⊗ by prior arrangement ⅊ ♨ ⚲ 🏠 ⚑ David Fereday.
Leisure driving range.
Location Sandfields Rd (2m N of Dudley,on A459)
Hotel ★★★62% Himley Country Club & Hotel, School Rd, HIMLEY
☎ (0902) 896716 76 ⇆ ⚑

SOLIHULL Map 07 SP17

Olton ☎ 021-705 1083
Parkland course with prevailing southwest wind.
18 holes, 6232yds, Par 69, SSS 71.
Club membership 600.
Visitors may not play Wed & with member only at weekends.
Societies by arrangement.
Green Fees £30 per day.
Facilities ⊗ & ⅏ by prior arrangement ⅊ ♨ ♀ ⚲ 🏠⚑
Leisure snooker.
Location Mirfield Rd (1m NW off A41)
Hotel ★★★63% St John's Swallow Hotel, 651 Warwick Rd, SOLIHULL
☎ 021-711 3000 177 ⇆ ⚑

Robin Hood ☎ 021-706 0061
Pleasant parkland course with easy walking and open to good views.Tree lined fairways and varied holes, culminating in two excellent finishing holes. Modern clubhouse.
18 holes, 6635yds, Par 72, SSS 72, Course record 68.
Club membership 700.
Visitors must contact in advance. With member only at weekends.
Societies must contact in advance.
Green Fees £35 per day; £29 per round.
Facilities ⅊ ♨ ♀ ⚲ 🏠⚑ Alan Harvey.
Location St Bernards Rd (2m W off B4025)
Hotel ★★★63% St John's Swallow Hotel, 651 Warwick Rd, SOLIHULL
☎ 021-711 3000 177 ⇆ ⚑

Shirley ☎ 021-744 6001
Fairly flat parkland course.
18 holes, 6510yds, Par 72, SSS 71.
Club membership 500.
Visitors may not play bank holidays & with member only at weekends. Handicap certificate is required.
Societies must contact in advance.
Green Fees £25 per round.
Facilities ⊗ ⅏ ⅊ & ♨ by prior arrangement ♀ ⚲ 🏠⚑ C J Wicketts.
Leisure snooker.
Location Stratford Rd, Monkpath (3m SW off A34)
Hotel ★★★67% Regency Hotel, Stratford Rd, Shirley, SOLIHULL ☎ 021-745 6119 112 ⇆ ⚑

┌─────────────────────────────────────┐
Phoneday - remember from 16 April 1995 all phone codes in the UK will change - see page 4 for details
└─────────────────────────────────────┘

STOURBRIDGE Map 07 SO98

Hagley Golf & Country Club ☎ (0562) 883701
Undulating parkland course set beneath the Clent Hills; there are superb views. Testing 15th, par 5, 557 yards.
18 holes, 6353yds, Par 72, SSS 72, Course record 71.
Club membership 670.
Visitors restricted Wed (Ladies Day) & with member only at weekends.
Societies Mon-Fri only, must apply in writing.
Green Fees £25 per day; £20 per round.
Facilities ⊗ ⅏ ⅊ ♨ ♀ ⚲ 🏠⚑ Iain Clark.
Leisure squash, caddy cars.
Location Wassell Grove, Hagley (1m E of Hagley off A456)
Hotel ★★64% Talbot Hotel, High St, STOURBRIDGE ☎ (0384) 394350 25 ⇆ ⚑

Stourbridge ☎ (0384) 395566
Parkland course.
18 holes, 6231yds, Par 70, SSS 70.
Club membership 720.
Visitors may not play Wed mornings & weekends unless with member. Must have a handicap certificate.
Societies must apply in writing.
Green Fees £25 per day.
Facilities ⊗ ⅏ by prior arrangement ⅊ ♨ ♀ ⚲ 🏠⚑ William H Firkins.
Leisure snooker.
Location Worcester Ln, Pedmore (2m from town centre)
Hotel ★★64% Talbot Hotel, High St, STOURBRIDGE ☎ (0384) 394350 25 ⇆ ⚑

SUTTON COLDFIELD Map 07 SP19

┌─────────────────────────────────────┐
THE BELFRY See page 203
└─────────────────────────────────────┘

Little Aston ☎ 021-353 2066
Parkland course.
18 holes, 6670yds, Par 72, SSS 73.
Club membership 250.
Visitors must contact in advance & have handicap certificate, but may not play at weekends.
Societies must apply in writing.
Green fees on application.
Facilities ⊗ ⅏ ⅊ ♀ ⚲ 🏠⚑ John Anderson.
Location Streetly (3.5m NW off A454)
Hotel ★★★69% Moor Hall Hotel, Moor Hall Dr, Four Oaks, Sutton Coldfield ☎ 021-308 3751 75 ⇆ ⚑

Moor Hall ☎ 021-308 6130
Parkland course. The 14th is a notable hole.
18 holes, 6249yds, Par 70, SSS 70.
Club membership 600.
Visitors must contact in advance. With member only weekends & bank holidays.
Societies must apply in writing.
Green fees £32 per day; £25 per round.
Facilities all catering by arrangement with steward tel:021-308 0103 ♀ ⚲ 🏠⚑⚑ Alan Partridge.
Leisure snooker.
Location Moor Hall Dr (2.5m n of town centre off A453)
Hotel ★★★69% Moor Hall Hotel, Moor Hall Dr, Four Oaks, Sutton Coldfield
☎ 021-308 3751 75 ⇆ ⚑

THE BELFRY

SUTTON COLDFIELD ☏(0675) 470301   Map 07 SP19

John Ingham writes: When professional people are commissioned to turn a piece of farmland into a golf course and hotel complex, they are flattered - and delighted. This happened to Peter Alliss and Dave Thomas, two celebrated tournament competitors. The challenge they were offered: turn an unsympathetic piece of land into a good golf course. The resulting Belfry Golf Club was opened in 1977.

Since that date the two architects have every reason to be proud. The course, set in 370 acres of parkland, has staged more than one of the popular Ryder Cup matches, and the two courses - the Brabazon and the Derby - named after two Lords, have received thousands of visitors. These visitors have been entertained with a kindly reception, enhanced by a really excellent hotel.

In the sixteen years since its establishment, the saplings and newly-created greens have settled down very well and presented a worthwhile face to the world. One of the big challenges of The Belfry are the lakes and many water hazards that gobble up wild shots. Many a famous player, such as Seve Ballesteros, has had balls sinking without trace at the Brabazon's famously testing 18th hole. This monster requires the player to clear the lake twice in its 455-yard drive to reach an uphill, three-tiered, 60-yard long green.

As a public course, The Belfry is open to all-comers every day. This obviously means a great deal of traffic, although there are many other worthwhile courses in the West Midlands such as Hansworth and Little Aston. However, The Belfry is excellently managed and kept in top condition by a team now fully experienced in catering for every golfer. Recently, bunkering and new tees have improved several of the holes and spectator mounding has improved viewing of the golf tournaments.

In its fine parkland setting the club has become well known for its accommodation and fine business facilities and, being so well placed for the NEC, Birmingham and the international airport, it attracts a variety of golfers.

Visitors	must contact in advance. A handicap certificate is required for the Brabazon course
Societies	must telephone in advance
Green fees	Brabazon £50 per round; Derby £20 per round
Facilities	⊗ ⅏ ⯊ ⯊ ⯊ ♀ ⇔ ᇲ ⛳ ↑ putting green, driving range, ⛳ (P McGovern)
Leisure	hard tennis courts, heated indoor swimming pool, squash, snooker, sauna, solarium, gym. Nightclub in grounds
Location	Lichfield Rd, Wishaw (exit junc 9 M42 4m E)

36 holes. Brabazon: 18 holes, 6905yds, Par 72, SSS 72. Course record 63
Derby: 18 holes, 6103yds Par70, SSS 70

WHERE TO STAY AND EAT NEARBY

HOTELS:

WISHAW

★★★★❀❀ 72% The Belfry, Lichfield Rd.☏ Curdworth (0675) 470301 219 ⇔ ⋔ French cuisine

★★★58% Moxhull Hall, Holly Lane. ☏ 021-329 2056, 20 ⇔ ⋔

LEA MARSTON

★★★68% Lea Marston Hotel and Leisure Complex. ☏ Curdworth (0675) 470468, 22 ⇔ ⋔

SUTTON COLDFIELD

★★★59% Sutton Court, 60-66 Lichfield Rd. ☏ 021-3 55 6071, 56 ⇔ ⋔ Annexe 8

★★★★❀❀ 75% New Hall, Walmley Rd. ☏ 021-378 2442. 62 ⇔ ⋔ International cuisine

Pype Hayes ☎ 021-351 1014
Attractive, fairly flat course with excellent greens.
18 holes, 5979yds, Par 71, SSS 68, course record 64.
Club membership 300.
Ssocieties   contact in advance.
Green fees   £7.80.
Facilities   ⊗ ⅷ ⤫ 🏌 ♨ 📠 ⛳ ⌢ James Bayliss.
Location   Eachelhurst Rd, Walmley (2.5m S off B4148)
Hotel   ★★★67% Marston Farm, Bodymoor Heath, Sutton Coldfield ☎ (0827) 872133 37 ⇆ ⌢

Sutton Coldfield ☎ 021-353 9633
A fine natural, heathland course, with tight fairways, gorse, heather and trees; which is surprising as the high-rise buildings of Birmingham are not far away.
18 holes, 6541yds, Par 72, SSS 71.
Club membership 600.
Visitors   must contact in advance & have handicap certificate.
Societies   must apply in writing.
Green fees   £30 per day.
Facilities   ⊗ ⅷ by prior arrangement 🏌 ⤫ ♨ 📠 ⌢ Jerry Hayes.
Leisure   snooker.
Location   Thornhill Rd, streetly (3m NW on B4138)
Hotel   ★★★69% Moor Hall Hotel, Moor Hall Dr, Four Oaks, Sutton Coldfield ☎ 021-308 3751 75 ⇆ ⌢

SUTTON COURT HOTEL

★★★

60-66 Lichfield Road, Sutton Coldfield
West Midlands B74 2NA
Telephone: 0121 355 6071   Fax: 0121 355 0083

BIRDIE WITHIN 5 MINUTES OF HOTEL

Play at the Belfry and stay at the Sutton Court Hotel. We're only 5 minutes away from this delux golf course. All our executive bedrooms are of a 5 star standard which are all individually designed. PJ's Restaurant enjoys an excellent reputation where the Chef de cuisine and his brigade of chefs prepare a variety of imaginative dishes from the finest of fresh produce. This fine Victorian building combines a chic atmosphere and excellent hospitality combined with elegant furnishings.
Golfing weekends available at special rates. Close to all amenities. Conference facilities available.

Walmley ☎ 021-373 0029
Pleasant parkland course with many trees. The hazards are not difficult.
18 holes, 6537yds, Par 72, SSS 72, course record 69.
Club membership 700.
Visitors   with member only at weekends. must contact in advance.
Societies   must contact in advance.
Green fees   £25 per round.
Facilities   ⊗ ⅷ 🏌 ⤫ (no catering mon) ♨ ♨ 📠 ⌢ M J Skerritt.
Leisure   snooker.
Location   Brooks Rd, Wylde Green (2m S off A5127)
Hotel   ★★★67% Marston Farm, Bodymoor Heath, Sutton Coldfield ☎ (0827) 872133 37 ⇆ ⌢

WALSALL   Map 07 SP09

Bloxwich ☎ Bloxwich (0922) 405724
Undulating parkland course with natural hazards and subject to strong north wind.
18 holes, 6286yds, Par 71, SSS 70.
Club membership 532.
Visitors   may not play at weekends.
Societies   must apply in writing.
Green Fees   £25 per day; £20 per round.
Facilities   ⊗ ⅷ 🏌 ⤫ ♨ 📠 ⌢ Gary Broadbent.
Leisure   snooker.
Location   Stafford Rd, Bloxwich (3m N of town centre on A34)
Hotel   ★★★66% Fairlawns Hotel, 178 Little Aston Road, Aldridge, WALSALL ☎ (0922) 55122 35 ⇆ ⌢

Calderfields ☎ (0922) 640540
Parkland course with lake.
18 holes, 6590yds, Par 73, SSS 72.
Club membership 700.
Visitors   no restrictions.
Societies   telephone in advance.
Green Fees   not confirmed.
Facilities   ⊗ ⅷ 🏌 ⤫ ♨ ♨ 📠 ⛳ ⌢ Roger Griffin.
Leisure   fishing.
Location   Aldridge Rd (on A454)
Hotel   ★★★66% Fairlawns Hotel, 178 Little Aston Road, Aldridge, WALSALL ☎ (0922) 55122 35 ⇆ ⌢

Walsall ☎ (0922) 613512
Well-wooded parkland course with easy walking.
18 holes, 6243yds, Par 70, SSS 70, Course record 65.
Club membership 700.
Visitors   may not play weekends & bank holidays.
Societies   must apply in writing.
Green Fees   £40 per day; £33 per round.
Facilities   ⊗ ⅷ by prior arrangement 🏌 ⤫ ♨ ♨ 📠 ⛳ Richard Lambert.
Leisure   snooker.
Location   The Broadway (1m S of town centre off A34)
Hotel   ★★★62% Boundary Hotel, Birmingham Rd, WALSALL ☎ (0922) 33555 98 ⇆ ⌢

WEST BROMWICH   Map 07 SP09

Dartmouth ☎ 021-588 2131
Meadowland course with undulating but easy walking. The 617 yd (par 5) first hole is something of a challenge.
9 holes, 6060yds, Par 71, SSS 70, Course record 66.
Club membership 350.

Visitors	with member only at weekends. May not play bank holidays or medal weekends.
Societies	must apply in writing.
Green Fees	£16.50 per day.
Facilities	⊗ & ⊤ by prior arrangement 🏌 ♣ ♀ ♨ 🏠 (Carl Yates.
Leisure	snooker, practice area, putting green.
Location	Vale St (E side of town centre off A4041)
Hotel	★★★63% West Bromwich Moat House, Birmingham Rd, WEST BROMWICH ☎ 021-553 6111 180 ⇆ ｆ

Sandwell Park ☎ 021-553 4637
Undulating parkland course situated in the Sandwell Valley.
18 holes, 6470yds, Par 71, SSS 72.
Club membership 600.

Visitors	must contact in advance. With member only weekends.
Societies	must apply in writing.
Green Fees	£32.50.
Facilities	⊗ ⊤ 🏌 ♣ ♀ ♨ 🏠 (Nigel Wylie.
Leisure	snooker.
Location	Birmingham Rd (SE side of town centre off A4040)
Hotel	★★★63% West Bromwich Moat House, Birmingham Rd, WEST BROMWICH ☎ 021-553 6111 180 ⇆ ｆ

WOLVERHAMPTON   Map 07 SO99

Oxley Park ☎ (0902) 20506
Parklands course with easy walking on the flat.
18 holes, 6028yds, Par 71, SSS 69.
Club membership 615.

Visitors	must contact in advance. Must be introduced by member during winter weekends.
Societies	must contact in advance.
Green Fees	not confirmed.
Facilities	⊗ (ex Mon) ⊤ by prior arrangement 🏌 ♣ ♀ ♨ 🏠 (Les Burlison.
Leisure	snooker.
Location	Stafford Rd, Bushbury (N of town centre off A449)
Hotel	★★68% Ely House Hotel, 53 Tettenhall Rd, WOLVERHAMPTON ☎ (0902) 311311 18 ⇆ ｆ

Penn ☎ (0902) 341142
Heathland course just outside the town.
18 holes, 6465yds, Par 70, SSS 71, Course record 67.
Club membership 620.

Visitors	must be member of recognised club, can only play weekdays & must use yellow tees.
Societies	must apply in writing.
Green Fees	£25 per day; £20 per round.
Facilities	⊗ (ex Sun & Mon) ⊤ 🏌 & ♣ (ex Sun,Mon & Wed) ♀ ♨ 🏠 ᵀ (A Briscoe.
Leisure	snooker.

Location	Penn Common, Penn (SW side of town centre off A449)
Hotel	★★★60% Park Hall Hotel, Park Drive, Goldthorn Park, WOLVERHAMPTON ☎ (0902) 331121 57 ⇆ ｆ

South Staffordshire ☎ (0902) 751065
A parkland course.
18 holes, 6500yds, Par 71, SSS 71.
Club membership 570.

Visitors	must contact in advance but may not play weekends & before 2pm Tue.
Societies	must contact in advance.
Green Fees	£30 per day; £27.50 per round.
Facilities	⊗ ⊤ 🏌 & ♣ ♀ ♨ 🏠 (Jim Rhodes.
Leisure	snooker, electric buggy.
Location	Danescourt Rd, Tettenhall (3m NW off A41)
Hotel	★★68% Ely House Hotel, 53 Tettenhall Rd, WOLVERHAMPTON ☎ (0902) 311311 18 ⇆ ｆ

Wergs ☎ (0902) 742225
Open parkland course.
18 holes, 6949yds, Par 72, SSS 73.
Club membership 300.

Visitors	no restrictions.
Societies	must contact in advance.
Green Fees	£12.50 per day (£15 weekends & bank holidays).
Facilities	⊗ ⊤ 🏌 ♣ ♀ ♨ 🏠 (M C Moseley.
Leisure	practice area, caddy cars.
Location	Keepers Ln, Tettenhall
Hotel	★★68% Ely House Hotel, 53 Tettenhall Rd, WOLVERHAMPTON ☎ (0902) 311311 18 ⇆ ｆ

WEST SUSSEX

ANGMERING   Map 04 TQ00

Ham Manor ☎ (0903) 783288
Two miles from the sea, this parkland course has fine springy turf and provides an interesting test in two loops of nine holes each.
18 holes, 6243yds, Par 70, SSS 70, Course record 62.
Club membership 850.

Visitors	must have a handicap certificate.
Societies	must contact in writing.
Green Fees	£25 (£35 weekends).
Facilities	⊗ ⊤ (Tue-Sat) 🏌 ♣ ♀ ♨ 🏠 ᵀ (Simon Buckley.
Leisure	snooker, bowling green, table tennis.
Location	0.75m SW
Hotel	★★★58% Chatsworth Hotel, Steyne, WORTHING ☎ (0903) 236103 107 ⇆ ｆ

For an explanation of symbols and abbreviations, see page 5

BOGNOR REGIS
Map 04 SZ99

Bognor Regis ☎ (0243) 865867
This flattish, parkland course has more variety than is to be found on some of the South Coast courses. The club is also known far and wide for its enterprise in creating a social atmosphere. The course is open to the prevailing wind.
18 holes, 6238yds, Par 70, SSS 70, Course record 64.
Club membership 650.

Visitors	restricted Tue; must play with member at weekends Apr-Oct. Must contact in advance and have a handicap certificate.
Societies	must contact in writing.
Green Fees	£25 per day/round (£30 weekends Nov-Mar).
Facilities	⊗ ⅃ ⚑ ♀ ♣ 盒 (A P Barr.
Location	Downview Rd, Felpham (1.5m NE off A259)
Hotel	★★63% Black Mill House Hotel, Princess Av, Aldwick, BOGNOR REGIS ☎ (0243) 821945 & 865596 22rm(18 ⇄ ♪)Annexe4rm

BURGESS HILL
Map 04 TQ31

Burgess Hill ☎ (0444) 870615
A new and attractive undulating 9-hole course bordered by a tributary of the River Adur. Many challenging holes with water hazards and established trees and shrubs.The course is notable in that it has the first putting green for wheelchair users in the world.
9 holes, 4433yds, Par 62, SSS 62.
Club membership 400.

Societies	book by phone or write.
Green Fees	£5 per 18 holes (£7 weekends & bank holidays).
Facilities	⊗ ⅃ ⅃ ⚑ ♀ ♣ 盒 ᵀ (Patrick Tallack.
Leisure	first putting green for wheelchair users.
Location	Cuckfield Rd (B2036)
Hotel	★★★♣75% Ockenden Manor, Ockenden Ln, CUCKFIELD ☎ (0444) 416111 22 ⇄ ♪

CHICHESTER
Map 04 SU80

Chichester Golf Centre ☎ (0243) 533833
Set amongst lush farmland, the Tower course has four lakes which bring water into play on seven holes. The Florida-style Cathedral course was opened in 1994. There is also a 9-hole Par 3 and a floodlit driving range.
Tower Course: 18 holes, 5956yds, Par 71, SSS 69, Course record 69.
Cathedral Course: 18 holes, 6461yds, Par 72, SSS 69.
Club membership 300.

Visitors	a strict dress code is in operation. It is advisable to contact in advance.
Societies	must contact in advance.
Green Fees	Tower: £14 per round (£19.50 weekends). Cathedral £25 per round (£30 weekends).
Facilities	⊗ ⅃ ⚑ ♣ 盒 ᵀ (Carl Rota.
Leisure	Par 3 9 hole course, buggies.
Location	Hoe Farm, Hunston (3m S of Chichester, on B2145 at Hunston)
Hotel	★★62% The Dolphin & Anchor, West St, CHICHESTER ☎ (0243) 785121 49 ⇄ ♪

COPTHORNE
Map 05 TQ33

Copthorne ☎ (0342) 712033 & 712508
Despite it having been in existence since 1892, this club remains one of the lesser known Sussex courses. It is hard to know why because it is most attractive with plenty of trees and much variety
18 holes, 6505yds, Par 71, SSS 71.
Club membership 600.

Visitors	restricted at weekends after 1pm.
Societies	Thu & Fri only; must contact well in advance.
Green Fees	£33 per day (£30 weekends & bank holidays after 1pm); £25 per round.
Facilities	⊗ ⅃ ⅃ ⚑ ♀ ♣ 盒 (Joe Burrell.
Location	Borers Arms Rd (E side of village junc 10 of M23 off A264)
Hotel	★★★★64% The Copthorne, Copthorne Way, COPTHORNE ☎ (0342) 714971 227 ⇄ ♪

Effingham Park ☎ (0342) 716528
Parkland course.
9 holes, 1749yds, Par 30.
Club membership 390.

Visitors	restricted at weekends after 12 noon.
Societies	Mon-Fri only, must write/telephone in advance.
Green Fees	£11 per 18 holes; £7.50 per 9 holes.
Facilities	⊗ ⅃ ⅃ ⚑ ♀ ♣ 盒 ᵀ ⌷ (Ian Dryden.
Leisure	heated indoor swimming pool, sauna, solarium, gymnasium, dance studio, jacuzzi, steam room.
Location	2m E on B2028
Hotel	★★★★68% The Copthorne Effingham Park, West Park Road, Copthorne, COPTHORNE ☎ (0342) 714994 122 ⇄ ♪

CRAWLEY
Map 04 TQ23

Cottesmore ☎ (0293) 528256
The old North Course is undulating with four holes are over water. The new South Course is shorter and less testing. But both are lined by silver birch, pine and oak, with rhododendrons ablaze in June.
Old Course: 18 holes, 6113yds, Par 72, SSS 70.
New South Course: 18 holes, 5469yds, Par 69, SSS 68.
Club membership 1300.

Visitors	may only play after noon on Old Course at weekends. Must contact in advance.
Societies	Mon, Wed & Fri Apr-1 Nov. Must contact in advance.
Green Fees	Old Course: £30 (£40 weekends). New Course: £20 (£28 weekends).
Facilities	⊗ ⅃ ⅃ ⚑ ♀ ♣ 盒 ᵀ ⌷ (
Leisure	hard tennis courts, heated indoor swimming pool, squash, sauna, solarium, gymnasium.
Location	Buchan Hill, Pease Pottage (3m SW 1m W of M23 junc 11)
Hotel	★★★60% Goffs Park Hotel, 45 Goffs Park Road, Crawley, CRAWLEY ☎ (0293) 535447 37 ⇄ ♪Annexe28 ⇄ ♪

Gatwick Manor ☎ (0293) 538587
Interesting, pay and play short course.
9 holes, 2492yds, Par 56, SSS 50.
Club membership 63.

Visitors	no restrictions.

Societies must telephone in advance.
Green Fees £3 per round.
Facilities ⊗ ⅏ ♀ 🏠 ⫯ 🏌 𝄞 C Jenkins.
Location Lowfield Heath (2m N on A23)
Hotel ★★★60% Goffs Park Hotel, 45 Goffs Park Road, Crawley, CRAWLEY
☎ (0293) 535447 37 ⇆ 🐾Annexe28 ⇆ 🐾

Ifield Golf & Country Club ☎ (0293) 520222
Parkland course.
18 holes, 6314yds, Par 70, SSS 70.
Club membership 800.
Visitors may not play after 3pm Fri; must play with member at weekends. Must contact in advance and have a handicap certificate.
Societies Mon-Wed afternoons & Thu.
Green Fees £27 per day; £20 per round.
Facilities ⊗ ⅏ 🏠 ♥ ♀ 🧍 🏠 𝄞 Jon Earl.
Leisure squash, snooker.
Location Rusper Rd, Ifield (1m W side of town centre off A23)
Hotel ★★★60% George Hotel, High St, CRAWLEY
☎ (0293) 524215 86 ⇆ 🐾

GOODWOOD
Map 04 SU80

> **Goodwood** ☎ Chichester (0243) 774968
> Downland course designed by the master architect, James Braid. Many notable holes, particularly the finishing ones: 17 down an avenue of beech trees and 18 along in front of the terrace. Superb views of the downs and the coast.
> *18 holes, 6401yds, Par 72, SSS 71, Course record 63.*
> *Club membership 900.*
> **Visitors** must contact in advance and have handicap certificate.
> **Societies** must contact in writing.
> **Green Fees** £28 per day (£38 weekends).
> **Facilities** ⊗ ⅏ by prior arrangement 🧍 ♥ ♀ 🧍 🏠 𝄞 Keith MacDonald.
> **Leisure** snooker.
> **Location** 4.5m NE of Chichester off A27
> **Hotel** ★★★67% Goodwood Park Hotel, Golf & Country Club, GOODWOOD
> ☎ (0243) 775537 88 ⇆ 🐾

HAYWARDS HEATH
Map 05 TQ32

Haywards Heath ☎ (0444) 414866
Pleasant parkland course with several challenging par 4s and 3s.
18 holes, 6204yds, Par 71, SSS 70, Course record 68.
Club membership 750.
Visitors must be a member of a recognised golf club and have a handicap certificate. Must contact in advance.

Societies Wed & Thu only.
Green Fees £27 per day; £22 per round (£35 per day; £30 per round weekends & bank holidays).
Facilities ⊗ ⅏ by prior arrangement 🧍 ♥ ♀ 🧍 🏠 𝄞 Michael Henning.
Location High Beech Ln (1.25m N off B2028)
Hotel ★★★★75% Ockenden Manor, Ockenden Ln, CUCKFIELD ☎ (0444) 416111 22 ⇆ 🐾

Paxhill Park ☎ (0444) 484467 & 484000
A relatively flat parkland course designed by Patrick Tallack.
18 holes, 6172yds, Par 71, SSS 69, Course record 65.
Club membership 500.
Visitors welcome but may not play weekend mornings.
Societies must contact in advance.
Green Fees £25 per day; £15 per round (£20 per round weekends).
Facilities ⊗ ⅏ by prior arrangement 🧍 ♥ ♀ (all day) 🧍 🏠 𝄞 Steve Dunkley.
Location East Mascalls Ln, Lindfield
Hotel ★★★60% The Birch Hotel, Lewes Rd, HAYWARDS HEATH ☎ (0444) 451565 53 ⇆ 🐾

HORSHAM
Map 04 TQ13

See Slinfold

LITTLEHAMPTON
Map 04 TQ00

> **Littlehampton** ☎ (0903) 717170
> A delightful seaside links in an equally delightful setting - and the only links course in the area.
> *18 holes, 6244yds, Par 70, SSS 70, Course record 66.*
> *Club membership 650.*
> **Visitors** must have handicap certificate.
> **Societies** welcome weekdays.
> **Green Fees** £24 per day (£30 weekends).
> **Facilities** ⊗ ⅏ by prior arrangement 🧍 ♥ ♀ 🧍 🏠 𝄞 Guy McQuitty.
> **Location** Rope Walk, West Beach (1m W off A259)
> **Hotel** ★★★66% Norfolk Arms Hotel, High St, ARUNDEL
> ☎ (0903) 882101 21 Annexe13 ⇆

MANNINGS HEATH
Map 04 TQ22

Mannings Heath ☎ Horsham (0403) 210228
The course meanders up hill and down dale over heathland with streams affecting 11 of the holes. Wooded valleys protect the course from strong winds. Famous holes at 12th (the 'Waterfall', par 3), 13th (the 'Valley', par 4).
18 holes, 6402yds, Par 73, SSS 71.
Club membership 710. ▶

MORE WAYS TO PLAY . . .

. . . an 18-hole championship course set in established parkland with lakes and streams . . . a 9-hole short course . . . a floodlit driving range . . . two resident golf professionals . . . a luxuriously appointed clubhouse, bar and restaurant . . . and a warm welcome for visitors and societies

AT SLINFOLD PARK GOLF CLUB, Stane St (A29), Slinfold, W. Sussex. Tel: 01403 791555

Slinfold Park
• GOLF & COUNTRY CLUB •

SOUTH LODGE HOTEL

Four star luxury in traditional Country House set in 90 acres of beautiful Sussex Parkland, with views over the South Downs.

Delicious cuisine by chef John Elliott, using local game and fish, with soft fruits and herbs from hotel's own walled garden.

Superbly appointed bedrooms and suites each individually decorated in true country house style.

Enjoy tennis, croquet, petanque, putting, fishing, horse riding or golf at our spectacular 18 hole course at Mannings Heath.

South Lodge is the perfect location for visiting the wealth of National Trust Gardens and Houses of Sussex.

For full details, please contact:
SOUTH LODGE HOTEL, Lower Beeding,
near Horsham, West Sussex RH13 6PS.
Telephone: 01403 891711.

Visitors	must contact in advance & have handicap certificate.
Societies	must contact in advance.
Green Fees	£27 per round (£35 weekends).
Facilities	⊗ ⫚ ⤶ 🍷 ♀ ⌂ 🏠 ⵑ ✆ Peter Harrison.
Leisure	hard tennis courts, fishing, snooker.
Location	Goldings Ln (N side of village)
Hotel	★★★★⩗74% South Lodge Hotel, Brighton Rd, LOWER BEEDING ☎ (0403) 891711 39 ⊂⊃

MIDHURST   Map 04 SU82

Cowdray Park ☎ (0730) 813599
Parkland course, hard walking up to 4th green.
18 holes, 6212yds, Par 70, SSS 70, Course record 68.
Club membership 700.

Visitors	may play after 9am on weekdays, 11am Sat & 3pm Sun. Must contact in advance and have a handicap certificate.
Societies	must contact in writing.
Green Fees	not confirmed.
Facilities	⊗ ⫚ by prior arrangement ⤶ 🍷 ♀ ⌂ 🏠 ⵑ ✆ Stephen Hall.
Location	1m E on A272
Hotel	★★★69% Spread Eagle Hotel, South St, MIDHURST ☎ (0730) 816911 37 ⊂⊃ ⍨Annexe4 ⍨

PULBOROUGH   Map 04 TQ01

West Sussex ☎ (0798) 872563
Heathland course.
18 holes, 6221yds, Par 68, SSS 70, Course record 61.
Club membership 800.

Visitors	must contact in advance and have a handicap certificate.
Societies	Wed & Thu only. Must contact in advance.
Green Fees	£40 per day; £30 per round (£45/£35 weekends).
Facilities	⊗ ⤶ 🍷 ♀ ⌂ 🏠 ✆ Tim Packham.
Location	Golf Club Ln, Wiggonholt (1.5m E off A283)
Hotel	★★★64% Roundabout Hotel, Monkmead Ln, WEST CHILTINGTON ☎ (0798) 813838 23 ⊂⊃ ⍨

PYECOMBE   Map 04 TQ21

Pyecombe ☎ (0273) 845372
Typical downland course on the inland side of the South Downs. Hilly, but magnificent views.
18 holes, 6278yds, Par 71, SSS 70, Course record 66.
Club membership 624.

Visitors	may only play after 9.15 weekdays, 2pm Sat & 3pm Sun.
Societies	must contact in advance.
Green Fees	£20 per day; £15 per round (£25/£20 weekends).
Facilities	⊗ ⤶ 🍷 ♀ ⌂ 🏠 ⵑ ✆ C R White.
Location	Clayton Hill (E side of village on A273)
Hotel	★★67% Whitehaven Hotel, 34 Wilbury Rd, Hove ☎ (0273) 778355 17 ⊂⊃ ⍨

SELSEY   Map 04 SZ89

Selsey ☎ (0243) 602203
Fairly difficult seaside course, exposed to wind and has natural ditches.
9 holes, 5932yds, Par 68, SSS 68.
Club membership 433.

Visitors	must have a handicap certificate, and play with member at weekends.
Societies	must contact in writing.
Green Fees	not confirmed.
Facilities	⊗ & ⫚ (ex Tue) ⤶ 🍷 ♀ ⌂ 🏠 ✆ Peter Grindley.
Leisure	hard tennis courts, bowling green.
Location	Golf Links Ln (1m N off B2145)
Hotel	★★★62% The Dolphin & Anchor, West St, CHICHESTER ☎ (0243) 785121 49 ⊂⊃ ⍨

SLINFOLD   Map 04 TQ13

Slinfold Park Golf & Country Club ☎ (0403) 791555
Opened for play in spring 1993, Slinfold course enjoys splendid views among mature trees. The 10th tee is spectacularly located on the centre of one of the two large landscaped lakes. The 166-yard 16th has water running in front of of the tee and everything sloping towards it!
Championship: 18 holes, 6407yds, Par 72, SSS 71, Course record 65.
Short: 9 holes, 1315yds, Par 28.
Club membership 600.

Visitors	subject to booking.
Societies	advance booking required, weekends not available.
Green Fees	Championship: £30 per day; £20 per round (£25 per round weekends). Short Course £8 per 18 holes; £5 per round.
Facilities	⊗ & ⅏ by prior arrangement ┗ ☟ ♀ ♨ ⌂ ↑ ໂ G McKay/D Tunn.
Leisure	19 bay driving range.
Location	Stane St (4m W on the A29)
Hotel	★★★70% Random Hall Hotel, Stane St, Slinfold, HORSHAM ☎ (0403) 790558 & 790852 15 ⇆ ໂⁿ

WEST CHILTINGTON   Map 04 TQ01

West Chiltington ☎ (0798) 813574
The Main Course is situated on gently undulating, well-drained greensand and offers panoramic views of the Sussex Downs. Three large double greens provide an interesting feature to this new course. Also 9-hole short course and 13-bay driving range.
18 holes, 6000yds, Par 70, SSS 69 or 9 holes, 3000yds, Par 28.
Club membership 750.

Visitors	it is advisable to contact the club in advance for weekends. Tee times can be booked in advance.
Societies	telephone for booking form.
Green Fees	£12.50; £5 after 5pm (£15/£7.50 weekends).
Facilities	⊗ ⅏ ┗ ☟ ♀ (all day) ♨ ⌂ ↑ ໂ R Tisdall.
Leisure	driving range.
Location	Broadford bridge Rd (on N side of village)
Hotel	★★★64% Roundabout Hotel, Monkmead Ln, WEST CHILTINGTON ☎ (0798) 813838 23 ⇆ ໂⁿ

WORTHING   Map 04 TQ10

Hill Barn Municipal ☎ (0903) 37301
Downland course with views of both Isle of Wight and Brighton.
18 holes, 6224yds, Par 70, SSS 70.
Club membership 1000.

Visitors	no restrictions.
Societies	must telephone in advance.
Green Fees	£10.50 (£12.50 weekends).
Facilities	⊗ ⅏ ┗ ☟ ♀ ♨ ⌂ ↑ ໂ A Higgins.
Leisure	croquet.
Location	Hill Barn Ln (N side of town at junction of A24/A27)
Hotel	★★★58% Chatsworth Hotel, Steyne, WORTHING ☎ (0903) 236103 107 ⇆ ໂⁿ

Worthing ☎ (0903) 60801
The High Course, short and tricky with entrancing views, will provide good entertainment. 'Lower Course' is considered to be one of the best downland courses in the country.
Lower Course: 18 holes, 6519yds, Par 71, SSS 72.
Upper Course: 18 holes, 5243yds, Par 66, SSS 66.
Club membership 1146.

Visitors	advisable to contact in advance.
Societies	must contact in writing 6 months in advance.
Green Fees	not confirmed.

Facilities	⊗ ⅏ ┗ ☟ ♀ ♨ ⌂ ໂ
Leisure	snooker.
Location	Links Rd (N side of town centre off A27)
Hotel	★★65% Ardington Hotel, Steyne Gardens, WORTHING ☎ (0903) 230451 47 ⇆ ໂⁿ

WEST YORKSHIRE

ALWOODLEY   Map 08 SE24

Alwoodley ☎ Leeds (0532) 681680
A fine heathland course with length, trees and abundant heather. Many attractive situations - together a severe test of golf.
18 holes, 6686yds, Par 72, SSS 72, Course record 67.
Club membership 250.

Visitors	must contact in advance, restricted Tue, weekends & bank holidays.
Societies	must apply in advance.
Green Fees	£35 per day (£45 weekends & bank holidays).
Facilities	⊗ & ⅏ by prior arrangement ┗ ☟ ♀ ♨ ⌂ ໂ John Green.
Location	Wigton Ln (5m N off A61)
Hotel	★★★63% Harewood Arms Hotel, Harrogate Rd, HAREWOOD ☎ (0532) 886566 24 ⇆ ໂⁿ

BAILDON   Map 07 SE13

Baildon ☎ (0274) 595162
Moorland course with much bracken rough. The 5th is a hard climb.
18 holes, 6225yds, Par 70, SSS 70, Course record 64.
Club membership 600.

Visitors	restricted Tue & weekends.
Societies	may not play Tue & weekends; must contact in advance.
Green Fees	£16 per day (£20 weekends & bank holidays).
Facilities	⊗ (ex Mon) ⅏ (ex Sun) ┗ ☟ ♀ ♨ ⌂ ↑ ໂ Richard Masters.
Leisure	snooker.
Location	Moorgate (N off A6038)
Hotel	★★★70% Hollings Hall, Hollins Hall, Baildon, SHIPLEY ☎ (0274) 530053 59 ⇆ ໂⁿ

BINGLEY   Map 07 SE13

Bingley St Ives ☎ Bradford (0274) 562436 & 511788
Parkland/moorland course.
18 holes, 6312yds, Par 71, SSS 71.
Club membership 650.

Visitors	restricted Mon-Fri after 4.30pm & Sat.
Societies	must apply in advance.
Green Fees	not confirmed.
Facilities	⊗ ⅏ ┗ ☟ ♀ ♨ ⌂ ໂ
Leisure	snooker.

▶

Location Golf Club House, St Ives Estate, Harden (0.75m W off B6429)

Hotel ★★★65% Oakwood Hall Hotel, Lady Ln, BINGLEY ☎ (0274) 564123 & 563569 16 ⇆ ⌕

BRADFORD   Map 07 SE13

Bradford Moor ☎ (0274) 638313
Parkland course, hard walking.
9 holes, 5880yds, Par 70, SSS 68, Course record 68.
Club membership 376.
Visitors must play with member after 4pm Fri, Sat, Sun and bank holidays.
Societies must contact in advance.
Green Fees £12 per day/round.
Facilities ⊗ ⊪ ⍾ ⬛ ♀ ⚒ 🏠 ⛳ ⌕ Ron Hughes.
Leisure snooker.
Location Scarr Hall, Pollard Ln (2m NE of city centre off A658)
Hotel ★★66% Park Drive Hotel, 12 Park Dr, BRADFORD ☎ (0274) 480194 11 ⇆ ⌕

Clayton ☎ (0274) 880047
Moorland course, difficult in windy conditions.
9 holes, 5407yds, Par 68, SSS 67.
Club membership 350.
Visitors may not play after 4pm on Sun.
Societies apply in writing to the Secretary or Captain.
Green Fees £12 per day; £10 per round (£12 per round weekends & bank holidays).
Facilities ⊗ & ⍾ (by arrangement,not Mon) ⍾ ⬛ ♀ (not Mon) ⚒
Leisure snooker.
Location Thornton View Rd, Clayton (2.5m SW of city centre on A647)
Hotel ★★★59% Novotel, Merrydale Rd, BRADFORD ☎ (0274) 683683 131 ⇆ ⌕

East Bierley ☎ (0274) 681023
Hilly moorland course with narrow fairways. Two par 3 holes over 200 yds.
9 holes, 4700yds, Par 64, SSS 63.
Club membership 200.
Visitors restricted Sat (am), Sun & Mon evening. Must contact in advance.
Societies must apply in writing.
Green Fees not confirmed.
Facilities ⊗ ⍾ ⍾ ⬛ ♀ ⚒
Leisure snooker.
Location South View Rd, East Bierley (4m SE of city centre off A650)
Hotel ★★★59% Novotel, Merrydale Rd, BRADFORD ☎ (0274) 683683 131 ⇆ ⌕

Headley ☎ (0274) 833481
Hilly moorland course, short but very testing, windy, fine views.
9 holes, 4914yds, Par 64, SSS 64.
Club membership 350.
Visitors must play with member at weekends. Must contact in advance.
Societies must telephone in advance.
Green Fees not confirmed.
Facilities ⚒
Location Headley Ln, Thornton (4m W of city centre off B6145 at Thornton)

Hotel ★★66% Park Drive Hotel, 12 Park Dr, BRADFORD ☎ (0274) 480194 11 ⇆ ⌕

Phoenix Park ☎ (0274) 667573
Very short, tight, moorland course, rather testing.
9 holes, 2491yds, Par 66, SSS 64, Course record 66.
Club membership 260.
Visitors restricted weekends.
Societies must apply in advance.
Green Fees not confirmed.
Facilities ♀ ⚒ 🏠
Location Phoenix Park, Thornbury (E side of city centre on A647)
Hotel ★★66% Park Drive Hotel, 12 Park Dr, BRADFORD ☎ (0274) 480194 11 ⇆ ⌕

Queensbury ☎ (0274) 882155
Undulating woodland/parkland course.
9 holes, 5400yds, Par 66, SSS 65, Course record 64.
Club membership 400.
Visitors restricted weekends. Must have a handicap certificate.
Societies must apply in advance.
Green Fees not confirmed.
Facilities ⊗ ⍾ by prior arrangement ⍾ ⬛ ♀ ⚒ 🏠 ⛳ ⌕ Geoff Howard.
Leisure snooker.
Location Brighouse Rd, Queensbury (4m from Bradford on A647)
Hotel ★★66% Park Drive Hotel, 12 Park Dr, BRADFORD ☎ (0274) 480194 11 ⇆ ⌕

South Bradford ☎ (0274) 679195
Hilly course with good greens, trees and ditches. Interesting short 2nd hole (par 3) 200 yds, well-bunkered and played from an elevated tee.
9 holes, 6028yds, Par 70, SSS 69.
Club membership 305.
Visitors restricted competition days and before 3.30pm weekends and bank holidays unless accompanied by member.
Societies must apply in writing.
Green Fees £14 per day (£22 weekends & bank holidays).
Facilities ⊗ ⍾ ⍾ ⬛ ♀ ⚒ 🏠 ⌕ Ian Marshall.
Leisure snooker.
Location Pearson Rd, Odsal (2m S of city centre off A638)
Hotel ★★★59% Novotel, Merrydale Rd, BRADFORD ☎ (0274) 683683 131 ⇆ ⌕

West Bowling ☎ (0274) 724449
Undulating, tree-lined parkland course. Testing hole: 'the coffin' short par 3, very narrow.
18 holes, 5657yds, Par 69, SSS 67.
Club membership 400.
Visitors restricted before 9.30am, 12-1.30pm & weekends. Must contact in advance and have a letter of introduction.
Societies must apply in writing.
Green Fees £24 per round (£30 weekends).
Facilities ⊗ ⍾ ⍾ ⬛ ♀ ⚒ 🏠 ⛳ ⌕ Allan Swaine.
Leisure snooker.
Location Newall Hall, Rooley Ln (S side of city centre off A638)
Hotel ★★★59% Novotel, Merrydale Rd, BRADFORD ☎ (0274) 683683 131 ⇆ ⌕

West Bradford ☎ West Bradford (0274) 542767
Parkland course, windy, especially 3rd, 4th, 5th and 6th
holes. Hilly but not hard.
18 holes, 5741yds, Par 69, SSS 68.
Club membership 440.
Visitors   restricted Sat.
Societies   must apply in writing.
Green Fees not confirmed.
Facilities   ⊗ 🍴 🛏 💺 ♀ (ex Mon) ⛳ 🏠
                  ♟ Nigel M Barber.
Leisure   snooker.
Location   Chellow Grange Rd (W side of city centre off
                  B6269)
Hotel   ★★★70% Hollings Hall, Hollins Hall, Baildon,
                  SHIPLEY ☎ (0274) 530053 59 ⇥ 🐾

CLECKHEATON   Map 08 SE12

Cleckheaton & District ☎ (0274) 851266
Parkland course with gentle hills.
18 holes, 5769yds, Par 71, SSS 68.
Club membership 550.
Visitors   must contact in advance and have an
                  introduction from own club.
Societies   weekdays only; must contact in advance.
Green Fees not confirmed.
Facilities   ⊗ (ex Mon) 🍴 by prior arrangement 🛏 (ex
                  2pm-4pm) 💺 (ex 2pm-4pm) ♀ ⛳ 🏠 ⚑
                  ♟ Mike Ingham.
Leisure   snooker.
Location   Bradford Rd (1.5m NW on A638 junc 26 M62)
Hotel   ★★★66% Gomersal Park Hotel, Moor Ln,
                  GOMERSAL ☎ (0274) 869386 52 ⇥ 🐾

DEWSBURY   Map 08 SE22

Hanging Heaton ☎ (0924) 461606
Arable land course, easy walking, fine views. Testing 4th
hole (par 3).
9 holes, 5400mtrs, Par 69, SSS 67.
Club membership 550.
Visitors   must play with member at weekends & bank
                  holidays. Must contact in advance.
Societies   must telephone in advance.
Green Fees £12 per day.
Facilities   ⊗ 🛏 💺 ♀ (ex Mon) ⛳ 🏠♟ S Hartley.
Leisure   snooker.
Location   White Cross Rd (0.75m NE off A653)
Hotel   ★★68% Healds Hall Hotel, Leeds Rd,
                  Liversedge, DEWSBURY
                  ☎ (0924) 409112 25 ⇥ 🐾

ELLAND   Map 07 SE12

Elland ☎ (0422) 372505
Parkland course.
9 holes, 2815yds, Par 66, SSS 66, Course record 64.
Club membership 300.
Visitors   must be members of recognised golf club.
Societies   must contact in writing.
Green Fees £12 (£20 weekends and bank holidays).
Facilities   ⊗ 🍴 🛏 💺 (no catering Mon) ♀ ⛳ 🏠
                  ♟ Michael Allison.
Location   Hammerstones, Leach Ln (1m SW)

Hotel   ★★69% Rock Inn Hotel & Churchills
                  Restaurant, HOLYWELL GREEN
                  ☎ (0422) 379721 18 ⇥ 🐾

FENAY BRIDGE   Map 08 SE11

Woodsome Hall ☎ Huddersfield (0484) 602971
A parkland course with good views and an historic clubhouse.
18 holes, 6080yds, Par 70, SSS 69.
Club membership 900.
Visitors   must contact in advance & have handicap
                  certificate. Restricted weekends & competitions.
Societies   must apply in writing.
Green Fees £25 per day (£30 weekends & bank holidays).
Facilities   ⊗ 🍴 by prior arrangement 🛏 💺 ♀ ⛳ 🏠
                  ♟ Michael Higginbottom.
Leisure   snooker.
Location   1.5m SW off A629
Hotel   ★★★70% Springfield Park Hotel, Penistone Rd,
                  KIRKBURTON ☎ (0484) 607788 46 ⇥ 🐾

GARFORTH   Map 08 SE43

Garforth ☎ Leeds (0532) 862021
Parkland course with fine views, easy walking.
18 holes, 6005yds, Par 69, SSS 69.
Club membership 500.
Visitors   must contact in advance and have handicap
                  certificate. With member only weekends & bank
                  holidays.
Societies   must apply in advance.
Green Fees not confirmed.
Facilities   ⊗ 🍴 🛏 💺 ♀ ⛳ 🏠 ⚑♟ K Findlater.
Leisure   snooker.
Location   1m N
Hotel   B Hilton National Leeds/Garforth, Wakefield
                  Rd, Garforth Rdbt, GARFORTH
                  ☎ (0532) 866556 144 ⇥ 🐾

GUISELEY   Map 08 SE14

Bradford ☎ (0943) 875570
Moorland course with eight par 4 holes of 360 yds or more.
18 holes, 6259yds, Par 71, SSS 71.
Club membership 600.
Visitors   must have a handicap certificate. May not play
                  Sun.
Societies   welcome Mon-Fri, must apply in advance.
Green Fees £25 per day; £20 per round (£32/£25 weekends).
Facilities   ⊗ 🍴 🛏 💺 (no catering weekends) ♀ (Mon-Fri)
                  ⛳ 🏠♟ Sydney Weldon.
Leisure   snooker.
Location   Hawksworth Ln (SW side of town centre off
                  A6038)
Hotel   ★★★53% Cow & Calf Hotel, Moor Top,
                  ILKLEY ☎ (0943) 607335 20 ⇥ 🐾

HALIFAX   Map 07 SE02

Halifax ☎ (0422) 244171
Hilly moorland course crossed by streams, natural hazards,
and offering fine views. Testing 172-yd 17th (par3).
18 holes, 6037yds, Par 70, SSS 70, Course record 66.
Club membership 500.   ▶

Visitors restricted competition days. Must contact in advance.
Societies must apply in advance.
Green Fees £20 per day (£30 weekends).
Facilities ⊗ ⅷ ⓑ ♥ (no catering Mon) ♀ ♣ 🏠 ⓕ Steven Foster.
Leisure snooker.
Location Bob Hall, Union Ln, Ogden (4m NW off A629)
Hotel ★★★74% Holdsworth House Hotel, Holmfield, HALIFAX ☎ (0422) 240024 40 ⇆ ⋒

Lightcliffe ☎ (0422) 202459
Heathland course.
9 holes, 5388yds, Par 68, SSS 68.
Club membership 545.
Visitors must be a member of a recognised Golf Club.
Societies must contact 21 days in advance.
Green Fees not confirmed.
Facilities ⊗ ⅷ by prior arrangement ⓑ ♥ ♀ ♣ 🏠 ⓕ Warren Locketty.
Location Knowle Top Rd, Lightcliffe (3.5m E on A58)
Hotel ★★★74% Holdsworth House Hotel, Holmfield, HALIFAX ☎ (0422) 240024 40 ⇆ ⋒

West End ☎ (0422) 353608
Semi-moorland course.
18 holes, 5951yds, Par 69, SSS 69.
Club membership 530.
Visitors not before 10am & 2pm. Must contact in advance & have handicap certificate.
Societies must apply in writing.
Green Fees £22 per day; £17 per round (£27/£20 weekends & bank holidays).
Facilities ⊗ ⅷ ⓑ ♥ (no catering Mon) ♀ ♣ 🏠 ⓕ David Rishworth.
Leisure snooker.
Location Paddock Ln, Highroad Well (W side of town centre off A646)
Hotel ★★★74% Holdsworth House Hotel, Holmfield, HALIFAX ☎ (0422) 240024 40 ⇆ ⋒

HEBDEN BRIDGE   Map 07 SD92

Hebden Bridge ☎ (0422) 842896
Moorland course with splendid views.
9 holes, 5113yds, Par 68, SSS 65, Course record 63.
Club membership 300.
Visitors advisable to contact in advance, restricted weekends.
Societies by arrangment with directors.
Green Fees £10 per day (£15 weekends).
Facilities ⓑ ♥ ♀ ♣
Leisure pool table, TV.
Location Mount Skip, Wadsworth (1.5m E off A6033)
Hotel ★★68% Hebden Lodge Hotel, New Rd, HEBDEN BRIDGE ☎ (0422) 845272 12 ⇆ ⋒

HOLYWELL GREEN   Map 07 SE01

Halifax Bradley Hall ☎ Halifax (0422) 374108
Moorland/parkland course, tightened by recent tree planting, easy walking.
18 holes, 6213yds, Par 70, SSS 70.
Club membership 608.

Visitors no under 17yrs.
Societies must apply in writing.
Green Fees £23 per day; £18 per round (£35/£28 weekends & bank holidays).
Facilities ⊗ ⅷ ⓑ ♥ ♀ ♣ 🏠 ⓕ
Leisure snooker.
Location S on A6112
Hotel ★★69% Rock Inn Hotel & Churchills Restaurant, HOLYWELL GREEN ☎ (0422) 379721 18 ⇆ ⋒

HUDDERSFIELD   Map 07 SE11

Bradley Park ☎ (0484) 539988
Parkland course, challenging with good mix of long and short holes. Also 14-bay floodlit driving range and 9-hole par 3 course, ideal for beginners. Superb views.
18 holes, 6220yds, Par 70, SSS 70, Course record 64.
Par 3: 9 holes, 1019yds, Par 27.
Club membership 300.
Visitors must contact for weekend play.
Societies welcome midweek only, must apply by letter.
Green Fees £8.50 per round (£10 weekends).
Facilities ⊗ ⅷ ⓑ ♥ ♀ ♣ 🏠 ⓟⓕ Parnel Reilly.
Leisure buggies, 14 bay floodlit driving range.
Location Off Bradley Rd (3m N on A6107)
Hotel ★★★67% The George Hotel, St George's Square, HUDDERSFIELD ☎ (0484) 515444 60 ⇆ ⋒

Crosland Heath ☎ (0484) 653216
Moorland course with fine views over valley.
18 holes, 5972yds, Par 70, SSS 70.
Club membership 350.
Visitors must contact in advance and have an introduction from own club.
Societies must telephone in advance.
Green Fees not confirmed.
Facilities ⊗ ⅷ ⓑ ♥ ♀ ♣ 🏠 ⓕ Richard Jessop.
Location Felk Stile Rd, Crosland Heath (SW off A62)
Hotel ★★★67% The George Hotel, St George's Square, HUDDERSFIELD ☎ (0484) 515444 60 ⇆ ⋒

Huddersfield ☎ (0484) 426203
A testing heathland course of championship standard laid out in 1891.
18 holes, 6364yds, Par 71, SSS 71.
Club membership 730.
Visitors restricted Tue (Ladies Day). Must contact in advance.
Societies welcome Mon-Fri, must apply in writing.
Green Fees not confirmed.
Facilities ⊗ ⅷ ⓑ ♥ by prior arrangement ♀ (by prior arrangement) ♣ 🏠 ⓕ Paul Carman.
Leisure snooker.
Location Fixby Hall, Lightridge Rd, Fixby (2m N off A641)
Hotel ★★★67% The George Hotel, St George's Square, HUDDERSFIELD ☎ (0484) 515444 60 ⇆ ⋒

Longley Park ☎ (0484) 422304
Lowland course.
9 holes, 5269yds, Par 66, SSS 66, Course record 63.
Club membership 440.

Visitors must contact in advance & have handicap
certificate, restricted Thu & weekends.
Societies must apply in writing.
Green Fees £13 per round (£16 weekends & bank holidays).
Facilities ⊗ 🍴 by prior arrangement 🛏 💺 ♀ ⅄ 🖼 ⛳
⅃ Paul Middleton.
Location Maple St, Off Somerset Rd (0.5m SE of town
centre off A629)
Hotel ★★★67% The George Hotel, St George's
Square, HUDDERSFIELD
☎ (0484) 515444 60 ⇔ ☈

ILKLEY   Map 07 SE14

Ben Rhydding ☎ (0943) 608759
Moorland/parkland course with splendid views over the
Wharfe valley.
9 holes, 4711yds, Par 65, SSS 64.
Club membership 300.
Visitors restricted Wed and weekends.
Green Fees not confirmed.
Location High Wood, Ben Rhydding (SE side of town)
Hotel ★★75% Rombalds Hotel & Restaurant, 11 West
View, Wells Rd, ILKLEY
☎ (0943) 603201 15 ⇔ ☈

Ilkley ☎ (0943) 600214
This beautiful parkland course is situated in Wharfedale
and the Wharfe is a hazard on each of the first seven
holes. In fact, the 3rd is laid out entirely on an island in
the middle of the river.
18 holes, 6262yds, Par 69, SSS 70.
Club membership 500.
Visitors advisable to contact in advance.
Societies welcome except Tue, Fri & weekends.
Green Fees £30 per day/round (£35 weekends & bank
holidays).
Facilities ⊗ 🍴 🛏 & 💺 by prior arrangement ♀ ⅄ 🖼
⛳ ⅃ John L Hammond.
Leisure fishing, snooker, caddy carts for hire.
Location Middleton (W side of town centre off A65)
Hotel ★★75% Rombalds Hotel & Restaurant, 11
West View, Wells Rd, ILKLEY
☎ (0943) 603201 15 ⇔ ☈

KEIGHLEY   Map 07 SE04

Branshaw ☎ Haworth (0535) 643235 & 647441
Picturesque moorland course with fairly narrow fairways and
good greens. Extensive views.
18 holes, 5858yds, Par 69, SSS 69.
Club membership 500.
Visitors must contact professional in advance.
Societies telephone professional (0535) 647441.
Green Fees £15 per day (£20 weekends).
Facilities ⊗ 🍴 🛏 💺 (no catering Mon) ♀ ⅄ 🖼
⅃ Stephen Bassil.
Location Branshaw Moor, Oakworth (2m SW on B6149)
Hotel ★★68% Dalesgate Hotel, 406 Skipton Rd,
Utley, KEIGHLEY ☎ (0535) 664930 21 ⇔ ☈

Keighley ☎ (0535) 604778
Parkland course with good views down the Aire Valley.
18 holes, 6149yds, Par 69, SSS 70, Course record 65.
Club membership 600.

Visitors restricted Sat & Sun. Must contact in advance.
Societies must apply in advance.
Green Fees not confirmed.
Facilities ⊗ 🍴 🛏 💺 ♀ ⅄ 🖼 ⅃ Mike Bradley.
Location Howden Park, Utley (1m NW of town centre off
B6143)
Hotel ★★68% Dalesgate Hotel, 406 Skipton Rd,
Utley, KEIGHLEY ☎ (0535) 664930 21 ⇔ ☈

LEEDS   Map 08 SE33

Brandon ☎ (0532) 737471
An 18-hole links type course enjoying varying degrees of
rough, water and sand hazards.
18 holes, 3650yds, Par 58, SSS 62.
Club membership 100.
Visitors must have own set of golf clubs.
Societies must telephone in advance.
Green Fees £7 per round (£7.50 weekend & bank holidays).
Facilities 💺 ⅄ 🖼
Location Holywell Ln, Shadwell
Hotel ★★★79% Haley's Hotel & Restaurant, Shire
Oak Rd, Headingley, LEEDS
☎ (0532) 784446 22 ⇔ ☈

Gotts Park ☎ (0532) 638232
Municipal parkland course; hilly and windy with narrow
fairways. Some very steep hills to some greens. A
challenging course requiring accuracy rather than length from
the tees.
18 holes, 4960yds, Par 65, SSS 64, Course record 63.
Club membership 300.
Visitors no restrictions.
Green Fees not confirmed.
Facilities 🛏 💺 ♀ (evenings) 🖼 ⛳ ⅃ John F Simpson.
Location Armley Ridge Rd (3m W of city centre off
A647)
Hotel ★★★★67% The Queen's, City Square, LEEDS
☎ (0532) 431323 190rm(188 ⇔ ☈)

Headingley ☎ (0532) 679573
An undulating course with a wealth of natural features
offering fine views from higher ground. Its most striking
hazard is the famous ravine at the 18th. Leeds's oldest course,
founded in 1892.
18 holes, 6298yds, Par 69, SSS 70.
Club membership 630.
Visitors must contact in advance. Restricted before 9.30
& 12-1.45pm.
Societies must telephone in advance and confirm in
writing.
Green Fees £30 per day; £25 per round (£36 per day/round
weekends & bank holidays).
Facilities ⊗ 🍴 🛏 💺 ♀ ⅄ 🖼 ⅃ Andrew Dyson.
Leisure snooker.
Location Back Church Ln, Adel (5.5m N of city centre off
A660)
Hotel B Forte Crest, Leeds Rd, BRAMHOPE
☎ (0532) 842911 126 ⇔ ☈

Horsforth ☎ (0532) 586819
Moorland course overlooking airport.
18 holes, 6243yds, Par 71, SSS 70, Course record 66.
Club membership 750.
Visitors restricted Sat & with member only Sun.
Societies must apply in writing.   ▶

Green Fees £24 per day; £20 per round (£30 per day
    weekends & bank holidays).
Facilities ⊗ ⅏ ᴌ ♖ ♀ ♨ 🏠 ⸙ Peter Scott.
Leisure snooker.
Location Layton Rise, Layton Rd, Horsforth (6.5m NW of
    city centre off A65)
Hotel B Forte Crest, Leeds Rd, BRAMHOPE
    ☎ (0532) 842911 126 ⇌ ┠

Leeds ☎ (0532) 658775
Parkland course with pleasant views.
18 holes, 6097yds, Par 69, SSS 69.
Club membership 600.
Visitors with member only weekends, yellow tees only.
    Must contact in advance.
Societies must apply in writing.
Green Fees not confirmed.
Facilities ⊗ ⅏ ᴌ ♖ (catering limited Mon) ♀ ♨ 🏠 ⸙
    ⸙ Simon Longster.
Leisure snooker.
Location Elmete Ln (5m NE of city centre on A6120 off
    A58)
Hotel ★★★79% Haley's Hotel & Restaurant, Shire
    Oak Rd, Headingley, LEEDS
    ☎ (0532) 784446 22 ⇌ ┠

Middleton Park Municipal ☎ (0532) 700449
Parkland course.
18 holes, 5263yds, Par 68, SSS 66, Course record 65.
Club membership 300.
Visitors no restrictions.
Green Fees not confirmed.
Facilities ♨ 🏠 ⸙
Location Middleton Park, Middleton (3m S off A653)
Hotel ★★★67% The Queen's, City Square, LEEDS
    ☎ (0532) 431323 190rm(188 ⇌ ┠)

Moor Allerton ☎ (0532) 661154
The Moor Allerton Club has 27 holes set in 220 acres of
undulating parkland, with magnificent views extending
across the Vale of York. The Championship Course was
designed by Robert Trent Jones, the famous American
course architect, and is the only course of his design in
the British Isles.
Lakes: 18 holes, 6314yds, Par 71, SSS 72.
Blackmoor: 18 holes, 6502yds, Par 71, SSS 72.
High Course: 18 holes, 6672yds, Par 72, SSS 73.
Club membership 1200.
Visitors restricted Sun.
Societies must apply in advance.
Green Fees £37 per day (£50 weekends). Reduced fees
    Nov-Mar.
Facilities ⊗ ⅏ ᴌ ♖ ♀ ♨ 🏠 ⸙ Richard Lane.
Leisure hard tennis courts, snooker, sauna, 6 bay
    covered driving range, caddy cars.
Location Coal Rd, Wike (5.5m N of city centre on
    A61)
Hotel ★★★63% Harewood Arms Hotel,
    Harrogate Rd, HAREWOOD
    ☎ (0532) 886566 24 ⇌ ┠

**For an explanation of symbols and
abbreviations, see page 5**

Moortown ☎ (0532) 686521
Championship course, tough but fair. Springy moorland
turf, natural hazards of heather, gorse and streams,
cunningly placed bunkers and immaculate greens.
18 holes, 6826yds, Par 71, SSS 74, Course record 69.
Club membership 550.
Visitors weekend by prior arrangement
Societies must apply in advance.
Green Fees £40 per day; £35 per round (£45/£40
    weekends).
Facilities ⊗ ⅏ ᴌ ♖ (all catering by prior
    arrangement on Mon) ♀ ♨ 🏠 ⸙
Leisure snooker.
Location Harrogate Rd, Alwoodley (6m N of city
    centre on A61)
Hotel ★★★63% Harewood Arms Hotel,
    Harrogate Rd, HAREWOOD
    ☎ (0532) 886566 24 ⇌ ┠

Oulton Park ☎ (0532) 823152
27-hole championship-length municipal course. Although
municipal, a dress rule is applied. 16-bay driving range.
*18 holes, 6550yds, Par 71, SSS 70 or 9 holes, 3299yds, Par
36, SSS 35.*
Club membership 500.
Visitors must wear golf shoes and abide by dress rules.
Societies contact in advance.
Green Fees £6.80 per 18 holes (£7.40 weekends). £4.40 per
    9 holes.
Facilities ⊗ ᴌ ♖ ♀ ♨ 🏠 ⸙ ⸙ Stephen Gromett.
Leisure buggies, driving range.
Location Rothwell (junc 30 on M62)
Hotel ★★★★75% Oulton Hall Hotel, Rothwell Ln,
    ROTHWELL ☎ (0532) 821000 152 ⇌ ┠

Roundhay ☎ (0532) 662695
Attractive municipal parkland course, natural hazards, easy
walking.
9 holes, 5166yds, Par 65, SSS 70.
Club membership 350.
Visitors no restrictions.
Societies must apply in advance to Leeds City Council.
Green Fees £6.90 per round (£7.40 weekends & bank
    holidays).
Facilities ᴌ ♖ ♀ ♨ 🏠 ⸙ Jim Pape.
Location Park Ln (4m NE of city centre off A58)
Hotel ★★★79% Haley's Hotel & Restaurant, Shire
    Oak Rd, Headingley, LEEDS
    ☎ (0532) 784446 22 ⇌ ┠

Sand Moor ☎ (0532) 685180
A beautiful, undulating course overlooking Lord
Harewood's estate and the Eccup Reservoir. The course
is wooded with some holes adjacent to water. The 12th is
perhaps the most difficult where the fairway falls away
towards the reservoir.
18 holes, 6429yds, Par 71, SSS 71, Course record 63.
Club membership 553.
Visitors restricted weekends & bank holidays.
Societies must apply in advance.
Green Fees £35 per day; £28 per round (£38 per round
    Sun & bank holidays).
Facilities ⊗ (Mon by prior arrangement) ⅏ by prior
    arrangement ᴌ ♖ ♀ ♨ 🏠 ⸙ Peter Tupling.
Leisure snooker, practice area.

Location	Alwoodley Ln (5m N of city centre off A61)
Hotel	B Forte Crest, Leeds Rd, BRAMHOPE
	☎ (0532) 842911 126 ⇔ ↖

South Leeds ☎ (0532) 700479
Parkland couse, windy, hard walking, good views.
18 holes, 5769yds, Par 69, SSS 68, Course record 59.
Club membership 632.

Visitors   must contact in advance & have handicap
certificate. No play weekends & bank holidays.
Societies   must apply in advance.
Green Fees £18 per day/round (£26 weekends & bank
holidays).
Facilities   ⊗ ⅢⅢ ▙ & 🍺 by prior arrangement ♀ ᐃ 📦
🍴 Mike Lewis.
Location   Gipsy Ln, Beeston (3m S of city centre off
A653)
Hotel   ★★★67% The Queen's, City Square, LEEDS
☎ (0532) 431323 190rm(188 ⇔ ↖)

Temple Newsam ☎ (0532) 645624
Two parkland courses. Testing long 13th (563 yds) on second
course.
Lord Irwin: 18 holes, 6460yds, Par 69, SSS 71.
Lady Dorothy: 18 holes, 6276yds, Par 70, SSS 70.
Club membership 520.

Visitors   no restrictions.
Societies   must apply in advance.
Green Fees not confirmed.
Facilities   ⊗ (weekends only) ▙ 🍺 (weekends only) ♀ ᐃ
📦 🍴 David Bulmer.
Leisure   snooker.
Location   Temple-Newsam Rd (3.5m E of city centre off
A63)
Hotel   ★★★79% Haley's Hotel & Restaurant, Shire
Oak Rd, Headingley, LEEDS
☎ (0532) 784446 22 ⇔ ↖

MARSDEN   Map 07 SE01

Marsden ☎ (0484) 844253
Moorland course with good views, natural hazards, windy.
9 holes, 5702yds, Par 68, SSS 68.
Club membership 200.

Visitors   must play with member at weekends.
Societies   Mon-Fri; must contact in advance.
Green Fees £10 (£15 bank holidays).
Facilities   ⊗ ⅢⅢ ▙ 🍺 (no catering Tue) ♀ ᐃ 📦
🍴 A J Bickerdike.
Leisure   hard tennis courts.
Location   Mount Rd, Hemplow (S side of A62)
Hotel   ★★★62% Briar Court Hotel, Halifax
Road,Birchencliffe, HUDDERSFIELD
☎ (0484) 519902 47 ⇔ ↖

MELTHAM   Map 07 SE01

Meltham ☎ Huddersfield (0484) 850227
Parkland course with good views. Testing 548 yd, 13th hole
(par 5).
18 holes, 6145yds, Par 70, SSS 70, Course record 65.
Club membership 535.

Visitors   restricted Sat & Wed (Ladies Day).
Societies   must apply in advance.

Green Fees £20 per day (£25 weekends & bank holidays).
Facilities   ⊗ ⅢⅢ ▙ 🍺 ♀ ᐃ 📦 🍴 Paul Davies.
Leisure   snooker.
Location   Thick Hollins Hall (SE side of village off
B6107)
Hotel   ★★★67% The George Hotel, St George's
Square, HUDDERSFIELD
☎ (0484) 515444 60 ⇔ ↖

MIRFIELD   Map 08 SE21

Dewsbury District ☎ (0924) 492399
Heathland/parkland course with panoramic view from top,
hard walking. Ponds in middle of 3rd fairway, left of 5th
green and 17th green.
18 holes, 6267yds, Par 71, SSS 71, Course record 64.
Club membership 650.

Visitors   restricted weekends before 4pm & bank
holidays. Must contact in advance.
Societies   must apply in advance.
Green Fees £20 per day; £16 per round (£18 per round
weekends & bank holidays).
Facilities   ⊗ ⅢⅢ by prior arrangement ▙ 🍺 ♀ ᐃ 📦 🍴
🍴 Nigel P Hirst.
Leisure   snooker, practice area.
Location   Sands Ln (1m S off A644)
Hotel   ★★★67% The George Hotel, St George's
Square, HUDDERSFIELD
☎ (0484) 515444 60 ⇔ ↖

MORLEY   Map 08 SE22

Howley Hall ☎ Batley (0924) 478417
Parkland course with easy walking and good views.
18 holes, 6058yds, Par 71, SSS 69.
Club membership 500.

Visitors   standard course only. Must contact in advance.
Societies   must apply in writing.
Green Fees £23 per day; £19 per round (£26 day/round
weekends & bank holidays).
Facilities   ⊗ ⅢⅢ by prior arrangement ▙ 🍺 ♀ ᐃ 📦 🍴
🍴 Stephen Spinks.
Leisure   snooker.
Location   Scotchman Ln (1.5m S on B6123)
Hotel   ★★66% Alder House Hotel, Towngate Rd, off
Healey Ln, BATLEY
☎ (0924) 444777 22rm(21 ⇔ ↖)

NORMANTON   Map 08 SE32

Normanton ☎ Wakefield (0924) 892943
A pleasant, flat course with tight fairways in places and an
internal out-of-bounds requiring accuracy.
9 holes, 5288yds, Par 66, SSS 66.
Club membership 250.

Visitors   may not play on Sun.
Societies   mid-week only.
Green Fees £10 (£17 weekends & bank holidays).
Facilities   ⊗ ⅢⅢ by prior arrangement ▙ 🍺 ♀ ᐃ 📦 🍴
🍴 Martin Evans.
Location   Snydale Rd (0.5m SE on B6133)
Hotel   ★★★63% Swallow Hotel, Queens St,
WAKEFIELD ☎ (0924) 372111 64 ⇔ ↖

OSSETT
Map 08 SE22

Low Laithes ☎ (0924) 273275
Testing parkland course.
18 holes, 6463yds, Par 72, SSS 71.
Club membership 575.
Visitors may not play weekends and bank holidays. Must contact in advance.
Societies welcome Mon-Fri, must apply in advance.
Green Fees £22 per day/round.
Facilities ⊗ ⅷ ⬤ ♀ ♨ 🏠 ⚑ 𝔩 P Browning.
Location Parkmill Ln, Flushdyke (1.5m SE off A128)
Hotel B Forte Posthouse, CRICK ☎ (0788) 822101 88 ⇔ 𝔫

OTLEY
Map 08 SE24

Otley ☎ (0943) 465329
An expansive course with magnificent views across Wharfedale. It is well-wooded with streams crossing the fairway. The 4th is a fine hole which generally needs two woods to reach the plateau green. The 17th is a good short hole.
18 holes, 6235yds, Par 70, SSS 70.
Club membership 700.
Visitors restricted Sat.
Societies must contact in advance.
Green Fees £23 per round.
Facilities ⊗ & ⅷ by prior arrangement ⬤ ♀ ♨ 🏠 ⚑ 𝔩 Simon Poot.
Leisure snooker, practice ground, trolleys.
Location Off West Busk Ln (1.5m SW off A6038)
Hotel B Forte Crest, Leeds Rd, BRAMHOPE ☎ (0532) 842911 126 ⇔ 𝔫

OUTLANE
Map 07 SE01

Outlane ☎ Halifax (0422) 374762
Moorland course.
18 holes, 6003yds, Par 71, SSS 69, Course record 67.
Club membership 500.
Visitors must contact in advance but may not play Sat & before 10.30am Sun.
Societies must contact 14 days in advance.
Green Fees £18 per day (£30 weekends & bank holidays).
Facilities ⊗ ⅷ ⬤ ♀ ♨ 🏠 ⚑ 𝔩 David Chapman.
Location Slack Ln (S side of village off A640)
Hotel ★★★68% Old Golf House Hotel, New Hey Rd, OUTLANE ☎ (0422) 379311 50 ⇔ 𝔫

PONTEFRACT
Map 08 SE42

Mid Yorkshire ☎ (0977) 704522
An 18-hole championship-standard course opened in 1992.
18 holes, 6500yds, Par 72, SSS 72, Course record 68.
Club membership 500.
Visitors must contact in advance, with member only at weekends.
Societies apply in writing to the secretary.
Green Fees not confirmed.
Facilities ⊗ ⅷ ⬤ ♀ ♨ 🏠 ⚑ 🚗 𝔩 Peter Scott.
Leisure golf academy with 28 driving bays.
Location Havercroft Ln, Darrington (2m SE)
Hotel ★★★67% Wentbridge House Hotel, WENTBRIDGE ☎ (0977) 620444 12 ⇔ 𝔫

Pontefract & District ☎ (0977) 792241
Parkland course.
18 holes, 6227yds, Par 72, SSS 70.
Club membership 800.
Visitors welcome except Wed & weekends. Must contact in advance and have a handicap certificate.
Societies welcome except Wed & weekends.
Green Fees £25 (£32 weekends & bank holidays).
Facilities ⊗ ⅷ ⬤ ♀ ♨ 🏠 Nick Newman.
Location Park Ln (1.5m W on B6134)
Hotel ★★★67% Wentbridge House Hotel, WENTBRIDGE ☎ (0977) 620444 12 ⇔ 𝔫

PUDSEY
Map 08 SE23

Calverley ☎ (0532) 569244
Two parkland courses on top of a hill. The course was established 10 years ago and has a few water hazards and some bunkers.
18 holes, 5527yds, Par 68, SSS 67 or 9 holes, 2137yds, Par 33.
Club membership 700.
Visitors no restrictions.
Societies contact in writing or telephone.
Green Fees £12 per 18 holes; £6 per 9 holes (£18 weekends & bank holidays).
Facilities ⊗ ⅷ ⬤ ♀ ♨ 🏠 ⚑ 𝔩 Derek Johnson.
Location Woodhall Ln
Hotel ★★66% Park Drive Hotel, 12 Park Dr, BRADFORD ☎ (0274) 480194 11 ⇔ 𝔫

Fulneck ☎ (0532) 565191
Picturesque, hilly parkland course. Compact but strenuous.
9 holes, 5432yds, Par 67, SSS 65.
Club membership 300.
Visitors must contact in advance. With member only weekends & bank holidays.
Societies must apply in writing.
Green Fees £12 per day.
Facilities ⊗ ⅷ ⬤ (catering by prior arrangement) ♀ ♨
Leisure pool table.
Location S side of town centre
Hotel ★★★59% Novotel, Merrydale Rd, BRADFORD ☎ (0274) 683683 131 ⇔ 𝔫

Woodhall Hills ☎ (0532) 564771
Meadowland course, prevailing SW winds, fairly hard walking. Testing holes: 8th, 377 yd (par 4); 14th, 206 yd (par 3).
18 holes, 6102yds, Par 71, SSS 69, Course record 66.
Club membership 612.
Visitors restricted Mon-Fri until 9.30am.
Societies must apply in writing.
Green Fees £20.50 per day/round (£25.50 weekends & bank holidays).
Facilities ⊗ (ex Mon) ⅷ ⬤ ♀ ♨ 🏠 𝔩 Darren Tear.
Leisure snooker, trolleys.
Location Calverley (2.5m NW off A647)
Hotel ★★66% Park Drive Hotel, 12 Park Dr, BRADFORD ☎ (0274) 480194 11 ⇔ 𝔫

> **For an explanation of symbols and abbreviations, see page 5**

RAWDON
Map 08 SE23

Rawdon Golf & Lawn Tennis Club ☎ (0532) 506040
Undulating parkland course.
9 holes, 5980yds, Par 72, SSS 69.
Club membership 700.
Visitors   must contact in advance & have handicap
certificate. With member only at weekends.
Societies   must contact in advance.
Green Fees   not confirmed.
Facilities   ⊗ ⊪ ⓑ 🍺 ♀ ♨ 🖐 🛈 Syd Wheldon.
Leisure   hard and grass tennis courts, snooker.
Location   Buckstone Dr (S side of town off A65)
Hotel   B Forte Crest, Leeds Rd, BRAMHOPE
☎ (0532) 842911 126 ⇆ 🐾

RIDDLESDEN
Map 07 SE04

Riddlesden ☎ Keighley (0535) 602148
Undulating moorland course with prevailing west winds,
some hard walking and beautiful views. Ten Par 3 holes and
spectacular 6th and 15th holes played over old quarry sites.
18 holes, 4247yds, Par 62, SSS 61.
Club membership 250.
Visitors   restricted before 2pm weekends.
Societies   must apply in writing.
Green Fees   £12 per round (£15 weekends).
Facilities   ⊗ ⊪ ⓑ 🍺 ♀ ♨
Location   Howden Rough (1m NW)
Hotel   ★★68% Dalesgate Hotel, 406 Skipton Rd,
Utley, KEIGHLEY
☎ (0535) 664930 21 ⇆ 🐾

SCARCROFT
Map 08 SE34

Scarcroft ☎ Leeds (0532) 892311
Undulating parkland course with prevailing west wind and
easy walking.
18 holes, 6031yds, Par 71, SSS 69.
Club membership 667.
Visitors   must contact in advance.
Societies   must contact in advance.
Green Fees   £30 per day; £25 per round (£35 weekends &
bank holidays).
Facilities   ⊗ ⊪ (ex Sun & Mon) ⓑ 🍺 ♀ (ex Sun) ♨ 🖐
⛳ 🛈 Martin Ross.
Leisure   snooker.
Location   Syke Ln (0.5m N of village off A58)
Hotel   ★★★63% Harewood Arms Hotel, Harrogate
Rd, HAREWOOD ☎ (0532) 886566 24 ⇆ 🐾

SHIPLEY
Map 07 SE13

Northcliffe ☎ Bradford (0274) 596731
Parkland course with magnificent views of moors. Testing 1st
hole (18th green 100 feet below tee).
18 holes, 5839yds, Par 71, SSS 68, Course record 66.
Club membership 657.
Visitors   no restrictions.
Societies   must apply in writing.
Green Fees   £20 per day (£25 weekends & bank holidays).
Facilities   ⊗ ⊪ ⓑ 🍺 (no catering Mon) ♀ ♨ 🖐
🛈 M Hillas.
Leisure   snooker.

Location   High Bank Ln (1.25m SW off A650)
Hotel   ★★★70% Hollings Hall, Hollins Hall, Baildon,
SHIPLEY ☎ (0274) 530053 59 ⇆ 🐾

SILSDEN
Map 07 SE04

Silsden ☎ Steeton (0535) 652998
Tight downland course which can be windy. Good views of
the Aire Valley.
14 holes, 4870yds, Par 65, SSS 64, Course record 61.
Club membership 300.
Visitors   may not play before 11am on Sun.
Societies   must apply in advance.
Green Fees   £10 per day (£16 weekends & bank holidays).
Facilities   ⓑ 🍺 ♀ ♨
Location   High Brunthwaite (1m E)
Hotel   ★★68% Dalesgate Hotel, 406 Skipton Rd,
Utley, KEIGHLEY ☎ (0535) 664930 21 ⇆ 🐾

SOWERBY
Map 07 SE02

Ryburn ☎ Halifax (0422) 831355
Moorland course, easy walking.
9 holes, 4984yds, Par 66, SSS 64, Course record 64.
Club membership 200.
Visitors   must contact in advance.
Societies   apply in writing.
Green Fees   not confirmed.
Facilities   ⊗ ⊪ ⓑ & 🍺 by prior arrangement ♀ ♨
Location   The Shaw, Norland (1m S of Sowerby Bridge
off A58)
Hotel   ★★69% The Hobbit Hotel, Hob Ln, Norland,
SOWERBY BRIDGE
☎ (0422) 832202 17 ⇆ 🐾 Annexe5 ⇆ 🐾

TODMORDEN
Map 07 SD92

Todmorden ☎ (0706) 812986
Pleasant moorland course.
9 holes, 5818yds, Par 68, SSS 68.
Club membership 250.
Visitors   restricted Sat, bank holidays & competition days.
Societies   must contact in advance.
Green Fees   £15 per day (£20 weekends).
Facilities   all catering by by prior arrangement ♀ ♨ 🖐
Location   Rive Rocks, Cross Stone Rd (NE off A646)
Hotel   ★★★64% Scaitcliffe Hall, Burnley Rd,
TODMORDEN ☎ (0706) 818888 13 ⇆ 🐾

WAKEFIELD
Map 08 SE32

City of Wakefield ☎ (0924) 367442 & 360282
Parkland course.
18 holes, 6299yds, Par 72, SSS 70.
Club membership 850.
Visitors   restricted weekends.
Societies   must apply in advance.
Green Fees   prices on application.
Facilities   ⊗ & ⊪ (book with steward) ⓑ 🍺 ♀ ♨ 🖐 ⛳
🛈 Roger Holland.
Location   Lupset Park, Horbury Rd (1.5m W of city centre
on A642)
Hotel   B Forte Posthouse, Queen's Dr, Ossett,
WAKEFIELD ☎ (0924) 276388 99 ⇆ 🐾

Painthorpe House ☎ (0924) 255083
Undulating meadowland course, easy walking.
9 holes, 4520yds, Par 62, SSS 62.
Club membership 150.
Visitors   restricted weekends.
Societies   must apply in advance.
Green Fees not confirmed.
Facilities   ⊗ ⊞ ⓛ ⬤ ♀ ♨ 🏠
Leisure   bowling green.
Location   Painthorpe Ln, Painthorpe, Crigglestone (2m S
           off A636)
Hotel   B Forte Posthouse, Queen's Dr, Ossett,
           WAKEFIELD ☎ (0924) 276388 99 ⇆ 👣

Wakefield ☎ (0924) 255104
A well-sheltered meadowland/heath course with easy walking
and good views.
18 holes, 6611yds, Par 72, SSS 72, Course record 66.
Club membership 550.
Visitors   strict dress code.
Societies   must apply in writing.
Green Fees £25 per day; £20 per round (£27 weekends &
           bank holidays).
Facilities   ⊗ & ⊞ by prior arrangement ⓛ ⬤ ♀ ♨ 🏠
           ⌀ I M Wright.
Leisure   snooker.
Location   Woodthorpe Ln, Sandal (3m S off A61)
Hotel   B Forte Posthouse, Queen's Dr, Ossett,
           WAKEFIELD ☎ (0924) 276388 99 ⇆ 👣

WETHERBY   Map 08 SE44

Wetherby ☎ (0937) 580089
Parkland course with fine views.
18 holes, 5888yds, Par 69, SSS 68, Course record 66.
Club membership 750.
Visitors   may not play 12-1.15pm weekdays, and all day
           Tue. Restricted times on Sat.
Societies   welcome Mon & Wed-Fri, must apply in
           writing.
Green Fees £28 per day; £23 per round (£34 per day/round
           weekends).
Facilities   ⊗ ⊞ ⓛ ⬤ (all catering by prior arrangement) ♀
           ♨ 🏠 ⌀ D Padgett.
Leisure   snooker.
Location   Linton Ln (1m W off A661)
Hotel   ★★★59% Wetherby Resort Hotel, Leeds Rd,
           WETHERBY ☎ (0937) 583881 72 ⇆ 👣

WIGHT, ISLE OF

COWES   Map 04 SZ49

Cowes ☎ (0983) 292303
Fairly level, tight parkland course with difficult par 3s and
Solent views.
9 holes, 5934yds, Par 70, SSS 68, Course record 66.
Club membership 300.
Visitors   restricted Thu, Fri & Sun mornings.

Societies   must contact in advance.
Green Fees £15 per day/round (£18 weekends).
Facilities   ⓛ ⬤ ♀ ♨ 🏹
Location   Crossfield Av (NW side of town)
Hotel   ★★62% Fountain Hotel, High St, COWES
           ☎ (0983) 292397 20 ⇆

EAST COWES   Map 04 SZ59

Osborne ☎ (0983) 295421
Undulating parkland course in the grounds of Osborne House.
Quiet and peaceful situation.
9 holes, 6276yds, Par 70, SSS 70.
Club membership 350.
Visitors   restricted Tue 9am-1pm & weekends before
           noon. Handicap certificate required.
Societies   must contact in advance.
Green Fees £16 per day (£19 weekends & bank holidays).
Facilities   ⊗ ⊞ by prior arrangement ⓛ ⬤ ♀ ♨ 🏠 🏹
           ⌀ Andrew Scullion.
Location   Osborne House Estate (E side of town centre off
           A3021)
Hotel   ★★61% Cowes Hotel, 260 Artic Rd, COWES
           ☎ (0983) 291541 15 ⇆ 👣

FRESHWATER   Map 04 SZ38

Freshwater Bay ☎ (0983) 752955
A downland/seaside links with wide fairways and spectacular
coastal views of the Solent and Channel.
18 holes, 5662yds, Par 68, SSS 68, Course record 64.
Club membership 600.
Visitors   may not play before 9.30am weekdays & 10am
           Sun.
Societies   must telephone in advance.
Green Fees not confirmed.
Facilities   ⊗ ⊞ ⓛ ⬤ ♀ ♨ 🏹
Location   Afton Down (0.5m E of village off A3055)
Hotel   ★★★64% Albion Hotel, FRESHWATER
           ☎ (0983) 753631 42 ⇆ 👣

NEWPORT   Map 04 SZ58

Newport ☎ (0983) 525076
Downland course, fine views.
9 holes, 5704yds, Par 68, SSS 67, Course record 65.
Club membership 340.
Visitors   may not play Wed noon-3.30pm or after 3pm Sat
           & noon Sun.
Societies   must telephone in advance.
Green Fees £15 per day (£17.50 weekends & bank holidays).
Facilities   ⊗ & ⊞ by prior arrangement ⓛ ⬤ ♀ ♨ 🏠 🏹
Location   St George's Down (1.5m S off A3020)
Hotel   ★★★57% Melville Hall Hotel, Melville St,
           SANDOWN ☎ (0983) 406526 33 ⇆ 👣

RYDE   Map 04 SZ59

Ryde ☎ (0983) 614809
Downland course with wide views over the Solent.
9 holes, 5287yds, Par 66, SSS 66.
Club membership 375.
Visitors   may not play Wed afternoons & Sun mornings.
Societies   must contact in writing.

Green Fees £15 (£20 weekends).
Facilities ⊗ ⓑ ♥ ♀ ⚑ 📠
Location Binstead Rd (1m W on A3054)
Hotel ★★65% Biskra House Beach Hotel, 17 Saint
Thomas's St, RYDE
☎ (0983) 567913 9 ⇥ 🐾

SANDOWN
Map 04 SZ58

Shanklin & Sandown ☎ (0983) 403217
Heathland course.
18 holes, 6000yds, Par 70, SSS 68, Course record 65.
Club membership 650.
Visitors must be member of a recognised club with a
handicap certificate. Must contact in advance.
Societies limited bookings; telephone in advance.
Green Fees £20/£25.
Facilities ⊗ ⌱ ⓑ ♥ ♀ ⚑ 📠 ꝑ 🍴 Peter Hammond.
Leisure snooker.
Location Fairway, Lake (1m NW)
Hotel ★★★59% Cliff Tops Hotel, Park Rd,
SHANKLIN ☎ (0983) 863262 88 ⇥ 🐾

VENTNOR
Map 04 SZ57

Ventnor ☎ (0983) 853326
Downland course subject to wind. Fine seascapes.
12 holes, 5767yds, Par 70, SSS 68.
Club membership 300.
Visitors may not play Fri noon-3.30pm or Sun mornings.
Societies must contact in advance.
Green Fees £12 per day (£14 weekends & bank holidays).
Facilities ⓑ ♥ ♀ ⚑ ꝑ
Leisure pool table.
Location Steep Hill Down Rd, Upper Ventnor (1m NW
off B3327)
Hotel ★★★62% Ventnor Towers Hotel, Madeira Rd,
VENTNOR ☎ (0983) 852277 27 ⇥ 🐾

● WILTSHIRE ●

BISHOPS CANNINGS
Map 04 SU06

North Wilts ☎ (0380) 860627
High, downland course with fine views.
18 holes, 6322yds, Par 70, SSS 70.
Club membership 800.
Visitors welcome, a handicap certificate is required at
weekends.
Societies must book in advance.
Green Fees £25 per day; £18 per round (£30 weekends).
Facilities ⊗ ⌱ by prior arrangement ⓑ ♥ ♀ ⚑ 📠
🍴 Graham Laing.
Leisure practice grounds, some caddy cars.
Location 2m NW
Hotel ★★★62% Bear Hotel, Market Place, DEVIZES
☎ (0380) 722444 24 ⇥ 🐾

CALNE
Map 03 ST97

Bowood Golf & Country Club ☎ (0249) 822228
A long, undulating course designed by Dave Thomas. Set in a
Grade I listed Capability Brown park full of mature trees and
acres of wildflowers, the course is a real test of golf. A 10-
bay driving range and grass teeing area are enhanced by a 3-
hole Academy course and putting greens
18 holes, 6890, Par 72, SSS 73, Course record 70.
Club membership 250.
Visitors welcome except before noon on Sat and Sun.
Societies booking by telephone or letter essential.
Green Fees £40 per 36 holes; £35 per 27 holes; £27 per 18
holes (Sat and bank holidays £32, Sun £27).
Facilities ⊗ ⌱ ⓑ ♥ ♀ ⚑ 📠 ꝑ 🏊
🍴 N Blenkarne, G Hanham.
Leisure caddy cars, driving range, putting green.
Location Off A6 between Chippenham & Calne
Hotel ★★61% Lansdowne Strand Hotel & Restaurant,
The Strand, CALNE
☎ (0249) 812488 21 ⇥ 🐾Annexe5 ⇥

CASTLE COMBE
Map 03 ST87

Castle Combe ☎ Chippenham (0249) 782982
Opened in 1992 and set in one of the finest locations in
England, this 18-hole Peter Alliss/Clive Clark course was
designed to marry neatly with the surrounding conservation
area. Many mature trees have been used to great effect giving
individuality and challenge to every shot. There are
spectacular holes at the 17th & 18th with lakes and waterfalls
making them memorable.
18 holes, 6340yds, Par 72, SSS 73, Course record 67.
Club membership 730.
Visitors no restrictions.
Societies contact in advance.
Green Fees £25/£20 per day; £29/25 (weekends & bank
holidays).
Facilities ⊗ ⌱ ⓑ ♥ ♀ ⚑ 📠 ꝑ 🍴 Christine Langford.
Leisure snooker, sauna.
Location 5m NW of Chippenham
Hotel ★★★★(red)🎖 Manor House Hotel, CASTLE
COMBE
☎ (0249) 782206 12 ⇥ 🐾Annexe24 ⇥ 🐾

CHIPPENHAM
Map 03 ST97

Chippenham ☎ (0249) 652040
Easy walking on downland course. Testing holes at 1st and
15th.
18 holes, 5559yds, Par 69, SSS 67, Course record 64.
Club membership 650.
Visitors must contact in advance and have a handicap
certificate.
Societies must contact in writing; handicap certificates
required.
Green Fees £20 per day (£25 weekends & bank holidays).
Facilities ⊗ & ⌱ (ex Mon) ⓑ ♥ ♀ ⚑ ꝑ
🍴 Bill Creamer.
Location Malmesbury Rd (1.5m N on A429)
Hotel ★★★★(red)🎖 Manor House Hotel, CASTLE
COMBE
☎ (0249) 782206 12 ⇥ 🐾Annexe24 ⇥ 🐾

DURNFORD, GREAT   Map 04 SU13

High Post ☎ Middle Woodford (072273) 356
An interesting downland course on Wiltshire chalk with
good turf and splendid views over the southern area of
Salisbury Plain. The par 3, 17th and the two-shot 18th
require good judgement.
18 holes, 6297yds, Par 70, SSS 70, Course record 64.
Club membership 600.

Visitors	a handicap certificate is required at weekends.
Societies	welcome except weekends.
Green Fees	£28 per day; £20 per round (£33/£25 weekends).
Facilities	⊗ ℳ ᴸ ⬛ ♀ ᐃ 🛍 ₵ Anthony John Harman.
Leisure	large practice ground.
Location	1.75m SE on A345
Hotel	★★★67% Rose & Crown Hotel, Harnham Rd, Harnham, SALISBURY ☎ (0722) 327908 28 ⇌ ℟

HIGHWORTH   Map 04 SU29

Highworth Community Golf Centre ☎ Swindon (0793)
766014
Public downland course, situated in a high position affording
good views.
9 holes, 3120yds, Par 35, SSS 35.
Club membership 170.

Visitors	no restrictions.
Societies	must telephone in advance.
Green Fees	not confirmed.
Facilities	⬛ 🛍 🍴 ₵ Mark Toombs.
Location	Swindon Rd
Hotel	B Forte Crest, Oxford Rd, Stratton St Margaret, SWINDON ☎ (0793) 831333 91 ⇌ ℟

KINGSDOWN   Map 03 ST86

Kingsdown ☎ Bath (0225) 742530
Fairly flat, open downland course with very sparse tree cover
but surrounding wood.
18 holes, 6445yds, Par 72, SSS 71, Course record 64.
Club membership 620.

Visitors	welcome except at weekends. Must contact in advance & handicap certificate required.
Societies	apply by letter.
Green Fees	£22 per day.
Facilities	⊗ ℳ & 🛍 (not Mon) ⬛ ♀ ᐃ 🛍 ₵ Andrew Butler.
Location	W side of village
Hotel	★★71% Box House Hotel & Restaurant, London Rd, BOX ☎ (0225) 744447 9 ⇌ ℟

MARLBOROUGH   Map 04 SU16

Marlborough ☎ (0672) 512147
Downland course open to prevailing wind. Extensive views.
18 holes, 6526yds, Par 72, SSS 71.
Club membership 920.

Visitors	restricted at certain times; must have a handicap certificate at weekends. Must contact in advance.
Societies	must telephone in advance.

Green Fees	£32 per day; £21 per round (£40 weekends).
Facilities	⊗ & ℳ by prior arrangement 🛍 ⬛ ♀ ᐃ 🛍 ₵ L Ross.
Location	The Common (N side of town centre on A345)
Hotel	★★★60% Castle & Ball Hotel, High St, MARLBOROUGH ☎ (0672) 515201 34 ⇌ ℟Annexe2 ⇌ ℟

OGBOURNE ST GEORGE   Map 04 SU27

Swindon ☎ (0672) 841327
Downland turf and magnificent greens.
18 holes, 6226yds, Par 71, SSS 70, Course record 66.
Club membership 800.

Visitors	welcome weekdays only, handicap certificate required. Must contact in advance.
Societies	must apply in advance.
Green Fees	£23 per day; £17 per round. Rates for juniors.
Facilities	⊗ ℳ by prior arrangement 🛍 ⬛ ♀ ᐃ 🛍 ₵ Colin Harraway.
Leisure	practice ground.
Location	N side of village on A436
Hotel	★★★72% Ivy House Hotel & Garden Restaurant, High St, MARLBOROUGH ☎ (0672) 515333 12 ⇌ ℟Annexe16 ⇌ ℟

SALISBURY   Map 04 SU12

Salisbury & South Wilts ☎ (0722) 742645
Gently undulating parkland course in country setting with
panoramic views of the cathedral and surrounding country.
Main Course: 18 holes, 6528yds, Par 70, SSS 71.
Old Course: 18 holes, 6177yds, Par 70, SSS 70.
Club membership 1010.

Visitors	welcome except for competitions days. Must contact in advance.
Societies	apply in writing.
Green Fees	£25 freedom of 27 holes; £12 9 hole. Course of Day (£40/£15 weekends).
Facilities	⊗ ℳ by prior arrangement 🛍 ⬛ ♀ ᐃ 🛍 🍴 ₵ Gary Emerson.
Leisure	snooker.
Location	Netherhampton (2m W on A3094)
Hotel	★★★67% Rose & Crown Hotel, Harnham Rd, Harnham, SALISBURY ☎ (0722) 327908 28 ⇌ ℟

SWINDON   Map 04 SU18

Broome Manor Golf Complex ☎ (0793) 532403
Two courses and a 20-bay floodlit driving range. Parkland
with water hazards, open fairways and short cut rough.
Walking is easy on gentle slopes.
18 holes, 6359yds, Par 71, SSS 70, Course record 67 or 9
holes, 2745yds, Par 66, SSS 67.
Club membership 1000.

Visitors	casual times available but advisable to contact in advance.
Societies	welcome Mon-Thu only.
Green Fees	£7.85 per 18 holes; £4.70 per 9 holes (£9.60/£5.80).
Facilities	⊗ ℳ 🛍 ⬛ ♀ ᐃ 🛍 🍴 ₵ Barry Sandry.
Leisure	driving range.
Location	Pipers Way (1.75m SE of town centre off B4006)

Hotel B Forte Crest, Oxford Rd, Stratton St Margaret, SWINDON ☎ (0793) 831333 91 ⇨ 🐾

TIDWORTH
Map 04 SU24

Tidworth Garrison ☎ Stonehenge (0980) 842301
A breezy, dry downland course with lovely turf, fine trees and views over Salisbury Plain and the surrounding area. The 3rd and 12th holes are notable. The 564-yard 13th, going down towards the clubhouse, gives the big hitter a chance to let fly.
18 holes, 6075yds, Par 69, SSS 69, Course record 65.
Club membership 850.
Visitors must contact in advance, weekend & bank holiday bookings may not be made until Thursday prior.
Societies must contact in writing.
Green Fees £18 per day.
Facilities ⊗ & 🕮 (ex Mon) 🖥 🍴 🍷 🎿 🏠 🥢 🌴 Terry Gosden.
Leisure practice area putting & chipping greens.
Location Bulford Rd (W side of village off A338)
Hotel ★★★59% Ashley Court, Micheldever Rd, ANDOVER ☎ (0264) 357344 9 ⇨ 🐾Annexe26 ⇨ 🐾

UPAVON
Map 04 SU15

Upavon ☎ Stonehenge (0980) 630787 & 630281
Downland course set on sides of infamous valley, with some wind affecting play. The 2nd, 9th, 11th and 18th are all par 3 to small greens. A well-drained course.
9 holes, 5589yds, Par 69, SSS 67, Course record 66.
Club membership 400.
Visitors must contact in advance and may not play before 11am at weekends. Handicap certificate required weekends.
Societies contact in advance.
Green Fees £16 per day; £12 per round (£24 weekends).
Facilities ⊗ 🕮 🖥 🍴 (all catering by arrangement) 🍷 🎿 🏠 🥢 🌴 Richard Blake.
Leisure hard tennis courts.
Location Douglas Av (2m E on A342)
Hotel ★★★62% Bear Hotel, Market Place, DEVIZES ☎ (0380) 722444 24 ⇨ 🐾

WARMINSTER
Map 03 ST84

West Wilts ☎ (0985) 212702
A hilltop course among the Wiltshire downs without trees and somewhat windswept. First-class springy turf with many interesting holes.
18 holes, 5709yds, Par 70, SSS 68, Course record 62.
Club membership 600.
Visitors with member only weekends, handicap certificate required. Must contact in advance.
Societies apply by letter.
Green Fees £24 per day/round (£35 weekends).
Facilities ⊗ by prior arrangement (ex Tue) 🕮 by prior arrangement (ex Sun-Tue) 🖥 🍴 🍷 🎿 🏠 🌴 John G Jacobs.
Location Elm Hill (N side of town centre off A350)

Hotel ★★★★♨69% Bishopstrow House Hotel, WARMINSTER ☎ (0985) 212312 32 ⇨ 🐾

WOOTTON BASSETT
Map 04 SU08

Wootton Bassett ☎ Swindon (0793) 849999
A Peter Alliss/Clive Clark design set in rolling Wiltshire countryside. A number of lakes add a challenge for both low and high handicappers.
18 holes, 6496yds, Par 72, SSS 71.
Club membership 730.
Visitors must have handicap certificate and contact in advance; limited at weekends.
Societies contact in advance.
Green Fees £30 per day; £20 per round.
Facilities ⊗ 🕮 🖥 🍴 🍷 🎿 🏠 🥢 B McAdams.
Leisure cart & trolley hire.
Location Leave M4 at junc 16, on A3102
Hotel ★★★66% Marsh Farm Hotel, Coped Hall, WOOTTON BASSETT ☎ (0793) 848044 4 ⇨ 🐾Annexe24 ⇨ 🐾

CHANNEL ISLANDS

ALDERNEY

ALDERNEY
Map 16

Alderney ☎ (0481) 822835 & 823609
Undulating seaside course with sea on all sides and offering magnificent views from its high tees and greens. Course designed by Frank Pennink.
9 holes, 2528yds, Par 32, SSS 65.
Club membership 560.
Visitors may not play before 10am at weekends.
Societies must contact in advance.
Green Fees not confirmed.
Facilities ⊗ 🖥 🍴 🍷 🎿 🏠 🥢
Leisure bowling green & boules pitch.
Location Route des CarriÈres (1m E of St Annes)
Hotel ★★66% Inchalla Hotel, St Anne, ALDERNEY ☎ (0481) 823220 11rm(9 ⇨ 1 🐾)

Each golf-course entry has a recommended AA-appointed hotel. For a wider choice of places to stay, consult *AA Hotels in Britain and Ireland* and *AA Inspected Bed and Breakfast in Britain and Ireland* available from your local book shop or AA shops

GUERNSEY

L'ANCRESSE VALE
Map 16

Royal Guernsey ☎ (0481) 47022
Not quite as old as its neighbour Royal Jersey, Royal Guernsey is a sporting course which was re-designed after World War II by Mackenzie Ross, who has many fine courses to his credit. It is a pleasant links, well-maintained, and administered by the States of Guernsey in the form of the States Tourist Committee. The 8th hole, a good par 4, requires an accurate second shot to the green set amongst the gorse and thick rough. The 18th, with lively views, needs a strong shot to reach the green well down below. The course is windy, with hard walking. There is a junior section.
18 holes, 6206yds, Par 70, SSS 70, Course record 64.
Club membership 1500.
Visitors must have a handicap certificate; may not play on Thu & Sat afternoons & Sun.
Green Fees £25 per day.
Facilities ⊗ ⅷ (Mon-Sat) ⅙ ♥ ♀ ♧ 🏠 ↑
⟨ Norman Wood.
Leisure snooker, driving range.
Location 3m N of St Peter Port
Hotel ★★★★68% St Pierre Park Hotel, Rohais, ST PETER PORT
☎ (0481) 728282 135 ⇆ 🐾

ST PETER PORT
Map 16

St Pierre Park Golf Club ☎ (0481) 727039 & 728282
Par 3 parkland course with delightful setting, with lakes, streams and many tricky holes.
9 holes, 2511yds, Par 54, SSS 48.
Club membership 220.
Visitors no restrictions.
Societies must contact in advance.
Green Fees not confirmed.
Facilities ⊗ ⅷ ⅙ ♥ ♀ ♧ 🏠 ↑ ⋈
Leisure hard tennis courts, heated indoor swimming pool, snooker, sauna, solarium, gymnasium, croquet & petanque.
Location Rohais (1m W off Rohais Rd)
Hotel ★★★★68% St Pierre Park Hotel, Rohais, ST PETER PORT ☎ (0481) 728282 135 ⇆ 🐾

JERSEY

GROUVILLE
Map 16

Royal Jersey ☎ Jersey (0534) 854416
A seaside links, historic because of its age: its centenary was celebrated in 1978. It is also famous for the fact that Britain's greatest golfer, Harry Vardon, was born in a little cottage on the edge of the course and learned his golf here.
18 holes, 6059yds, Par 70, SSS 70.
Club membership 1364.

Visitors restricted to 10am-noon & 2pm-4pm
Societies welcome Mon-Fri. Must apply in writing.
Green Fees £30 per round (£35 weekends & bank holidays).
Facilities ⊗ ⅷ ⅙ ♥ ♀ ♧ 🏠 ↑ ⟨ Tommy Horton.
Leisure snooker.
Location 4m E of St Helier off coast rd
Hotel ★★★63% Old Court House Hotel, GOREY ☎ (0534) 854444 58 ⇆ 🐾

LA MOYE
Map 16

La Moye ☎ Jersey (0534) 43401
Seaside championship links course (venue for the Jersey Open) situated in an exposed position on the south western corner of the island overlooking St Ouens Bay. Offers spectacular views, two start points, full course all year - no temporary greens.
18 holes, 6705yds, Par 72, SSS 72.
Club membership 1300.
Visitors must contact in advance and have a handicap certificate.
Societies must contact in advance.
Green Fees £55 per day (lunch incl); £35 per round (£40 weekends).
Facilities ⊗ ⅷ ⅙ ♥ ♧ 🏠 ↑ ⟨
Leisure snooker, practice ground.
Location W side of village off A13
Hotel ★★★★66% Atlantic Hotel, La Moye, ST BRELADE ☎ (0534) 44101 50 ⇆ 🐾

ST CLEMENT
Map 16

St Clement ☎ Jersey (0534) 21938
Very tight moorland course. Holes cross over fairways, impossible to play to scratch. Suitable for middle to high handicaps.
9 holes, 2244yds, Par 30.
Club membership 500.
Visitors must contact in advance.
Green Fees not confirmed.
Facilities ♧
Leisure hard tennis courts.
Location Jersey Recreation Grounds (E side of St Helier on A5)
Hotel ★★★★(red)⛊ Longueville Manor Hotel, ST SAVIOUR ☎ (0534) 25501 32 ⇆ 🐾

For an explanation of symbols and abbreviations, see page 5

Remember – prior to playing a stroke or making a practice swing the players should ensure that no one is standing close by. No one should move, talk or stand close to or directly behind the ball when a player is addressing the ball or making a stroke

ISLE OF MAN

CASTLETOWN
Map 06 SC26

Castletown Golf Links ☎ (0624) 822201
Set on the Langness Peninsula, this superb Championship course is surrounded on three sides by the sea, and holds many surprises from its Championship tees. The hotel offers many leisure facilities.
18 holes, 6713yds, Par 72, SSS 73, Course record 65.
Club membership 350.

Visitors	must book tee one month in advance unless a hotel resident.
Societies	must telephone in advance.
Green Fees	£25 per day Fri-Sun & bank holidays (£18 Mon-Thu).
Facilities	⊗ (Sun only) ⅏ 🏌 🍺 ♀ 🏊 🏠 ♈ 🏁 ♟ Murray Crowe.
Leisure	heated indoor swimming pool, fishing, snooker, sauna, solarium, putting green & croquet.
Location	Fort Island, Derbyhaven
Hotel	★★★65% Castletown Golf Links Hotel, Fort Island, CASTLETOWN ☎ (0624) 822201 58 ⇥ 🐾

DOUGLAS
Map 06 SC37

Pulrose ☎ (0624) 675952
Hilly, parkland and moorland course under the control of Douglas Corporation.
18 holes, 6080yds, Par 69, SSS 68, Course record 66.
Club membership 430.

Visitors	no restrictions.
Societies	must apply in writing.
Green Fees	not confirmed.
Facilities	🏌 🍺 ♀ 🏊 🏠 ♈ ♟ K Parry.
Location	1m W off A1
Hotel	★★★72% The Empress Hotel, Central Promenade, DOUGLAS ☎ (0624) 661155 102 ⇥ 🐾

ONCHAN
Map 06 SC47

King Edward Bay Golf & Country Club ☎ Douglas (0624) 620430
Club plays over King Edward Bay course. Hilly seaside links course with natural hazards and good views.
18 holes, 5457yds, Par 67, SSS 66.
Club membership 470.

Visitors	must have a handicap certificate.
Societies	must contact in advance.
Green Fees	not confirmed.
Facilities	⊗ (Tue-Sun) ⅏ (Tue-Sat) 🏌 🍺 ♀ 🏊 🏠 ♈ ♟ Donald Jones.
Leisure	snooker, sauna, solarium, Caddy cars for hire, also buggies.
Location	Howstrake, Groudle Rd (E side of town off A11)
Hotel	★★★65% Sefton Hotel, Harris Promenade, DOUGLAS ☎ (0624) 626011 80 ⇥ 🐾

PEEL
Map 06 SC28

Peel ☎ (062484) 2227 or 3456
Moorland course, with natural hazards and easy walking. Good views. 11th hole is a par 4, dog-leg.
18 holes, 5914yds, Par 69, SSS 68.
Club membership 600.

Visitors	not before 10.30am weekends & bank holidays. Must have a handicap certificate.
Societies	must contact in advance.
Green Fees	£13 per day (£17 weekends & bank holidays).
Facilities	⊗ 🏌 🍺 ♀ 🏊 🏠
Leisure	snooker.
Location	Rheast Ln (SE side of town centre on A1)
Hotel	★★★72% The Empress Hotel, Central Promenade, DOUGLAS ☎ (0624) 661155 102 ⇥ 🐾

PORT ERIN
Map 06 SC16

Rowany ☎ (0624) 834108 or 837072
Undulating seaside course with testing later holes.
18 holes, 5840yds, Par 70, SSS 69.
Club membership 600.

Visitors	must contact in advance & have handicap certificate.
Societies	weekends only; must contact in advance.
Green Fees	£13 per day (£18 weekends & bank holidays).
Facilities	⊗ ⅏ by prior arrangement 🏌 🍺 ♀ 🏊 🏠
Leisure	pool table & darts.
Location	Rowany Dr (N side of village off A32)
Hotel	★★★66% Cherry Orchard Hotel, Bridson St, PORT ERIN ☎ (0624) 833811 31 ⇥ 🐾

RAMSEY
Map 06 SC49

Ramsey ☎ (0624) 812244
Parkland course, with easy walking. Windy. Good views. Testing holes: 1st, par 5; 18th, par 3.
18 holes, 5657yds, Par 69, SSS 67.
Club membership 1000.

Visitors	restricted Tue mornings, Sat & Sun.
Societies	not Sat & Sun; must contact in writing.
Green Fees	Winter: £15 per day (£18 weekends & bank holidays).
Facilities	⊗ ⅏ by prior arrangement 🏌 🍺 ♀ 🏊 🏠 ♈ ♟ Calum Wilson.
Leisure	snooker, practice area, caddy cars for hire.
Location	Brookfield (SW side of town)
Hotel	★★★68% Grand Island Hotel, Bride Rd, RAMSEY ☎ (0624) 812455 54 ⇥ 🐾

> *Remember* – unless stated otherwise, two-ball matches should have precedence over and be entitled to pass any three- or four-ball match and any match playing a whole round may pass a match playing a shorter round

ℐCOTLAND

Land of the midnight tee-off

· ·

THE routine of most people on a golfing holiday is to enjoy the game during the day then fall in with the festivities at night. But, just for a change, how about going out there to chase birdies at a time when you are usually tucked up in bed merely dreaming about them?

In the north-east of Scotland they give you the chance, with midnight tournaments during a long summer night in mid-June. Royal Dornoch, the mecca for all golfers who visit that area, have a mixed foursomes tournament, and Brora and Wick have similar events, all open to visitors. 'It's a bit of fun', says Brora president Robin Wilson. 'We have a shotgun start at around 9pm and then finish at midnight. Some people use coloured golf balls and one year everyone played in fancy dress. We try to change the format every year. But although it is a light-hearted affair there is a nice trophy to be won, presented by a Canadian

gentleman who enjoyed himself here. And some English people donated a scratch cup.'

They tee off later at Wick. 'Near midnight, according to the weather', says club captain John Hunter. 'It's a real daft night and we top it off with a barbecue at the finish.' Visitors to Wick will enjoy the facilities of a new clubhouse from summer 1994 – the first major change to the building since the club was founded in 1870.

Royal Dornoch also holds the Carnegie Shield event, with a limit of 240, in August. Everyone plays two rounds and the qualifiers are put into flights of 32 for scratch and handicap match-play. The entry fee is £25, but if you are thinking about it, get your name in early as it's very popular. Tom Watson, the American five times Open Champion, played Dornoch in the 1980s and said it was one of the most

· ·

memorable experiences of a lifetime. It could be for you, too.

On the south side of Dornoch Firth, you can sample another rarity, a club where there is no-one around to collect your visitor's fees – Tarbat, at Portmahomack, trust visitors to leave their £6 all-day fee in an envelope at the clubhouse. 'We accept people on the basis of pay as you play and we expect them to be honest', says club secretary David Wilson. 'The greenkeeper tries to keep an eye on those who are on the course.'

The Scottish Highlands are clustered with courses that, once played, will make you want to return. Coming south through Inverness and along the Moray Firth there is Nairn, reckoned one of the best tests in the country. It is a traditional links, with the outward holes winding along the waters of the Firth. The four par threes are as good as you will find anywhere. Get the better of them and a good round is on the cards. Colin Montgomerie certainly did, winning the Scottish Amateur Championship there in 1987 before beginning his successful professional career. Other visitors in the past included Charlie Chaplin and former British Prime Minister Sir Harold Macmillan. Originally laid out by Andrew

Simpson in 1887 and later worked on by Tom Morris and James Braid. Nearby are other jewels like Elgin, Boat of Garten, Moray and Forres.

Apart from the golf, one of the great attractions of the Highlands is the malt whisky. Half of Scotland's malt whisky distilleries are situated in the valleys by the River Spey and as you follow the trail south you reach Grantown-on-Spey, one of the most popular courses for visitors to the area. Apart from the delights of the course you can enjoy breathtaking views. As you stand on the ninth tee you look straight towards the Crondale Hills, distinctly covered in heather. And, as you make your way along the last six holes, there is a wonderful view of the Cairngorm Mountains. A few miles away is another gem, Boat of Garten, a testing circuit of under 6,000 yards. The secret here is – keep the ball straight or you are in trouble.

A golfing trip to the Highlands is something you will never forget. When you have played there you want to return ... especially with the added attraction of a wee dram of malt!

IAN RIACH
Golf correspondent, *Scottish Sunday Express*

SCOTLAND

BORDERS

COLDSTREAM
Map 12 NT83

Hirsel ☎ (0890) 882678 & 882626
Parkland course, with hard walking and sheltered trees. Testing 3rd and 6th holes. A further 9 holes have been developed.
18 holes, 6092yds, Par 70, SSS 69.
Club membership 475.
Visitors restricted during competitions.
Societies contact for details.
Green Fees not confirmed.
Facilities ⊗ ⓑ ☕ (Apr-May, daily ex Tue, Jun-Sep daily) ♀ (Apr-Sep) ⚐ 🛏 ⛳
Location Kelso Rd (SW side of town off A678)
Hotel ★★★♨66% Tillmouth Park Hotel, CORNHILL-ON-TWEED
☎ (0890) 882255 12 ⇔ ⏃Annexe2 ⇔ ⏃

DUNS
Map 12 NT75

Duns ☎ (0361) 882717
Interesting upland course, with natural hazards of water and hilly slopes. Views south to the Cheviot Hills.
9 holes, 5846yds, Par 68, SSS 68, Course record 66.
Club membership 319.
Visitors welcome except competition days & Tue after 3pm.
Societies apply in writing.
Green Fees £10 per day/round (£5 Nov-15 Mar).
Facilities ⓑ (in season) ♀ (in season) ⚐
Location Longformacus Rd (1m W off A6105)
Hotel ★★★68% Marshall Meadows Country House Hotel, BERWICK-UPON-TWEED
☎ (0289) 331133 18 ⇔ ⏃

EYEMOUTH
Map 12 NT96

Eyemouth ☎ (08907) 50551
With the exception of a steep climb to the 1st tee, this is a compact, flat and popular seaside course. Fast smooth greens and fine views are typified by the 15th, played from an elevated tee to a green on a peninsula over a North Sea inlet.
9 holes, 4608mtrs, Par 66, SSS 65, Course record 60.
Club membership 250.
Visitors may not play before 10.30am Sat or noon Sun.
Societies apply in writing.
Green Fees not confirmed.
Facilities ♀ (evenings) ⚐ 🛏 ⌇ Craig Maltman.
Leisure snooker.
Location Gunsgreen House (E side of town)
Hotel ★★★65% Marshall Meadows Country House Hotel, BERWICK-UPON-TWEED
☎ (0289) 331133 18 ⇔ ⏃

GALASHIELS
Map 12 NT43

Galashiels ☎ (0896) 3724
Hillside course, superb views from the top; 10th hole very steep.
18 holes, 5185yds, Par 67, SSS 66.
Club membership 290.
Visitors no restrictions.
Societies must contact in advance.
Green Fees £14 per day; £10 per round (£16/£12 weekends).
Facilities ⊗ & ☕ by prior arrangement ♀ ⚐
Location Ladhope Recreation Ground (N side of town centre off A7)
Hotel ★★★65% Kingsknowes Hotel, Selkirk Rd, GALASHIELS
☎ (0896) 58375 11rm(10 ⇔ ⏃)

Torwoodlee ☎ (0896) 2260
Parkland course with natural hazards designed by James Braid. Testing 3rd hole (par 3).
9 holes, 5720yds, Par 68, SSS 68, Course record 64.
Club membership 300.
Visitors may not play Sat & Thu after 1pm.
Societies must contact in advance.
Green Fees £15 per day; £12 per round (£20/£15 weekends).
Facilities ⊗ (ex Tue) ⓜ ⓑ ☕ ♀ ⚐ 🛏
Location 1.75m NW off A7
Hotel ★★★64% Woodlands House Hotel & Restaurants, Windyknowe Rd, GALASHIELS
☎ (0896) 4722 9 ⇔ ⏃

HAWICK
Map 12 NT51

Hawick ☎ (0450) 72293
Hill course with good views.
18 holes, 5929yds, Par 68, SSS 69.
Club membership 690.
Visitors by arrangement at weekends.
Societies must contact in writing.
Green Fees £22 per day; £15 per round (£22 per round weekends).
Facilities ⊗ ⓜ ⓑ ☕ (all catering by arrangement) ♀ by arrangement 🛏 ⛳
Location Vertish Hill (SW side of town)
Hotel ★★71% Kirklands Hotel, West Stewart Place, HAWICK
☎ (0450) 372263 5 ⇔ ⏃Annexe7 ⇔ ⏃

INNERLEITHEN
Map 11 NT33

Innerleithen ☎ (0896) 830951
Moorland course, with easy walking. Burns and rivers are natural hazards. Testing 5th hole (100 yds) par 3.
9 holes, 2992yds, Par 68, SSS 69, Course record 67.
Club membership 260.
Visitors no restrictions.
Societies must contact in writing.
Green Fees £10 (£12 weekends).
Facilities ⊗ & ⓜ by prior arrangement ⓑ ☕ ♀ ⚐
Location Leithen Water, Leithen Rd (1.5m N on B709)
Hotel ★★★♨57% Tweed Valley Hotel & Restaurant, Galashiels Rd, WALKERBURN
☎ (0896) 870636 16 ⇔ ⏃

JEDBURGH

Map 12 NT62

Jedburgh ☎ (0835) 863587
Undulating parkland course, windy, with young trees.
9 holes, 5760yds, Par 68, SSS 67.
Club membership 265.

Visitors	restricted at weekends during competitions.
Societies	must contact at least one month in advance.
Green Fees	£10 per day.
Facilities	⊗ 🏌 💺 (catering weekends only Apr-Sep) 🏌 (Apr-Sep) ⛳ 🏠
Location	Dunion Rd (1m W on B6358)
Hotel	★★71% Kirklands Hotel, West Stewart Place, HAWICK ☎ (0450) 372263 5 ⇄ 🐾Annexe7 ⇄ 🐾
Additional hotel	QQQ Kenmore Bank Hotel, Oxnam Rd, JEDBURGH ☎ (0835) 862369 6 ⇄ 🐾

KELSO

Map 12 NT73

Kelso ☎ (0573) 223009
Parkland course. Easy walking.
18 holes, 6061yds, Par 70, SSS 69, Course record 63.
Club membership 450.

Visitors	restricted weekends & Mon-Fri 9-9.30am & 1-1.30pm.
Societies	apply in writing.
Green Fees	£20 per day; £12 per round (£25/£16 weekends).
Facilities	⊗ 🏌 🏌 💺 (no catering Mon & Tue) 🏌 ⛳ 🏠 🍴
Location	Racecourse Rd (N side of town centre off B6461)
Hotel	★★★58% Cross Keys Hotel, 36-37 The Square, KELSO ☎ (0573) 223303 24 ⇄ 🐾

KENMORE BANK HOTEL
JEDBURGH

AA
QQQ

Oxnam Road, Jedburgh TD8 8JJ
Tel: (01835) 862369
Open all year

COMMENDED

VISA

Access

MasterCard

FREEDOM OF THE FAIRWAYS in the Scottish borders!

Uncrowded golfing on 16 scenic courses from your Jedburgh base at Kenmore Bank, a small family run hotel with residential licence. Colour TV in all en-suite bedrooms.

4 nights B&B from £125 or 6 nights B&B from £184 inclusive of golf.

LAUDER

Map 12 NT54

Lauder ☎ (0578) 722526
Inland course and practice area on gently sloping hill.
9 holes, 3001yds, Par 72, SSS 70, Course record 70.
Club membership 200.

Visitors	restricted Wed 4.30-5.30pm and Sun before noon.
Societies	telephone in advance.
Green Fees	18 holes £7 (£8 weekends).
Facilities	⛳
Location	Galashiels Rd (on Galashiels Rd, off A68, 0.5m from Lauder)
Hotel	★★69% Buccleuch Arms Hotel, The Green, ST BOSWELLS ☎ (0835) 22243 19rm(17 ⇄ 🐾)

MELROSE

Map 12 NT53

Melrose ☎ (089682) 2855
Undulating tree-lined fairways with spendid views.
9 holes, 5579yds, Par 70, SSS 68, Course record 62.
Club membership 390.

Visitors	restricted at weekends, Apr-Oct.
Societies	must telephone in advance.
Green Fees	£14 per round/day.
Facilities	catering by arrangement 🏌 ⛳
Location	Dingleton (S side of town centre on B6359)
Hotel	★★★60% Burt's Hotel, The Square, MELROSE ☎ (089682) 2285 21 ⇄ 🐾

MINTO

Map 12 NT52

Minto ☎ Denholm (045087) 220
Pleasant, undulating parkland course featuring mature trees and panoramic views of Scottish Border country. Short but quite testing.
18 holes, 5460yds, Par 68, SSS 68.
Club membership 600.

Visitors	may not play before 10.15am & 3.15pm Sat-Sun or during a club medal competition. Handicap certificate required.
Societies	must contact in writing.
Green Fees	£18 per day; £12 per round (£25/£18 weekends & bank holidays).
Facilities	⊗ 🏌 (Apr-Oct) 🏌 💺 🏌 (Apr-Oct) ⛳ 🏠
Location	Denholm (S side of village)
Hotel	★★71% Kirklands Hotel, West Stewart Place, HAWICK ☎ (0450) 372263 5 ⇄ 🐾Annexe7 ⇄ 🐾

NEWCASTLETON

Map 12 NY48

Newcastleton ☎ Liddesdale (03873) 75257
Hill course.
9 holes, 5748yds, Par 70, SSS 68.

Visitors	restricted competition days.
Societies	must contact in advance.
Green Fees	£7 per day/round (£8 weekends).
Facilities	⛳
Location	Holm Hill (W side of village)
Hotel	★★56% Eskdale Hotel, Market Place, LANGHOLM ☎ (03873) 80357 & 81178 16rm(3 ⇄7 🐾)

PEEBLES Map 11 NT24

Peebles ☎ (0721) 720197
Parkland course with fine views.
18 holes, 6137yds, Par 70, SSS 69, Course record 64.
Club membership 600.
Visitors advised to contact for weekends, 3 ball play only.
Societies must be pre-booked with deposit.
Green Fees £20 per day; £13 per round (£27/£19 weekends).
Facilities ⊗ Ⅲ ℡ ☕ (no catering Tue) ♀ ⛁ ⌂ ↱
Leisure buggies for hire Apr-Oct.
Location Kirkland St (W side of town centre off A72)
Hotel ★★★68% Peebles Hydro Hotel, PEEBLES ☎ (0721) 720602 137 ⇨ ↱

ST BOSWELLS Map 12 NT53

St Boswells ☎ (0835) 23527
Attractive parkland course by the banks of the River Tweed; easy walking.
9 holes, 2625yds, Par 66, SSS 65.
Club membership 310.
Visitors play restricted after 4pm & on competition days.
Societies must contact in advance.
Green Fees £10 (£15 weekends).
Facilities ☕ ♀ ⛁
Leisure fishing.
Location N side of village off B6404
Hotel ★★69% Buccleuch Arms Hotel, The Green, ST BOSWELLS ☎ (0835) 22243 19rm(17 ⇨ ↱)

SELKIRK Map 12 NT42

Selkirk ☎ (0750) 22508
Pleasant moorland course set around Selkirk Hill. Unrivalled views.
9 holes, 5620yds, Par 68, SSS 67, Course record 61.
Club membership 364.
Visitors may not play Mon evening, competition/match days.
Societies must telephone in advance.
Green Fees £16 per day; £12 per round (£16 per round weekends).
Facilities ⊗ by prior arrangement ℡ ☕ ⛁
Location Selkirk Hill (1m S on A7)
Hotel ★★61% Heatherlie House Hotel, Heatherlie Park, SELKIRK ☎ (0750) 21200 7rm(6 ↱)

WEST LINTON Map 11 NT15

West Linton ☎ (0968) 660256 & 660589
Moorland course with beautiful views of Pentland Hills.
18 holes, 5864yds, Par 68, SSS 68, Course record 63.
Club membership 600.
Visitors may not play on competition days & before 1pm weekends.
Societies must contact in writing.
Green Fees £21 per day; £15 per round (£24 per round weekends).
Facilities ⊗ (ex Tue) ℡ (ex Tue) ☕ ♀ ⛁ ⌂ ⟨ Ricky Forrest.
Leisure caddy cars.
Location NW side of village off A702
Hotel ★★★68% Peebles Hydro Hotel, PEEBLES ☎ (0721) 720602 137 ⇨ ↱

CENTRAL

ABERFOYLE Map 11 NN50

Aberfoyle ☎ (0877) 382493
Scenic heathland course with mountain views.
18 holes, 5210yds, Par 66, SSS 66.
Club membership 665.
Visitors may not tee off before 10.30am Sat & Sun.
Societies must contact in advance.
Green Fees £16 per day; £12 per round (£24 per day; £16 per round weekends).
Facilities ⊗ Ⅲ ℡ ☕ (catering Apr-Sep) ♀ ⛁ ↱
Location Braeval (1m E on A81)
Hotel ★★73% Lake Hotel, PORT OF MENTEITH ☎ (08775) 258 13 ⇨ ↱

ALLOA Map 11 NS89

Alloa ☎ (0259) 722745
Undulating, wooded parkland course.
18 holes, 6230yds, Par 70, SSS 70.
Club membership 750.
Visitors no restrictions.
Societies may not play at weekends.
Green Fees £22 per day; £14 per round (£26 per day after 11am; £17 per round after 2pm weekends).
Facilities ⊗ Ⅲ ℡ ☕ ♀ ⛁ ⌂ ↱ ⟨ Bill Bennett.
Leisure snooker.
Location Schawpark, Sauchie (1.5m NE on A908)
Hotel ★★★64% Royal Hotel, Henderson St, BRIDGE OF ALLAN ☎ (0786) 832284 32 ⇨ ↱

Braehead ☎ (0259) 722078
Attactive parkland course at the foot of the Ochil Hills, and offering spectacular views.
18 holes, 6041yds, Par 70, SSS 69, Course record 64.
Club membership 800.
Visitors advisable to contact in advance.
Societies must contact in advance.
Green Fees £20 per day; £12 per round (£28/£20 weekends).
Facilities ⊗ Ⅲ ℡ ☕ ♀ ⛁ ⌂ ↱ ⟨ Paul Brookes.
Leisure practice area, caddy cars.
Location Cambus (1m W on A907)
Hotel ★★★64% Royal Hotel, Henderson St, BRIDGE OF ALLAN ☎ (0786) 832284 32 ⇨ ↱

ALVA Map 11 NS89

Alva ☎ (0259) 760431
A 9-hole course at the foot of the Ochil Hills which gives it its characteristic sloping fairways and fast greens.
9 holes, 2423yds, Par 66, SSS 64, Course record 63.
Club membership 308.

Visitors	may not play during medal competitions or Thu evening (Ladies night).
Societies	apply in writing or telephone in advance.
Green Fees	£12 per day; £7 per round (£10 per round weekends).
Facilities	ⓑ 🍴 ♀ ⅋
Location	Beauclerc St (7m from Stirling, A91 Stirling/St Andrews Rd)
Hotel	★★★64% Royal Hotel, Henderson St, BRIDGE OF ALLAN ☎ (0786) 832284 32 ⇄ ⋔

BONNYBRIDGE   Map 11 NS88

Bonnybridge ☎ (0324) 812822
Testing heathland course, with tightly guarded greens. Easy walking.
9 holes, 6060yds, Par 72, SSS 69.
Club membership 325.

Visitors	must contact in advance and be accompanied by member.
Societies	must contact in advance.
Green Fees	£10 per round.
Facilities	⊗ 🍴 ⓑ & 🍴 (weekends only or by arrangement) ♀ ⅋ 🏠
Location	Larbert Rd (1m NE off A883)
Hotel	★★★68% Inchyra Grange Hotel, Grange Rd, POLMONT ☎ (0324) 711911 43 ⇄ ⋔

BRIDGE OF ALLAN   Map 11 NS79

Bridge of Allan ☎ (0786) 832332
Parkland course, very hilly with good views of Stirling Castle and beyond to the Trossachs. Testing 1st hole, 221 yds (par 3) uphill 6 ft wall 25 yds before green.
9 holes, 4932yds, Par 66, SSS 65, Course record 62.
Club membership 400.

Visitors	restricted Sat.
Societies	must contact in advance.
Green Fees	not confirmed.
Facilities	Catering at weekends or by arrangement ♀ ⅋
Leisure	pool table.
Location	Sunnylaw (0.5m N off A9)
Hotel	★★★64% Royal Hotel, Henderson St, BRIDGE OF ALLAN ☎ (0786) 832284 32 ⇄ ⋔

CALLANDER   Map 11 NN60

Callander ☎ (0877) 330090
Parkland course, with fairly tightly guarded greens. Designed by Tom Morris Snr and overlooked by the Trossachs.
18 holes, 5125yds, Par 66, SSS 66, Course record 61.
Club membership 580.

Visitors	must have handicap certificate to play Wed & Sun.
Societies	apply in writing.
Green Fees	£18 per day; £14 per round (£22/£18 weekends).
Facilities	⊗ 🍴 by prior arrangement ⓑ 🍴 ♀ ⅋ 🏠 ⋔ 〔 William Kelly.
Leisure	caddy cars.
Location	Aveland Rd (E side of town off A84)
Hotel	★★★★68% Roman Camp Hotel, CALLANDER ☎ (0877) 330003 14 ⇄ ⋔

DOLLAR   Map 11 NS99

Dollar ☎ (0259) 742400
Compact hillside course.
18 holes, 5144yds, Par 68, SSS 66.
Club membership 500.

Visitors	no restrictions
Societies	must contact in advance.
Green Fees	£12 per day; £8 per round (£16 per day weekends).
Facilities	⊗ 🍴 ⓑ 🍴 ♀ ⅋ ⋔
Leisure	snooker.
Location	Brewlands House (0.5m N off A91)
Hotel	★★★64% Royal Hotel, Henderson St, BRIDGE OF ALLAN ☎ (0786) 832284 32 ⇄ ⋔

DRYMEN   Map 11 NS48

Buchanan Castle ☎ (0360) 60307
Parkland course, with easy walking and good views.
18 holes, 6086yds, Par 70, SSS 69.
Club membership 830.

Visitors	must be accompanied by member, contact in advance and have an introduction from own club.
Societies	must contact in advance.
Green Fees	not confirmed.
Facilities	⊗ & 🍴 by prior arrangement ⓑ 🍴 ♀ ⅋ 🏠 ⋔ 〔 Charles Dernie.
Location	1m W
Hotel	★★★67% Buchanan Highland Hotel, DRYMEN ☎ (0360) 60588 50 ⇄ ⋔

DUNBLANE   Map 11 NN70

Dunblane New Golf Club ☎ (0786) 823711
Well maintained parkland course, with reasonably hard walking. Testing 6th and 9th holes.
18 holes, 5876yds, Par 69, SSS 68.
Club membership 800.

Visitors	may play 9.30am-noon & 2.30-4pm Mon-Fri. Must contact in advance.
Societies	welcome Mon, Wed-Fri, contact in advance.
Green Fees	£23 per day; £16 per round.
Facilities	⊗ 🍴 ⓑ 🍴 ♀ ⅋ 🏠 ⋔ 〔 Bob Jamieson.
Leisure	caddy cars.
Location	Perth Rd (E side of town on A9)
Hotel	★★★(red)♨ Cromlix House Hotel, Kinbuck, DUNBLANE ☎ (0786) 822125 14 ⇄ ⋔

FALKIRK   Map 11 NS88

Falkirk ☎ (0324) 611061
Parkland course with trees, gorse and streams.
18 holes, 6282yds, Par 71, SSS 69, Course record 66.
Club membership 800.

Visitors	with member only at weekends.
Societies	telephone (0324) 612219 in advance.
Green Fees	£18 per day; £12 per round (weekdays).
Facilities	⊗ 🍴 ⓑ 🍴 ♀ ⅋ 🏠
Location	136 Stirling Rd, Camelon (1.5m W on A9)
Hotel	★★★68% Inchyra Grange Hotel, Grange Rd, POLMONT ☎ (0324) 711911 43 ⇄ ⋔

KILLIN   Map 11 NN53

Killin ☎ (0567) 820312
Parkland course with good views. Glorious setting.
9 holes, 5200yds, Par 66, SSS 65.
Club membership 250.
Visitors   may not play competition days.
Societies   apply in writing.
Green Fees not confirmed.
Facilities   ⊗ ⍟ ⅃ ♥ ♀ ♨ 🖦 ♈
Leisure   caddy cart elec & manual for hire.
Location   1m N on A827
Hotel   ★★66% Dall Lodge Country House Hotel, Main
                   St, KILLIN ☎ (0567) 820217 10 ⇄ ⋔

LARBERT   Map 11 NS88

Falkirk Tryst ☎ (0324) 562415 & 562054
Moorland course, fairly level with trees and broom, well-
bunkered. Winds can affect play.
18 holes, 6053yds, Par 70, SSS 69, Course record 64.
Club membership 900.
Visitors   with member only weekend & bank holidays.
Societies   apply in writing.
Green Fees £18 per day; £13 per round.
Facilities   ⊗ ⍟ (evening only) ⅃ ♥ ♀ ♨ 🖦
                   ⋔ Steven Dunsmore.
Location   86 Burnhead Rd (1m NE off A88/B905)
Hotel   ★★★68% Inchyra Grange Hotel, Grange Rd,
                   POLMONT ☎ (0324) 711911 43 ⇄ ⋔

Glenbervie Clubhouse ☎ (0324) 562605
Parkland course with good views.
18 holes, 6469yds, Par 70, SSS 70.
Club membership 600.
Visitors   must contact in advance, restricted at weekends.
Societies   apply in writing.
Green Fees £35 per day; £25 per round.
Facilities   ⊗ ⍟ ⅃ ♥ ♀ ♨ 🖦 ⋔ John Chillas.
Location   Stirling Rd (2m NW on A9)
Hotel   ★★★68% Inchyra Grange Hotel, Grange Rd,
                   POLMONT ☎ (0324) 711911 43 ⇄ ⋔

MUCKHART   Map 11 NO00

Muckhart ☎ (0259) 781423
Scenic heathland/downland course.
18 holes, 6192yds, Par 71, SSS 70.
Club membership 750.
Visitors   visitors welcome some weekends and from
                   10.30am-12.30pm and after 2.30pm.
Societies   must telephone in advance.
Green Fees £18 per day; £12.50 per round (£24/£18
                   weekends).
Facilities   ⊗ ⍟ ⅃ ♥ ♀ ♨ 🖦 ⋔ Keith Salmoni.
Location   SW of village off A91
Hotel   ★★★69% Green Hotel, 2 The Muirs,
                   KINROSS ☎ (0577) 863467 47 ⇄ ⋔

> ### For an explanation of symbols and
> ### abbreviations, see page 5

POLMONT   Map 11 NS97

Grangemouth ☎ (0324) 711500
Windy parkland course. Testing holes: 3rd, 4th (par 4's); 5th
(par 5); 7th (par 3) 216 yds over reservoir (elevated green);
8th, 9th, 18th (par 4's).
18 holes, 6314yds, Par 71, SSS 71.
Club membership 700.
Visitors   must contact in advance.
Societies   must contact in writing.
Green Fees £8.30 per day; £5.50 per round (£10.20/£7.40
                   weekends).
Facilities   ⊗ ⍟ ⅃ ♥ ♀ ♨ 🖦 ⋔
Leisure   pool tables.
Location   Polmont Hill (on unclass rd 0.5m N of M9 junc 4)
Hotel   ★★★68% Inchyra Grange Hotel, Grange Rd,
                   POLMONT ☎ (0324) 711911 43 ⇄ ⋔

Polmont ☎ (0324) 711277
Parkland course, hilly with few bunkers. Views of the River
Forth and Ochil Hills.
9 holes, 3031yds, Par 36.
Club membership 200.
Visitors   restricted Sat.
Societies   must telephone in advance.
Green Fees £7 per round (£12 Sun).
Facilities   ⊗ ⍟ ⅃ ♥ ♀
Location   Manuelrigg, Maddiston (E side of village off
                   A803)
Hotel   ★★★68% Inchyra Grange Hotel, Grange Rd,
                   POLMONT ☎ (0324) 711911 43 ⇄ ⋔

STIRLING   Map 11 NS79

Stirling ☎ (0786) 464098
Undulating parkland course with magnificent views. Testing
15th, 'Cotton's Fancy', 384 yds (par 4).
18 holes, 6438yds, Par 72, SSS 71, Course record 75.
Club membership 1000.
Visitors   may not play Sat & restricted Sun.
Societies   must telephone in advance.
Green Fees £23 per day; £17 per round.
Facilities   ⊗ ⍟ ⅃ ♥ ♀ ♨ 🖦 ⋔ Ian Collins.
Location   Queens Rd (W side of town on B8051)
Hotel   ★★57% King Robert Hotel, Glasgow Rd,
                   Bannockburn, STIRLING
                   ☎ (0786) 811666 53 ⇄ ⋔

TILLICOULTRY   Map 11 NS99

Tillicoultry ☎ (0259) 51337 & 50124
Parkland course at foot of the Ochil Hills entailing some hard
walking.
18 holes, 5358yds, Par 68, SSS 66.
Club membership 400.
Visitors   welcome except during club competitions.
Societies   apply in writing.
Green Fees not confirmed.
Facilities   ⊗ ⍟ by prior arrangement ⅃ ♥ ♀ ♨
Location   Alva Rd
Hotel   ★★★64% Royal Hotel, Henderson St,
                   BRIDGE OF ALLAN
                   ☎ (0786) 832284 32 ⇄ ⋔

DUMFRIES & GALLOWAY

CASTLE DOUGLAS Map 11 NX76

Castle Douglas ☎ (0556) 502801 or 502099
Parkland course, one severe hill.
9 holes, 2704yds, Par 34, SSS 33.
Club membership 500.

Visitors welcome except Tue & Thu after 4pm & Sun during competitions.
Societies apply by writing.
Green Fees £12 per day/round.
Facilities (summer only)
Location Abercromby Rd (W side of town)
Hotel ★★65% Douglas Arms, King St, CASTLE DOUGLAS ☎ (0556) 502231 22rm(15)

COLVEND Map 11 NX85

Colvend ☎ Rockcliffe (0556) 630398
Picturesque and challenging course on Solway coast. Superb views.
9 holes, 2322yds, Par 66, SSS 62.
Club membership 480.

Visitors restricted Tue, Thu & weekends in summer. No visitors after 5pm May-Jul.
Societies must telephone in advance.
Green Fees £12 per day.
Facilities (wknds only Oct-Mar) (wknds only Oct-Mar)
Leisure caddy carts/trollies.
Location Sandyhills (6m from Dalbeattie on A710 Solway Coast Rd)
Hotel ★★65% Clonyard House Hotel, COLVEND ☎ (0556) 630372 15

CUMMERTREES Map 11 NY16

Powfoot ☎ (0461) 700227
The hills of Cumbria, away beyond the Solway Firth, and from time to time a sight of the Isle of Man, make playing at this delightfully compact semi-links seaside course a scenic treat. Lovely holes include the 2nd, the 8th and the 11th.
18 holes, 6283yds, Par 71, SSS 70, Course record 65.
Club membership 820.

Visitors may not play Sat & only after 2.45pm on Sun. Must contact in advance.
Societies must book at least one week in advance.
Green Fees £15 per round (£16 Sun after 2.45pm).
Facilities Gareth Dick.
Location 0.5m off B724
Hotel ★★64% Golf Hotel, Links Av, POWFOOT ☎ (0461) 700254 19rm(14)

DUMFRIES Map 11 NX97

Dumfries & County ☎ (0387) 53585
Parkland course alongside River Nith, with views over the Queensberry Hills.
18 holes, 5928yds, Par 69, SSS 68.
Club membership 600.

AA ★★★
Let the tranquillity and splendour of the region entice you to spend a few days at HETLAND HALL, explore the Solway Coast, the Galloway Forest and the Borders.
Hetland Hall is situated by the main A75 Euro route, 8 miles from Dumfries and 22 miles from Carlisle.
Besides the many fitness facilities offered within the hotel and its extensive grounds, Dumfries & Galloway offers 24 Golf courses all in different glorious scenery.
Hetland Hall Hotel
CARRUTHERSTOWN,
DUMFRIES DG1 4JX
TEL: 01387 84201 FAX: 01387 84211
Best Western WORLDWIDE HOTELS

Visitors must contact in advance but may not play on Sat during Mar-Oct.
Societies apply in writing.
Green Fees not confirmed.
Facilities Gordon Gray.
Location Edinburgh Rd (1m NE off A701)
Hotel ★★★63% Station Hotel, 49 Lovers Walk, DUMFRIES ☎ (0387) 54316 32
Additional hotel ★★★66% Hetland Hall Hotel, CARRUTHERSTOWN ☎ (0387) 84201 27

Dumfries & Galloway ☎ (0387) 63848
Parkland course.
18 holes, 5803yds, Par 68, SSS 68.
Club membership 800.

Visitors may not play on competition days.
Societies apply in writing.
Green Fees not confirmed.
Facilities by prior arrangement Joe Fergusson.
Leisure snooker.
Location 2 Laurieston Av (W side of town centre on A75)
Hotel ★★★63% Station Hotel, 49 Lovers Walk, DUMFRIES ☎ (0387) 54316 32

GATEHOUSE-OF-FLEET Map 11 NX55

Gatehouse ☎ (0557) 814734
Set against a background of rolling hills with scenic views of Fleet Bay and the Solway Firth.
9 holes, 2398yds, Par 66, SSS 63.
Club membership 280. ▶

The Cally Palace Hotel
Gatehouse of Fleet, Dumfries & Galloway DG7 2DL
AA ★★★★

Set in its own grounds within 500 acres of Fleet Forest, The Cally Palace is one of the most beautiful locations in Scotland. 56 luxurious bedroom suites. Fine food and friendly, professional service. Within the grounds there is an 18 hole par 70 golf course much of it in mature wooded areas and around Cally Lake. Also, there is an indoor leisure centre, outdoor tennis, putting, croquet and boating.

– everything one could wish for –
for a week, a fortnight or just a few days

Telephone 01557 814341 for brochure

Visitors	no restrictions.
Societies	telephone (0557) 814459 in advance.
Green Fees	£10 per day/round.
Facilities	△
Location	Laurieston Rd (N side of village)
Hotel	★★★★♨66% Cally Palace Hotel, GATEHOUSE OF FLEET ☎ (0557) 814341 55 ⇄

GLENLUCE   Map 10 NX15

Wigtownshire County ☎ (0581) 300420
Seaside links course on the shores of Luce Bay, easy walking but affected by winds. The 12th hole, a dogleg with out of bounds to the right,is named after the course's designer, Gordon Cunnigham.
18 holes, 5823yds, Par 70, SSS 68, Course record 64.
Club membership 375.

Visitors	may not play on Wed evenings or during competitions.
Societies	must telephone (0581) 300589 in advance.
Green Fees	£19 per day ; £15 per round (£21/£17 weekends).
Facilities	⊗ ⅶ ᖯ 💼 🏵 △ 🎏 ⚑
Leisure	pool table, caddy cars(non motorised).
Location	Mains of Park (1.5m W off A75)
Hotel	★★★★68% North West Castle Hotel, STRANRAER ☎ (0776) 704413 71 ⇄ ⋔

GRETNA   Map 11 NY36

Gretna ☎ (0461) 38464
A nice parkland course on gentle hills. Opened in 1991, it offers a good test of skill.
9 holes, 3215yds, Par 72, SSS 71.
Club membership 250.

Visitors	no restrictions.
Societies	telephone in advance.
Green Fees	£8 per day (£10 weekends & bank holidays).
Facilities	△
Leisure	driving range.
Location	Kirtle View (0.5m W of Gretna on B721,signposted)
Hotel	★★66% Solway Lodge Hotel, Annan Rd, GRETNA ☎ (0461) 38266 3 ⇄ ⋔Annexe7 ⇄ ⋔

KIRKCUDBRIGHT   Map 11 NX65

Kirkcudbright ☎ (0557) 330314
Parkland course. Hilly, with hard walking. Good views.
18 holes, 5598yds, Par 67, SSS 67.
Club membership 500.

Visitors	welcome except during competitions.
Societies	contact the Secretary in advance.
Green Fees	£20 per day; £15 per round.
Facilities	⊗ ⅶ ᖯ 💼 ♀ △
Leisure	caddy cars.
Location	Stirling Crescent (NE side of town off A711)
Hotel	★★68% Selkirk Arms Hotel, Old High St, KIRKCUDBRIGHT ☎ (0557) 330402 14 ⇄ ⋔Annexe1 ⇄ ⋔

LANGHOLM   Map 11 NY38

Langholm ☎ no telephone
Hillside course with fine views, hard walking.
9 holes, 5744yds, Par 70, SSS 68.
Club membership 130.

Visitors	restricted Sat & Sun.
Societies	apply in writing or telephone in advance.
Green Fees	£10 per day/round.
Facilities	♀ (ex Tue & Thu)
Location	Whitaside (E side of village off A7)
Hotel	★★56% Eskdale Hotel, Market Place, LANGHOLM ☎ (03873) 80357 & 81178 16rm(3 ⇄7 ⋔)

LOCHMABEN   Map 11 NY08

Lochmaben ☎ (0387) 810552
Comfortable-walking parkland course between two lochs with fine old trees and fast greens all year round.
9 holes, 5304yds, Par 66, SSS 66.
Club membership 550.

Visitors	restricted weekday evenings & during competitions.
Societies	must contact in advance.
Green Fees	£12 per day (£14 weekends).
Facilities	⊗ ⅶ ᖯ 💼 ♀ △
Leisure	fishing, snooker.
Location	Castlehill Gate (S side of village off A709)
Hotel	★★★66% Dryfesdale Hotel, LOCKERBIE ☎ (0576) 202427 15 ⇄ ⋔

LOCKERBIE
Map 11 NY18

Lockerbie ☎ (0576) 202462
Parkland course with fine views and featuring the only pond hole in Dumfriesshire.
18 holes, 5418yds, Par 67, SSS 66.
Club membership 627.
Visitors   restricted Sun.
Societies   must contact in advance.
Green Fees   £14 per day (£18 per day Sat; £16 per round Sun).
Facilities   ⊗ & ⅷ by prior arrangement ⅊ ⅊ ⅊ ⅊
Leisure   caddy cars.
Location   Corrie Rd (E side of town centre off B7068)
Hotel   ★★★66% Dryfesdale Hotel, LOCKERBIE
☎ (0576) 202427 15 ⇔ ⬧

MOFFAT
Map 11 NT00

Moffat ☎ (0683) 20020
Scenic moorland course overlooking the town, with panoramic views.
18 holes, 5218yds, Par 69, SSS 66, Course record 60.
Club membership 375.
Visitors   restricted Wed afternoons.
Societies   must contact in advance.
Green Fees   £17 per day (£25 weekends & bank holidays).
Facilities   ⊗ ⅷ ⅊ ⅊ ⅊ ⅊ ⅊ ⅊
Leisure   snooker, darts, table tennis, pool table.
Location   Coatshill (1m SW off A701)
Hotel   ★★★65% Moffat House Hotel, High St, MOFFAT
☎ (0683) 20039 16 ⇔ ⬧Annexe4 ⇔ ⬧

MONREITH
Map 10 NX34

St Medan ☎ Port William (0988) 700358
Links course with panoramic views of the Solway and Isle of Man.
9 holes, 4552yds, Par 64, SSS 63, Course record 60.
Club membership 300.
Visitors   no restrictions.
Societies   apply in writing.
Green Fees   £10 per day; £40 per week; £6 per 9 holes.
Facilities   ⊗ ⅷ ⅊ ⅊ ⅊ ⅊
Leisure   pool table, video game.
Location   1m SE off A747
Hotel   ★★★♨64% Corsemalzie House Hotel, PORT WILLIAM ☎ (098886) 254 14 ⇔ ⬧

NEW GALLOWAY
Map 11 NX67

New Galloway ☎ (06443) 455
Set on the edge of the Galloway Hills and overlooking Loch Ken, the course has excellent tees and first class greens.
9 holes, 5006yds, Par 68, SSS 67, Course record 65.
Club membership 303.
Visitors   restricted on competition days.
Societies   apply in writing.
Green Fees   £10 per day.
Facilities   ⅊ (summer) ⅊ (summer) ⅊
Location   S side of town on A762
Hotel   ★★65% Douglas Arms, King St, CASTLE DOUGLAS ☎ (0556) 502231 22rm(15 ⇔ ⬧)

NEWTON STEWART
Map 10 NX46

Newton Stewart ☎ (0671) 402172
Parkland course in picturesque setting. Short but quite tight.
18 holes, 5970yds, Par 69, SSS 69.
Club membership 300.
Visitors   telephone for details.
Societies   must contact in advance.
Green Fees   £15 per day; £12 per round (£20/£16 weekends & bank holidays).
Facilities   ⊗ ⅷ by prior arrangement ⅊ ⅊ ⅊ ⅊ ⅊
Leisure   pool table.
Location   Kirroughtree Av, Minnigaff (0.5m N of town centre)
Hotel   ★★66% Creebridge House Hotel, NEWTON STEWART ☎ (0671) 402121 20 ⇔ ⬧

PORTPATRICK
Map 10 NX05

Portpatrick ☎ (0776) 810273
Seaside links-type course, set on cliffs overlooking the Irish Sea, with magnificent views.
Dunskey Course: 18 holes, 5843yds, Par 70, SSS 68.
Dinvin Course: 9 holes, 1504yds, Par 27.
Club membership 500.
Visitors   welcome except for competition days. A handicap certificate is required for 18 hole course.
Societies   must contact in advance.
Green Fees   18 holes: £21 per day; £14 per round (£25/£17 weekends) 9 holes: £12 per day; £6 per round.
Facilities   ⊗ ⅷ ⅊ ⅊ ⅊ ⅊ ⅊ ⅊
Leisure   caddy carts, practice ground.
Location   Golf Course Rd (300 yds right from war memorial)
Hotel   ★★★65% Fernhill Hotel, PORTPATRICK
☎ (0776) 810220 14 ⇔ ⬧Annexe6 ⇔ ⬧

SANQUHAR
Map 11 NS70

Sanquhar ☎ (0659) 50577
Moorland course, fine views.
9 holes, 5144mtr, Par 70, SSS 68, Course record 66.
Club membership 180.
Visitors   may not play competition days.
Societies   apply in writing.
Green Fees   not confirmed.
Facilities   ⊗ ⅷ ⅊ ⅊ (all catering by prior arrangement) ⅊
Leisure   snooker.
Location   Euchan Golf Course (0.5m SW off A76)
Hotel   ★★61% Mennockfoot Lodge Hotel, Mennock, SANQUHAR
☎ (0659) 50382 & 50477 1 ⇔Annexe8 ⇔ ⬧

SOUTHERNESS
Map 11 NX95

Southerness ☎ Kirkbean (038788) 677
Natural links, Championship course with panoramic views. Heather and bracken abound.
18 holes, 6564yds, Par 69, SSS 72, Course record 65.
Club membership 800.
Visitors   some restricted times.
Societies   must contact in advance.   ▶

Green Fees £24 per day (£32 weekends & bank holidays).
Facilities
Leisure caddy cars, practice area.
Location 3.5m S of Kirkbean off A710
Hotel ★★65% Clonyard House Hotel, COLVEND ☎ (0556) 630372 15

STRANRAER — Map 10 NX06

Stranraer ☎ Leswalt (0776) 870245
Parkland course with beautiful view of Lochryan.
18 holes, 6308yds, Par 70, SSS 71, Course record 66.
Club membership 596.

Visitors restricted at weekends.
Societies must telephone in advance.
Green Fees £12 per day; £16 per round (£21/£27 weekends).
Facilities by prior arrangement
Leisure snooker, trolleys, practice area.
Location Creachmore by Stranraer (2.5m NW on A718)
Hotel ★★★★68% North West Castle Hotel, STRANRAER ☎ (0776) 704413 71

THORNHILL — Map 11 NX89

Thornhill ☎ Dumfries (0848) 330546
Moorland/parkland course with fine views.
18 holes, 6011yds, Par 71, SSS 69.
Club membership 580.

Visitors no restrictions.
Societies must telephone in advance.
Green Fees £16 per day (£20 weekends).
Facilities
Location Blacknest (1m E of town off A92)
Hotel ★★72% Trigony House Hotel, Closeburn, THORNHILL ☎ (0848) 331211 9

WIGTOWN — Map 10 NX45

Wigtown & Bladnoch ☎ (0988) 403354
Slightly hilly parkland course with fine views over Wigtown Bay to Galloway Hills.
9 holes, 5462yds, Par 68, SSS 67.
Club membership 180.

Visitors may not play competition days.
Societies apply in writing.
Green Fees £15 per day; £10 per round.
Facilities
Location Lightlands Ter (SW on A714)
Hotel ★★66% Creebridge House Hotel, NEWTON STEWART ☎ (0671) 402121 20

FIFE

ABERDOUR — Map 11 NT18

Aberdour ☎ (0383) 860256
Parkland course with lovely views over Firth of Forth.
18 holes, 5460yds, Par 67, SSS 67, Course record 63.
Club membership 580.

Visitors may play weekdays only and must contact in advance.
Societies are advised to telephone in advance.
Green Fees not confirmed.
Facilities Gordon McCallum.
Location Seaside Place (S side of village)
Hotel ★★65% Woodside Hotel, High St, ABERDOUR ☎ (0383) 860328 21

AA ★★
The Woodside Hotel
High Street, Aberdour, Fife

Enjoy FREE GOLF when you stay with us!
Book your Tee-time on Aberdour's scenic 18 hole course.
You will enjoy our warm hospitality and excellent food.
You must visit our unique bar! – Taken from the RMS Orontes.
Conveniently located for Edinburgh.
St. Andrew's Golf Course is within easy driving distance.
Tel: 01383 860328 for brochure and tariff.

ANSTRUTHER — Map 12 NO50

Anstruther ☎ (0333) 310956 & 312283
Seaside links course with some excellent par 3 holes; always in good condition.
9 holes, 4144mtrs, Par 62, SSS 63.
Club membership 600.

Visitors advised to phone in advance.
Societies welcome except Jun-Aug. Must apply in writing.
Green Fees £11 per round (£15 weekends).
Facilities Jun-Aug
Location Shore Rd, "Marsfield" (SW off A917)
Hotel ★★59% Smugglers Inn, High St, ANSTRUTHER ☎ (0333) 310506 8

BURNTISLAND — Map 11 NT28

Burntisland Golf House Club ☎ (0592) 874093
This hill course has fine sea views.
18 holes, 5908yds, Par 69, SSS 69, Course record 65.
Club membership 780.

Visitors	no restrictions.
Societies	apply in writing.
Green Fees	£26 per day; £18 per round (£35/£25 weekends).
Facilities	⊗ ⍚ ⬛ 🛒 ♀ ⬍ ⬚ ⬩ Jacky Montgomery.
Leisure	caddy cars.
Location	Dodhead (1m E on B923)
Hotel	★★66% Inchview Hotel, 69 Kinghorn Rd, BURNTISLAND ☎ (0592) 872239 12 ⇌ ⬩

COWDENBEATH
Map 11 NT19

Cowdenbeath ☎ (0383) 511918
A parkland-based 9-hole golf course.
Dora Course: 9 holes, 6552yds, Par 72, SSS 71, Course record 72.
Club membership 400.

Visitors	no restrictions.
Societies	must telephone in advance.
Green Fees	£6.50 per day (£9.25 weekends).
Facilities	⊗ ⍚ ⬛ 🛒 ♀ ⬍ ⬚ ⬩
Leisure	caddy cars.
Location	Seco Place (6m E of Dunfermline)
Hotel	★★65% Woodside Hotel, High St, ABERDOUR ☎ (0383) 860328 21 ⇌ ⬩

CRAIL
Map 12 NO60

Crail Golfing Society ☎ (0333) 450278
Perched on the edge of the North Sea on the very point of the golfing county of Fife, the Crail Golfing Society's course at Balcomie is picturesque and sporting. And here again golf history has been made for Crail Golfing Society began its life in 1786. The course is highly thought of by students of the game both for its testing holes and the standard of its greens.
18 holes, 5720yds, Par 69, SSS 68.
Club membership 1100.

Visitors	must contact in advance, restricted 10am-noon & 2-4.30pm.
Societies	must telephone in advance.
Green Fees	£25 per day; £17 per round (£33/£22 weekends).
Facilities	⊗ ⍚ ⬛ 🛒 ♀ ⬍ ⬚ ⬩ Graheme Lennie.
Location	Balcomie Clubhouse, Fifeness (2m NE off A917)
Hotel	★★62% Balcomie Links Hotel, Balcomie Rd, CRAIL ☎ (0333) 450237 11 ⇌ ⬩

CUPAR
Map 11 NO31

Cupar ☎ (0334) 53549
Hilly parkland course with fine views over north east Fife.5th/14th hole is most difficult - uphill and into the prevailing wind.
9 holes, 5500yds, Par 68, SSS 65, Course record 62.
Club membership 450.

Visitors	welcome except Sat.
Societies	must contact in advance.
Green Fees	£10 per round/day (£12 weekends).
Facilities	⊗ ⍚ ⬛ 🛒 ♀ ⬍
Leisure	practice putting green.
Location	Hilltarvit (0.75m S off A92)
Hotel	★★★59% Fernie Castle Hotel, LETHAM ☎ (0337) 810381 15 ⇌ ⬩

DUNFERMLINE
Map 11 NT08

Canmore ☎ (0383) 724969
Undulating parkland course affording excellent views.
18 holes, 5474yds, Par 67, SSS 66.
Club membership 620.

Visitors	no restrictions. Sat not usually available.
Societies	apply in writing to secretary.
Green Fees	£18 per day; £12 per round (£25/£18 weekends).
Facilities	⊗ ⍚ ⬛ 🛒 ♀ ⬍ ⬚ ⬩
Location	Venturefair Av (1m N on A823)
Hotel	★★★62% King Malcolm Thistle, Queensferry Rd, Wester Pitcorthie, DUNFERMLINE ☎ (0383) 722611 48 ⇌ ⬩

Dunfermline ☎ (0383) 723534
Gently undulating parkland course with interesting contours. Sixteenth-century clubhouse.
18 holes, 6237yds, Par 72, SSS 70.
Par 3 course: 9 holes, 1144yds, Par 27.
Club membership 675.

Visitors	welcome Mon-Fri. Contact to check times.
Societies	must contact in advance.
Green Fees	£28 per day; £20 per round.
Facilities	⊗ (ex Mon) ⍚ by prior arrangement ⬛ 🛒 ♀ ⬍ ⬚ ⬩ Steve Craig.
Leisure	caddy cars.
Location	Pitfirrane, Crossford (2m W on A994)
Hotel	★★★62% King Malcolm Thistle, Queensferry Rd, Wester Pitcorthie, DUNFERMLINE ☎ (0383) 722611 48 ⇌ ⬩

Pitreavie ☎ (0383) 722591
Picturesque woodland course with panoramic view of the River Forth Valley. Testing golf.
18 holes, 6086yds, Par 70, SSS 69, Course record 65.
Club membership 700.

Visitors	welcome except for competition days.
Societies	must write or telephone in advance.
Green Fees	£19 per day; £14 per round (£25 per day weekends).
Facilities	⊗ ⍚ by prior arrangement ⬛ 🛒 ♀ ⬍ ⬚ ⬩ Jim Forrester.
Leisure	pool table.
Location	Queensferry Rd (SE side of town on A823)
Hotel	★★★62% King Malcolm Thistle, Queensferry Rd, Wester Pitcorthie, DUNFERMLINE ☎ (0383) 722611 48 ⇌ ⬩

ELIE
Map 12 NO40

Golf House Club ☎ (0333) 330301
One of Scotland's most delightful holiday courses with panoramic views over the Firth of Forth. Some of the holes out towards the rocky coastline are splendid. This is the course which has produced many good professionals, including the immortal James Braid.
18 holes, 6241yds, Par 70, SSS 70, Course record 62.
Club membership 650.

Visitors	may not play before 10am; no parties at weekends.
Societies	mid week only, except Jun-Aug.
Green Fees	£32 per day; £24 per round (£48/36 weekends). ▶

Facilities	⊗ ⊞ ⓚ ♥ ♀ ㊅ 🏠 ⼲ (Robin Wilson.
Leisure	caddy cars for hire.
Location	W side of village off A917
Hotel	★★★66% Old Manor Hotel, Leven Rd, LUNDIN LINKS ☎ (0333) 320368 19 ⇌ ⋔

FALKLAND   Map 11 NO20

Falkland ☎ (0337) 857404
A flat, well kept course with excellent greens and views of East Lomond Hill and Falkland Palace.
9 holes, 5216yds, Par 68, SSS 65, Course record 62.
Club membership 325.

Visitors	parties must make prior arrangements.
Societies	must contact in advance.
Green Fees	£8 per day (£12 weekends); £25 per weekly ticket.
Facilities	⊗ ⊞ ⓚ ♥ ♀ ㊅
Location	The Myre (N side of town on A912)
Hotel	★★63% Lomond Hills Hotel, Parliament Square, FREUCHIE ☎ (0337) 857329 & 857498 25 ⇌ ⋔

GLENROTHES   Map 11 NO20

Glenrothes ☎ (0592) 754561
Testing and hilly parkland course with burn crossed four times. Good views.
18 holes, 6444yds, Par 71, SSS 71, Course record 65.
Club membership 800.

THE LOMOND HILLS HOTEL
FREUCHIE Nr GLENROTHES, FIFE

Situated at the foot of the Lomond Hills, this old inn is an ideal place when visiting Fife. The hotel is close to many golf courses. Comfortable bedrooms, radio, TV/CH private facilities, candlelit restaurant. Leisure complex free to hotel guests.

Tel/Fax: (0337) 857329
AA   Tel: (0337) 857498
★★   BHCRA *Exechotel*

COMMENDED

THE FOREST HILLS HOTEL
THE SQUARE, AUCHTERMUCHTY, FIFE

Traditional Inn. In the square of the Royal Borough of Auchtermuchty (once a busy weaving centre) surrounding Forest/Hills once favoured deer/boar hunting. 10 bedrooms, 8 with facilities. Falkland Palace nearby, Edinburgh 30 miles. Well furnished. Bright bedrooms. Restaurant, Bistro, Cocktail Bar.

COMMENDED

Tel/Fax: (0337) 828318
Not AA   **2 lines**
appointed

Visitors	restricted some weekends.
Societies	write one month in advance.
Green Fees	£15 per day; £9 per round (£17/£11 weekends).
Facilities	⊗ ⊞ ⓚ ♥ ♀ ㊅
Location	Golf Course Rd (W side of town off B921)
Hotel	★★★69% Balgeddie House Hotel, Balgeddie Way, GLENROTHES ☎ (0592) 742511 18 ⇌ ⋔

KINCARDINE   Map 11 NS98

Tulliallan ☎ (0259) 730396
Partially hilly parkland course with testing 3rd hole (par 4).
18 holes, 5982yds, Par 69, SSS 69.
Club membership 525.

Visitors	restricted at weekends.
Societies	may not play on Sat; must contact in advance.
Green Fees	not confirmed.
Facilities	⊗ ⊞ ⓚ ♥ ♀ ㊅ 🏠 ⼲ (Steven Kelly.
Location	Alloa Rd (1m NW on A977)
Hotel	★★66% Dall Lodge Country House Hotel, Main St, KILLIN ☎ (0567) 820217 10 ⇌ ⋔

KINGHORN   Map 11 NT28

Kinghorn ☎ (0592) 890345
Municipal course, 300 ft above sea level with views over Firth of Forth and North Sea. Undulating and quite testing. Facilities shared by Kinghorn Ladies.
18 holes, 5269yds, Par 65, SSS 67.
Club membership 190.

Visitors	no restrictions.
Societies	must contact in writing.
Green Fees	£15 per day; £9 per round (£17/£11 weekends).
Facilities	⊗ ⊞ & ⓚ (weekends) ♥ ♀ ㊅
Location	Macduff Cres (S side of town on A921)
Hotel	★★★57% Dean Park Hotel, Chapel Level, KIRKCALDY ☎ (0592) 261635 20 ⇌ ⋔Annexe12 ⋔

KIRKCALDY   Map 11 NT29

Dunnikier Park ☎ (0592) 261599
Parkland, rolling fairways, not heavily bunkered, views of Firth of Forth.
18 holes, 6601yds, Par 72, SSS 72.
Club membership 600.

Visitors	no restrictions.
Societies	apply in writing to the Secretary.
Green Fees	£15 per day; £9 per round (£18/11 weekends).
Facilities	⊗ (ex Mon-Tue during Oct-Mar) ⊞ ⓚ ♥ ♀ ㊅ 🏠 (Jacky Montgomery.
Location	Dunnikier Way (2m N off A988)
Hotel	★★★57% Dean Park Hotel, Chapel Level, KIRKCALDY ☎ (0592) 261635 20 ⇌ ⋔Annexe12 ⋔

Kirkcaldy ☎ (0592) 260370
Parkland course.
18 holes, 6004yds, Par 71, SSS 70.
Club membership 725.

Visitors	may not play Sat. Must contact in advance.
Societies	apply in writing to the Secretary.
Green Fees	£20 per day; £15 per round (£25/£18 weekends).

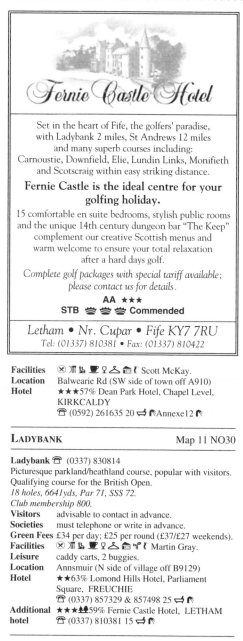

Fernie Castle Hotel

Set in the heart of Fife, the golfers' paradise, with Ladybank 2 miles, St Andrews 12 miles and many superb courses including: Carnoustie, Downfield, Elie, Lundin Links, Monifieth and Scotscraig within easy striking distance.

Fernie Castle is the ideal centre for your golfing holiday.

15 comfortable en suite bedrooms, stylish public rooms and the unique 14th century dungeon bar "The Keep" complement our creative Scottish menus and warm welcome to ensure your total relaxation after a hard days golf.

Complete golf packages with special tariff available; please contact us for details.

AA ★★★
STB ✿ ✿ ✿ Commended

Letham • Nr. Cupar • Fife KY7 7RU
Tel: (01337) 810381 • Fax: (01337) 810422

Facilities	⊗ ⫞ ⛳ ♥ ♀ ⩍ 🏌 Scott McKay.
Location	Balwearie Rd (SW side of town off A910)
Hotel	★★★57% Dean Park Hotel, Chapel Level, KIRKCALDY ☎ (0592) 261635 20 ⇌ 🐾Annexe12 🐾

LADYBANK   Map 11 NO30

Ladybank ☎ (0337) 830814
Picturesque parkland/heathland course, popular with visitors. Qualifying course for the British Open.
18 holes, 6641yds, Par 71, SSS 72.
Club membership 800.

Visitors	advisable to contact in advance.
Societies	must telephone or write in advance.
Green Fees	£34 per day; £25 per day (£37/£27 weekends).
Facilities	⊗ ⫞ ⛳ ♥ ♀ ⩍ 🏌 Martin Gray.
Leisure	caddy carts, 2 buggies.
Location	Annsmuir (N side of village off B9129)
Hotel	★★63% Lomond Hills Hotel, Parliament Square, FREUCHIE ☎ (0337) 857329 & 857498 25 ⇌ 🐾
Additional hotel	★★★♨59% Fernie Castle Hotel, LETHAM ☎ (0337) 810381 15 ⇌ 🐾

LESLIE   Map 11 NO20

Leslie ☎ Glenrothes (0592) 620040
Challenging parkland course.
9 holes, 2470yds, Par 62, SSS 64, Course record 59.
Club membership 200.

Visitors	no restrictions.
Societies	must apply to the Secretary.
Green Fees	not confirmed.
Facilities	⛳ & ♥ by prior arrangement ♀ ⩍
Location	Balsillie Laws (N side of town off A911)
Hotel	★★★69% Balgeddie House Hotel, Balgeddie Way, GLENROTHES ☎ (0592) 742511 18 ⇌ 🐾

LEUCHARS   Map 12 NO42

St Michael's ☎ (0334) 839365
Parkland course with open views over Fife and Tayside. The undulating course weaves its way through tree plantations. The short Par 4 7th, parallel to the railway and over a pond to a stepped green, poses an interesting challenge.
9 holes, 5158yds, Par 70, SSS 66.
Club membership 550.

Visitors	may not play on Sun before 1pm.
Societies	must apply in writing.
Green Fees	£12 per day.
Facilities	⊗ ⛳ ♥ ♀ ⩍
Location	NW side of village on A919
Hotel	★★★66% Scores Hotel, 76 The Scores, ST ANDREWS ☎ (0334) 472451 30 ⇌ 🐾

LEVEN   Map 11 NO30

Leven Golfing Society ☎ (0333) 426096
Plays over Leven Links - typical links course.
18 holes, 6435yds, Par 71, SSS 71.
Club membership 700.
▶

Remember – prior to playing a stroke or making a practice swing the players should ensure that no one is standing close by. No one should move, talk or stand close to or directly behind the ball when a player is addressing the ball or making a stroke

---

Remember – unless stated otherwise, two-ball matches should have precedence over and be entitled to pass any three- or four-ball match and any match playing a whole round may pass a match playing a shorter round

---

Remember – replace all divots, and repair ball-marks or damage by spikes on completion of the hole

Visitors start times restricted, phone for details (0333) 421390/428859

Societies apply in writing.

Green Fees £26 per day; £18 per round (£36/£24 weekends).

Facilities ⊗ �🍽 by prior arrangement 🛍 💺 ♀ 🏌 🏠 ♬ George Finlayson.

Leisure snooker, caddy cars.

Location Links Rd

Hotel ★★★66% Old Manor Hotel, Leven Rd, LUNDIN LINKS ☎ (0333) 320368 19 ⇆ 🏠

Leven Thistle ☎ (0333) 426333

Leven has the classic ingredients which make up a golf links in Scotland; undulating fairways with hills and hallows, out of bounds and a 'burn' or stream. A top class championship links course used for British Open final qualifying stages, it has fine views over Largo Bay.

18 holes, 6434yds, Par 71, SSS 71.

Club membership 500.

Visitors parties may not play on Sat.

Societies apply in writing to Link Joint Secretary, Promenade, Leven, Fife tel: (0333) 428859.

Green Fees £26 per day; £18 per round (£36 per day; £24 per round weekends).

Facilities ⊗ �🍽 🛍 💺 ♀ 🏌 🏠 ♬ G Finlayson.

Leisure pool table, carpet bowls, darts.

Location 3 Balfour St

Hotel ★★★66% Old Manor Hotel, Leven Rd, LUNDIN LINKS ☎ (0333) 320368 19 ⇆ 🏠

LOCHGELLY   Map 11 NT19

Lochgelly ☎ (0592) 780174

Parkland course with easy walking and often windy.

18 holes, 5491yds, Par 68, SSS 67.

Club membership 600.

Visitors no restrictions.

Societies must apply in writing.

Green Fees not confirmed.

Facilities (catering during season, weekends and Fri) ♀ 🏌

Location Cartmore Rd (W side of town off A910)

Hotel ★★★57% Dean Park Hotel, Chapel Level, KIRKCALDY ☎ (0592) 261635 20 ⇆ 🏠Annexe12 🏠

Lochore Meadows ☎ Ballingry (0592) 860086

Lochside course with natural stream running through, and woodland nearby. Country park offers many leisure facilities.

9 holes, 5554yds, Par 72, SSS 71, Course record 68.

Club membership 200.

Visitors no restrictions.

Societies must contact in advance.

Green Fees not confirmed.

Facilities ⊗ 🛍 💺 🏌

Leisure fishing, riding.

Location Lochore Meadows Country Park, Crosshill (2m N off B920)

Hotel ★★★69% Green Hotel, 2 The Muirs, KINROSS ☎ (0577) 863467 47 ⇆ 🏠

Phoneday - remember from 16 April 1995 all phone codes in the UK will change - see page 4 for details

---

LUNDIN LINKS   Map 12 NO40

Lundin ☎ (0333) 320202

The Leven Links and the course of the Lundin Club adjoin each other. The course is part seaside and part inland. The holes are excellent but those which can be described as seaside holes have a very different nature from the inland style ones.

18 holes, 6377yds, Par 71, SSS 71.

Club membership 830.

Visitors Mon-Fri 9am-3pm, Sat after 2.30pm, with member only on Sun.

Societies apply in writing.

Green Fees Mon-Fri £30 per day; £20 per round.

Facilities ⊗ �🍽 🛍 💺 (catering Tues-Fri) ♀ 🏠 ♬ D K Webster.

Leisure caddy cars available from professional.

Location Golf Rd (W side of village off A915)

Hotel ★★★66% Old Manor Hotel, Leven Rd, LUNDIN LINKS ☎ (0333) 320368 19 ⇆ 🏠

Lundin Ladies ☎ (0333) 320022

Short, lowland course with Roman stones on the second fairway, and coastal views.

9 holes, 4730yds, Par 68, SSS 67.

Club membership 350.

Visitors no restrictions.

Societies apply to Secretary.

Green Fees £6 per day (£7.50 weekends).

Facilities 💺 🏌

Location Woodilea Rd (W side of village off A915)

Hotel ★★★66% Old Manor Hotel, Leven Rd, LUNDIN LINKS ☎ (0333) 320368 19 ⇆ 🏠

The Old Manor Hotel
Near St Andrews

AA ★★★   COMMENDED

Family owned Country House overlooking Lundin and Leven Championship Courses. St. Andrews, Crail, Elie, Ladybank, close by, and over 30 courses within a half hour drive. Twenty en-suite Bedrooms, 2 Restaurants. Excellent food, fine wine and real ale. Golf Breaks for individuals and Societies.

Lundin Links, Fife KY8 6AJ
Tel: 01333 320368 Fax: 01333 320911

MARKINCH   Map 11 NO20

Balbirnie Park ☎ Glenrothes (0592) 752006
Scenic parkland course with several interesting holes.
18 holes, 6210yds, Par 71, SSS 70.
Club membership 800.
Visitors   must contact in advance.
Societies   apply in writing or telephone Mon-Fri, 9am-
                1pm.
Green Fees £26 per day; £19 per round (£34 per day; £27
                per round weekends).
Facilities ⊗ � 🛋 💺 ⚑ ⚘
Leisure   caddy cars.
Location   2m E of Glenrothes
Hotel   ★★★★♨73% Balbirnie House, Balbirnie Park,
                MARKINCH ☎ (0592) 610066 30 ⇥ 🐾

ST ANDREWS   Map 12 NO51

British Golf Museum ☎ (0334) 78880 (Situated
opposite Royal & Ancient Golf Club) Tells the
fascinating history of golf. Highly visual displays are
complemented by the use of visitor-activated touch
screens throughout the galleries. Exhibits take the
visitor from the misty origins of the game to the
present day. You will see amazing images, fascinating
collections of clubs, balls, fashion and memorabilia,
two period workshops and historic documents. An
audio-visual theatre shows historic golfing moments.
Shop. **Open**: May-Oct, daily 1000-1730.
☎ to confirm winter opening hours.
Admission: There is a charge. ☎ for details.

ST ANDREWS LINKS See page 241

SALINE   Map 11 NT09

Saline ☎ (0383) 852591
Hillside course with panoramic view of the Forth Valley.
9 holes, 5302yds, Par 68, SSS 66.
Club membership 416.
Visitors   advisable to contact in advance and may not play
                Sat.
Societies   telephone one week in advance.
Green Fees £8 per day (£10 Sun).
Facilities ⊗ � 🛋 & 💺 (catering by arrangement Tue) ⚑ ⚘
Leisure   putting green, practice nets.
Location   Kinneddar Hill (0.5m E at junc B913/914)
Hotel   ★★★62% King Malcolm Thistle, Queensferry
                Rd, Wester Pitcorthie, DUNFERMLINE
                ☎ (0383) 722611 48 ⇥ 🐾

TAYPORT   Map 12 NO42

Scotscraig ☎ Dundee (0382) 552515
A rather tight course on downland-type turf with an
abundance of gorse. The sheltered position of this Open
qualifying course ensures good weather throughout the
year.
18 holes, 6496yds, Par 71, SSS 71.
Club membership 650.
Visitors   restricted at weekends. Must contact in
                advance.   ▶

OLD COURSE HOTEL
The St Andrews Old Course Hotel & Spa is set in a
spectacular location overlooking the infamous 17th
Road Hole and the historic Royal and Ancient
Clubhouse. All 125 bedrooms, including 17 sumptuous
suites, have unrivalled views, some looking over the Old
Course to the sea, others towards the surrounding
countryside.
The Old Course Hotel is currently building its own
championship course, designed by five times Open
Champion Peter Thomson, at Craigtoun Park, two miles
inland from the hotel.
In its natural parkland setting the course will
complement St Andrews' famous links and will be ready
for play in 1995/96.
St Andrews Old Course Hotel
St Andrews Fife KY16 9SP
Tel: 01334 474371   Fax: 01334 474371

ON THE VERY DOORSTEP
OF THE HOME
OF GOLF

This famous 30 bedroom hotel is literally only
yards from the R & A clubhouse and the first tee
of the Old Course. Enjoying magnificent views of
the Bay, and only minutes walk from the historic
town centre, this is the ideal choice for your
golfing holiday in St. Andrews.
    Facilities include a coffee shop, two bars and a
respected restaurant.
    We are happy to assist in making bookings at
most local courses.

SCORES HOTEL
ST ANDREWS   AA ★★★

The Scores Hotel St. Andrews, Fife, KY16 9BB, Scotland
Tel: (01334) 472451   Fax: (01334) 473947

Societies	apply in writing.
Green Fees	on application.
Facilities	⊗ ⅢⅢ ⅃⅃ ⊒ ♀ ⅄ ⊞ ⅆ
Leisure	caddy cars.
Location	Golf Rd (S side of village off B945)
Hotel	★★★65% The Queen's Hotel, 160 Nethergate, DUNDEE ☎ (0382) 322515 47 ⇄ ⅀

THORNTON   Map 11 NT29

Thornton ☎ Glenrothes (0592) 771111
Undulating and fairly difficult parkland course.
18 holes, 5878yds, Par 70, SSS 69.
Club membership 650.
Visitors   restricted at weekends before 10am & between
                  12.30-2.30pm.
Societies   apply in advance.
Green Fees £18 per day; £12 per round (£27/£17 weekends).
Facilities   ⊗ ⅢⅢ ⅃⅃ ⊒ ♀ ⅄ ⊞
Location   Station Rd (1m E of town off A92)
Hotel   ★★★69% Balgeddie House Hotel, Balgeddie
                  Way, GLENROTHES
                  ☎ (0592) 742511 18 ⇄ ⅀

● GRAMPIAN

ABERDEEN   Map 15 NJ90

Balnagask ☎ (0224) 876407
Links course.
18 holes, 5486mtrs, SSS 69.
Visitors   no restrictions.
Societies   must contact in advance.
Facilities   ♀ ⅄
Location   St Fitticks Rd (2m E of city centre)
Hotel   ★★★64% Caledonian Thistle, 10 Union Ter,
                  ABERDEEN ☎ (0224) 640233 80 ⇄ ⅀

Bon Accord ☎ (0224) 633464
The club plays over King's Links coastal course; a municipal
course used by three clubs.
18 holes, 6433yds, Par 72, SSS 71.
Club membership 800.
Visitors   no restrictions.
Societies   welcome.
Green Fees not confirmed.
Facilities   ⊗ ⅃⅃ ⊒ ♀ ⅆ
Leisure   snooker.
Location   19 Golf Rd (0.75 NE of city centre)
Hotel   ★★★64% Caledonian Thistle, 10 Union Ter,
                  ABERDEEN ☎ (0224) 640233 80 ⇄ ⅀

Deeside ☎ (0224) 867697
An interesting riverside course with several tree-lined
fairways. A stream comes into play at 9 of the 18 holes on the
main course. There is a subsidiary 9-hole course.
18 holes, 6000yds, Par 69, SSS 69.
Club membership 600.

Visitors   must contact in advance but may not play on Sat
                  before 4pm & medal days.
Societies   Thu only by arrangement.
Green Fees £20 per round (£25 weekends & bank holidays).
Facilities   ⊗ ⅢⅢ ⅃⅃ ⊒ ♀ ⅄ ⊞ ⅆ Frank J Coutts.
Leisure   snooker.
Location   Bieldside (3m W of city centre off A93)
Hotel   ★★★★69% Ardoe House, Blairs, South
                  Deeside Rd, ABERDEEN
                  ☎ (0224) 867355 71 ⇄ ⅀

Hazelhead Public ☎ No telephone
A tree-lined course.
18 holes, 6595yds, Par 70, SSS 70.
Visitors   no restrictions.
Societies   must contact in advance.
Green Fees not confirmed.
Facilities   ⅄ ⊞ ⅆ
Location   Hazelhead (4m W of city centre off A944)
Hotel   ★★★★69% Ardoe House, Blairs, South
                  Deeside Rd, ABERDEEN
                  ☎ (0224) 867355 71 ⇄ ⅀

Kings Links ☎ (0224) 632269
A typical links course with no tree lines and plenty of
bunkers. The 14th hole is tricky - a long par 4 with a raised
green and not much fairway round the green. The course is
playable all year. Nearby there is a 6-hole course.
18 holes, 6384yds, Par 72, SSS 71.
Visitors   welcome.
Societies   contact for details.
Green Fees £4.30-£6.10.
Facilities   by arrangement with member clubs
Location   0.75m NE of city centre
Hotel   ★★★64% Caledonian Thistle, 10 Union Ter,
                  ABERDEEN ☎ (0224) 640233 80 ⇄ ⅀

Murcar ☎ (0224) 704370
Seaside links course, prevailing NE wind, hard-walking.
Testing 4th and 14th holes.
18 holes, 5809yds, Par 69, SSS 68.
Club membership 830.
Visitors   may not play Wed afternoon, Sat all day & Sun
                  mornings. Must contact in advance & have either
                  a letter of introduction or handicap certificate.
Societies   apply in writing.
Green Fees £20 per day; £16 per round (£22.50 per round
                  Sun & bank holidays).
Facilities   ⊗ & ⅢⅢ (ex Tue) ⅃⅃ ⊒ ♀ ⅄ ⊞ ⅆ Alan White.
Leisure   grass tennis courts, trolleys.
Location   Bridge of Don (5m NE of city centre off A92)
Hotel   ★★★66% The Craighaar, Waterton Rd,
                  Bucksburn, ABERDEEN
                  ☎ (0224) 712275 55 ⇄ ⅀

Nigg Bay ☎ (0224) 871286
Seaside course, hard walking. Plays over Balnagask Course.
18 holes, 5986yds, Par 70, SSS 69.
Club membership 800.
Visitors   no restrictions.
Societies   must contact in advance.
Green Fees £6.10 per round.
Facilities   ⅃⅃ ♀ ⅄
Location   St Fitticks Rd
Hotel   ★★★64% Caledonian Thistle, 10 Union Ter,
                  ABERDEEN ☎ (0224) 640233 80 ⇄ ⅀

ST. ANDREWS LINKS

ST ANDREWS, FIFE ☎ (0334) 475757   Map 12 N051

John Ingham writes: If golf has a mother, then without doubt it is St Andrews, the most famous links in all the world. Sir Winston Churchill is said to have claimed golf was invented by the Devil, and if this is so then the famous Old Course must be the Devil's playground. How can one reconcile these two thoughts; the birthplace and mother of the game - and yet the very Devil of a test?

The great Bobby Jones started by hating St Andrews and shredded his card into a hundred pieces, letting it blow in the wind. But eventually he came to love the place, and earn the affection of all golf. However you view St Andrews, you cannot ignore it. That master shot-maker from America, Sam Snead, took one look and claimed they should plant cattle fodder on the bumpy acres. Gary Player once said it should be towed out to sea, and sunk. But Jack Nicklaus loved it so much that when he won an Open title here, he threw his putter into the air. And he went away, and copied several of the St Andrews features in other courses that now decorate this earth.

St Andrews is much more than an 18-hole test. It is a whole experience and a walk in history. Name the famous players of yesteryear, and they played here, taking divots from the very spot that you can also take divots - merely by paying for a ticket. You too can wander out with your clubs to conquer some holes, maybe, and to be brought to a humbling halt by others.

Jack Nicklaus won his most remarkable victory on this course, thanks to an historic missed putt of just 3 feet 6 inches by Doug Sanders, who had needed a final hole par 4 to win the 1970 Open Championship. The all-time course record is 62, shot by Curtis Strange in the 1987 Dunhill Cup. Surely nobody can ever beat that?

Visitors	must telephone in advance
Societies	must telephone in advance
Green fees	Old course: £50; New Course £25; Jubilee £25, Eden £18; Strathyrum £14, Balgove £6 (18 holes)
Facilities	⌂ 🍴 ♿ (no bar, clubhouse open summer 95)
Location	NW of town off the A91

Old Course: 18 holes, 6566yds, Par 72, SSS 72
New (West Sands Rd): 18 holes, 6604yds, Par 71, SSS 72
Jubilee (West Sands Rd): 18 holes, 6284yds, Par 69, SSS 70
Eden (Dundee Rd): 18 holes, 6112yds, Par 70, SSS 69
Strathyrum): 18 holes, 5195yds, Par 69
Balgove 9 holes 3060 yds

WHERE TO STAY AND EAT NEARBY

HOTELS:

ST ANDREWS

★★★★(red)✿✿ 73% St Andrews Old Course, Old Station Rd. ☎ (0334) 474371. 125 🛏 ♿ Scottish & French cuisine

★★★✿ 71% St Andrews Golf, 40 The Scores. ☎ (0334) 472611. 23 🛏 ♿ Scottish & French cuisine

★★★✿ 66% Scores, 76 The Scores ☎ (0334) 472451. 30 🛏 ♿. British & French cuisine

RESTAURANTS:

CUPAR

✗✿✿✿ Ostlers Close, Bonnygate ☎ (0334) 655574 French & Swiss cuisine

PEAT INN

✗✗✿✿✿ The Peat Inn. ☎ (0334) 840206 French cuisine

Northern ☎ (0224) 636440
Exposed and windy seaside course, testing 10th hole. One of
three clubs playing over King's Links municipal course.
*King's Links: 18 holes, 6437, Par 72, SSS 72, Course record
65.*
Club membership 1000.
Visitors   restricted Sats.
Societies   must contact in advance.
Green Fees £6.30 per round.
Facilities   ⊗ (Wed,Fri,Sat & Sun) 〗Ⅲ (Sat) ⅛ ▆ ♀ △
Leisure   snooker, driving range.
Location   22 Golf Rd (adjacent to beach)
Hotel   ★★★64% Caledonian Thistle, 10 Union Ter,
              ABERDEEN ☎ (0224) 640233 80 ⇥ ☞

Royal Aberdeen ☎ (0224) 702571
Championship links course. Windy, easy walking.
*Balgownie: 18 holes, 6372yds, Par 70, SSS 71, Course
record 64.*
Silverburn: 18 holes, 4066yds, Par 64, SSS 60.
Club membership 640.
Visitors   may not play before 3.30pm Sat. Must contact in
              advance and have an introduction from own
              club.
Societies   must telephone in advance.
Green Fees not confirmed.
Facilities   ⊗ 〗Ⅲ by prior arrangement ⅛ ▆ ♀ (all day) △
              ☜ ♈ ⅃ Ronnie MacAskill.
Location   Balgownie, Bridge of Don (2.5m N of city
              centre off A92)
Hotel   ★★★64% Caledonian Thistle, 10 Union Ter,
              ABERDEEN ☎ (0224) 640233 80 ⇥ ☞

COUNTRY HOTEL AND RESTAURANT

Return to the Quality of Life

Varied à la carte menu
including vegetarian
dishes.
Seafood our speciality.
Only 10 minutes from
Royal Aberdeen
Murcar and Cruden
Bay courses.
A warm welcome
awaits you from the
Craig Family.

NEWBURGH, ABERDEENSHIRE
Tel: (01358) 789444

Westhill ☎ (0224) 740159
A highland course.
18 holes, 5921yds, Par 69, SSS 69.
Club membership 600.
Visitors   restricted Mon-Fri 4pm-7pm & Sat all day. Must
              contact in advance.
Societies   must contact in advance.
Green Fees not confirmed.
Facilities   ⊗ & 〗Ⅲ by prior arrangement ⅛ ▆ ♀ △ ☜ ⅃
Location   Westhill Heights, Westhill, Skene (6m NW of
              city centre off A944)
Hotel   ★★★62% Westhill Hotel, WESTHILL
              ☎ (0224) 740388 37 ⇥ ☞Annexe14 ⇥ ☞

ABOYNE   Map 15 NO59

Aboyne ☎ (03398) 86328
Beautiful parkland with outstanding views. Two lochs on course.
18 holes, 5910yds, Par 68, SSS 68.
Club membership 900.
Visitors   no restrictions.
Societies   prior booking essential.
Green Fees not confirmed.
Facilities   ⊗ 〗Ⅲ ⅛ ▆ ♀ △ ☜ ♈ ⅃
Location   Formaston Park (E side of village, N of A93)
Hotel   ★★67% Birse Lodge Hotel, Charleston Rd,
              ABOYNE ☎ (03398) 86253 & 86254
              12 ⇥ ☞Annexe4 ⇥

ALFORD   Map 15 NJ51

Alford ☎ (09755) 62178
A flat parkland course in scenic countryside. Divided into
sections by a road, a railway and a burn.
18 holes, 5290yds, Par 69, SSS 66.
Club membership 538.
Visitors   advisable to contact in advance.
Societies   must contact in advance.
Green Fees not confirmed.
Facilities   ⊗ & 〗Ⅲ by prior arrangement ⅛ ▆ ♀ △
Location   Montgarrie Rd
Hotel   ★★★(red)♨ Kildrummy Castle Hotel,
              KILDRUMMY ☎ (09755) 71288 16 ⇥ ☞

AUCHENBLAE   Map 15 NO77

Auchenblae ☎ Laurencekirk (0561) 378869
Picturesque, small, undulating parkland course offering good
views.
9 holes, 2174yds, Par 32, SSS 30, Course record 60.
Club membership 78.
Visitors   restricted Wed & Fri evenings.
Societies   must telephone (0561) 320331 in advance.
Green Fees not confirmed.
Location   0.5m NE
Hotel   ★★60% County Hotel, Arduthie Rd,
              STONEHAVEN ☎ (0569) 764386 14 ⇥ ☞

BALLATER   Map 15 NO39

Ballater ☎ (03397) 55567
Moorland course with testing long holes and beautiful scenery.
18 holes, 5638yds, Par 67, SSS 68.
Club membership 620.

Banchory Lodge Hotel

| AA 3 RED STARS | STB 4 CROWNS Highly Commended | LES ROUTIERS CASSEROLE |

Banchory, Kincardineshire AB31 3HS
Tel: Banchory 01330 822625 Fax: 01330 825019
Banchory Lodge Hotel has an unrivalled setting at the confluence of the River Feugh and Dee. Guests can overlook the river whilst enjoying the hospitable atmosphere and high standard of cuisine and comfort. This former Georgian mansion house is within a few minutes of the centre of Banchory and 18 miles inland from Aberdeen.

Visitors must phone Pro shop (03397) 55658 for weekend play.
Societies must telephone in advance.
Green Fees £24 per day; £16 per round (£28.80/£19.20 weekends).
Facilities ⊗ ⅷ ⅃ ☒ ♀ ♨ 🏠 🍴 ⏻
Leisure hard tennis courts, fishing, snooker, bowling club & putting green.
Location Victoria Rd (W side of town)
Hotel ★★★67% Darroch Learg Hotel, Braemar Rd, BALLATER
🕿 (03397) 55443 15 ⇌ 🏾Annexe5 ⇌ 🏾

BANCHORY   Map 15 NO69

Banchory 🕿 (0330) 822365
Sheltered parkland course situated beside the River Dee, with easy walking and woodland scenery. 11th and 12th holes are testing.
18 holes, 5245yds, Par 67, SSS 66, Course record 60.
Club membership 1000.
Visitors must contact in advance.
Societies must book in advance.
Green Fees £19 per day (£21 weekends).
Facilities ⊗ ⅷ ⅃ ☒ ♀ ♨ 🏠 🍴 ⏻ Charles Dernie.
Leisure snooker.
Location Kinneskie Rd (A93, 300 yds from W end of High St)
Hotel ★★★(red)♨ Banchory Lodge Hotel, BANCHORY 🕿 (0330) 822625 22 ⇌ 🏾

BANFF   Map 15 NJ66

Duff House Royal 🕿 (0261) 812062
Well-manicured flat parkland, bounded by woodlands and River Deveron. Well bunkered and renowned for its large, two-tier greens.
18 holes, 6161yds, Par 68, SSS 69, Course record 63.
Club membership 1000.
Visitors a handicap certificate is preferred. Some time restrictions.
Societies must apply in writing.
Green Fees £16 per day; £12 per round (£24/£18 weekends).
Facilities ⊗ ⅷ ⅃ ☒ ♀ ♨ 🏠 🍴 ⏻ Bob Strachan.
Leisure snooker.
Location The Barnyards (0.5m S on A98)
Hotel ★★★54% Banff Springs Hotel, Golden Knowes Rd, BANFF 🕿 (0261) 812881 30 ⇌ 🏾

For an explanation of symbols and abbreviations, see page 5

BRAEMAR   Map 15 NO19

Braemar 🕿 (03397) 41618
Flat course, set amid beautiful countryside on Royal Deeside, with River Clunie running through several holes. The 2nd hole is one of the most testing in the area.
18 holes, 5000yds, Par 65, SSS 64, Course record 61.
Club membership 400.
Visitors are advised to book 24 hours in advance to play at weekends.
Societies must contact secretary in advance.
Green Fees £14 per day; £10 per round (£17 per day; £13 per round weekends).
Facilities ⊗ ⅷ ⅃ ☒ ♀ ♨ 🏠 🍴
Location Cluniebank Rd (0.5m S)
Hotel ★★★68% Invercauld Arms, BRAEMAR 🕿 (03397) 41605 68 ⇌ 🏾

BUCKIE   Map 15 NJ46

Buckpool 🕿 (0542) 832236
Windy, seaside course, with easy walking. Overlooking Moray Firth, its fairways are lined by whin and broom.
18 holes, 6257yds, Par 70, SSS 70, Course record 64.
Club membership 350.
Visitors may not play on competition days.
Societies booking advisable.
Green Fees £15 per day; £8 per round (£20/£12 weekends).
Facilities ⊗ ⅷ ⅃ ☒ (all catering during high season) ♀ ♨
Leisure squash, snooker, caddy cars for hire.
Location Barhill Rd, Buckpool (W side of town off A990)
Hotel ★★61% Mill House Hotel, Tynet, BUCKIE 🕿 (0542) 850233 15 ⇌ 🏾

Strathlene 🕿 (0542) 831798
Windy seaside links course with magnificent view. A special feature of the course is approach shots to raised greens (holes 4,5,6 & 13).
18 holes, 5925yds, Par 69, SSS 68, Course record 65.
Club membership 350.
Visitors no restrictions.
Societies must telephone in advance.
Green Fees £14 per day; £10 per round (£18/12 weekends).
Facilities ⊗ ⅃ ☒ ♀ ♨ 🏠
Leisure trolleys for hire.
Location Strathlene Rd (3m E on A942)
Hotel ★★61% Mill House Hotel, Tynet, BUCKIE 🕿 (0542) 850233 15 ⇌ 🏾

CAIRNBULG
Map 15 NK06

Inverallochy ☎ (0346) 582000
Windy seaside links course with natural hazards, tricky par 3s and easy walking. Panoramic views of North Sea at every hole.
18 holes, 5137yds, Par 64, SSS 65, Course record 60.
Club membership 300.

Visitors	restricted at weekends and competition days
Societies	apply in writing.
Green Fees	£10 per day.
Facilities	⅃ & 🍺 (evenings and weekends) ⌖
Location	24 Shore St (E side of village off B9107)
Hotel	★★64% Tufted Duck Hotel, ST COMBS ☎ (0346) 582481 & 582482/3 18 ⇌ 🏠

CRUDEN BAY
Map 15 NK03

Cruden Bay ☎ (0779) 812285
A seaside links which provides golf of a high order. It was designed by a master architect, Tom Simpson, and although changed somewhat from his original design it is still a great golf course. Magnificent views.
Cruden Bay: 18 holes, 6370yds, Par 70, SSS 71.
St Olaf: 9 holes, 5106yds, Par 64, SSS 62.
Club membership 1050.

Visitors	restricted on Wed & competition days.
Societies	apply in writing.
Green Fees	Cruden Bay £22 per day (£30 weekends); St Olaf £12 per day (£17 weekends).
Facilities	⊗ ⅏ ⅃ 🍺 ⌖ 🏠 ⅌ ℓ Robbie Stewart.
Leisure	practice range.
Location	SW side of village on A975
Hotel	★★★66% Waterside Inn, Fraserburgh Rd, PETERHEAD ☎ (0779) 471121 70 ⇌ 🏠 Annexe40 ⇌ 🏠
Additional hotel	★★65% Udny Arms Hotel, Main St, NEWBURGH ☎ (0358) 789444 26 ⇌ 🏠

CULLEN
Map 15 NJ56

Cullen ☎ (0542) 840685
Interesting links on two levels with rocks and ravines offering some challenging holes. Spectacular scenery.
18 holes, 4610yds, Par 63, SSS 62, Course record 58.
Club membership 650.

Visitors	no restrictions.
Societies	apply in advance.
Green Fees	£10 per day (£13 weekends).
Facilities	⊗ ⅏ by prior arrangement ⅃ 🍺 (catering Apr-Oct) ⅂ ⌖
Location	The Links (0.5m W off A98)
Hotel	★★61% Mill House Hotel, Tynet, BUCKIE ☎ (0542) 850233 15 ⇌ 🏠

DUFFTOWN
Map 15 NJ33

Dufftown ☎ (0340) 820325
A short and undulating inland course with good views. Highest hole over 1000 ft above sea level.
18 holes, 5308yds, Par 67, SSS 67, Course record 68.
Club membership 300.

Visitors	Tue & Wed evening course not available until after 6pm.
Societies	must contact in advance.

Green Fees	£15 per day; £12 per round.
Facilities	⅂ ⌖ ⅌
Leisure	caddy cars for hire.
Location	0.75m SW off B9009
Hotel	★★★74% Craigellachie Hotel, CRAIGELLACHIE ☎ (0340) 881204 30 ⇌ 🏠

ELGIN
Map 15 NJ26

Elgin ☎ (0343) 542338
Possibly the finest inland course in the north of Scotland, with undulating greens and compact holes that demand the highest accuracy. There are thirteen par 4's and one par 5 hole on its parkland layout.
18 holes, 6401yds, Par 69, SSS 71.
Club membership 906.

Visitors	restricted until 10.05am at weekends. A handicap certificate is required. An advance telephone call is required if more than four people intend to play.
Societies	contact in advance.
Green Fees	£22 per day; £15 per round (£30/£22 weekends).
Facilities	⊗ & ⅏ by prior arrangement ⅃ 🍺 ⅂ ⌖ 🏠 ℓ Ian P Rodger.
Leisure	practice area.
Location	Hardhillock, Birnie Rd, New Elgin (1m S off A941)
Hotel	★★★69% Mansfield House Hotel, Mayne Rd, ELGIN ☎ (0343) 540883 17 ⇌ 🏠

ELLON
Map 15 NJ93

McDonald ☎ (0358) 720576
Tight, parkland course with streams and a pond.
18 holes, 5986yds, Par 70, SSS 69.
Club membership 710.

Visitors	no restrictions.
Green Fees	not confirmed.
Facilities	⅂ ⌖
Location	Hospital Rd (0.25m N on A948)
Hotel	★66% Meldrum Arms Hotel, The Square, OLDMELDRUM ☎ (0651) 872238 7 🏠

FORRES
Map 14 NJ05

Forres ☎ (0309) 672949
An all-year parkland course laid on light, well-drained soil in wooded countryside. Walking is easy despite some hilly holes. A test for the best golfers.
18 holes, 6240yds, Par 70, SSS 69, Course record 63.
Club membership 950.

Visitors	welcome although club competitions take priority. Weekends may be restricted in summer.
Societies	must telephone 2-3 weeks in advance.
Green Fees	not confirmed.
Facilities	⊗ ⅏ ⅃ 🍺 ⅂ ⌖ 🏠 ⅌ ℓ Sandy Aird.
Location	Muiryshade (SE side of town centre off B9010)
Hotel	★★68% Ramnee Hotel, Victoria Rd, FORRES ☎ (0309) 672410 20 ⇌ 🏠

FRASERBURGH
Map 15 NJ96

Fraserburgh ☎ (0346) 518287
Testing seaside course.

18 holes, 6279yds, Par 70, SSS 70, Course record 64.
Club membership 700.
Visitors   no restrictions.
Societies   must contact in advance.
Green Fees £12 per day (£16 weekends).
Facilities   ⊗ ⫪ ⯖ ⯊ (No catering Mon) ⚲ ⌷ ☖
Location   Corbie Hill (1m SE on B9033)
Hotel   ★★64% Tufted Duck Hotel, ST COMBS
               ☎ (0346) 582481 & 582482/3 18 ⇥ ৈ

GARMOUTH   Map 15 NJ36

Garmouth & Kingston ☎ Spey Bay (0343) 870388
Seaside course with several parkland holes and tidal waters.
Naturally flat.
18 holes, 5656yds, Par 67, SSS 67, Course record 64.
Club membership 400.
Visitors   restricted on competition days.
Societies   must telephone in advance.
Green Fees £15 per day; £10 per round (£20/£15 weekends).
Facilities   all catering by prior arrangement ⚲ (weekends) ⌷
Leisure   caddy cars for hire-donation to charity.
Location   In village on B9015
Hotel   ★★★69% Mansefield House Hotel, Mayne Rd,
               ELGIN ☎ (0343) 540883 17 ⇥ ৈ

HOPEMAN   Map 15 NJ16

Hopeman ☎ (0343) 830578
Links-type course with beautiful views over the Moray Firth.
The 12th hole, called the Priescach, is a short hole with a
drop of 100 feet from tee to green. It can require anything
from a wedge to a wood depending on the wind.
18 holes, 5511yds, Par 67, SSS 67, Course record 66.
Club membership 600.
Visitors   restricted Tue 5pm-6pm & weekends.
Societies   apply by letter 2 weeks in advance.
Green Fees £12 per day, £8 after 3pm (£17/£12 weekends).
Facilities   ⊗ ⫪ ⯖ ⯊ ⚲ ⌷ ☖ ⛳
Leisure   pool table, caddy cars.
Location   E side of village off B9012
Hotel   ★★★69% Mansefield House Hotel, Mayne Rd,
               ELGIN ☎ (0343) 540883 17 ⇥ ৈ

HUNTLY   Map 15 NJ53

Huntly ☎ (0466) 792643
A parkland course lying between the Rivers Deveron and Bogie.
18 holes, 5399yds, Par 67, SSS 66.
Club membership 820.
Visitors   may not play before 8am.
Societies   must contact the secretary.

Green Fees not confirmed.
Facilities   ⊗ ⫪ ⯖ ⯊ & ⯊ by prior arrangement ⚲ ⌷ ☖
Leisure   pool table.
Location   Cooper Park (0.25m through School Arch N side
               of Huntly)
Hotel   ★★⯖⯊59% Castle Hotel, HUNTLY
               ☎ (0466) 792696 21rm(20 ⇥ ৈ)

INVERURIE   Map 15 NJ72

Inverurie ☎ (0467) 624080
Parkland course, part of which is exposed and windy, and
part through wooded area.
18 holes, 5711yds, Par 69, SSS 68, Course record 67.
Club membership 585.
Visitors   no restrictions.
Green Fees £12 per day (£18 weekends).
Facilities   ⊗ ⫪ by prior arrangement ⯖ ⯊ ⚲ ⌷ ☖
Location   Davah Wood, Blackhall Rd (W side of town off
               A96)
Hotel   ★★★67% Strathburn Hotel, Burghmuir Dr,
               INVERURIE ☎ (0467) 624422 25 ⇥ ৈ

KEITH   Map 15 NJ45

Keith ☎ (0542) 882469
Parkland course, with natural hazards over first 9 holes.
Testing 7th hole, 232 yds, par 3.
18 holes, 5614yds, Par 69, SSS 68, Course record 65.
Club membership 410.
Visitors   advisable to telephone in advance.
Societies   by arrangement with club secretary
Green Fees £10 per day (£15 weekends).
Facilities   ⊗ ⫪ ⯖ ⯊ & ⯊ by prior arrangement ⚲ ⌷
Leisure   pool table.
Location   Fife Park (NW side of town centre off A96)
Hotel   ★★★74% Craigellachie Hotel,
               CRAIGELLACHIE ☎ (0340) 881204 30 ⇥ ৈ

KEMNAY   Map 15 NJ71

Kemnay ☎ (0467) 642225
Undulating parkland course with superb views. A stream
crosses four holes.
18 holes, 5903yds, Par 70, SSS 68.
Club membership 650.
Visitors   may not play Tue & Thu evenings or before
               11am on Sun.
Societies   must telephone in advance.
Green Fees £15 per day; £10 per round (£18/£12 weekends).
Facilities   ⯊ (phone for details of catering) ⚲ ⌷ ☖
Leisure   caddy cars.   ▶

The Castle Hotel

Set in our own grounds we offer peace and tranquillity along with comfortable accommodation and good food. Huntly Golf Club is on our doorstep and there are numerous others all within an hours drive. We are happy to assist in making bookings at most courses.

Telephone: (01466) 792696 • Fax (01466) 792641

HUNTLY • ABERDEENSHIRE • AB54 4SH

Location Monymusk Rd (W side of village on B993)
Hotel ★★★62% Westhill Hotel, WESTHILL
    ☎ (0224) 740388 37 ⇆ ⚑Annexe14 ⇆ ⚑

LOSSIEMOUTH   Map 15 NJ27

Moray ☎ (0343) 812018
Two fine Scottish Championship links courses, known as
Old and New (Moray), and situated on the Moray Firth
where the weather is unusually mild.
Old Course: 18 holes, 6643yds, Par 71, SSS 72.
New Course: 18 holes, 6005yds, Par 69, SSS 69.
Club membership 1300.
Visitors must contact in advance, restricted at
    weekends.
Societies must contact in advance.
Green Fees Old Course: £26 per day; £21 per round
    (£35/£30 weekends). New Course: £20 per
    day; £15 per round (£25/£20 weekends).
Facilities ⊗ ⅏ by prior arrangement ⮞ ♥ ♀ ⚘ 🏠
    ✆ Alistair Thomson.
Location Stotfield Rd (N side of town)
Hotel ★★★69% Mansfield House Hotel, Mayne
    Rd, ELGIN ☎ (0343) 540883 17 ⇆ ⚑

MACDUFF   Map 15 NJ76

Royal Tarlair ☎ (0261) 32897
Seaside clifftop course, can be windy. Testing 13th, 'Clivet'
(par 3).
18 holes, 5866yds, Par 71, SSS 68, Course record 64.
Club membership 576.
Visitors no restrictions.
Societies apply in writing.
Green Fees not confirmed.
Facilities ⊗ ⅏ ⮞ ♥ ♀ ⚘
Location Buchan St (0.75m E off A98)
Hotel ★★60% The Highland Haven, Shore St,
    MACDUFF ☎ (0261) 32408 20 ⇆ ⚑

NEWBURGH ON YTHAN   Map 15 NJ92

Newburgh on Ythan ☎ Newburgh (0358) 789438
Seaside course adjacent to bird sanctuary. Testing 550-yd dog
leg (par 5).
9 holes, 6404yds, Par 72, SSS 70, Course record 69.
Club membership 300.
Visitors restricted Tue & Sat.
Societies must telephone in advance.
Green Fees not confirmed.
Location E side of village on A975
Hotel ★★65% Udny Arms Hotel, Main St,
    NEWBURGH ☎ (0358) 789444 26 ⇆ ⚑
    See advertisement on page 242

NEWMACHAR   Map 15 NJ81

Newmachar ☎ (0651) 863002
Championship-standard parkland course designed by Dave
Thomas and opened in 1991. Several lakes affect five of the
holes and there are well developed birch and Scots pine trees.
*Hawkshill: 18 holes, 6623yds, Par 72, SSS 74, Course
record 68.*
Club membership 750.

Visitors must contact in advance & have handicap
    certificate, restricted at weekends.
Societies apply in writing.
Green Fees £24 per day; £16 per round (£30/£20 weekends).
Facilities ⊗ ⅏ ⮞ ♥ ♀ ⚘ 🏠 ✆ Glenn Taylor.
Leisure caddy cars, motorised golf buggies.
Location Swailend (2m N of Dyce, off A947)
Hotel ★★★67% Strathburn Hotel, Burghmuir Dr,
    INVERURIE ☎ (0467) 624422 25 ⇆ ⚑

OLDMELDRUM   Map 15 NJ82

Old Meldrum ☎ (0651) 872648
Parkland course with tree-lined fairways and superb views.
Challenging 196 yard, Par 3, 11th over two ponds to a green
surrounded by bunkers.
18 holes, 5988yds, Par 70, SSS 69, Course record 69.
Club membership 800.
Visitors may not play during Club competitions. Must
    contact in advance. To book tee time tel: (0651)
    873555.
Societies apply in writing.
Green Fees £10 per day (£15 weekends); weekly ticket
    (Mon-Fri) £35.
Facilities ⊗ ⅏ ⮞ ♥ ♀ ⚘ 🏠
Location Kirkbrae (E side of village off A947)
Hotel ★66% Meldrum Arms Hotel, The Square,
    OLDMELDRUM ☎ (0651) 872238 7 ⚑

PETERHEAD   Map 15 NK14

Peterhead ☎ (0779) 472149
Natural links course bounded by the sea and the River Ugie.
Old Course: 18 holes, 6173yds, Par 70, SSS 70.
New Course: 9 holes, 2237yds, Par 62, SSS 62.
Club membership 600.
Visitors telephone for details.
Societies apply in writing.
Green Fees Old Course: £14 per day/round (£18 weekends).
    New Course: £6 per day/round.
Facilities ⊗ & ⅏ by prior arrangement ⮞ ♥ ♀ ⚘
Leisure pool table.
Location Craigewan Links (N side of town centre off
    A952)
Hotel ★★★66% Waterside Inn, Fraserburgh Rd,
    PETERHEAD
    ☎ (0779) 471121 70 ⇆ ⚑Annexe40 ⇆ ⚑

PORTLETHEN   Map 15 NO99

Portlethen ☎ Aberdeen (0224) 782575
Set in pleasant parkland, this new course features mature
trees and a stream which affects a number of holes.
18 holes, 6735yds, Par 72, SSS 72.
Club membership 650.
Visitors may not play after 4pm weekdays. Must play
    with member Sat & Sun.
Societies apply in writing.
Green Fees £18 per day; £12 per round.
Facilities ⊗ ⅏ ⮞ ♥ ♀ ⚘ 🏠 ✆ Muriel Thompson.
Leisure snooker, darts, pool table.
Location Badentoy Rd
Hotel ★★60% County Hotel, Arduthie Rd,
    STONEHAVEN ☎ (0569) 764386 14 ⇆ ⚑

ROTHES
Map 15 NJ24

Rothes ☎ (0340) 831443
A hilly course opened in 1990 on an elevated site overlooking the remains of Rothes castle and the Spey valley. The 2nd fairway and most of the 3rd are sheltered by woodland. The ground alongside the 5th & 6th falls away steeply.
9 holes, 4956yds, Par 68, SSS 64, Course record 65.
Club membership 300.
Visitors no restrictions.
Societies apply in advance in writing.
Green Fees £8 per round (£10 weekends).
Facilities ⊗ by prior arrangement ♀ (evening & weekends) ☆
Location Blackhall (9m S of Elgin on A941)
Hotel ★★★⚓⚓63% Rothes Glen Hotel, ROTHES ☎ (0340) 831254 & 831255 16 ⇆ ♦

SPEY BAY
Map 15 NJ36

Spey Bay ☎ Fochabers (0343) 820424
Seaside links course over gently undulating banks and well-drained ground. Good views along Moray coast. Driving range.
18 holes, 6092yds, Par 71, SSS 69.
Club membership 177.
Visitors telephone for details.
Societies must contact in advance.
Green Fees £15 per day;£10 per round (£18/£13 weekends).
Facilities ⊗ ♭ ♀ ☆ 🏠 ⚐ ⋈
Leisure hard tennis courts, fishing, caravan site, putting & driving range.
Location 4.5m N of Fochabers on B9104
Hotel ★★61% Mill House Hotel, Tynet, BUCKIE ☎ (0542) 850233 15 ⇆ ♦

STONEHAVEN
Map 15 NO88

Stonehaven ☎ (0569) 762124
Challenging meadowland course overlooking sea with three gullies and splendid views.
18 holes, 5103yds, Par 66, SSS 65.
Club membership 840.
Visitors must contact in advance, restricted at weekends.
Societies must contact in advance.
Green Fees £13 per day (£18 weekends).
Facilities ⊗ ℿ by prior arrangement ♭ ♥ ♀ ☆ 🏠
Leisure snooker.
Location Cowie (1m N off A92)
Hotel ★★60% County Hotel, Arduthie Rd, STONEHAVEN ☎ (0569) 764386 14 ⇆ ♦

TARLAND
Map 15 NJ40

Tarland ☎ (03398) 81413
Difficult upland course, but easy walking.
9 holes, 5816yds, Par 66, SSS 68.
Club membership 260.
Visitors welcome except for competition days. Advisable to contact in advance for weekends.
Societies must telephone in advance.
Green Fees £12 per day (£15 weekends).
Facilities ⊗ ℿ ♭ ♥ ♀ ☆
Location Aberdeen Rd (E side of village off B9119)

Hotel ★★67% Birse Lodge Hotel, Charleston Rd, ABOYNE ☎ (03398) 86253 & 86254 12 ⇆ ♦Annexe4 ⇆

TORPHINS
Map 15 NJ60

Torphins ☎ (03398) 82115
Heathland/parkland course built on a hill with views of the Cairngorms.
9 holes, 4684yds, Par 64, SSS 64, Course record 64.
Club membership 370.
Visitors must contact in advance. Restricted weekends, members only Tues after 5pm.
Societies must contact in writing.
Green Fees £10 per day (£12 weekends).
Facilities snacks tea & coffee (weekends Apr-Oct) ☆
Location Golf Rd (0.25m W of village off A980)
Hotel ★★★64% Tor-na-Coille Hotel, BANCHORY ☎ (0330) 822242 24 ⇆ ♦

TURRIFF
Map 15 NJ74

Turriff ☎ (0888) 62982
A well-maintained parkland course alongside the River Deveron in picturesque surroundings. 6th and 12th particularly challenging in a testing course.
18 holes, 6145yds, Par 69, SSS 69, Course record 63.
Club membership 860.
Visitors may not play before 10am weekends. Must contact in advance.
Societies apply in writing to the secretary.
Green Fees £16 per day; £13 per round (£22/£17 weekends).
Facilities  ⊗ ℿ (ex Wed) ♭ ♥ ♀ ☆ 🏠 ⚐
𝄡 Robin Smith.
Leisure caddy cars.
Location Rosehall (1m W off B9024)
Hotel ★★★54% Banff Springs Hotel, Golden Knowes Rd, BANFF ☎ (0261) 812881 30 ⇆ ♦

HIGHLAND

ALNESS
Map 14 NH66

Alness ☎ (0349) 883877
A short, but testing, parkland course with beautiful views over the Cromarty Firth and the Black Isle.
9 holes, 2606yds, Par 66, SSS 64, Course record 62.
Club membership 230.
Visitors restricted during competitions.
Societies must telephone in advance.
Green Fees not confirmed.
Facilities ♭ ♥ ♀ ☆ ⚐
Location Ardross Rd (0.5m N off A9)
Hotel ★★★64% Morangie House Hotel, Morangie Rd, TAIN ☎ (0862) 892281 13 ⇆ ♦

> For an explanation of symbols and abbreviations, see page 5

BOAT OF GARTEN

Map 14 NH91

Boat of Garten ☎ (0479) 831282
This parkland course was cut out from a silver birch forest though the fairways are adequately wide. There are natural hazards of broom and heather, good views and walking is easy. A round provides great variety.
18 holes, 5837yds, Par 69, SSS 69.
Club membership 400.

Visitors	must contact in advance and have a handicap certificate. Restricted weekdays 9.30am-5.30pm.
Societies	must telephone in advance.
Green Fees	£16 per day (£21 weekends).
Facilities	⊗ ⅢⅡ Ⅱ ♥ ♀ △ 🖻
Leisure	hard tennis courts, caddy cars.
Location	E side of village
Hotel	★★★64% Boat Hotel, BOAT OF GARTEN ☎ (0479) 831258 32 ➪ ↾

BONAR BRIDGE

Map 14 NH69

Bonar Bridge-Ardgay ☎ (054982) 248
Wooded moorland course with picturesque views of hills and loch.
9 holes, 4626yds, Par 66, SSS 63, Course record 66.
Club membership 240.

Visitors	restricted during competitions.
Societies	apply in advance.
Green Fees	£8 per day.
Facilities	⊗ & ♥ (May-Sep) △

Location	0.5m E
Hotel	★★66% Dornoch Castle Hotel, Castle St, DORNOCH ☎ (0862) 810216 4 ➪ ↾Annexe13 ➪ ↾

BRORA

Map 14 NC90

Brora ☎ (0408) 621417
Typical seaside links with little rough and fine views. Some testing holes.
18 holes, 6110yds, Par 69, SSS 69.
Club membership 550.

Visitors	welcome except for competition days.
Societies	must contact in advance.
Green Fees	£15 per day.
Facilities	⊗ ⅢⅡ Ⅱ ♥ ♀ △ 🖻 ⍾
Leisure	caddy cars.
Location	Golf Rd (E side of village)
Hotel	★★★62% The Links Hotel, Golf Rd, BRORA ☎ (0408) 621225 21 ➪ ↾

CARRBRIDGE

Map 14 NH92

Carrbridge ☎ (0479) 841623
Short part-parkland, part-moorland course with magnificent views of the Cairngorms.
9 holes, 5300yds, Par 71, SSS 66, Course record 64.
Club membership 600.

Visitors	restricted Sun, competition days and after 5pm Wed May-Sep.
Societies	must contact in advance.

GOLF WEEKS AND TEE BREAKS

AA ★ ★ ★

Situated overlooking the beautiful but challenging Boat of Garten Golf Course - the 'Gleneagles' of the Highlands - the Boat Hotel offers you Master Classes with our resident Professional, or, excellent value Tee Break holidays with golf on any of six local courses. Individual tuition available throughout the year.

For Golf Brochure Contact:
Suzanne MacLean,
The Boat Hotel, Boat of Garten,
Inverness-shire. PH24 3BH
Tel: 01479 831258 Fax: 01479 831414

FAIRWINDS HOTEL AND CHALETS

Carrbridge, Inverness-shire PH23 3AA
Telephone and Fax: 01479 841240

AA
selected

What is important to a Golfer?
Golf Courses. We have 7 within easy reach
But after the golf, what then?

Return to a friendly welcome, pleasant comfortable surroundings – all our bedrooms are en-suite – and high standards of personal attention. Relax in the Ptarmigan Lounge Bar before enjoying a meal in our spacious Conservatory Restaurant:- we pride ourselves on our varied menus including vegetarian dishes. Alternatively stay in one of our 2 or 3 bedroom self catering Chalets or Studio Apartment.

Please write or phone for full details to Mrs E. Reed

Green Fees £9-£10 per day (£11 weekends).
Facilities ⓑ 🍽 (catering Apr-Oct) ⚷ ⅋
Leisure caddy cars.
Location N side of village
Hotel ★★71% Dalrachney Lodge, CARRBRIDGE
☎ (0479) 841252 10 ⇄ ⬥
Additional QQQQ Fairwinds Hotel, CARRBRIDGE
hotel ☎ (0479) 841240 5 ⇄ ⬥
See advertisement on page 248

DORNOCH
Map 14 NH78

Royal Dornoch ☎ (0862) 810219
Very challenging seaside championship links, designed
by Tom Morris and John Sutherland.
18 holes, 6591yds, Par 70, SSS 72, Course record 67.
Struie: 18 holes, 5321yds, Par 68, SSS 70.
Club membership 900.
Visitors handicap of 24 for gentlemen (ladies 35).
Must contact in advance and have a
handicap certificate.
Societies must telephone in advance.
Green Fees not confirmed.
Facilities ⊗ ⅲ ⓑ 🍽 ⓠ ⚷ ⚑ ⅋ ℓ W E Skinner.
Leisure hard tennis courts, fishing, riding.
Location Golf Rd (E side of town)
Hotel ★★66% Dornoch Castle Hotel, Castle St,
DORNOCH
☎ (0862) 810216 4 ⇄ ⬥Annexe13 ⇄ ⬥

★★
Dornoch Castle

**DORNOCH,
SUTHERLAND
IV25 3SD**
Tel. (01862) 810216
Fax: (01862) 810981

Play GOLF on the famous Royal Dornoch Championship
Course, and stay at the charming Dornoch Castle. Your
room looks out over lovely sheltered formal gardens and the
magnificent Dornoch Firth. All have private facilities: those
in the new wing have modern decor, while those in the
Castle enjoy the highest level of traditional atmosphere and
elegance. Beaches and golf courses are within walking
distance. Superb food ("Taste of Scotland" recommended) in
one of the finest Restaurants of the area with a cellar to
match will make your visit an experience not to be
forgotten. Regular performances of the Dornoch Pipe Band
on Saturday nights in summer.

STB 😊😊😊😊 COMMENDED

DURNESS
Map 14 NC46

Durness ☎ (0971) 511364 & 511209
A 9-hole course set in tremendous scenery overlooking
Balnakeil Bay. Part links and part inland with water hazards.
Off alternative tees for second 9 holes giving surprising
variety. Tremendous last hole played across the sea to the
green over 100 yards away.
9 holes, 5545yds, Par 70, SSS 68, Course record 72.
Club membership 100.
Visitors restricted 10am-noon on Sun.
Societies must telephone in advance.
Green Fees £8 per day.
Facilities 🍽 ⚷ ⅋
Location Balnakeil (1m W of village)
Hotel ★★★65% Kinlochbervie Hotel,
KINLOCHBERVIE ☎ (0971) 521275 14 ⇄ ⬥

FORT AUGUSTUS
Map 14 NH30

Fort Augustus ☎ (0320) 366460
Moorland course, with narrow fairways and good views.
Bordered by the tree-lined Caledonian Canal.
9 holes, 5454yds, Par 67, SSS 68, Course record 69.
Club membership 170.
Visitors no restrictions.
Societies welcome.
Green Fees not confirmed.
Facilities ⓑ 🍽 ⓠ ⚷ ⅋
Location Markethill (1m SW on A82)
Hotel ★★67% Lovat Arms Hotel,
FORT AUGUSTUS
☎ (0320) 366206 & 366204 21 ⇄ ⬥

FORTROSE
Map 14 NH75

Fortrose & Rosemarkie ☎ (0381) 620733 & 620529
Seaside links course, set on a peninsula with sea on three
sides. Easy walking, good views. Designed by James Braid;
the club was formed in 1888.
18 holes, 5973yds, Par 71, SSS 69, Course record 64.
Club membership 765.
Visitors restricted 8.45-10.15am & 1-2.15 then 4.45-
6.30pm.
Societies must telephone in advance.
Green Fees £18 per day; £13 per round (£18 per round
weekends).
Facilities ⊗ ⓑ 🍽 (bar meals by arrangement) ⓠ ⚷ ⚑ ⅋
Location Ness Rd East (E side of town centre)
Hotel ★★66% Royal Hotel, Marine Ter,
CROMARTY ☎ (0381) 600217 10 ⇄ ⬥

FORT WILLIAM
Map 14 NN17

Fort William ☎ (0397) 704464
Moorland course with fine views. Tees and greens very good,
but fairways can be very soft in wet weather.
18 holes, 5640yds, Par 70, SSS 68.
Club membership 200.
Visitors no restrictions.
Societies must contact in writing.
Green Fees not confirmed.
Facilities ⓑ 🍽 ⓠ ⚷ ⅋
Location 3m NE on A82 ▶

Hotel   ★★★75% Moorings Hotel, Banavie,
FORT WILLIAM
☎ (0397) 772797 21 ⇆ ⋔Annexe3 ⋔

GAIRLOCH   Map 14 NG87

Gairloch ☎ (0445) 2407
Fine seaside links course running along Gairloch Sands with
good views over the sea to Skye. In windy conditions each
hole is affected.
9 holes, 4577yds, Par 62, SSS 63.
Club membership 350.
Visitors   no restrictions.
Societies   must telephone in advance.
Green Fees £10 per day.
Facilities   ♖ ⌂ ⚑
Location   1m S on A832
Hotel   ★★62% The Old Inn, Flowerdale, GAIRLOCH
☎ (0445) 2006 14 ⇆ ⋔

GOLSPIE   Map 14 NH89

Golspie ☎ (0408) 633266
Founded in 1889, Golspie's seaside course offers easy
walking and natural hazards including beach heather and
whins. Spectacular scenery.
18 holes, 5836yds, Par 68, SSS 68.
Club membership 480.
Visitors   restricted on competition days.
Societies   must telephone in advance.
Green Fees £12 per day/round (£16 weekends & bank
holidays).

TYREE HOUSE HOTEL

The Square,
Grantown-on-Spey,
Morayshire
Telephone: (01479) 2615

Tyree House is centrally situated in the
town of Grantown-on-Spey. Ideal for
family holidays, only 10 minutes through
the town to the golf course, fishing,
bowling green and tennis courts. The hotel
has full central heating with nine tastefully
decorated bedrooms all having private
facilities, complimentary tea & coffee and
TV. A comfortable residents lounge is
situated on the first floor with views across
the sqwuare and guests are welcome to
make use of the lounge at all times. Dinner
is available in the hotel's à la carte
restaurant, The Tyrone Suite open every
evening. Ample parking space.

Facilities   ⊗ ⋔ by prior arrangement ♖ ♛ ♀ ⌂ 🏠
Location   Ferry Rd (0.5m S off A9)
Hotel   ★★62% Golf Links Hotel, GOLSPIE
☎ (0408) 633408 9 ⇆ ⋔

GRANTOWN-ON-SPEY   Map 14 NJ02

Grantown-on-Spey ☎ (0479) 872079 (summer) & 872715
Parkland and woodland course. Part easy walking, remainder
hilly. The 7th to 13th really sorts out the golfers.
18 holes, 5745yds, Par 70, SSS 68.
Club membership 600.
Visitors   restricted 8am-10am weekends.
Societies   telephone in advance, or write in winter.
Green Fees £13 per day (£18 weekends).
Facilities   ⊗ ♖ ♛ (catering Apr-Oct) ♀ (Apr-Oct) ⌂ 🏠
⚑ (Bill Mitchell.
Leisure   putting green.
Location   Golf Course Rd (E side of town centre)
Hotel   ★★63% Seafield Lodge Hotel, Woodside Av,
GRANTOWN-ON-SPEY
☎ (0479) 872152 14 ⇆ ⋔
Additional   ★73% Tyree House, 8 The Square,
hotel   GRANTOWN-ON-SPEY
☎ (0479) 872615 9 ⋔

HELMSDALE   Map 14 ND01

Helmsdale ☎ (0431) 821240
Sheltered, undulating course following the line of the
Helmsdale River.
9 holes, 1825yds, Par 62, SSS 62.
Club membership 137.
Visitors   no restrictions.
Societies   apply in writing.
Green Fees not confirmed.
Facilities   ⌂
Location   Golf Rd (NW side of town on A896)
Hotel   ★★★62% The Links Hotel, Golf Rd, BRORA
☎ (0408) 621225 21 ⇆ ⋔

INVERGORDON   Map 14 NH76

Invergordon ☎ (0349) 852715
Fairly easy but windy parkland course, with good views over
Cromarty Firth. Very good greens. Clubhouse situated 1m
from course close to middle of town.
9 holes, 6028yds, Par 68, SSS 69, Course record 65.
Club membership 300.
Visitors   no restrictions.
Societies   must telephone in advance.
Green Fees not confirmed.
Facilities   ♖ & ♛ (Sat only) ♀ (Sat, Tue & Thu eve) ⌂
Location   King George St (W side of town centre on B817)
Hotel   ★★★64% Morangie House Hotel, Morangie
Rd, TAIN ☎ (0862) 892281 13 ⇆ ⋔

If you know of a golf course that
welcomes visitors and is not already in
this guide, we should be grateful for
information

INVERNESS   Map 14 NH64

Inverness ☎ (0463) 239882
Fairly flat parkland course with burn running through it.
Windy in winter. The 14th is one of the most difficult Par 4's
in the north of Scotland.
18 holes, 6226yds, Par 69, SSS 70.
Club membership 1050.
Visitors   restricted at weekends.
Societies   must telephone in advance.
Green Fees   £22 per day; £16 per round (£24/£20 weekends
                  & bank holidays).
Facilities   ⊗ ℳ by prior arrangement ⅃ ■ ♀ ⚐ ⌂ ⌇
                  ⌇ Alistair P Thomson.
Location   Culcabock
Hotel   ★★★★67% Kingsmills Hotel, Culcabock Rd,
                  INVERNESS
                  ☎ (0463) 237166 78 ⇆ ⌇Annexe6 ⇆ ⌇

Torvean ☎ (0463) 711434
Municipal parkland course, easy walking, good views.
18 holes, 5784yds, Par 69, SSS 68, Course record 66.
Club membership 403.
Visitors   must contact in advance, restricted on
                  competition days.
Societies   must telephone in advance.
Green Fees   £11.20 per day; £8.40 per round (£12.70/£9.80
                  weekends).
Facilities   ⊗ (weekends only) ⅃ (Mon-Fri) ■ ♀ (summer)
                  ⚐ ⌂ ⌇
Leisure   trolleys.
Location   Glenurquhart Rd (1.5m SW on A82)
Hotel   ★★★68% Dunain Park Hotel, INVERNESS
                  ☎ (0463) 230512 12rm(10 ⇆ ⌇)

KINGUSSIE   Map 14 NH70

Kingussie ☎ (0540) 661374
Hilly upland course with natural hazards and magnificent
views. Stands about 1000ft above sea level at its highest
point, and the River Gynack comes into play on five holes.
18 holes, 5555yds, Par 66, SSS 67, Course record 64.
Club membership 700.
Visitors   restricted weekends.
Societies   must telephone (0540) 661600 to book.
Green Fees   £15 per day; £12 per round (£18 & £14 weekends).
Facilities   ⊗ (Jun-Sep. Weekends other times) ⅃ ■ ♀
                  (Apr-Oct) ⚐ ⌂ ⌇
Location   Gynack Rd (0.25m N off A86)
Hotel   ★69% Osprey Hotel, Ruthven Rd, KINGUSSIE
                  ☎ (0540) 661510 8rm(7 ⇆ ⌇)

LOCHCARRON   Map 14 NG83

Lochcarron ☎ (05202) 257
Seaside links course with some parkland with an interesting
2nd hole. A short course but great accuracy is required. There
are plans to extend to 18-holes on an additional 500 acres.
9 holes, 1750yds, SSS 60.
Club membership 150.
Visitors   restricted Fri evening & Sat 2-5pm.
Societies   welcome but restricted Fri evening & Sat 2-5pm.
Green Fees   £18 per week; £8 per day; £5 per 18 holes.
Facilities   no catering ⌇

Location   East End (1m E)
Hotel   ★★65% Lochcarron Hotel, LOCHCARRON
                  ☎ (05202) 226 10rm(9 ⇆ ⌇)

LYBSTER   Map 15 ND23

Lybster
Picturesque, short heathland course, easy walking.
9 holes, 1896yds, Par 62, SSS 62.
Club membership 80.
Visitors   no restrictions.
Societies   must contact in advance.
Green Fees   not confirmed.
Facilities   ⚐ ⌇
Location   Main St (E side of village)
Hotel   ★★63% Portland Arms, LYBSTER
                  ☎ (05932) 208 19 ⇆ ⌇

MUIR OF ORD   Map 14 NH55

Muir of Ord ☎ (0463) 870825
Old established (1875), heathland course with tight fairways
and easy walking. Testing 11th, 'Castle Hill' (par 3).
18 holes, 5202yds, Par 67, SSS 66, Course record 61.
Club membership 700.
Visitors   not permitted during specified draw times for
                  medal tees. Restricted 11am-12.30pm Sat & Sun
                  unless by prior arrangement.
Societies   apply in writing.
Green Fees   £8-£12 per round/day (£10-£15 weekends).
Facilities   ⊗ ⅃ ■ ♀ ⚐ ⌂ ⌇ ⌇ Graham Vivers.
Leisure   snooker.
Location   Great North Rd (S side of village on A862)
Hotel   ★★★66% Priory Hotel, The Square, BEAULY
                  ☎ (0463) 782309 22 ⇆ ⌇

NAIRN   Map 14 NH85

Nairn ☎ (0667) 453208
Championship, seaside links founded in 1887 and created
from a wilderness of heather and whin. Designed by A.
Simpson, old Tom Morris and James Braid. Opening
holes stretch out along the shoreline with the turn for
home at the 10th. Regularly chosen for national
championships.
18 holes, 6722yds, Par 72, SSS 71, Course record 65.
Club membership 1150.
Visitors   restricted until 10.30am weekends.
Societies   telephone at least 6 weeks in advance.
Green Fees   £37 per day; £26 per round (£42/£32
                  weekends).
Facilities   ⊗ ℳ by prior arrangement ⅃ ■ ♀ ⚐ ⌂
                  ⌇ ⌇ Robin Fyfe.
Leisure   snooker, 9 hole course.
Location   Seabank Rd
Hotel   ★★★★60% Golf View Hotel, Seabank Rd,
                  NAIRN ☎ (0667) 452301 47 ⇆ ⌇

Nairn Dunbar ☎ (0667) 452741
Links course with sea views and testing gorse-and-whin-lined
fairways. Breezy at holes 6, 7 and 8. Testing hole: 'Long
Peter' (527 yds).
18 holes, 6431yds, Par 71, SSS 71, Course record 68.
Club membership 700.

▶

Visitors must contact in advance & have handicap certificate.
Societies must contact in advance.
Green Fees £22 per day; £17 per round (£27/£22 weekends).
Facilities ⊗ 🍞 ☕ 🍷 △ 🛒 ⛳ 🧑 Brian Mason.
Location Lochloy Rd (E side of town off A96)
Hotel ★★59% Carnach House Hotel, Delnies, NAIRN ☎ (0667) 452094 14rm(13 🛁 🚿)

NETHY BRIDGE — Map 14 NJ02

Abernethy ☎ (0479) 821305
Picturesque moorland course.
9 holes, 4986yds, Par 66, SSS 66.
Club membership 300.
Visitors restricted during club matches.
Societies must telephone in advance.
Green Fees £9 per day (£12 weekends).
Facilities ⊗ by prior arrangement 🍞 ☕ △ ⛳
Leisure trolleys.
Location N side of village on B970
Hotel ★★★🏡🏡68% Muckrach Lodge Hotel, DULNAIN BRIDGE ☎ (047985) 257 10 🛁 🚿 Annexe2 🛁 🚿

NEWTONMORE — Map 14 NN79

Newtonmore ☎ (0540) 673328 & 673878
Inland course beside the River Spey. Beautiful views and easy walking. Testing 17th hole (par 3).
18 holes, 5880yds, Par 70, SSS 68, Course record 64.
Club membership 450.
Visitors no restrictions.
Societies apply in writing.
Green Fees £18 per day; £12 per round (£20/£14 weekends).
Facilities ⊗)Ⅲ 🍞 ☕ (all catering Apr-Oct ex Tue) 🍷 △ 🛒 ⛳ 🧑 Robert Henderson.
Location Golf Course Rd (E side of town off A9)
Hotel ★★69% Columba House Hotel, Manse Rd, KINGUSSIE ☎ (0540) 661402 7 🛁 🚿

PORTMAHOMACK — Map 14 NH98

Tarbat ☎ (086287) 236
Picturesque links course with magnificent views.
9 holes, 5046yds, Par 66, SSS 65.
Club membership 180.
Visitors no restrictions.
Societies must telephone in advance.
Green Fees not confirmed.
Facilities ☕ △
Location E side of village
Hotel ★★★64% Morangie House Hotel, Morangie Rd, TAIN ☎ (0862) 892281 13 🛁 🚿

REAY — Map 14 NC96

Reay ☎ (084781) 288
Picturesque seaside links with natural hazards, following the contours of Sandside Bay. Tight and testing.
18 holes, 5884yds, Par 69, SSS 68, Course record 64.
Club membership 450.
Visitors restricted competition days
Societies apply in writing.
Green Fees £10 per day.
Facilities 🍞 (summer) ☕ 🍷 △
Location 0.5m E off A836
Hotel ★★64% Melvich Hotel, MELVICH ☎ (06413) 206 14 🚿

STRATHPEFFER — Map 14 NH45

Strathpeffer Spa ☎ (0997) 421219
Upland course with many natural hazards (no sand bunkers), hard walking and fine views. Testing 3rd hole (par 3) across loch.
18 holes, 4792yds, Par 65, SSS 65, Course record 60.
Club membership 550.
Visitors may not play during club competition times or until after 10.30am on Sun.
Societies apply in writing.
Green Fees £15 per day; £10 per round (£15 weekends).
Facilities ⊗)Ⅲ (by arrangement weekends) 🍞 ☕ 🍷 △ 🛒 ⛳
Location 0.25m N of village off A834
Hotel ★★64% Holly Lodge Hotel, STRATHPEFFER ☎ (0997) 21254 7rm(3 🛁 3 🚿)

TAIN — Map 14 NH78

Tain ☎ (0862) 892314
Heathland/links course with river affecting 3 holes; easy walking, fine views.
18 holes, 6238yds, Par 70, SSS 70, Course record 62.
Club membership 600.
Visitors must contact in advance and may not play on competition days.
Societies must book in advance.
Green Fees £12 per round (£18 weekends).
Facilities ⊗)Ⅲ by prior arrangement 🍞 ☕ 🍷 △ 🛒
Leisure caddy cars.
Location Golf Links (E side of town centre off B9174)
Hotel ★★★64% Morangie House Hotel, Morangie Rd, TAIN ☎ (0862) 892281 13 🛁 🚿

THURSO — Map 15 ND16

Thurso ☎ (0847) 63807
Parkland course, windy, but with fine views of Dunnet Head and the Orkney Islands.
18 holes, 5818yds, Par 69, SSS 69.
Club membership 366.
Visitors no restrictions.
Societies must telephone in advance.
Green Fees £10 per day.
Facilities ⊗ 🍞 ☕ 🍷 △ 🛒 ⛳
Location Newlands of Geise (2m SW on B874)
Hotel ★★63% Pentland Hotel, Princes St, THURSO ☎ (0847) 63202 53rm(28 🛁 11 🚿)

WICK — Map 15 ND35

Wick ☎ (0955) 2726
Typical seaside links course, windy, easy walking.
18 holes, 5976yds, Par 69, SSS 69, Course record 63.
Club membership 352.
Visitors no restrictions.
Societies apply in writing or telephone in advance.
Green Fees not confirmed.

Facilities	🏌 🍺 ♀
Location	Reiss (3.5m N off A9)
Hotel	★★60% Mackay's Hotel, Union St, WICK ☎ (0955) 2323 26rm(23 ⇆1 🐾)

LOTHIAN

ABERLADY   Map 12 NT47

Kilspindie ☎ (0875) 870358
Seaside course, short but tight and well-bunkered. Testing holes: 2nd, 3rd, 4th and 7th.
18 holes, 5410yds, Par 69, SSS 66.
Club membership 600.
Visitors   no restrictions.
Societies   must contact in advance.
Green Fees not confirmed.
Facilities   ⊗ high tea (Apr-Oct) 🏌 🍺 ♀ 👗 🏠
                  ✦ Graham J Sked.
Location   W side of village off A198
Hotel   ★★65% Kilspindie House Hotel, Main St, ABERLADY ☎ (0875) 870682 26 ⇆ 🐾

Luffness New ☎ Gullane (0620) 843114 & 843336
Seaside course.
18 holes, 6122yds, Par 69, SSS 69, Course record 62.
Club membership 700.
Visitors   must contact in advance but may not play at weekends & bank holidays.
Societies   must contact in writing.
Green Fees £40 per day; £27 per round.
Facilities   ⊗ 🍺 ♀ 👗 🏠
Leisure   caddies.
Location   1m E on A198
Hotel   ★★★(red)🍴 Greywalls Hotel, Muirfield, GULLANE ☎ (0620) 842144 17 ⇆ 🐾Annexe5 ⇆ 🐾

BATHGATE   Map 11 NS96

Bathgate ☎ (0506) 630505
Moorland course. Easy walking. Testing 11th hole, par 3.
18 holes, 6328yds, Par 71, SSS 70.
Club membership 650.
Visitors   must contact in advance & may not play on competition days.
Societies   must contact in advance.
Green Fees not confirmed.
Facilities   ♀ 👗 🏠✦
Location   Edinburgh Rd (E side of town off A89)
Hotel   ★★60% Dreadnought Hotel, 17/19 Whitburn Rd, BATHGATE ☎ (0506) 630791 19rm(18 ⇆ 🐾)

BONNYRIGG   Map 11 NT36

Broomieknowe ☎ 031-663 9317
Easy walking mature parkland course laid out by Ben Sayers and extended by James Braid. Elevated site with excellent views.

18 holes, 5754yds, Par 68, SSS 68, Course record 64.
Club membership 450.
Visitors   restricted Wed, weekends & bank holidays; a handicap certificate is preferred.
Societies   must contact in writing and pay a deposit.
Green Fees not confirmed.
Facilities   ⊗ 🍽 & 🏌 (ex Mon) 🍺 ♀ 👗 🏠✦
                  ✦ Mark Patchett.
Location   36 Golf Course Rd (0.5m NE off B704)
Hotel   ★★61% Eskbank Motor Hotel, 29 Dalhousie Rd, DALKEITH ☎ 031-663 3234 16 ⇆ 🐾

BROXBURN   Map 11 NT07

Niddry Castle ☎ (0506) 891097
A 9-hole parkland course. While not very long, it requires accurate golf to score well.
9 holes, 5514yds, Par 70, SSS 67.
Club membership 320.
Visitors   advisable to contact at weekends, restricted during competition time.
Societies   must contact in advance.
Green Fees £8 per round (£11 weekends).
Facilities   🍺 👗
Location   Castle Rd, Winchburgh (9m W of Edinburgh off junc 1)
Hotel   ★★★57% Forth Bridges Moat House, Forth Bridge, SOUTH QUEENSFERRY ☎ 031-331 1199 108 ⇆ 🐾

DALKEITH   Map 11 NT36

Newbattle ☎ 031-663 2123
Undulating parkland course on three levels, surrounded by woods.
18 holes, 6012yds, Par 69, SSS 69.
Club membership 650.
Visitors   restricted before 4pm on weekdays; may not play at weekends. Handicap certificate required.
Societies   must contact in advance.
Green Fees not confirmed.
Facilities   ⊗ 🏌 🍺 ♀ 👗 🏠✦ David Torrance.
Location   Abbey Rd (SW side of town off A68)
Hotel   ★★61% Eskbank Motor Hotel, 29 Dalhousie Rd, DALKEITH ☎ 031-663 3234 16 ⇆ 🐾

DUNBAR   Map 12 NT67

Dunbar ☎ (0368) 862317
Another of Scotland's old links. It is said that it was some Dunbar members who first took the game of golf to the North of England. The club dates back to 1856. The wind, if blowing from the sea, is a problem.
18 holes, 6426yds, Par 71, SSS 71, Course record 64.
Club membership 650.
Visitors   booking in advance recommended.
Societies   booking in advance recommended.
Green Fees £25 per day (£40 weekends).
Facilities   ⊗ 🏌 🏌 🍺 ♀ (all day) 👗 🏠✦
                  ✦ Derek Small.
Location   East Links (0.5m E off A1087)
Hotel   ★★62% Bayswell Hotel, Bayswell Park, DUNBAR ☎ (0368) 862225 13 ⇆ 🐾

AA ★★   STB 🏠🏠🏠🏠 Commended
Les Routiers
LOGIS (GB)

Redheugh Hotel

Bayswell Park, Dunbar
East Lothian EH42 1AE

Small private licensed hotel set in the heart of "Golf Country" yet only 28 miles from Edinburgh. All 10 Rooms en-suite, with TV, telephone etc. Your Tee Times arranged for you on 14 different courses within ½ hour drive. Special "Golf Breaks" and "Group Rates" available.

**Please telephone (01368) 862793
for more information**

Winterfield ☎ (0368) 863562
Seaside course with superb views.
18 holes, 5220yds, SSS 64.
Club membership 200.
Visitors   must contact in advance.
Green Fees not confirmed.
Facilities   ♀⚲🏠🏌
Location   North Rd (W side of town off A1087)
Hotel   ★★62% Bayswell Hotel, Bayswell Park, DUNBAR ☎ (0368) 862225 13 ⇆ 📻
Additional ★★64% Redheugh Hotel, Bayswell Park,
hotel   DUNBAR ☎ (0368) 862793 10 ⇆ 📻

EDINBURGH   Map 11 NT27

Baberton ☎ 031-453 4911
Parkland course.
18 holes, 6098yds, Par 69, SSS 69.
Club membership 1000.
Visitors   may not play at weekends.
Societies   must contact in advance.
Green Fees £25 per day; £17 per round.
Facilities   ⊗ 🏛🍴🍺♀⚲🏠🏌 Kenneth Kelly.
Location   Juniper Green (5m W of city centre off A70)
Hotel   ★★★66% Bruntsfield Hotel, 69/74 Bruntsfield Place, EDINBURGH ☎ 031-229 1393 50 ⇆ 📻

Braid Hills ☎ 031-447 6666
Municipal heathland course with good views of Edinburgh and the Firth of Forth.
18 holes, 6172yds, Par 70, SSS 68 or 4832yds, Par 65.

Visitors   may not play on Sat mornings.
Societies   apply in writing to Leisure Management Unit, Edinburgh District Council, 141 London Road, Edinburgh.
Green Fees not confirmed.
Facilities   ⚲🏠🏌🏌 J Boath.
Location   Braid Hills Approach (2.5m S of city centre off A702)
Hotel   ★★★62% Braid Hills Hotel, 134 Braid Rd, Braid Hills, EDINBURGH ☎ 031-447 8888 68 ⇆ 📻

Bruntsfield Links Golfing Society ☎ 031-336 1479
Parkland course with good views of Forth Estuary. 4th and 14th holes testing.
18 holes, 6407yds, Par 71, SSS 71.
Club membership 1000.
Visitors   may not play at weekends. Must contact in advance and have an introduction from own club.
Societies   must contact in advance.
Green Fees apply for details.
Facilities   ⊗ 🏛 by prior arrangement 🍺♀⚲🏠 Brian MacKenzie.
Location   32 Barnton Av, Davidsons-Mains (4m NW of city centre off A90)
Hotel   ★★★63% Barnton Thistle, Queensferry Rd, Barnton, EDINBURGH ☎ 031-339 1144 50 ⇆ 📻

Carrick Knowe ☎ 031-337 1096
Flat parkland course. Played over by two clubs, Carrick Knowe and Carrick Vale.
18 holes, 6299yds, Par 71, SSS 70, Course record 64.
Club membership 450.
Visitors   must have an introduction from own club.
Green Fees not confirmed.
Location   Carrick Knowe Municipal, Glendevon Park (3m W of city centre, S of A8)
Hotel   B Forte Posthouse, Corstorphine Rd, EDINBURGH ☎ 031-334 0390 200 ⇆ 📻

Craigmillar Park ☎ 031-667 0047
Parkland course, with good views.
18 holes, 5859yds, Par 70, SSS 68, Course record 65.
Club membership 520.
Visitors   must play with member at weekends & after 3pm on weekdays.
Societies   must contact in writing.
Green Fees £23 per day; £15 per round.
Facilities   ⊗ & 🏛 by prior arrangement 🍺♀⚲🏠🏌 Brian McGhee.
Location   1 Observatory Rd (2m S of city centre off A7)
Hotel   ★★★57% Donmaree Hotel, 21 Mayfield Gardens, EDINBURGH ☎ 031-667 3641 17 ⇆ 📻
Additional QQ Glenisla Hotel, 12 Lygon Rd, EDINBURGH
hotel   ☎ 031-667 4877 7rm(4 📻)
                 See advertisiement on page 255

Dalmahoy Hotel Golf & Country Club
☎ 031-333 1845
Two upland courses, one Championship.
East: 18 holes, 6677yds, Par 72, SSS 72.
West: 18 holes, 5185yds, Par 68, SSS 66.
Club membership 700.

Glenisla Hotel

12 Lygon Road, Edinburgh EH16 5QB.
Telephone: 0131-667 4877
Fax: 0131-667 4098

A small family run hotel situated in quiet area of the city, ten minutes from Princes Street and on main bus route. Surrounded by golf courses and within easy reach of Commonwealth Pool and Holyrood Palace. The Hotel is nicely furnished and decorated to a high standard. Full central heating, all bedrooms with shower & toilet, tea, coffee and hair dryers. Licensed restaurant for residents and non residents. Residents' TV lounge. Ample parking. Open all year.
Please send for brochure.

Ashcroft Farmhouse

Ashcroft is a new farmhouse built on a 5 acre smallholding. All rooms are on the ground floor. Bedrooms equipped with tea/coffee making facilities and colour TV. Relax with early morning tea in bed before being tempted with full Scottish breakfast with home-made sausage, local produce and even Whisky marmalade. Ideal base for touring, golfing or sightseeing.
No smoking, sorry.
Derek & Elizabeth Scott,
Ashcroft Farmhouse, East Calder,
near Edinburgh.
Tel: 01506 881810   Fax: 01506 884327
Prices from £22.

Visitors	weekend by application.
Societies	must telephone for details.
Green Fees	Day Ticket £50. East Course £34 per round; West Course £24 per round (£46/£34 weekends).
Facilities	⊗ ⅋Ⅲ ⓛ 💺 ♈ ♀ △ 🏠 ♈ 🏠 ℓ Brian Anderson.
Leisure	hard tennis courts, heated indoor swimming pool, squash, snooker, sauna, solarium, gymnasium, pull trolleys,electric trolleys/buggies.
Location	Kirknewton (7m W of city centre on A71)
Hotel	★★★★69% Dalmahoy Hotel, Golf & Country Club, Kirknewton, EDINBURGH ☎ 031-333 1845 116 ⇌ ♞
Additional hotel	QQQQ Ashcroft Farmhouse, EAST CALDER ☎ (0506) 881810 6 ♞

Duddingston ☎ 031-661 7688
Parkland, semi-seaside course with burn as a natural hazard. Testing 11th hole. Easy walking and windy.
18 holes, 6647yds, Par 72, SSS 72.
Club membership 700.

Visitors	may not play at weekends.
Societies	Tue & Thu only. Must contact in advance.
Green Fees	£27.50 per day; £21 per round.
Facilities	⊗ ⅋Ⅲ by prior arrangement ⓛ 💺 ♀ △ 🏠 ♈ ℓ Alastair McLean.
Location	Duddingston Rd West (2.5m SE of city centre off A1)

Hotel	★★★57% Donmaree Hotel, 21 Mayfield Gardens, EDINBURGH ☎ 031-667 3641 17 ⇌ ♞

Kingsknowe ☎ 031-441 1145
Hilly parkland course with prevailing SW winds.
18 holes, 5979yds, Par 69, SSS 69.
Club membership 800.

Visitors	must contact in advance.
Societies	may not play at weekends and must contact in advance.
Green Fees	£20 per day; £16 per round (£25 per round weekends).
Facilities	⊗ 💺 ♀ △ 🏠 ℓ Andrew Marshall.
Leisure	snooker, caddy car hire.
Location	326 Lanark Rd (4m SW of city centre on A70)
Hotel	★★★66% Bruntsfield Hotel, 69/74 Bruntsfield Place, EDINBURGH ☎ 031-229 1393 50 ⇌ ♞

Liberton ☎ 031-664 3009
Undulating, wooded parkland course.
18 holes, 5299yds, Par 67, SSS 67.
Club membership 650.

Visitors	may only play before 5pm on Tue & Thu Apr-Sep. Must contact in advance.
Societies	must contact in writing.
Green Fees	not confirmed.
Facilities	△ 🏠 ℓ
Location	297 Gilmerton Rd (3m SE of city centre on A7)
Hotel	★★61% Eskbank Motor Hotel, 29 Dalhousie Rd, DALKEITH ☎ 031-663 3234 16 ⇌ ♞

Lothianburn ☎ 031-445 2206
Hillside course with a 'T' shaped wooded-area, situated in the Pentland foothills. Sheep on course. Testing in windy conditions.
18 holes, 5750yds, Par 71, SSS 69, Course record 63.
Club membership 850.
Visitors	may not play on competition days. Some restrictions at weekends.
Societies	must contact in writing.
Green Fees	£18 per day; £12 per round (£23/£18 weekends).
Facilities	⊗ Ⅷ ⓛ ♥ (no catering Wed) ♀ ⚹ 🖼 ℓ Kurt Mungall.
Location	106A Biggar Rd, Fairmilehead (4.5m S of city centre on A702)
Hotel	★★★62% Braid Hills Hotel, 134 Braid Rd, Braid Hills, EDINBURGH ☎ 031-447 8888 68 ⇆ ↑

Merchants of Edinburgh ☎ 031-447 1219
Testing hill course.
18 holes, 4889mtrs, Par 64, SSS 64.
Club membership 700.
Visitors	must play with member at weekends and after 4pm Wed.
Societies	must contact in writing.
Green Fees	£12 per day/round.
Facilities	⊗ & ⅧI (ex Wed and Thu) ⓛ ♥ ♀ ⚹ 🖼
Location	10 Craighill Gardens (2m SW of city centre off A702)
Hotel	★★★62% Braid Hills Hotel, 134 Braid Rd, Braid Hills, EDINBURGH ☎ 031-447 8888 68 ⇆ ↑

Mortonhall ☎ 031-447 6974
Moorland course with views over Edinburgh.
18 holes, 6557yds, Par 72, SSS 71.
Club membership 650.
Visitors	must have letter of introduction.
Societies	may not play at weekends. Must contact in advance.
Green Fees	£25 per day; £20 per round (£35/£30 weekends).
Facilities	⊗ (ex Sat & Mon) ⅧI by prior arrangement ⓛ ♥ ♀ ⚹ 🖼 ℓ D B Horn.
Leisure	caddy cars, buggy.
Location	Braid Rd (3m S of city centre off A702)
Hotel	★★★62% Braid Hills Hotel, 134 Braid Rd, Braid Hills, EDINBURGH ☎ 031-447 8888 68 ⇆ ↑

Murrayfield ☎ 031-337 3478
Parkland course on the side of Corstorphine Hill, with fine views.
18 holes, 5725yds, Par 70, SSS 68, Course record 64.
Club membership 775.
Visitors	may not play at weekends.
Green Fees	£26 per day; £20 per round.
Facilities	⊗ (Tue-Fri) ⓛ (Mon-Fri) ♥ ♀ ⚹ 🖼 ↑ ℓ
Location	43 Murrayfield Rd (2m W of city centre off A8)
Hotel	B Forte Posthouse, Corstorphine Rd, EDINBURGH ☎ 031-334 0390 200 ⇆ ↑

Portobello ☎ 031-669 4361
Public parkland course, easy walking.
9 holes, 2400yds, Par 32, SSS 32, Course record 62.
Club membership 70.
Visitors	may not play Sat 8.30-10am & 12.30-2pm and on competition days.

Societies	must contact in advance.
Green Fees	not confirmed.
Facilities	↑
Location	Stanley St (3m E of city centre off A1)
Hotel	★★★57% Donmaree Hotel, 21 Mayfield Gardens, EDINBURGH ☎ 031-667 3641 17 ⇆ ↑

Prestonfield ☎ 031-667 1273
Parkland course with beautiful views.
18 holes, 6216yds, Par 70, SSS 70, Course record 62.
Club membership 800.
Visitors	may not play between 8-10.30am and noon-1pm Sat & before 11.30am Sun.
Societies	must contact in advance.
Green Fees	£25 per day; £17 per round (£35 per day; £25 per round weekends & bank holidays).
Facilities	⊗ ⅧI by prior arrangement ⓛ ♥ ♀ ⚹ 🖼 ℓ Graham MacDonald.
Leisure	caddy cars, practise area, putting green.
Location	Priestfield Rd North (1.5m S of city centre off A68)
Hotel	★★★57% Donmaree Hotel, 21 Mayfield Gardens, EDINBURGH ☎ 031-667 3641 17 ⇆ ↑

Ravelston ☎ 031-332 2486
Parkland course.
9 holes, 5322yds, Par 66, SSS 66, Course record 66.
Club membership 610.
Visitors	must contact in advance & have handicap certificate, but may not play at weekends & bank holidays.
Green Fees	£15 per round.
Facilities	♥ ⚹
Location	24 Ravelston Dykes Rd (3m W of city centre off A90)
Hotel	B Forte Posthouse, Corstorphine Rd, EDINBURGH ☎ 031-334 0390 200 ⇆ ↑

Royal Burgess ☎ 031-339 2075
No mention of golf clubs would be complete without mention of the Royal Burgess, which was instituted in 1735, thus being the oldest golfing society in the world. Its course is a pleasant parkland, and one with very much variety. A club which all those interested in the history of the game should visit.
18 holes, 6111yds, Par 71, SSS 71, Course record 66.
Club membership 620.
Visitors	must contact in advance. Gentlemen only.
Societies	must contact in advance.
Green Fees	£38 per day; £28 per round (£45 weekends & bank holidays).
Facilities	⊗ ⅧI (Tue-Fri only) ⓛ ♥ ♀ ⚹ 🖼 ↑ ℓ George Yuille.
Location	181 Whitehouse Rd, Barnton (5m W of city centre off A90)
Hotel	★★★63% Barnton Thistle, Queensferry Rd, Barnton, EDINBURGH ☎ 031-339 1144 50 ⇆ ↑

Silverknowes ☎ 031-336 3843
Public links course on coast overlooking the Firth of Forth.
18 holes, 6216yds, Par 71, SSS 70.
Club membership 500.
Visitors	no restrictions.

Societies   must contact in advance in writing.
Green Fees £6.80 per round.
Location   Silverknowes, Parkway (4m NW of city centre N
                of A902)
Hotel   ★★59% Murrayfield Hotel, 18 Corstorphine Rd,
                EDINBURGH
                ☎ 031-337 1844 23 ⇆ ☏Annexe10 ☏

Swanston ☎ 031-445 2239
Hillside course with steep climb at 12th & 13th holes.
18 holes, 5024yds, Par 66, SSS 65.
Club membership 500.
Visitors   may not play on competition days. Must contact
                in advance.
Societies   telephone for details on 031-445 4002
Green Fees £15 per day; £10 per round (£18/£12 weekends
                & public holidays).
Facilities ⊗ ⅷ ᖚ ♛ ♀ ⚲ 🏠 ☏ Scott Maxwell.
Location   111 Swanston Rd, Fairmilehead (4m S of city
                centre off B701)
Hotel   ★★★62% Braid Hills Hotel, 134 Braid Rd,
                Braid Hills, EDINBURGH
                ☎ 031-447 8888 68 ⇆ ☏

Torphin Hill ☎ 031-441 1100
Beautiful hillside, heathland course, with fine views of
Edinburgh and the Forth Estuary.
18 holes, 4597mtrs, Par 67, SSS 66.
Club membership 410.
Visitors   must contact in advance but may not play on
                competition days.
Societies   must contact in advance.
Green Fees not confirmed.
Facilities ⊗ ⅷ ᖚ ♛ ♀ ⚲ 🏠 🏌
Location   Torphin Rd, Colinton (5m SW of city centre S of
                A720)
Hotel   ★★★62% Braid Hills Hotel, 134 Braid Rd,
                Braid Hills, EDINBURGH
                ☎ 031-447 8888 68 ⇆ ☏

Turnhouse ☎ 031-539 5937 & 031-339 1014
Hilly, parkland/heathland course, good views.
18 holes, 6171yds, Par 69, SSS 69.
Club membership 750.
Visitors   must be accompanied by a member & may not
                play at weekends or on competition days.
Societies   must contact in writing.
Green Fees £20 per day; £14 per round.
Facilities ⊗ ᖚ ♛ ♀ ⚲ 🏠 🏌 ☏ John Murray.
Leisure   practice area.
Location   Turnhouse Rd (6m W of city centre N of A8)
Hotel   ★★★63% Barnton Thistle, Queensferry Rd,
                Barnton, EDINBURGH
                ☎ 031-339 1144 50 ⇆ ☏

Greenburn ☎ (0501) 770292
Exposed rolling course with sparse tree cover. Water hazards
from a pond and a burn.
18 holes, 6045yds, Par 71, SSS 69.
Club membership 800.
Visitors   restricted during competitions.
Societies   by prior arrangement.
Green Fees £17 per day; £11.50 per round (£21.50/£14.50
                weekends).

Facilities ⊗ ⅷ ᖚ ♛ (no catering Tue) ♀ ⚲ 🏠 ☏
Location   6 Greenburn Rd (3m SW of Whitburn)
Hotel   ★★60% Dreadnought Hotel, 17/19 Whitburn Rd,
                BATHGATE ☎(0506) 630791 19rm(18 ⇆ ☏)

Gifford ☎ (0620) 810267 & 810591
Parkland course, with easy walking.
9 holes, 6101yds, Par 71, SSS 69, Course record 65.
Club membership 504.
Visitors   restricted Tue, Wed & weekends.
Green Fees £10 per day (£10 per round weekends).
Facilities ⚲
Location   Edinburgh Rd (1m SW off B6355)
Hotel   ★★68% Tweeddale Arms Hotel, GIFFORD
                ☎ (0620) 810240 16 ⇆ ☏

Gullane ☎ (0620) 842255
Gullane is a delightful village and one of Scotland's great
golf centres. Gullane club was formed in 1882. There are
three Gullane courses and the No 1 is of championship
standard. It differs from most Scottish courses in as much
as it is of the downland type and really quite hilly. The
first tee is literally in the village. The views from the top
of the course are magnificent and stretch far and wide in
every direction - in fact, it is said that 14 counties can be
seen from the highest spot.
Course No 1: 18 holes, 6466yds, Par 71, SSS 71.
Course No 2: 18 holes, 6219yds, Par 71, SSS 70.
Course No 3: 18 holes, 5128yds, Par 66, SSS 65.
Club membership 1200.
Visitors   limited start time for visitors on No 1 course
                at weekends.
Societies   must contact in writing.
Green Fees £16-£53 per day; £10.50-£37 per round
                (£19-£56 per day; £12.50-£47 per round
                weekends).
Facilities ⊗ ⅷ by prior arrangement ᖚ ♛ (dress rules
                in clubhouse) ♀ ⚲ 🏠 🏌 ☏ Jimmy Hume.
Leisure   6 hole childrens course.
Location   At west end of village on A198
Hotel   ★★★(red)♨ Greywalls Hotel, Muirfield,
                GULLANE
                ☎ (0620) 842144 17 ⇆ ☏Annexe5 ⇆ ☏

MUIRFIELD See page 259
(Honourable Company of Edinburgh Golfers)

Haddington ☎ (062082) 3627
Inland course, tree-lined and bunkered, but not hilly.
18 holes, 6280yds, Par 71, SSS 70.
Club membership 600.
Visitors   may not play between 7am-10am & noon-2pm at
                weekends. Must contact in advance.
Societies   must contact in advance; deposits required.
Green Fees not confirmed.
Facilities ⊗ ⅷ ᖚ ♛ (catering weekends only mid Oct-
                Mar) ♀ ⚲ 🏠 ☏ John Sandilands.   ▶

Leisure   pool table.
Location   Amisfield Park (E side off A613)
Hotel   ★★68% Tweeddale Arms Hotel, GIFFORD
               ☎ (0620) 810240 16 ⇄ ⌧

LINLITHGOW   Map 11 NS97

Linlithgow ☎ (0506) 842585
Slightly hilly parkland course in beautiful setting.
18 holes, 5800yds, Par 70, SSS 68.
Club membership 400.
Visitors   may not play Sat. Must book in advance Sun.
Societies   must contact in writing.
Green Fees not confirmed.
Facilities ⊗ ⓛ & ▣ (in season except Tue) ♀ ⚘ ☖
                ⟨ Derek Smith.
Location   Braehead (1m S off Bathgate Road off A803)
Hotel   ★★★68% Inchyra Grange Hotel, Grange Rd,
                POLMONT ☎ (0324) 711911 43 ⇄ ⌧

West Lothian ☎ (0506) 826030
Hilly parkland course with superb views of River Forth.
18 holes, 6340yds, Par 71, SSS 71, Course record 64.
Club membership 500.
Visitors   may not play after 4pm midweek. Weekends by
                arrangement. Must contact in advance
Societies   must telephone in advance.
Green Fees not confirmed.
Facilities ⚘
Location   Airngath Hill (1m S off A706)
Hotel   ★★★68% Inchyra Grange Hotel, Grange Rd,
                POLMONT ☎ (0324) 711911 43 ⇄ ⌧

LIVINGSTON   Map 11 NT06

Deer Park Golf & Country Club
☎ (0506) 38843 & 31037
Long testing course, nearly flat, championship standard.
18 holes, 6636yds, Par 71, SSS 72.
Club membership 700.
Visitors   no restrictions.
Societies   telephone or write
Green Fees £20.50 per day; £15 per round (£35/£25
                weekends).
Facilities ⊗ ⫢ ⓛ ▣ ♀ ⚘ ☖ ⌁ ⟨ Bill Yule.
Leisure   heated indoor swimming pool, squash, snooker,
                sauna, solarium, gymnasium, golf buggies,
                trolleys, ten pin bowling.
Location   Golfcourse Rd (N side of town off A809)
Hotel   ★★60% Dreadnought Hotel, 17/19 Whitburn
                Rd, BATHGATE
                ☎ (0506) 630791 19rm(18 ⇄ ⌧)

Pumpherston ☎ (0506) 32869
Undulating parkland course with testing 6th hole (par 3), and
view of Pentland Hills.
9 holes, 5154yds, Par 64, SSS 65, Course record 61.
Club membership 350.
Visitors   must be accompanied by a member.
Societies   weekdays only. Must apply in writing.
Green Fees not confirmed.
Facilities ⊗ ⫢ ⓛ ▣ ♀ ⚘
Location   Drumshoreland Rd, Pumpherston (1m E
                between A71 & A89)

Hotel   ★★60% Dreadnought Hotel, 17/19 Whitburn
               Rd, BATHGATE
               ☎ (0506) 630791 19rm(18 ⇄ ⌧)

LONGNIDDRY   Map 12 NT47

Longniddry ☎ (0875) 852141
Undulating seaside links and partial parkland course. One
of the numerous courses which stretch east from
Edinburgh right to Dunbar. The inward half is more open
and less testing than the wooded outward half.
18 holes, 6219yds, Par 68, SSS 70, Course record 63.
Club membership 950.
Visitors   must contact in advance & have a handicap
                certificate; must play with member at
                weekends but may not play on bank
                holidays or competition days.
Societies   must contact in writing.
Green Fees £35 per day; £25 per round.
Facilities ⊗ ⫢ ⓛ ▣ ♀ ⚘ ☖ ⌁ ⟨ John Gray.
Location   Links Rd (W side of village off A198)
Hotel   ★★65% Kilspindie House Hotel, Main St,
                ABERLADY ☎ (0875) 870682 26 ⇄ ⌧

MUSSELBURGH   Map 11 NT37

Musselburgh ☎ 031-665 2005
Testing parkland course with natural hazards including trees
and a burn, easy walking.
18 holes, 6614yds, Par 71, SSS 73, Course record 65.
Club membership 800.
Visitors   must contact in advance. May not play before
                9.30am weekdays & before 10am weekends.
Societies   must contact in advance.
Green Fees £25 per day; £17 per round (£30/£21 weekends).
Facilities ⊗ ⫢ by prior arrangement ⓛ ▣ (no catering
                Tue) ♀ (restricted Tue) ⚘ ☖ ⌁ ⟨
Leisure   golf cars, caddy cars.
Location   Monktonhall (1m S on B6415)
Hotel   ★★★57% Donmaree Hotel, 21 Mayfield
                Gardens, EDINBURGH
                ☎ 031-667 3641 17 ⇄ ⌧

Musselburgh Old Course ☎ 031-655 5438
A links type course.
9 holes, 2371yds, Par 33, SSS 33, Course record 67.
Club membership 70.
Visitors   may not play at weekends.
Societies   must contact in advance.
Green Fees not confirmed.
Facilities ♀ ⚘
Location   Millhill (1m E of town off A1)
Hotel   ★★★57% Donmaree Hotel, 21 Mayfield
                Gardens, EDINBURGH
                ☎ 031-667 3641 17 ⇄ ⌧

NORTH BERWICK   Map 12 NT58

Glen ☎ (0620) 895288 & 892726
An interesting course with a good variety of holes. The views
of the town, the Firth of Forth and the Bass Rock are
breathtaking.
18 holes, 6086yds, Par 69, SSS 69, Course record 64.
Club membership 500.   ▶

ℳUIRFIELD
(Honourable Company of Edinburgh Golfers)

GULLANE ☎(0620) 842123.   Map 12 NT 48

John Ingham writes: Ask an American superstar to name the best golf course in Great Britain, or maybe even in the entire world, and the likely answer will be Muirfield. It certainly features in the top ten of any meaningful selection.

Purely on shape and balance, the course has everything. Ask competitors in the Open Championship what they think of the last nine holes, and they will tell you it can wreck the stoutest heart. But ask Isoa Aoki of Japan what he thinks, and he will smile and maybe tell of his course record 63 here.

Established in 1744, it is just ten years older than the Royal & Ancient itself but not as old as Royal Blackheath. However, these dates show that Muirfield certainly has seniority and tradition. Quite simply, it is exclusive and entirely excellent. Muirfield has staged some outstanding Open Championships with one, I suspect, standing out in people's minds more than any other.

Back in 1972, Tony Jacklin was Europe's best player and looked set to prove it again at Muirfield when he had appeared to wear down Lee Trevino, the defending champion. At the 71st hole, Trevino seemed to be frittering away strokes as he mishit a shot downwind through the dry, fast, green. The next few minuteswere truly hair-raising 'I was mad' recalled Trevino. 'My next shot from the bank was strictly a give-up one. And the ball went straight in the hole.' Jacklin had chipped up, well short. Then he missed his putt, turned for the return putt, and missed again. We all did mental arithmetic. Jacklin had blown it and when he bogeyed the last, furious at himself, he suddenly wasn't the winner - Trevino was.

Those of us who were there recall Trevino had holed one bunker shot, and chipped in three times. Muirfield looked on his brilliance with favour and sad Jacklin never won an Open again.

Membership 625

Visitors accepted on Tuesdays and Thursdays: also Friday mornings September-June. Must contact in advance

Societies telephone in advance. But also restricted to Tuesdays, Thursdays: and Friday mornings September-June

Green fees £64 per day; £48 per round

Facilities ⊗ ☎ ♀ ♨

Location Duncur Rd (off A198 on NE side of village)

18 holes, 6601 yards, Par 70, SSS 73

WHERE TO STAY AND EAT NEARBY

HOTELS:

ABERLADY

★★ 65% Kilspindie House, Main St. ☎(0875) 870682. 26⇆ ↾

GULLANE

★★★(red) ⊛⊛ ♨♨ Greywalls, Muirfield. ☎(0620) 842144. 17 ⇆ ↾ Annexe 5 ⇆ ↾

NORTH BERWICK

★★★ 65% The Marine, Cromwell Rd. ☎(0620) 892406. 83 ⇆ ↾ International cuisine

★★ 62% Nether Abbey, 20 Dirleton Ave. ☎(0620) 892802. 16 (10 ⇆ ↾)

★★ 63% Point Garry, West Bay Rd. ☎(0620) 892380. 16(12 ⇆ ↾) International cuisine

RESTAURANT:

GULLANE

✕⊛⊛⊛ La Potinière, Main St. ☎(0620) 843214. French cuisine

Visitors	booking advisable.
Societies	must telephone in advance.
Green Fees	£17 per day; £11.50 per round (£21/£15 weekends).
Facilities	⊗ ⅲ by prior arrangement ⅊ ⧠ ♀ ⚷ 🏠 ↑
Leisure	caddy cars.
Location	East Links, Tantallon Ter (E side of town centre)
Hotel	★★62% Nether Abbey Hotel, 20 Dirleton Av, NORTH BERWICK ☎ (0620) 892802 16rm(4 ⇆6 ↑)

North Berwick ☎ (0620) 892135

Another of East Lothian's famous courses, the links at North Berwick is still popular. A classic championship links, it has many hazards including the beach, streams, bunkers, light rough and low walls. The great hole on the course is the 15th, the famous 'Redan', selected for televisions best 18 in the UK. Used by both the Tantallon and Bass Rock Golf Clubs.

18 holes, 6315yds, Par 71, SSS 70, Course record 66.
Club membership 500.

Visitors	must contact in advance.
Societies	must contact in advance.
Green Fees	not confirmed.
Facilities	⊗ ⅲ by prior arrangement ⅊ ⧠ ♀ ⚷ 🏠 ↑ ⚑ D Huish.
Leisure	caddy cars available.
Location	New Clubhouse, Beach Rd (W side of town on A198)

The Castle Inn

**Dirleton, North Berwick,
East Lothian EH39 5EP**

Fully licensed hotel with 8 bedrooms, 4 en suite. Accommodates 14. Cask conditioned ales. Bar lunches & suppers.

Warm, friendly atmosphere. Surrounded by many well known golf courses – North Berwick, Muirfield, Gullane and Luffness

Open all year.

Telephone: (01620) 850221

Hotel	★★★65% The Marine Hotel, Cromwell Rd, NORTH BERWICK ☎ (0620) 892406 83 ⇆ ↑
Additional hotel	Q Castle Inn, DIRLETON ☎ (0620) 850221 4 ⇆ ↑Annexe4rm

---

PENICUIK   Map 11 NT25

Glencorse ☎ (0968) 677177

Picturesque parkland course with burn affecting ten holes. Testing 5th hole (237 yds) par 3.
18 holes, 5205yds, Par 64, SSS 66.
Club membership 650.

Visitors	must contact in advance, restricted at weekends.
Societies	Mon-Thu only; must contact in advance.
Green Fees	£22 per day; £16 per round.
Facilities	⊗ ⅲ ⅊ ⧠ ♀ ⚷ 🏠 ⚑ Cliffe Jones.
Leisure	caddy cars.
Location	Milton Bridge (1.5m N on A701)
Hotel	★★★62% Braid Hills Hotel, 134 Braid Rd, Braid Hills, EDINBURGH ☎ 031-447 8888 68 ⇆ ↑

PRESTONPANS   Map 11 NT37

Royal Musselburgh ☎ (0875) 810276

Tree-lined parkland course overlooking Firth of Forth.
18 holes, 6237yds, Par 70, SSS 70.
Club membership 900.

Visitors	must contact in advance, restricted Fri afternoons & weekends.
Societies	must contact in writing.
Green Fees	£30 per day; £18 per round (£30 per round weekends).
Facilities	⊗ ⅲ by prior arrangement ⅊ ⧠ ♀ ⚷ 🏠 ↑ ⚑ John Henderson.
Leisure	snooker.
Location	Prestongrange House (W side of town centre off A59)
Hotel	★★65% Kilspindie House Hotel, Main St, ABERLADY ☎ (0875) 870682 26 ⇆ ↑

RATHO   Map 11 NT17

Ratho Park ☎ 031-333 1252

Flat parkland course.
18 holes, 5900yds, Par 69, SSS 68, Course record 63.
Club membership 720.

Visitors	must contact in advance.
Societies	must contact in writing.
Green Fees	£30 per day; £20 per round (£30 weekends).
Facilities	⊗ ⅲ ⅊ ⧠ ♀ ⚷ 🏠 ⚑ Alan Pate.
Leisure	snooker, caddy cars, pool table.
Location	0.75m E, N of A71
Hotel	B Forte Posthouse, Corstorphine Rd, EDINBURGH ☎ 031-334 0390 200 ⇆ ↑

> **If visiting a brand new course, be sure to telephone before your visit to confirm the course information is correct**

SOUTH QUEENSFERRY   Map 11 NT17

Dundas Parks ☎ 031-331 5603 (evenings only)
Parkland course situated on the estate of Lady Jane Stewart-Clark, with excellent views. For 18 holes, the 9 are played twice.
9 holes, 6024yds, Par 70, SSS 69, Course record 66.
Club membership 500.
Visitors   must contact in advance.
Societies   must contact in advance.
Green Fees £8 per day.
Facilities   ⊗ & ▼ by prior arrangement ⚲
Leisure   practice ground, bunker & driving bay.
Location   c/o Secretary, 38 Society Rd (1m S on A8000)
Hotel   ★★★57% Forth Bridges Moat House, Forth
                 Bridge, SOUTH QUEENSFERRY
                 ☎ 031-331 1199 108 ⇆ ℟

UPHALL   Map 11 NT07

Uphall ☎ (0506) 856404
Windy parkland course, easy walking.
18 holes, 5567yds, Par 69, SSS 67, Course record 62.
Club membership 500.
Visitors   restricted weekends.
Societies   must contact in advance.
Green Fees £18 per day; £13 per round (£25/£17 weekends).
Facilities   ⊗ ⅲ � ▼ ♀ ⚲ ⌂ ⌤℟ Gordon Law.
Location   W side of village on A899
Hotel   ★★60% Dreadnought Hotel, 17/19 Whitburn
                 Rd, BATHGATE
                 ☎ (0506) 630791 19rm(18 ⇆ ℟)

WEST CALDER   Map 11 NT06

Harburn ☎ (0506) 871256
Moorland, reasonably flat.
18 holes, 5853yds, Par 69, SSS 68, Course record 62.
Club membership 600.
Visitors   may not play after 2.30pm.
Societies   must contact in writing.
Green Fees £18.50 per day; £12.50 per round (£25 per day;
                 £18.50 per round weekends).
Facilities   ⊗ ⅼ ▼ (Apr-Sep ex no catering Tue) ♀ ⚲ ⌂
                 ℟ Tom Stangoe.
Leisure   caddy cars for hire.
Hotel   ★★★60% The Hilcroft Hotel, East Main St,
                 WHITBURN ☎ (0501) 740818 30 ⇆ ℟

WHITBURN   Map 11 NS96

Polkemmet Country Park ☎ (0501) 743905
Public parkland course surrounded by mature woodland and rhododendron bushes. 15-bay floodlit driving range.
9 holes, 2969mtrs, Par 37.
Visitors   no restrictions.
Societies   must contact in advance.
Green Fees £2/£2.80 per round (£3.50 Sun).
Facilities   ⊗ ⅲ ⅼ ▼ ♀
Leisure   floodlit 15 bay driving range.
Location   2m W off B7066
Hotel   ★★★60% The Hilcroft Hotel, East Main St,
                 WHITBURN ☎ (0501) 740818 30 ⇆ ℟

STRATHCLYDE

AIRDRIE   Map 11 NS76

Airdrie ☎ (0236) 762195
Picturesque parkland course with good views.
18 holes, 6004yds, Par 69, SSS 69.
Club membership 450.
Visitors   must contact in advance. With member only
                 weekends & bank holidays.
Societies   apply in writing.
Green Fees not confirmed.
Facilities   ⊗ ⅲ ⅼ ▼ ♀ ⚲ ⌂ ℟ A McCloskey.
Leisure   snooker.
Location   Rochsoles (1m N on B802)
Hotel   ★★★65% Garfield House Hotel, Cumbernauld
                 Rd, STEPPS
                 ☎ 041-779 2111 27 ⇆ ℟Annexe19 ⇆ ℟

Easter Moffat ☎ (0236) 842878
Moorland/parkland course.
18 holes, 6221yds, Par 72, SSS 70.
Club membership 450.
Visitors   may only play on weekdays.
Societies   must contact in advance.
Green Fees £18 per day; £12 per round.
Facilities   ⊗ ⅲ by prior arrangement ⅼ ▼ ♀ ⚲ ⌂
                 ℟ Brian Dunbar.
Location   Mansion House, Plains (2m E on old Edinburgh-
                 Glasgow road)
Hotel   ★★★65% Garfield House Hotel, Cumbernauld
                 Rd, STEPPS
                 ☎ 041-779 2111 27 ⇆ ℟Annexe19 ⇆ ℟

AYR   Map 10 NS32

Belleisle ☎ (0292) 441258
Parkland course with beautiful sea views. First-class conditions.
Belleisle Course: 18 holes, 6540yds, Par 70, SSS 71.
Seafield Course: 18 holes, 5498yds, Par 68, SSS 67.
Visitors   advised to contact in advance.
Societies   advised to contact in advance.
Green Fees Belleisle £15 per round; Seafield £10 per round.
                 Daily ticket (one round per course) £22.
Facilities   ⊗ ⅲ ⅼ ▼ ♀ ⚲ ⌂ ⌤℟ David Gemmell.
Leisure   children's animal menagerie, caddy cars.
Location   Belleisle Park (2m S on A719)
Hotel   ★★68% Pickwick Hotel, 19 Racecourse Rd,
                 AYR ☎ (0292) 260111 15 ⇆ ℟

Dalmilling ☎ (0292) 263893
Meadowland course, with easy walking.
18 holes, 5724yds, Par 69, SSS 68.
Club membership 140.
Visitors   must contact in advance.
Societies   must contact in advance.
Green Fees £18 per day; £10 per round.
Facilities   ⊗ ⅲ ⅼ & ▼ (catering by arrangement Tue) ♀
                 ⚲ ⌂ ⌤℟ Philip Cheyney.
Leisure   caddy cars for hire.
Location   Westwood Av (1.5m E of town centre off A719)
Hotel   ★★★59% Carlton Toby Hotel, 187 Ayr Rd,
                 PRESTWICK ☎ (0292) 76811 39 ⇆ ℟

BALLOCH   Map 10 NS38

Cameron House Hotel & Country Estate ☎ (0389) 57211
Only available for residents of the hotel or a party booked in
advance. A challenging 9-hole course with water hazards.
The Wee Demon: 9 holes, 2266yds, Par 32.
Club membership 200.
Visitors   must be residents or party booked in advance.
Societies   apply in writing.
Green Fees £14 per day.
Facilities ⊗ ⫴ ⅃ ♨ ♞ ♟ ♈ ⋈
Leisure   hard tennis courts, heated indoor swimming
                pool, squash, fishing, snooker, sauna, solarium,
                gymnasium, marina offering
                charters,watersports.
Location   Loch Lomond
Hotel   ★★★★72% Cameron House Hotel and Country
                Estate, BALLOCH ☎ (0389) 55565 68 ⇌ ↟

BALMORE   Map 11 NS57

Balmore ☎ (0360) 620240
Parkland course with fine views.
18 holes, 5516yds, Par 66, SSS 67.
Club membership 700.
Visitors   must contact in advance and be accompanied by
                member.
Societies   must contact in advance.
Green Fees £25 per day; £15 per round.
Facilities ♨ ⛶
Location   N off A807
Hotel   ★★★65% Black Bull Thistle, Main St,
                MILNGAVIE ☎ 041-956 2291 27 ⇌ ↟

BARASSIE   Map 10 NS33

Kilmarnock (Barassie) ☎ Troon (0292) 313920
A magnificent seaside course, relatively flat with much
heather. The turf and greens are quite unequalled. The
15th is a testing par 3 at 220 yards.
18 holes, 6473yds, Par 71, SSS 71, Course record 63.
Club membership 500.
Visitors   with member only Wed & weekends.
                Restricted Mon, Tue, Thu & Fri afternoons.
                Must contact in advance,
Societies   must telephone in advance and confirm in
                writing.
Green Fees £31/£40 per day; £23/£30 per round.
Facilities ⊗ ⫴ ♨ ⅃ ♟ ♈ ⛶ ↟ (W R Lockie.
Leisure   caddy cars for hire.
Location   29 Hillhouse Rd (E side of village on B746)
Hotel   ★★★★63% Marine Highland Hotel,
                TROON ☎ (0292) 314444 72 ⇌ ↟

BARRHEAD   Map 11 NS45

Fereneze ☎ 041-881 1519
Hilly moorland course, with a good view at the end of a hard
climb to the 3rd, then levels out.
18 holes, 5821yds, Par 70, SSS 68.
Club membership 700.
Visitors   must contact in advance but may not play at
                weekends.
Societies   apply in writing.

Green Fees £20 per day/round.
Facilities ⊗ & ⫴ by prior arrangement ♨ ⅃ ♟ ♈ ⛶ ↟
                (Darren Robinson.
Leisure   pool table, satellite tv.
Location   Fereneze Av (NW side of town off B774)
Hotel   ★★63% Dalmeny Park Country House,
                Lochlibo Rd, BARRHEAD
                ☎ 041-881 9211 18rm(4 ⇌10 ↟)

BEARSDEN   Map 11 NS57

Bearsden ☎ 041-942 2351
Parkland course, with 16 greens and 11 teeing grounds. Easy
walking and views over city.
9 holes, 6014yds, Par 68, SSS 69, Course record 65.
Club membership 550.
Visitors   must be accompanied by and play with member.
Societies   apply by letter at least 1 month in advance.
Green Fees £2.
Facilities ⊗ & ♨ (Mon & Tue only in winter) ⅃ ♟ ♈ ⛶
Location   Thorn Rd (1m W off A809)
Hotel   ★★★65% Black Bull Thistle, Main St,
                MILNGAVIE ☎ 041-956 2291 27 ⇌ ↟

Douglas Park ☎ 041-942 2220
Parkland course with wide variety of holes.
18 holes, 5957yds, Par 69, SSS 69, Course record 64.
Club membership 900.
Visitors   may not play Mon & Fri. Must be accompanied
                by member and must contact in advance.
Societies   must telephone in advance.
Green Fees not confirmed.
Facilities ⊗ ⫴ by prior arrangement ♨ ⅃ ♟ ♈ ⛶ ↟
                (David Scott.
Leisure   caddy cars.
Location   Hillfoot (E side of town on A81)
Hotel   ★★★65% Black Bull Thistle, Main St,
                MILNGAVIE ☎ 041-956 2291 27 ⇌ ↟

Glasgow ☎ 041-942 2011
One of the finest parkland courses in Scotland.
18 holes, 5968yds, Par 70, SSS 69.
Club membership 800.
Visitors   must contact in advance & have handicap
                certificate.
Green Fees £35 per day; £30 per round.
Facilities ⊗ ♨ ⅃ ♟ (members guest only) ♟ ⛶ ↟
                (J Steven.
Location   Killermont (SE side off A81)
Hotel   ★★★65% Black Bull Thistle, Main St,
                MILNGAVIE ☎ 041-956 2291 27 ⇌ ↟

Windyhill ☎ 041-942 2349
Hard walking parkland/moorland course; testing 12th hole.
18 holes, 6254yds, Par 71, SSS 70, Course record 65.
Club membership 675.
Visitors   may not play at weekends. Must contact in
                advance.
Societies   must apply to secretary in writing.
Green Fees £15 per day.
Facilities ⊗ ⫴ ♨ ⅃ ♟ ♈ ⛶ ↟ (G Collinson.
Leisure   caddy car hire, golf club hire.
Location   Windyhill (2m NW off B8050)
Hotel   ★★★65% Black Bull Thistle, Main St,
                MILNGAVIE ☎ 041-956 2291 27 ⇌ ↟

BEITH
Map 10 NS35

Beith ☎ (0505) 503166
Hilly course, with panoramic views over 7 counties.
9 holes, 2559yds, Par 68, SSS 68.
Club membership 400.
Visitors may not play on Sat, Sun after 1pm or weekdays
after 5pm.
Societies apply in writing.
Green Fees £10 per day; £8 per round (£12 Sun).
Facilities ⬧
Location Threepwood Rd (1.5m NE off A737)
Hotel ★★★62% Bowfield Country Club Hotel, Lands
of Bowfield, HOWWOOD
☎ (0505) 705225 12 ⇄ ⋒

BELLSHILL
Map 11 NS76

Bellshill ☎ (0698) 745124
Parkland course.
18 holes, 6205yds, Par 70, SSS 70.
Club membership 600.
Visitors may not play between 4-7pm May-Aug.
Societies apply in writing in advance.
Green Fees £12 per day (£15 weekends & bank holidays).
Facilities ⊗ & ⧨ by prior arrangement ⬧ ⬤ ♀ ⬧
Location Community Rd, Orbiston (1m SE off A721)
Hotel ★★62% Silvertrees Hotel, Silverwells Crescent,
BOTHWELL
☎ (0698) 852311 7 ⇄ ⋒Annexe19 ⇄ ⋒

BIGGAR
Map 11 NT03

Biggar ☎ (0899) 20618
Flat parkland course, easy walking and fine views.
18 holes, 5416yds, Par 67, SSS 66, Course record 63.
Club membership 240.
Visitors restricted at certain times. Must contact in
advance. Smart casual wear required (no jeans).
Societies telephone (0899) 20319 to book in advance.
Green Fees £9 per day (£13 weekends & bank holidays).
Facilities ⊗ ⧨ ⬧ & ⬤ by prior arrangement ♀ ⬧ ⬔
Leisure hard tennis courts, caravan park, boating pond,
play area.
Location The Park, Broughton Rd (S side of town)
Hotel ★★★68% Shieldhill Hotel, Quothquan,
BIGGAR ☎ (0899) 20035 11 ⇄ ⋒

BISHOPBRIGGS
Map 11 NS67

Bishopbriggs ☎ 041-772 1810
Parkland course with views to Campsie Hills.
18 holes, 6041yds, Par 69, SSS 69, Course record 63.
Club membership 600.
Visitors must be accompanied by member, contact in
advance and have an introduction from own club.
Societies apply in writing to the Committee one month in
advance.
Green Fees not confirmed.
Facilities ⊗ ⧨ ⬧ ⬤ ♀ ⬧ ⬔
Leisure snooker.
Location Brackenbrae Rd (0.5m NW off A803)
Hotel ★★★65% Black Bull Thistle, Main St,
MILNGAVIE ☎ 041-956 2291 27 ⇄ ⋒

Cawder ☎ 041-772 5167
Two parkland courses; Cawder Course is hilly, with 5th, 9th,
10th, 11th-testing holes. Keir Course is flat.
Cawder Course: 18 holes, 6295yds, Par 70, SSS 71.
Keir Course: 18 holes, 5877yds, Par 68, SSS 68.
Club membership 1150.
Visitors must contact in advance & may play on
weekdays only.
Societies must contact in writing.
Green Fees £23 per day.
Facilities ⊗ ⧨ ⬧ ⬤ ♀ ⬧ ⬔ ⋔ ⸙
Location Cadder Rd (1m NE off A803)
Hotel ★★★65% Black Bull Thistle, Main St,
MILNGAVIE ☎ 041-956 2291 27 ⇄ ⋒

BISHOPTON
Map 10 NS47

Erskine ☎ (0505) 862302
Parkland course.
18 holes, 6287yds, Par 71, SSS 70.
Club membership 700.
Visitors must be accompanied by member and must have
a handicap certificate.
Societies apply in writing.
Green Fees £20 per round; £30 per day.
Facilities ⊗ ⬧ ⬤ ♀ ⬧ ⬔ ⸙ Peter Thomson.
Location 0.75 NE off B815
Hotel B Forte Posthouse, North Barr, ERSKINE
☎ 041-812 0123 166 ⇄ ⋒

BONHILL
Map 10 NS37

Vale of Leven ☎ Alexandria (0389) 52351
Hilly moorland course, tricky with many natural hazards -
gorse, burns, trees. Overlooks Loch Lomond.
18 holes, 5162yds, Par 67, SSS 66, Course record 61.
Club membership 640.
Visitors may not play Sat Apr-Sep.
Societies apply to the secretary.
Green Fees £15 per day; £10 per round (£20/£15 weekends
& holidays).
Facilities ⊗ ⧨ & ⬧ (ex Tue) ⬤ ♀ ⬧ ⬔ ⋔
Location North Field Rd (E side of town off A813)
Hotel ★★66% Dumbuck Hotel, Glasgow Rd,
DUMBARTON ☎ (0389) 34336 22 ⇄ ⋒

BOTHWELL
Map 11 NS75

Bothwell Castle ☎ (0698) 853177
Flat parkland course in residential area.
18 holes, 6243yds, Par 71, SSS 70.
Club membership 1200.
Visitors may only play Mon-Fri 9.30am-noon & 2-
3.30pm.
Societies apply in writing.
Green Fees not confirmed.
Facilities ⊗ ⧨ ⬧ ⬤ ♀ ⬧ ⬔ ⸙ Gordon Niven.
Leisure caddy cars.
Location Blantyre Rd (NW off village off B7071)
Hotel ★★62% Silvertrees Hotel, Silverwells Crescent,
BOTHWELL
☎ (0698) 852311 7 ⇄ ⋒Annexe19 ⇄ ⋒

BRIDGE OF WEIR   Map 10 NS36

Ranfurly Castle ☎ Johnstone (0505) 612609 or 614795
A highly challenging, 240 acre, picturesque moorland course.
18 holes, 6284yds, Par 70, SSS 70, Course record 64.
Club membership 360.
Visitors   weekdays only, must have a handicap certificate.
Societies   Tues am only, apply in writing.
Green Fees   £27 per day; £22 per round.
Facilities   ⊗ & ⅷ by prior arrangement Ⅼ ♥ ♀ ⚐ 🖻 ⚐
                  (Tom Eckford.
Leisure   caddy cars & clubs for hire.
Location   The Clubhouse, Golf Rd (5m NW of Johnstone)
Hotel   ★★★62% Bowfield Country Club Hotel, Lands
              of Bowfield, HOWWOOD
              ☎ (0505) 705225 12 ⇆ ♛

BURNSIDE   Map 11 NS66

Blairbeth ☎ 041-634 3355
Parkland course.
18 holes, 5481yds, Par 70, SSS 67, Course record 64.
Club membership 400.
Visitors   introduced by a member or by arrangement with
               Secretary.
Societies   apply in writing.
Green Fees   £16 per day Mon-Fri.
Facilities   ⊗ ⅷ Ⅼ ♥ ♀ ⚐
Location   S off A749
Hotel   ★★★63% Macdonald Thistle, Eastwood Toll,
              GIFFNOCK ☎ 041-638 2225 56 ⇆ ♛

Cathkin Braes ☎ 041-634 6605
Moorland course, prevailing westerly wind, small loch hazard
at 5th hole.
18 holes, 6208yds, Par 71, SSS 71.
Club membership 890.
Visitors   must contact in advance & have handicap
               certificate but may not play at weekends.
Societies   apply in writing.
Green Fees   £30 per day; £20 per round.
Facilities   ⊗ ⅷ Ⅼ ♥ (catering by arrangement) ♀ ⚐ ⚐
               (Stephen Bree.
Location   Cathkin Rd (1m S on B759)
Hotel   ★★★63% Macdonald Thistle, Eastwood Toll,
              GIFFNOCK ☎ 041-638 2225 56 ⇆ ♛

CAMBUSLANG   Map 11 NS66

Cambuslang ☎ 041-641 3130
Parkland course.
9 holes, 6072yds, Par 70, SSS 69, Course record 65.
Club membership 200.
Visitors   must contact in advance and have an
               introduction from own club.
Societies   weekdays only; must contact in writing.
Green Fees   not confirmed.
Facilities   ⊗ Ⅼ ♥ ♀ ⚐
Location   Westburn Dr (0.25m N off A724)
Hotel   ★★62% Silvertrees Hotel, Silverwells Crescent,
              BOTHWELL
              ☎ (0698) 852311 7 ⇆ ♛Annexe19 ⇆ ♛

CARDROSS   Map 10 NS37

Cardross ☎ (0389) 841213
Undulating parkland course, testing with good views.
18 holes, 6496yds, Par 71, SSS 71.
Club membership 800.
Visitors   may not play at weekends unless introduced by
               member.
Societies   must contact in writing.
Green Fees   not confirmed.
Facilities   ⊗ ⅷ Ⅼ ♥ ♀ ⚐ 🖻 ⚐ (
Leisure   caddy car hire.
Location   Main Rd (In centre of village on A814)
Hotel   ★★★56% Commodore Toby Hotel, 112 West
              Clyde St, HELENSBURGH
              ☎ (0436) 676924 45 ⇆ ♛

CARLUKE   Map 11 NS85

Carluke ☎ (0555) 771070
Parkland course with views over the Clyde Valley. Testing
11th hole, par 3.
18 holes, 5811yds, Par 70, SSS 68, Course record 64.
Club membership 800.
Visitors   until 4pm weekdays only. Must contact in
               advance & have handicap certificate.
Societies   apply in writing.
Green Fees   not confirmed.
Facilities   ⊗ ⅷ Ⅼ (ex Thu) ♥ ♀ ⚐ 🖻 ⚐
               (Andrew Brooks.
Location   Mauldslie Rd, Hallcraig (1m W off A73)
Hotel   ★★★64% Popinjay Hotel, Lanark Rd,
              ROSEBANK
              ☎ (0555) 860441 38 ⇆ ♛Annexe5 ⇆ ♛

CARNWATH   Map 11 NS94

Carnwath ☎ (0555) 840251
Picturesque parkland course slightly hilly, with small greens
calling for accuracy. Panoramic views.
18 holes, 5953yds, Par 70, SSS 69.
Club membership 470.
Visitors   restricted after 5pm, no visitors Sat.
Societies   apply in writing or telephone.
Green Fees   not confirmed.
Facilities   catering by arrangement ♀ ⚐ ⚐
Location   1 Main St (W side of village on A70)
Hotel   ★★★64% Popinjay Hotel, Lanark Rd,
              ROSEBANK
              ☎ (0555) 860441 38 ⇆ ♛Annexe5 ⇆ ♛

CARRADALE   Map 10 NR83

Carradale ☎ (05833) 387
Pleasant seaside course built on a promontory overlooking
the Isle of Arran. Natural terrain and small greens are the
most difficult natural hazards. Described as the most sporting
9-hole course in Scotland. Testing 7th hole (240 yds), par 3.
9 holes, 2387yds, Par 66, SSS 64, Course record 62.
Club membership 300.
Visitors   no restrictions
Societies   welcome.
Green Fees   £6 per day.
Facilities   ⚐

Location S side of village
Hotel ★★62% Royal Hotel, Main St,
CAMPBELTOWN
☎ (0586) 552017 16rm(8 ⇄4 ⋒)

CLARKSTON Map 11 NS55

Cathcart Castle ☎ 041-638 0082
Tree-lined parkland course, with undulating terrain.
18 holes, 5832yds, Par 68, SSS 68.
Club membership 990.
Visitors must have a letter of introduction from own club.
Societies Tue & Thu only; must apply in writing.
Green Fees £25 per day; £17 per round.
Facilities ⊗ ⫽ ⅃ ♥ ♀ ♨ ⌂ ⏲ David Naylor.
Location Mearns Rd (0.75m SW off A726)
Hotel ★★★63% Macdonald Thistle, Eastwood Toll,
GIFFNOCK ☎ 041-638 2225 56 ⇄ ⋒

CLYDEBANK Map 11 NS56

Clydebank & District ☎ Duntocher (0389) 873289
An undulating parkland course established in 1905
overlooking Clydebank.
18 holes, 5823yds, Par 68, SSS 68, Course record 64.
Club membership 825.
Visitors handicap certificate is required. Round only,
weekdays only. Must tee off before 4pm.
Societies must apply in writing.
Green Fees £12 per round.
Facilities ⊗ ⫽ & ⅃ (during season) ♥ ♀ ♨ ⌂
⏲ David Pirie.
Leisure pool table.
Location Glasgow Rd, Hardgate (2m E of Erskine Bridge)
Hotel ★★★65% Patio Hotel, 1 South Av, Clydebank
Business Park, CLYDEBANK
☎ 041-951 1133 80 ⇄ ⋒

Clydebank Municipal ☎ 041-941 1331
Hilly, compact parkland course with tough finishing holes.
18 holes, 5349yds, Par 67, SSS 67.
Visitors no restrictions.
Societies contact in advance.
Green Fees £4.30 per round (£4.70 Sun).
Facilities Cafeteria ♨ ⌂ ⏲ ⏲
Location Overtoun Rd, Dalmur (2m NW of town centre)
Hotel ★★★65% Patio Hotel, 1 South Av, Clydebank
Business Park, CLYDEBANK
☎ 041-951 1133 80 ⇄ ⋒

COATBRIDGE Map 11 NS76

Drumpellier ☎ (0236) 424139
Parkland course.
18 holes, 6227yds, Par 71, SSS 70, Course record 60.
Club membership 700.
Visitors must contact in advance and may not play
weekends or public holidays.
Societies telephone for details.
Green Fees £25 per day; £18 per round.
Facilities ⊗ ⫽ ⅃ ♥ ♀ ♨ ⌂ ⏲ Kenneth Hutton.
Leisure pool table.
Location Drumpellier Av (0.75m W off A89)
Hotel ★★★62% Bothwell Bridge Hotel, 89 Main St,
BOTHWELL ☎ (0698) 852246 76 ⇄ ⋒

CUMBERNAULD Map 11 NS77

Dullatur ☎ (0236) 723230
Parkland course, with natural hazards and wind. Testing 17th
hole, par 5.
18 holes, 6219yds, Par 70, SSS 70.
Club membership 656.
Visitors may not play on competition days & must play
with member at weekends. Must contact in
advance.
Societies must contact in writing.
Green Fees £25 per day; £15 per round after 1pm.
Facilities catering by arrangement ♀ ♨ ⌂ ⏲
⏲ D Sinclair.
Leisure snooker, caddy cars available for hire.
Location Dullatur (1.5m N)
Hotel ★★★★64% Westerwood Hotel Golf And
Country Club, 1 St Andrews Dr, Westerwood,
CUMBERNAULD ☎ (0236) 457171 47 ⇄ ⋒

Palacerigg ☎ (0236) 734969
Parkland course.
18 holes, 6444yds, Par 72, SSS 71.
Club membership 400.
Visitors no restrictions.
Societies apply in writing to the Secretary.
Green Fees not confirmed.
Facilities ⊗ (Wed-Sun) ⅃ ♥ ♀ ⌂
Leisure pool table.
Location Palacerigg Country Park (2m S)
Hotel ★★★★64% Westerwood Hotel Golf And
Country Club, 1 St Andrews Dr, Westerwood,
CUMBERNAULD ☎ (0236) 457171 47 ⇄ ⋒

Westerwood Hotel Golf & Country Club
☎ (0236) 457171
Undulating parkland/woodland course designed by Dave
Thomas and Seve Ballesteros. Holes meander through silver
birch, firs, heaths and heathers, and the spectacular 15th, 'The
Waterfall', has its green set against a 40ft rockface. Buggie
track. Hotel facilities.
18 holes, 6721yds, Par 73, SSS 72.
Club membership 250.
Visitors no restrictions.
Societies by prior arrangement.
Green Fees £35 per day; £22.50 per round (£45/£27.50
weekends).
Facilities ⊗ ⫽ ⅃ ♥ ♀ ♨ ⌂ ⏲ ⋈ ⏲ Steven Killen.
Leisure hard tennis courts, heated indoor swimming
pool, snooker, solarium, gymnasium, driving
range, golf school & putting.
Location St Andrews Dr (adjacent to A80)
Hotel ★★★★64% Westerwood Hotel Golf And
Country Club, 1 St Andrews Dr, Westerwood,
CUMBERNAULD ☎ (0236) 457171 47 ⇄ ⋒

DALMALLY Map 10 NN12

Dalmally ☎ (0838) 200370 & 200281
A 9-hole flat parkland course alongside the River Orchy. The
course is surrounded by mountains and there are plenty of
water hazards.
9 holes, 2217yds, Par 64, SSS 62, Course record 65.
Club membership 100.

▶

Visitors	no visitors on Sun between 9-10 & 1-2.
Societies	telephone in advance.
Green Fees	£7 per day.
Facilities	catering by prior arrangement ⌂
Leisure	fishing.
Location	Old Saw Mill (on A85, 1.5m W of Dalmally)
Hotel	★★67% Brander Lodge Hotel, Bridge of Awe, TAYNUILT ☎ (08662) 243 & 225 20 ⇆ ☏

DUMBARTON   Map 10 NS37

Dumbarton ☎ (0389) 32830
Flat parkland course.
18 holes, 5992yds, Par 71, SSS 69, Course record 64.
Club membership 500.

Visitors	may not play weekends & public holidays.
Societies	advance booking with secretary.
Green Fees	£16 per day.
Facilities	⊗ & ⅏ by prior arrangement ⬛ ♀ ⌂
Location	Broadmeadow (0.25m N off A814)
Hotel	★★66% Dumbuck Hotel, Glasgow Rd, DUMBARTON ☎ (0389) 34336 22 ⇆ ☏

DUNOON   Map 10 NS17

Cowal ☎ (0369) 5673
Moorland course. Panoramic views of Clyde Estuary and surrounding hills.
18 holes, 6251yds, Par 70, SSS 70, Course record 64.
Club membership 550.

Visitors	handicap certificate preferred or club membership.
Societies	must telephone in advance.
Green Fees	£20 per day; £13 per round (£30/£20 weekends).
Facilities	⊗ ⅏ ⓛ ⬛ ♀ ⌂ ⌷ ⌿ ⎰
Leisure	caddy cars.
Location	Ardenslate Rd (1m N)
Hotel	★★76% Enmore Hotel, Marine Pde, Kirn, DUNOON ☎ (0369) 2230 11 ⇆ ☏

EAGLESHAM   Map 11 NS55

Bonnyton ☎ (03553) 2781
Windy, moorland course.
18 holes, 6255yds, Par 72, SSS 71.
Club membership 950.

Visitors	welcome weekdays only, must contact in advance.
Societies	must telephone in advance.
Green Fees	£25 per day.
Facilities	⊗ ⅏ ⓛ ⬛ ♀ ⌂ ⌷ ⌿ ⎰ Kendal McWade.
Location	0.25m SW off B764
Hotel	★★★61% Bruce Swallow Hotel, Cornwall St, EAST KILBRIDE ☎ (03552) 29771 78 ⇆ ☏

EAST KILBRIDE   Map 11 NS65

East Kilbride ☎ (03552) 20913
Parkland and hill course. Very windy. Testing 7th, 9th and 14th holes.
18 holes, 6419yds, Par 71, SSS 71.
Club membership 800.

Visitors	by appointment. Must be a member of recognised golfing society.

Societies	must telephone in advance & submit formal application.
Green Fees	not confirmed.
Facilities	⊗ ⅏ ⓛ ⬛ ♀ ⌂ ⎰ ⌿ ⎰ A Taylor.
Location	Chapelside Rd, Nerston (0.5m N off A749)
Hotel	★★★61% Bruce Swallow Hotel, Cornwall St, EAST KILBRIDE ☎ (03552) 29771 78 ⇆ ☏

Torrance House ☎ (03552) 48638
A parkland course.
18 holes, 6415yds, Par 72, SSS 69, Course record 71.
Club membership 1000.

Visitors	welcome, may book up to six days in advance.
Societies	Mon-Fri. Apply in writing to John Dunlop, East Kilbride District Council, Civic Centre, East Kilbride.
Green Fees	£13.80 per round.
Facilities	⊗ ⅏ & ⓛ by prior arrangement ⬛ ♀ ⌂ ⌿ ⌷ John Dunlop.
Leisure	snooker, practice area, caddy cars.
Location	Calderglen Country Park, Strathaven Rd (1.5m SE of Kilbride on A726)
Hotel	★★★61% Bruce Swallow Hotel, Cornwall St, EAST KILBRIDE ☎ (03552) 29771 78 ⇆ ☏

GALSTON   Map 11 NS53

Loudoun ☎ (0563) 821993
Pleasant, testing parkland course.
18 holes, 5600yds, Par 67, SSS 68, Course record 61.
Club membership 550.

Visitors	must contact in advance. No play at weekends.
Societies	must contact in advance.
Green Fees	£25 per day; £15 per round.
Facilities	⊗ ⅏ ⓛ ⬛ ♀ ⌂ ⌷ ⌿
Location	Edinburgh Rd (NE side of town on A71)
Hotel	★★★65% Strathaven Hotel, Hamilton Rd, STRATHAVEN ☎ (0357) 21778 10 ⇆ ☏

GARTCOSH   Map 11 NS66

Mount Ellen ☎ (0236) 872277
Downland course with 73 bunkers. Testing hole: 10th ('Bedlay'), 156 yds, par 3.
18 holes, 5525yds, Par 68, SSS 68, Course record 60.
Club membership 500.

Visitors	may play Mon-Fri 9am-4pm. Must contact in advance.
Societies	must contact in advance.
Green Fees	£18 two rounds, £12 per round.
Facilities	⊗ ⅏ (Sat & Sun 8-10pm) ⓛ ⬛ ♀ ⌂ ⎰ ⌷ Iain Bilsborough.
Leisure	petrol buggy hire £10 per round.
Location	0.75m N off A752
Hotel	★★★65% Garfield House Hotel, Cumbernauld Rd, STEPPS ☎ 041-779 2111 27 ⇆ ☏ Annexe19 ⇆ ☏

> A golf course name printed in ***bold italics*** means we have been unable to verify information with the club's management for the current year

GIRVAN   Map 10 NX19

Brunston Castle ☎ Dailly (0465) 81471
Sheltered inland parkland course. A championship design by
Donald Steel, the course is bisected by the River Girvan and
shaped to incorporate all the natural surroundings. It finishes
with the 17th 185 yards over a man made lake. Driving range.
Burns: 18 holes, 6792yds, Par 72, SSS 72.
Club membership 200.
Visitors   must contact in advance.
Societies   must contact in advance.
Green Fees £30 per day; £20 per round (£35/£25 weekends).
Facilities   ⊗ ⅢI by prior arrangement ⅃ ☕ ♀ ♈ 🖼 ☂
                   ⌀ Derek J McKenzie.
Leisure   fishing, driving range, buggies, caddy cars.
Location   Dailly (6m SE of Turnberry)
Hotel   ★★61% King's Arms Hotel, Dalrymple St,
                    GIRVAN ☎ (0465) 3322 25 ⇆ ⋔

Girvan ☎ (0465) 4272
Municipal seaside and parkland course. Testing 17th hole
(223-yds) uphill, par 3. Good views.
18 holes, 5098yds, Par 64, SSS 65.
Club membership 175.
Visitors   no restrictions.
Societies   may not play Jul & Aug.
Green Fees not confirmed.
Facilities   ♀ ♈
Location   Golf Course Rd (N side of town off A77)
Hotel   ★★61% King's Arms Hotel, Dalrymple St,
                    GIRVAN ☎ (0465) 3322 25 ⇆ ⋔

GLASGOW   Map 11 NS56

Alexandra ☎ 041-556 3991
Parkland course, hilly with some woodland.
9 holes, 2800yds, Par 34.
Club membership 250.
Visitors   no restrictions.
Societies   no prior arrangement required.
Green Fees £2.10 summer; £1.75 winter.
Facilities   ♈
Leisure   practice area.
Location   Alexandra Park, Alexandra Pde (2m E of city
                    centre off M8/A8)
Hotel   ★★★68% The Town House Hotel, West George
                    St, GLASGOW ☎ 041-332 3320 34 ⇆ ⋔

Cowglen ☎ 041-632 0556
Parkland course with good views over Clyde valley to
Campsie Hills.
18 holes, 5976yds, Par 69, SSS 69, Course record 63.
Club membership 775.
Visitors   play on shorter course. Must contact in advance
                    and have a handicap certificate. No visitors at
                    weekends.
Societies   must telephone in advance.
Green Fees £25 per day; £18 per round (weekdays).
Facilities   ⊗ ⅢI ⅃ ☕ ♀ ♈ 🖼 ⌀ John McTear.
Location   Barrhead Rd (4.5m SW of city centre on B762)
Hotel   ★★★63% Macdonald Thistle, Eastwood Toll,
                    GIFFNOCK ☎ 041-638 2225 56 ⇆ ⋔

Haggs Castle ☎ 041-427 1157
Wooded, parkland course where Scottish National
Championships and the Glasgow and Scottish Open have
been held. Quite difficult.
18 holes, 6464yds, Par 72, SSS 71.
Club membership 960.
Visitors   may not play at weekends. Must contact in
                    advance and have a handicap certificate.
Societies   apply in writing in advance.
Green Fees £36 per day; £24 per round.
Facilities   ⊗ ⅢI ⅃ ☕ ♀ ♈ 🖼 ☂ ⌀
Location   70 Dumbreck Rd, Dumbreck (2.5m SW of
                    city centre on B768)
Hotel   ★★★58% Sherbrooke Castle Hotel, 11
                    Sherbrooke Av, Pollokshields, GLASGOW
                    ☎ 041-427 4227 10 ⇆ ⋔Annexe11 ⇆ ⋔

Kirkhill ☎ 041-641 8499
Meadowland course designed by James Braid.
18 holes, 5889yds, Par 69, SSS 69, Course record 63.
Club membership 650.
Visitors   must play with member at weekends. Must
                    contact in advance.
Societies   must contact in advance.
Green Fees not confirmed.
Facilities   ⊗ (ex Mon) ⅢI by prior arrangement ⅃ (ex Mon
                    and Thu) ☕ ♀ ♈
Location   Greenless Rd, Cambuslang (5m SE of city centre
                    off A749)
Hotel   ★★★59% Stuart Hotel, 2 Cornwall Way,
                    EAST KILBRIDE ☎ (03552) 21161 39 ⇆ ⋔

Knightswood ☎ 041-959 2131
Parkland course within easy reach of city. Two dog-legs.
9 holes, 2700yds, Par 33, SSS 33.
Club membership 60.
Visitors   no restrictions.
Societies   welcome.
Green Fees £2.10 summer; £1.75 winter.
Location   Lincoln Av (4m W of city centre off A82)
Hotel   ★★★62% Jurys Pond Hotel, Great Western Rd,
                    GLASGOW ☎ 041-334 8161 134 ⇆ ⋔

Lethamhill ☎ 041-770 6220
Municipal parkland course.
18 holes, 5859yds, Par 70, SSS 68.
Visitors   must have an introduction from own club.
Societies   must contact in advance.
Facilities   ♈
Location   1240 Cumbernauld Rd, Millerston (3m NE of
                    city centre on A80)
Hotel   ★★★65% Garfield House Hotel, Cumbernauld
                    Rd, STEPPS
                    ☎ 041-779 2111 27 ⇆ ⋔Annexe19 ⇆ ⋔

Linn Park ☎ 041-637 5871
Municipal parkland course with six par 3's in outward half.
18 holes, 4952yds, Par 65, SSS 65, Course record 61.
Club membership 80.
Visitors   no restrictions.
Green Fees not confirmed.
Facilities   ♈
Location   Simshill Rd (4m S of city centre off B766)
Hotel   ★★★61% Bruce Swallow Hotel, Cornwall St,
                    EAST KILBRIDE ☎ (03552) 29771 78 ⇆ ⋔

Pollok ☎ 041-632 1080
Parkland course with woods and river.
18 holes, 6257yds, Par 71, SSS 70, Course record 62.
Club membership 460.
Visitors   must play with member at weekends. Must contact in advance and have a handicap certificate.
Societies   Mon-Thu only; must contact in writing.
Green Fees £26 per round; £33 per day.
Facilities   ⊗ ⅏ by prior arrangement ⓑ 🍺 ♀ ♨
Location   90 Barrhead Rd (4m SW of city centre on A762)
Hotel   ★★★63% Tinto Firs Thistle, 470 Kilmarnock Rd, GLASGOW ☎ 041-637 2353 28 ⇆ ⋔

Williamwood ☎ 041-637 1783
Inland course, fairly hilly with wooded areas, a small lake and pond.
18 holes, 5878yds, Par 67, SSS 69.
Club membership 450.
Visitors   must be introduced by and play with member.
Green Fees not confirmed.
Facilities   🍴 ⋔
Location   Clarkston Rd (5m S of city centre on B767)
Hotel   ★★★63% Macdonald Thistle, Eastwood Toll, GIFFNOCK ☎ 041-638 2225 56 ⇆ ⋔

GOUROCK   Map 10 NS27

Gourock ☎ (0475) 631001
Moorland course with hills and dells. Testing 8th hole, par 5. Magnificent views over Firth of Clyde.
18 holes, 6492yds, Par 73, SSS 73, Course record 64.
Club membership 720.

THE
Glynhill
HOTEL
AND LEISURE CLUB   ★★★

The gateway to Scotland hotel offering businessmen and tourists alike a quality product and service. Facilities range from Diplomat Suites, American style bedrooms, convention centre, gourmet and carverie restaurants, all complemented by a luxurious leisure centre. Privately owned, excellent value golf break packages and well located hotel for the West of Scotland's superb golf courses.
Glasgow International Airport 1 mile
(300 yards M8 junc 27)
The Glynhill Hotel and Leisure Club
169 Paisley Road, Renfrew PA4 8XB
Tel: 0141 886 5555   Fax: 0141 885 2838

Visitors   by introduction or with member.
Societies   welcome weekdays, must contact in advance.
Green Fees £22 per day; £15 per round (£25/£18 weekends).
Facilities   ⊗ ⅏ ⓑ 🍺 ♀ ♨ 🍴 ⋔ A M Green.
Leisure   caddy car.
Location   Cowal View (SW side of town off A770)
Hotel   ★★★♨62% Manor Park Hotel, SKELMORLIE ☎ (0475) 520832 10 ⇆ ⋔Annexe13 ⇆ ⋔

GREAT CUMBRAE ISLAND (MILLPORT)
                                      Map 10 NS15

Millport ☎ (0475) 530305
Pleasantly situated on the west side of Cumbrae looking over Bute to Arran and the Mull of Kintyre. Exposure means conditions may vary according to wind strength and direction. A typical seaside resort course welcoming visitors.
18 holes, 5828yds, SSS 68, Course record 64.
Club membership 550.
Visitors   no restrictions.
Societies   advance booking with secretary for over 12 people, tee time with starter if 6-12.
Green Fees £15 per day; £11 per round (£20 weekends & bank holidays).
Facilities   ⊗ ⅏ ⓑ 🍺 ♀ ♨ 🍴 ⋔ Grieg McQueen.
Leisure   caddy cars for hire.
Location   Golf Rd (approx 4m from ferry slip)
Hotel   ★★★66% Brisbane House, 14 Greenock Rd, Esplanade, LARGS ☎ (0475) 687200 23 ⇆ ⋔

GREENOCK   Map 10 NS27

Greenock ☎ (0475) 720793
Testing moorland course with panoramic views of Clyde Estuary.
18 holes, 5838yds, Par 68, SSS 68.
Club membership 730.
Visitors   may not play Sat. Must contact in advance and have a handicap certificate.
Societies   must telephone in advance.
Green Fees not confirmed.
Facilities   ⊗ ⅏ ⓑ 🍺 (No catering Mon) ♀ ♨ 🍴 ⋔ Graham Ross.
Location   Forsyth St (SW side of town off A770)
Hotel   ★★★♨62% Manor Park Hotel, SKELMORLIE ☎ (0475) 520832 10 ⇆ ⋔Annexe13 ⇆ ⋔

Whinhill ☎ (0475) 21064
Picturesque heathland public course.
18 holes, 5454yds, Par 66, SSS 68.
Visitors   may only use club facilities with member.
Green Fees not confirmed.
Location   Beith Rd (1.5m SW off B7054)
Hotel   ★★★♨62% Manor Park Hotel, SKELMORLIE ☎ (0475) 520832 10 ⇆ ⋔Annexe13 ⇆ ⋔

HAMILTON   Map 11 NS75

Hamilton ☎ (0698) 282872
Beautiful parkland course.
18 holes, 6281yds, Par 70, SSS 70.
Club membership 480.

Visitors must be accompanied by member.
Green Fees not confirmed.
Facilities ♀♨🏠🛈
Location Riccarton, Ferniegair (1.5m SE on A72)
Hotel ★★62% Silvertrees Hotel, Silverwells Crescent, BOTHWELL
☎ (0698) 852311 7 ⇆ 🏨Annexe19 ⇆ 🏌

Strathclyde Park ☎ (0698) 266155
Municipal parkland course.
9 holes, 3147yds, Par 36, SSS 70, Course record 64.
Club membership 180.
Visitors advised to book in advance.
Societies must contact in advance.
Green Fees £2.25 per round.
Facilities ⊗ 🎱 🖳 🍺 ♀♨🏠🛈 William Walker.
Leisure driving range, practice area.
Location Mote Hill (N side of town off B7071)
Hotel ★★62% Silvertrees Hotel, Silverwells Crescent, BOTHWELL
☎ (0698) 852311 7 ⇆ 🏨Annexe19 ⇆ 🏌

HELENSBURGH   Map 10 NS28

Helensburgh ☎ (0436) 74173
Sporting moorland course with superb views of Loch Lomond and River Clyde.
18 holes, 6058yds, Par 69, SSS 69, Course record 64.
Club membership 850.
Visitors may not play at weekends.
Societies must contact in writing.
Green Fees £23 per day; £15 per round.
Facilities 🎱 by prior arrangement 🖳 🍺 ♀♨🏠🛉
🛈 Robert Farrell.
Leisure practice area, caddy cars.
Location 25 East Abercromby St (NE side of town off B832)
Hotel ★★★56% Commodore Toby Hotel, 112 West Clyde St, HELENSBURGH
☎ (0436) 676924 45 ⇆ 🏌

IRVINE   Map 10 NS33

Glasgow ☎ (0294) 311347
A lovely seaside links. The turf of the fairways and all the greens is truly glorious and provides tireless play. Established in 1787, this is the ninth oldest course in the world and is a qualifying course for the Open Championship.
18 holes, 6502yds, Par 71, SSS 72.
Club membership 1150.
Visitors must contact in advance but may not play mornings at weekends & bank holidays.
Societies apply to secretary.
Green Fees £33 per day; £27 per round (£30 afternoon round weekends).
Facilities ⊗ 🎱 by prior arrangement 🖳 🍺 ♀♨🏠
Location Gailes (2m S off A737)
Hotel ★★★★52% Hospitality Inn, Annick Rd, Annickwater, IRVINE
☎ (0294) 274272 128 ⇆ 🏌

Irvine ☎ (0294) 275626
Testing links course; only two short holes.
18 holes, 6400yds, Par 71, SSS 71, Course record 65.
Club membership 450.
Visitors may not play before 3pm Sat & Sun. Must contact in advance.
Societies are welcome weekdays, telephone (0294) 275979 to book in advance.
Green Fees not confirmed.
Facilities ⊗ 🎱 🖳 🍺 ♀♨🏠🛈 Keith Erskine.
Location Bogside (N side of town off A737)
Hotel ★★★★52% Hospitality Inn, Annick Rd, Annickwater, IRVINE
☎ (0294) 274272 128 ⇆ 🏌

Irvine Ravenspark ☎ (0294) 279550
Parkland course.
18 holes, 6702yds, Par 71, SSS 71, Course record 65.
Club membership 550.
Visitors may not play Sat 7am-2pm.
Societies may not play Sat. Must telephone in advance.
Green Fees £10 per day; £6.70 per round (£15/£10 weekends).
Facilities ⊗ 🎱 🖳 🍺 (no catering Tue and Thu) ♀♨🏠
🛈 Peter Bond.
Location N side of town on A737
Hotel ★★★★70% Montgreenan Mansion House Hotel, Montgreenan Estate, KILWINNING
☎ (0294) 557733 21 ⇆ 🏌

Western Gailes ☎ (0294) 311649
A magnificent seaside links with glorious turf and wonderful greens. The view is open across the Firth of Clyde to the neighbouring islands. It is a well-balanced course crossed by 3 burns. There are 2 par 5's, the 6th and 14th, and the 11th is a testing 445-yd, par 4, dog-leg.
18 holes, 6664yds, Par 71, SSS 73, Course record 65.
Visitors welcome Mon, Tue, Wed & Fri. Must contact in advance and have a handicap certificate.
Societies must contact in advance.
Green Fees not confirmed.
Facilities ⊗ 🎱 🖳 🍺 ♀♨
Leisure caddies & caddy cars for hire.
Location Gailes by Irvine (2m S off A737)
Hotel ★★★★70% Montgreenan Mansion House Hotel, Montgreenan Estate, KILWINNING
☎ (0294) 557733 21 ⇆ 🏌

JOHNSTONE   Map 10 NS46

Cochrane Castle ☎ (0505) 320146
Fairly hilly parkland course,wooded with two small streams running through it.
18 holes, 6226yds, Par 70, SSS 70, Course record 65.
Club membership 580.
Visitors may not play at weekends. Must contact in advance.
Societies may not play at weekends.
Green Fees £22 per day; £16 per round.
Facilities ⊗ 🎱 & 🖳 🍺 (limited catering on Mon & Thu after 1pm) ♀♨🏠🛈 Stuart Campbell.
Leisure caddy car for hire.
Location Scott Av, Craigstone (0.5m W off A737)
Hotel ★★★65% Glynhill Hotel & Leisure Club, Paisley Rd, RENFREW
☎ 041-886 5555 125 ⇆ 🏌

Elderslie ☎ (0505) 322835
Parkland course, undulating, with good views.
18 holes, 6175yds, Par 70, SSS 70.
Club membership 940.
Visitors	may not play at weekends & bank holidays. Must contact club in advance and have a handicap certificate.
Societies	must telephone in advance.
Green Fees	£23.50 per day, £17.10 per round.
Facilities	⊗ ⅢⅢ ᖫ ▰ ♀ ♨ ⚑ Richard Bowman.
Leisure	snooker, caddy cars.
Location	63 Main Rd, Elderslie (E side of town on A737)
Hotel	★★★62% Bowfield Country Club Hotel, Lands of Bowfield, HOWWOOD ☎ (0505) 705225 12 ⇔ ♙

KILBIRNIE   Map 10 NS35

Kilbirnie Place ☎ (0505) 683398
Easy walking parkland course.
18 holes, 5400yds, Par 69, SSS 67.
Club membership 400.
Visitors	no restrictions.
Societies	must contact in advance.
Green Fees	not confirmed.
Facilities	⊗ ᖫ ▰ ♀ ♨
Location	Largs Rd (1m W on A760)
Hotel	★★68% Elderslie Hotel, John St, Broomfields, LARGS ☎ (0475) 686460 25rm(9 ⇔4 ♙)

KILMACOLM   Map 10 NS36

Kilmacolm ☎ (050587) 2139
Moorland course, easy walking, fine views. Testing 7th, 13th and 14th holes.
18 holes, 5964yds, Par 69, SSS 68.
Club membership 800.
Visitors	must contact in advance, restricted weekends.
Societies	apply in writing.
Green Fees	£25 per day; £20 per round.
Facilities	⊗ & ⅢⅢ by prior arrangement ᖫ ▰ ♀ ♨ ⚑ ⚑ David Stewart.
Location	Porterfield Rd (SE side of town off A761)
Hotel	★★★★68% Gleddoch House Hotel, LANGBANK ☎ (0475) 540711 33 ⇔ ♙

KILMARNOCK   Map 11 NS43

Annanhill ☎ (0563) 21644
Municipal, tree-lined parkland course played over by private clubs.
18 holes, 6269yds, Par 71, SSS 70.
Club membership 350.
Visitors	no visitors Sat.
Societies	must telephone in advance.
Green Fees	not confirmed.
Facilities	⊗ (ex Tue & Thu) ᖫ ▰ ♀ ♨
Location	Irvine Rd (1m W on A71)
Hotel	★★★★75% Chapeltoun House Hotel, STEWARTON ☎ (0560) 482696 8 ⇔ ♙

Caprington ☎ (0563) 23702
Municipal parkland course.
18 holes, 5718yds, Par 69, SSS 68.
Club membership 400.

Visitors	may not play on Sat.
Societies	must contact in advance.
Green Fees	£6.50 per round (£14 per day weekends).
Facilities	⊗ ⅢⅢ ᖫ ▰ (catering weekends only) ♀ ♨ ⚑
Leisure	snooker.
Location	Ayr Rd (1.5m S on B7038)
Hotel	★★★★75% Chapeltoun House Hotel, STEWARTON ☎ (0560) 482696 8 ⇔ ♙

KILSYTH   Map 11 NS77

Kilsyth Lennox ☎ (0236) 824115
Hilly moorland course, hard walking. Course and facilities revamped with 18-holes after a serious fire early in 1993.
18 holes, 5912yds, Par 70, SSS 69.
Club membership 400.
Visitors	must play with member at weekends.
Societies	must contact in writing.
Green Fees	£12 per day; £8 per round (£16/£12 weekends).
Facilities	♨ ⚑ ⚑ R Abercrombie.
Location	Tak Ma Doon Rd (N side of town off A803)
Hotel	★★★64% Kirkhouse Inn, STRATHBLANE ☎ (0360) 770621 15 ⇔ ♙

KIRKINTILLOCH   Map 11 NS67

Hayston ☎ 041-776 1244
An undulating, tree-lined course with a sandy subsoil.
18 holes, 6042yds, Par 70, SSS 69.
Club membership 440.
Visitors	must apply to secretary.
Societies	apply in writing.
Green Fees	£15 per round.
Facilities	⊗ ⅢⅢ ᖫ ▰ ♀ ♨ ⚑ ⚑ Steven Barnett.
Leisure	practice ground, caddy cars.
Location	Campsie Rd (1m NW off A803)
Hotel	★★★64% Kirkhouse Inn, STRATHBLANE ☎ (0360) 770621 15 ⇔ ♙

Kirkintilloch ☎ 041-776 1256
Parkland course in rural setting.
18 holes, 5269yds, Par 70, SSS 66.
Club membership 650.
Visitors	must be introduced by member.
Societies	apply in writing.
Green Fees	not confirmed.
Facilities	♨ ⚑
Location	Campsie Rd (1m NW off A803)
Hotel	★★★64% Kirkhouse Inn, STRATHBLANE ☎ (0360) 770621 15 ⇔ ♙

LANARK   Map 11 NS84

Lanark ☎ (0555) 663219
Chosen as one of the pre-qualifying tests for the Open Championship held at Lanark from 1977 to 1983. The address of the club, 'The Moor', gives some indication as to the kind of golf to be found there. Golf has been played at Lanark for well over a century and the Club dates from 1851.
18 holes, 6423yds, Par 70, SSS 71, Course record 62.
Club membership 850.

Visitors	must contact in advance, restricted until 4pm weekdays only.
Societies	may not play at weekends. Telephone in advance.
Green Fees	£34 per day; £22 per round. 9 hole £4.
Facilities	⊗ & ⅷ ⓫ & 🍺 (Apr-Sep) ♀ 🏌 🏠 ⚑ ⚑ Ron Wallace.
Location	The Moor (E side of town centre off A73)
Hotel	★★★64% Popinjay Hotel, Lanark Rd, ROSEBANK ☎ (0555) 860441 38 ⇆ ⚑Annexe5 ⇆ ⚑

LANGBANK   Map 10 NS37

Gleddoch Golf and Country Club ☎ (0475) 540304
Parkland and heathland course with other sporting facilities available to temporary members. Good views over Firth of Clyde.
18 holes, 5661yds, Par 68, SSS 67.
Club membership 600.
Visitors   must contact in advance.
Societies   must contact in advance.
Green Fees £25 per day.
Facilities ⊗ ⅷ ⓫ 🍺 ♀ 🏌 🏠 ⚑ ⚑ Keith Campbell.
Leisure   grass tennis courts, heated indoor swimming pool, squash, riding, snooker, sauna, archery, clay pigeon shooting.
Location   B789-Old Greenock Road
Hotel   ★★★♨68% Gleddoch House Hotel, LANGBANK ☎ (0475) 540711 33 ⇆ ⚑

LARGS   Map 10 NS25

Largs ☎ (0475) 673594
A parkland, tree-lined course with views to the Clyde coast and Arran Isles.
18 holes, 6220yds, Par 70, SSS 71, Course record 64.
Club membership 850.
Visitors   may not play weekends & competition days. Must contact in advance.
Societies   apply in writing.
Green Fees £24 per day; £18 per round.
Facilities ⊗ ⅷ ⓫ 🍺 ♀ 🏌 🏠 ⚑ ⚑
Location   Irvine Rd (1m S of town centre on A78)
Hotel   ★★68% Elderslie Hotel, John St, Broomfields, LARGS ☎ (0475) 686460 25rm(9 ⇆4 ⚑)

Routenburn ☎ (0475) 673230
Heathland course with fine views over Firth of Clyde.
18 holes, 5675yds, Par 68, SSS 68.
Club membership 500.
Visitors   no restrictions.
Societies   apply in writing.
Green Fees £10 per day; £6 per round (£15/£10 weekends).
Facilities ⊗ ⓫ 🍺 (no catering Tue) ♀ 🏌 🏠 ⚑ J Grieg McQueen.
Leisure   caddy car for hire.
Location   Routenburn Rd (1m N off A78)
Hotel   ★★★♨62% Manor Park Hotel, SKELMORLIE ☎ (0475) 520832 10 ⇆ ⚑Annexe13 ⇆ ⚑

LARKHALL   Map 11 NS75

Larkhall ☎ (0698) 881113
Small, inland parkland course.
9 holes, 6700yds, Par 72, SSS 71, Course record 69.
Club membership 250.
Visitors   restricted Tue & Sat.
Green Fees not confirmed.
Facilities ⓫ (weekends only) ♀
Location   Burnhead Rd (E side of town on B7019)
Hotel   ★★★64% Popinjay Hotel, Lanark Rd, ROSEBANK ☎ (0555) 860441 38 ⇆ ⚑Annexe5 ⇆ ⚑

LEADHILLS   Map 11 NS81

Leadhills ☎ (0659) 74222
A testing, hilly course with high winds. At 1500ft above sea level it has the privilege of being the is the highest golf course in Great Britain.
9 holes, 4354yds, Par 66, SSS 64.
Club membership 80.
Visitors   no restrictions.
Societies   must telephone in advance.
Green Fees not confirmed.
Location   E side of village off B797
Hotel   ★★61% Mennockfoot Lodge Hotel, Mennock, SANQUHAR ☎ (0659) 50382 & 50477 1 ⇆Annexe8 ⇆ ⚑

LENNOXTOWN   Map 11 NS67

Campsie ☎ (0360) 310244
Scenic hillside course.
18 holes, 5515yds, Par 70, SSS 67, Course record 65.
Club membership 560.
Visitors   restricted after 4pm weekdays and all day Sat & Sun. Must contact in advance.
Societies   must contact one month in advance.
Green Fees £20 per day; £12 per round (£15 per round weekends).
Facilities ⓫ 🍺 ♀ 🏌 🏠 ⚑ Mark Brennan.
Location   Crow Rd (0.5m N on B822)
Hotel   ★★★64% Kirkhouse Inn, STRATHBLANE ☎ (0360) 770621 15 ⇆ ⚑

LENZIE   Map 11 NS67

Lenzie ☎ 041-776 1535
Pleasant moorland course.
18 holes, 5984yds, Par 69, SSS 69.
Club membership 850.
Visitors   must have introduction by member or by prior arrangement with secretary.
Societies   apply in writing.
Green Fees £20 per day; £12.50 per round.
Facilities ♀ 🏌 🏠 ⚑ Jim McCallum.
Leisure   caddy cars.
Location   19 Crosshill Rd (S side of town on B819)
Hotel   ★★★65% Garfield House Hotel, Cumbernauld Rd, STEPPS ☎ 041-779 2111 27 ⇆ ⚑Annexe19 ⇆ ⚑

LESMAHAGOW   Map 11 NS83

Holland Bush ☎ (0555) 893484
Fairly difficult, tree-lined municipal parkland and moorland
course. 1st half is flat, while 2nd half is hilly. No bunkers.
18 holes, 6110yds, Par 72, SSS 70, Course record 63.
Club membership 500.
Visitors   no restrictions.
Societies   must contact in advance.
Green Fees not confirmed.
Facilities ⊗ ⅲ ⅼ ♥ ♀ △ 🏠 ⑂ ⟨ Ian Rae.
Location   Acretophead
Hotel   ★★★65% Strathaven Hotel, Hamilton Rd,
                STRATHAVEN ☎ (0357) 21778 10 ⇌ ⧉

LOCHWINNOCH   Map 10 NS35

Lochwinnoch ☎ (0505) 842153
Parkland course, slightly hilly in middle, with testing golf.
Overlooks bird sanctuary and boating loch.
18 holes, 6243yds, Par 71, SSS 70.
Club membership 650.
Visitors   may not play at weekends and bank holidays
                unless accompanied by member. Restricted
                during competition days.
Societies   apply in writing to club administrator.
Green Fees £20 per day; £15 per round.
Facilities ⊗ ⅲ by prior arrangement ⅼ ♥ ♀ △ 🏠
                ⟨ Gerry Reilly.
Location   Burnfoot Rd (W side of town off A760)
Hotel   ★★★62% Bowfield Country Club Hotel, Lands
                of Bowfield, HOWWOOD
                ☎ (0505) 705225 12 ⇌ ⧉

MACHRIHANISH   Map 10 NR62

Machrihanish ☎ (0586) 810213
Magnificent seaside links of championship status. The
1st holes is the famous drive across the Atlantic. Sandy
soil allows for play all year round. Large greens, easy
walking, windy. Fishing.
18 holes, 6228yds, Par 70, SSS 70.
Club membership 850.
Visitors   no restrictions.
Societies   apply in writing.
Green Fees not confirmed.
Facilities ⊗ ⅲ ⅼ ♥ by prior arrangement ♀ △ 🏠
                ⟨ Kenneth Campbell.
Location   5m W of Campbeltown on B843
Hotel   ★★63% Seafield Hotel, Kilkerran Rd,
                CAMPBELTOWN
                ☎ (0586) 554385 3 ⧉Annexe6 ⧉

MAUCHLINE   Map 11 NS42

Ballochmyle ☎ (0290) 550469
Wooded parkland course.
18 holes, 5952yds, Par 70, SSS 69.
Club membership 840.
Visitors   may not play on Sat or on Mon from Oct-Mar
                except with member.
Societies   apply in writing.
Green Fees £25 per day; £18 per round (£30 Sat & Sun day
                ticket).

Facilities ⊗ ⅼ ♥ ♀ △ 🏠
Leisure   squash, snooker.
Location   Ballochmyle (1m SE on B705)
Hotel   ★★57% Royal Hotel, 1 Glaisnock St,
                CUMNOCK ☎ (0290) 420822 10rm(2 ⇌3 ⧉)

MAYBOLE   Map 10 NS20

Maybole Municipal
Hilly parkland course.
9 holes, 2635yds, Par 33, SSS 65, Course record 64.
Club membership 100.
Visitors   no restrictions.
Societies   must contact in advance.
Green Fees not confirmed.
Location   Memorial Park
Hotel   ★★(red)♣♣ Ladyburn, MAYBOLE
                ☎ (06554) 585 8rm(4 ⇌3 ⧉)

MILNGAVIE   Map 11 NS57

Clober ☎ 041-956 1685
Parkland course. Testing 5th hole, par 3.
18 holes, 5042yds, Par 65, SSS 65, Course record 61.
Club membership 600.
Visitors   may not play before 4.30pm Mon-Thu and
                before 4pm Fri & last Tue in month (Mar-Sep).
                Must play with member weekends and bank
                holidays.
Societies   must contact in advance.
Green Fees £10 per round.
Facilities ⊗ ⅲ & ⅼ (summer) ♥ ♀ △ 🏠
Leisure   caddy carts for hire.
Location   Craigton Rd (NW side of town)
Hotel   ★★★65% Black Bull Thistle, Main St,
                MILNGAVIE ☎ 041-956 2291 27 ⇌ ⧉

Dougalston ☎ 041-956 5750
Tree-lined with water features.
18 holes, 6683yds, Par 72, SSS 71.
Visitors   must contact in advance.
Societies   must contact in advance.
Green Fees not confirmed.
Facilities ⊗ ⅲ ⅼ ♥ ♀ △ ⑂
Location   Strathblane Rd (NE side of town on A81)
Hotel   ★★★65% Black Bull Thistle, Main St,
                MILNGAVIE ☎ 041-956 2291 27 ⇌ ⧉

Hilton Park ☎ 041-956 4657
Moorland courses set amidst magnificent scenery.
Hilton: 18 holes, 6054yds, Par 70, SSS 70.
Allander: 18 holes, 5374yards, Par 69, SSS 67.
Club membership 1200.
Visitors   must contact in advance but may not play at
                weekends.
Societies   weekdays only by prior arrangement.
Green Fees £20 per round; £26 two rounds.
Facilities ♀ △ 🏠 ⑂ ⟨
Location   Stockiemuir Rd (3m NW on A809)
Hotel   ★★★65% Black Bull Thistle, Main St,
                MILNGAVIE ☎ 041-956 2291 27 ⇌ ⧉

Milngavie ☎ 041-956 1619
Moorland course, hard walking, sometimes windy, good
views. Testing 1st and 4th holes (par 4).
18 holes, 5818yds, Par 68, SSS 68.
Club membership 700.
Visitors   must contact in advance.
Societies   apply in writing.
Green Fees not confirmed.
Facilities   ♀ ⚲
Location   Laigh Park (1.25m N)
Hotel   ★★★65% Black Bull Thistle, Main St,
                 MILNGAVIE ☎ 041-956 2291 27 ⇥ ⋒

MOTHERWELL   Map 11 NS75

Colville Park ☎ (0698) 263017
Parkland course. First nine, tree-lined, second nine, more
exposed. Testing 10th hole par 3, 16th hole par 4.
18 holes, 6265yds, Par 71, SSS 70.
Club membership 790.
Visitors   with member only except for parties. Must
                 contact in advance in writing.
Societies   weekdays only, apply in writing.
Green Fees £20 per day.
Facilities   ⊗ ⊞ ⓛ ♟ ♀ ⚲ 🏠
Leisure   snooker, 2 bowling greens, sailing, fishing club.
Location   New Jerviston House, Jerviston Estate (1.25m
                 NE on A723)
Hotel   ★★62% Silvertrees Hotel, Silverwells Crescent,
                 BOTHWELL
                 ☎ (0698) 852311 7 ⇥ ⋒Annexe19 ⇥ ⋒

MUIRHEAD   Map 11 NS66

Crow Wood ☎ 041-779 4954
Parkland course.
18 holes, 6249yds, Par 71, SSS 70, Course record 62.
Club membership 700.
Visitors   must contact in advance but may not play at
                 weekends & bank holidays.
Societies   maximum 32, apply in writing.
Green Fees £24 per day; £16 per round.
Facilities   ⊗ ⊞ ⓛ ♟ ♀ ⚲ 🏠 ⍵ Alan Kershaw.
Leisure   snooker, caddy cars.
Location   Garnkirk House (0.5m W on A80)
Hotel   ★★★65% Garfield House Hotel, Cumbernauld
                 Rd, STEPPS
                 ☎ 041-779 2111 27 ⇥ ⋒Annexe19 ⇥ ⋒

NEW CUMNOCK   Map 11 NS61

New Cumnock ☎ (0290) 32037
Parkland course.
9 holes, 5176yds, Par 68, SSS 65, Course record 62.
Club membership 240.
Visitors   restricted on Sun competition days; not before
                 4pm.
Societies   apply in writing to the Secretary, 23 Castlemains
                 Avenue, New Cumnock.
Green Fees not confirmed.
Facilities   ⚲
Location   Lochhill (0.75m N on A76)
Hotel   ★★57% Royal Hotel, 1 Glaisnock St,
                 CUMNOCK ☎ (0290) 420822 10rm(2 ⇥3 ⋒)

NEWTON MEARNS   Map 11 NS55

East Renfrewshire ☎ Loganswell (03555) 258
Undulating moorland with loch; prevailing SW wind.
18 holes, 6097yds, Par 70, SSS 70.
Club membership 500.
Visitors   must contact in advance.
Societies   must contact in advance.
Green Fees not confirmed.
Facilities   ⊗ ⊞ ⓛ ♟ ♀ ⚲ 🏠 ⍵
Location   Pilmuir (3m SW on A77)
Hotel   ★★★63% Macdonald Thistle, Eastwood Toll,
                 GIFFNOCK ☎ 041-638 2225 56 ⇥ ⋒

Eastwood ☎ Loganswell (03555) 261
Moorland course.
18 holes, 5864yds, Par 68, SSS 68.
Club membership 900.
Visitors   welcome by appointment.
Societies   must contact in advance.
Green Fees £26 per day; £18 per round.
Facilities   ⊗ ⊞ ⓛ ♟ ♀ ⚲ 🏠 ⍵ Alan McGinness.
Leisure   pool table.
Location   Muirshield (2.5m S on A77)
Hotel   ★★★63% Macdonald Thistle, Eastwood Toll,
                 GIFFNOCK ☎ 041-638 2225 56 ⇥ ⋒

Whitecraigs ☎ 041-639 4530
Beautiful parkland course.
18 holes, 6230yds, Par 70, SSS 70.
Club membership 1150.
Visitors   must contact in advance and have a handicap
                 certificate. With member only weekends and
                 bank holidays.
Societies   apply in writing.
Green Fees £28 per day; £23 per round (weekdays).
Facilities   ⊗ ⊞ ⓛ ♟ ♀ ⚲ 🏠 ⍵ Alistair Forrow.
Location   72 Ayr Rd (1.5m NE on A77)
Hotel   ★★★63% Macdonald Thistle, Eastwood Toll,
                 GIFFNOCK ☎ 041-638 2225 56 ⇥ ⋒

OBAN   Map 10 NM83

Glencruitten ☎ (0631) 62868
There is plenty of space and considerable variety of hole
on this downland course - popular with holidaymakers. In
a beautiful, isolated situation, the course is hilly and
testing, particularly the 1st and 12th, par 4's, and 10th
and 15th, par 3's.
18 holes, 4250yds, Par 61, SSS 63, Course record 55.
Club membership 620.
Visitors   restricted Thu & Sat.
Societies   must contact in writing.
Green Fees £12.50 per day; £10 per round.
Facilities   ⊗ ⊞ ⓛ ♟ ♀ ⚲ 🏠 ⍵
Location   Glencruitten Rd (NE side of town centre off
                 A816)
Hotel   ★★★58% Caledonian Hotel, Station
                 Square, OBAN ☎ (0631) 63133 70 ⇥

For an explanation of symbols and
abbreviations, see page 5

PAISLEY   Map 11 NS46

Barshaw ☎ 041-889 2908
Municipal parkland course.
18 holes, 5703yds, Par 68, SSS 67.
Club membership 77.
Visitors   no restrictions.
Green Fees not confirmed.
Facilities ⬝
Location   Barshaw Park (1m E off A737)
Hotel   ★★★65% Glynhill Hotel & Leisure Club,
                Paisley Rd, RENFREW
                ☎ 041-886 5555 125 ⇆ ☈

Paisley ☎ 041-884 3903
Moorland course, windy but with good views.
18 holes, 6220yds, Par 70, SSS 70.
Club membership 700.
Visitors   must contact in advance & have handicap
                certificate. Visitors not admitted after 4pm, on
                weekends or public holidays.
Societies   apply in writing.
Green Fees £24 per day; £16 per round.
Facilities ⊗ & ⅢＩ by prior arrangement ⬝ ☕ ♀ ⬝ ☖
                Ɩ Grant Gilmour.
Leisure   snooker, trolley hire.
Location   Braehead (S side of town off B774)
Hotel   ★★★65% Glynhill Hotel & Leisure Club,
                Paisley Rd, RENFREW
                ☎ 041-886 5555 125 ⇆ ☈

Ralston ☎ 041-882 1349
Parkland course.
18 holes, 6071yds, Par 71, SSS 69.
Club membership 750.
Visitors   must be accompanied by member.
Green Fees not confirmed.
Facilities ♀ ⬝ ☖
Location   Strathmore Av, Ralston (2m E off A737)
Hotel   ★★★66% Swallow Hotel, 517 Paisley Rd West,
                GLASGOW ☎ 041-427 3146 117 ⇆ ☈

PORT GLASGOW   Map 10 NS37

Port Glasgow ☎ (0475) 704181
A moorland course set on a hilltop overlooking the Clyde,
with magnificent views to the Cowal hills.
18 holes, 5712yds, Par 68, SSS 68, Course record 63.
Club membership 390.
Visitors   may not play on Sat. Must contact in advance.
Societies   apply in writing.
Green Fees not confirmed.
Facilities ⊗ ⅢＩ ⬝ ☕ (catering on request) ♀
Location   Devol Rd (1m S)
Hotel   ★★★★68% Gleddoch House Hotel,
                LANGBANK ☎ (0475) 540711 33 ⇆ ☈

PRESTWICK   Map 10 NS32

Prestwick ☎ (0292) 77404
Seaside links with natural hazards and fine views.
18 holes, 6544yds, Par 71, SSS 72.
Club membership 575.

Visitors   restricted Thu; may not play at weekends.
                Must contact in advance and have a
                handicap certificate.
Societies   must contact in writing.
Green Fees not confirmed.
Facilities ⬝ ☖ ☇ Ɩ F C Rennie.
Location   2 Links Rd (in town centre off A79)
Hotel   ★★62% Parkstone Hotel, Esplanade,
                PRESTWICK ☎ (0292) 77286 15 ⇆ ☈

Prestwick St Cuthbert ☎ (0292) 77101
Parkland course with easy walking, natural hazards and
sometimes windy.
18 holes, 6470yds, Par 71, SSS 71.
Club membership 820.
Visitors   must contact in advance but may not play at
                weekends & bank holidays.
Societies   apply in writing.
Green Fees not confirmed.
Facilities ⊗ ⅢＩ (ex Thu) ⬝ ☕ ♀ ⬝
Leisure   limited number of caddy cars available.
Location   East Rd (0.5m E of town centre off A77)
Hotel   ★★63% St Nicholas Hotel, 41 Ayr Rd,
                PRESTWICK ☎ (0292) 79568 17rm(13 ⇆ ☈)

Prestwick St Nicholas ☎ (0292) 77608
Seaside links course with whins, heather and tight fairways. It
provides easy walking and has an unrestricted view of the
Firth of Clyde.
18 holes, 5952yds, Par 69, SSS 69.
Club membership 700.
Visitors   except weekends & public holidays. Must
                contact in advance.
Societies   must contact in advance.
Green Fees £30 per day; £20 per round.
Facilities ⊗ ⅢＩ ⬝ ☕ ♀ ⬝ ☖ ☇ Ɩ
Location   Grangemuir Rd (S side of town off A79)
Hotel   ★★62% Parkstone Hotel, Esplanade,
                PRESTWICK ☎ (0292) 77286 15 ⇆ ☈

RENFREW   Map 11 NS46

Renfrew ☎ (041886) 6692
Tree-lined parkland course.
18 holes, 6818yds, Par 72, SSS 73, Course record 67.
Club membership 700.
Visitors   must be accompanied by member, contact in
                advance and have an introduction from own club.
Green Fees not confirmed.
Facilities ⊗ ⅢＩ ⬝ ☕ ♀ ⬝ ☖
Location   Blythswood Estate, Inchinnan Rd (0.75m W off A8)
Hotel   ★★★65% Glynhill Hotel & Leisure Club,
                Paisley Rd, RENFREW
                ☎ 041-886 5555 125 ⇆ ☈

RIGSIDE   Map 11 NS83

Douglas Water ☎ Douglas Water (0555) 880361
A 9-hole course of 3,000 yards with good variety and some
hills and spectacular views. An interesting course with a
challenging longest hole of 564 yards but, overall, not too
testing for average golfers.
9 holes, 5890yds, Par 72, SSS 69.
Club membership 250.

Visitors   no restrictions weekdays or Sun, competitions on
                  Sat normal restrictions.
Societies   apply in writing/telephone in advance.
Green Fees   £5 gents; £3 ladies (£8/£5 weekends &
                  bankholidays).
Facilities   ⊗ & ⏝ by prior arrangement 🎱 ♣ ♀ (prior
                  arrangement) ⛷
Location   Old School, Ayr Rd (Ayr rd A70)
Hotel   ★★★68% Tinto Hotel, Symington, BIGGAR
                  ☎ (08993) 454 29 ⇆ 🏌

SHOTTS   Map 11 NS86

Shotts ☎ (0501) 820431 & 826628
Moorland course.
18 holes, 6204yds, Par 70, SSS 70, Course record 63.
Club membership 900.
Visitors   welcome weekdays, must contact in advance.
Societies   apply by letter, weekdays only.
Green Fees   £17 per day (£20 weekends); low season £12 per
                  day.
Facilities   ⊗ ⏝ 🎱 ♣ ♀ (all day) ⛷ 🏠 🍴 Sandy Strachan.
Location   Blairhead (2m from M8 off Benhar Road)
Hotel   ★★★60% The Hilcroft Hotel, East Main St,
                  WHITBURN ☎ (0501) 740818 30 ⇆ 🏌

SKELMORLIE   Map 10 NS16

Skelmorlie ☎ (0475) 520152
Parkland/moorland course with magnificent views over Firth
of Clyde. Designed by James Braid, the club celebrated its
centenary in 1991. The first five holes are played twice.
18 holes, 5056yds, Par 64, SSS 65.
Club membership 400.
Visitors   must contact in advance, restricted Sat.
Societies   apply in writing to the secretary.
Green Fees   £14 per day; £10 per 18 holes (Sat 18 holes £11
                  after 4pm, Sun £17 per day/£11 per round).
Facilities   ⊗ ⏝ 🎱 (all by arrangement at weekends) ♣ ♀
                  ⛷ ⛳
Leisure   fishing.
Location   Beithglass (E side of village off A78)
Hotel   ★★★♨62% Manor Park Hotel,
                  SKELMORLIE
                  ☎ (0475) 520832 10 ⇆ 🏌Annexe13 ⇆ 🏌

SOUTHEND   Map 10 NR60

Dunaverty ☎ (0586) 830677
Undulating, seaside course.
18 holes, 4597yds, Par 66, SSS 64.
Club membership 250.
Visitors   no restrictions.
Societies   apply in writing.
Green Fees   £12 per day; £9 per round.
Facilities   ⊗ ♣ ⛷ 🏠
Location   10m S of Campbeltown on B842
Hotel   ★★62% Royal Hotel, Main St,
                  CAMPBELTOWN
                  ☎ (0586) 552017 16rm(8 ⇆4 🏌)

┌───┐
│ For an explanation of symbols and   │
│ abbreviations, see page 5   │
└───┘

STEVENSTON   Map 10 NS24

Ardeer ☎ (0294) 464542
Parkland course with natural hazards.
18 holes, 6500yds, Par 72, SSS 72, Course record 64.
Club membership 560.
Visitors   may not play Sat.
Societies   must contact in advance.
Green Fees   not confirmed.
Facilities   ⊗ ⏝ 🎱 ♣ ♀ ⛷ 🏠
Leisure   snooker.
Location   Greenhead (0.5m N off A78)
Hotel   ★★★♨70% Montgreenan Mansion House
                  Hotel, Montgreenan Estate, KILWINNING
                  ☎ (0294) 557733 21 ⇆ 🏌

STRATHAVEN   Map 11 NS64

Strathaven ☎ (0357) 20421
Gently undulating, tree-lined, Championship parkland course
with panoramic views over town and Avon valley.
18 holes, 6206yds, Par 71, SSS 70, Course record 66.
Club membership 950.
Visitors   welcome weekdays only. Must contact in
                  advance.
Societies   Tue only.
Green Fees   £26 per day; £18 per round.
Facilities   ⊗ ⏝ 🎱 ♣ ♀ ⛷ 🏠 🍴
Location   Overton Av, Glasgow Rd (NE side of town on
                  A726)
Hotel   ★★★65% Strathaven Hotel, Hamilton Rd,
                  STRATHAVEN ☎ (0357) 21778 10 ⇆ 🏌

TARBERT   Map 10 NR86

Tarbert ☎ (0880) 820565
Beautiful moorland course. Four fairways crossed by streams.
9 holes, 4460yds, Par 66, SSS 64.
Club membership 110.
Visitors   may not play competition days.
Societies   apply in writing.
Green Fees   £8 per 18 holes; £5 per 9 holes; £10 per day.
Facilities   ♀ (Sat pm)
Location   1m W on B8024
Hotel   ★★★♨65% Stonefield Castle Hotel,
                  TARBERT, ☎ (0880) 820836 33 ⇆ 🏌

TIGHNABRUAICH   Map 10 NR97

Kyles of Bute ☎ (0700) 811603
Moorland course which is hilly and exposed to wind. Good
views of the Kyles of Bute.
9 holes, 4778yds, Par 66, SSS 64.
Club membership 160.
Visitors   no restrictions.
Societies   must give 3 weeks prior notice.
Green Fees   £6 per day.
Facilities   ♣ ⛷ ⛳
Location   1.25m S off B8000
Hotel   ★★73% Kilfinan Hotel, KILFINAN
                  ☎ (070082) 201 11 ⇆

TROON
Map 10 NS33

ROYAL TROON See page 277

Troon Municipal ☎ (0292) 312464
Three links courses, two championship.
Lochgreen course: 18 holes, 6785yds, Par 74, SSS 73, Course record 66.
Darley: 18 holes, 6501yds, Par 71, SSS 71, Course record 65.
Fullerton: 18 holes, 4822yds, Par 64, SSS 63, Course record 59.
Club membership 3000.
Visitors   must contact in advance.
Societies   apply in writing.
Green fees not confirmed.
Facilities   ⊗ ℳ ᵫ ♥ ♀ ⚐ 🏠 ᵀ ℓ Gordon McKinley.
Location   Harling Dr (100yds from railway station)
Hotel   ★★62% Craiglea Hotel, South Beach, Troon
                        ☎ (0292) 311366 20rm(10 ⇆ ☞)

TURNBERRY
Map 10 NS20

TURNBERRY HOTEL GOLF COURSES See page 279

UDDINGSTON
Map 11 NS66

Calderbraes ☎ (0698) 813425
Parkland course with good view of Clyde Valley. Testing 4th hole (par 4), hard uphill.
9 holes, 5046yds, Par 66, SSS 67, Course record 65.
Club membership 230.
Visitors   weekdays before 5pm.
Societies   welcome.
Green Fees £10 per day.
Facilities   ⊗ ℳ ᵫ ♥ ♀ ⚐
Location   57 Roundknowe Rd (1.5m NW off A74)
Hotel   ★★65% Redstones Hotel, 8-10 Glasgow Rd,
                        UDDINGSTON
                        ☎ (0698) 813774 & 814843 18rm(16 ⇆ ☞)

UPLAWMOOR
Map 10 NS45

Caldwell ☎ (0505) 850329
Parkland course.
18 holes, 6228yds, Par 70, SSS 70, Course record 62.
Club membership 600.
Visitors   restricted weekends & bank holidays. Must
                        contact in advance.
Societies   apply in writing.
Green Fees £24 per day; £18 per round.
Facilities   ⊗ ℳ & ᵫ (not weekends or holidays) ♥ ♀ ⚐
                        🏠 ℓ Stephen Forbes.
Leisure   caddy cars for hire.
Location   0.5m SW A736
Hotel   ★★63% Dalmeny Park Country House,
                        Lochlibo Rd, BARRHEAD
                        ☎ 041-881 9211 18rm(4 ⇆10 ☞)

> For an explanation of symbols and
> abbreviations, see page 5

WEST KILBRIDE
Map 10 NS24

West Kilbride ☎ (0294) 823911
Seaside links course on Firth of Clyde, with fine views of Isle of Arran from every hole.
18 holes, 5974yds, Par 70, SSS 69.
Club membership 920.
Visitors   may not play at weekends. Must have a handicap
                        certificate.
Societies   Tue & Thu only; must contact in advance.
Green Fees £29 per day; £18 per round.
Facilities   ⊗ ℳ by prior arrangement ᵫ ♥ ♀ ⚐ 🏠
                        ℓ Gregor Howie.
Leisure   snooker.
Location   Fullerton Dr (W side of town off A78)
Hotel   ★★68% Elderslie Hotel, John St, Broomfields,
                        LARGS ☎ (0475) 686460 25rm(9 ⇆4 ☞)

WISHAW
Map 11 NS75

Wishaw ☎ (0698) 372869
Parkland course with many tree-lined areas. Bunkers protect 17 of the 18 greens.
18 holes, 6051yds, Par 69, SSS 69.
Club membership 980.
Visitors   welcome midweek before 5pm, Sun after
                        10.30am, not Sat.
Societies   apply by letter 4 weeks in advance.
Green Fees £12 per round; £20 per day (£25 per day Sun).
Facilities   ⊗ ℳ ᵫ ♥ ♀ ⚐ ℓ John Campbell.
Location   55 Cleland Rd (NW side of town off A721)
Hotel   ★★★64% Popinjay Hotel, Lanark Rd,
                        ROSEBANK
                        ☎ (0555) 860441 38 ⇆ ☞Annexe5 ⇆ ☞

TAYSIDE

ABERFELDY
Map 14 NN84

Aberfeldy ☎ (0887) 820535
Flat, parkland course, situated by River Tay near the famous Wade Bridge and Black Watch Monument.
9 holes, 5466yds, Par 67, SSS 67.
Club membership 250.
Visitors   are advised to book in advance and must do so at
                        weekends Jun-Aug.
Societies   must contact in advance.
Green Fees £16 per day ticket; £11 per 18 holes; £7 per 9
                        holes.
Facilities   ⊗ ᵫ ♥ ♀ ⚐ 🏠
Location   Taybridge Rd (N side of town centre)
Hotel   ★★60% The Weem, Weem, ABERFELDY
                        ☎ (0887) 820381 12 ⇆ ☞
                        See advertisement on page 279
Additional   ★★58% Glenfarg Hotel, Main St, GLENFARG
hotel   ☎ (0577) 830241 15 ⇆ 🍴
                        See advertisement on page 278

ROYAL TROON

TROON ☎ (0292) 311555   Map 10 NS33

John Ingham writes: When Jack Nicklaus first played Royal Troon in the 1962 Open, he was 22 and hit the ball a long way. At that time Nicklaus told me 'There are only two holes that I might not reach with my second shot. My favourite shot is the drive, which I hit up to 350 yards. Just before I swing,' he said, 'all my concentration is directed on one thing and that is to give the ball as big a hit - and as square a hit - as I physically can.'

While sheer length from the back tees at Royal Troon is a great advantage, bearing in mind the full course measures 7097 yards, where you hit the ball is more important than how far. The reason is that this championship links-type course is peppered with bunkers not visible from the tee.

That particular Open was won by Arnold Palmer, in those days a longish hitter as well. However, Palmer also had a delightful putting touch, essential for Royal Troon greens, which can prove hard to read.

Royal Troon is one of the finest links in the world and in an American list appears at number 36. Created in 1878, it was then mercifully free of jumbo jets from nearby Prestwick and has provided entertaining and testing golf for players from all over the world. Greg Norman holds the record with a 10-under-par round of 64. A round which put him in a tie for the 1989 Open which he lost to Mark Calcavecchia.

In the 1960s I played a round at this grand links with the late Henry Longhurst, a good club single figure man who had once won the German Amateur championship. To my best drives, lashed in the breeze, he would just hiss 'Wrong line' and, sure enough, when we got up the fairway, the ball would be submerged in soft sand. In fact I'm told there are 365 bunkers, one for every day of the year!

The Marine Higland hotel is on the edge of the course and, as there are 22 other courses in the area, this makes a great place for a holiday.

So great is Royal Troon, in fact, that the Royal and Ancient has announced that the 1997 Open will again be staged there - for the seventh time since 1923!

Membership 500 (male only)

Visitors may not play Wed, Fri, weekends and public holidays.Must write in advance and have a letter of introduction from own club and a handicap certificate. Ladies and under 18s may only play on the Portland

Societies apply in writing

Green fees £78 per day (Portland only £48) inc lunch.To be paid 2 months in advance

Facilities ⊗ ▥ ♿ ☟ ♀ ♨ ☖ 𝅘 𝄞 (R B Anderson)

Location Craigend Rd (S side of town on B749)

36 holes. Old Course: 18 holes, 7097yds, Par 73, SSS 74, course record 64 (Greg Norman)
Portland: 18 holes, 6274yds, Par 71, SSS 71

WHERE TO STAY AND EAT NEARBY

HOTEL

TROON

★★★ ❀❀ ▲▲ 79% Lochgreen House, Monktenhill Rd, Southwood ☎(0292) 313343. 7 ⇆ 𝄞

★★★★ ❀ 63% Marine Highland. ☎ (0292) 314444, 72 ⇆ 𝄞 International cuisine

★★★ ❀❀ 69% Highgrove House ☎ (0292) 312511. 9 ⇆ 𝄞 French cuisine

★★★ ❀ 66% Piersland House, Craigend Rd. ☎ (0292) 314747. 15 ⇆ 𝄞 Annexe 4 ⇆ British & Continental cuisine

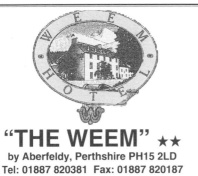

"THE WEEM" ★★
by Aberfeldy, Perthshire PH15 2LD
Tel: 01887 820381 Fax: 01887 820187

Nestling under the spectacular Weem Rock in glorious Breadalbane, you will find this traditional yet fully refurbished 17th century country inn providing the ideal base for a superb holiday in the very heart of Scotland. With the widest selection of excellent golf courses, game fishing, shooting and stalking not to mention water sports, trekking, superb walking, the active will never have a dull moment! For those who prefer a more leisurely time . . . we have some of the finest scenery in the world.

Meanwhile back at "THE WEEM"

you will find comfort, excellent cuisine and a unique atmosphere. You will be pampered and guaranteed many a lighthearted moment . . . "The Weem" breeds contentment and laughter.

ALYTH   Map 15 NO24

Alyth ☎ (08283) 2268
Windy, heathland course with easy walking.
18 holes, 6226yds, Par 70, SSS 70, Course record 66.
Club membership 850.
Visitors   advance booking advisable Must contact in advance.
Societies   must contact in advance.
Green Fees £25 per day; £17 per round (£30/£22 weekends).
Facilities   ⊗ ⋔ 🏌 ▆ ♀ ♨ 🏠 ⚑
Location   Pitcrocknie (1m E on B954)
Hotel   ★★♨67% Altamount House Hotel, Coupar Angus Rd, BLAIRGOWRIE
                  ☎ (0250) 873512 & 873814 7 ⇆ ⎘

ARBROATH   Map 12 NO64

Arbroath ☎ (0241) 875837
Municipal seaside links course, with bunkers guarding greens. Played upon by Arbroath Artisan Club.
18 holes, 6090yds, Par 70, SSS 69.
Club membership 600.
Visitors   no restrictions, but visitors prefered mid-week.
Societies   must telephone in advance; deposit required.
Green Fees £16 per day; £10 per round (£24/£15 weekends).
Facilities   ⊗ ⋔ 🏌 (ex Thu) ▆ ♀ ♨ 🏠 ⚑ ⎘ Lindsay Ewart.
Location   Elliot (2m SW on A92)
Hotel   ★★62% Hotel Seaforth, Dundee Rd, ARBROATH ☎ (0241) 72232 20 ⇆ ⎘

Letham Grange ☎ (0241) 890373
Two courses of great variety. Old Course is set in wooded estate with attractive lochs and burns. New Course is shorter and less arduous but deceptive.
Old Course: 18 holes, 6614yds, Par 73, SSS 73.
New Course: 18 holes, 5528yds, Par 68, SSS 68.
Club membership 780.
Visitors   restricted Tue & weekends on Old Course. Must contact in advance.
Societies   must contact in advance.
Green Fees Old Course: May-Sep £30 per day; £20 per round (£50/£25 weekends). New Course: May-Sep £18 per day; £12 per round (£30/£18 weekends).
Facilities   ⊗ ⋔ 🏌 ▆ ♀ ♨ 🏠 ⚑ ⎘ ⚑ David F G Scott.
Leisure   powered buggies, practice area.
Location   Colliston (4m N on A993)
Hotel   ★★★63% Letham Grange Hotel, Colliston, ARBROATH ☎ (0241) 890373 19 ⇆ ⎘
                  See advertisement on page 280

AUCHTERARDER   Map 11 NN91

Auchterarder ☎ (0764) 662804
Parkland course with easy walking.
18 holes, 5757yds, Par 69, SSS 68.
Club membership 650.
Visitors   restricted on competition days. Must contact in advance,
Societies   must contact 2 months in advance.
Green Fees not confirmed.
Facilities   ⊗ ⋔ 🏌 ▆ ♀ ♨ 🏠 ⚑ ⚑ Gavin Baxter.
Leisure   caddy cars, trolleys.
Location   Orchil Rd (0.75m SW on A824)
Hotel   ★★★★(red) The Gleneagles Hotel, AUCHTERARDER
                  ☎ (0764) 662231 234 ⇆ ⎘   ▶

★★
The GLENFARG
HOTEL

CARNOUSTIE ★ Ladybank ★ Crail ★ Scotscraig ★ ST ANDREWS
★ Downfield ★ GLENEAGLES ★ Taymouth Castle ★ DALMAHOV
★ Lundin Links ★ ROSEMOUNT ★ Elie ★ Crieff ★ MURRAYSHALL
. . . The golfers hotel . . .
YOUR ONLY WORRY WILL BE CHOOSING WHERE TO PLAY . . .
Situated in the heart of Scotland's golfing country, yet only 35 mins from Edinburgh and St Andrews, this friendly popular hotel is the perfect setting for your golf break. The hotel is happy to organise all your golfing requirements. A busy group package service includes discounted rates and full itinerary planning. All bedrooms are en suite with full facilities. Real ale bar. Extensive bar menu. Candlelit restaurant.
Write or phone for full information and brochure.
GLENFARG, PERTHSHIRE PH2 9NU   Tel: (01577) 830241   Fax: (01577) 830665

TURNBERRY HOTEL GOLF COURSES

TURNBERRY ☎ (0655) 31000   Map 10 NS20

John Ingham writes: The hotel is sumptuous, the Ailsa and Arran courses beneath it are total magic. The air reaches down into your inner lung and of all places in Scotland, Turnberry has to be among the finest.

Tunberry is delightfully off the beaten track and, although the courses are principally for residents of the hotel, if you wish to fly in, then Prestwick Airport is only seventeen miles from the first tee. What makes the place so desirable is the warmness of the welcome and, course professional Bob Jamieson will tell you, this is literally so on occasions, as the links is on the friendliest of gulf streams.

The Ailsa course has been the venue for the Open in 1977 and 1986 and hosted it again in 1994. It was here in the 1977 Open, that Jack Nicklaus put up such a brave fight against Tom Watson. Then, in 1986, we had a wondrous victory from Greg Norman. He has fond memories of Turnberry, where a few hours after the prize-giving he was able to sit with his wife on the edge of the great links, drinking champagne, and watching the moon roll round the pure white lighthouse out by the 9th green.

Without any doubt, Turnberry is the stuff of dreams and you must go there if you possibly can.

Visitors   The golf courses are principally for residents of the hotel, so must contact in advance

Societies   contact in advance as courses are principally for residents of the hotel

Green fees   Arran Course: 29 Mar-23 Oct £30; 24 Oct-27 Mar £15
Ailsa Course: 29 Mar-23 Oct £50; 27 Mar-24 Oct £30 - both fees include a round on Arran if played on same day

Facilities   ⊗ 乂 﨟 ☕ ♀ 🍴 🏠 ♟ ⌘ (R SJamieson)

Leisure   tennis (hardcourt), indoor-heated swimming pool, squash, snooker, complete health spa

Location   N side of village, on A719

36 holes. Ailsa Course: 18 holes, 6440 yds, Par 69, SSS 72, Course record 63 (Greg Norman & Maric Hayes) Arran Course: 18 holes, 6014yds, Par 69, SSS 70. Course record 65 (E Macintosh/C Ronald/S McGregor)

WHERE TO STAY AND EAT NEARBY

HOTELS:

GIRVAN
★★ 61% King's Arms, Dalrymple St. ☎ (0465) 3322. 25 ⇌ 🐾
Scottish & French cuisine

MAYBOLE
★★❀♨ 80% Ladyburn. ☎ Crosshill (06554) 585. 8(7 ⇌ 🐾)

TURNBERRY
★★★★★(red)❀❀ 80% Turnberry Hotel and Golf Courses. ☎ (0655) 31000
132 ⇌ 🐾 Scottish & French cuisine

★★★ 70% Malin Court. ☎ (0655) 31457. 17 ⇌ 🐾

· LETHAM · GRANGE ·

HOTEL & GOLF COURSES

AA ★★★   STB 🏆🏆🏆🏆 Commended

Letham Grange is a de-luxe,
20 bedroom, former Victorian mansion
with award winning cuisine.

The 300 acre estate has two 18 hole
golf courses.

The Old Course is Championship Standard
Tree lined parkland and open rolling
fairways, with water playing a major role,
the course is both scenic and dramatic.

The New Course is easier, but deceptive.

Only minutes from Arbroath and Carnoustie.

Colliston, By Arbroath, Angus DD11 4RL
Telephone: 01241 890373   Fax: 01241 890414

DUCHALLY HOUSE
★★★ · HOTEL · 🌸 ♨

Duchally House is set in 27 acres of grounds overlooking the lovely Perthshire countryside and just 2
miles off the main A9 Stirling to Perth road. Less than
one hour's drive from both Glasgow and Edinburgh.
This fine country house offers the best of food and
wines in a relaxed and friendly atmosphere. Ten golf
courses within 30 minutes drive. Open fires in public
rooms and an original Victorian billiard room.
From £35 to £50 per person B&B sharing
Special short inclusive breaks
Conference, wedding and meeting facilities available.
For further information and brochure contact
Duchally House Hotel
Near Auchterarder, Perthshire PH3 1PN
Tel: 01764 663071.   Fax: 01764 662464

Additional   ★★★♨68% Duchally House Hotel,
hotel   AUCHTERARDER
                ☎ (0764) 663071 13rm(12 ⇄ ℝ)

Gleneagles Hotel ☎ (0764) 662231
Famous moorland courses designed by James Braid. The
King's has heather and gorse threatening wayward shots;
The Queen's is more heavily wooded with a variety of
dog-leg holes and the Loch-an-Eerie to negotiate.
Sumptuous hotel offers unrivalled sports and leisure
activities. Course record holder on King's Course is Ian
Woosnam. The new championship Monarchs Course,
designed by Jack Nicklaus, was opened at the end of 1992.
Kings Course: 18 holes, 6471yds, Par 70, SSS 71.
Queens Course: 18 holes, 5965yds, Par 68, SSS 69.
Wee Course: 9 holes, 1481yds, Par 27.
Monarch Course: 18 holes, 6551yds, Par 72, SSS 71.
Club membership 780.
Visitors   must be hotel residents or the guest of a club
                member. A handicap certificate is not
                required. Must contact in advance.
Societies   must be resident in the hotel.
Green Fees £50 per 18 holes; £13 per 9 holes.
Facilities ⊗ ⅲ 🏌 ▨ (catering available to hotel
                guests) ♀⚑🏠 ⚓🎯ℓ Greg Schofield.
Leisure   hard and grass tennis courts, heated indoor
                swimming pool, squash, fishing, riding,
                snooker, sauna, solarium, gymnasium,
                croquet, bowls, pitch & putt & cycling.
Location   2m SW of A823
Hotel   ★★★★★(red) The Gleneagles Hotel,
                AUCHTERARDER
                ☎ (0764) 662231 234 ⇄ ℝ

BARRY   Map 12 NO53

Panmure ☎ (0241) 855120
A nerve-testing, adventurous course set amongst
sandhills - its hazards belie the quiet nature of the
opening holes. This tight links has been used as a
qualifying course for the Open Championship, and
features Ben Hogan's favourite hole, the dog-leg 6th,
which heralds the toughest stretch, around the turn.
18 holes, 6317yds, Par 70, SSS 70, Course record 62.
Club membership 700.
Visitors   may not play Sat. Parties of 6 or more must
                contact in advance.
Societies   must contact secretary in advance.
Green Fees £35 per day; £23 per round.
Facilities ⊗ ⅲ by prior arrangement 🏌 ▨♀🏠
                ⚓ℓ Andew Cullen.
Leisure   buggy, caddy cars, caddies.
Location   Burnside Rd (S side of village off A930)
Hotel   ★★62% Glencoe Hotel, Links Pde,
                CARNOUSTIE
                ☎ (0241) 853273 11rm(3 ⇄5 ℝ)

BLAIR ATHOLL   Map 14 NN86

Blair Atholl ☎ (0796) 481407
Parkland course, river runs alongside 3 holes, easy walking.
9 holes, 5710yds, Par 70, SSS 69.
Club membership 400.
Visitors   no restrictions.
Societies   must contact in advance.
Green Fees £10 per day (£12 weekends).

KINLOCH HOUSE HOTEL

AA ★★★ (red) ۞۞

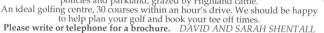

By Blairgowrie, Perthshire, PH10 6SG
Telephone: Blairgowrie (01250) 884 237 Fax: (01250) 884 333
With its oak panelled hall and magnificent gallery, Kinloch House is a
fine example of a Scottish country house – set in 20 acres of wooded
policies and parkland, grazed by Highland cattle.
An ideal golfing centre, 30 courses within an hour's drive. We should be happy
to help plan your golf and book your tee off times.
Please write or telephone for a brochure. *DAVID AND SARAH SHENTALL*

Facilities	⊗ 🝙 🍺 ♀ 🏋 ⛳
Leisure	caddy cars.
Location	0.5m S off B8079
Hotel	★★64% Atholl Arms Hotel, BLAIR ATHOLL
	☎ (0796) 481205 30 ⇥ 🐾

BLAIRGOWRIE

Map 15 NO14

Blairgowrie ☎ (0250) 872622
Two 18-hole heathland courses, also a 9-hole course.
Rosemount Course: 18 holes, 6588yds, Par 72, SSS 72.
Lansdowne Course: 18 holes, 6895yds, Par 72, SSS 73.
Wee Course: 9 holes, 4654yds, Par 64, SSS 63.
Club membership 1200.
Visitors must contact in advance & have handicap
certificate, restricted Wed, Fri & weekends.
Societies must contact in writing.
Green Fees not confirmed.
Facilities ⊗ 🍴 🝙 🍺 ♀ 🏋 🏠 ⛳ ☍ Gordon Kinnoch.
Location Rosemount (2m S off A93)

Glencoe

HOTEL

Links Parade, Carnoustie DD7 7JF
Tel: 01241 853273 Fax: 01241 853319
AA ★★ "Par excellence"

*The 'Golf Hotel' in
Carnoustie, directly opposite
the last green of the
championship golf course.
Family run hotel, offering
excellent cuisine and
accommodation.
Golfing parties welcome.*

Hotel	★★★(red)🏌 Kinloch House Hotel,
	BLAIRGOWRIE
	☎ (0250884) 237 21 ⇥ 🐾

BRECHIN

Map 15 NO56

Brechin ☎ (0356) 622383
Rolling parkland course, with easy walking and good views
of Strathmore Valley and Grampian Mountains. The course
was extended in 1993.
18 holes, 6100yds, Par 70, SSS 69.
Club membership 650.
Visitors may not play at weekends when competitions are
being held.
Societies must contact in advance.
Green Fees £17 per day; £12 per round (£25/£16 weekends
& bank holidays).
Facilities ⊗ 🍴 🝙 🍺 ♀ 🏋 🏠 ⛳ ☍ Stephen Rennie.
Leisure squash, pool table.
Location Trinity (1m N on B966)
Hotel ★★56% Northern Hotel, Clerk St, BRECHIN
☎ (0356) 622156 & 625505 20rm(4 ⇥ 12 🐾)

CARNOUSTIE

Map 12 NO53

CARNOUSTIE GOLF LINKS See page 283

COMRIE

Map 11 NN72

Comrie ☎ (0764) 670055
Scenic highland course.
9 holes, 5250yds, Par 70, SSS 69, Course record 64.
Club membership 400.
Visitors restricted Mon & Tue after 4.30pm.
Societies must contact in advance.
Green Fees £10 per day (£12 weekends).
Facilities ⊗ (summer only) 🍺 🏋 ⛳
Location E side of village off A85
Hotel ★★63% Comrie Hotel, Drummond St,
COMRIE
☎ (0764) 670239 9 ⇥ 🐾Annexe2 ⇥

A golf course name printed in ***bold
italics*** means we have been unable to
verify information with the club's
management for the current year

CRIEFF   Map 11 NN82

Crieff ☎ (0764) 652909
This course is what you might call 'up and down' but the turf is beautiful and the highland air fresh and invigorating. There are views from the course over Strathearn. Of the two courses the Ferntower is the more challenging. Both parkland, the Dornock has one water hazard.
Ferntower: 18 holes, 6402yds, Par 71, SSS 71, Course record 66.
Dornock: 9 holes, 4772yds, Par 64, SSS 63.
Club membership 570.
Visitors   must have a handicap certificate. Must contact in advance.
Societies   must contact in advance.
Green Fees Ferntower £27 per day, £16 per round (£34/£20 weekends); Dornock £11 per 18 holes (£13 weekends).
Facilities   ⊗ �🏛 ⬥ 🍺 ♀ 🛆 🏠 ⛳
           ⏱ D Murchie & J M Stark.
Location   Perth Rd (0.5m NE on A85)
Hotel   ★★69% Murray Park Hotel, Connaught Ter, CRIEFF ☎ (0764) 653731 21 ⇄

DUNDEE   Map 11 NO43

Caird Park ☎ (0382) 453606
Municipal parkland course.
18 holes, 5494yds, Par 69, SSS 68.
Club membership 400.
Visitors   no restrictions.
Societies   must contact Dundee District Council on (0382) 23141 in advance.
Green Fees £20 per day; £12 per round.
Facilities   ⊗ ⬥ 🍺 ♀ 🏠 ⛳ ⏱ J Black.
Location   Mains Loan (1.5m N of city centre off A972)
Hotel   ★★★65% The Queen's Hotel, 160 Nethergate, DUNDEE ☎ (0382) 322515 47 ⇄ 🐾

Camperdown ☎ (0382) 621145
Parkland course. Testing 2nd hole.
18 holes, 5999yds, Par 71, SSS 69.
Club membership 600.
Visitors   must contact in advance.
Societies   must contact in advance.
Green Fees not confirmed.
Facilities   🛆 🏠 ⏱
Leisure   hard tennis courts, riding.
Location   Camperdown House, Camperdown Park (3m NW of city centre off A923)
Hotel   ★★★63% Angus Thistle, 101 Marketgait, DUNDEE ☎ (0382) 26874 58 ⇄ 🐾

Downfield ☎ (0382) 825595
A fine inland course of recent Championship rating set in undulating woodland to the north of Dundee. The Gelly burn provides a hazard for several holes.
18 holes, 6804yds, Par 73, SSS 73.
Club membership 733.
Visitors   must telephone (0382) 89246 for start time on day of play.
Societies   must contact in advance.
Green Fees £36 per day; £24 per round.
Facilities   ⊗ ⏛ ⬥ 🍺 ♀ 🛆 🏠 ⛳

Leisure   snooker.
Location   Turnberry Av (N of city centre off A923)
Hotel   ★★★63% Angus Thistle, 101 Marketgait, DUNDEE ☎ (0382) 26874 58 ⇄ 🐾

DUNKELD   Map 11 NO04

Dunkeld & Birnam ☎ (0350) 727524
Interesting heathland course with spectacular views of surrounding countryside.
9 holes, 5264yds, Par 68, SSS 66.
Club membership 300.
Visitors   may not play on competition days.
Societies   must telephone in advance.
Green Fees on application.
Facilities   ⊗ ⏛ ⬥ 🍺 ♀ 🛆 🏠 ⛳
Leisure   caddy car hire.
Location   Fungarth (1m N of village on A923)
Hotel   ★★★63% Birnam Hotel, Birnam, DUNKELD ☎ (0350) 727462 28 ⇄ 🐾

DUNNING   Map 11 NO01

Dunning ☎ (0764) 684372 & 684747
Parkland course.
9 holes, 4836yds, Par 66, SSS 64.
Club membership 580.
Visitors   may not play on Sat before 4pm or Sun before 1pm. With member only after 5pm Mon-Fri.
Societies   must contact in advance in writing.
Green Fees £8 per day.
Facilities   🍺 (Mon-Fri) 🛆
Location   Rollo Park (off A9 NW)
Hotel   ★★★♨68% Duchally House Hotel, AUCHTERARDER ☎ (0764) 663071 13rm(12 ⇄ 🐾)

EDZELL   Map 15 NO66

Edzell ☎ (0356) 647283
This delightful course is situated in the foothills of the Scottish Highlands and provides good golf as well as conveying to everyone who plays there a feeling of peace and quiet. The village of Edzell is one of the most picturesque in Scotland.
18 holes, 6348yds, Par 71, SSS 70.
Club membership 910.
Visitors   restricted at certain times. Must have a handicap certificate.
Societies   must contact in advance.
Green Fees £24 per day; £16 per round (£33 per day; £22 per round weekends & bank holidays).
Facilities   ⊗ ⏛ ⬥ 🍺 ♀ 🛆 🏠 ⛳ ⏱ A J Webster.
Location   S side of village on B966
Hotel   ★★★60% Glenesk Hotel, High St, EDZELL ☎ (0356) 648319 25rm(23 ⇄ 🐾)

Phoneday - remember from 16 April 1995 all phone codes in the UK will change - see page 4 for details

CARNOUSTIE GOLF LINKS

CARNOUSTIE ☎ (0241) 853789   Map 12 NO53

John Ingham writes: You love it, or hate it - but you respect it. Carnoustie can be a graveyard. Simply standing up to the buffeting is bad enough, but those closing holes, across the Barry Burn (or into it) are a prospect which can gnaw at the mind. The burn twists through the links like an angry serpent and has to be crossed no fewer than seven times.

Back in 1953 they came to see Ben Hogan play in the Open Championship. This little man from Texas had a magic about him, and the huge terrifying links, the dread of any short hitter, certainly promised to be a platform on which to examine the finest golfer of his day, and maybe of any day.

Not since 1860 had any golfer won the Open on his first attempt. Certainly Hogan hadn't come to this awesome place for the money which, in those days, was a pittance. He had come to prove he was the best player in the world. That was pressure!

When Mr Hogan saw the 'Stone Age' course, dating back to the birth of the game, he was shocked because it lacked trees and colour, and looked drab. But he beat the 7200-yard monster course for the 1953 Championship, which was, as they say, something else.

'Winning the British Open at Carnoustie gave me my greatest pleasure' he told the *Fort Worth Star-Telegram*. 'Certainly the other victories were pleasurable, but none gave me the feeling, the desire to perform, that gripped me in Scotland'.

Sadly, Hogan never returned and then the great links was taken from the Open Championship rota. Today there are hopes it may be re-instated.

Visitors	must contact golf links in advance. Restricted hours. Must have a handicap certificate for Championship course
Societies	prior arrangement required either in writing or by telephone
Green fees	Championship: £63 per day; £36 per round Burnside: £21 per day; £14 per round; Buddon Links: £15 per day; £10 per round. Combination day tickets: Championship & Burnside £43 ; Championship & Buddon Links £4; Burnside & Buddon Links £19
Facilities	⛪
Location	Links Parade (SW side of town, off A930)

54 holes. Championship Course: 18 holes, 6936 yds, Par 72, SSS 74, Course record 65 (Jack Newton, Aus) Burnside Course: 18 holes, 6020 yds, Par 68, SSS 69 Buddon Links: 18 holes, 5196 yds, Par 66, SSS 66

WHERE TO STAY AND EAT NEARBY

HOTELS:

ARBROATH
★★★ 63% Letham Grange, Colliston, ☎ Gowanbank (0241) 890373 19 ⇥

CARNOUSTIE
★★ 63% Carlogie House, Carlogie Rd ☎ (0241) 853185. 11 ⇥ 📻

★★62% Glencoe, Links Pde. ☎ (0241) 853273. 11(8 ⇥ 📻) Scottish & French cuisine

LETHAM
★★★ ♨ 59% Fernie Castle. ☎ (0337) 810381. 15 ⇥ 📻

RESTAURANT:

INVERKEILOR
✗ ⊛ Gordon's, Homewood House, Main St. ☎ (0241) 830364 Scottish & French cuisine

FORFAR
Map 15 NO45

Forfar ☎ (0307) 462120 & 463773
Moorland course with wooded, undulating fairways and fine views.
18 holes, 5522mtrs, Par 69, SSS 69, Course record 64.
Club membership 850.
Visitors   no restrictions.
Societies   must contact in advance.
Green Fees £20 per day; £16 per round (£30 weekends & bank holidays).
Facilities   ♀⚲🏠⟊
Location   Cunninghill, Arbroath Rd (1m E on A932)
Hotel   ★★★♨64% Idvies House Hotel, Letham, FORFAR ☎ (0307) 818787 10 ⇋ ♞

GLENSHEE (SPITTAL OF)
Map 15 NO16

Dalmunzie ☎ Glenshee (0250) 885224
Well maintained Highland course with difficult walking. Testing 5th hole. Small but good greens.
9 holes, 2035yds, Par 30, SSS 30.
Club membership 53.
Visitors   restricted Sun 10.30-11.30am.
Societies   must contact by telephone.
Green Fees £8 per day; £5 per round.
Facilities   ⊗ ▥ by prior arrangement ⌸ ⛊ ♀⟊ ⋈
Leisure   hard tennis courts, fishing, stalking & shooting.
Location   Dalmunzie Estate (2m NW of Spittal of Glenshee)
Hotel   ★★♨65% Dalmunzie House Hotel, SPITTAL OF GLENSHEE ☎ (0250) 885224 18rm(16 ⇋ ♞)

KENMORE
Map 14 NN74

Kenmore ☎ Aberfeldy (0887) 830226
Testing course in mildly undulating natural terrain. Beautiful views in tranquil setting by Loch Tay.
9 holes, 6052yds, Par 70, SSS 69, Course record 70.
Club membership 150.
Visitors   restricted Thur evenings and during club competitions.
Societies   apply in writing or telephone.
Green Fees £15 per day; £10 per 18 holes; £7per 9 holes (£16/£11/£8 weekends).
Facilities   ⊗ ▥ ⌸ ⛊ ♀⚲🏠⟊ ⋈
Leisure   hard tennis courts, fishing, riding, caddy cars, petrol buggy,petanque.
Location   Taymouth Holiday Centre
Hotel   ★★62% Fortingall Hotel, FORTINGALL ☎ (0887) 830368 & 830368 9rm(8 ⇋ ♞)

Taymouth Castle ☎ (0887) 830228
Parkland course set amidst beautiful mountain and loch scenery. Easy walking. Fishing.
18 holes, 6066yds, Par 69, SSS 69, Course record 63.
Club membership 200.
Visitors   must contact in advance.
Societies   must telephone in advance.
Green Fees not confirmed.
Facilities   ⊗ ⌸ ⛊ ♀⚲🏠⟊⟊ Alex Marshall.

Leisure   fishing.
Location   1m E on A827
Hotel   ★★62% Fortingall Hotel, FORTINGALL ☎ (0887) 830367 & 830368 9rm(8 ⇋ ♞)

KINROSS
Map 11 NO10

Green Hotel ☎ (0577) 863407
Two interesting and picturesque parkland courses, with easy walking.
Red Course: 18 holes, 6257yds, Par 72, SSS 70.
Blue Course: 18 holes, 6456yds, Par 71, SSS 71.
Club membership 450.
Visitors   must contact in advance.
Societies   must contact in advance.
Green Fees not confirmed.
Facilities   ⚲🏠⟊⋈⟊
Leisure   hard tennis courts, heated indoor swimming pool, squash, fishing, sauna, solarium, gymnasium.
Location   NE side of town on B996
Hotel   ★★★69% Green Hotel, 2 The Muirs, KINROSS ☎ (0577) 863467 47 ⇋ ♞

Kinross Beeches Park ☎ (0577) 862237
Parkland course on the banks of Loch Leven.
Blue Course: 18 holes, 6456yds, Par 71, SSS 71, Course record 66.
Red Course: 18 holes, 6257yds, Par 72, SSS 70, Course record 70.
Club membership 540.
Visitors   no restrictions.

THE IDEAL
GREEN
FOR GOLFERS

JUST A SHORT IRON FROM THE FRONT DOOR YOU WILL FIND THE FIRST TEES OF OUR OWN TWO SCENIC GOLF COURSES. BOTH OFFER AN ENJOYABLE AND STIMULATING CHALLENGE WHETHER YOU'RE A HOLIDAY GOLFER OR LOW HANDICAP PLAYER.
OUR 47 MODERN SPACIOUS BEDROOMS ARE ALL WELL APPOINTED AND INCLUDE SATELLITE TV. INDOOR LEISURE COMPLEX FEATURES INDOOR POOL, SAUNA, SOLARIUM, SQUASH COURT AND FITNESS AREA. OVER 50 OTHER GREAT COURSES WITHIN AN HOUR'S EASY DRIVE INCLUDING ST. ANDREWS, GLENEAGLES AND CARNOUSTIE.

THE GREEN
H O T E L
2 The Muirs, Kinross, Scotland KY13 7AS.
Tel: (01577) 863467. Fax: (01577) 863180

Green Fees Blue Course: £14 per round (£20 weekends & bank holidays). Red Course: £20 per day (£30 weekends & bank holidays).
Facilities ⊗ ⓑ ⚑ ♀ ⚐ 龠 ℑ ℓ Stuart Geraghty.
Leisure caddy cars.
Location NE side of town on B996
Hotel ★★★69% Green Hotel, 2 The Muirs, KINROSS ☎ (0577) 863467 47 ⇆ ♠
Additional hotel ★★63% Bridgend Hotel, High St, KINROSS ☎ (0577) 863413 15 ⇆ ♠

KIRRIEMUIR   Map 15 NO35

Kirriemuir ☎ (0575) 573317
Parkland and heathland course set at the foot of the Angus glens, with good view.
18 holes, 5553yds, Par 68, SSS 67, Course record 62.
Club membership 600.
Visitors must play with member at weekends.
Societies must apply in advance
Green Fees £19 per day; £14 per round.
Facilities ⊗ 爪 ⓑ ⚑ ♀ ⚐ 龠 ℑ ℓ A Caira.
Leisure caddy cars for hire.
Location Northmuir (1m N off B955)
Hotel ★★★♨72% Castleton House Hotel, GLAMIS ☎ (0307) 840340 6 ⇆ ♠

MILNATHORT   Map 11 NO10

Milnathort ☎ Kinross (0577) 864069
Undulating parkland course.
9 holes, 5969yds, Par 71, SSS 69, Course record 65.
Club membership 400.
Visitors must contact in advance.
Societies must contact in writing; deposit required.
Green Fees £10 per day (£15 weekends).
Facilities ⊗ 爪 & ℑ by prior arrangement ⚑ ♀ ⚐
Location South St (S side of town on A922)
Hotel ★★★69% Green Hotel, 2 The Muirs, KINROSS ☎ (0577) 863467 47 ⇆ ♠

MONIFIETH   Map 12 NO43

Monifieth ☎ (0382) 532767
The chief of the two courses at Monifieth is the Medal Course. It has been one of the qualifying venues for the Open Championship on more than one occasion. A seaside links, but divided from the sand dunes by a railway which provides the principal hazard for the first few holes. The 10th hole is outstanding, the 17th is excellent and there is a delightful finishing hole. The other course here is the Ashludie, and both are played over by a number of clubs who share the links.
Medal Course: 18 holes, 6651yds, Par 71, SSS 72.
Ashludie Course: 18 holes, 5123yds, SSS 64.
Club membership 1500.
Visitors must contact in advance. Restricted to after 2pm Sat & after 10am Sun.
Societies must contact in advance.
Green Fees not confirmed.
Facilities ⊗ 爪 ⓑ ⚑ ♀ ⚐ 龠 ℑ ℓ Ian McLeod.
Location The Links (NE side of town on A930)
Hotel ★★63% Carlogie House Hotel, Carlogie Rd, CARNOUSTIE ☎ (0241) 853185 11 ⇆ ♠

MONTROSE   Map 15 NO75

Montrose Links Trust ☎ (0674) 672932
The links at Montrose like many others in Scotland are on commonland and are shared by three clubs. The Medal course at Montrose - the fifth oldest in the world - is typical of Scottish seaside links, with narrow, undulating fairways and problems from the first hole to the last. The Broomfield course is flatter and easier.
Medal Course: 18 holes, 6443yds, Par 71, SSS 71.
Broomfield Course: 18 holes, 4815yds, Par 66, SSS 63.
Club membership 1155.
See advertisement inside Back Cover
Visitors may not play on the Medal Course on Sat & before 10am on Sun. Must have a handicap certificate for medal Course.
Societies must telephone at least 7 days in advance.
Green Fees Medal: £24 per day; £14 per round (£33/£21 weekends). £76 weekly. Broomfield: £13 per day; £9 per round (£20/£13 weekends). £50 weekly.
Facilities ⊗ 爪 ⓑ ⚑ ♀ ⚐ 龠 ℑ ℓ
Leisure caddy cars for hire.
Location Traill Dr (NE side of town off A92)
Hotel ★★★61% Park Hotel, 61 John St, MONTROSE ☎ (0674) 73415 59rm(48 ⇆5 ♠)

MUTHILL   Map 11 NN81

Muthill ☎ (0764) 681523
Parkland course with fine views. Not too hilly, tight with narrow fairways.
9 holes, 4700yds, Par 66, SSS 63.
Club membership 400.
Visitors restricted on match nights.
Green Fees £8 per day (£12 weekends).
Facilities ⚑ ♀ ⚐
Location Peat Rd (W side of village off A822)
Hotel ★★69% Murray Park Hotel, Connaught Ter, CRIEFF ☎ (0764) 653731 21 ⇆

PERTH   Map 11 NO12

Craigie Hill ☎ (0738) 620829 & 622644
Slightly hilly, parkland course. Good views over Perth.
18 holes, 5379yds, Par 66, SSS 66, Course record 60.
Club membership 610.
Visitors must contact in advance but may not play on Sat.
Societies must contact in writing.
Green Fees £15 per day; £10 per round (£20 Sun).
Facilities ⊗ (ex Tue) ⓑ ⚑ ♀ ⚐ 龠 ℑ Frank Smith.
Location Cherrybank (1m SW of city centre off A952)
Hotel ★★★60% The Royal George, Tay St, PERTH ☎ (0738) 624455 42 ⇆ ♠

King James VI ☎ (0738) 625170
Parkland course, situated on island in the middle of River Tay. Easy walking.
18 holes, 6038yds, Par 70, SSS 69, Course record 62.
Club membership 675.
Visitors must contact in advance but may not play on Sat.
Societies may not play on Sat. Must contact in writing.
Green Fees £18 per day; £12 per round (£24 per day weekends £15 weekends after 10am). ▶

The Bein Inn ★★
Glenfarg
Perthshire PH2 9PY
Tel: (01577) 830216 Fax: (01577) 830211

**Under new experienced ownership.
Golf and food is our priority.**
Nestling in beautiful Glenfarg, eight miles
south of Perth just off the M90, is where you
will find the Bein Inn. A 17th century Drovers
Inn full of atmosphere.
Edinburgh, Perth, Dundee and St Andrews are
all within easy motoring distance.
A golfers' paradise with St Andrews,
Gleneagles, Carnoustie and many more
excellent courses within easy reach.
Special Bargain Break prices available
throughout the year.
Just that little bit different

Facilities	⊗ ⅷ ⌾ 🍺 ♀ 🏌 📷 ⌜
Leisure	caddy cars, buggy for hire.
Location	Moncrieffe Island (SE side of city centre)
Hotel	★★★61% Queens Hotel, Leonard St, PERTH
	☎ (0738) 442222 50rm(40 ⇆9 📷)
Additional	★★64% Bein Inn Hotel, GLENFARG
hotel	☎ (0577) 830216 9rm(7 ⇆)Annexe4 ⇆ 📷

Murrayshall Country House Hotel
☎ New Scone (0738) 551171
This course is laid out in 130 acres of parkland with tree-lined
fairways. Hotel and driving range.
18 holes, 6446yds, Par 73, SSS 71.
Club membership 300.

Visitors	no restrictions.
Societies	must contact in advance.
Green Fees	£30 per day; £20 per round (£40 per day; £25
	per round weekends).
Facilities	⊗ ⅷ ⌾ 🍺 ♀ 🏌 📷 ⌜ 🏌 ⌜ Neil Macintosh.
Leisure	hard tennis courts, driving range, putting green,
	croquet.
Location	Murrayshall, Scone (E side of village off A94)
Hotel	★★★75% Murrayshall Country House Hotel
	& Golf Course, New Scone, PERTH
	☎ (0738) 551171 19 ⇆ 📷

If visiting a brand new course, be sure
to telephone before your visit to
confirm the course information is
correct

PITLOCHRY
Map 14 NN95

Pitlochry ☎ (0796) 472792
A varied and interesting heathland course with fine views
and posing many problems. Its SSS permits few errors in
its achievement.
18 holes, 5811yds, Par 69, SSS 68.
Club membership 400.

Visitors	may not play before 9.30am.
Societies	must contact in writing.
Green Fees	not confirmed.
Facilities	⊗ ⅷ by prior arrangement ⌾ 🍺 ♀ 🏌 📷
	🏌 ⌜ George Hampton.
Location	Pitlochry Estate Office (N side of town off
	A924)
Hotel	★★★★71% Pine Trees Hotel, Strathview
	Ter, PITLOCHRY
	☎ (0796) 472121 20rm(19 ⇆ 📷)
Additional	★★73% Killiecrankie Hotel,
hotel	KILLIECRANKIE
	☎ (0796) 473220 10 ⇆ 📷

ST FILLANS
Map 11 NN62

St Fillans ☎ (0764) 685312
Fairly flat, beautiful parkland course. Wonderfully rich in
flora, animal and bird life.
9 holes, 5680yds, Par 69, SSS 68, Course record 66.
Club membership 400.

Visitors	may not play on Sat mornings.
Societies	may not play in Jul & Aug. Booking fee
	required.

The
Killiecrankie
Hotel AA ★★ 73% ☺☺

A charmingly appointed hotel in a spectacular setting
overlooking the historic Pass of Killiecrankie, within
easy reach of Perthshire's many golf courses. Five
minutes' drive from Blair Atholl and Pitlochry
courses, and within easy reach of scenic Taymouth
Castle, Dunkeld, Strathtay and Blairgowrie.
Ten pretty bedrooms, including one suite,
exceptionally good food and an easy atmosphere, the
hotel is an ideal place to relax and unwind. Closed
January and February.

**For details of brochure and tariff, please contact
Colin and Carole Anderson,
Killiecrankie Hotel, Killiecrankie,
By Pitlochry, Perthshire.
Tel: 01796 473220 or Fax: 01796 472451**

Green Fees not confirmed.
Facilities ⊗ ⅃▯ ☕ ⚲ 🏠 ⛳
Leisure fishing.
Location E side of village off A85
Hotel ★★★66% The Four Seasons Hotel, ST
FILLANS ☎ (0764) 685333 12 ⇌ ↾

STRATHTAY   Map 14 NN95

Strathtay ☎ Dunkeld (0350) 727797
A wooded mainly hilly course with pleasing panoramic
views. 5th hole 'Spion Kop' is especially difficult. It is steep,
with heavy rough on both sides of the hilly fairway and an
unsighted green of the back of the hill which is affected by
winds.
9 holes, 4082yds, Par 63, SSS 63.
Club membership 158.
Visitors restricted May-Sep; Sun 12.30-5pm & Mon 6-
8pm.
Societies by letter or telephone to Secretary T D Lind,
Lorne Cottage, Dalguise, Dunkeld, Perthshire
PH8 0JX.
Green Fees £30 weekly; £8 per day (£10 weekends).
Facilities ⚲
Location Eastern end of minor rd to Weem, off A827
Hotel ★★(red)⚘ Farleyer House Hotel,
ABERFELDY
☎ (0887) 820332 11rm(9 ⇌ ↾)

SCOTTISH ISLANDS

ARRAN, ISLE OF

BLACKWATERFOOT   Map 10 NR82

Shiskine ☎ Shiskine (0770) 860226
Unique 12-hole links course with gorgeous outlook to the
Mull of Kintyre.
12 holes, 2990yds, Par 42, SSS 42.
Visitors no restrictions.
Societies must contact in writing.
Green Fees not confirmed.
Facilities ⊗ ☕ ⚲ 🏠
Leisure hard tennis courts, all weather bowling green.
Location Shore Rd (W side of village off A841)
Hotel ★★63% The Lagg Hotel, Kilmory, BRODICK
☎ (0770) 870255 15 ⇌ ↾

BRODICK   Map 10 NS03

Brodick ☎ (0770) 302349
Short seaside course, very flat.
18 holes, 4405yds, Par 62, SSS 62, Course record 61.
Club membership 552.
Visitors must contact in advance but may not play on
competition days.
Societies must contact in advance.
Green Fees £12 per day; £8 per round (£14/£9 weekends).

Facilities ⅃▯ ☕ ⚲ 🏠 ⛳ Peter McCalla.
Leisure caddy cars, practice area.
Location N side of village
Hotel ★★★75% Auchrannie Country House Hotel,
BRODICK
☎ (0770) 302234 & 302235 28 ⇌ ↾

CORRIE   Map 10 NS04

Corrie ☎ (0770) 810223
A heathland course on the coast with beautiful mountain
scenery. An upward climb to 6th hole, then a descent from
the 7th. All these holes are subject to strong winds in bad
weather.
9 holes, 3896yds, Par 62, SSS 61.
Club membership 220.
Visitors restricted Sat when medal games played.
Societies must contact in advance.
Green Fees not confirmed.
Facilities ⊗ ∭ ☕ 🏠 ⛳
Location Sannox (2m N on A841)
Hotel ★★★75% Auchrannie Country House Hotel,
BRODICK
☎ (0770) 302234 & 302235 28 ⇌ ↾

LAMLASH   Map 10 NS03

Lamlash ☎ (0770) 600296
Undulating heathland course with magnificent views of the
mountains and sea.
18 holes, 4611yds, Par 64, SSS 63, Course record 62.
Club membership 400.
Visitors no restrictions.
Societies must contact in writing.
Green Fees £10 per day (£12 weekends).
Facilities ⊗ ∭ ☕ ⅃▯ ⚲ 🏠 ⛳
Leisure caddy cars.
Location 0.75m N on A841
Hotel ★★68% Glenisle Hotel, LAMLASH
☎ (0770) 600559 & 600258 13 ⇌ ↾

LOCHRANZA   Map 10 NR95

Lochranza ☎ (0770) 830273
Level parkland course by the sea. River crosses four holes.
Nine large greens, 18 tees.
9 holes, 5569yds, Par 70, SSS 70, Course record 74.
Visitors no restrictions; course closed Oct-mid May.
Societies must telephone in advance.
Green Fees £8 for 18 holes; £5 for 9 holes.
Facilities ☕ ⚲ 🏠 ⛳
Leisure caravan site, trolleys for hire.
Hotel ★★63% The Lagg Hotel, Kilmory, BRODICK
☎ (0770) 870255 15 ⇌ ↾

MACHRIE   Map 10 NR83

Machrie Bay ☎ Brodick (0770) 850261
Fairly flat seaside course. Designed at turn of century by
William Fernie.
9 holes, 2143yds, Par 32.
Club membership 285.

▶

Visitors no restrictions.
Societies must contact in advance.
Green Fees £5 per day/round.
Facilities 🍺 (Apr-Sep) ⛳
Leisure hard tennis courts, fishing.
Location 9m W of Brodick via String Rd
Hotel ★★63% The Lagg Hotel, Kilmory, BRODICK
　　　　　☎ (0770) 870255 15 ⇄ 🐾

WHITING BAY   Map 10 NS02

Whiting Bay ☎ (0770) 700487
Heathland course.
18 holes, 4405yds, Par 63, SSS 63.
Club membership 290.
Visitors no restrictions.
Green Fees not confirmed.
Facilities ♀
Location NW side of village off A841
Hotel ★★63% The Lagg Hotel, Kilmory, BRODICK
　　　　　☎ (0770) 870255 15 ⇄ 🐾

BUTE, ISLE OF

KINGARTH   Map 10 NS05

Kingarth ☎ Kilchattan Bay (070083) 648
Flat seaside course with good fenced greens.
9 holes, 2497yds, Par 64, SSS 64, Course record 65.
Club membership 120.
Visitors restricted Sat until after 12.30pm.
Societies apply in advance.
Green Fees £6 per day.
Facilities ⛳
Location Kingarth, Rothesay (1m W off A844)
Hotel ★59% St Ebba Hotel, 37 Mountstuart Rd,
　　　　　Craigmore, ROTHESAY
　　　　　☎ (0700) 502683 11 ⇄ 🐾

PORT BANNATYNE   Map 10 NS06

Port Bannatyne ☎ (0700) 505223
Seaside hill course with panoramic views. Difficult hole: 4th
(par 3).
13 holes, 4503yds, Par 68, SSS 63, Course record 61.
Club membership 200.
Visitors no restrictions.
Societies must telephone in advance.
Green Fees £8 per day.
Facilities 🍴 🍺 ⛳
Location Bannatyne Mains Rd (W side of village off
　　　　　A844)
Hotel ★59% St Ebba Hotel, 37 Mountstuart Rd,
　　　　　Craigmore, ROTHESAY
　　　　　☎ (0700) 502683 11 ⇄ 🐾

ROTHESAY   Map 10 NS06

Rothesay ☎ (0700) 502244
A scenic island course designed by James Braid and Ben
Sayers. The course is fairly hilly, with views of the Firth of
Clyde, Rothesay Bay or the Kyles of Bute from every hole.
Winds are a regular feature which makes the two par 5 holes
extremely challenging.
18 holes, 5043yds, Par 69, SSS 65, Course record 62.
Club membership 350.
Visitors pre-booking essential for weekends, telephone
　　　　　professional.
Societies contact in advance, booking essential at weekends.
Green Fees £12 daily (£18 weekends).
Facilities ⊗ 🍴 🍔 🍺 ♀ ⛳ 🛍 🐾 ♟ James Dougal.
Leisure caddy cars.
Location Canada Hill (off road to Kingarth)
Hotel ★59% St Ebba Hotel, 37 Mountstuart Rd,
　　　　　Craigmore, ROTHESAY
　　　　　☎ (0700) 502683 11 ⇄ 🐾

COLONSAY, ISLE OF

SCALASAIG   Map 10 NR39

Colonsay ☎ Colonsay (09512) 316
Traditional links course on natural machair (hard wearing
short grass), challenging, primitive. Colonsay Hotel, 2 miles
away, is the headquarters of the club, offering
accommodation and facilities.
18 holes, 4775yds, Par 72, SSS 72.
Club membership 120.
Visitors no restrictions.
Societies apply in writing.
Green Fees not confirmed.
Facilities ♟
Location 2m W on A870
Hotel ★74% Colonsay Hotel, SCALASAIG
　　　　　☎ (09512) 316 10rm(1 ⇄ 7 🐾)Annexe1rm

ISLAY, ISLE OF

PORT ELLEN   Map 10 NR34

Machrie Hotel ☎ (0496) 302310
Championship links course opened in 1891, where golf's
first £100 Open Championship was played in 1901. Fine
turf and many blind holes. Par 4.
18 holes, 6226yds, Par 71, SSS 70, Course record 66.
Visitors must be member of a recognised golf club
　　　　　and have a handicap certificate.
Societies must contact in advance.

Green Fees not confirmed.
Facilities ⊗ ∭ 🛏 🍺 ♀ 🏠 ⚲ 🎣
Leisure fishing, riding, snooker, clay pigeon shooting.
Location Machrie (4m N off A846)
Hotel ★★58% Lochside Hotel, 19 Shore St, BOWMORE ☎ (0496) 810244 8 ⇥ ♞

Visitors no restrictions.
Societies must contact in advance.
Green Fees £10 per day/round; £35 per week.
Facilities ⚲
Location 0.5m N off A848
Hotel ★★★69% Western Isles Hotel, TOBERMORY ☎ (0688) 2012 27 ⇥ ♞

LEWIS, ISLE OF

STORNOWAY   Map 13 NB43

Stornoway ☎ (0851) 702240
Picturesque, tree-lined parkland course, fine views. The 11th hole, 'Dardanelles' - most difficult par 5.
18 holes, 5178yds, Par 68, SSS 66, Course record 62.
Club membership 450.
Visitors no golf on Sun.
Societies must telephone in advance.
Green Fees £10 per day.
Facilities 🛏 🍺 ♀ 🏖 🏠 ⚲
Leisure trolleys, pool table.
Location Lady Lever Park (N side of town centre off A857)
Hotel ★★★67% Caberfeidh Hotel, STORNOWAY ☎ (0851) 702604 46 ⇥ ♞

MULL, ISLE OF

CRAIGNURE   Map 10 NM73

Craignure ☎ (06802) 370
A flat links course, overlooking the sea.
9 holes, 2218mtrs, Par 64, SSS 64.
Club membership 70.
Visitors may not play on competition days.
Societies must contact in advance.
Green Fees £8 per day.
Facilities 🏖
Location Scallastle (1m N on A849)
Hotel ★★★69% Western Isles Hotel, TOBERMORY ☎ (0688) 2012 27 ⇥ ♞

TOBERMORY   Map 13 NM55

Tobermory ☎ (0688) 2020
A physically demanding, hilly seaside cliff-top course. No sand-bunkers, superb views over the Sound of Mull. Testing 3rd hole (par 3) and interesting 7th much affected by the winds.
9 holes, 4921yds, Par 64, SSS 64.
Club membership 100.

ORKNEY

KIRKWALL   Map 16 HY41

Orkney ☎ (0856) 872457
Open parkland course with few hazards and superb views over Kirkwall and Islands.
18 holes, 5411yds, Par 70, SSS 68, Course record 65.
Club membership 410.
Visitors may not play on competition days.
Societies advance contact preferred.
Green Fees £10 per day; £35 per week; £50 per fortnight.
Facilities 🛏 & 🍺 (lunchtime & evenings in summer) ♀ 🏖 🏠 ⚲
Location Grainbank (0.5m W off A965)
Hotel ★★65% Ayre Hotel, Ayre Rd, KIRKWALL ☎ (0856) 873001 34rm(30 ⇥ ♞)

STROMNESS   Map 16 HY20

Stromness ☎ (0856) 850772
Testing parkland/seaside course with easy walking. Beautiful holiday course with magnificent views of Scapa Flow.
18 holes, 4762yds, Par 65, SSS 64, Course record 61.
Club membership 250.
Visitors restricted 5-7pm.
Societies must contact in advance.
Green Fees £10 per day.
Facilities ♀ 🏖
Leisure hard tennis courts, bowls & putting.
Location S side of town centre off A965
Hotel ★★65% Ayre Hotel, Ayre Rd, KIRKWALL ☎ (0856) 873001 34rm(30 ⇥ ♞)

WESTRAY   Map 16 HY44

Westray ☎ (08577) 373
Interesting, picturesque seaside course, easy walking.
9 holes, 2405yds, Par 33.
Club membership 60.
Visitors No restrictions.
Green Fees £3 per day.
Facilities ⚲
Location 1m NW of Pierowall off B9066
Hotel ★★65% Ayre Hotel, Ayre Rd, KIRKWALL ☎ (0856) 873001 34rm(30 ⇥ ♞)

For an explanation of symbols and abbreviations, see page 5

SHETLAND

LERWICK   Map 16 HU44

Dale ☎ Gott (059584) 369
Challenging moorland course, hard walking. A burn runs the full length of the course and provides a natural hazard. Testing holes include the 3rd (par 4), 5th (par 4).
18 holes, 5776yds, Par 68, SSS 70, Course record 69.
Club membership 370.
Visitors   restricted on competition days.
Societies   must contact in advance.
Green Fees £8 per day.
Facilities   ⓑ ♀ ᐃ
Location   PO Box 18 (4m N on A970)
Hotel   ★★★60% Lerwick Hotel, 15 South Rd,
                  LERWICK ☎ (0595) 2166 34 ⇆ ⋔

WHALSAY, ISLAND OF   Map 16 HU56

Whalsay ☎ Symbister (08066) 481
The most northerly golf course in Britain, with a large part of it running round the coastline, offering spectacular holes in an exposed but highly scenic setting. There are no cut fairways as yet, these are defined by marker posts, with preferred lies in operation all year round.
18 holes, 6009yds, Par 70, SSS 70, Course record 65.
Club membership 112.
Visitors   are advised to telephone, and on arrival on
                  Whalsay call at the shop by the harbour.
Societies   must contact in advance.
Green Fees £5 per day; £20 per week.
Facilities   ᐃ
Location   Skaw Taing
Hotel   ★★★♨67% Busta House Hotel, BRAE
                  ☎ (080622) 506 20 ⇆ ⋔

SKYE, ISLE OF

SCONSER   Map 13 NG53

Isle of Skye ☎ (0478) 612341
Seaside course, often windy, splendid views.
9 holes, 4796yds, Par 66, SSS 63.
Club membership 210.
Visitors   welcome except Wed after 5pm & Sat 9.30-
                  10.30am.
Societies   welcome.
Green Fees £8 per round.
Facilities   ᐃ
Location   0.5m E of village on A850
Hotel   ★★70% Rosedale Hotel, PORTREE
                  ☎ (0478) 613131 20 ⇆ ⋔Annexe3 ⇆ ⋔

SOUTH UIST, ISLE OF

ASKERNISH   Map 13 NF72

Askernish ☎ No telephone
Golfers play on machair (hard-wearing short grass), close to the Atlantic shore.
9 holes, 5312yds, Par 68, SSS 67.
Club membership 20.
Visitors   no restrictions.
Societies   welcome.
Green Fees not confirmed.
Facilities   ⋔
Location   Lochboisdale (5m NW of Lochboisdale off
                  A865 via ferry)

WALES
Courses of history

GOLFERS who visit Wales will find exactly what they are looking for. If you are a low-handicap 'tiger' there are some of the most testing courses in the world and if you like things a bit easier there is a wide range of links, parkland and mountain courses, some set in quite incredible landscapes.

And there is a touch of the unexpected. For instance, at Pennard, west of Swansea on the Gower Peninsula, there is a castle and a disused church on the course. A service is held near the church ruin once a year, although it is visited by off-line players regularly during the week! Another off-beat aspect to the club are the wild ponies which roam over the course, necessitating fenced-off greens to keep them off the putting surfaces. A few years ago animal lovers were entertained at Southerndown – one of the principality's best courses – by a sheepdog

called Shep, who took it upon himself to keep the sheep off the greens. Curiously, although Shep is now gone, the sheep still stay clear of the greens!

For a bit of history there is Tenby, the oldest course in Wales, formed in 1888, which is within the Pembrokeshire Coast National Park. It is a source of merriment for the members of this championship links that the first president was Sir Charles Phillips, then the Minister for Lunacy!

Since Tenby set the ball rolling more than 120 courses have been built in Wales, including Royal Porthcawl, reckoned to be among the best you will find anywhere. Michael Bonallack, secretary of the Royal and Ancient, won the second of his five British Amateur Championships there in 1965 and there was a proud moment for Wales in 1980 when Duncan Evans became the first Welsh winner of the Amateur at

Porthcawl. The course, 22 miles west of Cardiff, has played host to dozens of men's and women's amateur and professional tournaments, including the 1961 Dunlop Masters. It is not over long at 6,691 yards, but with its cleverly placed bunkers is a stern test. You can see the Bristol Channel from every hole on the course.

Royal St David's, in the north, is another course that has held its share of major tournaments and internationals. Within the Snowdonia National Park, this links is overlooked by Harlech Castle, built by Edward I and classed as a World Heritage Listed Site. Overlooked by mountains, and with some of the holes running alongside Cardigan Bay, Royal St David's, an easy walking course with superb greens, is a delight to play.

In an area rich in golf there are four private courses on Anglesey, all close to the coast, at Rhosneigr, Bull Bay, Baron Hill and Holyhead, plus a nine-hole public course at Llangefni. And there is a gem in Criccieth, a hilly course on the Lleyn Peninsula close to Porthmadog. The course provides truly spectacular views of the bay. Further down the coast there is a tougher test, the beautiful championship links at Aberdovey at the mouth of the Dovey Estuary.

Moving across to the heart of Wales, almost in the centre, is the Llandrindod course at Llandrindod Wells, which opened with a flourish at the turn of the century with a match involving three Open Champions – Harry Vardon, James Braid and J H Taylor – and local professional George Humble.

And what about playing in two countries on the same course? This happens at Llanymynech at Pant, where the 4th, 5th and 6th holes sneak their way into England before the course returns to Wales. Ian Woosnam likes it – he holds the record of 65. One of Wales most celebrated courses, St Pierre, is also near the border – only two miles on the Welsh side of the Severn Bridge. It is the former home of both the Dunlop Masters and the Epson Grand Prix of Europe Match-play Championship. If you want to follow in the footsteps of Seve Ballesteros, Bernhard Langer and Ian Woosnam, who all won there, it's the place for you.

IAN RIACH
Golf correspondent, *Scottish Sunday Express*

WALES

CLWYD

ABERGELE
Map 06 SH97

Abergele & Pensarn ☎ (0745) 824034
A beautiful parkland course with views of the Irish Sea and
Gwrych Castle. There are splendid finishing holes, a testing
par 5, 16th; a 185 yd, 17th to an elevated green, and a superb
par 5 18th with out of bounds just behind the green.
18 holes, 6520yds, Par 72, SSS 71.
Club membership 1200.
Visitors restricted Tue.
Societies must contact in writing.
Green Fees £22 per day (£28 weekends & bank holidays).
Facilities ⊗ ⅷ ⅙ 🍺 (no catering Mon) ♀ ♨ 🏠
ℓ Iain R Runcie.
Leisure snooker, trolleys for hire, practice area.
Location Tan-y-Goppa Rd (0.5m W off A547/A55)
Hotel ★★64% Kinmel Manor Hotel, St Georges Rd,
ABERGELE ☎ (0745) 832014 42 ⇥ ⋒
Additional ★★★60% Colwyn Bay Hotel, Penmaenhead,
hotel COLWYN BAY ☎ (0492) 516555 43 ⇥ ⋒

★★★

THE COLWYN BAY HOTEL

Penmaenhead
Old Colwyn
Colwyn Bay
Clwyd LL29 9LD
Tel: 01492 516555
Fax: 01492 515565
Previously called Hotel 70°

Occupying an enviable position commanding panoramic
views of the Irish Sea, Colwyn Bay and the dramatic
mountains of Snowdonia from all rooms.
This splendid modern Hotel offers a very high standard of
comfort, service and luxury through-out. All bedrooms en
suite with full facilities and sea views.
Elegant restaurant serving excellent cuisine in superb
surroundings.
Ideally located for touring Snowdonia National Park and
Conwy. Numerous golf courses nearby for the discerning
golf enthusiast.
Excellent conference and banqueting facilities available
for up to 200 persons.

BRYNFORD
Map 07 SJ17

Holywell ☎ Holywell (0352) 710040 & 713937
Exposed moorland course, with bracken and gorse flanking
undulating fairways. 720 ft above sea level.
18 holes, 6025yds, Par 70, SSS 69, Course record 70.
Club membership 500.
Visitors may not play weekends and competition times.
Societies must have handicap certificates, telephone in
advance.
Green Fees £12 per day (£18 weekends & bank holidays).
Facilities ⊗ (ex Mon) ⅷ ⅙ 🍺 ♀ ♨ 🏠 ℓ Martin Carty.
Leisure snooker.
Location Brynford (1.25m SW off B5121)
Hotel ★★65% Stamford Gate Hotel, Halkyn Rd,
HOLYWELL
☎ (0352) 712942 & 712968 12 ⇥ ⋒

CHIRK
Map 07 SJ23

Chirk Golf & Country Club ☎ (0691) 774407
Overlooked by the National Trust's Chirk Castle, is a
championship-standard 18-hole course with a 664 yard, par 5
at the 9th - one of the longest in Europe. Also a 9-hole course,
driving range and golf academy.
Canal Course: 18 holes, 6956yds, Par 72, SSS 74.
Mine Rock: 9 holes, 1141yds, Par 27.
Club membership 475.
Visitors advisable to contact in advance. Some times
restricted to members.
Societies must telephone for provisional booking.
Green Fees 18 holes: £22 per day; £15 per round (£28/£19
weekends). 9 holes: £4 per round (£5 weekends).
Facilities ⊗ ⅷ ⅙ 🍺 ♀ ♨ 🏠 🥕 🏌 ℓ James Waugh.
Leisure fishing, riding, snooker, trolleys and buggies for
hire.
Location 5m N of Oswestry
Hotel ★★★63% Bryn Howel Hotel & Restaurant,
LLANGOLLEN
☎ (0978) 860331 38 ⇥ ⋒

COLWYN BAY
Map 06 SH87

Old Colwyn ☎ (0492) 515581
Hilly, meadowland course with sheep and cattle grazing on it
in parts.
9 holes, 5000yds, Par 68, SSS 66.
Club membership 300.
Visitors no restrictions.
Societies must contact in advance.
Green Fees not confirmed.
Facilities ⊗ ⅷ ⅙ 🍺 ♀ (weekends) ♨
Location Woodland Av, Old Colwyn (E side of town
centre on B5383)
Hotel ★★69% Hopeside Hotel, Princes Dr, West End,
COLWYN BAY ☎ (0492) 533244 19 ⇥ ⋒
See advertisement on page 294

> A golf course name printed in ***bold
> italics*** means we have been unable to
> verify information with the club's
> management for the current year

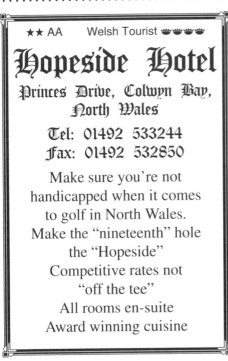

★★ AA   Welsh Tourist 🏴🏴🏴🏴

Hopeside Hotel
Princes Drive, Colwyn Bay, North Wales

Tel: 01492 533244
Fax: 01492 532850

Make sure you're not handicapped when it comes to golf in North Wales. Make the "nineteenth" hole the "Hopeside" Competitive rates not "off the tee"
All rooms en-suite
Award winning cuisine

DENBIGH   Map 06 SJ06

Bryn Morfydd Hotel ☎ (0745) 78280
In a beautiful setting in the Vale of Clwyd, the original 9-hole Duchess course was designed by Peter Alliss in 1982. In 1992, the 18-hole Dukes course was completed: a parkland course designed to encourage use of finesse in play.
Dukes: 18 holes, 5650yds, Par 71, SSS 68, Course record 69.
Duchess: 9 holes, Par 27.
Club membership 350.
Visitors   advance reservation advisable.
Societies   apply in writing for society rates.
Green Fees £10 Dukes; £4 Duchess per 18 holes (£5 weekends and bank holidays).
Facilities   ⊗ ⅢⓁ 🍷 ♀ ⚙ 🏨 ⛳ 🏹
Leisure   outdoor swimming pool, electric trolley hire.
Location   Llanrhaedr (on A525 between Denbigh and Ruthin)
Hotel   ★★★62% Oriel House Hotel, Upper Denbigh Rd, ST ASAPH ☎ (0745) 582716 19 ⇥ ⋒

Denbigh ☎ (0745) 814159
Parkland course, giving a testing and varied game. Good views.
18 holes, 5581yds, Par 68, SSS 67.
Club membership 750.
Visitors   may not play before 9.30am weekdays or 10.30am weekends.
Societies   must telephone in advance.
Green Fees not confirmed.
Facilities   ⚙ 🏨 ⛳ 🏹 ⌂

Leisure   snooker.
Location   Henllan Rd (1.5m NW on B5382)
Hotel   ★★★65% Talardy Park Hotel, The Roe, ST ASAPH ☎ (0745) 584957 18 ⇥ ⋒

EYTON   Map 07 SJ34

Plassey ☎ (0978) 780020
A 10-hole course currently being extended to 18 holes (for 1995). The course is naturally contoured parkland with water hazards. It is within a caravan park and all park facilities are available to golfers.
10 holes, 2812yds, Par 36, SSS 37, Course record 38.
Club membership 200.
Societies   telephone then confirm in writing.
Green Fees £4 per 10 holes (£5 weekends & bank holidays).
Facilities   ⊗ Ⅲ Ⓛ 🍷 ♀ ⚙ 🏨 ⛳
Leisure   heated indoor swimming pool, fishing, solarium.
Location   2.5m off A483 Chester/Oswestry
Hotel   ★★65% Cross Lanes Hotel & Restaurant, Cross Lanes, Bangor Rd, MARCHWIEL ☎ (0978) 780555 18 ⇥ ⋒

FLINT   Map 07 SJ27

Flint ☎ (0352) 732327
Parkland course incorporating woods and streams. Excellent views of Dee estuary.
9 holes, 5953yds, Par 69, SSS 69, Course record 65.
Club membership 330.
Visitors   with member only at weekends.
Societies   apply in advance.
Green Fees £12 per day.
Facilities   ⊗ Ⅲ Ⓛ 🍷 (catering by arrangement) ♀ ⚙
Leisure   hard tennis courts, snooker.
Location   Cornist Park (1m W)
Hotel   ★★★64% New Chequers Country House Hotel, Chester Rd, NORTHOP HALL ☎ (0244) 816181 27 ⇥ ⋒

HAWARDEN   Map 07 SJ36

Hawarden ☎ (0244) 531447
Parkland course with comfortable walking and good views.
18 holes, 5564yds, Par 68, SSS 67.
Club membership 650.
Visitors   with member or by appointment. Must contact in advance and have a handicap certificate.
Societies   apply in writing.
Green Fees £26 per day; £20 per round.
Facilities   ⊗ Ⅲ Ⓛ 🍷 ♀ ⚙ 🏨 ⋒
Location   Groomsdale Ln (W side of town off B5125)
Hotel   ★★★64% New Chequers Country House Hotel, Chester Rd, NORTHOP HALL ☎ (0244) 816181 27 ⇥ ⋒

LLANGOLLEN   Map 07 SJ24

Vale of Llangollen ☎ (0978) 860906
Parkland course, set in superb scenery by the River Dee.
18 holes, 6661yds, Par 72, SSS 72.
Club membership 660.
Visitors   must contact in advance. Restricted club competition days.

Societies apply in writing.
Green Fees on request.
Facilities ⊗ ⊞ ⅃ ▥ ♀ ⅍ ⌂ ⊓ℓ D I Vaughan.
Location Holyhead Rd (1.5m E on A5)
Hotel ★★★63% Bryn Howel Hotel & Restaurant, LLANGOLLEN ☎ (0978) 860331 38 ⇥ ♜

MOLD

Map 07 SJ26

Old Padeswood ☎ Buckley (0244) 547401
Meadowland course, undulating in parts.
18 holes, 6639yds, Par 72, SSS 72.
Club membership 600.
Visitors welcome, subject to tee availability.
Societies must contact in advance.
Green Fees £16 per round (£20 weekends).
Facilities ⊗ & ⊞ by prior arrangement ▥ ▥ ♀ ⅍ ⌂ ⊓ℓ Tony Davies.
Leisure fishing, riding, par 3, caddy cars.
Location Station Rd, Padeswood (3m SE off A5118)
Hotel ★★64% Bryn Awel Hotel, Denbigh Rd, MOLD ☎ (0352) 758622 7 ⇥ ♜Annexe10 ⇥ ♜

Padeswood & Buckley ☎ (0244) 550537
Gently undulating parkland course, with natural hazards and good views of the Welsh Hills.
18 holes, 5823yds, Par 68, SSS 68, Course record 66.
Club membership 600.
Visitors Sat & Sun by arrangement.
Societies must contact in advance.
Green Fees £20 (£25 weekends & bank holidays).
Facilities ⊗ ⊞ ⅃ ▥ ♀ ⅍ ⌂ ⊓ℓ David Ashton.
Leisure snooker, caddy cars, buggies.
Location The Caia, Station Ln (3m SE off A5118)
Hotel ★★64% Bryn Awel Hotel, Denbigh Rd, MOLD ☎ (0352) 758622 7 ⇥ ♜Annexe10 ⇥ ♜

NORTHOP

Map 07 SJ26

Northop Country Park ☎ (0352) 840440
Designed by former British Ryder Cup captain, John Jacobs, the parkland course gives the impression of having been established for many years. No two holes are the same and designed to allow all year play.
18 holes, 6750yds, Par 72, SSS 72.
Club membership 500.
Visitors advisable to prebook.
Societies apply in writing or by telephone.
Green Fees £25 per round (£35 weekends & bank holidays).
Facilities ⊗ (Sun or by arrangement) ⊞ (ex Sun) ▥ ▥ ♀ ⅍ ⌂ℓ David Llewllyn.
Leisure hard tennis courts, snooker, sauna, solarium, gymnasium.
Location 150 yds from Connahs Quay turnoff on A55
Hotel ★★★★69% St Davids Park Hotel, St Davids Park, EWLOE ☎ (0244) 520800 121 ⇥ ♜
See Inside Back Cover

PANTYMWYN

Map 07 SJ16

Mold ☎ (0352) 740318 & 741513
Meadowland course with some hard walking and natural hazards. Fine views.
18 holes, 5548yds, Par 67, SSS 67, Course record 63.
Club membership 600.

Visitors may not play on captains day, or when county matches are held.
Societies apply in writing.
Green Fees £16 per day (£21 per day/£18 per round weekends and bank holidays).
Facilities ⊗ ⊞ by prior arrangement ▥ ▥ ♀ ⅍ ⌂ ⊓ℓ Martin Carty.
Location E side of village
Hotel ★★64% Bryn Awel Hotel, Denbigh Rd, MOLD ☎ (0352) 758622 7 ⇥ ♜Annexe10 ⇥ ♜

PRESTATYN

Map 06 SJ08

Prestatyn ☎ (0745) 854320
Very flat seaside links exposed to stiff breeze. Testing holes: 9th, par 4, bounded on 3 sides by water; 10th, par 4; 16th, par 4.
18 holes, 6808yds, Par 72, SSS 73.
Club membership 650.
Visitors welcome except Sat & Tue mornings. Must contact in advance & have handicap certificate.
Societies must contact in advance.
Green Fees £18 per day (£25 weekends & bank holidays).
Facilities ⊗ ⊞ ⅃ ▥ ♀ ⅍ ⌂ ⊓ℓ Malcolm Staton.
Leisure snooker.
Location Marine Rd East (0.5m N off A548)
Hotel ★★★65% Graig Park Hotel & Country Club, DYSERTH ☎ (0745) 571022 12 ⇥ ♜

St Melyd ☎ (0745) 854405
Parkland course with good views of mountains and Irish Sea. Testing 1st hole (423 yds) par 4. 18 tees.
9 holes, 5829yds, Par 68, SSS 68, Course record 65.
Club membership 400.
Visitors must contact in advance.
Societies must telephone in advance.
Green Fees £15 per day (£19 weekends).
Facilities ⊗ ⊞ ⅃ ▥ ♀ ⅍ ⌂ℓ Richard Bladbury.
Leisure snooker.
Location The Paddock, Meliden Rd (0.5m S on A547)
Hotel ★★★65% Graig Park Hotel & Country Club, DYSERTH ☎ (0745) 571022 12 ⇥ ♜

RHUDDLAN

Map 06 SJ07

Rhuddlan ☎ (0745) 590217
Attractive, gently undulating parkland course with good views. Well bunkered with trees and water hazards. The 476 yard 8th and 431 yard 11th require both length and accuracy. The clubhouse has been refurbished.
18 holes, 6482yds, Par 71, SSS 71.
Club membership 953.
Visitors must contact in advance & have handicap certificate. Sun with member only.
Societies must contact in advance.
Green Fees £20 per day (£25 per round Sat & bank holidays).
Facilities ⊗ ⊞ ⅃ ▥ ♀ ⅍ ⌂ ⊓ℓ Ian Worsley.
Leisure snooker, practice ground.
Location Meliden Rd (E side of town on A547)
Hotel ★★★62% Oriel House Hotel, Upper Denbigh Rd, ST ASAPH ☎ (0745) 582716 19 ⇥ ♜

RHYL

Map 06 SJ08

Rhyl ☎ (0745) 353171
Seaside course.
9 holes, 3109yds, Par 35, SSS 35.
Club membership 350.
Visitors restricted Sun in summer. Must contact in advance.
Societies must contact in advance.
Green Fees £12 day/round (£15 weekends & bank holidays).
Facilities ⊗ ⑂ (ex Mon) ⓑ ♥ ♀ ⚘ ☎ ⫟
Leisure snooker.
Location Coast Rd (1m E on A548)
Hotel ★★61% Hotel Marina, Marine Dr, RHYL
☎ (0745) 342371 26rm(20 ⇆2 ⚑)

RUABON

Map 07 SJ34

Pen-y-cae ☎ (0978) 821195
An architecturally designed and built 9-hole course with an opening hole from an elevated tee wooded to one side and backed by trees and a river. The 2nd at 262 yards crosses water twice as the river meanders down the fairway. Th 5th is very narrow being wooded on either side and with a slight dogleg. The 6th also a par 3, needs a high shot to clear the mature birch in the path.
9 holes, 2008yds, Par 32, SSS 31, Course record 30.
Club membership 200.
Visitors no restrictions.
Societies telephone or write in advance.
Green Fees £7 per 18 holes; £4.50 per 9 holes (£9/£5.50 weekends).
Facilities ⊗ & ⑂ (most days) ⓑ ☎ ⫟ ⚑ Nick Rothe.
Location Ruabon Rd, Pen-y-cae (1m off A5)
Hotel ★★57% Wynnstay Arms, High St, RUABON
☎ (0978) 822187 9rm(6 ⇆)

RUTHIN

Map 06 SJ15

Ruthin-Pwllglas ☎ (0824) 703427
Hilly parkland course in elevated position with panoramic views. Stiff climb to 3rd and 9th holes.
10 holes, 5362yds, Par 66, SSS 66.
Club membership 380.
Visitors welcome except for competition days.
Societies apply in writing.
Green Fees not confirmed.
Facilities ⊗ & ⑂ by prior arrangement ♀ ⚘
Location Pwllglas (2.5m S off A494)
Hotel ★★★63% Ruthin Castle, RUTHIN
☎ (0824) 702664 58 ⇆ ⚑

WREXHAM

Map 07 SJ35

Wrexham ☎ (0978) 261033
Inland, sandy course with easy walking. Testing dog-legged 7th hole (par 4), and short 14th hole (par 3) with full carry to green.
18 holes, 6078yds, Par 70, SSS 69.
Club membership 650.
Visitors may not play competition days, and are advised to contact in advance.
Societies welcome except for Tue, Wed & weekends.
Green Fees on application.

Facilities ⊗ ⑂ ⓑ ♥ ♀ ⚘ ☎ ⫟ ⚑ David Larvin.
Leisure snooker.
Location Holt Rd (1.75m NE on A534)
Hotel ★★★64% Wynnstay Arms, High Street/Yorke St, WREXHAM ☎ (0978) 291010 76 ⇆ ⚑

DYFED

ABERYSTWYTH

Map 06 SN58

Aberystwyth ☎ (0970) 615104
Undulating meadowland course. Testing holes: 16th (The Loop) par 3; 17th, par 4; 18th, par 3. Good views over Cardigan Bay.
18 holes, 6150yds, Par 70, SSS 70, Course record 68.
Club membership 400.
Visitors must contact in advance at weekends & bank holidays.
Societies must contact in advance.
Green Fees Apr-Sep: £18 per day; £15 per round (£20/£18 weekends). Oct-Mar: £12 per day (£15 weekends).
Facilities ⊗ ⑂ ⓑ ♥ ♀ ⚘ ☎ ⫟ ⚑ Kevin Bayliss.
Location Brynymor Rd (N side of town)
Hotel ★★67% Belle Vue Royal Hotel, Marine Ter, ABERYSTWYTH
☎ (0970) 617558 37rm(32 ⇆ ⚑)

AMMANFORD

Map 03 SN61

Glynhir ☎ Llandybie (0269) 850472
Parkland course with good views, latter holes close to Upper Loughor River. The 14th is a 394-yd dog leg.
18 holes, 6090yds, Par 69, SSS 69, Course record 66.
Club membership 700.
Visitors with member only weekends. No visitors Sun. Must contact in advance and have a handicap certificate.
Societies welcome weekdays only. Must apply in writing.
Green Fees £15 per day ; £8 winter (£20/£10 weekends & bank holidays).
Facilities ⊗ (Tue-Fri) ⑂ (Sat & Sun) ⓑ ♥ ♀ ⚘ ☎ ⫟ ⚑ Ian Roberts.
Location Glynhir Rd, Llandybie (2m N of Ammanford)
Hotel ★★67% Mill at Glynhir, Glyn-Hir, Llandybie, AMMANFORD ☎ (0269) 850672 11 ⇆ ⚑

BORTH

Map 06 SN69

Borth & Ynyslas ☎ (0970) 871202
Seaside links, over 100 years old, with strong winds at times. Some narrow fairways.
18 holes, 6116yds, Par 69, SSS 70, Course record 65.
Club membership 500.
Visitors may not play before 10.30am or between 1.30-2.30pm at weekends.
Societies must contact in advance.
Green Fees £16 (£22 weekends & bank holidays and in Aug).

Facilities ⊗ & ⅷ by prior arrangement ⓛ (weekends) ☕ 🍴⌗🏠🍴 J G Lewis.
Leisure caddy cars, practice area.
Location 0.5m N on B4353
Hotel ★★65% Four Seasons Hotel, 50-54 Portland St, ABERYSTWYTH
☎ (0970) 612120 14rm(13 ⇥ 🕭)

BURRY PORT   Map 02 SN40

Ashburnham ☎ (0554) 833846
This course has a lot of variety. In the main it is of the seaside type although the holes in front of the clubhouse are of an inland character. They are, however, good holes which make a very interesting finish. Course record holder, Sam Torrance.
18 holes, 6916yds, Par 72, SSS 73, Course record 67.
Club membership 750.
Visitors special times available. Must contact in advance and have an introduction from own club.
Societies apply in writing.
Green Fees not confirmed.
Facilities ⊗ⅷⓛ☕🍴⌗🏠🍴 Robert Ryder.
Leisure pool table.
Location Cliffe Ter (W side of town on B4311)
Hotel ★★★60% Diplomat Hotel, Felinfoel, LLANELLI
☎ (0554) 756156 23 ⇥ 🕭Annexe8 ⇥ 🕭

Cliff Hotel
GWBERT, CARDIGAN, WEST WALES
TEL: CARDIGAN (01239) 613241

AA ★★★ Hotel in breathtaking position on cliffs overlooking Cardigan Bay. Outdoor pool, Squash, Gym, Snooker, Sauna. FREE Golf on hotel's own 9-hole course. Cardigan Golf Course (18 holes) only ½ mile away. Bargain breaks available. Also self-catering in Gate House.

CARDIGAN   Map 02 SN14

Cardigan ☎ (0239) 612035
A links course, very dry in winter, with wide fairways, light rough and gorse. Every hole overlooks the sea.
18 holes, 6641yds, Par 72, SSS 72.
Club membership 500.
Visitors may not play between 1-2pm. Must have a handicap certificate.
Societies must telephone in advance.
Green Fees £15 per day (£20 weekends and bank holidays).
Facilities ⊗ⅷⓛ☕🍴⌗🏠🍴
Leisure squash.
Location Gwbert-on-Sea (3m N off B4548)
Hotel ★★★56% Cliff Hotel, GWBERT
☎ (0239) 613241 75 ⇥ 🕭

CARMARTHEN   Map 02 SN42

Carmarthen ☎ (0267) 281588
Hilltop course with good views.
18 holes, 6210yds, Par 71, SSS 71, Course record 68.
Club membership 700.
Visitors no restrictions.
Societies must contact in advance.
Green Fees £18 (£25 weekends & bank holidays). Reduction in winter.
Facilities ⊗ & ⅷ (ex Wed) ⓛ☕🍴⌗🏠🍴 Pat Gillis.
Location Blaenycoed Rd (4m NW)
Hotel ★★★62% The Ivy Bush Royal, Spilman St, CARMARTHEN ☎ (0267) 235111 75 ⇥ 🕭

GWBERT-ON-SEA   Map 02 SN15

Cliff Hotel ☎ (0239) 613241
This is a short course with 2 Par 4's and the remainder are challenging Par 3's. Particularly interesting holes are played across the sea on to a small island.
9 holes, 1545yds, Par 29, SSS 29, Course record 29.
Club membership 80.
Visitors no restrictions.
Societies telephone in advance.
Green Fees £5.50 per day (£6.50 weekends).
Facilities ⊗ⅷⓛ☕🍴⌗🍴🏌
Leisure heated outdoor swimming pool, squash, snooker, sauna, solarium, gymnasium, caddy car.
Hotel ★★★56% Cliff Hotel, GWBERT
☎ (0239) 613241 75 ⇥ 🕭

HAVERFORDWEST   Map 02 SM91

Haverfordwest ☎ (0437) 764523
Parkland course in attractive surroundings.
18 holes, 6005yds, Par 70, SSS 69, Course record 68.
Club membership 720.
Visitors restricted Wed & Thu.
Societies must telephone in advance & confirm in writing.
Green Fees £15 per day (£20 weekends).
Facilities ⊗ⅷⓛ☕🍴⌗🏠🍴 Alex Pile.
Leisure caddy cars.
Location Arnolds Down (1m E on A40)
Hotel ★★64% Hotel Mariners, Mariners Square, HAVERFORDWEST
☎ (0437) 763353 30 ⇥ 🕭

KIDWELLY — Map 02 SN40

Pontnewydd Golf Centre ☎ (0554) 810278
In the Gwendraeth valley, a new 18-hole parkland course with greens well protected by the planting of 35,000 trees. There is a covered practice area and 9-hole course under construction.
18 holes, 6173yds, Par 70, SSS 69, Course record 68.
Club membership 300.

Visitors advisable to book for weekends.
Societies must contact in advance.
Green Fees £11.25 per round (£13 weekends & bank holidays).
Facilities ⊗ � 🏔 🍴 ♀ 🛄 📷 🛜 ⚑ Ian Roberts.
Leisure covered practice area.
Location Trimsaran (4.5m E, off B4317)
Hotel ★★★62% The Ivy Bush Royal, Spilman St, CARMARTHEN ☎ (0267) 235111 75 ⇆ 🐾

LLANGYBI — Map 02 SN65

Cilgwyn ☎ (057045) 286
Picturesque parkland course in secluded valley, with natural hazards of ponds, stream and woodland.
9 holes, 5309yds, Par 68, SSS 67, Course record 67.
Club membership 260.

Visitors no restrictions.
Societies must telephone in advance and confirm in writing.
Green Fees £15 per day ; £10 per round (£22/£15 weekends & bank holidays).
Facilities ⊗ � 🏔 🍴 ♀ 🛄 📷 🛜
Leisure pool table.
Location 0.5m NW off A485
Hotel ★★★★67% Falcondale Country House Hotel, LAMPETER ☎ (0570) 422910 19 ⇆ 🐾

LLANRHYSTUD — Map 06 SN56

Penrhos Golf & Country Club ☎ Llanon (0974) 202999
Beautifully scenic course incorporating five lakes and spectacular coastal and inland views. Many leisure facilities.
18 holes, 6641yds, Par 72, SSS 72, Course record 75.
Club membership 300.

Visitors must contact in advance and should have a handicap certificate.
Societies must contact in advance.
Green Fees £20 per day; £15 per round (£25/£18 weekends & bank holidays).
Facilities ⊗ � by prior arrangement (Wed, Fri & Sat) 🏔 🍴 ♀ 🛄 📷 🛜 ⚑ Paul Diamond.
Leisure hard tennis courts, heated indoor swimming pool, fishing, sauna, solarium, gymnasium, bowls, shooting, buggies, trolleys.
Location 0.5m SE on B4337
Hotel ★★★★66% Conrah Hotel, Ffosrhydygaled, Chancery, ABERYSTWYTH ☎ (0970) 617941 11 ⇆ 🐾Annexe9 ⇆ 🐾

LLANSTEFFAN — Map 02 SN31

Llansteffan ☎ (026783) 526
A Pay and Play downland course with superb views of the sea and Gower Coast. Quite challenging in a sea breeze!
9 holes, 2165yds, Par 30, Course record 33.

Visitors no restrictions.
Societies contact in advance for bank holidays.
Green Fees £3 per 9 holes.
Facilities catering facilities under construction. 📷 🛜
Location S of Carmarthen off B4312
Hotel ★★66% Forge Restaurant & Motel, ST CLEARS ☎ (0994) 230300 Annexe18 ⇆ 🐾

MILFORD HAVEN — Map 02 SM90

Milford Haven ☎ (0646) 692368
Parkland course with excellent greens and views of the Milford Haven waterway.
18 holes, 6030yds, Par 71, SSS 70.
Club membership 450.

Visitors no restrictions, advisable to contact in advance.
Societies telephone to book.
Green Fees not confirmed.
Facilities ⊗ & � by prior arrangement (ex Tue) 🏔 🍴 ♀ 🛄 📷 🛜 ⚑ Stephen Laidler.
Location Woodbine House, Hubberston (1.5m W)
Hotel ★★63% Lord Nelson Hotel, Hamilton Ter, MILFORD HAVEN ☎ (0646) 695341 32 ⇆ 🐾

NEWPORT — Map 02 SN03

Newport (Pemb) ☎ (0239) 820244
Seaside links course, with easy walking and good view of the Preselli Hills and Newport Bay.
9 holes, 5815yds, Par 70, SSS 69.
Club membership 220.

Visitors no restrictions.
Societies must telephone in advance.
Green Fees not confirmed.
Facilities ⊗ � 🏔 🍴 ♀ 🛄 📷 🛜 ⚑ 🍽 ⚑ Colin Parsons.
Leisure buggies.
Location The Golf Club (1.25m N)
Hotel ★★63% Trewern Arms, NEVERN ☎ (0239) 820395 9 ⇆ 🐾

PEMBROKE DOCK — Map 02 SM90

South Pembrokeshire ☎ (0646) 683817
Parkland course overlooking the Cleddau River.
9 holes, 5804yds, Par 70, SSS 69.
Club membership 350.

Visitors must contact in advance, restricted weekends & club competitions.
Societies apply in writing.
Green Fees not confirmed.
Facilities 🏔 🍴 ♀ 🛄
Leisure snooker.
Location Defensible Barracks (SW side of town centre off B4322)
Hotel ★★59% Old Kings Arms, Main St, PEMBROKE ☎ (0646) 683611 21 ⇆ 🐾

ST DAVID'S — Map 02 SM72

St David's City ☎ (0437) 720312
Links course with alternative tees for 18 holes. Panoramic views of St David's Head and Ramsey Island.
9 holes, 5961yds, Par 70, SSS 70, Course record 67.
Club membership 200.

PENALLY ABBEY ★★★ ◉
Penally, Tenby, Dyfed SA70 7PY
Telephone: (01834) 843033 Fax: (01834) 844714

Penally Abbey, one of Pembrokeshire's loveliest country houses, is an 11 bedroom, gothic style, stone built mansion. Situated in an elevated position, adjacent to the church, on the village green in the picturesque floral village of Penally, 2 miles from Tenby.

Visitors	welcome. No sharing of golf bags.
Societies	must telephone in advance.
Green Fees	not confirmed.
Facilities	⌂
Location	Whitesands Bay (2m W overlooking Whitesands Bay)
Hotel	★★★65% Warpool Court Hotel, ST DAVID'S ☎ (0437) 720300 25 ⇌ ◖

TENBY   Map 02 SN10

Tenby ☎ (0834) 842978
The oldest club in Wales,this fine old seaside links, with sea views and natural hazards provides good golf.
18 holes, 6232yds, Par 69, SSS 71.
Club membership 650.

Visitors	subject to competition & tee reservation. Must produce handicap certificate.
Societies	must telephone in advance.
Green Fees	£18 per day (£22.50 weekends & bank holidays).
Facilities	♀⌂◖◖
Leisure	snooker.
Location	The Burrows
Hotel	★★★67% Atlantic Hotel, Esplanade, TENBY ☎ (0834) 842881 & 844176 40 ⇌ ◖
Additional hotel	★★80% Penally Abbey Country House, Penally, TENBY ☎ (0834) 843033 8 ⇌ ◖Annexe4 ⇌

GWENT

ABERGAVENNY   Map 03 SO21

Monmouthshire ☎ (0873) 853171 & 852532
This parkland course is very picturesque, with the beautifully wooded River Usk running alongside. There are a number of par 3 holes and a testing par 4 at the 15th.
18 holes, 5961yds, Par 72, SSS 70.
Club membership 700.

Visitors	must play with member at weekends. Must contact in advance & have handicap certificate.
Societies	must contact in writing.
Green Fees	£21 per day (£26 weekends & bank holidays).

Facilities	⊗ (ex Tue) 🍽 by prior arrangement ▤ (ex Tue) ■♀⌂◖◖◖ Philip Worthing.
Leisure	fishing.
Location	Gypsy Ln, LLanfoist (2m S off B4269)
Hotel	★★70% Llanwenarth Arms Hotel, Brecon Rd, ABERGAVENNY ☎ (0873) 810550 18 ⇌ ◖

Wernddu Golf Centre ☎ (0873) 856223
A 9-hole course with a total 18-hole playing length of 3,850 yards. 9th hole, Par 3 has a green protected by two ponds. There is also a 26-bay flooodlit driving range and a practice putting green.
9 holes, 2002yds, Par 32, SSS 30.
Club membership 70.

Visitors	correct golf attire must be worn.
Societies	apply in advance in writing.
Green Fees	£10 per 18 holes; £6 per 9 holes.
Facilities	⊗ 🍽 ▤ ■♀⌂◖◖◖ A A Ashmead.
Leisure	pitch & putt, driving range.
Location	1.5m NE on B4521 off A465
Hotel	★★70% Llanwenarth Arms Hotel, Brecon Rd, ABERGAVENNY ☎ (0873) 810550 18 ⇌ ◖

BETTWS NEWYDD   Map 03 SO30

Alice Springs ☎Nantyderry (0873) 880772 & 880708
Two 18-hole undulating parkland courses set back to back with magnificent views of the Usk Valley. The Queen's course has testing 7th and 15th holes. The King's Course which opened in summer 1992, is 6662yds long.
Queens: 18 holes, 6041yds, Par 67, SSS 69.
Kings: 18 holes, 6662yds, Par 72, SSS 71.
Club membership 350.

Visitors	should contact the club in advance for weekend play.
Societies	must telephone in advance.
Green Fees	not confirmed.
Facilities	⊗ 🍽 ▤ ■♀⌂◖ Jim Howard.
Hotel	★★★63% Glen-yr-Afon House Hotel, Pontypool Rd, USK ☎ (0291) 672302 & 673202 27rm(26 ⇌ ◖)

BLACKWOOD   Map 03 ST19

Blackwood ☎ (0495) 223152
Heathland course with sand bunkers. Undulating, with hard walking. Testing 2nd hole par 4. Good views.
9 holes, 5304yds, Par 66, SSS 66, Course record 64.
Club membership 250.   ▶

Visitors	must contact in advance & have handicap certificate. Must play with member at weekends & bank holidays.
Societies	may not play weekends & bank holidays.
Green Fees	£12 per day (£15 weekends & bank holidays).
Facilities	⌣
Location	Cwmgelli (0.75m N off A4048)
Hotel	★★★53% Maes Manor Hotel, BLACKWOOD ☎ (0495) 224551 & 220011 8 ⇄Annexe14 ⇄

CAERWENT   Map 03 ST49

Dewstow ☎ Caldicot (0291) 430444

A newly-established, picturesque parkland course with spectacular views over the Severn estuary towards Bristol. Testing holes include the Par three 7th, which is approached over water, some 50 feet lower than the tee. There is also a 26-bay floodlit driving range.

18 holes, 6100yds, Par 72, SSS 70, Course record 74.
Club membership 500.

Visitors	may book two days in advance.
Societies	apply in writing or telephone secretary.
Green Fees	not confirmed.
Facilities	⊗ ⑂ ㋡ ▬ ♀ ⌂ ☎ ℹ Mark Kedward.
Leisure	floodlit golf range.
Location	0.5m S of A48 at Caerwent
Hotel	★★★69% St Pierre Hotel, Golf & Country Club, St Pierre Park, CHEPSTOW ☎ (0291) 625261 104 ⇄ ℹ Annexe42 ⇄ ℹ

CHEPSTOW   Map 03 ST59

St Pierre Hotel Golf and Country Club
☎ (0291) 625261

Parkland/meadowland championship course.There are two golf courses, the Old and the Mathern. The Old is home to the Epson Grand Prix of Europe, and is one of Britain's major courses. Its long par 5, 12th hole of 545 yds, tests even the finest golfers. St Pierre, with its delightful 14th-century mansion was discovered over 30 years ago by retired businessman Bill Graham. He said 'I saw this deer park almost by accident. I liked the mature trees and the atmosphere of the place - so I bought it!' With Ken Cotton and golf coach Bill Cox, they transformed the mansion into a club house and the park into two golf courses that became famous and staged professional tournaments within a very short time. Today the courses attract many visitors. The club professional Renton Doig and his staff can tell stories of many well-known stars doing well, and of one Arwyn Griffiths who arrived on the 18th tee needing a par 3 for an amazing round of 63. This hole must be played over water and, unhappily for Mr Griffiths, he took an 11. Although shattered at failing to establish a record he still won the competition and was able to celebrate at the excellent 19th hole.

Old Course: 18 holes, 6700yds, Par 71, SSS 73.
Mathern Course: 18 holes, 5762yds, Par 68, SSS 68.
Club membership 900.

Visitors	must contact in advance & have handicap certificate.
Societies	must make an advance reservation.
Green Fees	not confirmed.
Facilities	⊗ ⑂ ㋡ ▬ ♀ ⌂ ☎ ℹ ⊨ ℹ Renton Doig.

★★★

ST PIERRE HOTEL,

GOLF & COUNTRY CLUB

St Pierre Park Chepstow Gwent NY6 6YA

Telephone: (01291) 625261

Leisure	hard tennis courts, heated indoor swimming pool, squash, snooker, sauna, solarium, gymnasium, badminton, crown bowling & croquet.
Location	St Pierre Park (3m SW off A48)
Hotel	★★★69% St Pierre Hotel, Golf & Country Club, St Pierre Park, CHEPSTOW ☎ (0291) 625261 104 ⇄ ℹ Annexe42 ⇄ ℹ

CWMBRAN   Map 03 ST29

Green Meadow Golf & Country Club
☎ (0633) 869321 & 862626

Undulating parkland course with panoramic views. The 7th hole is played partly down hill with the front half of the green enclosed with water; the 13th is exposed to winds with large mature trees along righthand side of green.

18 holes, 5806yds, Par 72, SSS 70, Course record 66.
Club membership 470.

Visitors	restricted during club competitions, Dress code; no jeans,t shirts, shorts or trainers.
Societies	telephone for brochure.
Green Fees	£12 per 18 holes weekdays.
Facilities	⊗ ⑂ ㋡ ▬ ♀ ⌂ ⌂
Leisure	26 bay driving range,caddy cars for hire.
Location	Treherbert Rd, Croesyceiliog (5m N of junct 26 M4, off A4042)
Hotel	★★★★61% Parkway Hotel, Cwmbran Dr, CWMBRAN ☎ (0633) 871199

Pontnewydd ☎ (0633) 482170
Mountainside course, with hard walking. Good views across
the Severn Estuary.
10 holes, 5353yds, Par 68, SSS 67, Course record 63.
Club membership 250.
Visitors   must play with member weekends & bank
                holidays.
Green Fees not confirmed.
Facilities ♀ ⅄
Location   Maesgwyn Farm, West Pontnewydd (N side of
                town centre)
Hotel   ★★★★61% Parkway Hotel, Cwmbran Dr,
                CWMBRAN ☎ (0633) 871199

LLANWERN   Map 03 ST38

Llanwern ☎ (0633) 412029
Two parkland courses.
New Course: 18 holes, 6115yds, Par 70, SSS 69.
Old Course: 9 holes, 5237yds, Par 67, SSS 67.
Club membership 850.
Visitors   must be a member of a recognised golf club.
Societies   must contact in writing.
Green Fees New: £20 per day (£25 weekends); Old: £15 per
                day.
Facilities ⊗ ⅢⅢ ⅃ ⬛ ♀ ⅄ 🏠 ⎰ Stephen Price.
Leisure   snooker.
Location   Tennyson Av (0.5m S off A455)
Hotel   ★★★★63% Celtic Manor Hotel, Coldra Woods,
                NEWPORT ☎ (0633) 413000 73 ⇌ 🐾

MONMOUTH   Map 03 SO51

Monmouth ☎ (0600) 712212
Parkland course in scenic setting. High, undulating land with
good views. Testing 1st and 4th holes.
18 holes, 5698yds, Par 69, SSS 69.
Club membership 500.
Visitors   no restrictions.
Societies   Mon-Fri only, telephone in advance.
Green Fees £15 per day.
Facilities ⊗ ⅢⅢ ⅃ ⬛ ♀ ⅄ 🏠
Location   Leasebrook Ln (1.5m NE off A40)
Hotel   ★★★58% Kings Head Hotel, Agincourt Square,
                MONMOUTH
                ☎ (0600) 712177 29rm(27 ⇌ 🐾)

Rolls of Monmouth ☎ (0600) 715353
A hilly and challenging parkland course encompassing
several lakes and ponds and surrounded by woodland. Set
within a beautiful private estate complete with listed
mansion.
18 holes, 6723yds, Par 72, SSS 72.
Club membership 200.
Visitors   must contact in advance and may not play
                on open days.
Societies   must contact in advance.
Green Fees £30 per day (£35 weekends & bank
                holidays).
Facilities ⊗ ⅢⅢ ⅃ ⬛ ♀ ⅄ 🏠 ⎰
Location   The Hendre (4m W on B4233)
Hotel   ★★★58% Kings Head Hotel, Agincourt
                Square, MONMOUTH
                ☎ (0600) 712177 29rm(27 ⇌ 🐾)

NANTYGLO   Map 03 SO11

West Monmouthshire ☎ (0495) 310233
Mountain and heathland course with picturesque views, hard
walking and natural hazards. Testing 3rd hole, par 5, and 7th
hole, par 4.
18 holes, 6118yds, Par 71, SSS 69.
Club membership 700.
Visitors   welcome, must be guest of member for play on
                Sun.
Societies   must telephone 1 week in advance.
Green Fees £15 per day (Mon-Sat).
Facilities ⊗ ⅃ ⬛ ♀ ⅄ 🏠 ⎰
Location   Pond Rd (0.25m W off A467)
Hotel   ★★★57% Angel Hotel, Cross St,
                ABERGAVENNY ☎ (0873) 857121 29 ⇌ 🐾

NEWPORT   Map 03 ST38

Newport ☎ (0633) 896794 & 892643
An undulating parkland course, part-wooded. The 2nd
hole is surrounded by bunkers - a difficult hole. The 11th
hole is a bogey 4 and the fairway runs through an avenue
of trees, making a straight drive preferable. Set 300ft
above sea level, it offers fine views.
18 holes, 6431yds, Par 72, SSS 71, Course record 64.
Club membership 700.
Visitors   must contact in advance & have handicap
                certificate. With member only on Sat.
Societies   must contact in writing.
Green Fees £30 per day (£40 Sat & Sun).
Facilities ⊗ ⅢⅢ ⅃ ⬛ ♀ ⅄ 🏠 ⎰ ⎰ Roy Skuse.
Location   Great Oak, Rogerstone (3m NW of city
                centre off B4591)
Hotel   ★★★★63% Celtic Manor Hotel, Coldra
                Woods, NEWPORT
                ☎ (0633) 413000 73 ⇌ 🐾
                See advertisement on page 302

Parc ☎ (0633) 680933
A challenging but enjoyable 18-hole course with water
hazards and accompanying wildlife. The 38-bay driving
range is floodlit until 10pm.
18 holes, 5512yds, Par 70, SSS 68, Course record 67.
Club membership 520.
Visitors   no restrictions.
Societies   contact in advance.
Green Fees £18 per day; £10 per round (£18/£12 weekends).
Facilities ⊗ ⅢⅢ ⅃ ⬛ ♀ ⅄ 🏠 ⎰ Brian Edwarda.
Leisure   38 bay driving range.
Location   Church Ln, Coedkernew (4m SW of A48)
Hotel   ★★★61% Wentloog Resort Hotel,
                CASTLETON ☎ (0633) 680591 55 ⇌ 🐾

Tredegar Park ☎ (0633) 895219
A parkland course with River Ebbw and streams as
natural hazards. The ground is very flat with narrow
fairways and small greens. The 17th hole (par 3) is
played on to a plateau where many players spoil their
medal round.
18 holes, 6095yds, Par 71, SSS 70.
Club membership 800.
Visitors   must be a member of a recognised golf club.
Societies   must contact in advance.

▶

EGON RONAY

Celtic Manor

HOTEL, GOLF
& COUNTRY CLUB

AA ★★★★

Two Exciting New Courses
At One Of The Finest Hotels
In Wales And The West
OPEN SPRING 1995
IAN WOOSNAM
AFFILIATED TOURING PROFESSIONAL
THE IDEAL VENUE FOR
BUSINESS, CONFERENCE, LEISURE BREAKS
GOLFING BREAKS

72 BEDROOMS
2 RESTAURANTS
6 CONFERENCE SUITES
SWIMMING POOL AND LEISURE FACILITIES

**THE CELTIC MANOR HOTEL,
COLDRA WOODS, NEWPORT NP6 2YA**
TEL: 01633 413000 FAX: 01633 412910

Green Fees	£15-£23 per day (£30 weekends & bank holidays).
Facilities	⊗ ⒤ ⓛ ⓜ ⓤ ⓨ ⓐ ⓕ ⓣ ⓘ M L Morgan.
Leisure	snooker.
Location	Bassaleg Rd (2m SW off A467 exit 27 of M4)
Hotel	★★★67% Kings Hotel, High St, NEWPORT ☎ (0633) 842020 47 ⇥ ℞

PONTYPOOL   Map 03 SO20

Pontypool ☎ (0495) 763655
Undulating, mountain course with magnificent views.
18 holes, 6046yds, Par 69, SSS 69.
Club membership 600.

Visitors	must have a handicap certificate.
Societies	must contact secretary in advance.
Green Fees	£16.50 per day (£22.50 weekends & bank holidays).
Facilities	⊗ ⒤ ⓛ ⓜ ⓤ ⓨ ⓐ ⓕ ⓣ ⓘ
Leisure	snooker, pratice area.
Location	Trevethin (1.5m N off A4043)
Hotel	★★★63% Glen-yr-Afon House Hotel, Pontypool Rd, USK ☎ (0291) 672302 & 673202 27rm(26 ⇥ ℞)

Phoneday - remember from 16 April
1995 all phone codes in the UK will
change - see page 4 for details

Woodlake Park Golf & Country Club
☎ Usk (0291) 673933
Undulating parkland course with magnificent views over
Llandegfedd Reservoir. Superb green constructed to USGA
specification. Holes 4, 7 & 16 are Par 3's which are
particularly challenging. Holes 6 & 17 are long Par 4's which
can be wind affected. An indoor golf centre with
chipping/pitching & 4 bunker positions, plus an indoor
driving range (from Autumn 1994) ensure golf can be played
whatever the weather!
18 holes, 6305yds, Par 71, SSS 70, Course record 71.
Club membership 300.

Visitors	must observe dress code.
Societies	booking required.
Green Fees	£27.50 per day; £20 per round (£30/£25 weekends & bank holidays).
Facilities	⊗ ⒤ ⓛ ⓜ ⓤ ⓨ ⓐ ⓕ ⓣ ⓘ Clive Coombs.
Leisure	fishing, snooker, electric trolleys & caddy cars.
Location	Glascoed (overlooking Llandegfedd Reservoir)
Hotel	★★★63% Glen-yr-Afon House Hotel, Pontypool Rd, USK ☎ (0291) 672302 & 673202 27rm(26 ⇥ ℞)

TREDEGAR   Map 03 SO10

Tredegar and Rhymney ☎ Rhymney (0685) 840743
Mountain course with lovely views.
9 holes, 5504yds, Par 68.
Club membership 194.

Visitors	no restrictions.
Societies	must contact in writing.
Green Fees	not confirmed.
Facilities	ⓛ ⓜ ⓨ ⓐ
Location	Cwmtysswg, Rhymney (1.75m SW on B4256)
Hotel	★★68% Tregenna Hotel, Park Ter, MERTHYR TYDFIL ☎ (0685) 723627 & 382055 24 ⇥ ℞

GWYNEDD

ABERDOVEY   Map 06 SN69

Aberdovey ☎ (0654) 767210
A beautiful championship course at the mouth of the
Dovey estuary, Aberdovey has all the true characteristics
of a seaside links. It has some fine holes among them the
3rd, the 12th, an especially good short hole, and the 15th.
There are some striking views to be had from the course.
18 holes, 6445yds, Par 71, SSS 71, Course record 67.
Club membership 850.

Visitors	members have priority between 8-10am & 12.30-2pm.
Societies	apply in writing to the secretary.
Green Fees	£30 per day; £20 per round (£36/£25 weekends).
Facilities	⊗ ⒤ ⓛ ⓜ ⓤ ⓨ ⓐ ⓕ ⓘ John Davies.
Leisure	snooker, caddy cars.
Location	0.5m W on A493
Hotel	★★★67% Trefeddian Hotel, ABERDOVEY ☎ (0654) 767213 46 ⇥ ℞

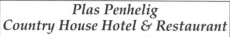

Plas Penhelig
Country House Hotel & Restaurant

Aberdovey, Gwynedd LL35 0NA
Telephone: (01654) 767676
Fax: (01654) 767783

An award winning country house situated by the sea with delightful views over the Dovey Estuary. Built in 1909, the hotel stands in seven acres of grounds including a beautiful walled kitchen garden, nine hole putting green and croquet lawn. Guests can indulge in an assortment of activities or visit the many places of interest in the vicinity. The beautiful house, with its oak-panelled entrance hall, stained glass windows and oak staircase, has been well developed by the Richardson family into a beautifully appointed hotel. An ideal venue for small wedding receptions, conferences and private parties. The fruit, vegetables and salads are provided by the hotel's gardens with local meat, game and fish all used.

Please write or call for brochure.

AA　　　Welsh Tourist Board Highly Commended
★★★　　　👑👑👑

Additional hotel ★★★🏠65% Plas Penhelig Country House Hotel, ABERDOVEY
☎ (0654) 767676 12 🛏 🐾

ABERSOCH
Map 06 SH32

Abersoch ☎ (0758) 712622
Seaside links, with five parkland holes.
18 holes, 5994yds, Par 69, SSS 69.
Club membership 700.
Visitors must have a handicap certificate.
Societies must apply in writing.
Green Fees £15 per day.
Facilities ⊗ ⏶ 🝀 💻 ♀ ♨ 🏠
Location S side of village
Hotel ★★★63% Abersoch Harbour Hotel, ABERSOCH
☎ (0758) 712406 9 🛏 🐾Annexe5 🛏 🐾

AMLWCH
Map 06 SH49

See under Anglesey, Isle of

A golf course name printed in ***bold italics*** means we have been unable to verify information with the club's management for the current year

---

ANGLESEY, ISLE OF
Map 06

Golf Courses on the island of Anglesey are listed below.

AMLWCH
Map 06 SH49

Bull Bay ☎ (0407) 830960
Wales's northernmost course, Bull Bay is a pleasant coastal, heathland course with natural meadow, rock, gorse and wind hazards. Views from all tees across Irish Sea to Isle of Man.
18 holes, 6217yds, Par 70, SSS 70, Course record 68.
Club membership 800.
Visitors must have handicap certificate or equivalent.
Societies must contact in advance.
Green Fees £20 per day; £15 per round (£25/20 weekends & bank holidays).
Facilities ⊗ ⏶ 🝀 💻 ♀ ♨ 🏠 ♦ Neil Dunroe.
Location 1m W on A5025
Hotel ★★57% Trecastell Hotel, Bull Bay, AMLWCH
☎ (0407) 830651 12rm(8 🛏3 🐾)

BEAUMARIS
Map 06 SH67

Baron Hill ☎ (0286) 810231
Undulating course with natural hazards of rock and gorse. Testing 3rd and 4th holes (par 4's). Nole 5/14 plays into the prevailing wind with an elevated tee across two streams. The hole is between two gorse covered mounds.
9 holes, 5062mtrs, Par 68, SSS 67.
Club membership 400.
Visitors restrictions but ladies have priority on Tue.
Societies apply in writing.
Green Fees £12 per day.
Facilities ♨
Location 1m SW off A545
Hotel ★★68% Bishopsgate House Hotel, 54 Castle St, BEAUMARIS ☎ (0248) 810302 10 🛏 🐾

HOLYHEAD
Map 06 SH28

Holyhead ☎ (0407) 763279
Treeless, undulating seaside course which provides a varied and testing game, particularly in a south wind. The fairways are bordered by gorse, heather and rugged outcrops of rock. Accuracy from most tees is paramount as there are 43 fairway and greenside bunkers and lakes. Designed by James Braid. Indoor driving range.
18 holes, 6056yds, Par 70, SSS 70, Course record 63.
Club membership 1309.
Visitors must contact in advance & have handicap certificate.
Societies must telephone in advance.
Green Fees £20 per day (£25 weekends & bank holidays).
Facilities ⊗ ⏶ 🝀 💻 ♀ ♨ 🏠 🍴 ♦ Stephen Elliot.
Leisure snooker, indoor driving range.
Location Trearddur Bay (1.25m S on B4545)
Hotel ★★★72% Trearddur Bay Hotel, TREARDDUR BAY
☎ (0407) 860301 31 🛏 🐾

LLANGEFNI   Map 06 SH47

Llangefni (Public) ☎ (0248) 722193
Picturesque parkland course designed by Hawtree & Son.
9 holes, 1342yds, Par 28, SSS 28.
Visitors   no restrictions.
Societies   must contact in advance.
Facilities   ⌷ 🏠 ⚐ 🍴 ⏍
Location   1.5m off A5
Hotel   ★★★(red)🏨 Tre-Ysgawen Hall, Capel Coch,
         LLANGEFNI ☎ (0248) 750750 19 ⇥ ⏏

RHOSNEIGR   Map 06 SH37

Anglesey ☎ (0407) 811202
Links course, low and fairly level with sand dunes and tidal
river.
18 holes, 5713yds, Par 68, SSS 68.
Club membership 400.
Visitors   welcome, some times are reserved for members.
Societies   apply in writing.
Green Fees not confirmed.
Facilities   ⊗ 🍴 by prior arrangement 🍺 🍽 ⌷ ⌷ 🏠
         ⏏ Paul Lovell.
Leisure   darts, pool table, golf practice ground.
Location   Station Rd (NE side of village on A4080)
Hotel   ★★★72% Trearddur Bay Hotel,
         TREARDDUR BAY
         ☎ (0407) 860301 31 ⇥ ⏏

BALA   Map 06 SH93

Bala ☎ (0678) 520359
Mountainous course with natural hazards. All holes except
first and last affected by wind.
10 holes, 5980yds, Par 66, SSS 64.
Club membership 250.
Visitors   must telephone in advance for weekends & bank
         holidays.
Societies   must telephone in advance.
Green Fees £12 per day (£15 per round weekends & bank
         holidays).
Facilities   🍺 🍽 ⌷ 🏠 ⚐ 🍴
Leisure   snooker.
Location   Penlan (0.5m SW off A494)
Hotel   ★★63% Plas Coch Hotel, High St, BALA
         ☎ (0678) 520309 10 ⇥ ⏏

BANGOR   Map 06 SH57

St Deiniol ☎ (0248) 353098
Elevated parkland course with panoramic views of
Snowdonia, Menai Straits, and Anglesey.
18 holes, 5068mtrs, Par 68, SSS 67.
Club membership 500.
Visitors   restricted weekends.
Societies   must contact in writing.
Green Fees £12 (£16 weekends).
Facilities   ⊗ 🍴 🍺 🍽 (no catering on Mon) ⌷ 🏠 🏠
Leisure   snooker.
Location   Penybryn (E side of town centre off A5122)
Hotel   ★★★67% Menai Court Hotel, Craig y Don Rd,
         BANGOR ☎ (0248) 354200 13 ⇥ ⏏

BEAUMARIS   Map 06 SH67

See under Anglesey, Isle of

BETWS-Y-COED   Map 06 SH75

Betws-y-Coed ☎ (0690) 710556
Attractive flat meadowland course set between two rivers in
Snowdonia National Park.
9 holes, 4996yds, Par 64, SSS 64.
Club membership 350.
Visitors   no restrictions.
Societies   must telephone in advance.
Green Fees £15 per day (£20 weekends & bank holidays).
Facilities   ⊗ 🍴 🍺 🍽 (no catering Mon) ⌷ 🏠
Location   NE side of village off A5
Hotel   ★★★66% Royal Oak, Holyhead Rd,
         BETWS-Y-COED ☎ (0690) 710219 27 ⇥ ⏏

CAERNARFON   Map 06 SH46

Caernarfon ☎ (0286) 673783 & 678359
Parkland course with gentle gradients.
18 holes, 5891yds, Par 69, SSS 69, Course record 68.
Club membership 745.
Visitors   may not play competition days.
Societies   must apply in advance.
Green Fees £18 (£22 weekends & bank holidays).
Facilities   ⊗ 🍴 🍺 🍽 ⌷ 🏠
Location   Llanfaglan (1.75m SW)
Hotel   ★★64% Stables Hotel, LLANWNDA
         ☎ (0286) 830711 & 830935 Annexe14 ⇥ ⏏

CONWY   Map 06 SH77

Conwy (Caernarvonshire)
   ☎ Aberconwy (0492) 592423
This course close by the old town of Conwy is a real
seaside links with gorse, rushes, sandhills and fine old
turf. There are plenty of natural hazards, the gorse
providing more than its share. The course has a
spectacular setting between sea and mountains.
18 holes, 6647yds, Par 72, SSS 72.
Club membership 960.
Visitors   must have a certified club handicap.
         Restricted weekends & competitions.
Societies   must contact in advance.
Green Fees £22 per round (£27 weekends & bank holidays).
Facilities   ⊗ (ex Tue) 🍴 (ex Mon and Tue) 🍺 🍽 ⌷
         ⌷ 🏠 ⏏ Peter Lees.
Leisure   caddy cars.
Location   The Morfa (1m W of town centre on A55)
Hotel   ★★★64% Sychnant Pass Hotel, Sychnant
         Pass Rd, CONWY
         ☎ (0492) 596868 13 ⇥ ⏏

CRICCIETH   Map 06 SH43

Criccieth ☎ (0766) 522154
Hilly course on Lleyn Peninsula. Good views.
18 holes, 5787yds, Par 69, SSS 68, Course record 65.
Club membership 234.
Visitors   no restrictions.

Societies no restrictions.
Green Fees not confirmed.
Facilities ⊗ ⅲ ㇄ ■ ♀ ⚹ 🏠
Location Ednyfed Hill (1m NE)
Hotel ★★★🏨67% Bron Eifion Country House Hotel, CRICCIETH ☎ (0766) 522385 19 ⇄ ♠

DOLGELLAU · · · · · · · · · · · · · · · Map 06 SH71

Dolgellau ☎ (0341) 422603
Undulating parkland course. Good views of mountains and Mawddach estuary.
9 holes, 4671yds, Par 66, SSS 63, Course record 63.
Club membership 280.
Visitors may not play on Sat.
Societies must contact in advance.
Green Fees £12 (£15 weekends & bank holidays).
Facilities ⊗ ⅲ ㇄ ■ ♀ ⚹ 🏠
Location Pencefn Rd (0.5m N)
Hotel ★★64% Royal Ship Hotel, Queens Square, DOLGELLAU
☎ (0341) 422209 24rm(18 ⇄ ♠)

FFESTINIOG · · · · · · · · · · · · · · · Map 06 SH74

Ffestiniog ☎ (076676) 2637
Moorland course set in Snowdonia National Park.
9 holes, 4570yds, Par 68, SSS 66.
Club membership 150.
Visitors welcome except during competitions.
Societies must telephone in advance.
Green Fees £8.50 per day.
Facilities ⚹
Location Y Cefn (1m E on B4391)
Hotel ★★(red)🏨 Maes y Neuadd Hotel, TALSARNAU
☎ (0766) 780200 12 ⇄ ♠Annexe4 ⇄ ♠

HARLECH · · · · · · · · · · · · · · · · · Map 06 SH53

Royal St Davids ☎ (0766) 780361
Championship links, with easy walking and natural hazards.
18 holes, 6427yds, Par 69, SSS 72.
Club membership 750.
Visitors pre booking essential, must be member of recognised golf club & hold current handicap certificate.
Societies telephone in advance and confirm in writing.
Green Fees £24 per day (£30 weekends & bank holidays).
Facilities ⊗ ⅲ ㇄ ■ ♀ ⚹ 🏠 ⚍ John Barnett.
Leisure caddy cars & buggies for hire.
Location W side of town on A496
Hotel ★★61% Ty Mawr Hotel, LLANBEDR
☎ (034123) 440 due to change to (0341) 241440 10 ⇄ ♠

HOLYHEAD · · · · · · · · · · · · · · · · Map 06 SH28

See under Anglesey, Isle of

LLANDUDNO · · · · · · · · · · · · · · · Map 06 SH78

Llandudno (Maesdu) ☎ (0492) 876450
Part links, part parkland, this championship course starts and finishes on one side of the main road, the remaining holes, more seaside in nature, being played on the other side. The holes are pleasantly undulating and present a pretty picture when the gorse is in bloom. Often windy, this varied and testing course is not for beginners.
18 holes, 6530yds, Par 73, SSS 72, Course record 66.
Club membership 1100.
Visitors welcome although some times are restricted. Must be member of a club with handicap certificate.
Societies must apply in advance, must be members of a recognised golf club.
Green Fees £22 per day (£30 weekends & bank holidays).
Facilities ⊗ ⅲ ㇄ ■ ♀ ⚹ 🏠 ⚍ ⚍ Simon Boulden.
Leisure snooker.
Location Hospital Rd (S side of town centre on A546)
Hotel ★★★67% Imperial Hotel, The Promenade, LLANDUDNO
☎ (0492) 877466 100 ⇄ ♠

North Wales ☎ (0492) 875325
Challenging seaside links with superb views of Anglesey and Snowdonia.
18 holes, 6132yds, Par 71, SSS 69.
Club membership 750.
Visitors must contact in advance & have handicap certificate, some times are restricted weekdays & weekends.
Societies must telephone in advance.
Green Fees £22 per day (£28 weekends & bank holidays).
Facilities ⊗ ⅲ ㇄ ■ ♀ ⚹ 🏠 ⚍ ⚍ Richard Bradbury.
Leisure snooker, practice ground.
Location 72 Bryniau Rd, West Shore (W side of town on A546)
Hotel ★★(red) St Tudno Hotel, Promenade, LLANDUDNO ☎ (0492) 874411 21 ⇄ ♠

Rhos-on-Sea ☎ Colwyn Bay (0492) 549641 & 549100
Seaside course, with easy walking and panoramic views.
18 holes, 6064yds, Par 69, SSS 69.
Club membership 400.
Visitors advised to contact in advance.
Societies booking essential, telephone in advance.
Green Fees £15 per day (£20 weekends).
Facilities ⊗ ⅲ by prior arrangement ㇄ ■ ♀ ⚹ 🏠 ⚑ ⚍ Matthew Jones.
Leisure snooker.
Location Penrhyn Bay (0.5m W off A546)
Hotel ★★★62% Gogarth Abbey Hotel, West Shore, LLANDUDNO ☎ (0492) 876211 40 ⇄ ♠

LLANFAIRFECHAN · · · · · · · · · · Map 06 SH67

Llanfairfechan ☎ (0248) 680144
Hillside course with panoramic views of coast.
9 holes, 3119yds, Par 54, SSS 57.
Club membership 350.
Visitors no restrictions. ▶

· ·

Societies apply in writing to the secretary.
Green Fees £10 per day (£15 weekends & bank holidays).
Facilities ⊗ ⊪ & ⓑ by prior arrangement ♀ ⌂
Location Fford Llannerch (W side of town on A55)
Hotel ★★★64% Sychnant Pass Hotel, Sychnant Pass Rd, CONWY ☎ (0492) 596868 13 ⊨ ⏷

LLANGEFNI Map 06 SH47

*See under **Anglesey, Isle of***

MORFA NEFYN Map 06 SH24

Nefyn & District ☎ (0758) 720218
Seaside course, with parkland fairways and good views. Testing golf along cliff edge. Large clubhouse with excellent facilities. Course record holder Ian Woosnam.
18 holes, 6301yds, Par 72, SSS 71.
Club membership 800.
Visitors must have a handicap certificate.
Societies apply in writing to the secretary.
Green Fees £25 per day; £20 per round (£35/£25 weekends & bank holidays).
Facilities ⊗ ⊪ ⓑ ♥ ♀ ⌂ ⌚ ⏷ John Froom.
Leisure snooker, caddy cars & motorised buggies for hire.
Location 0.75m NW
Hotel ★★♨76% Plas Bodegroes Restaurant, PWLLHELI ☎ (0758) 612363 8 ⊨ ⏷

PENMAENMAWR Map 06 SH77

Penmaenmawr ☎ (0492) 623330
Hilly course with magnificent views across the bay to Llandudno and Anglesey. Dry-stone wall natural hazards.
9 holes, 5306yds, Par 67, SSS 66.
Club membership 600.
Visitors no restrictions.
Societies must telephone in advance.
Green Fees £15 per day (£18 weekends & bank holidays).
Facilities ⊗ & ⊪ by prior arrangement ⓑ ♥ ♀ ⌂
Leisure bowling, darts, pool table.
Location Cae Maen Pavilion (1.5m NE off A55)
Hotel ★★★62% The Castle, High St, CONWY ☎ (0492) 592324 29 ⊨ ⏷

PORTHMADOG Map 06 SH53

Porthmadog ☎ (0766) 514124 & 513828
Seaside links,very interesting but with easy walking and good views.
18 holes, 6240yds, Par 70, SSS 70.
Club membership 900.
Visitors must contact in advance.
Societies must apply in writing.
Green Fees not confirmed.
Facilities ⊗ ⊪ ⓑ ♥ ♀ ⌂ ⌚ ⏷ Peter Bright.
Leisure snooker.
Location Morfa Bychan (1.5m SW)
Hotel ★★62% Plas Isa Hotel, Porthmadog Rd, CRICCIETH ☎ (0766) 522443 14 ⊨ ⏷

PWLLHELI Map 06 SH33

Pwllheli ☎ (0758) 612520
Easy walking on flat seaside course with outstanding views of Snowdon, Cader Idris and Cardigan Bay.
18 holes, 6091yds, Par 69, SSS 69, Course record 66.
Club membership 880.
Visitors restricted Tue,Thu & weekends.
Societies must telephone in advance.
Green Fees not confirmed.
Facilities ⊗ ⊪ ⓑ ♥ ♀ ⌂ ⌚ ⏷ G D Verity.
Leisure snooker.
Location Golf Rd (0.5m SW off A497)
Hotel ★★♨76% Plas Bodegroes Restaurant, PWLLHELI ☎ (0758) 612363 8 ⊨ ⏷

RHOSNEIGR Map 06 SH37

*See under **Anglesey, Isle of***

MID GLAMORGAN

ABERDARE Map 03 SO00

Aberdare ☎ (0685) 871188 & 872797
Mountain course with parkland features overlooking Cynon Valley.
18 holes, 5845yds, Par 69, SSS 69, Course record 63.
Club membership 600.
Visitors must contact in advance & have handicap certificate but may only play on Sat with member.
Societies must contact by phone & confirm in writing.
Green Fees £14 per day (£18 Sun & bank holidays).
Facilities ⊗ & ⊪ (ex Mon) ⓑ ♥ by prior arrangement ♀ ⌂ ⌚ ⏷ A W Palmer.
Leisure snooker.
Location Abernant (0.75m E)
Hotel ★★★59% Baverstock Hotel, The Heads Of Valley Rd, MERTHYR TYDFIL ☎ (0685) 386221 53 ⊨ ⏷

BARGOED Map 03 ST19

Bargoed ☎ (0443) 830143
Mountain parkland course, testing par 4, 13th hole.
18 holes, 5836yds, Par 70, SSS 70, Course record 67.
Club membership 500.
Visitors must play with member at weekends.
Societies must contact in advance.
Green Fees £15 per day/round.
Facilities ⊗ ⊪ ⓑ ♥ ♀ ⌂
Location Heolddu (NW side of town)
Hotel ★★★53% Maes Manor Hotel, BLACKWOOD ☎ (0495) 224551 & 220011 8 ⊨ Annexe14 ⏷

★ ★ ★

St. Mary's Hotel, Golf & Country Club

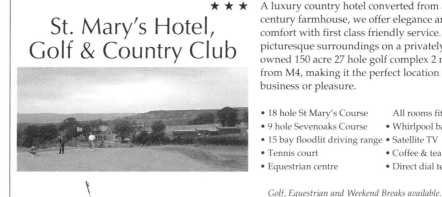

A luxury country hotel converted from a 17th century farmhouse, we offer elegance and comfort with first class friendly service. Set in picturesque surroundings on a privately owned 150 acre 27 hole golf complex 2 mins from M4, making it the perfect location for business or pleasure.

- 18 hole St Mary's Course
- 9 hole Sevenoaks Course
- 15 bay floodlit driving range
- Tennis court
- Equestrian centre

All rooms fitted with:
- Whirlpool baths
- Satellite TV
- Coffee & tea facilities
- Direct dial telephone

Golf, Equestrian and Weekend Breaks available.

Please call us for a FREE video and brochure and sample for yourselves "The Magic of St. Mary's".

St. Mary's Golf Club Ltd. St. Mary's Hill Pencoed, South Glamorgan CF35 5EA.
Hotel Reservation: Tel: (01656) 861100 Fax: (01656) 863400

BRIDGEND   Map 03 SS97

Southerndown ☏ (0656) 880476
Downland championship course with rolling fairways and fast greens. The par-3 5th is played across a valley and the 18th, with its split level fairway, is a demanding finishing hole. Superb views.
18 holes, 6417yds, Par 70, SSS 72, Course record 64. Club membership 720.

Visitors	must contact in advance & have handicap certificate. With member only Sun (Oct-Mar).
Societies	must contact in advance.
Green Fees	£30 per day; £20 per round afternoons (£36/£30 weekends).
Facilities	⊗ ⅲ 🏌 ⚑ ♀ 🏆 🏠 🌳 D G McMonagle.
Leisure	snooker, practice shed.
Location	Ewenny (3m SW on B4524)
Hotel	★★★61% Heronston Hotel, Ewenny, BRIDGEND ☏ (0656) 668811 76 ⇥ 🐾
Additional hotel	★★★72% Coed-y-Mwstwr Hotel, Coychurch, BRIDGEND ☏ (0656) 860621 23 ⇥ 🐾

CAERPHILLY   Map 03 ST18

Caerphilly ☏ (0222) 883481 & 86344
Undulating mountain course with woodland. Good views especially from 10th hole, 700 ft above sea level. An additional four holes constructed in 1994.
14 holes, 6028yds, Par 73, SSS 71, Course record 68. Club membership 792.

▶

Coed-y-Mwstwr

An elegant late-Victorian mansion, tastefully converted into a Luxury Hotel and Restaurant for the discerning. Situated only 4 miles from 6 first class golf courses.

In the 17 acre grounds are a swimming pool and tennis court; the hotel also has a snooker room.

The focal point of the Hotel is undoubtedly the oak-panelled Restaurant, renowned for its Good food, fine wine and friendly attentive service. 2½ miles from exit 35 off M4. Turn off on to A473 towards Bridgend – approx 1 mile turn right into Coychurch Village Centre – well signposted from Esso filling station.

AT COYCHURCH, Nr. BRIDGEND, MID-GLAMORGAN CF35 6AF.
Tel: (01656) 860621

Visitors must contact in advance & have a handicap certificate & membership of a recognised golf club. May only play with member at weekends & bank holidays.
Societies must contact in advance.
Green Fees £20 per day/round.
Facilities ⊗ ⅷ by prior arrangement ⓑ (no catering Mon) ♀⚑🏠🍴 Richard Barter.
Leisure snooker, billiards/snooker.
Location Pencapel Mountain Rd (0.5m S on A469)
Hotel ★★★73% Manor Parc Country Hotel & Restaurant, Thornhill Rd, Thornhill, CARDIFF ☎ (0222) 693723 12 ⇔ 🐾

Mountain Lakes & Castell Heights ☎ (0222) 861128 & 886666
The 9-hole Castell Heights course within the Mountain Lakes complex was established in 1982 on a 45-acre site. In 1988 a further 18-hole course was designed by Bob Sandow to take advantage of 150-acres of mountain heathland, combining both mountain top golf and parkland. Most holes are tree lined and there are 16 'lakes' as hazards. Host of major PGA tournaments.
Mountain Lakes: 18 holes, 6343yds, Par 72, SSS 73.
Castell Heights: 9 holes, 5376yds, Par 68, SSS 64.
Club membership 600.
Visitors to Mountain Lakes must be a member of another club or have a handicap certificate.
Societies written or telephone notice in advance.
Green Fees Mountain Lakes: £20 per day; £15 per round. Castell Heights £5.50 per 9 holes.
Facilities ⊗ ⅷ ⓑ 🍺 (prior notice advisable) ♀⚑🏠🍴 🍴 Sion Bebb.
Leisure driving range 20 bay.
Location Blaengwynlais (near Black Lock Inn, Caerphilly Mountain)
Hotel ★★★73% Manor Parc Country Hotel & Restaurant, Thornhill Rd, Thornhill, CARDIFF ☎ (0222) 693723 12 ⇔ 🐾

Virginia Park Golf & Bowling Club ☎ (0222) 863919
Beside Caerphilly leisure centre, the course is totally flat but with plenty of trees and bunkers and 2 lakes. It is a tight, challenging course with 6 par 4 and 3 par 3 holes. Also a 20-bay flodlit driving range.
9 holes, 5132yds, Par 66.
Club membership 400.
Visitors spiked golf shoes must be worn & conventional golf attire (no jeans, tracksuits, tee shirts, trainers.
Societies apply in writing.
Green Fees £11 per 18 holes; £6 per 9 holes.
Facilities ⊗ ⓑ 🍺 ♀⚑🏠🍴
Leisure driving range, leisure centre adjacent.
Location Virginia Park (off Pontyewindy Rd)
Hotel ★★★73% Manor Parc Country Hotel & Restaurant, Thornhill Rd, Thornhill, CARDIFF ☎ (0222) 693723 12 ⇔ 🐾

CREIGIAU (CREIYIAU)   Map 03 ST08

Creigiau ☎ Cardiff (0222) 890263
Downland course, with small greens.
18 holes, 5979yds, Par 70, SSS 69.
Club membership 850.

Visitors must be a member of a recognised golf club. Must play with member at weekends.
Societies must contact in writing.
Green Fees £21 per day.
Facilities ⊗ ⅷ ⓑ 🍺 ♀⚑🏠🍴 Mark Maddison.
Location 6m NW of Cardiff on A4119
Hotel ★★★69% Miskin Manor Hotel, MISKIN ☎ (0443) 224204 35 ⇔ 🐾

MAESTEG   Map 03 SS89

Maesteg ☎ (0656) 732037 & 735742
Reasonably flat hill-top course with scenic views.
18 holes, 5900yds, Par 70, SSS 69, Course record 64.
Club membership 700.
Visitors must be a member of a recognised golf club & have a handicap certificate.
Societies weekdays only. Must contact in advance.
Green Fees £15 per day (£20 weekends & bank holidays).
Facilities ⊗ ⅷ ⓑ 🍺 ♀⚑🏠🍴 W Evans.
Location Mount Pleasant, Neath Rd (0.5m W off B4282)
Hotel ★★★60% Aberavan Beach Hotel, PORT TALBOT ☎ (0639) 884949 52 ⇔

MAESYCWMMER   Map 03 ST19

Bryn Meadows ☎ Blackwood (0495) 225590 or 224103
A heavily wooded parkland course with panoramic views of the Brecon Beacons.
18 holes, 6132yds, Par 72, SSS 69, Course record 66.
Club membership 540.
Visitors may not play Sun mornings. Must contact in advance.
Societies Tue & Thu only.
Green Fees £17.50 per round (£22.50 weekends).
Facilities ⊗ ⅷ ⓑ 🍺 ♀⚑🏠🍴 ♙ Bruce Hunter.
Leisure heated indoor swimming pool, sauna, gymnasium, caddy cars.
Location The Bryn (on the A4048 Blackwood to Ystrad Mynach rd)
Hotel ★★★53% Maes Manor Hotel, BLACKWOOD ☎ (0495) 224551 & 220011 8 ⇔Annexe14 ⇔

MERTHYR TYDFIL   Map 03 SO00

Merthyr Tydfil (Cilanws) ☎ (0685) 723308
Mountain-top course with good views and water hazards. Requires accuracy off the tee.
11 holes, 5956yds, Par 70, SSS 69.
Club membership 200.
Visitors may not play on Sun.
Societies must contact in writing.
Green Fees not confirmed.
Facilities ♀
Location Cilsanws, Cefn Coed (2m NW off A470)
Hotel ★★66% Nant Ddu Lodge Hotel, Cwm Taf, Merthyr Tydfil ☎ (0685) 379111 14 ⇔ 🐾

Morlais Castle ☎ (0685) 722822
Beautiful moorland course in National Park adjacent to Brecon Beacons. Rocky terrain off the fairways makes for a testing game.
18 holes, 6320yds, Par 71, SSS 71.
Club membership 400.

Visitors	must contact in advance for weekends.
Societies	weekdays only; must telephone in advance & confirm in writing.
Green Fees	£14 per day (£16 weekends & bank holidays).
Facilities	⊗ ⅋Ⅲ ﹗﹗ Ⅾ ⅋
Location	Pant, Dowlais (2.5m N off A465)
Hotel	★★66% Nant Ddu Lodge Hotel, Cwm Taf, Merthyr Tydfil ☎ (0685) 379111 14 ⇆ 𝄐

MOUNTAIN ASH   Map 03 ST09

Mountain Ash ☎ (0443) 478770
Mountain course.
18 holes, 5553yds, Par 69, SSS 68, Course record 64.
Club membership 600.

Visitors	must play with member at weekends and must have a handicap certificate.
Societies	must contact in writing.
Green Fees	£18 per day.
Facilities	⊗ & Ⅲ by prior arrangement ﹗ ﹗﹗ Ⅾ ⅋ 🏠 𝄐 C Hiscox.
Leisure	caddy cars available.
Location	Cefnpennar (1m NW off A4059)
Hotel	★★★59% Baverstock Hotel, The Heads Of Valley Rd, MERTHYR TYDFIL ☎ (0685) 386221 53 ⇆ 𝄐

NELSON   Map 03 ST19

Whitehall ☎ (0443) 740245
Windy hilltop course. Testing 4th hole (225 yds) par 3, and 6th hole (402 yds) par 4. Pleasant views.
9 holes, 5666yds, Par 69, SSS 68, Course record 63.
Club membership 300.

Visitors	must be a member of a recognised golf club & have a handicap certificate. Must contact in advance to play at weekends.
Societies	must contact in writing 4 weeks in advance.
Green Fees	£15 per day.
Facilities	⊗ & Ⅲ by prior arrangement ﹗ ﹗﹗ Ⅾ ⅋
Location	The Pavilion (2m W off A470)
Hotel	★★★63% Llechwen Hall Hotel, Llanfabon, PONTYPRIDD ☎ (0443) 742050 11 ⇆ 𝄐

PENCOED   Map 03 SS98

St Mary's Hotel Golf & Country Club ☎ (0656) 861100
A parkland course with many American style features. The Par 3 13th called 'Alcatraz' has a well deserved reputation.
St Mary's: 18 holes, 5120yds, Par 67, SSS 66, Course record 67.
Sevenoaks: 9 holes, 2426yds, Par 35, SSS 34.
Club membership 1100.

Visitors	must produce a handicap certificate.
Societies	telephone Kay Brazell.
Green Fees	St Mary's: £12 per 18 holes (£15 weekends). Sevenoaks: £2.50 per 9 holes (£4 weekends).
Facilities	⊗ Ⅲ ﹗ ﹗﹗ Ⅾ ⅋ 🏠 ╬╬ 🏌 𝄐 Jason Harris.
Leisure	hard tennis courts, riding, 15 bay driving range.
Location	St Mary Hill
Hotel	★★★70% St Mary's Hotel & Country Club, St Marys Golf Club, PENCOED ☎ (0656) 861100 24 ⇆ 𝄐

See advertisement on page 307

PENRHYS   Map 03 ST09

Rhondda ☎ Tonypandy (0443) 441384
Mountain course with good views.
18 holes, 6206yds, Par 70, SSS 70.
Club membership 700.

Visitors	restricted Sun.
Societies	must contact in advance.
Green Fees	£15 (£20 weekends).
Facilities	⊗ Ⅲ ﹗ ﹗﹗ Ⅾ ⅋ 🏠 🏌 Rhys Davies.
Leisure	snooker.
Location	Golf Club House (0.5m W off B4512)
Hotel	★★55% Wyndham Hotel, Dunraven Place, BRIDGEND ☎ (0656) 652080 & 657431 28rm(25 ⇆)

PONTYPRIDD   Map 03 ST09

Pontypridd ☎ (0443) 409904 & 402359
Well-wooded mountain course with springy turf. Good views of the Rhondda Valleys and coast.
18 holes, 5721yds, Par 69, SSS 68.
Club membership 850.

Visitors	must play with member on weekends & bank holidays. Must have a handicap certificate.
Societies	weekdays only. Must apply in writing.
Green Fees	£18.
Facilities	⊗ & Ⅲ (ex Thu) ﹗ ﹗﹗ Ⅾ ⅋ 🏠 𝄐 Wade Walters.
Leisure	snooker.
Location	Ty Gwyn Rd (E side of town centre off A470)
Hotel	★★★66% Heritage Park Hotel, Coed Cae Rd, Trehafod, PONTYPRIDD ☎ (0443) 687057 50 ⇆ 𝄐

PORTHCAWL   Map 03 SS87

Royal Porthcawl ☎ (0656) 782251
This championship-standard heathland/downland links course is always in sight of the sea, and has hosted many major tournaments.
18 holes, 6409yds, Par 72, SSS 73.
Club membership 800.

Visitors	must contact in advanced & have handicap certificate. Restricted at weekends & bank holidays.
Societies	must contact in writing.
Green Fees	£35 per day; £27.50 per round.
Facilities	⊗ Ⅲ by prior arrangement ﹗ ﹗﹗ Ⅾ ⅋ 🏠 ╬╬ 𝄐 Peter Evans.
Location	1.5m NW of town centre
Hotel	★★★60% Seabank Hotel, The Promenade, PORTHCAWL ☎ (0656) 782261 61 ⇆ 𝄐

PYLE   Map 03 SS88

Pyle & Kenfig ☎ Porthcawl (0656) 783093
Links and downland course, with sand-dunes. Easy walking. Often windy.
18 holes, 6081mtrs, Par 71, SSS 73, Course record 68.
Club membership 1089.

Visitors	must play with member at weekends. Must have a handicap certificate.
Societies	weekdays only. Must contact in advance. ▶

Green Fees £31 per day, £26 per round.
Facilities ⊗ ∭ by prior arrangement 🏌 ♥ ♀ ♨ 🏠
🍴 Robert Evans.
Location Waun-Y-Mer (S side of Pyle off A4229)
Hotel ★★★60% Seabank Hotel, The Promenade,
PORTHCAWL ☎ (0656) 782261 61 ⇔ ♠

TALBOT GREEN   Map 03 ST08

Llantrisant & Pontyclun ☎ Llantrisant (0443) 222148
Parkland course.
12 holes, 5712yds, Par 68, SSS 68.
Club membership 600.
Visitors must have a club membership card & handicap
certificate and should be accompanied by a
member.
Societies apply in writing.
Green Fees not confirmed.
Facilities ♨ 🏠 🍴 🍴
Location Llanelry Rd (N side of village off A473)
Hotel ★★★69% Miskin Manor Hotel, MISKIN
☎ (0443) 224204 35 ⇔ ♠

POWYS

BRECON   Map 03 SO02

Brecon ☎ (0874) 622004
Parkland course, with easy walking. Natural hazards include
two rivers on its boundary. Good river and mountain scenery.
9 holes, 5218yds, Par 66, SSS 66, Course record 61.
Club membership 420.
Visitors restricted on competition days.
Societies must contact in writing.
Green Fees not confirmed.
Facilities ⊗ & ∭ by prior arrangement 🏌 ♀ ♨
Location Newton Park (0.75m W of town centre on A40)
Hotel ★★64% Castle of Brecon Hotel, Castle Square,
BRECON
☎ (0874) 624611 37 ⇔ ♠ Annexe12 ♠

Cradoc ☎ (0874) 623658
Parkland with wooded areas, lakes and spectacular views
over the Brecon Beacons. Challenging golf.
18 holes, 6301yds, Par 71, SSS 71, Course record 65.
Club membership 700.
Visitors must contact in advance. Restricted on Sun.
Societies must contact 7 days in advance.
Green Fees £18 (£20 Sat).
Facilities ⊗ & ∭ (ex Mon) 🏌 ♥ ♀ ♨ 🏠
🍴 Douglas Beattie.
Location Penoyre Park, Cradoc (2m N on B4520)
Hotel ★★64% Castle of Brecon Hotel, Castle Square,
BRECON
☎ (0874) 624611 37 ⇔ ♠ Annexe12 ♠

For an explanation of symbols and
abbreviations, see page 5

BUILTH WELLS   Map 03 SO05

Builth Wells ☎ (0982) 553296
Well guarded greens and a stream running thorough the
centre of the course add interest to this 18-hole undulating
parkland course. The clubhouse is a converted 16th-century
Welsh long house.
18 holes, 5376yds, Par 66, SSS 67, Course record 64.
Club membership 400.
Visitors must have handicap certificate.
Societies by prior arrangement.
Green Fees £15 per day (£20 weekends).
Facilities ⊗ ∭ 🏌 ♥ ♀ ♨ 🏠 🍴 🍴 Roy Truman.
Leisure trolley hire.
Location The Clubhouse, Golf Links Rd (N of A483)
Hotel ★★★▲63% Caer Beris Manor Hotel,
BUILTH WELLS ☎ (0982) 552601 22 ⇔ ♠

CAERSWS   Map 06 SO09

Maesmawr ☎ (0686) 688303
A 9-hole, Par 3 course with sand bunkers and three ponds.
9 holes, 2554yds, Par 54, SSS 54, Course record 63.
Club membership 85.
Visitors restricted during competition time.
Societies telephone in advance.
Green Fees not confirmed.
Facilities ♥ ♀ ♨ 🏠 🍴
Leisure 12 bay floodlit driving range.
Location Mid Wales Golf Centre (6m W of Newtown)
Hotel ★★62% Elephant & Castle, Broad St,
NEWTOWN
☎ (0686) 626271 25 ⇔ ♠ Annexe11 ⇔ ♠

KNIGHTON   Map 07 SO27

Knighton ☎ (0547) 528646
Hill course with hard walking.
9 holes, 5320yds, Par 68, SSS 66, Course record 65.
Club membership 150.
Visitors may not play on Sun until after 4.30pm.
Societies must contact in advance.
Green Fees £8 per day (£10 weekends & bank holidays).
Facilities ∭ by prior arrangement 🏌 ♥ ♀ ♨
Location Frydd Wood (0.5m S off B4355)
Hotel ★★★64% The Knighton Hotel, Broad St,
KNIGHTON ☎ (0547) 520530 15 ⇔ ♠

LLANDRINDOD WELLS   Map 03 SO06

Llandrindod Wells ☎ (0597) 822010 & 823873
Moorland course, designed by Harry Vardon, with easy
walking and panoramic views. One of the highest courses in
Wales. (1,100 ft above sea level).
18 holes, 5759yds, Par 68, SSS 67.
Club membership 650.
Visitors no restrictions.
Societies must telephone in advance.
Green Fees £12 per day (£20 weekends & bank holidays).
Facilities ⊗ ∭ 🏌 ♥ (no catering Tue) ♀ ♨ 🏠 🍴
Location 1m SE off A483
Hotel ★★★62% Hotel Metropole, Temple St,
LLANDRINDOD WELLS
☎ (0597) 823700 121 ⇔ ♠

LLANGATTOCK   Map 03 SO21

Old Rectory ☎ (0873) 810373
Sheltered course with easy walking.
9 holes, 2225yds, Par 53, SSS 54, Course record 53 or 53yds.
Club membership 200.
Visitors   no restrictions.
Societies   must contact in advance.
Green Fees £12 per day.
Facilities ⊗ ⊞ ⓑ 🍷 ♀ ♨ ⛳
Location   SW of village
Hotel   ★★⚑70% Gliffaes Country House Hotel,
               CRICKHOWELL
               ☎ (0874) 730371 19 ⇆ ⓡAnnexe3 ⇆ ⓡ

LLANIDLOES   Map 06 SN98

St Idloes ☎ (0686) 412559
Hill-course, slightly undulating but walking is easy. Good
views.
9 holes, 5320yds, Par 66, SSS 66, Course record 59.
Club membership 350.
Visitors   may not play on Sun mornings. Must have a
                 handicap certificate.
Societies   must contact in advance.
Green Fees £10 (£12 weekends).
Facilities ⓑ 🍷 (lunchtime & early evening) ♀ ♨
Location   Penrhallt (1m N off B4569)
Hotel   ★★67% Glansevern Arms Hotel, Pant Mawr,
               LLANGURIG ☎ (05515) 240 7 ⇆ ⓡ

MACHYNLLETH   Map 06 SH70

Machynlleth ☎ (0654) 702000
Lowland course with mostly natural hazards.
9 holes, 5726yds, Par 68, SSS 67.
Club membership 247.
Visitors   may not play during competitions & Thu 12.30-
                 3pm
Societies   must contact in advance.
Green Fees £12 per day (£15 weekends & bank holidays).
Facilities ⓑ & 🍷 (noon-2pm) ♀ (noon-2pm) ♨ ⛳
Location   Ffordd Drenewydd (0.5m E off A489)
Hotel   ★★64% Wynnstay Arms Hotel, Maengwyn St,
               MACHYNLLETH ☎ (0654) 702941 20 ⇆ ⓡ

NEWTOWN   Map 06 SO19

St Giles ☎ (0686) 625844
Inland country course with easy walking. Testing 2nd hole,
par 3, and 4th hole, par 4. River Severn skirts four holes.
9 holes, 5936yds, Par 70, SSS 68, Course record 63.
Club membership 400.
Visitors   restricted Thu & Sat afternoons & Sun
                 mornings. Must have a handicap certificate.
Societies   must contact in advance in writing.
Green Fees £12.50 per day (£15 weekends & bank holidays).
Facilities ⊗ ⊞ ⓑ 🍷 (no catering Mon) ♀ (ex Mon) ♨
               ⓑ ⛳ ⓡ D P Owen.
Leisure   fishing.
Location   Pool Rd (0.5m NE on A483)
Hotel   ★★62% Elephant & Castle, Broad St,
               NEWTOWN
               ☎ (0686) 626271 25 ⇆ ⓡAnnexe11 ⇆ ⓡ

WELSHPOOL   Map 07 SJ20

Welshpool ☎ Castle Caerinion (0938) 83249
Undulating, hilly, heathland course with bracing air. Testing
holes are 2nd (par 5), 14th (par 3), 17th (par 3) and a
memorable 18th.
18 holes, 5708yds, Par 70, SSS 69, Course record 68.
Club membership 550.
Visitors   restricted at weekends.
Societies   must book in advance.
Green Fees £10 per day (£20 weekends & bank holidays).
Facilities ⊗ by prior arrangement ⓑ 🍷 ♀ ♨ 🏠
Location   Golfa Hill (3m W off A458)
Hotel   ★★65% Royal Oak Hotel, WELSHPOOL
               ☎ (0938) 552217 24 ⇆ ⓡ

———————————————— • ————————————————

SOUTH GLAMORGAN

———————————————— • ————————————————

BARRY   Map 03 ST16

Brynhill ☎ (0446) 720277 & 735061
Meadowland course with some hard walking. Prevailing west
wind.
18 holes, 6077yds, Par 71, SSS 69.
Club membership 500.
Visitors   must have a handicap certificate. May not play
                 on Sun.
Societies   weekdays only.
Green Fees £20 (£25 Sat).
Facilities ⊗ ⊞ ⓑ 🍷 ♀ ♨ 🏠 ⓡ
Leisure   snooker.
Location   Port Rd (1.25m N on B4050)
Hotel   ★★★57% Mount Sorrell Hotel, Porthkerry Rd,
               BARRY ☎ (0446) 740069 45 ⇆ ⓡ

RAF St Athan ☎ St Athan (0446) 797186 & 751043
This is a very windy course with wind straight off the sea to
make all holes interesting. Further interest is added by this
being a very tight course with lots of trees.
9 holes, 6452yds, Par 71, SSS 71.
Club membership 350.
Visitors   not Sun am.
Societies   apply by letter.
Green Fees £10 (£15 weekends & bank holidays).
Facilities ⊗ ⊞ ⓑ 🍷 ♀ ♨ ⓡ Neil Gillette.
Location   St Athan (between Barry & Llantwit Major)
Hotel   ★★66% West House Country Hotel &
               Restaurant, West St, LLANTWIT MAJOR
               ☎ (0446) 792406 & 793726 21 ⇆ ⓡ

St Andrews Major
A new 9-hole, Pay and Play course with 6 Par 4s and 1 Par 5.
9 holes, 3100yds, Par 35.
Club membership 500.
Visitors   must have own clubs and be appropriately
                 dressed including golf shoes.
Societies   contact in advance.
Green Fees not confirmed.

▶

Facilities ⊗ ⅷ (summer only) ⅙ � ♀ ♨ ⩍ ☖ ⌁ ⍪
Location Coldbrook Rd, Argae Ln, nr Cadoxton (off Barry new link road)
Hotel ★★★⯭74% Egerton Grey Country House Hotel, Porthkerry, BARRY ☎ (0446) 711666 10 ⇆ ⍜

CARDIFF Map 03 ST17

Cardiff ☎ (0222) 753320
Parkland course, where trees form natural hazards. Interesting variety of holes, mostly bunkered.
18 holes, 6016yds, Par 70, SSS 70.
Club membership 930.
Visitors must play with member at weekends.
Societies Thu only.
Green Fees £28 per round.
Facilities ⊗ ⅷ ⅙ ▣ ♀ ♨ ⩍ ⌁ Terry Hanson.
Location Sherborne Av, Cyncoed (3m N of city centre)
Hotel B Forte Posthouse, Pentwyn Rd, Pentwyn, CARDIFF ☎ (0222) 731212 142 ⇆ ⍜

Llanishen ☎ (0222) 755078
Mountain course, with hard walking overlooking the Bristol Channel.
18 holes, 5296yds, Par 68, SSS 66.
Club membership 900.
Visitors must play with member at weekends & bank holidays. Must contact in advance and have a handicap certificate.
Societies Thu only.
Green Fees £22 per day.
Facilities ⊗ ⅷ ⅙ & ▣ (ex Mon) ♀ ♨ ⩍ ⌁
Leisure snooker.
Location Cwm Lisvane (5m N of city centre off A469)
Hotel B Forte Posthouse, Pentwyn Rd, Pentwyn, CARDIFF ☎ (0222) 731212 142 ⇆ ⍜

Peterstone ☎ (0633) 680009
Parkland course with abundant water features and several long drives (15th, 601yds).
18 holes, 6600yds, Par 71, SSS 70.
Club membership 735.
Visitors must have reasonable golfing ability and correct dress code. Book by phone.
Societies must apply in advance.
Green Fees £20 per day; £15 per round (£27.50/£22.50 weekends).
Facilities ⊗ ⅷ (Wed-Sat) ⅙ ▣ ♀ ♨ ⩍ ⌁ Michael Pycroft.
Leisure fishing, snooker, buggies.
Location Peterstone, Wentloog (SW Newport, A48 Castleton, through Marshfield)
Hotel B Forte Posthouse, Pentwyn Rd, Pentwyn, CARDIFF ☎ (0222) 731212 142 ⇆ ⍜

Radyr ☎ (0222) 842408
Hillside, parkland course which can be windy. Good views.
18 holes, 6031yds, Par 69, SSS 70, Course record 63.
Club membership 870.
Visitors must play with member at weekends. Must contact in advance and have an introduction from own club.
Societies must contact in advance.
Green Fees not confirmed.
Facilities ⊗ ⅷ ⅙ ▣ ♀ ♨ ⩍ ⌁ Steve Gough.

Leisure snooker.
Location Drysgol Rd, Radyr (4.5m NW of city centre off A4119)
Hotel ★★★★58% Cardiff Park Thistle, Park Place, CARDIFF ☎ (0222) 383471 119 ⇆ ⍜

St Mellons ☎ (0633) 680408
This parkland course comprises quite a few par-3 holes and provides some testing golf. It is indeed a challenge to the single handicap golfer. The 12th hole runs over a stream, making an accurate drive virtually essential.
18 holes, 6080yds, Par 70, SSS 70.
Club membership 800.
Visitors must contact in advance & have handicap certificate. With member only at weekends.
Societies must telephone in advance.
Green Fees not confirmed.
Facilities ⊗ ⅷ ⅙ ▣ ♀ ♨ ⩍ ⌁
Leisure caddy car for hire.
Location St Mellons (5m NE off A48)
Hotel B Forte Posthouse, Pentwyn Rd, Pentwyn, CARDIFF ☎ (0222) 731212 142 ⇆ ⍜

Whitchurch ☎ (0222) 620985
Well manicured parkland course, with easy walking.
18 holes, 6319yds, Par 71, SSS 70, Course record 62.
Club membership 1000.
Visitors must have a handicap certificate. Restricted Sat (Apr-Oct), Sun (Oct-Apr).
Societies Thu only. Must contact in writing.
Green Fees £25 (£30 weekends & bank holidays).
Facilities ⊗ ⅷ ⅙ ▣ ♀ ♨ ⩍ ☖ ⌁ Eddie Clark.
Location Whitchurch (4m N of city centre on A470)
Hotel ★★★★58% Cardiff Park Thistle, Park Place, CARDIFF ☎ (0222) 383471 119 ⇆ ⍜

DINAS POWIS Map 03 ST17

Dinas Powis ☎ (0222) 512727
Parkland/downland course with views over the Bristol Channel and the seaside resort of Barry.
18 holes, 5377yds, Par 67, SSS 66.
Club membership 620.
Visitors must play with member at weekends. Must have an introduction from own club.
Societies must contact in advance.
Green Fees £20 per day (with member only weekends).
Facilities ⊗ ⅷ ⅙ ▣ ♀ ♨ ⩍ ⌁ G Bennett.
Location Old High Walls (NW side of village)
Hotel ★★★57% Mount Sorrell Hotel, Porthkerry Rd, BARRY ☎ (0446) 740069 45 ⇆ ⍜

PENARTH Map 03 ST17

Glamorganshire ☎ Cardiff (0222) 701185
Parkland course, overlooking the Bristol Channel.
18 holes, 6181yds, Par 70, SSS 70.
Club membership 1000.
Visitors must be a member of a recognised golf club & have a handicap certificate. May not play on competition & society days. Must contact in advance.
Societies Thu & Fri only. Must contact in advance.
Green Fees £24 per day (£30 weekends & bank holidays).
Facilities ⊗ ⅷ ⅙ ▣ ♀ ♨ ⩍ ⌁ Andrew Kerr Smith.

Leisure squash, snooker.
Location Lavernock Rd (S side of town centre on B4267)
Hotel ★65% Walton House Hotel, 37 Victoria Rd, PENARTH ☎ (0222) 707782 13rm(11 ⇌ ♠)

WENVOE
Map 03 ST17

Wenvoe Castle ☎ Cardiff (0222) 594371
Parkland course which is hilly for first 9 holes. Lake, situated 280 yds from tee at 10th hole, is a hazard.
18 holes, 6422yds, Par 72, SSS 71, Course record 68.
Club membership 600.
Visitors must be a member of a recognised golf club & have a handicap certificate. Must play with member at weekends. Must contact in advance and have an introduction from own club.
Societies must contact in writing.
Green Fees not confirmed.
Facilities ⊗ ⅲ ╚ ☕ ♀ ♨ ♨ (R J Wyer.
Location 1m S off A4050
Hotel ★★★♣74% Egerton Grey Country House Hotel, Porthkerry, BARRY ☎ (0446) 711666 10 ⇌ ♠

WEST GLAMORGAN

CLYDACH
Map 03 SN60

Inco ☎ (0792) 844216
Flat meadowland course.
12 holes, 6303yds, Par 71, SSS 70.
Club membership 300.
Visitors no restrictions.
Societies must contact in advance.
Green Fees not confirmed.
Facilities ╚ ♀ ♨
Location 0.75m SE on B4291
Hotel ★★62% Oak Tree Parc Hotel, Birchgrove Rd, BIRCHGROVE ☎ (0792) 817781 10 ⇌ ♠

GLYNNEATH
Map 03 SN80

Glynneath ☎ (0639) 720452
Attractive hillside golf overlooking the Vale of Neath in the foothills of the Brecon Beacons National Park. Reasonably level farmland/wooded course.
18 holes, 5560yds, Par 68, SSS 67, Course record 67.
Club membership 580.
Visitors restricted starting times at weekend.
Societies welcome mid-week. Must book in advance.
Green Fees £15 per day; £12 per round (£18 per day weekends).
Facilities ╚ ☕ ♀ ♨ ♨
Leisure snooker.
Location Pen-y-graig, Pontneathvaughan (2m NE on B4242)
Hotel ★★62% Oak Tree Parc Hotel, Birchgrove Rd, BIRCHGROVE ☎ (0792) 817781 10 ⇌ ♠

NEATH
Map 03 SS79

Neath ☎ (0639) 643615 & 632759
Mountain course, with spectacular views. Testing holes: 10th par 4; 12th par 5; 15th par 4.
18 holes, 6492yds, Par 72, SSS 72, Course record 66.
Club membership 700.
Visitors with member only weekends & bank holidays.
Societies should either telephone or write in advance.
Green Fees £17 per day.
Facilities ⊗ ⅲ by prior arrangement ╚ ☕ ♀ ♨ ♨ ⚲ (E M Bennett.
Leisure snooker.
Location Cadoxton (2m NE off A4230)
Hotel ★★65% Castle Hotel, The Parade, NEATH ☎ (0639) 641119 & 643581 28 ⇌ ♠

Swansea Bay ☎ Skewen (0792) 814153
Fairly level seaside links with part-sand dunes.
18 holes, 6605yds, Par 72, SSS 70.
Club membership 500.
Visitors must have a handicap certificate.
Societies must book in advance.
Green Fees not confirmed.
Facilities ⊗ ⅲ by prior arrangement ╚ ☕ ♀ ♨ ♨ (Mike Day.
Leisure riding, snooker.
Location Jersey Marine (4m SW off A48)
Hotel ★★65% Castle Hotel, The Parade, NEATH ☎ (0639) 641119 & 643581 28 ⇌ ♠

PONTARDAWE
Map 03 SN70

Pontardawe ☎ (0792) 863118
Meadowland course situated on plateau 600 ft above sea-level with good views over Bristol Channel and Brecon Beacons.
18 holes, 6162yds, Par 70, SSS 70.
Club membership 700.
Visitors must contact in advance, but may not play on weekends.
Societies welcome weekdays by prior arrangement.
Green Fees £19 per day.
Facilities ⊗ ⅲ by prior arrangement ╚ ☕ ♀ ♨ ♨ (Gary Hopkins.
Leisure snooker.
Location Cefn Llan (N side of town centre M4 junc 45 off A4067)
Hotel ★★62% Oak Tree Parc Hotel, Birchgrove Rd, BIRCHGROVE ☎ (0792) 817781 10 ⇌ ♠

PONTLLIW
Map 02 SS69

Allt-y-Graban ☎ Pontardulais (0792) 885757
A new course opened for 1994.It is a 9-hole course but with plans for 12 holes. There are 6 par-4 holes and 3 par-3 holes. The 4th is a challenging hole with a blind tee shoot into the valley and a dogleg to the left onto an elevated green.
9 holes, 4420yds, Par 66, SSS 61.
Club membership 100.
Visitors no restrictions for 1994/5.
Societies telephone in advance.
Green Fees £9 per 18 holes; £6 per 9 holes.
Facilities catering planned for summer 1994 ▶

Location Allt-y-Graban Rd
Hotel ★★★61% Fforest Hotel, Pontardulais Rd,
Fforestfach, SWANSEA
☎ (0792) 588711 34 ⇆ ↑

PORT TALBOT
Map 03 SS78

British Steel Port Talbot ☎ (0639) 814182
A 9 hole course with two lakes. All the holes are affected by
crosswinds and the 7th, Par 3, is alongside a deep stream, so
is very tight.
9 holes, 4726yds, Par 64, SSS 62, Course record 64.
Club membership 270.
Visitors may not play on competition days.
Societies telephone or write to the secretary.
Green Fees £7 per 18 holes.
Facilities ⊗ ᴸᴸ ♀ ⌂
Leisure hard tennis courts, snooker, bowls greens in
summer.
Location Sports & Social Club, Margam
Hotel ★★★60% Aberavan Beach Hotel,
PORT TALBOT
☎ (0639) 884949 52 ⇆

SOUTHGATE
Map 02 SS58

Pennard ☎ (0792) 233131
Undulating, cliff-top seaside links with good coastal views.
18 holes, 6289yds, Par 71, SSS 71, Course record 66.
Club membership 779.
Visitors a handicap certificate is required.
Societies welcome except weekends & bank holidays,
must apply by letter.
Green Fees £24 (£30 weekends & bank holidays).
Facilities ⊗ & ∭ by prior arrangement ᴸᴸ 🍺 ♀ (times
vary) ⌂ ⌂ ↑ ↑ M V Bennett.
Leisure squash, snooker.
Location 2 Southgate Rd (NW side of village)
Hotel ★★65% Nicholaston House Hotel, Nicholaston,
PENMAEN ☎ (0792) 371317 11 ⇆

SWANSEA
Map 03 SS69

Clyne ☎ (0792) 401989
Moorland course, very open to the wind and with grazing
rights for local commoners.
18 holes, 6323yds, Par 70, SSS 71, Course record 64.
Club membership 800.
Visitors must be member of a club with handicap
certificate and contact in advance.
Societies must telephone in advance.
Green Fees not confirmed.
Facilities ⊗ ∭ ᴸᴸ 🍺 (no catering Mon) ♀ ⌂ 🏠
↑ Mark Bevan.
Leisure snooker, practice facilities.
Location 120 Owls Lodge Ln, The Mayals, Blackpyl
(3.5m SW on B4436 off A4067)
Hotel ★★69% Langland Court, Langland Court Rd,
LANGLAND
☎ (0792) 361545 16 ⇆ ↑Annexe5 ⇆ ↑

Langland Bay ☎ (0792) 366023
Parkland course overlooking Gower coast. The par 4, 6th is
an uphill dog-leg open to the wind, and the par 3, 16th (151
yds) is aptly named 'Death or Glory'.
18 holes, 5857yds, Par 70, SSS 69.
Club membership 850.
Visitors no restrictions.
Societies must telephone in advance.
Green Fees £24 summer; £18 winter (£26/£20 weekends).
Facilities ⊗ ∭ ᴸᴸ 🍺 (no catering Mon) ♀ ⌂ 🏠 ↑
Location Langland Bay (6m W on A4067)
Hotel ★★69% Langland Court, Langland Court Rd,
LANGLAND
☎ (0792) 361545 16 ⇆ ↑Annexe5 ⇆ ↑

Morriston ☎ (0792) 796528
Pleasant parkland course.
18 holes, 5800yds, Par 68, SSS 68.
Club membership 580.
Visitors must have handicap certificate.
Societies apply in writing.
Green Fees £18 per day (£25 weekends & bank holidays).
Facilities ⊗ ∭ ᴸᴸ 🍺 (no catering on Mon) ♀ ⌂ 🏠 ↑
↑ D A Rees.
Location 160 Clasemont Rd (5m N on A48)
Hotel ★★62% Oak Tree Parc Hotel, Birchgrove Rd,
BIRCHGROVE
☎ (0792) 817781 10 ⇆ ↑

UPPER KILLAY
Map 02 SS59

Fairwood Park ☎ Swansea (0792) 203648 & 297849
Championship parkland course on Gower coast with good
views and easy walking.
18 holes, 6741yds, Par 72, SSS 72.
Club membership 720.
Visitors welcome except when championship or club
matches are being held. Must contact in advance.
Societies must contact in advance.
Green Fees £25 per day (£30 weekends & bank holidays).
Facilities ⊗ ∭ ᴸᴸ 🍺 ♀ ⌂ 🏠 ↑ ↑
Leisure snooker.
Location Blackhills Ln (1.5m S off A4118)
Hotel ★71% Windsor Lodge Hotel, Mount Pleasant,
SWANSEA
☎ (0792) 642158 & 652744 18rm(12 ⇆4 ↑)

YSTALYFERA
Map 03 SN70

Palleg ☎ (0639) 842193
Heathland course liable to become heavy going after winter
rain.
9 holes, 6400yds, Par 72, SSS 72.
Club membership 200.
Visitors restricted Sat (Apr-Sep) & Sun mornings in
winter.
Societies must contact two months in advance.
Green Fees not confirmed.
Facilities ⊗ (Sun only) ᴸᴸ (Thu & Sat) ♀ (ex Mon) ⌂
Location Lower Cwm-twrch (1.5m N off A4068)
Hotel ★★62% Oak Tree Parc Hotel, Birchgrove Rd,
BIRCHGROVE
☎ (0792) 817781 10 ⇆ ↑

For an explanation of symbols and
abbreviations, see page 5

NORTHERN IRELAND

Top courses for top players

ONE day last year four Americans discovered to their cost just how difficult Royal Portrush can be. By the time they had reached the 16th hole they did not have a golf ball left among them, having lost 53!

There were extenuating circumstances. The wind was blowing wildly and, as their round was between Portrush's hosting of the British Amateur Championship and the North of Ireland Championship, the rough had been allowed to grow to a fierce height. In normal conditions Royal Portrush is difficult, but playable, and a must for any golfing visitor to the North of Ireland. Regularly rated among the top 20 courses in the world, it is the only club in Northern Ireland to have hosted the Open Championship. That was back in 1951 and the winner, Max Faulkner, was so in love with the place and so much in form that, before his final round, he signed his autograph 'Max Faulkner, Open Champion'.

One of the highlights of the year at Portrush is the Black Bush tournament, one of the world's biggest amateur events with an entry of 1,200, which is held in June. The Portstewart, Castlerock and Ballycastle courses are also used and there are prizes for individual and team performances. Competitors enter from other parts of the British Isles, America, Canada and elsewhere. A two-day ladies' tournament is held at Bushfoot at the same time.

Another venue not to be missed in this country of marvellous golf is Royal County Down, set on the sand dunes beside the town of Newcastle, where the Mountains of Mourne sweep down to the sea. Founded in 1889, the club employed the legendary Tom Morris to lay out the course. His fee was four guineas, but as he said at the time it was 90 per cent on the way to being a golf course before he got to work putting in tees, greens and bunkers. Also rated highly on the list of the world's top courses, it was one of the first links layouts to have two loops of nine holes starting and finishing at the clubhouse.

A treat awaits those who play at Portstewart Golf Club, a close challenger for the title of Northern Ireland's top course. Weaker holes have been replaced by seven new holes in the sandhills behind the first green – the work being done by their own staff at a cost of £100,000, peanuts when you consider the cost of golf course construction nowadays.

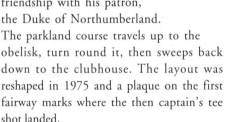

Golfers at the County Armagh club play round the obelisk, a huge structure built in 1782 by Richard Robinson, Archbishop of Armagh, to commemorate his friendship with his patron, the Duke of Northumberland. The parkland course travels up to the obelisk, turn round it, then sweeps back down to the clubhouse. The layout was reshaped in 1975 and a plaque on the first fairway marks where the then captain's tee shot landed.

Physical features also form a part of many Irish courses such as the Malone club where a 22-acre lake is the focal point. It comes into play at several holes, especially the par three 15th, where the tee and green are built on the lake with little but water in between. The lake also provides a stern finish, catching any shots sliced from the 18th tee. Ardglass is a cliff-top course on the south-east coast of County Down, providing a view of the Isle of Man on a clear day. It has a strong Viking influence, which is shown in some local names, and alongside the clubhouse are the remains of the first Norman castle built in 1177. Four cannons, in front of the clubhouse, are relics of smuggling and piracy in the area.

Such is the beauty of Irish courses that even Belvoir Park close to the centre of Belfast, is as tranquil as a country course, for huge mature trees line every fairway making you forget you are so close to the city. The course was built in 1927 by Harry Colt – whose other courses included Sunningdale – with the use of teams of horses and hand ploughs.

There are many golfing delights for those who go to Northern Ireland for golf. And there is another advantage – it's cheap.

IAN RIACH
Golf correspondent, *Scottish Sunday Express*

NORTHERN IRELAND

CO ANTRIM

ANTRIM
Map 01 D5

Massereene ☎ (0849) 428096
The first nine holes are parkland, while the second, adjacent to the shore of Lough Neagh, have more of a links character with sandy ground.
18 holes, 6614yds, Par 72, SSS 71.
Club membership 900.
Visitors welcome except for Sat which is competition day.
Societies apply in writing.
Green Fees £18 (£23 weekends).
Facilities ⊗ ⅢⓁ ♕ ♀⚐ 🏠⚑⚓ ꞁ Jim Smyth.
Leisure snooker, indoor bowling in winter.
Location 51 Lough Rd (1m SW of town)
Hotel ★★★62% Adair Arms Hotel, Ballymoney Rd, BALLYMENA ☎ (0266) 653674 39 ⇔ 🐾

BALLYCASTLE
Map 01 D6

Ballycastle ☎ (02657) 62536
An unusual mixture of terrain beside the sea, with magnificent views from all parts. The first five holes are inland type; the middle holes on the Warren are links type and the rest, on high ground, are heath type.
18 holes, 5177mtrs, Par 71, SSS 68.
Club membership 921.
Visitors are welcome during the week.
Societies apply in writing.
Green Fees £13 per day (£18 per round weekends).
Facilities ⊗ & Ⅲ by prior arrangement Ⓛ ♕ ♀⚐ 🏠 ꞁ Ian McLaughlin.
Leisure snooker.
Location Cushendall Rd (between Portrush & Cushendall (A2))
Hotel ★★57% Thornlea Hotel, 6 Coast Rd, CUSHENDALL ☎ (02667) 71223 13rm(1 ⇔11 🐾)

BALLYCLARE
Map 01 D5

Ballyclare ☎ (0960) 322696 & 342352
Parkland course with lots of trees and shrubs and water hazards provided by the river, streams and lakes.
18 holes, 5745mtrs, Par 71, SSS 72.
Club membership 980.
Visitors may not play at weekends before 3pm.
Societies must contact in writing.
Green Fees £14 per round (£20 weekends & bank holidays).
Facilities ⊗ Ⅲ Ⓛ ♀⚐
Leisure snooker.
Location 25 Springdale Rd (1.5m N)
Hotel ★★★69% Stormont Hotel, 587 Upper Newtonards Rd, BELFAST ☎ (0232) 658621 106 ⇔ 🐾

BALLYGALLY
Map 01 D5

Cairndhu ☎ Larne (0574) 583248
Built on a hilly headland, this course is both testing and scenic, with wonderful coastal views.
18 holes, 5598mtrs, Par 70, SSS 69.
Club membership 875.
Visitors may not play on Sat.
Societies must contact in writing.
Green Fees £12 (£20 Sun).
Facilities ⊗ Ⅲ Ⓛ ♕ ♀⚐ 🏠⚑ ꞁ Robert Walker.
Leisure snooker.
Location 192 Coast Rd (4m N of Larne on coast road)
Hotel ★★★61% Ballygally Castle Hotel, 274 Coast Rd, BALLYGALLY ☎ (0574) 583212 30 ⇔

BALLYMENA
Map 01 D5

Ballymena ☎ (0266) 861487
Parkland course of level heathland with plenty of bunkers.
18 holes, 5654yds, Par 68, SSS 67.
Visitors may not play on Tue or Sat.
Societies must contact in advance.
Green Fees not confirmed.
Facilities ⊗ Ⅲ Ⓛ ♀⚑ ꞁ James Gallagher.
Leisure snooker, bowling green.
Location 128 Raceview Rd (2m E on A42)
Hotel ★★★62% Adair Arms Hotel, Ballymoney Rd, BALLYMENA ☎ (0266) 653674 39 ⇔ 🐾

CARRICKFERGUS
Map 01 D5

Carrickfergus ☎ (09603) 363713 & 351803
Parkland course, fairly level but nevertheless demanding, with a notorious water hazard at the 1st. Well maintained and with nice views.
18 holes, 5759yds, Par 68, SSS 68.
Club membership 815.
Visitors restrictions at weekends.
Societies must contact in advance.
Green Fees £13 (£18 weekends & bank holidays).
Facilities ⊗ Ⅲ Ⓛ ♕ ♀⚐ 🏠 ꞁ Raymond Stevenson.
Leisure snooker, caddy cars.
Location 25 North Rd (9m NE of Belfast on A2)
Hotel ★★★58% Chimney Corner Hotel, 630 Antrim Rd, NEWTOWNABBEY ☎ (0232) 844925 & 844851 63 ⇔ 🐾

Greenisland ☎ (0232) 862236
9 holes, 5536mtrs, Par 71, SSS 68.
Visitors welcome, may be restricted on Sat.
Societies by prior arrangement.
Green Fees not confirmed.
Facilities catering available
Location 156 Upper Rd, Greenisland
Hotel ★★★58% Chimney Corner Hotel, 630 Antrim Rd, NEWTOWNABBEY ☎ (0232) 844925 & 844851 63 ⇔ 🐾

CUSHENDALL
Map 01 D6

Cushendall ☎ (02667) 71318
Scenic course with spectacular views over the Sea of Moyle and Red Bay to the Mull of Kintyre. The River Dall winds

through the course, coming into play in seven of the nine holes.
9 holes, 4386mtrs, Par 66, SSS 63.
Club membership 714.

Visitors　restricted on Sun.
Societies　must contact in writing.
Green Fees　£8 per day (£10 weekends & bank holidays).
Facilities　⊗ ∭ & 🝯 by prior arrangement � ♀⅄
Location　21 Shore Rd
Hotel　★★57% Thornlea Hotel, 6 Coast Rd, CUSHENDALL
　　　　　☎ (02667) 71223 13rm(1 ⇋11 🐾)

LARNE　　　　　　　　　　　　　Map 01 D5

Larne ☎ Islandmagee (0960) 382228
An exposed part links, part heathland course offering a good test, particularly on the last three holes along the sea shore.
9 holes, 6066yds, Par 70, SSS 69, Course record 66.
Club membership 450.

Visitors　may not play on Sat before 5.30pm.
Societies　apply in writing.
Green Fees　£8 per round (£15 weekends & bank holidays).
Facilities　⊗ ∭ & 🝯 (weekends or by prior arrangement) � ♀⅄
Leisure　snooker, indoor bowling.
Location　54 Ferris Bay Rd, Islandmagee
Hotel　★★★61% Ballygally Castle Hotel, 274 Coast Rd, BALLYGALLY ☎ (0574) 583212 30 ⇋

LISBURN　　　　　　　　　　　　Map 01 D5

Aberdelghy ☎ (0846) 662738
This parkland course has no bunkers but the par-3 3rd high on the hill and the 5th hole over the dam provide a challenge. The par-4 6th hole is a long dog leg.
9 holes, 2192mtrs, Par 33, SSS 65.
Club membership 150.

Visitors　restricted Sat 8-11am.
Societies　telephone in advance.
Green Fees　£6 per 18 holes; £3.20 per 9 holes (£6.50/£3.70 weekends & bank holidays.
Facilities　⅄ 🝮 ⑂ ☕ Ian Murdoch.
Leisure　practice area, lessons, trolley hire.
Location　Bell's Ln, Lambeg (1.5m N of Lisburn off A1)
Hotel　B Forte Crest, Kingsway, Dunmurry, BELFAST ☎ (0232) 612101 82 ⇋ 🐾

Lisburn ☎ (0846) 677216
Meadowland course, fairly level, with plenty of trees and shrubs. Challenging last three holes.
18 holes, 6572yds, Par 72, SSS 72, Course record 64.
Club membership 1000.

Visitors　must play with member at weekends.
Societies　must contact in writing.
Green Fees　not confirmed.
Facilities　⊗ ∭ ▇ ♀⅄ 🝮 ⑂ ☕ B R Campbell.
Leisure　snooker.
Location　Blaris Lodge, 68 Eglantine Rd (2m from town on A1)
Hotel　★★★69% Stormont Hotel, 587 Upper Newtonards Rd, BELFAST
　　　　　☎ (0232) 658621 106 ⇋ 🐾

MAZE　　　　　　　　　　　　　　Map 01 D5

Down Royal Park ☎ Lisburn (0846) 621339
The 9-hole Valley course and the 18-hole Down Royal Park are easy walking, undulating heathland courses. Down Royal's 2nd hole is 628yards and thought to be among the best par 5 holes in Ireland.
Down Royal Park: 18 holes, 6824yds, Par 72, Course record 73.
Valley: 9 holes, 2500yds, Par 33.

Visitors　no restrictions.
Societies　reservations in advance.
Green Fees　£12 weekdays (£14 Sat, £17 Sun & bank holidays).
Facilities　⊗ ∭ 🝯 ▇ (No catering on Mon) ♀⅄ ☕
Location　Dunygarton Rd (inside Down Royal Race Course)
Hotel　★★★61% Dukes Hotel, 65 University St, BELFAST ☎ (0232) 236666 21 ⇋ 🐾

PORTBALLINTRAE　　　　　　　Map 01 C6

Bushfoot ☎ (02657) 31317
A seaside links course with superb views in an area of outstanding beauty. A challenging par-3 7th is ringed bybunkers with out-of-bounds left, while the 3rd has a blind approach. Also a putting green and pitch & putt course.
9 holes, 5876yds, Par 70, SSS 68, Course record 62.
Club membership 863.

Visitors　may not play Sat-Sun in Jul & Aug unless with member.
Societies　must contact in advance.
Green Fees　£12-£15 per 18 holes.
Facilities　⊗ ∭ 🝯 ▇ ♀⅄ ⑂
Leisure　snooker, putting.
Location　50 Bushfoot Rd, Portballintrae (off Ballaghmore rd)
Hotel　★★60% Beach House Hotel, The Sea Front, PORTBALLINTRAE
　　　　　☎ (02657) 31214 32 ⇋ 🐾

PORTRUSH　　　　　　　　　　　Map 01 C6

ROYAL PORTRUSH　See page 319

WHITEHEAD　　　　　　　　　　Map 01 D5

Whitehead ☎ (0960) 353631
Undulating parkland course with magnificent sea views.
18 holes, 6426yds, Par 72, SSS 71.
Club membership 850.

Visitors　may not play on Sat. Must play with member on Sun.
Societies　must contact in advance.
Green Fees　£11 (£17 Sun).
Facilities　🝯 ▇ ♀⅄ 🝮 ⑂ Thomas Loughran.
Leisure　snooker.
Location　McCrae's Brae (0.5m N)
Hotel　★★★58% Chimney Corner Hotel, 630 Antrim Rd, NEWTOWNABBEY
　　　　　☎ (0232) 844925 & 844851 63 ⇋ 🐾

ROYAL PORTRUSH

PORTRUSH ☎(0265) 822311   **Map 01 D4**

John Ingham writes: It was more than thirty years ago that I first saw Royal Portrush, but the memory lingers on. That week in 1960, the great Joe Carr won the British Amateur Championship for his third, and last, time. But everyone there was a winner; the sun shone, and the course glistened as the foaming ocean was almost blown inland on to the briar roses that dotted the rough.

What a splendid seaside paradise this is, I wrote in a London evening newspaper, whose readers were keen to follow players such as Joe Carr and Michael Bonallack. There among the gallery was the late Fred Daly, winner of the 1947 Open and the only Irisman ever to win.

The man who designed this course was Harry S Colt, a name that appears as a creator of many fine courses. This one is considered among the six best in the United Kingdom. It is spectacular, breathtaking, but one of the tightest driving tests known to man because, if you get in the long stuff, you may stay there. On a clear day, you have a fine view of Islay and the Paps of Jura - seen from the 3rd tee. Then there's the Giant's Causeway, from the 5th, as good a downhill dogleg hole as you'll find anywhere.

While the greens have to be 'read' from the start, there are fairways up and down valleys, and holes called Calamity Corner and Purgatory for good reason. The second hole, called Giant's Grave, is 509 yards but there's an even longer one waiting for you at the 17th, while the last hole, a 479-yarder, nearly cost Max Faulkner his 1951 Open title. He hit a crooked drive, and had to bend his second shot with a wooden club. Dressed in primrose-coloured slacks, his colourful plumage and out-going attitude attracted most of the small crowd.

The Open did not return to Portrush and championship golf is the loser because the place is a gem. Founded in 1888, it was also the venue of the first professional golf event held in Ireland, when in 1895, Sandy Herd beat Harry Vardon in the final.

You'll love it.

Membership 1300

Visitors must contact in advance, and have a letter of introduction from their own club. Restricted Saturday and Sunday morning

Societies must apply in writing.

Green fees Dunluce Links £37.50 per day (£45 weekends); Valley Links £15 per day (£20 weekends); Skerries Course: £2

Facilities ⊗ ⅗ ⅃ ♨ ☂ ♀ (all day) ⛳ 🏠 ⅂ 2 practice grounds, caddies & caddy cars ⅂ (Dai Stevenson)

Leisure snooker

Location Bushmills Rd (0.5m from Portrush on main road to Bushmills)

45 holes. Dunluce Links: 18 holes, 6794 yds, Par 72, SSS 73, course record 66
Valley Links: 18 holes, 6273 yds, Par 70, SSS 70, course record 65
Skerries Course: 9 holes, 1187 yds

WHERE TO STAY AND EAT NEARBY

HOTELS:
PORTRUSH
★★★ 60% Causeway Coast, 36 Ballyreagh Rd. ☎ (0265) 822435
21 ⇆ ⋔ British & French cuisine

RESTAURANT:
PORTRUSH
✕ ✕ ❀❀ Ramore, The Harbour.
☎(0265) 824313. French cuisine

CO ARMAGH

ARMAGH   Map 01 C5

County Armagh ☎ (0861) 522501
Mature parkland course with excellent views of Armagh city
and its surroundings.
18 holes, 5641mtrs, Par 70, SSS 69, Course record 65.
Club membership 1000.
Visitors   may not play noon-3pm on Sat or noon-2pm on
              Sun. Must contact in advance.
Societies   must contact in writing.
Green Fees   not confirmed.
Facilities   ⊗ ⅲ ┗ & ▦ (all ex Mon) ♀ ⚑ 🏠
              (Alan Rankin.
Leisure   snooker.
Location   The Demesne (On the Newry road)
Hotel   ★★★69% Stormont Hotel, 587 Upper
              Newtonards Rd, BELFAST
              ☎ (0232) 658621 106 ⇆ 🐾

LURGAN   Map 01 D5

Craigavon Golf & Ski Centre ☎ (0762) 326606
Parkland course with a lake and stream providing water hazards.
18 holes, 6496yds, Par 72, SSS 72.
Visitors   no restrictions.
Societies   must contact in advance.
Green Fees   not confirmed.
Facilities   ⊗ ⅲ ▦ ⚑ 🏠 ✛ (Des Paul.
Leisure   putting green, floodlit driving range.
Location   Turmoyra Ln (2m N at Silverwood off the M1)
Hotel   ★★★69% Stormont Hotel, 587 Upper
              Newtonards Rd, BELFAST
              ☎ (0232) 658621 106 ⇆ 🐾

Lurgan ☎ (0762) 322087
Testing parkland course bordering Lurgan Park Lake with a
need for accurate shots. Drains well in wet weather and suits
a long straight hitter.
18 holes, 5836mtrs, Par 70, SSS 70.
Club membership 800.
Visitors   may not play Wed & Sat.
Societies   must contact in writing.
Green Fees   £15 (£20 weekends & bank holidays).
Facilities   ⊗ ⅲ ┗ ▦ ♀ ⚑ 🏠 (Des Paul.
Leisure   snooker, putting green, practice area.
Location   The Demesne (0.5m from town centre near
              Lurgan Park)
Hotel   ★★★69% Stormont Hotel, 587 Upper
              Newtonards Rd, BELFAST
              ☎ (0232) 658621 106 ⇆ 🐾

PORTADOWN   Map 01 D5

Portadown ☎ (0762) 355356
Well wooded parkland course on the banks of the River
Bann, which features among the water hazards.
18 holes, 5621mtrs, Par 70, SSS 70, Course record 65.
Club membership 1014.
Visitors   may not play on Tue & Sat.
Societies   must contact in advance.

Green Fees   not confirmed.
Facilities   ⊗ ⅲ ┗ ▦ ♀ ⚑ 🏠 ✛ (Paul Stevenson.
Leisure   squash, snooker, indoor bowling.
Location   192 Gilfrod Rd (SE via A59)
Hotel   ★★★69% Stormont Hotel, 587 Upper
              Newtonards Rd, BELFAST
              ☎ (0232) 658621 106 ⇆ 🐾

TANDRAGEE   Map 01 D5

Tandragee ☎ (0762) 841272
Pleasant hilly parkland with mature trees.
18 holes, 5519mtrs, Par 69, SSS 67.
Club membership 1085.
Visitors   may not play Thu & Fri afternoon or on Sat &
              Sun before 2pm unless by prior arrangement.
Societies   Mar-Sep; must contact in writing.
Green Fees   £12 per day/round (£18 Sun & public holidays).
Facilities   ⊗ ⅲ ┗ ▦ (no catering Mon) ♀ ⚑ 🏠 ✛
              (Erill Maney.
Leisure   snooker, sauna, gymnasium.
Location   Markethill Rd (on B3 out of Tandragee towards
              Markethill)
Farmhouse   QQQQ Brook Lodge Farmhouse, 79 Old
              Ballynahinch Rd, Cargacroy, LISBURN
              ☎ (0846) 638454 5rm(3 🐾)

CO BELFAST

BELFAST   Map 01 D5

See also The Royal Belfast, Hollywood, Co Down.

Balmoral ☎ (0232) 381514
Parkland course, mainly level, with tree-lined fairways and a
stream providing a water hazard.
18 holes, 6238yds, Par 69, SSS 70.
Visitors   preferred Mon & Thu.
Societies   must contact in advance.
Green Fees   not confirmed.
Facilities   ⊗ ⅲ ♀ ✛ (Geoff Bleakley.
Location   518 Lisburn Rd (3m SW)
Hotel   ★★★69% Stormont Hotel, 587 Upper
              Newtonards Rd, BELFAST
              ☎ (0232) 658621 106 ⇆ 🐾

Cliftonville ☎ (0232) 744158
Parkland course with rivers bisecting two fairways.
9 holes, 5706mtrs, Par 70, SSS 70, Course record 66.
Club membership 430.
Visitors   may not play on Sat or on Sun mornings.
Societies   must contact in writing.
Green Fees   not confirmed.
Facilities   ⅲ by prior arrangement ♀ ⚑ 🏠
Leisure   snooker.
Location   44 Westland Rd (Between Cavehill Rd &
              Cliftonville Circus)
Hotel   ★★★69% Stormont Hotel, 587 Upper
              Newtonards Rd, BELFAST
              ☎ (0232) 658621 106 ⇆ 🐾

Dunmurry ☎ (0232) 610834

Maturing very nicely, this tricky parkland course has several memorable holes which call for skilful shots.

18 holes, 5348mtrs, Par 69, SSS 68, Course record 68.

Club membership 870.

Visitors	may not play Tue, Thu & Sat after 5pm. Play restricted Fri & to after 12.30pm Sun.
Societies	must contact in writing.
Green Fees	£14 (£20 weekends & bank holidays).
Facilities	⊗ ⫟ ᛋ ♥ (no catering Mon) ♀ ♨ ⌂ ⛳ ℓ Paul Leonard.
Leisure	snooker.
Location	91 Dunmurry Ln
Hotel	★★★69% Stormont Hotel, 587 Upper Newtonards Rd, BELFAST ☎ (0232) 658621 106 ⇌ ☟

Fortwilliam ☎ (0232) 370770

Parkland course in most attractive surroundings. The course is bisected by a lane.

18 holes, 5771yds, Par 69, SSS 68.

Visitors	preferred weekday mornings.
Societies	preferred Thu. Must contact in advance.
Green Fees	not confirmed.
Facilities	⊗ ⫟ ♀ ℓ Peter Hanna.
Leisure	snooker, practice fairway.
Location	Downview Ave (Off Antrim road)
Hotel	★★★69% Stormont Hotel, 587 Upper Newtonards Rd, BELFAST ☎ (0232) 658621 106 ⇌ ☟

Knockbracken Golf, Ski & Leisure ☎ (0232) 401811

Inland parkland course which has recently been refurbished.

18 holes, 5391yds, Par 67, SSS 68.

Club membership 400.

Visitors	must contact in advance at weekends & bank holidays.
Societies	must contact in writing.
Green Fees	not confirmed.
Facilities	⊗ ⫟ ᛋ ♥ ♀ ♨ ⌂ ⛳ ℓ D Jones/E Logue/G Loughrey.
Leisure	snooker, driving ranges, bowls, ski slope.
Location	24 Ballymaconaghy Rd
Hotel	★★★69% Stormont Hotel, 587 Upper Newtonards Rd, BELFAST ☎ (0232) 658621 106 ⇌ ☟

Malone ☎ (0232) 612758

Two parkland courses, extremely attractive with a large lake, mature trees and flowering shrubs and bordered by the River Lagan. Very well maintained and offering a challenging round.

Course 1: 18 holes, 6433yds, Par 71, SSS 71.

Course 2: 9 holes, 5784yds, SSS 68.

Club membership 1300.

Visitors	may not play on 18 hole course on Tue, Wed & Sat.
Societies	apply in writing to council.
Green Fees	not confirmed.
Facilities	⊗ ⫟ ᛋ ♥ ♀ ⌂ ℓ
Location	240 Upper Malone Rd, Dunmurry (4.5m S)
Hotel	★★★69% Stormont Hotel, 587 Upper Newtonards Rd, BELFAST ☎ (0232) 658621 106 ⇌ ☟

Ormeau ☎ (0232) 641069 & 640999

Parkland.

9 holes, 2653mtrs, Par 68, SSS 65.

Visitors	welcome weekdays & Sun. Sat after 4.30pm.
Societies	contact in advance.
Green Fees	not confirmed.
Facilities	bar & restaurant facilities
Leisure	snooker.
Location	Ravenshill Rd (S of city centre)
Hotel	★★★61% Dukes Hotel, 65 University St, BELFAST ☎ (0232) 236666 21 ⇌ ☟

Shandon Park ☎ (0232) 401856

Fairly level parkland offering a pleasant challenge.

18 holes, 6261yds, Par 70, SSS 70.

Club membership 1100.

Visitors	may not play on competition days. Must contact in advance and have a handicap certificate.
Societies	may play Mon & Fri only, applications to club.
Green Fees	£20 (£25 weekends).
Facilities	⊗ ⫟ ᛋ ♥ ♀ ♨ ⌂ ⛳ ℓ Barry Wilson.
Leisure	snooker.
Location	73 Shandon Park (Off Knock road)
Hotel	★★★69% Stormont Hotel, 587 Upper Newtonards Rd, BELFAST ☎ (0232) 658621 106 ⇌ ☟

DUNDONALD
Map 01 D5

Knock ☎ Belfast (0232) 483251

Parkland course with huge trees, deep bunkers and a river cutting across several fairways. This is a hard but fair course and will test the best of golfers.

18 holes, 6407yds, Par 70, SSS 71.

Club membership 850.

Visitors	with member only on Sat.
Societies	must contact in advance.
Green Fees	£20 per day (£25 weekends & bank holidays).
Facilities	⊗ ⫟ ᛋ ♥ ♀ ♨ ⌂ ⛳ ℓ Gordon Fairweather.
Leisure	snooker.
Location	Summerfield
Hotel	★★★★67% Culloden Hotel, HOLYWOOD ☎ (0232) 425223 91 ⇌ ☟

NEWTOWNBREDA
Map 01 D5

The Belvoir Park ☎ Belfast (0232) 491693

This undulating parkland course is not strenuous to walk, but is certainly a test of your golf, with tree-lined fairways and a particularly challenging finish at the final four holes.

18 holes, 6501yds, Par 71, SSS 71, Course record 66.

Club membership 1076.

Visitors	may not play between 1 & 2pm or on Sat.
Societies	must contact in writing.
Green Fees	£25 per day (£30 Wed, Sun & holidays).
Facilities	⊗ ⫟ ᛋ ♥ ♀ ♨ ⌂ ⛳ ℓ Maurice Kelly.
Leisure	snooker, practice facilities.
Location	73 Church Rd (3m from centre off Saintfield/Newcastle rd)
Hotel	★★★69% Stormont Hotel, 587 Upper Newtonards Rd, BELFAST ☎ (0232) 658621 106 ⇌ ☟

CO DOWN

ARDGLASS
Map 01 D5

Ardglass ☎ (0396) 841219
A scenic cliff-top seaside course with spectacular views and some memorable holes.
18 holes, 5515mtrs, Par 70, SSS 69.
Club membership 762.
Visitors must contact in advance at weekends.
Societies must contact in advance.
Green Fees £15 per day (£20 weekends & bank holidays).
Facilities ⊗ & 〗 by prior arrangement ⓑ (weekends only) ☒ ♀ ⌂ 🍴 ♟ Kevin Dorrian.
Leisure snooker.
Location Castle Pl
Hotel ★★★63% Slieve Donard Hotel, NEWCASTLE
☎ (03967) 23681 120 ⇆

ARDMILLAN
Map 01 D5

Mahee Island ☎ Killinchy (0238) 541234
An undulating parkland course, almost surrounded by water, with magnificent views of Strangford Lough and its islands, with Scrabo Tower in the background.
9 holes, 5588yds, Par 68, SSS 67, Course record 65.
Club membership 490.
Visitors may not play on Wed after 4pm or Sat before 5pm.
Societies restricted Wed evenings, Sat & some Sun ; must contact in advance.
Green Fees £10 per round (£15 weekends & public holidays).
Facilities ⌂ 🍴
Leisure pool table.
Location Comber (On Comber/Killyleagh road 0.5m from Comber)
Hotel ★★★69% Stormont Hotel, 587 Upper Newtonards Rd, BELFAST
☎ (0232) 658621 106 ⇆ ♞

BALLYNAHINCH
Map 01 D5

Spa ☎ (0238) 562365
Parkland course with tree-lined fairways and scenic views of the Mourne Mountains.
18 holes, 5938mtrs, Par 72, SSS 72.
Club membership 890.
Visitors must contact in advance but may not play on Sat; must play with member on Sun.
Societies must contact in advance.
Green Fees not confirmed.
Facilities ⊗ ⓑ ☒ ♀ ⌂
Leisure snooker.
Location 20 Grove Rd
Hotel ★★★63% Slieve Donard Hotel, NEWCASTLE
☎ (03967) 23681 120 ⇆

BANBRIDGE
Map 01 D5

Banbridge ☎ (08206) 62211
A picturesque course with excellent views of the Movene mountains. The holes are not long, but are tricky, and six new holes opened in 1992 completed the 18.

18 holes, 5003mtrs, Par 69, SSS 67, Course record 66.
Club membership 700.
Visitors may not play Tue, Sat or before 11am on Sun.
Societies must contact in writing.
Green Fees not confirmed.
Facilities ⊗ 〗 ⓑ ☒ by prior arrangement ♀ ⌂
Location 116 Huntly Rd (0.5m along Huntly road)
Hotel ★★★63% Slieve Donard Hotel, NEWCASTLE
☎ (03967) 23681 120 ⇆

BANGOR
Map 01 D5

Bangor ☎ (0247) 270922
Undulating parkland course in the town. It is well maintained and pleasant and offers a challenging round, particularly at the 5th.
18 holes, 6490yds, Par 71, SSS 70.
Club membership 1150.
Visitors preferred on Mon & Wed. (Tue is Ladies day, no visitors Sat).
Societies Mon & Wed. Must contact in advance.
Green Fees £17 (£23 Sun & bank holidays).
Facilities ⊗ 〗 ⓑ ☒ ♀ ⌂ 🍴
Location Broadway (1m from town on Donaghadee road)
Hotel ★★★64% Old Inn, 15 Main St, CRAWFORDSBURN
☎ (0247) 853255 32 ⇆ ♞

Carnalea ☎ (0247) 270368
A scenic course on the shores of Belfast Lough.
18 holes, 5574yds, Par 68, SSS 67.
Club membership 1100.
Visitors no restrictions.
Societies must contact in writing.
Green Fees £11 (£15 weekends & bank holidays).
Facilities ⊗ 〗 ⓑ ☒ ♀ ⌂ 🍴 ♟
Leisure snooker.
Location Station Rd
Hotel ★★★64% Old Inn, 15 Main St, CRAWFORDSBURN
☎ (0247) 853255 32 ⇆ ♞

Clandeboye ☎ (0247) 271767
Parkland/heathland courses. The Dufferin is the championship course and offers a tough challenge. Nevertheless, the Ava has much to recommend it, with a notable 2nd hole.
Dufferin Course: 18 holes, 6469yds, Par 71, SSS 71.
Ava Course: 18 holes, 5656yds, Par 70, SSS 68.
Club membership 1200.
Visitors must play with member at weekends.
Societies Mon-Wed & Fri, Apr-Sep; Mon & Wed, Oct-Mar. Must contact in advance.
Green Fees not confirmed.
Facilities ⊗ 〗 ⓑ ☒ ♀ ⌂ 🍴 ♟ Peter Gregory.
Location Tower Rd, Conlig, Newtownards (2m S on A21)
Hotel ★★★64% Old Inn, 15 Main St, CRAWFORDSBURN
☎ (0247) 853255 32 ⇆ ♞

Helen's Bay ☎ (0247) 852815
A parkland course on the shores of Belfast Lough. The 4th hole Par 3 is particularly challenging as the green is screened by high trees.
9 holes, 5176mtrs, Par 68, SSS 67, Course record 67.
Club membership 780.

Visitors no restrictions Mon, Wed & Fri. Tue after
2.30pm with member. Thu off course by 5pm.
Sat play on after 6pm.
Societies welcome Mon, Wed & Fri, apply in writing.
Green Fees £12 (£15 weekends & bank holidays).
Facilities ⊗ ℿ ⅃ ▆ ♀ ⅄
Location Golf Rd, Helen's Bay (A2 from Belfast)
Hotel ★★★64% Old Inn, 15 Main St,
CRAWFORDSBURN
☎ (0247) 853255 32 ⇌ ⋔

CLOUGHEY   Map 01 D5

Kirkistown Castle ☎ Portavogie (02477) 71233
A seaside semi-links popular with visiting golfers because of
its quiet location. The course is exceptionally dry and remains
open when others in the area have to close. The Par 4 10th is
particularly distinctive with a long drive and a slight dogleg
to a raised green with a gorse covered motte waiting for the
wayward approach shot.
18 holes, 6167yds, Par 69, SSS 70, Course record 68.
Club membership 950.
Visitors must contact in advance, restricted Fri &
weekends.
Societies must contact in advance.
Green Fees £13 (£25 weekends).
Facilities ⊗ ℿ ⅃ ▆ ♀ ⅄ 🏠 ⋔ ⅃ Jonathon Peden.
Leisure snooker, full practice facilities.
Location 142 Main Rd, Cloughey
Hotel ★★★64% Old Inn, 15 Main St,
CRAWFORDSBURN
☎ (0247) 853255 32 ⇌ ⋔

DONAGHADEE   Map 01 D5

Donaghadee ☎ (0247) 883624
Undulating seaside course requiring a certain amount of
concentration. Splendid views.
18 holes, 6098yds, Par 71, SSS 69, Course record 64.
Club membership 1223.
Visitors may not play Sat.
Societies telephone in advance.
Green Fees £14 (£18 Sun).
Facilities ⊗ ℿ ⅃ ▆ (no catering Mon) ♀ ⅄ 🏠 ⋔ ⅃
Leisure snooker.
Location Warren Rd
Hotel ★★★64% Old Inn, 15 Main St,
CRAWFORDSBURN
☎ (0247) 853255 32 ⇌ ⋔

DOWNPATRICK   Map 01 D5

Bright Castle ☎ (0396) 841319
Parkland course in elevated position with views of the
Mountains of Mourne. A good challenge for the energetic
golfer.
18 holes, 7300yds, Par 74, SSS 74.
Visitors no restrictions.
Societies must contact in advance.
Green Fees not confirmed.
Facilities ⅃
Location 14 Coniamstown Rd, Bright (5m S)
Hotel ★★★63% Slieve Donard Hotel, NEWCASTLE
☎ (03967) 23681 120 ⇌

Downpatrick ☎ (0396) 612152 & 615947
This undulating parkland course has recently been extended,
with Hawtree & Son as architects. It provides a good
challenge.
18 holes, 6400yds, Par 70, SSS 69.
Club membership 800.
Visitors must contact in advance for groups of 20 or
more. May not play 7.30-10.30am at weekends
& bank holidays.
Societies must telephone in advance.
Green Fees £14 per day (£18 weekends & bank holidays).
Facilities ⊗ (summer only) ℿ ⅃ ▆ ♀ ⅄ 🏠 ⋔
Leisure snooker, putting green.
Location 43 Saul Rd (1.5m from town centre)
Hotel ★★64% Enniskeen Hotel, 98 Bryansfold Rd,
NEWCASTLE ☎ (03967) 22392 12 ⇌ ⋔

HOLYWOOD   Map 01 D5

Holywood ☎ (0232) 422138
Hilly parkland course with some fine views and providing an
interesting game.
18 holes, 5425mtrs, Par 69, SSS 68, Course record 64.
Club membership 800.
Visitors may not play between 1.30-2.15pm or on Sat.
Societies must contact in writing.
Green Fees not confirmed.
Facilities ⊗ ℿ ⅃ ▆ ♀ ⅄ 🏠 ⋔ ⅃ Michael Bannon.
Leisure snooker.
Location Nuns Wall, Demesne Rd
Hotel ★★★★67% Culloden Hotel, HOLYWOOD
☎ (0232) 425223 91 ⇌ ⋔

The Royal Belfast ☎ Belfast (0232) 428165
On the shores of Belfast Lough, this attractive course
consists of wooded parkland on undulating terrain which
provides a pleasant, challenging game.
18 holes, 5963yds, Par 70, SSS 69.
Club membership 1200.
Visitors may not play on Wed or Sat before 4.30pm;
must be accompanied by a member or
present a letter of introduction from their
own golf club.
Societies must contact in writing.
Green Fees £25 per round (£30 Sat after 4.30pm, Sun &
bank holidays).
Facilities ⊗ ℿ ⅃ ▆ ♀ ⅄ 🏠 ⋔ ⅃
Leisure hard tennis courts, squash, snooker, caddy cars.
Location Station Rd, Craigavad (2m E on A2)
Hotel ★★★★67% Culloden Hotel,
HOLYWOOD
☎ (0232) 425223 91 ⇌ ⋔

KILKEEL   Map 01 D5

Kilkeel ☎ (06937) 62296
Picturesquely situated at the foot of the Mourne Mountains,
Kilkeel was recently upgraded to an 18-hole course. Eleven
holes now have tree-lined fairways with the remainder in
open parkland. The 13th hole is testing and a well positioned
tee shot is essential.
18 holes, 6576yds, Par 72, SSS 72.
Club membership 700.
Visitors restricted Sun mornings & Tue & Sat. Must
contact in advance.

▶

Societies   must contact in writing.
Green Fees   £13 (£16 weekends & bank holidays).
Facilities   ⊗ �🁢 🕭 ▆ ⚑ ⛴
Location   Mourne Park (on Newry road)
Hotel   ★★(red) Glassdrumman Lodge, 85 Mill Rd,
                  ANNALONG
                  ☎ (03967) 68451 9 ⇥ ↸

MAGHERALIN   Map 01 D5

Edenmore ☎ (0846) 611310 & 619199
Set in mature parkland with gently rolling slopes. There are 9
well-established holes and an additional 9 holes opened in the
summer of 1994. The original Par 5 4th is played across a
lake and between two large oak trees. The Par 3 8th has an
elevated tee and a green nestled among lime trees.
18 holes, Par 71, SSS 70.
Club membership 200.
Visitors   members have priority Sat before noon. Closed
                  Sundays.
Societies   for larger societies telephone in advance.
Green Fees   £8 per 18 holes; £5 per 9 holes (£10/£7
                  weekends & bank holidays).
Facilities   ⊗ �🁢 by prior arrangement ▆ ⛴ 🕭 ⛴
Location   Edenmore House, 70 Drumnabreeze Rd
Hotel   B Forte Crest, Kingsway, Dunmurry, BELFAST
                  ☎ (0232) 612101 82 ⇥ ↸

NEWCASTLE   Map 01 D5

Royal County Down ☎ (03967) 23314
The remoteness of the links of the Royal County Down
and the backdrop of the Mountains of Mourne make this
a particularly exhilarating course to play, and there is a
wide variety in the challenges it presents. The greens,
always in good condition, can be tricky to read and some
of the tee shots are blind. The natural terrain of sand
dunes and gorse bushes may add to the hazards, but they
also contribute to the scenic beauty of the course.
Championship Course: 18 holes, 6969yds, Par 71, SSS 73.
No 2 Course: 18 holes, 4087yds, Par 65, SSS 60.
Visitors   may not play on Sat; may not play on
                  Championship Course Sat, Sun am & Wed
                  pm.
Societies   must contact in advance.
Green Fees   Championship: £43 per round (summer);
                  £32 (winter)(£55 per round weekends).
Facilities   ⊗ 🕭 ▆ ⚑ ⛴ 🕭 ⛴ ⛴ Kevan Whitson.
Leisure   heated indoor swimming pool, sauna,
                  solarium, gymnasium, trolleys.
Hotel   ★★★63% Slieve Donard Hotel,
                  NEWCASTLE ☎ (03967) 23681 120 ⇥

NEWTOWNARDS   Map 01 D5

Scrabo ☎ (0247) 812355
Hilly and picturesque, this course offers a good test of golf.
18 holes, 5699mtrs, Par 71, SSS 71, Course record 65.
Club membership 947.
Visitors   may not play on Sat.
Societies   must telephone in advance.
Green Fees   £15 (£20 weekends & bank holidays).
Facilities   ⊗ 🁢 🕭 ▆ (no catering Mon) ⚑ ⛴ 🕭 ⛴
                  ⛴ Gordon Fairweather.
Leisure   snooker.

Location   233 Scrabo Rd
Hotel   ★★★69% Stormont Hotel, 587 Upper
                  Newtonards Rd, BELFAST
                  ☎ (0232) 658621 106 ⇥ ↸

WARRENPOINT   Map 01 D5

Warrenpoint ☎ (06937) 53695
Parkland course with marvellous views and a need for
accurate shots.
18 holes, 6288yds, Par 71, SSS 70.
Club membership 1120.
Visitors   preferred Mon, Thu & Fri.
Societies   must contact in advance.
Green Fees   £16 (£22 weekends).
Facilities   ⊗ 🁢 🕭 ▆ ⚑ ⛴ 🕭 ⛴ ⛴ Nigel Shaw.
Leisure   squash, snooker.
Location   Lower Dromore Rd (1m W)
Hotel   ★★★63% Slieve Donard Hotel, NEWCASTLE
                  ☎ (03967) 23681 120 ⇥

CO FERMANAGH

ENNISKILLEN   Map 01 C5

Ashwoods Golf Centre ☎ (0365) 325321 & 322908
Only 1 mile from Lough Erne, this course is open
meadowland. It has been well planted with many young trees.
9 holes, 1290yds, Par 27.
Visitors   no restrictions.
Societies   must book in advance.
Green Fees   £4 per 18 holes, driving range £2 per 70 golf
                  balls.
Facilities   ⛴ 🕭 ⛴ ⛴ Thomas Loughran.
Location   Sligo Rd
Hotel   ★★★57% Killyhevlin Hotel, ENNISKILLEN
                  ☎ (0365) 323481 22 ⇥ ↸Annexe26rm

Castle Hume ☎ (0365) 327077
Castle Hulme is a particularly scenic and challenging course. Set
in undulating parkland with large rolling greens, rivers, lakes and
water hazards all in play on a championship standard course.
18 holes, 6500yds, Par 72, SSS 72, Course record 72.
Club membership 150.
Visitors   handicap required.
Societies   apply in writing & telephone for bookings.
Green Fees   £10 per round (£12 weekends & bankholidays).
Facilities   ⊗ 🁢 🕭 ▆ ⚑ ⛴ 🕭 ⛴
Leisure   caddy car for hire.
Location   Castle Hume (4m from Enniskillen on the
                  Belleek Rd)
Hotel   ★★★57% Killyhevlin Hotel, ENNISKILLEN
                  ☎ (0365) 323481 22 ⇥ ↸Annexe26rm

Enniskillen ☎ (0365) 325250
Meadowland course in Castle Coole estate.
18 holes, 5588mtrs, Par 71, SSS 69, Course record 67.
Club membership 500.
Visitors   restricted Tue and weekends.
Societies   must contact club steward in advance.

Green Fees £10 per day (£12 weekends & bank holidays).
Facilities ⊗ & 🍴 by prior arrangement 🛍 ⬛ ♀ 🏌 ⚑
Leisure snooker.
Location Castlecoole (1m E)
Hotel ★★★57% Killyhevlin Hotel, ENNISKILLEN
☎ (0365) 323481 22 ⇆ 🐾Annexe26rm

CO LONDONDERRY

AGHADOWEY
Map 01 C6

Brown Trout Golf & Country Inn ☎ Coleraine (0265) 868209
A challenging course with two par 5s. During the course of the 9 holes, players have to negotiate water 7 times and all the fairways are lined with densely packed fir trees.
9 holes, 2519mtrs, Par 70, SSS 68.
Club membership 150.
Visitors no restrictions.
Societies must contact by telephone.
Green Fees £8 per round (£12 weekends).
Facilities ⊗ 🍴 🛍 ⬛ ♀ 🏌 ⚑ 🐾 ⚓ Ken Revie.
Leisure riding.
Location 209 Agivey Rd (junc of A54 & B66)
Hotel ★★67% Brown Trout Golf & Country Inn, 209 Agivey Rd, AGHADOWEY
☎ (0265) 868209 17 ⇆ 🐾

CASTLEDAWSON
Map 01 C5

Moyola Park ☎ (0648) 68468
Parkland course with some difficult shots, calling for length and accuracy. The Moyola River provides a water hazard at the 8th.
18 holes, 6517yds, Par 71, SSS 71, Course record 70.
Club membership 900.
Visitors may not play Fri after 2pm. Must play with member Sat and may only play 1.30-2.30pm (by prior arrangement) Sun.
Societies must contact in advance.
Green Fees £12 per day (£22 weekends).
Facilities ⊗ 🍴 🛍 ⬛ ♀ 🏌 🛍 ⚓ Vivian Teague.
Leisure snooker.
Location Shanemullagh (3m NE of Magherafelt)
Hotel ★★★62% Adair Arms Hotel, Ballymoney Rd, BALLYMENA ☎ (0266) 653674 39 ⇆ 🐾

CASTLEROCK
Map 01 C6

Castlerock ☎ Coleraine (0265) 848314
A most exhilarating course with three superb par 4s, four testing short holes and two par 5s. After an uphill start, the hazards are many, including the river and a railway, and both judgement and accuracy are called for. A challenge in calm weather, any trouble from the elements will test your golf to the limits.
Mussenden: 18 holes, 6687yds, Par 73, SSS 72.
Bann: 9 holes, 2457mtrs, Par 35, SSS 33.
Club membership 960.

Visitors may not play at weekends or Fri during May-Aug.
Societies must contact in advance.
Green Fees not confirmed.
Facilities 🍴 🛍 ⬛ ♀ 🏌 🛍 ⚑ ⚓ Robert Kelly.
Leisure snooker.
Location 65 Circular Rd (6m from Coleraine on A2)
Hotel ★★★60% Causeway Coast Hotel, 36 Ballyreagh Rd, PORTRUSH
☎ (0265) 822435 21 ⇆ 🐾

KILREA
Map 01 C5

Kilrea ☎ no telephone
A relatively short undulating inland course with tight fairways and small greens. The opening hole is a long par 3, particularly into the wind.
9 holes, 3956mtrs, Par 62, SSS 62, Course record 61.
Club membership 300.
Visitors welcome but not permitted after 5pm Wed or Sat during competitions.
Societies contact Trevor Moore, 42 Maghera St, Kilrea. tel:(02665) 41316
Green Fees £8 (£10 weekends) subject to review.
Facilities 🏌
Location Drumagarner Rd
Hotel ★★★62% Adair Arms Hotel, Ballymoney Rd, BALLYMENA ☎ (0266) 653674 39 ⇆ 🐾

LIMAVADY
Map 01 C6

Roe Park ☎ (05047) 22212
A parkland course opened in 1992 on an historic Georgian estate. The course surrounds the original buildings and a driving range has been created in the old walled garden. Final holes 15-18 are particularly memorable with water, trees, out-of-bounds, etc to provide a testing finish.
18 holes, 6373yds, Par 70, SSS 71.
Club membership 280.
Visitors no restrictions.
Societies telephone bookings available.
Green Fees £15 per round (£20 weekends & bank holidays).
Facilities ⬛ 🏌 🛍 ⚓ Seamus Duffy.
Leisure caddy cars, driving range, practice bunker.
Location Roe Park (on Ballykelly rd A2)
Hotel ★★★66% Everglades Hotel, Prehen Rd, LONDONDERRY ☎ (0504) 46722 52 ⇆ 🐾

LONDONDERRY
Map 01 C5

City of Derry ☎ (0504) 46369
Two parkland courses on undulating parkland with good views and lots of trees. The 9-hole course will particularly suit novices.
Prehen: 18 holes, 6406yds, Par 71, SSS 71, Course record 68.
Dunhugh Course: 9 holes, 4708yds, Par 63.
Club membership 732.
Visitors must make a booking to play on Prehen Course at weekends or before 4.30pm on weekdays.
Societies must contact in advance.
Green Fees not confirmed.
Facilities ⊗ & 🍴 by prior arrangement 🛍 (summer only) ⬛ by prior arrangement ♀ 🏌 🛍 ⚓ Michael Doherty. ▶

Leisure   snooker.
Location 49 Victoria Rd (2m S)
Hotel   ★★★66% Everglades Hotel, Prehen Rd,
              LONDONDERRY ☎ (0504) 46722 52 ⇥ ℟

PORTSTEWART   Map 01 C6

Portstewart ☎ (0265) 833209
Three links courses with spectacular views, offering a
testing round on the Strand course in particular.
Strand: 18 holes, 6784yds, Par 72, SSS 72.
Town: 18 holes, 4733yds, Par 64, SSS 62.
3: 9 holes, 2622yds, Par 32.
Visitors   preferred on weekdays.
Societies   must contact in advance.
Green Fees not confirmed.
Facilities ⊗ ⑭ ♀ ☗ ⟨ Alan Hunter.
Leisure   snooker, indoor bowling.
Location   117 Strand Rd
Hotel   ★★★60% Causeway Coast Hotel, 36
                Ballyreagh Rd, PORTRUSH
                ☎ (0265) 822435 21 ⇥ ℟

● CO TYRONE ●

COOKSTOWN   Map 01 C5

Killymoon ☎ (06487) 63762
Parkland course on elevated, well drained land.
18 holes, 5498mtrs, Par 70, SSS 68.
Club membership 650.
Visitors   may not play on Sat afternoons. Must contact in
                advance and have a handicap certificate.
Societies   must contact in advance.
Green Fees £14 per day (£18 per round weekends & bank
                holidays).
Facilities ⊗ & ⑭ by prior arrangement ⓑ ☟ ♀ ☗ 🖿
                ⟨ Barry Hamill.
Leisure   snooker, caddy cars.
Location   200 Killymoon Rd
Hotel   ★★65% Royal Arms Hotel, 51 High St,
                OMAGH ☎ (0662) 243262 21 ⇥ ℟

DUNGANNON   Map 01 C5

Dungannon ☎ (08687) 22098 or 27338
Parkland course with five par 3s and tree-lined fairways.
18 holes, 5433mtrs, Par 71, SSS 68.
Club membership 480.
Visitors   may not play on Sat.
Societies   must contact secretary in advance.
Green Fees £8/£10 per day (£11/£13 weekends & bank
                holidays).
Facilities ⊗ & ⑭ (weekends only) ♀ ☗ 🖿
Leisure   snooker.
Location   34 Springfield Ln (0.5m outside town on
                Donaghmore road)
Hotel   ★★65% Royal Arms Hotel, 51 High St,
                OMAGH ☎ (0662) 243262 21 ⇥ ℟

NEWTOWNSTEWART   Map 01 C5

Newtownstewart ☎ (06626) 61466 & 61829
Parkland course bisected by a stream.
18 holes, 5468mtrs, Par 70, SSS 69, Course record 65.
Club membership 700.
Visitors   times may be booked in advance, restricted at
                weekends.
Societies   must contact in advance.
Green Fees £10 per round (£15 weekends & bank holidays).
Facilities ⊗ ⓑ ☟ (all catering by prior arrangement) ♀ by
                prior arrangement ☗ 🖿 ☗
Leisure   snooker, caddy cars.
Location   38 Golf Course Rd (2m SW on B84)
Hotel   ★★65% Royal Arms Hotel, 51 High St,
                OMAGH ☎ (0662) 243262 21 ⇥ ℟

OMAGH   Map 01 C5

Omagh ☎ (0662) 243160
Undulating parkland course beside the River Drumnagh.
18 holes, 5636mtrs, Par 71, SSS 70, Course record 73.
Club membership 824.
Visitors   may not play on Tue & Sat.
Societies   must contact in advance.
Green Fees £10 (£15 weekends & bank holidays).
Facilities ⓑ ☟ (11.30-1.30 & 4.30-11) ♀ ☗
Leisure   snooker.
Location   83a Dublin Rd (On S outskirts of town)
Hotel   ★★65% Royal Arms Hotel, 51 High St,
                OMAGH ☎ (0662) 243262 21 ⇥ ℟

STRABANE   Map 01 C5

Strabane ☎ (0504) 382271 & 382007
Testing parkland course with the River Mourne running
alongside and creating a water hazard.
18 holes, 5552mtrs, Par 69, SSS 69.
Club membership 550.
Visitors   may not play on Sat.
Societies   must contact in writing.
Green Fees not confirmed.
Facilities ⓑ & ☟ by prior arrangement ♀ ☗
Leisure   snooker.
Location   Ballycolman Rd
Hotel   ★★65% Royal Arms Hotel, 51 High St,
                OMAGH ☎ (0662) 243262 21 ⇥ ℟

NICK

Faldo found perfect peace when he visited Mount Juliet for the 1993 Irish Open Championship. Each night, after his round and practice session, he took his rod to the River Nore and fished for salmon and trout. He caught a few, won the tournament, and returned home a happy man. Of the golf course he said: 'It is the best prepared in Europe. Other courses hosting tournaments should come here and see the standards for themselves.'

High praise indeed, but this Jack Nicklaus-designed layout, built on a former stud farm near Thomastown, Co Kilkenny, 73 miles south of Dublin, is on 1,500 acres of rolling countryside that offers everything a visiting golfer could want. If things are not going well for you on the course there is the David Leadbetter Golf School, opened this year, to help put you back on the track, and there is a swimming pool, fitness and aerobics room and other keep-fit activities.

The course, full-length 7,142 yards, is tough, but forward tees for the amateur help to reduce its tigerish features. When Nicklaus played with Christy O'Connor Senior at the official opening in 1991 he generously offered to allow O'Connor, then aged 67, to play from the blue, forward tees. O'Connor would have none of it, played from the same back tees as Nicklaus, and won the match. Mount Juliet, the flagship of the courses Nicklaus designed outside the United States, was the last port of call for golfers who visited his golfing creations this year.

Discovering the new courses in the Republic of Ireland can be exciting for the golfing visitor, who will unearth some picturesque gems. For instance, as you head from Mount Juliet to Dublin you will find the Kilkea Castle Club which has been designed around the oldest inhabited castle in Ireland. The 12th-century castle is in view all the way round. You meet more than your share of water during the 18 holes. The River Griese has to be crossed on eight holes and there are two lakes, one of which stands between the 15th tee and the haven of the fairway.

There is water to be negotiated, too, at the Arnold Palmer-designed K Club, of which the River Liffey is one of 11 water features. The river divides to form the island of Inismor, just below the terraced approaches to nineteenth-century Straffan House, providing the setting for the green at the 7th, the longest hole on the course at 605 yards. Palmer said he wanted the course to be a blend of pleasure, skill and challenge and it is certainly that, although there are up to four tee boxes at most tees to take the sting out of it all for the higher handicap players. The course opened in 1991 and has played host to the Irish PGA Championship and the Johnnie Walker PGA Cup in 1992.

Christy O'Connor Senior describes the 1st at Knockanally Golf and Country Club as the most difficult opening hole in golf. The clubhouse, housed in a nineteenth-century mansion, provides panoramic views of the plains of Kildare, with the inward nine holes sweeping down to a stream which feeds the 'alligator farm', a pond that has claimed many wayward shots to the 10th, 11th and 13th greens. The Irish match-play championship has been held on the course. The accolade for the best final hole goes to St Margaret's Golf and Country Club, a new course half-an-hour from Dublin, that has already won its way into the top 30 Irish clubs decided by the Irish Golf Institute. Sam Torrance was impressed and says of the 18th: 'It's the best finishing hole I've ever seen and is possibly the most exciting in the world.'

If you want to have a taste of history then the Luttrellstown Castle Golf and Country Club is the place for you. The castle, part of which dates back to the 14th century, has had many dignitaries as guests, including Queen Victoria, President Ronald Reagan and Prince Rainier and Princess Grace of Monaco. Six miles from Dublin, the course is in a 560 acre estate which includes a tennis court, swimming pool and facilities for horse riding the shooting. The ninth, 10th, 11th and 12th holes work round the ornamental lakes. The water hazard at the 3rd is framed by the backdrop of the Dublin Mountains.

IAN RIACH
Golf correspondent, *Scottish Sunday Express*

REPUBLIC OF IRELAND

CO CARLOW

CARLOW   Map 01 C3

Carlow ☎ (0503) 31695
Created in 1922 to a design by Tom Simpson, this testing
and enjoyable course is set in a wild deer park, with
beautiful dry terrain and a varied character. With sandy
sub-soil, the course is playable all year round. There are
water hazards at the 2nd, 10th and 11th.
18 holes, 5599mtrs, Par 70, SSS 69, Course record 65.
Club membership 1000.

Visitors	are welcome, although play is limited on Tue and difficult on Sat & Sun. Must contact in advance.
Societies	must book in advance.
Green Fees	IR£20 per day (IR£25 weekends & bank holidays).
Facilities	⊗ 🏌 ⅏ 🍺 ♀ ⌕ ⛳ ⚲ ⛳ Andrew Gilbert.
Leisure	caddy cars and clubs for hire.
Location	Deerpark (2m N of Carlow)
Hotel	★★52% Royal Hotel, CARLOW ☎ (0503) 31621 34 ⇆ ⓕ

CO CAVAN

BALLYCONNELL   Map 01 C4

Slieve Russell Hotel Golf & Country Club ☎ (049) 26444
An 18-hole course with a new 9-hole Par 3 to complement
it. On the main course, the 2nd plays across water while
the 16th has water surrounding the green. The course
finishes with a 519 yard, Par 5 18th.
18 holes, 6580yds wh, Par 72, SSS 72.
Club membership 210.

Visitors	no restrictions, telephone to book in advance.
Societies	write or telephone in advance.
Green Fees	IR£22 per round (IR£30 Sat). Reduced rate for hotel residents.
Facilities	⊗ ⅏ 🏌 🍺 ♀ ⌕ 🏠 ⛳ ⚲ ⛳ Liam McCool.
Leisure	hard tennis courts, heated indoor swimming pool, squash, snooker, sauna, solarium, gymnasium, trolley & buggy hire.
Location	1.5m E of Ballyconnell
Hotel	★★61% Royal Hotel, BOYLE ☎ (079) 62016 16 ⇆ ⓕ

BELTURBET   Map 01 C4

Belturbet ☎ Cavan (049) 22287
Beautifully maintained parkland course with predominantly
family membership and popular with summer visitors.
9 holes, 5480yds, Par 68, SSS 65, Course record 64.
Club membership 150.

Visitors	restrictions the same as for members.

Societies	must contact secretary or captain in advance.
Green Fees	not confirmed.
Facilities	⊗ & ⅏ by prior arrangement 🏌 🍺 ♀ ⚲
Leisure	snooker.
Location	Erne Hill
Hotel	★★★⚑75% Cromleach Lodge Country House Hotel, Ballindoon, CASTLEBALDWIN ☎ (071) 65155 10 ⇆ ⓕ

BLACKLION   Map 01 C5

Blacklion ☎ (072) 53024
Parkland course established in 1962, with coppices of
woodland and mature trees. The lake comes into play on two
holes and there are some magnificent views of the lake,
islands and surrounding hills. It has been described as one of
the best maintained nine-hole courses in Ireland.
9 holes, 5614mtrs, Par 72, SSS 69.
Club membership 200.

Visitors	may not play on Sun mornings and occasional competition days.
Societies	must contact in advance.
Green Fees	IR£6 per day (IR£7 weekends).
Facilities	🏌 & 🍺 (pm only) ♀ (pm only) ⚲
Location	Toam
Hotel	★★★69% Sligo Park Hotel, Pearse Rd, SLIGO ☎ (071) 60291 89 ⇆ ⓕ

CAVAN   Map 01 C4

County Cavan ☎ (049) 31541
Parkland course.
18 holes, 5519mtrs, Par 70, SSS 69.

Visitors	welcome but restricted at weekends.
Societies	contact for details.
Green Fees	IR£10 (IR£12 weekends).
Facilities	full catering facilities available
Leisure	snooker.
Location	Drumelis (on Killeshandra rd)
Hotel	★★★65% Ballymascanlon House Hotel, DUNDALK ☎ (042) 71124 36 ⇆

VIRGINIA   Map 01 C4

Virginia ☎ (049) 47235
9 holes, 4900mtrs, Par 64, SSS 62.

Visitors	welcome.
Green Fees	not confirmed.
Facilities	catering in Park Hotel
Location	By Lough Ramor
Hotel	★★57% Conyngham Arms Hotel, SLANE ☎ (041) 24155 16rm(15 ⇆ ⓕ)

CO CLARE

CLONLARA   Map 01 B3

Clonlara Golf & Leisure ☎ (061) 354141
A 9-hole parkland course, Par 35, on the banks of the River
Shannon with views of Clare Hills. Set in grounds of 63 acres
surrounding the 17th century Landscape House, there is ▶

also a leisure complex for self-catering holidays.
9 holes, 5328mtrs, Par 70, SSS 68.
Club membership 70.

Visitors	players only no accompanying persons.
Societies	welcome subject to availability prior notice required.
Green Fees	IR£8 per 18 holes (IR£10 weekends & bank holidays).
Facilities	⅏ by prior arrangement ⓛ 🍺 ♀ 占 ⅎ 🐾
Leisure	hard tennis courts, sauna.
Location	7m NE of Limerick
Hotel	★★★★68% Castletroy Park Hotel, Dublin Rd, LIMERICK ☎ (061) 335566 107 ⇄ 🐾

ENNIS
Map 01 B3

Ennis ☎ (065) 24074
On rolling hills, this immaculately manicured course presents an excellent challenge to both casual visitors and aspiring scratch golfers, with tree-lined fairways and well protected greens.
18 holes, 5318mtrs, Par 69, SSS 68.
Club membership 1000.

Visitors	must contact in advance & be a member of a golf club.
Societies	apply in writing.
Green Fees	IR£15 per day.
Facilities	⊗ ⅏ by prior arrangement ⓛ 🍺 ♀ 占 🏠 ⅎ ⅈ Martin Ward.
Leisure	snooker, caddy cars.
Location	Drumbiggle
Hotel	★★★65% Auburn Lodge Hotel, Galway Rd, ENNIS ☎ (065) 21247 100 ⇄ 🐾

KILKEE
Map 01 B3

Kilkee ☎ (065) 56048
Well established course on the cliffs of Kilkee Bay, with beautiful views.
18 holes, 6500yds, Par 71, SSS 68.
Club membership 600.

Visitors	may not play on certain competition days.
Societies	must contact in writing.
Green Fees	IR£15 per day.
Facilities	⊗ ⅏ ⓛ 🍺 ♀ 占 🏠 ⅎ
Leisure	squash, fishing, sauna, pitch & putt,caddies/caddy cars for hire.
Location	East End
Hotel	★★59% Halpin's Hotel, Erin St, KILKEE ☎ (065) 56032 12 ⇄ 🐾

KILRUSH
Map 01 B3

Kilrush ☎ (065) 51138
Parkland course extended to 18 holes in summer of 1994.
9 holes, 2793yds, SSS 67.

Visitors	welcome, contact for details.
Societies	by prior arrangement.
Green Fees	IR£10.
Facilities	♀
Location	Parknamoney
Hotel	★★59% Halpin's Hotel, Erin St, KILKEE ☎ (065) 56032 12 ⇄ 🐾

LAHINCH
Map 01 B3

Lahinch ☎ (065) 81003
Originally designed by Tom Morris and later modified by Dr Alister MacKenzie, Lahinch has hosted every important Irish amateur fixture and the Home Internationals. The par five 5th - The Klondike - is played along a deep valley and over a huge dune; the par three 6th may be short, but calls for a blind shot over the ridge of a hill to a green hemmed in by hills on three sides.
Old Course: 18 holes, 6702yds, Par 72, SSS 73.
Castle Course: 18 holes, 4786mtrs, Par 67, SSS 66.
Club membership 1583.

Visitors	handicap limit, men 28, ladies 36
Societies	apply in writing
Green Fees	not confirmed.
Facilities	⊗ ⅏ ⓛ 🍺 ♀ 占 🏠 ⅎ ⅈ R McCavery.
Location	2m W of Ennisstymon on N67
Hotel	★★70% Sheedy's Spa View Hotel & Orchid Restaurant, LISDOONVARNA ☎ (065) 74026 11 ⇄ 🐾

MILLTOWN MALBAY
Map 01 B3

Spanish Point ☎ (065) 84219
A 9-hole links course with 3 elevated greens and 4 elevated tees. The 8th hole is a 75-metre par 3, locally known as 'the Terror'.
9 holes, 6032yds, Par 64, SSS 63.
Club membership 200.

Visitors	no restrictions.
Societies	apply in writing to the secretary.
Green Fees	IR£10 per day.
Facilities	ⓛ 🍺 ♀ 占 ⅎ
Leisure	cars/caddies.
Hotel	★★★67% Old Ground Hotel, O'Connell St, ENNIS ☎ (065) 28127 58 ⇄ 🐾

NEWMARKET-ON-FERGUS
Map 01 B3

Drumoland Castle ☎ (061) 368444 & 368144
Set in 200 acres of parkland, the course is enhanced by numerous trees and a lake. Three holes are played around the lake which is in front of the castle.
18 holes, 5646mtrs, Par 71, SSS 71, Course record 67.
Club membership 550.

Visitors	handicap certificate required.
Societies	contact in advance.
Green Fees	IR£20 (IR£25 weekends).
Facilities	⊗ ⅏ ⓛ 🍺 ♀ 占 🏠 ⅎ 🐾 ⅈ Philip Murphy.
Leisure	hard tennis courts, fishing, riding, snooker, tuition, caddys, caddy cars & buggys.
Location	2m N, on main Limerick/Galway rd
Hotel	★★★65% Auburn Lodge Hotel, Galway Rd, ENNIS ☎ (065) 21247 100 ⇄ 🐾

SCARRIFF
Map 01 B3

East Clare ☎ (061) 921322
Beside Lough Derg, East Clare was opened in June 1992 as a 9-hole course in 148 acre site with natural trees and water on well-drained land. An 18-hole championship course deigned by Arthur Spring is in preparation.
9 holes, 3252yds, Par 70, SSS 70, Course record 68.
Club membership 130.

Visitors   no restrictions unless there is a club competition or a society playing.
Societies   apply in writing, deposit required.
Green Fees IR£5 (to be increased when front 9 are in play).
Facilities   🏌 💺 🛎 ⛳
Location   Bodyke
Hotel   ★★★67% Old Ground Hotel, O'Connell St, ENNIS ☎ (065) 28127 58 ⇆ ℝ

SHANNON AIRPORT   Map 01 B3

Shannon ☎ (061) 471849
Superb parkland course with tree-lined fairways, strategically placed bunkers, water hazards and excellent greens, offering a challenge to all levels of players - including the many famous golfers who have played here.
18 holes, 6874yds, Par 72, SSS 74.
Club membership 800.
Visitors   must contact in advance & have handicap certificate. Restricted play at certain times.
Societies   must contact in writing.
Green Fees IR£20 per day (IR£25 weekends & bank holidays).
Facilities   ⊗ �🍴 🏌 💺 ♀ 🛎 📷 ⛳ 𝒷 Artie Pyke.
Leisure   putting green, practice facilities.
Location   2m from Shannon Airport
Hotel   ★★★63% Fitzpatrick Bunratty Shamrock Hotel, BUNRATTY ☎ (061) 361177 115 ⇆ ℝ

CO CORK

BANDON   Map 01 B2

Bandon ☎ (023) 41111
Lovely parkland course in pleasant rural surroundings.
18 holes, 5663mtrs, Par 70, SSS 69, Course record 66.
Club membership 800.
Visitors   welcome but may not play during club competitions. Must contact in advance.
Societies   must apply in writing.
Green Fees IR£12 per day (IR£15 weekends & bank holidays).
Facilities   ⊗ �🍴 🏌 💺 ♀ 🛎 📷 ⛳ 𝒷 Paddy O'Boyle.
Leisure   hard tennis courts, caddy cars.
Location   Castlebernard
Hotel   ★★63% Innishannon House Hotel, INNISHANNON ☎ (021) 775121 13 ⇆ ℝ

BANTRY   Map 01 A2

Bantry Park ☎ (027) 50579
An undulating 9-hole course with some magnificent sea views.
9 holes, 5882mtrs, Par 72, SSS 70.
Club membership 230.
Visitors   course is restricted only during competition times.
Societies   must apply in writing to Mr J Sheenan, Ardnagaoithe, Bantry.
Green Fees not confirmed.
Facilities   🛎 ⛳
Location   Donemark
Hotel   ★★★♨69% Sea View Hotel, BALLYLICKEY ☎ (027) 50073 & 50462 17 ⇆ ℝAnnexe 5rm

BLARNEY   Map 01 B2

Muskerry ☎ (021) 385297 & 385104
An adventurous game is guaranteed at this course, with its wooded hillsides and the meandering Shournagh River coming into play at a number of holes. The 15th is a notable hole - not long, but very deep - and after that all you need to do to get back to the clubhouse is stay out of the water.
18 holes, 6327yds, Par 71, SSS 70.
Club membership 706.
Visitors   may not play Wed afternoon & Thu morning. Must play with member at weekends.
Societies   must telephone in advance and then confirm in writing.
Green Fees IR£15 per day.
Facilities   ⊗ 💺 ♀ 🛎 📷 ⛳ 𝒷
Leisure   snooker.
Location   Carrigrohane (7.5m NW of Cork)
Hotel   ★★★68% Blarney Park Hotel, BLARNEY ☎ (021) 385281 76 ⇆ ℝ

CASTLETOWNBERE   Map 01 A2

Berehaven ☎ (027) 70039
Seaside links founded in 1902.
9 holes, 2380mtrs, Par 69, SSS 66.
Club membership 200.
Visitors   no restrictions.
Societies   must telephone (027) 70469 in advance.
Green Fees not confirmed.
Facilities   💺 (Jun-Aug) 🛎 ⛳
Leisure   hard tennis courts, outdoor swimming pool, fishing.
Location   Millcove (2m E on Glen Garriff Rd)
Hotel   ★★★♨69% Sea View Hotel, BALLYLICKEY ☎ (027) 50073 & 50462 17 ⇆ ℝAnnexe5rm

CHARLEVILLE   Map 01 B2

Charleville ☎ (063) 81257
Wooded parkland course offering not too strenuous walking.
18 holes, 6434yds, Par 71, SSS 70, Course record 68.
Club membership 700.
Visitors   only prebooked at weekends.
Societies   must telephone in advance.
Green Fees IR£12 (IR£15 weekends & bank holidays).
Facilities   ⊗ �🍴 🏌 💺 ♀ 🛎
Leisure   caddy cars available.
Location   Ardmore
Hotel   ★★★♨70% Longueville House Hotel, MALLOW ☎ (022) 47156 & 47306 16 ⇆ ℝ

CLONAKILTY   Map 01 B2

Dunmore ☎ (023) 33352
A hilly, rocky 9-hole course overlooking the Atlantic.
9 holes, 4080mtrs, Par 64, SSS 61.
Visitors   welcome, contact for details.
Societies   by prior arrangement.
Green Fees IR£10 per 9 hole.
Facilities   bar & restaurant facilities in Dunmore House
Location   Muckross (3.5m S of Clonakilty)
Hotel   ★★60% Courtmacsherry, COURTMACSHERRY ☎ (023) 46198 15rm(9 ⇆)

CORK
Map 01 B2

Cork ☎ (021) 353451
This championship-standard course is always kept in
superb condition and is playable all year round. It has
holes at the water's edge and holes in a disused quarry.
18 holes, 6115mtrs, Par 72, SSS 72.
Club membership 705.
Visitors	may not play 12.30-2pm or on Thu (Ladies Day), and only after 2.30pm Sat & Sun.
Societies	must contact in advance.
Green Fees	IR£23 per day (IR£26 weekends).
Facilities	⊗ ⅲ ⓛ ▇ ♀ ⚘ ⌂ ☈ ⚑ { Ted Higgins.
Location	Little Island (5m E, on N25)
Hotel	★★★★68% Jurys Hotel, Western Rd, CORK ☎ (021) 276622 185 ⇆ ⋔

Fitzpatrick Silver Springs ☎ (021) 505128
Five Par 4s and 4 Par 3s make up this short 9-hole course. The
4th has a 189 metre drive with out of bounds on the righthand.
9 holes, 2000mtrs, Par 32, SSS 32, Course record 26.
Club membership 100.
Visitors	welcome after societies & members.
Societies	apply by telephone.
Green Fees	IR£8 for visitors.
Facilities	⊗ ⅲ ⓛ ▇ ♀ ⚘ ⚑ ⋈
Leisure	tennis courts, heated indoor swimming pool, squash, snooker, sauna, solarium, gymnasium, indoor tennis, golf lessons.
Location	Tivoli (1m E of city centre)
Hotel	★★★★62% Fitzpatrick Silver Springs Hotel, Tivoli, CORK ☎ (021) 507533 109 ⇆ ⋔

Mahon Municipal ☎ (021) 362480
Municipal course which stretches alongside the river estuary,
with some holes across water.
18 holes, 4818mtrs, Par 67, SSS 66.
Club membership 380.
Visitors	may not play mornings at weekends.
Green Fees	IR£8.50 per day (IR£9.50 weekends & bank holidays).
Facilities	⊗ ⅲ ⓛ ▇ ♀ ⚘ ⌂ ☈
Location	Blackrock (2m from city centre)
Hotel	★★★★62% Fitzpatrick Silver Springs Hotel, Tivoli, CORK ☎ (021) 507533 109 ⇆ ⋔

DONERAILE
Map 01 B2

Doneraile ☎ (022) 24137
Parkland.
9 holes, 5528yds, SSS 66.
Visitors	no restrictions
Societies	welcome.
Green Fees	IR£10.
Facilities	meals available
Location	Off T11
Hotel	★★★⚔70% Longueville House Hotel, MALLOW ☎ (022) 47156 & 47306 16 ⇆ ⋔

DOUGLAS
Map 01 B2

Douglas ☎ Cork (021) 362055 & 895297
Level inland course overlooking the city of Cork. Suitable for
golfers of all ages and abilities.

18 holes, 5664mtrs, Par 70, SSS 69.
Club membership 750.
Visitors	may not play Tue or Sat & Sun before 2.30pm.
Societies	must contact in advance.
Green Fees	IR£17 per round (IR£19 weekends & bank holidays).
Facilities	⊗ ⅲ ⓛ ▇ ♀ ⚘ ⌂ ☈ ⚑ {
Leisure	snooker.
Hotel	★★★★68% Jurys Hotel, Western Rd, CORK ☎ (021) 276622 185 ⇆ ⋔

FERMOY
Map 01 B2

Fermoy ☎ (025) 31472
Rather exposed heathland course, bisected by a road.
18 holes, 6370yds, Par 70, SSS 69.
Visitors	preferred on weekdays.
Green Fees	not confirmed.
Facilities	⊗ ⅲ ⓛ ♀ ⚑
Location	Corrin Cross (2m SW)
Hotel	★★★⚔70% Longueville House Hotel, MALLOW ☎ (022) 47156 & 47306 16 ⇆ ⋔

GLENGARRIFF
Map 01 B2

Glengarriff ☎ (027) 63150
Founded 1935.
9 holes, 2042mtrs, SSS 62.
Visitors	welcome, details not supplied
Societies	apply to club.
Green Fees	IR£10.
Location	On N71
Hotel	★★★57% Westlodge Hotel, BANTRY ☎ (027) 50360 90 ⇆ ⋔

KINSALE
Map 01 B2

Kinsale ☎ (021) 772197
Founded 1912.
9 holes, 5332yds, SSS 68.
Visitors	welcome but late play at weekends.
Societies	by arrangement.
Green Fees	IR£12.
Facilities	catering available ♀ { Finbar Condon.
Location	Ringenane, Belgooly (on main Cork/Kinsale rd)
Hotel	★★★70% Trident Hotel, Worlds End, KINSALE ☎ (021) 772301 58 ⇆ ⋔

LITTLE ISLAND
Map 01 B2

Harbour Point ☎ (021) 353094
A new championship-standard course in rolling countryside
on the banks of the River Lee at Cork's scenic harbour. A
distinctive and testing course for every standard of golfer.
18 holes, 6063yds, Par 72, SSS 72, Course record 72.
Club membership 250.
Visitors	must contact in advance.
Societies	telephone for bookings.
Green Fees	IR£10 per round before 11am Mon, Wed, Thu & Fri; IR£20 other times.
Facilities	⊗ ⅲ ⓛ ▇ ♀ ⚘ ⌂ ⚑
Leisure	caddy cars, all weather driving range.
Location	Clash Rd (5m E of Cork)
Hotel	★★68% Ashbourne House Hotel, GLOUNTHAUNE ☎ (021) 353319 & 353310 26 ⇆ ⋔

MACROOM
Map 01 B2

Macroom ☎ (026) 41072
A particularly scenic parkland course located on undulating ground along the banks of the River Sullane. Bunkers and mature trees make a variable and testing course and the 18th has a 50 yards carry over the river to the green.
18 holes, 5574mtrs, Par 72, SSS 70, Course record 65.
Club membership 500.

Visitors	restricted during weekends of major club competitions. Timesheet operates at all weekends.
Societies	apply in writing.
Green Fees	IR£10 (IR£12 weekends & bank holidays).
Facilities	⊗ ᾲ ♨ ♥ ♀ ♈
Leisure	caddy cars for hire.
Location	Lackaduve (through castle entrance in town square)
Hotel	★★66% Castle Hotel, Main St, MACROOM ☎ (026) 41074 26 ⇆ ℟

MALLOW
Map 01 B2

Mallow ☎ (022) 21145
A well wooded parkland course overlooking the Blackwater Valley, Mallow is straightforward, but no less a challenge for it. The front nine is by far the longer, but the back nine is demanding in its call for accuracy and the par 3 18th provides a tough finish.
18 holes, 5687yds, Par 72, SSS 70.

Visitors	preferred on Mon, Wed, Thu & Fri.
Societies	apply in writing.
Green Fees	not confirmed.
Facilities	⊗ ᾲ ♨ ♥ ♀ ♈ ℟
Leisure	hard tennis courts, squash, snooker, sauna.
Location	Ballyellis
Hotel	★★★▲▲70% Longueville House Hotel, MALLOW ☎ (022) 47156 & 47306 16 ⇆ ℟

MIDLETON
Map 01 C2

East Cork ☎ (021) 631687
A well wooded course calling for accuracy of shots.
18 holes, 5207mtrs, Par 69, SSS 67.
Club membership 511.

Visitors	may not play Sun mornings.
Societies	must apply in writing.
Green Fees	not confirmed.
Facilities	⊗ ♨ ♥ ♀ ♈
Leisure	squash, fishing, riding, snooker.
Location	Gortacrue (on the A626)
Hotel	★★★71% Midleton Park, MIDLETON ☎ (021) 631767 40 ⇆ ℟

MITCHELSTOWN
Map 01 B2

Mitchelstown ☎ (025) 24072
Originally a 9-hole course, from summer of 1994 an additional 6 holes added to give a 5,300 metre course.
15 holes, 5300mtrs, Par 67, SSS 67, Course record 64.
Club membership 500.

Visitors	Ladies have priority on Wed, Mens competitions on Sun, prior booking for green fees preferred on Sun.
Societies	apply in writing or telephone (025) 24519
Green Fees	IR£10 per day.
Facilities	♨ ♥ ♀ ♈

Location	Limerick Rd, Gurrane (0.75m on Limerick rd from Mitchelstown)
Hotel	★★★▲▲70% Longueville House Hotel, MALLOW ☎ (022) 47156 & 47306 16 ⇆ ℟

MONKSTOWN
Map 01 B2

Monkstown ☎ (021) 841376
Undulating parkland course with five tough finishing holes.
18 holes, 5669mtrs, Par 70, SSS 69, Course record 66.
Club membership 960.

Visitors	restricted Tue & busy weekends. Must contact in advance.
Societies	must apply in writing.
Green Fees	IR£20 Mon-Thu; IR£23 Fri-Sun.
Facilities	⊗ ᾲ ♨ ♥ ♀ ⊿ ⊜ ♈ ℟ Batt Murphy.
Leisure	practice ground, caddy cars.
Location	Parkgariffe
Hotel	★★★★68% Jurys Hotel, Western Rd, CORK ☎ (021) 276622 185 ⇆ ℟

SKIBBEREEN
Map 01 B2

Skibbereen & West Carbery ☎ (028) 21227 & 22340
Expanded to an 18-hole course in May 1993. Slightly hilly course in scenic location.
18 holes, 4656mtrs, Par 72, SSS 70.
Club membership 376.

Visitors	advisable to contact in advance.
Societies	apply in writing.
Green Fees	not confirmed.
Facilities	⊗ ᾲ ♨ ♥ ♀ ⊿ ♈
Leisure	caddy cars, pool table.
Location	Licknavar (20m S of Bantry, off N71)
Hotel	★★★57% Westlodge Hotel, BANTRY ☎ (027) 50360 90 ⇆ ℟

YOUGHAL
Map 01 C2

Youghal ☎ (024) 92787
For many years the host of various Golfing Union championships, Youghal offers a good test of golf and is well maintained for year-round play. There are panoramic views of Youghal Bay and the Blackwater estuary.
18 holes, 5700mtrs, Par 70, SSS 69, Course record 67.
Club membership 600.

Visitors	may not play Wed (Ladies Day) and should contact in advance for weekends.
Societies	must apply in writing a few months in advance.
Green Fees	not confirmed.
Facilities	⊗ ᾲ by prior arrangement ♨ ♥ ♀ ⊿ ⊜ ♈ ℟ Ciaran Carroll.
Location	Knockaverry
Hotel	★★63% Devonshire Arms Hotel and Restaurant, Pearse Square, YOUGHAL ☎ (024) 92827 & 92018 10 ⇆ ℟

A golf course name printed in ***bold italics*** means we have been unable to verify information with the club's management for the current year

CO DONEGAL

BALLINTRA　　　　　　　　　　　　　　Map 01 B5

Donegal ☎ (073) 34054
This massive links course was opened in 1973 and provides a world-class facility in peaceful surroundings. It is a very long course with some memorable holes, including five par 5s, calling for some big hitting. Donegal is the home club of former Curtis Cup captain, Maire O'Donnell.
18 holes, 6243mtrs, Par 73, SSS 73.
Club membership 550.

Visitors	no restrictions.
Societies	must apply in writing well in advance.
Green Fees	IR£14per day (IR£18 weekends & bank holidays).
Facilities	⊗ 🅱 🍺 ♀ ⚒
Leisure	buggies, caddy cars.
Location	Murvagh, Laghy (6m S of Donegal on Ballyshannon road)
Hotel	★★★72% Sand House Hotel, ROSSNOWLAGH ☎ (072) 51777 42 ⇥ 📠

BALLYBOFEY　　　　　　　　　　　　　Map 01 C5

Ballybofey & Stranorlar ☎ (074) 31093
A most scenic course incorporating pleasant valleys backed by mountains with three of its holes bordered by a lake. There are three Par 3s on the first nine and two on the second. The most difficult hole is the long uphill Par 4 16th. The only Par 5 is the 7th.
18 holes, 5366mtrs, Par 68, SSS 68, Course record 64.
Club membership 450.

Visitors	may play on weekdays. Advisable to book in advance
Green Fees	IR£12 per day weekdays (per round weekends).
Facilities	⊗ & 🍲 by prior arrangement 🅱 🍺 ♀ ⚒
Leisure	squash.
Location	Stranorlar (0.25m from Stranorlar)
Hotel	★★★59% Kee's Hotel, Stranolar, BALLYBOFEY ☎ (074) 31018 35 ⇥ 📠

BALLYLIFFEN　　　　　　　　　　　　Map 01 C6

Ballyliffin ☎ Carndonagh (077) 76119
The Old course is a links course with rolling fairways. There is a new 18-hole course under construction designed by Craddock & Ruddy & Co.
18 holes, 6384yds, Par 72, SSS 70, Course record 67.
Club membership 803.

Visitors	telephone in advance.
Societies	telephone in advance.
Green Fees	IR£10 (IR£15 weekend & bank holidays).
Facilities	⊗ & 🅱 by prior arrangement 🍺 ♀ ⚒
Leisure	caddy cars for hire.
Hotel	★★63% Strand Hotel, BALLYLIFFEN ☎ (077) 76107 12 ⇥ 📠

> **For an explanation of symbols and abbreviations, see page 5**

BUNCRANA　　　　　　　　　　　　　Map 01 C6

Buncrana Municipal ☎ (077) 62279
A 9-hole course with a very challenging Par-3 3rd with all carry out of bounds on either side.
9 holes, 2125yds, Par 62, SSS 60, Course record 59.
Club membership 100.

Visitors	during open competitions only visitors with club handicaps.
Societies	write in advance.
Green Fees	IR£6 men, IR£4 ladies, IR£2 juniors.
Facilities	🅱 ♀ ⚒ 🏠
Location	Ballmacarry
Hotel	★★63% Strand Hotel, BALLYLIFFEN ☎ (077) 76107 12 ⇥ 📠

North West ☎ (077) 61715
A traditional-style links course on gently rolling sandy terrain with some long par 4s. Good judgement is required on the approaches and the course offers a satisfying test coupled with undemanding walking.
18 holes, 6203yds, Par 69, SSS 69, Course record 63.
Club membership 500.

Visitors	no restrictions.
Societies	must contact in advance.
Green Fees	IR£10 (IR£15 weekends).
Facilities	⊗ 🍲 (Thu, Fri & Sat) 🅱 🍺 ♀ ⚒ 🏠 🍴 Seamus McBriarty.
Leisure	snooker, practice area, putting green.
Location	Lisfannon, Fahan
Hotel	★★63% Strand Hotel, BALLYLIFFEN ☎ (077) 76107 12 ⇥ 📠

BUNDORAN　　　　　　　　　　　　　Map 01 B5

Bundoran ☎ (072) 41302
This popular course, acknowledged as one of the best in the country, runs along the high cliffs above Bundoran beach and has a difficult par of 69. Designed by Harry Vardon, it offers a challenging game of golf in beautiful surroundings and has been the venue for a number of Irish golf championships.
18 holes, 5599mtrs, Par 69, SSS 70.
Club membership 400.

Visitors	must contact in advance.
Societies	must contact in advance.
Green Fees	IR£12 (IR£14 weekends & bank holidays).
Facilities	🅱 ♀ ⚒ 🏠 🍴 ♀ 🍲
Leisure	hard tennis courts, heated indoor swimming pool, sauna, gymnasium, caddy cars.
Hotel	★★67% Dorrians Imperial Hotel, BALLYSHANNON ☎ (072) 51147 26 ⇥ 📠

DUNFANAGHY　　　　　　　　　　　Map 01 C6

Dunfanaghy ☎ Letterkenny (074) 36335
Overlooking Sheephaven Bay, the course has a flat central area with three streams to negotiate. At the Port-na-Blagh end there are five marvellous holes, including one across the beach, while the Horn Head end is a real golfing test.
18 holes, 5066mtrs, Par 68, SSS 66, Course record 65.
Club membership 350.

Visitors	restricted on Sat & Sun mornings.
Societies	must telephone in advance.
Green Fees	IR£11 per round (IR£13 weekends).

Facilities ⬛ ♀ ⚲ 🏠 ⛏
Leisure trolley hire.
Location Kill (On N56)
Hotel ★★68% Arnold's Hotel, DUNFANAGHY
☎ (074) 36208 & 36142 34 ⇆ 🐾

GREENCASTLE   Map 01 C6

Greencastle ☎ (077) 81013
A typical links course along the shores of Lough Foyle, surrounded by rocky headlands and sandy beaches. In 1992 to celebrate its centenary, the course increased to 18 holes.
18 holes, 5118mtrs, Par 69, SSS 67.
Club membership 600.
Visitors no restrictions.
Societies telephone in advance.
Green Fees IR£10 (IR£15 weekends).
Facilities ⊗ & ⫙ by prior arrangement ⬛ ♀ ⚲
Location Moville
Hotel ★58% Malin Hotel, MALIN
☎ (077) 70606 & 70645 12rm(2 ⇆)

LETTERKENNY   Map 01 C5

Letterkenny ☎ (074) 21150
The fairways are wide and generous, but the rough, when you find it, is short, tough and mean. The flat and untiring terrain on the shores of Lough Swilly provides good holiday golf. Many interesting holes include the intimidating 1st with its high tee through trees and the tricky dog-leg of the 2nd hole.
18 holes, 6239yds, Par 70, SSS 71, Course record 67.
Club membership 500.
Visitors preferred Mon-Fri. Advisable to contact in advance for weekends and bank holidays.
Societies apply by writing or telephone.
Green Fees not confirmed.
Facilities ⊗ ⫙ by prior arrangement ⬛ ♀ ⚲ ⛏
Leisure snooker, table tennis.
Location Barnhill (2m from town on Rathmelton road)
Hotel ★★67% Hotel Clanree, LETTERKENNY
☎ (074) 24369 21 ⇆ 🐾

NARIN   Map 01 B5

Narin & Portnoo ☎ (075) 45107
Seaside links with every hole presenting its own special feature. The Par 4 5th, for instance, demands a perfectly placed drive to get a narrow sight of the narrow entrance to the elevated green. Cross winds from the sea can make some of the Par 4s difficult to reach with two woods.
18 holes, 5225mtrs, Par 69, SSS 68.
Visitors preferred on weekdays.
Green Fees not confirmed.
Facilities ⬛ ♀
Location 6m from Ardara
Hotel ★★★61% The Hyland Central Hotel, The Diamond, DONEGAL ☎ (073) 21027 70 ⇆ 🐾

PORTSALON   Map 01 C6

Portsalon ☎ (074) 59459
Another course blessed by nature. The three golden beaches of Ballymastocker Bay lie at one end, while the beauty of Lough Swilly and the Inishowen Peninsula beyond is a

distracting but pleasant feature to the west. Situated on the Fanad Peninsula, this lovely links course provides untiring holiday golf at its best.
18 holes, 5379mtrs, Par 69, SSS 68, Course record 67.
Club membership 350.
Visitors may not play on competition days.
Societies must apply in writing to club secretary.
Green Fees IR£10 per day.
Facilities ⊗ ⫙ ⬛ & ⬛ (Fri-Sun only in winter) ♀ ⚲
Leisure caddy cars.
Hotel ★56% Pier Hotel, RATHMULLAN
☎ (074) 58178 16rm(11 ⇆ 🐾)

RATHMULLAN   Map 01 C6

Otway ☎ (074) 58319
9 holes, 4234yds, Par 64, SSS 60.
Visitors welcome.
Societies contact for details.
Green Fees not confirmed.
Location Saltpans (W shore of Loch Swilly)
Hotel ★★★⚬⚓62% Fort Royal Hotel, Fort Royal, RATHMULLAN
☎ (074) 58100 11 ⇆ 🐾Annexe4 ⇆

ROSAPENNA   Map 01 C6

Rosapenna ☎ (074) 55301
Dramatic links course offering a challenging round. Originally designed by Tom Morris and later modified by James Braid and Harry Vardon, it includes such features as bunkers in mid fairway. The best part of the links runs in the low valley along the ocean.
18 holes, 6271yds, Par 70, SSS 71.
Club membership 200.
Visitors no restrictions.
Societies must contact in advance.
Green Fees not confirmed.
Facilities ⫙ ⬛ ⬛ ♀ ⚲ 🏠 ⛏ ⚒ ⛏ Simon Byrne.
Leisure hard tennis courts, snooker.
Location Downings
Hotel ★★68% Arnold's Hotel, DUNFANAGHY
☎ (074) 36208 & 36142 34 ⇆ 🐾

CO DUBLIN

BALBRIGGAN   Map 01 D4

Balbriggan ☎ Dublin (01) 8412229
A parkland course with great variations and good views of the Mourne and Cooley mountains.
18 holes, 5881mtrs, Par 71, SSS 71.
Club membership 600.
Visitors no restrictions.
Societies must apply in writing.
Green Fees IR£14 per round (IR£18 weekends).
Facilities ⊗ ⫙ ⬛ ⬛ ♀ ⚲
Leisure snooker, caddy cars for hire.
Location Blackhall
Hotel ★★★63% The Grand Hotel, MALAHIDE
☎ (01) 8450000 100 ⇆ 🐾

BRITTAS   Map 01 D4

Slade Valley ☎ (01) 582183 & 582139
This is a course for a relaxing game, being fairly easy and in pleasant surroundings.
18 holes, 5345mtrs, Par 69, SSS 68, Course record 64.
Club membership 800.
Visitors   preferred on Mon, Thu & Fri. Restricted weekends.
Societies   telephone in advance
Green Fees   IR£15 per round.
Facilities   ⊗ ⅀ ♨ ♥ ♀ ⚲ 🏠 ⚑ (John Dignam.
Leisure   snooker, caddy cars.
Location   Lynch Park (9m SW of Dublin on N81)
Hotel   ★★★56% Downshire House Hotel,
                  BLESSINGTON
                  ☎ (045) 65199 14 ⇆ ⚑Annexe11 ⇆ ⚑

CLOGHRAN   Map 01 D4

Forrest Little ☎ (01) 8401183
Testing parkland course.
18 holes, 5865mtrs, Par 70, SSS 70.
Visitors   preferred weekday mornings.
Green Fees   not confirmed.
Facilities   ♨ ♀ 🏠 ⚑ (Tony Judd.
Location   6m N of Dublin on N1
Hotel   ★★★61% Marine Hotel, Sutton Cross,
                  DUBLIN ☎ (01) 8322613 27 ⇆ ⚑

CLONSILLA   Map 01 D4

Luttrellstown Castle ☎ (01) 8213237
18 holes, 6447mtrs, Par 72, SSS 73, Course record 68.
Club membership 250.
Visitors   restricted 2.30-4pm weekdays, 8.30-10 & 12.30-
                  2pm weekends & bank holidays.
Societies   must book in advance.
Green Fees   IR£30 per 18 holes (IR£35 weekends).
Facilities   ⊗ ⅀ ♨ ♥ ♀ ⚲ 🏠 ⚑ ⚲(
Leisure   hard tennis courts, heated outdoor swimming
                  pool, fishing, riding, snooker, caddy cars, carts.
Location   Porterstown rd
Hotel   ★★★57% Finnstown Country House Hotel &
                  Golf Course, Newcastle Rd, LUCAN
                  ☎ (01) 6280644 25 ⇆ ⚑

DONABATE   Map 01 D4

Balcarrick ☎ (01) 8436228
A 9-hole parkland course which is due to be extended to 18 holes during 1994/1995.
18 holes, 5954mtrs, Par 72, SSS 71.
Visitors   contact for details.
Societies   contact for details.
Green Fees   IR£10 (IR£15 weekends).
Location   Corballis
Hotel   ★★★63% The Grand Hotel, MALAHIDE
                  ☎ (01) 8450000 100 ⇆ ⚑

Beaverstown ☎ Dublin (01) 8436439 & 8436721
Well wooded course with water hazards at more than half of the holes.
18 holes, 5855mtrs, Par 71, SSS 71, Course record 69.
Club membership 800.

Visitors   may not play 12.30-1.30pm daily & must contact
                  in advance to play on Wed, Sat or Sun.
Societies   must contact in writing.
Green Fees   IR£12 (IR£20 weekends & bank holidays).
Facilities   ⊗ ⅀ ♨ ♥ ♀ ⚲
Leisure   snooker, caddy cars.
Location   Beaverstown (5m from Dublin Airport)
Hotel   ★★★63% The Grand Hotel, MALAHIDE
                  ☎ (01) 8450000 100 ⇆ ⚑

Corballis Public ☎ (01) 8436583
Well maintained coastal course with excellent greens.
18 holes, 4971yds, Par 65, SSS 64.
Visitors   no restrictions.
Societies   book by telephone and confirm by letter.
Green Fees   IR£7 per round (IR£8 weekends).
Facilities   ⊗ ⅀ ♨ ♥ ♀ ⚲ 🏠 ⚑
Leisure   caddy cars.
Location   Corballis
Hotel   ★★★63% The Grand Hotel, MALAHIDE
                  ☎ (01) 8450000 100 ⇆ ⚑

Donabate ☎ (01) 8436346
Level parkland course.
18 holes, 5704yds, Par 70, SSS 69.
Visitors   may not play on Wed or at weekends.
Green Fees   not confirmed.
Facilities   ⊗ ⅀ ♨ ♥ ♀ 🏠 ⚑ (Hugh Jackson.
Hotel   ★★★63% The Grand Hotel, MALAHIDE
                  ☎ (01) 8450000 100 ⇆ ⚑

The Island ☎ (01) 8436104
Links course on a promontory, with sea inlets separating some of the fairways. Accuracy as well as length of shots are required on some holes and sand hills provide an additional challenge.
18 holes, 6053mtrs, Par 71, SSS 72.
Club membership 800.
Visitors   preferred on Mon, Tue & Fri.
Societies   must apply in advance.
Green Fees   not confirmed.
Facilities   ⊗ ⅀ ♨ ♥ ♀ ⚲
Location   Corballis
Hotel   ★★★63% The Grand Hotel, MALAHIDE
                  ☎ (01) 8450000 100 ⇆ ⚑

DUBLIN   Map 01 D4

Carrickmines ☎ (01) 2955972
Meadowland course.
9 holes, 6100yds, Par 71, SSS 69.
Visitors   with member only Sat, Sun & bank holidays.
Societies   contact for details.
Green Fees   IR£15 (IR£18 Sun).
Facilities   limited catering available
Location   Carrickmines (7m S of Dublin)
Hotel   ★★★59% Victor Hotel, Rochestown Av, DUN
                  LAOGHAIRE
                  ☎ (01) 2853555 & 2853102 64 ⇆ ⚑

Castle ☎ (01) 4904207
A tight, tree-lined parkland course which is very highly regarded by all who play there.
18 holes, 5653mtrs, Par 70, SSS 69, Course record 63.
Club membership 1150.
Visitors   restricted at weekends.

Societies	must apply in writing.
Green Fees	IR£25.
Facilities	⊗ ⅢＬ ♥ ♀ ⚐ ⚑ ﹝ David Kinsella.
Leisure	snooker, caddy cars.
Location	Woodside Dr, Rathfarnham
Hotel	★★★★64% Jurys Hotel and Towers, Pembroke Rd, Ballsbridge, DUBLIN ☎ (01) 6605000 284 ⇄ ﹝Annexe100 ⇄ ﹝

Clontarf ☎ (01) 8331892

The nearest golf course to Dublin city, with a historic building as a clubhouse, Clontarf is a parkland type course bordered on one side by a railway line. There are several testing and challenging holes including the 12th, which involves playing over a pond and a quarry.
18 holes, 5459mtrs, Par 69, SSS 68, Course record 66.
Club membership 1000.

Visitors	must contact in advance. May not play on Tue between 1.30 & 2.30pm & Fri after 3pm; must play with member at weekends. Mon is Ladies Day. Dress code must be observed.
Societies	Tue & Fri. Must contact in writing.
Green Fees	not confirmed.
Facilities	⊗ Ⅲ Ｌ ♥ ♀ ⚐ ⚑ ⌦ ﹝ Joe Craddock.
Leisure	snooker, bowling green.
Location	Donnycarney House, Malahide Rd
Hotel	★★★63% Central Hotel, 1-5 Exchequer St, DUBLIN 2 ☎ (01) 6797302 70 ⇄ ﹝

Corrstown ☎ (01) 8640533

A new course with the first 9 holes in play - a pleasant parkland setting well sheltered by mature trees. An additional 18-hole championship standard course is due to open in Spring 1995. It has been designed by Eddie B. Connaughton to test the best golfers.
Parkland: 18 holes, 6838yds, Par 72.
Championship: 9 holes, 3053yds, Par 70, SSS 69.
Club membership 800.

Visitors	welcome to play 9 hole course but with member only weekdays. Further 18 Holes due to open Easter 1995.
Societies	by arrangement.
Green Fees	IR£5 per 9 holes.
Facilities	⊗ Ⅲ by prior arrangement ♀ (due to open 1995) ⚐ ⚑
Leisure	caddy cars, practice area.
Location	Killsallaghan (W of Dublin Airport via St Margarets)
Hotel	★★★63% The Grand Hotel, MALAHIDE ☎ (01) 8450000 100 ⇄ ﹝

Deer Park Hotel & Golf Course ☎ (01) 8322624

Claiming to be Irelands largest golf/hotel complex, be warned that its popularity makes it extremely busy at times and only hotel residents can book tee-off times.
St Fintans: 18 holes, 6647yds, Par 72, SSS 73.
Old 9: 9 holes, 3130yds, Par 35.
Par 3: 12 holes, 1810yds, Par 36.
Club membership 200.

Visitors	no restrictions. There may be delays especially Sun mornings.
Societies	must contact by telephone.
Green Fees	IR£9 (IR£10 weekends) 18 holes; IR£5 (IR£6 weekends) 9 holes.
Facilities	⊗ Ⅲ Ｌ ♥ ♀ ⚐ ⚑ ⌦
Leisure	snooker.
Location	Howth (On right 0.5m before Howth Harbour)

| Hotel | ★★★60% Howth Lodge Hotel, HOWTH ☎ (01) 8321010 46 ⇄ ﹝ |

Edmonstown ☎ (01) 4931082 & 4932462

A popular and testing parkland course situated at the foot of the Dublin Mountains in the suburbs of the city. An attractive stream flows in front of the 4th and 6th greens.
18 holes, 5663mtrs, Par 70, SSS 69.
Club membership 700.

Visitors	must contact in advance as there are daily restrictions.
Societies	must contact in writing.
Green Fees	IR£20 (IR£25 weekends).
Facilities	⊗ Ⅲ Ｌ ♥ ♀ ⚐ ﹝ Andrew Crofton.
Leisure	snooker.
Location	Edmondstown Rd, Edmondstown
Hotel	★★★68% Doyle Montrose Hotel, Stillorgan Rd, DUBLIN ☎ (01) 2693311 180 ⇄ ﹝

Elm Park Golf & Sports Club ☎ (01) 2693438

Interesting parkland course requiring a degree of accuracy, particularly as half of the holes involve crossing the stream.
18 holes, 5422mtrs, Par 69, SSS 68.
Club membership 1750.

Visitors	telephone before arrival.
Societies	apply in writing.
Green Fees	IR£30 per round (IR£35 weekends).
Facilities	⊗ Ⅲ Ｌ ♥ ♀ ⚐ ⚑ ⌦ ﹝
Leisure	grass tennis courts.
Location	Nutley House (3m from city centre)
Hotel	★★★★64% Jurys Hotel and Towers, Pembroke Rd, Ballsbridge, DUBLIN ☎ (01) 6605000 284 ⇄ ﹝Annexe100 ⇄ ﹝

Foxrock ☎ (01) 2895668

A well-treed parkland course.
9 holes, 5667mtrs, Par 70, SSS 69.

Visitors	welcome but contact in advance, no green fees Tue & weekends.
Societies	contact for details.
Green Fees	IR£20 per day.
Facilities	limited catering ♀ ﹝ Tony O'Connor.
Location	Torquay Rd, Foxrock
Hotel	★★★59% Victor Hotel, Rochestown Av, DUN LAOGHAIRE ☎ (01) 2853555 & 2853102 64 ⇄ ﹝

Grange ☎ (01) 932889

Wooded parkland course .
18 holes, 5517mtrs, Par 68, SSS 69.

Visitors	preferred on weekdays.
Green Fees	not confirmed.
Facilities	⊗ Ⅲ Ｌ ♀ ⚐ ﹝ W Sullivan.
Location	Rathfarnham (6m from city centre)
Hotel	★★★68% Doyle Montrose Hotel, Stillorgan Rd, DUBLIN ☎ (01) 2693311 180 ⇄ ﹝

Howth ☎ (01) 8323055

A moorland course with scenic views of Dublin Bay. It is very hilly and presents a good challenge for the athletic golfer.
18 holes, 5618mtrs, Par 71, SSS 69.
Club membership 1257.

Visitors	may not play on Wed, Sat or Sun. Contact in advance if more than 4 in party.
Societies	must apply in writing.
Green Fees	IR£16 Mon-Thu; IR£18 Fri. ▶

Finnstown Country House Hotel & Golf Course ★★★

Newcastle Road, Lucan, Co Dublin
Tel: 00 3531 628044   Fax: 00 3531 6281088

Finnstown Country House is only eight miles from Dublin city centre. Situated off the main road and on 50 acres of mature woodlands, guests may relax and enjoy the friendly atmosphere and service of a small grade A country house hotel together with the amenities of today and a fine Restaurant. The hotel has its own wooded walks, 9 hole golf course, hard tennis courts, outdoor pool, gymnasium, saunas and Turkish bath.

A beautiful place in a great location.

Facilities   ⓑ 🍷 ♀ ⅄ 🏌 (John McGuirk.
Leisure   snooker.
Location   St Fintan's, Carrickbrack Rd, Sutton
Hotel   ★★★61% Marine Hotel, Sutton Cross, DUBLIN ☎ (01) 8322613 27 ➪ ௳

Milltown ☎ (01) 4976090
Level parkland course on the outskirts of the city.
18 holes, 5638mtrs, Par 71, SSS 69, Course record 67.
Club membership 1200.
Visitors   with member only on Sun and after 5pm daily. Must contact in advance.
Societies   welcome.
Green Fees   not confirmed.
Facilities   ⊗ ⅏ ⓑ 🍷 ♀ ⅄ 🏌 (John Harnett.
Leisure   snooker.
Location   Lower Churchtown Rd
Hotel   ★★★★64% Jurys Hotel and Towers, Pembroke Rd, Ballsbridge, DUBLIN ☎ (01) 6605000 284 ➪ ௳Annexe100 ➪ ௳

Newlands ☎ (01) 4593157
Mature parkland course offering a testing game.
18 holes, 5714mtrs, Par 71, SSS 70.
Club membership 1000.
Visitors   must contact in advance and may play Mon, Thu, Fri and Wed mornings only.
Societies   must write in writing.
Green Fees   not confirmed.
Facilities   ⊗ (Mon-Fri) ⅏ (by prior arrangement winter) ⓑ 🍷 ♀ ⅄ 🏌 🏌 (Karl O'Donnell.
Location   Clondalkin
Hotel   ★★★56% Doyle Green Isle Hotel, Clondalkin, DUBLIN ☎ (01) 593406 48 ➪ ௳Annexe35 ➪ ௳

Rathfarnham ☎ (01) 4931201
Parkland course designed by John Jacobs in 1962.
9 holes, 5833mtrs, Par 71, SSS 70.
Club membership 592.
Visitors   may not play Tue, Sat, Sun or Thu pm.
Societies   must apply in writing.
Green Fees   IR£20.
Facilities   ⓑ 🍷 ♀ ⅄ 🏌 (Brian O'Hara.
Location   Newtown
Hotel   ★★★★64% Jurys Hotel and Towers, Pembroke Rd, Ballsbridge, DUBLIN ☎ (01) 6605000 284 ➪ ௳Annexe100 ➪ ௳

Royal Dublin ☎ (01) 8336346 & 8331262
A popular course with visitors, for its design subtleties, for the condition of the links and the friendly atmosphere. Founded in 1885, the club moved to its present site in 1889 and received its Royal designation in 1891. A notable former club professional was Christie O'Connor. Along with its many notable holes, Royal Dublin has a fine and testing finish. The 18th is a sharply dog-legged par 4, with out of bounds along the right-hand side. The decision to try the long carry over the 'garden' is one many visitors have regretted.
18 holes, 6267mtrs, Par 72, SSS 73, Course record 63.
Club membership 875.
Visitors   must contact in advance & have handicap certificate. Green fees not accepted on Wed, Sat or 10.30-12.30pm Sun.
Societies   must apply in writing.
Green Fees   IR£35 per round including caddy car hire (IR£45 weekends).
Facilities   ⊗ ⅏ ⓑ 🍷 (no catering Mon after 2.30pm) ♀ ⅄ 🏌 🏌 (Leonard Owens.
Leisure   snooker, sauna, practice ground & nets, putting green.
Location   North Bull Island, Dollymount
Hotel   ★★★63% Central Hotel, 1-5 Exchequer St, DUBLIN 2 ☎ (01) 6797302 70 ➪ ௳

St Anne's ☎ (01) 8336471
Links course, recently extended from 9 holes to 18.
18 holes, 5660mtrs, Par 70, SSS 69.
Club membership 500.
Visitors   telephone for restrictions. Must have an introduction from own club.
Societies   must apply in writing.
Green Fees   not confirmed.
Facilities   ⊗ ⅏ ⓑ 🍷 ♀ ⅄ 🏌 (Paddy Skerritt.
Location   North Bull Island, Dollymount
Hotel   ★★★63% Central Hotel, 1-5 Exchequer St, DUBLIN 2 ☎ (01) 6797302 70 ➪ ௳

St Margaret's Golf & Country Club
☎ (01) 8640400 & (01) 8640416
A championship standard course which measures nearly 7,000 yards off the back tees, but flexible teeing offers a fairer challenge to the middle and high handicap golfer. Plenty of water hazards and mounding. The Par 5 8th hole is set to become notorious - featuring lakes to the left and right of the tee and a third lake in front of the green. Ryder Cup player, Sam Torrance, has described the 18th as 'possibly the strongest and most exciting in the world'.
18 holes, 6629yds, Par 73, SSS 72, Course record 69.
Visitors   no restrictions.
Societies   pre booking recommended.
Green Fees   IR£30 (IR£35 weekends).

Facilities	⊗ ⊤ ৳ ☞ ♀ △ 盒 ⚑ ⚏ Ciaran Monaghan.
Leisure	caddy cars,caddies,tuition,golf clinic.
Location	St Margaret's (3m NW)
Hotel	★★★61% Marine Hotel, Sutton Cross, DUBLIN ☎ (01) 8322613 27 ⇄ ☏

Stackstown ☎ (01) 4942338 & 4941993
Pleasant course in scenic surroundings.
18 holes, 5925mtrs, Par 72, SSS 72, Course record 70.
Club membership 1042.

Visitors	preferred Mon-Fri.
Societies	telephone in advance and confirm in writing.
Green Fees	not confirmed.
Facilities	⊗ ⊤ ৳ ☞ ♀ △ 盒 ⚏ Michael Kavanach.
Leisure	snooker, sauna.
Location	Kellystown Rd, Rathfarnham (9m S of city centre)
Hotel	★★★68% Doyle Montrose Hotel, Stillorgan Rd, DUBLIN ☎ (01) 2693311 180 ⇄ ☏

Sutton ☎ (01) 8324875
Founded in 1890.
9 holes, 5226mtrs, Par 70, SSS 67.

Visitors	welcome except for competition days, contact for further details.
Societies	by prior arrangement.
Green Fees	IR£15 (IR£20 weekends).
Facilities	catering by prior arrangement ⚏ Nicky Lynch.
Leisure	lessons can be arranged.
Location	Cush Point, Burrow Rd, Sutton (approx 7m NE of city)
Hotel	★★★60% Howth Lodge Hotel, HOWTH ☎ (01) 8321010 46 ⇄ ☏

DUN LAOGHAIRE · Map 01 D4

Dun Laoghaire ☎ Dublin (01) 2803916
This is a well wooded parkland course, not long, but requiring accurate club selection and placing of shots. The course was designed by Harry Colt in 1918.
18 holes, 5272mtrs, Par 69, SSS 68, Course record 64.
Club membership 1050.

Visitors	may not play Sat.
Societies	must apply in writing.
Green Fees	IR£25.
Facilities	⊗ & ⊤ (Apr-Oct) ৳ ☞ ♀ △ 盒 ⚑ ⚏ Owen Mulhall.
Location	Eglinton Park, Tivoli Rd
Hotel	★★★59% Victor Hotel, Rochestown Av, DUN LAOGHAIRE ☎ (01) 2853555 & 2853102 64 ⇄ ☏

KILLINEY · Map 01 D4

Killiney ☎ Dublin (01) 2851983
The course is on the side of Killiney Hill with picturesque views over south Dublin and the Wicklow Mountains.
9 holes, 5626mtrs, Par 69, SSS 69, Course record 65.
Club membership 480.

Visitors	welcome Thu, Sat & Sun am.
Green Fees	IR£17 (IR£20 weekends & bank holidays).
Facilities	৳ ☞ ♀ △ 盒 ⚑ ⚏ P O'Boyle.
Leisure	snooker.
Location	Ballinclea Rd
Hotel	★★★71% Fitzpatrick Castle Hotel, KILLINEY ☎ (01) 2840700 90 ⇄ ☏

KILTERNAN · Map 01 D4

Kilternan Golf & Country Club Hotel ☎ (01) 2955559
Interesting and testing course overlooking Dublin Bay.
18 holes, 4914mtrs, Par 68, SSS 67, Course record 69.
Club membership 789.

Visitors	may not play before 1.30pm at weekends.
Societies	apply in writing/telephone in advance.
Green Fees	IR£12 (IR£16 weekends).
Facilities	⊗ ⊤ ৳ ☞ ♀ △ 盒 ⚑ ⛟ ⚏
Leisure	hard tennis courts, heated indoor swimming pool, fishing, riding, snooker, sauna, solarium, gymnasium, dry ski slope, indoor tennis, night club.
Hotel	★★★71% Fitzpatrick Castle Hotel, KILLINEY ☎ (01) 2840700 90 ⇄ ☏

LUCAN · Map 01 D4

Finnstown Fairways ☎ (01) 6280644
A flat parkland 9-hole course based in grounds originally laid out in the 18th century. Very challenging 6th and 7th holes among many mature trees.
9 holes, 2695yds, Par 68, SSS 66.
Club membership 200.

Visitors	time sheet in use.
Societies	must reserve in advance.
Green Fees	IR£10 per day (IR£12 weekends).
Facilities	⊗ ⊤ ৳ ☞ ♀ △ ⚑ ⛟
Leisure	hard tennis courts, heated outdoor swimming pool, sauna, solarium, gymnasium, turkish bath.
Location	Newcastle Rd (off N4)
Hotel	★★★57% Finnstown Country House Hotel & Golf Course, Newcastle Rd, LUCAN ☎ (01) 6280644 25 ⇄ ☏

Hermitage ☎ (01) 6265049
Part level, part undulating course bordered by the River Liffey and offering some surprises.
18 holes, 6034mtrs, Par 71, SSS 70, Course record 65.
Club membership 1100.

Visitors	must contact in advance and have an introduction from own club.
Societies	must telephone well in advance.
Green Fees	not confirmed.
Facilities	⊗ ⊤ (times vary with season) ৳ ☞ ♀ △ 盒 ⚑ ⚏ David Daly.
Leisure	snooker.
Location	Ballydowd
Hotel	★★★57% Finnstown Country House Hotel & Golf Course, Newcastle Rd, LUCAN ☎ (01) 6280644 25 ⇄ ☏

Lucan ☎ Dublin (01) 6282106
Founded in 1902 as a 9-hole course and only recently extended to 18 holes, Lucan involves playing across both the main road and a lane which bisects the course.
18 holes, 5958mtrs, Par 71, SSS 71.
Club membership 780.

Visitors	with member only Sat & Sun, after 1pm Wed. Must contact in advance.
Societies	must apply in writing.
Green Fees	IR£16.
Facilities	৳ ☞ ♀ △
Location	Celbridge Rd

▶

Hotel   ★★★54% Lucan Spa Hotel, LUCAN
☎ (01) 6280494 50 ⇌ 🟏

MALAHIDE   Map 01 D4

Malahide ☎ (01) 8461611
Parkland courses with water hazards at a number of holes.
Blue Course: 9 holes, 2888mtrs, Par 71, SSS 70.
Red Course: 9 holes, 2820mtrs, Par 71, SSS 70.
Yellow Course: 9 holes, 2632mtrs, Par 70, SSS 69.
Club membership 900.
Visitors   must contact in advance.
Societies   must contact in advance.
Green Fees IR£21 per 18 holes (IR£31 weekends & bank
holidays).
Facilities   ⊗ ⊞ ⅊ ▬ ♀ ⚘ ⌂ ⚙ ⚔ David Barton.
Leisure   snooker, caddy cars, caddies.
Location   Beechwood, The Grange (1m from coast road at
Portmarnock)
Hotel   ★★★63% The Grand Hotel, MALAHIDE
☎ (01) 8450000 100 ⇌ 🟏

PORTMARNOCK   Map 01 D4

PORTMARNOCK See page 341

RATHCOOLE   Map 01 D4

Beech Park ☎ Dublin (01) 580100
Relatively flat parkland with heavily wooded fairways.
18 holes, 5730mtrs, Par 72, SSS 70, Course record 67.
Club membership 750.
Visitors   restricted on some days, telephone in advance.
Societies   apply in writing.
Green Fees not confirmed.
Facilities   ⊗ ⊞ ⅊ ▬ ♀ ⚘
Leisure   snooker.
Location   Johnstown
Hotel   ★★★57% Finnstown Country House Hotel &
Golf Course, Newcastle Rd, LUCAN
☎ (01) 6280644 25 ⇌ 🟏

SKERRIES   Map 01 D4

Skerries ☎ (01) 8491567
Tree-lined parkland course on gently rolling countryside,
with sea views from some holes. The 1st and 18th are
particularly challenging. The club can be busy on some days,
but is always friendly.
18 holes, 5994mtrs, Par 73, SSS 72.
Club membership 900.
Visitors   must contact in advance.
Societies   must contact well in advance in writing.
Green Fees not confirmed.
Facilities   ⊗ ⊞ by prior arrangement ⅊ ▬ ♀ ⚘ ⌂ ⚙ ⌘
⚔ Jimmy Kinsella.
Leisure   snooker.
Hotel   ★★★63% The Grand Hotel, MALAHIDE
☎ (01) 8450000 100 ⇌ 🟏

TALLAGHT   Map 01 D4

Ballinascorney ☎ (01) 512516
A meadowland course founded in 1971.
18 holes, 5465yds, Par 71, SSS 67.
Visitors   weekdays only.
Societies   contact for details.
Green Fees IR£10 (no weekend play).
Facilities   ♀
Location   Ballinascorney (10m SW of Dublin)
Hotel   ★★★56% Doyle Green Isle Hotel, Clondalkin,
DUBLIN
☎ (01) 593406 48 ⇌ 🟏Annexe35 ⇌ 🟏

CO GALWAY

BALLINASLOE   Map 01 B4

Ballinasloe ☎ (0905) 42126
Well maintained parkland course, recently extended from a
par 68 to a par 72.
18 holes, 6445yds, Par 72, SSS 70.
Club membership 800.
Visitors   may not play on Sun.
Societies   welcome on weekdays, apply in writing.
Green Fees IR£10 weekdays (IR£12 weekends & bank holidays).
Facilities   ⊗ & ⊞ (summer only by arrangement) ⅊ & ▬
(by prior arrangement in winter) ♀ ⚘
Leisure   caddy cars available.
Location   Rossgloss
Hotel   ★★★62% Hayden's Hotel, BALLINASLOE
☎ (0905) 42347 50 ⇌ 🟏

BALLYCONNEELY   Map 01 A4

Connemara ☎ Clifden (095) 23502 & 23602
This championship links course is situated on the verge of
the Atlantic Ocean in a most spectacular setting, with the
Twelve Bens Mountains in the background. Established as
recently as 1973, it is a tough challenge, due in no small
part to its exposed location, with the back 9 the equal of
any in the world. The last six holes are exceptionally long.
18 holes, 6173mtrs, Par 72, SSS 73.
Club membership 800.
Visitors   must contact in advance and have a
handicap certificate.
Societies   must contact in writing.
Green Fees IR£10/IR£18 per round.
Facilities   ⊗ ⊞ ⅊ ▬ ♀ ⚘ ⌂ ⚙
Leisure   buggies, caddy cars, caddies.
Location   9m SW of Clifton
Hotel   ★★★54% Abbeyglen Castle Hotel, Sky Rd,
CLIFDEN ☎ (095) 21201 40 ⇌ 🟏

GALWAY   Map 01 B4

Galway ☎ (091) 22033
Designed by Dr Alister MacKenzie, this course is inland
by nature, although some of the fairways run close to the ▶

PORTMARNOCK

PORTMARNOCK ☎DUBLIN (01)8462 968   Map 01 D4

John Ingham writes: The night before our fourball tackled Portmarnock was spent, as I recall, in Dublin. Guinness in that city seems smoother, while the conversation with locals, ranged from why no southern Irish player ever won the Open to how such a small nation can boast so many great writers, wits and actors.

I can thoroughly recommend this preparation, prior to facing one of the world's great golfing challenges - providing you only intend playing eighteen holes in one day! Frankly, you will have to reach into the base of your golf bag to pull out every shot if you want to play to your handicap on this superb links.

An opening birdie, downwind, made me wonder what the fuss was about. Two hours later, with a backswing too fast and the breeze now something near a gale, I decided that a test of 7182 yards off the back tees was too man-size for me. Maybe it would be more enjoyable on a calm, summer evening!

I remember the course not for the way it humiliated me, but for the 1960 Canada Cup where I watched Sam Snead and Arnold Palmer winning with such skillful play. Even so, both took 75 in one round while scores by the mighty Gary Player ranged from 65 to 78.

There are no blind shots, unless you drive into sandhills. This is natural golf with no unfair carries off the tee and the only damage to your card is self-inflicted. True, there are a couple of holes of 560 yards and the 522-yard 16th is frightening as you tee up in a fierce wind.

It's incredible to think that Portmarnock was 'discovered' almost by accident in 1893 by a Mr Pickeman and the course architect, Ross. They had rowed a boat from Sutton to the peninsula where they came across a wilderness of bracken, duneland and natural-looking bunkers made by God. They were inspired to create the course, built a shack for a clubhouse and talked about the only real hazard left - a cow that devoured golf balls.

Today it's so very different - with a modern clubhouse filled with members delighted to belong to such an internationally well-known establishment.

Membership 1100

Visitors must apply in writing. Restricted Saturday, Sunday and public holidays

Societies must apply in writing

Green fees Monday-Friday (excluding public holidays) Men £IR40, Ladies £IR30: Saturday, Sunday & public holidays – Men only £IR50 per day

Facilities ⊗ ⍟ 🕭 ♀ (all day) 🏌 🛎 ⛳ ♪ (Joey Purcell)

Location 12m from Dublin. 1m from village down Golf Rd

27 holes. Old Course: 18 holes, 7182 yds, Par 72, SSS 75, course record 74 (Sandy Lyle)
New Course: 9 holes, 3478yds, Par 37

WHERE TO STAY AND EAT NEARBY

HOTELS:
HOWTH
★★★ 60% Howth Lodge.
☎(01) 8321010. 46 🛏 🏮
Irish & French cuisine

MALAHIDE
★★★ 63% Grand. ☎(01) 8450000.
100 🛏 🏮 European cuisine

ocean. The terrain is of gently sloping hillocks with plenty of trees and furze bushes to catch out the unwary. Although not a long course, it provided a worthy challenge as the venue of the Celtic International Tournament in 1984 and continues to delight the visiting golfer.
18 holes, 6376yds, Par 70, SSS 70.
Club membership 1050.

Visitors	preferred on weekdays, except Tue.
Societies	must apply in writing.
Green Fees	IR£20 per day.
Facilities	⊗ ⅷ ⓛ ♥ ♀ ⚲ ⌂ ⅌ ₵ Don Wallace.
Location	Blackrock, Salthill (2m W in Salthill)
Hotel	★★★★67% Great Southern Hotel, Eyre Square, GALWAY ☎ (091) 64041 114 ⇌ ↰

Glenlo Abbey ☎ (091) 26666
A championship course overlooking the magnificent Lough Corrib but only 10 minutes from the centre of Galway city. Nine fairways but large double green with two flags and four tee postions allows 18 diffent holes. The Par 3, 4th hole is on an island-like green extending into the lough.
18 holes, Par 72, SSS 72.

Visitors	pay as you play course due to open in Jul'94.
Societies	telephone in advance.
Green Fees	not confirmed.
Facilities	⊗ ⅷ ⓛ ♥ ♀ ⚲ ⌂ ⅌ ↰
Leisure	fishing, sauna, gymnasium.
Location	Bushy Park (on N59 Galway/Clifden rd)
Hotel	★★★★64% Glenlo Abbey, Bushypark, GALWAY ☎ (091) 26666 42 ⇌ ↰

GORT   Map 01 B3

Gort ☎ (091) 31336
A 9-hole course, bisected by a railway line and with out of bounds on most holes, six of which are bunkered.
9 holes, 2587mtrs, Par 34, SSS 67.
Club membership 320.

Visitors	may not play on Sun mornings or Wed evenings.
Societies	must contact club secretary or bar manager in advance.
Green Fees	IR£8 per round.
Facilities	ⓛ ♥ ♀ ⚲ ⅌
Location	Laughtyshaughnessy
Hotel	★★★★59% Corrib Great Southern Hotel, Dublin Rd, GALWAY ☎ (091) 55281 due to change to 755281 180 ⇌ ↰

LOUGHREA   Map 01 B3

Loughrea ☎ Galway (091) 41049
An excellent parkland course with good greens and extended in 1992 to 18-holes. The course has an unusual feature in that it incorporates a historic souterrain (underground shelter/food store).
9 holes, 5860yds, Par 68, SSS 67.
Club membership 290.

Visitors	may not play Sun mornings.
Societies	must contact in advance.
Green Fees	not confirmed.
Facilities	ⓛ ♥ ♀ ⚲
Location	Bullaun Rd
Hotel	★★★62% Hayden's Hotel, BALLINASLOE ☎ (0905) 42347 50 ⇌ ↰

MOUNTBELLEW   Map 01 B4

Mountbellew ☎ (0905) 79259
A 9-hole wooded parkland course with 2 quarries and penalty drains to provide hazards.
9 holes, 5143mtrs, Par 69, SSS 66.

Visitors	welcome.
Societies	by prior arrangement.
Green Fees	IR£7 (IR£10 weekends).
Facilities	light catering,meals by arrangement
Location	Ballinasloe (of N63 midway between Roscommon/Galway)
Hotel	★★★62% Hayden's Hotel, BALLINASLOE ☎ (0905) 42347 50 ⇌ ↰

ORANMORE   Map 01 B3

Athenry ☎ (091) 94466
Wooded parkland course, recently extended to 18 holes.
18 holes, 6100yds, Par 70, SSS 69.
Club membership 600.

Visitors	may not play on Sun.
Societies	must telephone in advance.
Green Fees	IR£15 per round.
Facilities	⊗ ⅷ ⓛ ♥ ♀ ⚲ ⌂ ⅌
Leisure	caddy cars.
Location	Palmerstown
Hotel	★★★★59% Corrib Great Southern Hotel, Dublin Rd, GALWAY ☎ (091) 55281 due to change to 755281 180 ⇌ ↰

Galway Bay Golf & Country Club
☎ (091) 90500 & 90503
A championship golf course surrounded on three sides by the Atlantic Ocean and featuring water hazards on a number of holes. Each hole has its own characteristics made more obvious by the everchanging seaside winds.
18 holes, 6101mtrs, Par 72, SSS 70, Course record 67.
Club membership 350.

Visitors	no restrictions.
Societies	contact in writing, telephone or fax.
Green Fees	IR£25 per round (IR£30 weekends & bank holidays).
Facilities	⊗ ⅷ ⓛ ♥ ♀ ⚲ ⌂ ⅌ ↰ ₵ Eugene O'Connor.
Leisure	sauna, practice ground,trolley & buggy hire.
Location	Renville
Hotel	★★★★64% Glenlo Abbey, Bushypark, GALWAY ☎ (091) 26666 42 ⇌ ↰

OUGHTERARD   Map 01 B4

Oughterard ☎ (091) 82131
Well maintained parkland course with mature trees and shrubs. Some very challenging holes.
18 holes, 6060yds, Par 70, SSS 69, Course record 68.
Club membership 830.

Visitors	preferred Mon-Fri. Avoid Wed (Ladies Day).
Societies	must apply in writing.
Green Fees	not confirmed.
Facilities	⊗ ⅷ ⓛ ♥ ♀ ⚲ ⌂ ⅌ ₵ Michael Ryan.
Leisure	snooker, caddies, caddy cars.
Location	1m from town on Galway road
Hotel	★★★63% Connemara Gateway Hotel, OUGHTERARD ☎ (091) 82328 62 ⇌ ↰

$\mathscr{B}$ALLYBUNION

BALLYBUNION ☎ (068) 27146   Map 01 A3

John Ingham writes: Since golf is a state of mind over muscle and a great day on the links is exhilarating, it is my view that memorable fairways tend not to be decorated with artificial lakes that are fun only for ducks and golf ball manufacturers.

Some of the best courses look natural, even though they may have been helped along by skilful architects such as Colt, Hawtree or Mackenzie. And in the Emerald Isle, it is entirely appropriate that, back in 1906, a Mr Murphy built Ballybunion on the West Coast of Ireland. Believe me, there are few greater adventures waiting to be tackled and not to play this old course is a crime.

In an American list of the world's top 100 courses, Ballybunion is in there at number eight and the reason is simple: it probably represents the ultimate links on as wild a stretch as you will find. The Atlantic waves crash into the shore and no golfer will ever feel closer to nature as he hunts his ball and flights it through crosswinds and breathtaking views. This course is a star even in a part of Ireland that is wall-to-wall golf courses of the highest calibre. The experience of taking on this classic will be remembered as long as you live.

There are now two courses at Ballybunion, separated only by a 19th hole that has heard all the wondrous stories before, as well as hosting such great names as Tom Watson, five times winner of the Open. Likeable Tom can't speak highly enough of the place and claims that before anyone builds a golf course, they should play Ballybunion.

Membership 1500

Visitors	must contact in advance, and have a handicap certificate (maximum handicap 24; women 36)
Societies	must book in advance
Green fees	Old Course: £30 per round; Cashen Course: £20 per round. An additional £5 per course charged mid-July-end Sept. Day ticket £45 (but Old Course cannot be played twice)
Facilities	⊗ ⍢ ⛿ ⬛ ⚲ ⚒ 🗄 ⛳ caddy cars ♞ (Brian O'Callaghan)
Leisure	private fishing, sauna
Location	Sandhill Rd

36 holes. Old Course: 18 holes, 6603 yds, Par 71, SSS 72
Carshen Course: 18 holes, 6477 yds, Par 71, SSS 72

WHERE TO STAY AND EAT NEARBY

HOTELS:
BALLYBUNION
★★ 56% Golf Hotel, Main Street.
☎ (068) 27111 85 ⇔ 🐾
Irish & French cuisine

PORTUMNA   Map 01 B3

Portumna ☎ (0509) 41059
Parkland course with mature trees.
18 holes, 5205mtrs, Par 68, SSS 67, Course record 66.
Club membership 500.
Visitors   must contact in advance to play on Sun.
Societies   must contact in writing.
Green Fees IR£10.
Facilities 🏌 ⚑ ♀ ⚲ 🏐
Leisure   caddy cars.
Location   2.5m from town on Woodford/Ennis road
Hotel   ★★62% County Arms Hotel, BIRR
                ☎ (0509) 20791 & 20193 18 ⇄ 📞

RENVYLE   Map 01 A4

Renvyle House Hotel ☎ (095) 43511
Pebble Beach course at Renvyle House is an exceptionally
demanding Par 3. Exposed to Atlantic winds, crosswinds are
a regular feature. A lake comes into play on 3 holes on one of
which is a drive over water. On 4 holes pebble beach and the
sea demand precision.
9 holes, 1453yds, Par 27, Course record 34.
Club membership 122.
Visitors   no restrictions.
Societies   telephone in advance.
Green Fees IR£10 per day.
Facilities ⊗ ⫴ 🏌 ⚑ ♀ 🏐 ⚲
Leisure   hard tennis courts, heated outdoor swimming pool,
               fishing, riding, snooker, croquet, lawn bowling.
Hotel   ★★★68% Renvyle House Hotel, RENVYLE
                ☎ (095) 43511 65 ⇄ 📞

TUAM   Map 01 B4

Tuam ☎ (093) 24354
Interesting course with plenty of trees and bunkers.
18 holes, 6377yds, Par 73, SSS 70.
Visitors   preferred Mon-Fri.
Green Fees not confirmed.
Facilities 🏌 ♀ ⚲ 🏐
Location   Barnacurragh (0.5m from town on Athenry road)
Hotel   ★★★71% Ardilaun House Hotel, Taylor's Hill,
                GALWAY ☎ (091) 21433 92 ⇄ 📞

• CO KERRY •

BALLYBUNION   Map 01 A3

BALLYBUNION See page 343

BALLYFERRITER   Map 01 A2

Ceann Sibeal ☎ (066) 56255 & 56408
This most westerly golf course in Europe has a magnificent
scenic location. It is a traditional links course with beautiful
turf, many bunkers, a stream that comes into play on 14 holes
and, usually, a prevailing wind.

18 holes, 6600yds, Par 72, SSS 71.
Club membership 400.
Visitors   no restrictions.
Societies   must telephone in advance.
Green Fees IR£23 per day; IR£18 per round.
Facilities ⊗ ⫴ 🏌 ⚑ ♀ ⚲ 🏐 📞 { Dermot O'Connor.
Leisure   practice ground,caddy cars available.
Hotel   ★★★70% Skellig Hotel, DINGLE
                ☎ (066) 51144 115 ⇄ 📞

GLENBEIGH   Map 01 A2

Dooks ☎ Tralee (066) 68205
Old-established course on the sea shore between the
Kerry mountains and Dingle Bay. Sand dunes are a
feature (the name Dooks is a derivation of the Gaelic
word for sand bank) and the course offers a fine
challenge in a superb Ring of Kerry location.
18 holes, 6010yds, Par 70, SSS 68.
Club membership 580.
Visitors   no restrictions.
Societies   must apply in writing.
Green Fees IR£16 per round.
Facilities ⊗ 🏌 ⚑ ♀ ⚲
Leisure   caddy cars.
Hotel   ★★★56% Gleneagle Hotel, KILLARNEY
                ☎ (064) 31870 177 ⇄ 📞

KENMARE   Map 01 A2

Kenmare ☎ (064) 41291
Parkland course situated at the head of Kenmare Bay in very
picturesque surroundings.

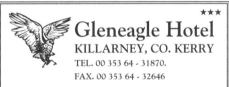

★★★
Gleneagle Hotel
KILLARNEY, CO. KERRY
TEL. 00 353 64 - 31870.
FAX. 00 353 64 - 32646.

Located in 25 acres of landscaped parkland, on the
banks of the river Flesk, adjacent to the 25,000 acre
National Park – the Gleneagle is ideally situated for
a wide range of leisure holidays and general and
special activities.

With 3 bars, 3 restaurants, 3 conference rooms and
170 en-suite bedrooms, it is the ideal choice for
meetings, seminars with a full business and social
programme. Swimming pool, sauna, gym, jacuzzi,
steam room, pitch and putt, tennis, squash,
children's playground, creche – all on site. Lake
cruises, coach tours, fishing, golf, pony trekking,
cycle hire etc. are all arranged by the hotel.

Free colour brochure available.

IRELAND'S LEADING
LEISURE HOTEL

9 holes, 5950yds, Par 71, SSS 69.
Club membership 250.
Visitors   enquire for weekends.
Societies   must contact secretary in writing.
Green Fees IR£12.50 per 18 holes.
Facilities   ⮂ 🍴 ♀ ⚄ 🏠 ⛳
Leisure   caddy cars for hire.
Location   Kilgarvan Rd
Hotel   ★★★★(red)⚕ Park Hotel, KENMARE
                ☎ (064) 41200 50 ⇥ 🏌

KILLARNEY   Map 01 B2

Killarney Golf & Fishing Club ☎ (064) 31034
Both of the courses are parkland with tree-lined fairways,
many bunkers and small lakes which provide no mean
challenge. Mahoney's Point Course has a particularly
testing par 5, 4, 3 finish and both courses call for great
skill from the tee. Killarney has been the venue for many
important events, including the Irish Open in 1991, and is
a favourite of many famous golfers
Mahony's Point: 18 holes, 6152mtrs, Par 72.
Killeen: 18 holes, 6475mtrs, Par 72.
Club membership 1400.
Visitors   must contact in advance & have a handicap
                certificate.
Societies   must telephone in advance.
Green Fees IR£26 per round.
Facilities   ⊗ 🏮 ⮂ 🍴 ♀ ⚄ 🏠 ⛳ ♪
Leisure   sauna, gymnasium.
Location   O'Mahony's Point (on Ring of Kerry road)
Hotel   ★★★★75% Aghadoe Heights Hotel,
                KILLARNEY ☎ (064) 31766 60 ⇥ 🏌
Additional ★★★56% Gleneagle Hotel, KILLARNEY
hotel   ☎ (064) 31870 177 ⇥ 🏌

PARKNASILLA   Map 01 A2

Parknasilla ☎ (064) 45122
Short, tricky 9-hole course, with 18 different tees which make
the second 9 more interesting.
9 holes, 2447yds, Par 35, SSS 65.
Club membership 40.
Visitors   may not play on competition days.
Societies   must contact in advance.
Green Fees IR£10 per day 18 holes.
Facilities   🏮 ⮂ ♀ ⚄ 🏠 ⛳ ♪ Charles McCarthy.
Leisure   hard tennis courts, heated indoor swimming
                pool, riding, snooker, sauna.
Hotel   ★★★★73% Great Southern Hotel,
                PARKNASILLA
                ☎ (064) 45122 25 ⇥ 🏌Annexe59 ⇥ 🏌

TRALEE   Map 01 A2

Tralee ☎ (066) 36379
The first Arnold Palmer designed course in Europe, the
magnificent 18-hole links are set in spectacular scenery
on the Barrow peninsula. Perhaps the most memorable
hole is the par four 17th which plays from a high tee,
across a deep gorge to a green perched high against a
backdrop of mountains.
18 holes, 6252mtrs, Par 73.
Club membership 1000.

Visitors   may play before 4.30pm on weekdays but
                only 10.30am-12.15pm on Wed & 11am-
                12.30pm at weekends & bank holidays.
                Must have a handicap certificate.
Societies   weekdays only; must contact in writing.
Green Fees not confirmed.
Facilities   ⊗ 🏮 ⮂ 🍴 ♀ ⚄ 🏠
Leisure   motorised buggies available & hand carts.
Location   West Barrow (8m W of Tralee on Spa-Fenit
                road)
Hotel   ★★★63% The Brandon Hotel, TRALEE
                ☎ (066) 23333 160 ⇥ 🏌

WATERVILLE   Map 01 A2

Waterville House & Golf Links ☎ (0667) 4102
On the western tip of the Ring of Kerry, this course is
highly regarded by many top golfers. The feature holes
are the par five 11th, which runs along a rugged valley
between towering dunes, and the par three 17th, which
features an exceptionally elevated tee. Needless to say,
the surroundings are beautiful.
18 holes, 6549yds, Par 72, SSS 74, Course record 70.
Club membership 250.
Visitors   must have a handicap certificate.
Societies   must contact in advance.
Green Fees not confirmed.
Facilities   ⊗ 🏮 ⮂ 🍴 ♀ ⚄ 🏠 ⛳ 🏌 ♪ Liam Higgins.
Leisure   heated outdoor swimming pool, fishing,
                riding, snooker, sauna, caddy cars,caddies
                senior/junior,clinic.4
Hotel   ★★64% Derrynane Hotel,
                CAHERDANIEL ☎ (0667) 5136 75 ⇥

CO KILDARE

ATHY   Map 01 C3

Athy ☎ (0507) 31729
A meadowland course approaching its centenary year having
been founded in 1906.
18 holes, 5500mtrs, Par 72, SSS 69.
Visitors   welcome weekdays.
Societies   contact for infromation.
Green Fees IR£10-IR£15.
Facilities   catering by arrangement
Location   Geraldine (2m N of Athy)
Hotel   ★★52% Royal Hotel, CARLOW
                ☎ (0503) 31621 34 ⇥ 🏌

CARBURY   Map 01 C4

Highfield ☎ (0405) 31021
A relatively flat parkland course but with interesting
undulations, especially by the fast flowing stream which runs
through many holes. The 7th doglegs over the lake, the 10th
is a great Par 5 with a challenging green, the 14th Par 3 is
over rushes onto a plateau green (out of bounds on lift) and
the 18th Par 3 green is tucked between bunkers and a huge
chestnut tree.   ▶

18 holes, 5707mtrs, Par 72, SSS 70.
Club membership 200.
Visitors preference given to members in competition & pre booked groups.
Societies telephone in advance, write for Sat & Sun mornings.
Green Fees IR£6 per 18 holes; IR£5 per 9 holes (IR£8 per 18 holes weekends & bank holidays).
Facilities 🏠 💺 ⛳ ⛳
Leisure caddy cars, practice range.
Location Highfield House (9m from Enfield)
Hotel ★★56% Curryhills House Hotel, PROSPEROUS ☎ (045) 68150 10 ⇔ 🐾

CASTLEDERMOT   Map 01 C3

Kilkea Castle ☎ (0503) 45156
A beautiful new course opened in the summer of 1994 in the grounds of a 12th-century castle - visible from all over the course. The River Griese and two lakes create numerous water hazards.
18 holes, 6200mtrs, Par 71.
Visitors welcome contact for details.
Societies welcome, contact for details.
Green Fees available on request.
Facilities ⊗ �🍴 🏠 💺 restaurant at club & Castle Hotel ⚑ ⛳🏠
Hotel ★★52% Royal Hotel, CARLOW ☎ (0503) 31621 34 ⇔ 🐾

CLANE   Map 01 C4

Clongowes ☎ (045) 21295
Parkland.
18 holes.
Visitors welcome, contact for further details.
Societies contact for details.
Green Fees not confirmed.
Facilities lunch & dinner available
Location Clongowes Wood, College Naas

DONADEA   Map 01 C4

Knockanally Golf & Country Club ☎ (045) 69322
Home of the Irish International Professional Matchplay championship, this parkland course is set in a former estate, with a Palladian-style clubhouse.
18 holes, 6485yds, Par 72, SSS 72, Course record 66.
Club membership 320.
Visitors may not play on Sun 8.30am-noon.
Societies must contact in writing.
Green Fees not confirmed.
Facilities ⊗ & �🍴 by prior arrangement 🏠 💺 ⚑ ⛳ 🏠 ⛳ ⛏ Peter Hickey.
Leisure fishing.
Location 3m off main Dublin-Galway road
Hotel ★★56% Curryhills House Hotel, PROSPEROUS ☎ (045) 68150 10 ⇔ 🐾

KILDARE   Map 01 C3

Cill Dara ☎ (045) 21295
Only 1 mile from the famous Curragh racecourse, this 9-hole parkland course is unusual in having links type soil as well as plenty of trees.
9 holes, 5738mtrs, Par 71, SSS 70.

Visitors welcome.
Societies contact for details.
Green Fees IR£10 per 18 holes; IR£5 per 9 holes.
Facilities catering for societies by arrangement ⚑⛏ D Sherlock & J Bulger.
Location Cill Dara, Little Curragh (1m E of Kildare)
Hotel ★★★56% Hotel Montague, Portlaoise, EMO ☎ (0502) 26154 75 ⇔ 🐾

Curragh ☎ (045) 41238
A particularly challenging course, well wooded and with lovely scenery all around.
18 holes, 6003mtrs, Par 72, SSS 71.
Club membership 900.
Visitors preferred on Mon, Thu & Fri.
Societies apply in writing.
Green Fees IR£14 per round (IR£18 weekends & bank holidays).
Facilities ⊗ �🍴 🏠 💺 ⚑ ⛳ 🏠 ⛳ ⛏ Phil Lawlor.
Leisure snooker, caddy cars for hire.
Location Curragh (Off N7 between Newbridge & Kildare)
Hotel ★★56% Curryhills House Hotel, PROSPEROUS ☎ (045) 68150 10 ⇔ 🐾

KILL   Map 01 D4

Killeen ☎ (045) 66003 & 66045
Set in pleasant countryside, the attractive course is characterised by its many lakes. It provides a challenge to test the skills of the moderate enthusiast and the more experienced golfer.
18 holes, 4979mtrs, Par 69, SSS 66, Course record 71.
Club membership 300.
Visitors may not play at weekends before 10am.
Societies must contact in advance.
Green Fees not confirmed.
Facilities ⊗ & �🍴 by prior arrangement 🏠 💺 ⚑ ⛳ 🏠 ⛳
Leisure snooker, putting green.
Location Off N7 at Kill signposted
Hotel ★★★71% Barberstown Castle, STRAFFAN ☎ (01) 6288157 & 6288206 10 ⇔ 🐾

NAAS   Map 01 D4

Bodenstown ☎ (045) 97096
The old course in Bodenstown has ample fairways and large greens, some of which are raised, providing more than a fair test of golf. The Ladyhill course is a little shorter and tighter, but still affords a fair challenge.
Bodenstown: 18 holes, 5788mtrs, Par 72, SSS 70.
Ladyhill: 18 holes, 5278mtrs, Par 71, SSS 68.
Club membership 650.
Visitors may not play on Bodenstown course at weekends.
Societies must contact by telephone.
Green Fees not confirmed.
Facilities ⊗ ⍵ 🏠 💺 ⚑ ⛳
Leisure snooker.
Location Sallins (4m from town near Bodenstown graveyard)
Hotel ★★★56% Downshire House Hotel, BLESSINGTON ☎ (045) 65199 14 ⇔ 🐾 Annexe11 ⇔ 🐾

Naas ☎ (045) 97509
Scenic parkland course with different tees for the return 9.
9 holes, 3000mtrs, Par 36, SSS 70, Course record 68.
Club membership 800.

Visitors   may not play on Sun, Tue or Thu.
Societies   must contact in advance.
Green Fees   not confirmed.
Facilities   ⓛ ☕ ♟ ⛳ ⛹
Leisure   snooker.
Location   Kerdiffstown (1m from town on Sallins-
Johnstown road)
Hotel   ★★★56% Downshire House Hotel,
BLESSINGTON
☎ (045) 65199 14 ⇄ ⓡ Annexe11 ⇄ ⓡ

STRAFFAN   Map 01 D4

Castlewarden ☎ (01) 588218
Founded in 1990, Castlewarden is maturing into a delightful
parkland course.
18 holes, 5681mtrs, Par 72, SSS 69.
Visitors   welcome contact for details.
Societies   by prior application.
Green Fees   IR£12-IR£17.50.
Facilities   catering contact for details ♟ ⓒ Gerry Egan.
Leisure   lessons available.
Location   Between Naas/Newlands Cross
Hotel   ★★★★★♣♣82% The Kildare Hotel & Country
Club, STRAFFAN
☎ (01) 6273333 36 ⇄ ⓡ Annexe9 ⇄ ⓡ

Kildare Hotel & Country Club ☎ (01) 6273333
Known as The K-Club, this course is growing in
reputation. Designed by Arnold Palmer, its 6,456 metre
length is a challenge to even the best golfers. Covering
177 acres of prime Kildare woodland there are 14 man-
made lakes as well as the River Liffey to create water
hazards. There is the promise of a watery grave at the
monster 7th (Par 5, 520 metres) and at the 17th the tee
shot is to the green on the water's edge. There is also a
practise area and driving range.
18 holes, 6163mtrs, Par 72, SSS 72, Course record 68.
Club membership 297.
Visitors   restricted at members times only, Sun-Fri
1.30-2.30pm, Sat 11am-3pm.
Societies   telephone & write in advance, societies not
allowed on Sat and at members tee-off times.
Green Fees   IR£85 includes trolley hire, use of practice
range, tees & markers plus a sleeve of golf balls.
Facilities   ⊗ �ℸ ⓛ ☕ ♟ ⛳ ⊞ ⌇ ⛹ ⓒ Ernie Jones.
Leisure   hard and grass tennis courts, heated indoor
swimming pool, squash, fishing, riding,
snooker, sauna, solarium, gymnasium,
practice area,driving range,caddies.
Hotel   ★★★★★♣♣82% The Kildare Hotel &
Country Club, STRAFFAN
☎ (01) 6273333 36 ⇄ ⓡ Annexe9 ⇄ ⓡ

CO KILKENNY

CALLAN   Map 01 C3

Callan ☎ (056) 25136
Meadowland.
9 holes, 5722mtrs, Par 72, SSS 68.
Visitors   welcome.

Societies   weekdays & Sat morning.
Green Fees   IR£8.
Facilities   snacks available ♟
Location   Geraldine
Hotel   ★★★65% Hotel Kilkenny, College Rd,
KILKENNY ☎ (056) 62000 60 ⇄ ⓡ

CASTLECOMER   Map 01 C3

Castlecomer ☎ (056) 41139
9 holes, 5923mtrs, Par 71, SSS 71.
Visitors   welcome Mon-Sat book in advance.
Societies   welcome Mon-Sat.
Green Fees   not confirmed.
Facilities   snacks & lunches to order
Location   Drumgoole (10m N of Kilkenny)
Hotel   ★★52% Royal Hotel, CARLOW
☎ (0503) 31621 34 ⇄ ⓡ

KILKENNY   Map 01 C3

Kilkenny ☎ (056) 22125 & 65400
One of Ireland's most pleasant inland courses, noted for
its tricky finishing holes and its par threes. Features of
the course are its long 11th and 13th holes and the
challenge increases year by year as thousands of trees
planted over the last 30 years or so are maturing. As host
of the Kilkenny Scratch Cup annually, the course is
permanently maintained in championship condition. The
Irish Dunlop Tournament and the Irish Professional
Matchplay Championship have also been held here.
18 holes, 5824mtrs, Par 71, SSS 70, Course record 65.
Club membership 1000.
Visitors   restricted weekends & Tue. Must contact in
advance.
Societies   must contact in advance.
Green Fees   IR£15 per day (IR£17 weekends).
Facilities   ⊗ ⍨ ⓛ ☕ ♟ ⛳ ⊞ ⌇ ⓒ Noel Leahy.
Leisure   snooker, caddies, caddy cars.
Location   Glendine (1m from centre on Castlecomer road)
Hotel   ★★★65% Hotel Kilkenny, College Rd,
KILKENNY ☎ (056) 62000 60 ⇄ ⓡ

THOMASTOWN   Map 01 C3

Mount Juliet Hotel ☎ (056) 24725 & 24455
The 18-hole Signature course designed by Jack Nicklaus
takes full advantage of the mature landscape and natural
beauty of the 1,500 acre Mount Juliet estate with the
elegant 18th century mansion at its heart. Only opened in
1991, the course quickly established its reputation and
hosted the Irish Open in 1993 and 1994. It has been
called the 'Augusta' of Europe and the design has
ensured it is playable all year round. The course is
challenging even to professional golfers but is equally
rewarding for higher handicap golfers. For 1994, a David
Leadbetter Golf Academy was opened to provide tution
for all standards of golfer.
18 holes, 7100yds, Par 72, SSS 74, Course record 65.
Visitors   no restrictions.
Societies   book in advance by telephone.
Green Fees   prices for non-residents IR£45-IR£90 per 36
holes; IR£30-IR£60 per 18 holes (IR£60-
IR£95/IR£40-IR£65 weekends). IR£20 per 9
holes 17 Oct-31 Mar only (IR£25 weekends).▶

Facilities	⊗ ⅢⅠ ﻬ ♥ ♀ ♨ ⊕ ❡ ⋈
	♟ Todd Pyle, Nick Bradley.
Leisure	hard and grass tennis courts, heated indoor swimming pool, fishing, riding, snooker, sauna, gymnasium, caddy cars,clay target shooting,archery.
Location	N9 Dublin/Waterford rd
Hotel	★★★★♨75% Mount Juliet Hotel, THOMASTOWN ☎ (056) 24455 32 ⇔

CO LAOIS

ABBEYLEIX

Map 01 C3

Abbeyleix ☎ (0502) 31450
9 holes, 5626mtrs, Par 70, SSS 68.
Visitors	welcome.
Societies	contact for details.
Green Fees	not confirmed.
Location	Rathmoyle
Hotel	★★60% Killeshin Hotel, Dublin Rd, PORTLAOISE ☎ (0502) 21663 44 ⇔ ♜

MOUNTRATH

Map 01 C3

Mountrath ☎ (0502) 32558
Small picturesque course at the foot of the Slieve Bloom Mountains in central Ireland. The course is in the process of being extended to 18 holes, due to be completed by summer 1994.
9 holes, 4634mtrs, Par 68, SSS 66.
Club membership 300.
Visitors	no restrictions.
Societies	must contact in advance.
Green Fees	IR£7 (IR£8 weekends).
Facilities	ﻬ ♥ ♀ ♨
Location	Knockanina (1.5m from town on Dublin-Limerick road)
Hotel	★★60% Killeshin Hotel, Dublin Rd, PORTLAOISE ☎ (0502) 21663 44 ⇔ ♜

PORTARLINGTON

Map 01 C3

Portarlington ☎ Portlaoise (0502) 23115
Lovely parkland course designed around a pine forest. It is bounded on the 16th and 17th by the River Barrow which makes the back 9 very challenging.
18 holes, 5673mtrs, Par 71, SSS 69, Course record 70.
Club membership 400.
Visitors	restricted Tue-Ladies Day, Sat & Sun societies and club competitions.
Societies	must contact in writing.
Green Fees	IR£10 (IR£12.50 weekends & bank holidays).
Facilities	⊗ ⅢⅠ ﻬ ♥ ♀ ♨
Leisure	caddy cars for hire.
Location	Garryhinch (4m from town on Mountmellick road)
Hotel	★★★56% Hotel Montague, Portlaoise, EMO ☎ (0502) 26154 75 ⇔ ♜

PORTLAOISE

Map 01 C3

The Heath ☎ (0502) 46533
One of the oldest clubs in Ireland. The course is set in pretty countryside and offers a good challenge.
18 holes, 5721mtrs, Par 71, SSS 70.
Club membership 800.
Visitors	preferred on weekdays.
Societies	apply in writing
Green Fees	IR£10 per round (IR£16 weekends and bank holidays).
Facilities	⊗ & ⅢⅠ by prior arrangement ﻬ ♥ ♀ ♨ ⊕ ❡
	♟ Eddie Doyle.
Leisure	snooker, driving range, caddy cars.
Location	5m NE
Hotel	★★60% Killeshin Hotel, Dublin Rd, PORTLAOISE ☎ (0502) 21663 44 ⇔ ♜

RATHDOWNEY

Map 01 C3

Rathdowney ☎ Roscrea (0505) 46170
Apleasant 9-hole course. 1st is difficult with out-of-bounds along the right. 5th, Par 3 has out-of-bounds very close to left. Plans are in hand for conversion to 18-holes.
9 holes, 6196yds, Par 70, SSS 69.
Club membership 250.
Visitors	may not play on Captain's, Lady Captain's,President & Lady President's Days or Sat pm & Sun. Ladies have priority on Wed. Welcome during open week 1-10th Jul'94.
Societies	must apply in writing and pay deposit to confirm booking.
Green Fees	IR£6 per day.
Facilities	some catering during Open Week & Sun ♀ (open week & Sun) ♨
Location	0.5m SE
Hotel	★★68% Leix County Hotel, BORRIS-IN-OSSORY ☎ (0505) 41213 19 ⇔

CO LEITRIM

BALLINAMORE

Map 01 C4

Ballinamore ☎ (078) 44346
A very dry and very testing 9-hole parkland course along the Ballinamore/Ballyconnell Canal.
9 holes, 5680yds, Par 68, SSS 66.
Club membership 100.
Visitors	restricted occasionally. Must contact in advance.
Societies	must contact in writing.
Green Fees	IR£5 per day.
Facilities	ﻬ ♥ ♀ ♨
Leisure	fishing.
Hotel	★★61% Royal Hotel, BOYLE ☎ (079) 62016 16 ⇔ ♜

> **For an explanation of symbols and abbreviations, see page 5**

CO LIMERICK

ADARE
Map 01 B3

Adare Manor ☎ (061) 396204
An 18-hole parkland course, Par 69, in an unusual setting. In the grounds of an ancient monastery, the course surrounds the ruins of a castle, a friary and an abbey.
18 holes, 5800yds, Par 69, SSS 69.
Club membership 600.
Visitors weekends by prior arrangement.
Societies by prior arrangement, preferably in writing.
Green Fees IR£15 per round (IR£20 weekends).
Facilities ⓑ ♥ ♀ ♨ 🍽 ꝑ
Leisure caddy cars & caddies available.
Hotel ★★★★♨76% Adare Manor, ADARE
☎ (061) 396566 28 ⇆ ☞Annexe36 ⇆ ☞

LIMERICK
Map 01 B3

Castletroy ☎ (061) 335753 & 335261
Parkland course with out of bounds on the left of the first two holes. The long par five 10th features a narrow entrance to a green guarded by a stream. The par three 13th has a panoramic view of the course and surrounding countryside from the tee and the 18th is a daunting finish, with the drive played towards a valley with the ground rising towards the green which is protected on both sides by bunkers. In recent years the club has hosted the finals of the Irish Mixed Foursomes and the Senior Championships.
18 holes, 5793mtrs, Par 69, SSS 71.
Club membership 1066.
Visitors must contact in advance & have handicap certificate but may not play Sun or 1-2.30pm weekdays.
Societies must contact in advance.
Green Fees IR£20 per day/round.
Facilities ⊗ ⍢ ⓑ ♥ ♀ ♨ 🍽 ꝑ ⸉ Noel Cassidy.
Leisure snooker, caddy cars & motorised buggy for hire.
Location Castletroy (3m from city on Dublin road)
Hotel ★★★69% Jurys Hotel, Ennis Rd, LIMERICK
☎ (061) 327777 95 ⇆ ☞

Limerick ☎ (061) 414083
Tree-lined parkland course which hosted the 1991 Ladies Senior Interprovincial matches. The club are the only Irish winners of the European Cup Winners Team Championship.
18 holes, 5938mtrs, Par 72, SSS 71, Course record 69.
Club membership 1324.
Visitors may not play after 4pm or on Tue & weekends.
Societies must contact in writing.
Green Fees IR£20 per day.
Facilities ⊗ ⓑ ♥ ♀ ♨ 🍽 ꝑ ⸉ John Cassidy.
Leisure snooker, caddy cars.
Location Ballyclough (3m S on Fedamore Road)
Hotel ★★★69% Jurys Hotel, Ennis Rd, LIMERICK
☎ (061) 327777 95 ⇆ ☞

NEWCASTLE WEST
Map 01 B3

Newcastle West ☎ (069) 76500
A new course set in 150 acres of unspoilt countryside, built to the highest standards on sandy free draining soil. A practice ground and driving range are included. Hazards on the course include lakes, bunkers, streams and trees. A signature hole is

likely to be the Par 3 6th playing 185 yards over a lake.
18 holes, 6041yds, Par 71.
Club membership 600.
Visitors restricted Sat & Sun mornings.
Societies contact in advance.
Green Fees IR£15 per round.
Facilities ⊗ by prior arrangement ⓑ ♥ ♀ ♨ ꝑ
Leisure caddy cars.
Location Ardagh (2m off N21 between Limerick & Killarney)
Hotel ★★★★♨76% Adare Manor, ADARE
☎ (061) 396566 28 ⇆ ☞Annexe36 ⇆ ☞

LONGFORD
Map 01 C4

County Longford ☎ (043) 46310
A lovely 18-hole parkland course with lots of trees.
18 holes, 5494mtrs, Par 70, SSS 69.
Visitors very welcome.
Societies by prior arrangement.
Green Fees not confirmed.
Facilities catering available ♀
Location Glack (E of town)
Hotel ★★★63% Abbey Hotel, Galway Rd, ROSCOMMON
☎ (0903) 26240 & 26505 20 ⇆ ☞

CO LOUTH

ARDEE
Map 01 D4

Ardee ☎ (041) 53227
Pleasant parkland course with mature trees and a stream.
18 holes, 6100yds, Par 69, SSS 69.
Visitors may normally play on weekdays (except Wed).
Green Fees not confirmed.
Facilities ⍢ ⓑ ♀
Location Townparks
Hotel ★★★65% Ballymascanlon House Hotel, DUNDALK ☎ (042) 71124 36 ⇆

BALTRAY
Map 01 D4

County Louth ☎ Drogheda (041) 22329
Generally held to have the best greens in Ireland, this links course was designed by Tom Simpson to have well guarded and attractive greens without being overly dependant on bunkers. It provides a good test for the modern champion, notably as the annual venue for the East of Ireland Amateur Open.
18 holes, 6577yds, Par 73, SSS 72, Course record 66.
Club membership 1000.
Visitors must contact in advance and have a handicap certificate
Societies must contact in writing.
Green Fees IR£27 per round (IR£35 weekends).
Facilities ⍢ ⓑ ♥ ♀ ♨ 🍽 ꝑ ⸉ Paddy McGuirk.
Leisure hard tennis courts, snooker.
Location 5m NE of Drogheda
Hotel ★★★62% Boyne Valley Hotel, DROGHEDA ☎ (041) 37737 35 ⇆ ☞

DUNDALK   Map 01 D4

Dundalk ☎ (042) 21731
A tricky course with extensive views.
18 holes, 6115mtrs, Par 72, SSS 72.
Club membership 1000.
Visitors   must contact in advance and may not play Tue or Sun.
Societies   must apply in writing in advance.
Green Fees not confirmed.
Facilities   ⊗ ⅏ ᴸ ☕ ♀ ♨ 🏳 ⏱ ⅊ James Cassidy.
Leisure   sauna, caddy cars.
Location   Blackrock (2.5m S on coast road)
Hotel   ★★★65% Ballymascanlon House Hotel, DUNDALK ☎ (042) 71124 36 ⇥

Killinbeg ☎ (042) 39303
Opened in 1991 and designed by Eddie Hackett, this undulating 12-hole parkland course has mature woodland and river features.
12 holes, 3322yds, Par 72, SSS 69.
Club membership 100.
Visitors   no restrictions.
Societies   apply by telephone or in writing in advance.
Green Fees IR£7 per day (IR£10 weekends & bank holidays) if busy prices are for a round..
Facilities   ⅏ ᴸ ☕ ♀ ♨ ⏱
Location   Killin Park (Bridge-a-Crinn)
Hotel   ★★★65% Ballymascanlon House Hotel, DUNDALK ☎ (042) 71124 36 ⇥

GREENORE   Map 01 D4

Greenore ☎ Dundalk (042) 73212
Situated amidst beautiful scenery on the shores of Carlingford Lough, the trees here are an unusual feature on a links course. There are quite a number of water facilities, tight fairways and very good greens.
18 holes, Par 71, SSS 71, Course record 68.
Club membership 500.
Visitors   must contact in advance at weekends. A letter of introduction is desirable, but not essential.
Societies   must contact in writing well in advance.
Green Fees not confirmed.
Facilities   ⊗ ⅏ ᴸ ☕ ♀ ♨
Hotel   ★★★65% Ballymascanlon House Hotel, DUNDALK ☎ (042) 71124 36 ⇥

TERMONFECKIN   Map 01 D4

Seapoint ☎ (041) 22333
A very long championship links course of 7,000 yards with a particularly interesting 17th hole.
18 holes, 7000yds, Par 72, SSS 71, Course record 69.
Club membership 200.
Visitors   no restrictions.
Societies   apply in writing.
Green Fees IR£17 (IR£22 weekends & bank holidays).
Facilities   ⊗ ⅏ ᴸ ☕ ♀ ♨ 🏳 ⏱
Leisure   caddy cars.
Hotel   ★★★62% Boyne Valley Hotel, DROGHEDA ☎ (041) 37737 35 ⇥ 🐾

CO MAYO

BALLINA   Map 01 B4

Ballina ☎ (096) 21050
Undulating but mostly flat inland course. Planned to be extended to 18 holes during 1995.
9 holes, 5700yds, Par 70, SSS 67, Course record 64.
Club membership 448.
Visitors   restricted Sun, Sat variable hours depending on competitions/society visits.
Societies   apply in writing or telephone in advance.
Green Fees IR£10 per 18 holes.
Facilities   ᴸ ☕ ♀ ♨
Leisure   caddy cars.
Location   Mosgrove, Shanaghy (1m outside town on Bonnocolon Rd)
Hotel   ★★★61% Downhill Hotel, BALLINA ☎ (096) 21033 50 ⇥ 🐾

BALLINROBE   Map 01 B4

Ballinrobe ☎ (092) 41448
Mainly flat terrain with some very interesting features. Although no other club plays on the course, its landlords, The Ballinrobe Race Company, hold races there five or six times a year.
9 holes, 5790yds, Par 72, SSS 68, Course record 67.
Club membership 400.
Visitors   may not play on Tue after 5pm or on Sat and Sun.
Societies   must contact Secretary in advance on (092) 41659.
Green Fees IR£8 per day; IR£10 per day Jun-Aug.
Facilities   ᴸ (summer only) ☕ ♀ ♨
Leisure   snooker, practice area.
Location   Castlebar Rd
Hotel   ★★★62% Breaffy House Hotel, CASTLEBAR ☎ (094) 22033 40 ⇥

BALLYHAUNIS   Map 01 B4

Ballyhaunis ☎ (0907) 30014
Undulating parkland course with 9 holes, 10 greens and 18 tees.
18 holes, 5393mtrs, Par 69, SSS 68.
Club membership 220.
Visitors   may not play Thu & Sun. Must contact in advance.
Societies   must apply in writing or telephone.
Green Fees IR£8 per day.
Facilities   ᴸ ☕ ♀ ♨
Leisure   putting green, caddy cars for hire.
Location   Coolnaha
Hotel   ★★★62% Breaffy House Hotel, CASTLEBAR ☎ (094) 22033 40 ⇥

BELMULLET   Map 01 A5

Belmullet ☎ (097) 82123
9 holes, 5272mtrs, Par 72, SSS 67.
Visitors   welcome.
Societies   contact for details.
Green Fees not confirmed.
Hotel   ★★★61% Downhill Hotel, BALLINA ☎ (096) 21033 50 ⇥ 🐾

CASTLEBAR   Map 01 B4

Castlebar ☎ (094) 21649
Pleasant parkland course with a particularly interesting 9th hole.
18 holes, 5698mtrs, Par 71, SSS 69, Course record 66.
Club membership 600.

Visitors	restricted during club competitions and society visits, contact club in advance.
Societies	must contact in advance.
Green Fees	IR£15 per day; IR£10 per round.
Facilities	🅱 ☕ (Mar-Oct) ♀ ⛳ ⛳
Leisure	caddy cars for hire.
Location	Rocklands (1m from town on Belcarra road)
Hotel	★★★62% Breaffy House Hotel, CASTLEBAR ☎ (094) 22033 40 ⇥

CLAREMORRIS   Map 01 B4

Claremorris ☎ (094) 71527
A 9-hole parkland course on hilly terrain. There are plenty of trees and a drain across the course.
9 holes, 5600mtrs, Par 70, SSS 69.

Visitors	no restrictions.
Societies	welcome weekdays, contact for details.
Green Fees	IR£8 per day.
Facilities	catering by prior arrangement
Location	Castlemagarrett (1.5m from town)
Hotel	★★★62% Breaffy House Hotel, CASTLEBAR ☎ (094) 22033 40 ⇥

KEEL   Map 01 A4

Achill ☎ (098) 43456
Seaside links in a scenic location on the edge of the Atlantic Ocean.
9 holes, 2723yds, Par 70, SSS 66, Course record 69.
Club membership 50.

Visitors	no restrictions.
Societies	must telephone in advance.
Green Fees	IR£4 per round.
Facilities	⛳ ⛳
Location	Achill Island, Westport
Hotel	★★★🅰🅰74% Newport House Hotel, NEWPORT ☎ (098) 41222 & 41154 13 ⇥ ⬤Annexe7 ⇥ ⬤

SWINFORD   Map 01 B4

Swinford ☎ (094) 51378 & 51379
A pleasant parkland course with good views of the beautiful surrounding countryside.
9 holes, 5901yds, Par 70, SSS 68.
Club membership 467.

Visitors	no restrictions.
Societies	must contact in writing.
Green Fees	IR£7 per 18 hole round.
Facilities	🅱 & ☕♀⛳
Leisure	squash, fishing, riding, snooker.
Location	Brabazon Park
Hotel	★★★62% Breaffy House Hotel, CASTLEBAR ☎ (094) 22033 40 ⇥

WESTPORT   Map 01 B4

Westport ☎ (098) 25113
This is a beautiful course with wonderful views of Clew Bay, with its 365 islands, and the holy mountain called Croagh Patrick, famous for the annual pilgrimage to its summit. Golfers indulge in a different kind of penance on this challenging course with many memorable holes. Perhaps the most exciting is the par five 15th, 580 yards long and featuring a long carry from the tee over an inlet of Clew Bay.
18 holes, 6959yds, Par 73, SSS 73, Course record 68.
Club membership 650.

Visitors	may not play Wed 8-9.30pm & 1.45-3pm, or Sat & Sun 8-10am & 1-3pm.
Societies	must write for application form.
Green Fees	IR£12-IR£15 (IR£15-IR£18 weekends & bank holidays).
Facilities	 Alex Mealia.
Leisure	caddy cars available,caddies arranged.
Location	Carrowholly
Hotel	★★★61% Hotel Westport, WESTPORT ☎ (098) 25122 49 ⇥ ⬤

CO MEATH

BETTYSTOWN   Map 01 D4

Laytown & Bettystown ☎ (041) 27170
A very competitive and trying links course, home of famous golfer, Des Smyth.
18 holes, 5652mtrs.
Club membership 950.

Visitors	may not play 1-2pm. Must contact in advance.
Societies	must contact in writing.
Green Fees	not confirmed.
Facilities	⛳ ⛳ ⛳ ⛳
Leisure	tennis courts, snooker.
Hotel	★★★62% Boyne Valley Hotel, DROGHEDA ☎ (041) 37737 35 ⇥ ⬤

DUNSHAUGHLIN   Map 01 D4

Black Bush ☎ (01) 8250021
Recently constructed 18-hole course in lovely parkland, with a lake providing a hazard at the 1st.
Course 1: 18 holes, 6930yds, Par 72, SSS 73.
Course 2: 9 holes, 3020yds, Par 35, SSS 35.
Club membership 850.

Visitors	may not play Tue afternoons.
Societies	must apply in writing.
Green Fees	not confirmed.
Facilities	⊗ & ⅢⅢ by prior arrangement (Mon-Fri) 🅱 ☕♀⛳
Leisure	snooker, driving range.
Location	Thomastown (1.5m from village on Dublin-Navan road)
Hotel	★★★57% Finnstown Country House Hotel & Golf Course, Newcastle Rd, LUCAN ☎ (01) 6280644 25 ⇥ ⬤

KELLS   Map 01 C4

Headfort ☎ (046) 40146
A delightful parkland course which is regarded as one of
the best of its kind in Ireland. There are ample
opportunities for birdies, but even if these are not
achieved, Headfort provides for a most pleasant game.
18 holes, 6480yds, Par 72, SSS 70, Course record 65.
Club membership 650.
Visitors   restricted Tues Ladies Day, Sat & Sun Mens
               competitions, not after 4pm on other days.
Societies   must contact in writing.
Green Fees   IR£15 (IR£18 weekends).
Facilities   ⚒ 🏠 (Brendan McGovern.
Leisure   snooker.
Hotel   ★★57% Conyngham Arms Hotel, SLANE
               ☎ (041) 24155 16rm(15 ⇄ ⧫)

NAVAN   Map 01 C4

Royal Tara ☎ (046) 25244 & 25508
Pleasant parkland course with plenty of variety. Situated close
to the Hill of Tara, the ancient seat of the Kings of Ireland.
*18 holes, 5757mtrs, Par 71, SSS 70 or 9 holes, 3184yds, Par
35, SSS 35.*
Club membership 1000.
Visitors   preferred Mon, Thu & Fri.
Societies   welcome Mon & Thu-Sat, apply in writing or
               telephone.
Green Fees   IR£14 per round (IR£18 weekends & bank holidays).
Facilities   ⊗ ⚒ (summer only) ⚒ ⚑ ♀ ⚒ 🏠 ⚒
               (Adam Whiston.
Leisure   snooker.
Location   Bellinter (6m from town on N3)
Hotel   ★★57% Conyngham Arms Hotel, SLANE
               ☎ (041) 24155 16rm(15 ⇄ ⧫)

TRIM   Map 01 C4

Trim ☎ (046) 31463
Extended in 1990 to form a big 18-hole parkland course. The
new part blends well with the old and is only distinguished by a
plentiful planting of young trees. Four very challenging Par 5's.
18 holes, 6720mtrs, Par 73, SSS 72.
Visitors   welcome some restrictions telephone for details.
Societies   not Sun, enquiries welcome.
Green Fees   IR£12 (IR15 weekends & bank holidays).
Facilities   catering facilities ♀
Location   Mewtownmoynagh (3m outside Trim on
               Trim/Longwood rd)
Hotel   ★★57% Conyngham Arms Hotel, SLANE
               ☎ (041) 24155 16rm(15 ⇄ ⧫)

● CO MONAGHAN ●

CARRICKMACROSS   Map 01 C4

Nuremore ☎ Dundalk (042) 61438
Picturesque parkland course of championship length
incorporating the drumlins and lakes which are a natural feature
of the Monaghan countryside. Precision is required on the 10th

---

to drive over a large lake and between a narrow avenue of trees.
18 holes, 6206mtrs, Par 72, SSS 73.
Club membership 275.
Visitors   restricted for short periods at weekends.
Societies   must contact in advance.
Green Fees   IR£18 per day (IR£20 weekends & bank
               holidays).
Facilities   ⊗ ⚒ ⚒ ⚑ ♀ ⚒ 🏠 ⚒ ⊨ (Maurice Cassidy.
Leisure   grass tennis courts, heated indoor swimming
               pool, squash, fishing, snooker, sauna, solarium,
               gymnasium, 2 motorised caddy cars available,
               tuition.
Location   S on Dublin road
Hotel   ★★★65% Ballymascanlon House Hotel,
               DUNDALK ☎ (042) 71124 36 ⇄

CASTLEBLAYNEY   Map 01 C4

Castleblayney ☎ (042) 40197
Scenic course on Muckno Park estate, adjacent to Muckno
Lake and Blayney Castle.
9 holes, 5345yds, Par 68, SSS 66, Course record 68.
Club membership 175.
Visitors   may not play during competitions.
Societies   must contact in advance.
Green Fees   not confirmed.
Facilities   ⚒
Leisure   hard tennis courts.
Location   Onomy
Hotel   ★★★65% Ballymascanlon House Hotel,
               DUNDALK ☎ (042) 71124 36 ⇄

CLONES   Map 01 C5

Clones ☎ (047) 56017
Parkland course set in Drumlin country. Due to limestone
belt, the course is very dry and playable all year round. There
is a timesheet in operation on Sundays.
9 holes, 5880yds, Par 68, SSS 68, Course record 65.
Club membership 250.
Visitors   time sheet in operation on Sun, visitors should
               ring in advance, no problem other days.
Societies   apply in writing.
Green Fees   IR£6 (IR£10 weekends).
Facilities   ⊗ ⚒ ⚒ ⚑ ♀ ⚒
Location   Hilton Park (2.5m from Clones, Scotshouse rd)
Hotel   ★★★65% Ballymascanlon House Hotel,
               DUNDALK ☎ (042) 71124 36 ⇄

MONAGHAN   Map 01 C5

Rossmore ☎ (047) 81316
An undulating parkland course amidst beautiful countryside. At
the time of going to press the course was being extended from 9 to
18 holes.
18 holes, 6000yds, Par 70, SSS 68.
Club membership 350.
Visitors   may not play on competition days.
Societies   must contact in writing.
Green Fees   IR£8 per day (IR£10 weekends).
Facilities   ⊗ ⚒ ⚒ ⚑ (no catering Mon) ♀ ⚒
Leisure   snooker.
Location   Rossmore Park (2m S on Coothill road)
Hotel   ★★★65% Ballymascanlon House Hotel,
               DUNDALK ☎ (042) 71124 36 ⇄

CO OFFALY

BIRR
Map 01 C3

Birr ☎ (0509) 20082
The course has been laid out over undulating parkland utilising the natural contours of the land. The sandy subsoil means that the course is playable all year round.
18 holes, 6262yds, Par 70, SSS 70.
Club membership 450.
Visitors may not play on Sun except 11am-noon; some restrictions on Sat.
Societies must contact in writing.
Green Fees IR£10 per round (IR£12 weekends).
Facilities ⊗ & ﷽ by prior arrangement 🏐 💺 ♀ 📥
Leisure caddy cars.
Location Glenns
Hotel ★★62% County Arms Hotel, BIRR
☎ (0509) 20791 & 20193 18 ⇆ 🐾

EDENDERRY
Map 01 C4

Edenderry ☎ (0405) 31072
A most friendly club which offers a relaxing game in pleasant surroundings. In 1992 the course was extended to 18 holes.
18 holes, 6121mtrs, Par 73, SSS 72.
Club membership 600.
Visitors restricted Thu & weekends.
Societies may not play on Thu & Sun; must contact the secretary in writing.
Green Fees IR£9 per round.
Facilities ⊗ ﷽ 🏐 💺 ♀ 📥
Leisure pool table.
Hotel ★★56% Curryhills House Hotel, PROSPEROUS ☎ (045) 68150 10 ⇆ 🐾

TULLAMORE
Map 01 C4

Tullamore ☎ (0506) 21439
Well wooded parkland course.
18 holes, 6322yds, Par 71, SSS 70, Course record 64.
Club membership 980.
Visitors Contact in advance. Restricted Tue & weekends.
Societies must contact in writing.
Green Fees IR£12 per round (IR£15 weekends).
Facilities ⊗ ﷽ 🏐 💺 ♀ 📥 📠 🐾 ﴾ Donagh McArdle.
Location Brookfield (2.5m SW on Kinnity road)
Hotel ★★★58% Prince Of Wales Hotel, ATHLONE ☎ (0902) 72626 72 ⇆ 🐾

CO ROSCOMMON

ATHLONE
Map 01 C4

Athlone ☎ (0902) 92073 & 92234
A picturesque course with a panoramic view of Lough Ree. It is a tight, difficult course with some outstanding holes.
18 holes, 5922mtrs, Par 71, SSS 71.
Club membership 1100.
Visitors Not Sun, competition days, Sat a.m.
Societies must contact in advance.
Green Fees IR£12 (IR£15 weekends).
Facilities ⊗ & ﷽ by prior arrangement 🏐 💺 ♀ 📥 📠 🐾 ﴾ Martin Quinn.
Leisure snooker.
Location Hodson Bay (4m from town beside Lough Ree)
Hotel ★★★63% Hodson Bay Hotel, Hodson Bay, KILTOOM ☎ (0902) 92446 46 ⇆ 🐾

BALLAGHADERREEN
Map 01 B4

Ballaghaderreen ☎ (0907) 60295
Mature 9-hole course with an abundance of trees. Accuracy off the tee is vital for a good score. Small protected greens require a good short-iron plan.
9 holes, 5727yds, Par 70, SSS 66, Course record 59.
Club membership 150.
Visitors no restrictions.
Societies apply in writing or telephone Sec (0907) 60029 during office hours.
Green Fees IR£6 per day.
Facilities 🏐 & 💺 by prior arrangement ♀ (prior arrangement) 📥
Location 3m W of town
Hotel ★★61% Royal Hotel, BOYLE ☎ (079) 62016 16 ⇆ 🐾

BOYLE
Map 01 B4

Boyle ☎ (079) 62594
Situated on a low hill and surrounded by beautiful scenery, this is an undemanding course with generous fairways and semi-rough.
9 holes, 5324yds, Par 67, SSS 66, Course record 65.
Club membership 260.
Visitors no restrictions.
Societies must contact in writing.
Green Fees IR£5 per day.
Facilities 🏐 & 💺 (May-Sep) ♀ 📥 🐾
Location Roscommon Rd
Hotel ★★61% Royal Hotel, BOYLE ☎ (079) 62016 16 ⇆ 🐾

CARRICK-ON-SHANNON
Map 01 C4

Carrick-on-Shannon ☎ (079) 67015
A pleasant 9-hole course overlooking the River Shannon.
9 holes, 5545mtrs, Par 70, SSS 68.
Club membership 200.
Visitors restricted on competition days & some Sun.
Societies must contact in advance.
Green Fees not confirmed.
Facilities 🏐 💺 ♀ 📥 🐾
Leisure snooker.
Location Woodbrook (4m W beside N4)
Hotel ★★61% Royal Hotel, BOYLE ☎ (079) 62016 16 ⇆ 🐾

CASTLEREA
Map 01 B4

Castlerea ☎ (0907) 20068
The clubhouse is virtually at the centre of Castlerea course with ▶

7 tees visible. A pleasant parkland very near the centre of town.
9 holes, 4974mtrs, Par 68, SSS 66.

Visitors	welcome.
Societies	contact for details.
Green Fees	IR£7 (IR£10 weekends).
Facilities	catering during summer ⚲
Location	Clonalis (on Dublin/Castlebar road)
Hotel	★★★63% Abbey Hotel, Galway Rd, ROSCOMMON ☎ (0903) 26240 & 26505 20 ⇆ ♙

ROSCOMMON　　　　　　　　　　　Map 01 B4

Roscommon ☎ (0903) 26382 & 26062
Roscommon is in the process of changing to 18 holes and will
only be open for limited play in August 1995. The new
rolling parkland course will have championship tees (6,200
metres), medal & society tees.
11 holes, 5784mtrs, Par 72, SSS 70, Course record 64.
Club membership 550.

Visitors	Not Sun, some Sats, Tue is ladies day.
Societies	prior arrangement in writing or by telephone.
Green Fees	IR£10 per day.
Facilities	⊗ by prior arrangement ⓛ ⚑ ⚲ ⚘
Leisure	caddy cars, practice ground.
Location	Mote Park (0.5m S of Roscommon town)
Hotel	★★★63% Abbey Hotel, Galway Rd, ROSCOMMON ☎ (0903) 26240 & 26505 20 ⇆ ♙

CO SLIGO

BALLYMOTE　　　　　　　　　　　Map 01 B4

Ballymote ☎ (071) 83460
Although Ballymote was founded in 1940, it has a new
course only opened in July 1993. This is a 9-hole parkland
course with some trees.
9 holes, 4601mtrs, SSS 65.

Visitors	welcome.
Societies	contact for details.
Green Fees	IR£5 per day.
Facilities	snacks
Location	Carrigans (1m N)
Hotel	★★★♨75% Cromleach Lodge Country House Hotel, Ballindoon, CASTLEBALDWIN ☎ (071) 65155 10 ⇆ ♙

ENNISCRONE　　　　　　　　　　　Map 01 B5

Enniscrone ☎ (096) 36297
In a magnificent situation with breathtaking views of
mountain, sea and rolling countryside, this course offers
some unforgettable golf. It offers an exciting challenge
among its splendid sandhills. A particularly favourite hole
is the tenth, with a marvellous view from the elevated tee.
18 holes, 6620yds, Par 72, SSS 72.
Club membership 700.

Visitors	may not play before 10.30am or between 1.30 & 3pm on Sun.
Societies	must telephone in advance.
Green Fees	not confirmed.
Facilities	⊗ ⵒ ⓛ ⚑ ⚲ ⚘ ⚘ ♟
Location	0.5m S on Ballina road

Hotel	★★★61% Downhill Hotel, BALLINA ☎ (096) 21033 50 ⇆ ♙

SLIGO　　　　　　　　　　　　　Map 01 B5

County Sligo ☎ (071) 77134 or 77186
Now considered to be one of the top links courses in Ireland,
County Sligo is host to a number of competitions. Set in an
elevated position on cliffs above three large beaches, the
prevailing winds provide an additional challenge.
18 holes, 6003mtrs, Par 71, SSS 72, Course record 66.
Club membership 1032.

Visitors	must contact in advance. Must play on medal course (white tee markers).
Societies	must contact in writing & pay a deposit.
Green Fees	IR£27 per day; IR£16 per round (IR£22 per round weekends & bank holidays).
Facilities	⊗ ⵒ ⓛ ⚑ ⚲ ⚘ 🖥 ♟ ℓ Leslie Robinson.
Leisure	buggies, caddy cars, practice area.
Location	Rosses Point (off N15 to Donegal)
Hotel	★★★58% Ballincar House Hotel, Rosses Point Rd, SLIGO ☎ (071) 45361 26 ⇆ ♙

Strandhill ☎ (071) 68188
This scenic course is situated between Knocknarea Mountain
and the Atlantic, offering golf in its most natural form amid
the sand dunes of the West of Ireland. This is a course where
accuracy will be rewarded.
18 holes, 5045mtrs, Par 69, SSS 68.

Visitors	preferred on weekdays, except Thu.
Green Fees	not confirmed.
Facilities	⊗ ⵒ by prior arrangement ⓛ ⚲
Location	Strandhill (5m from town)
Hotel	★★★58% Ballincar House Hotel, Rosses Point Rd, SLIGO ☎ (071) 45361 26 ⇆ ♙

TOBERCURRY　　　　　　　　　　　Map 01 B4

Tobercurry ☎ (071) 85849
A 9-hole parkland course designed by Edward Hackett. The
8th hole, a Par 3, is regarded as being one of the most testing
in the west of Ireland.
9 holes, 5478mtrs, Par 70, SSS 69, Course record 71.
Club membership 200.

Visitors	may be restricted on Sun.
Societies	apply in writing or telephone in advance.
Green Fees	IR£6 per 18 holes.
Facilities	⚘
Location	0.25m from Tobercurry
Hotel	★★★61% Downhill Hotel, BALLINA ☎ (096) 21033 50 ⇆ ♙

CO TIPPERARY

CARRICK-ON-SUIR　　　　　　　　　Map 01 C2

Carrick-on-Suir ☎ (051) 40047
9 holes, 5948yds, Par 70, SSS 68.

Visitors	may not play on Sun.
Societies	contact for details.
Green Fees	not confirmed.

Facilities	catering available by prior booking
Location	Garvonne (2m SW)
Hotel	★★★70% Minella Hotel, CLONMEL ☎ (052) 22388 & 22717 45 ⇆ 📷

CLONMEL   Map 01 C2

Clonmel ☎ (052) 24050
Set in the scenic, wooded slopes of the Comeragh Mountains, this is a testing course with lots of open space and plenty of interesting features.
18 holes, 5785mtrs, Par 71, SSS 70.
Club membership 850.

Visitors	may not play at weekends & bank holidays. Must contact in advance.
Societies	must contact in writing.
Green Fees	IR£13 per round (IR£15 weekends).
Facilities	⊗ (summer only) ⵊ by prior arrangement ⓑ ❢ ♀ ⚲ 🏠 ⵑ ⵊ Robert Hayes.
Leisure	snooker, bowls, pool table, table tennis.
Location	Lyreanearla, Mountain Rd
Hotel	★★★70% Minella Hotel, CLONMEL ☎ (052) 22388 & 22717 45 ⇆ 📷

NENAGH   Map 01 B3

Nenagh ☎ (067) 31476
Interesting gradients call for some careful approach shots.
18 holes, 5996yds, Par 69, SSS 68, Course record 64.
Club membership 700.

Visitors	preferred weekdays.
Societies	must apply in writing.
Green Fees	IR£12 per round (IR£15 weekends).
Facilities	⊗ ⵊ ⓑ ❢ ♀ ⚲ 🏠 ⵑ ⵊ John Coyle.
Location	Graigue (at Beechwood, 5m from town)
Hotel	★★★60% Castle Oaks House Hotel, CASTLECONNELL ☎ (061) 377666 11 ⇆ 📷

ROSCREA   Map 01 C3

Roscrea Golf Club ☎ (0505) 21130
An 18-hole parkland course.
18 holes, 5750mtrs, Par 71, SSS 70.
Club membership 420.

Visitors	on Sun by arrangement.
Societies	apply in writing to Hon Secretary.
Green Fees	IR£10 per day (IR£12 weekends).
Facilities	⊗ ⵊ ⓑ ❢ ♀ ⚲ ⵑ
Leisure	snooker, caddy car for hire.
Location	Derryvale (N7, Dublin side of Roscrea)
Hotel	★★68% Leix County Hotel, BORRIS-IN-OSSORY ☎ (0505) 41213 19 ⇆

TEMPLEMORE   Map 01 C3

Templemore ☎ (0504) 31400
Parkland course with newly planted trees. Level walking.
9 holes, Par 68, SSS 67, Course record 68.
Club membership 220.

Visitors	may not play on Sun during Special Events & Open weeks.
Societies	must contact in advance.
Green Fees	not confirmed.
Facilities	❢ by prior arrangement ♀ ⚲
Location	Manna South (0.5m S)

Hotel	★★68% Leix County Hotel, BORRIS-IN-OSSORY ☎ (0505) 41213 19 ⇆

THURLES   Map 01 C3

Thurles ☎ (0504) 21983
Superb parkland course with a difficult finish at the 18th.
18 holes, 5904mtrs, Par 72, SSS 71.
Club membership 700.

Visitors	preferred on Mon, Wed, Thu & Fri.
Societies	must book one year in advance.
Green Fees	not confirmed.
Facilities	⊗ & ⵊ by prior arrangement ⓑ ❢ ♀ 🏠 ⵑ ⵊ Sean Hunt.
Leisure	squash, snooker.
Location	1m from town on Cork road
Hotel	★★★★♣70% Cashel Palace Hotel, CASHEL ☎ (062) 61411 20 ⇆

TIPPERARY   Map 01 C3

Tipperary ☎ (062) 51119
Recently extended to 18-holes, this parkland course has plenty of trees and bunkers and water at three holes.
18 holes, 5805mtrs, Par 72, SSS 70.

Visitors	welcome but restricted on Sun.
Societies	by prior arrangement.
Green Fees	IR£10 per day.
Facilities	snacks available ♀
Location	Rathanny (1m S)
Hotel	★56% Royal Hotel, Bridge St, TIPPERARY ☎ (062) 51204 & 51285 16 ⇆ 📷

CO WATERFORD

DUNGARVAN   Map 01 C2

Dungarvan ☎ (058) 41605
Opened in June 1993. A championship-standard course beside Dungarvan Bay, with seven lakes and hazards placed to challenge all levels of golfer.
18 holes, 6134mtrs, Par 72, SSS 72.
Club membership 750.

Visitors	no restrictions. Advisable to book in advance for weekends.
Societies	must telephone in advance and confirm in writing.
Green Fees	IR£12 per round (IR£15 weekends).
Facilities	⊗ ⵊ ⓑ ❢ ♀ ⚲ 🏠 ⵑ ⵊ Derry Kiely.
Leisure	caddy cars.
Location	Knocknagrannagh (off N25 Waterford/Youghal)
Hotel	★★★59% Lawlors Hotel, DUNGARVAN ☎ (058) 41122 & 41056 89 ⇆ 📷

West Waterford ☎ (058) 43216
Designed by Eddie Hackett, the course is on 150 acres of rolling parkland by the Brickey River. The first nine are on a large plateau with a stream which comes into play at the 3rd and 4th holes.
18 holes, 6004mtrs, Par 72, SSS 74, Course record 69.
Club membership 100.

Visitors	pre book for tee times.
Societies	telephone to ensure a tee time & booking. ▶

Green Fees IR£15 (IR£20 weekends & bank holidays).
Facilities ⊗ 〗⫪ ⤶ ♥ ♀ ⚘ 👜 🛈 ⛴
Leisure fishing, caddy cars,caddies,tuition available.
Location Coolcormack (approx 3m W of Dungarvan, off N25)
Hotel ★★★59% Lawlors Hotel, DUNGARVAN
🕾 (058) 41122 & 41056 89 ⇆ 🐾

LISMORE   Map 01 C2

Lismore 🕾 (058) 54026
Picturesque tree-dotted sloping course on the banks of the
Blackwater River.
9 holes, 5291mtrs, Par 69, SSS 67.
Club membership 450.
Visitors may not play Sun. Ladies have priority Wed.
Societies must telephone in advance to play on weekdays
(contact in writing for weekends).
Green Fees IR£8 per round (IR£10 weekends & bank
holidays).
Facilities (summer & weekends only) ♀ ⚘ ⤶ & ♥
Leisure caddy cars.
Location Ballyin
Hotel ★★★59% Lawlors Hotel, DUNGARVAN
🕾 (058) 41122 & 41056 89 ⇆ 🐾

TRAMORE   Map 01 C2

Tramore 🕾 (051) 86170
This course has matured nicely over the years to become a
true championship test. Most of the fairways are lined by
evergreen trees, calling for accurate placing of shots, and the
course is continuing to develop.
18 holes, 5999mtrs, Par 72, SSS 73.
Club membership 1203.
Visitors preferred on weekdays.
Societies apply in writing.
Green Fees IR£17 (IR£20 weekends & bank holidays).
Facilities ⊗ 〗⫪ ⤶ ♥ ♀ ⚘ 👜 🛈 ⛴ Paul McDaid.
Leisure squash, snooker.
Location Newtown Hill
Hotel ★★★★⚘75% Waterford Castle Hotel, The
Island, WATERFORD 🕾 (051) 78203 19 ⇆ 🐾

WATERFORD   Map 01 C2

Waterford 🕾 (051) 78489
Undulating parkland course in pleasant surroundings.
18 holes, 6237yds, Par 71, SSS 70.
Visitors preferred on weekdays.
Green Fees not confirmed.
Facilities ⊗ 〗⫪ ⤶ ♀ 👜 ⛴ E Condon.
Location Newrath (1m N)
Hotel ★★★65% Jurys Hotel, Ferrybank,
WATERFORD 🕾 (051) 32111 98 ⇆ 🐾

CO WESTMEATH

MOATE   Map 01 C4

Moate 🕾 (0902) 81271
Extended in 1994 to 18 holes, the course is parkland with

---

trees. Although the original 9-holes did not have water
hazards the new section has a lake.
9 holes, 4879mtrs, Par 68, SSS 66.
Visitors welcome contact for details.
Societies contact for details.
Green Fees IR£7 (IR£10 weekends).
Facilities bar snacks
Location E of Athlone
Hotel ★★★58% Prince Of Wales Hotel, ATHLONE
🕾 (0902) 72626 72 ⇆ 🐾

MULLINGAR   Map 01 C4

Mullingar 🕾 (044) 48366
The wide rolling fairways between mature trees provide
parkland golf at its very best. The course, designed by the
great James Braid, offers a tough challenge and annually
hosts the Mullingar Scratch Cup. It has also been the venue
of the Irish Professional Championship.
18 holes, 6451yds, Par 72, SSS 71.
Club membership 900.
Visitors preferred on weekdays, except Wed.
Societies must contact in advance.
Green Fees not confirmed.
Facilities ⊗ 〗⫪ ⤶ ♥ ♀ ⚘ 👜 🛈 ⛴ John Burns.
Leisure snooker.
Location 3m W
Hotel ★★★58% Prince Of Wales Hotel,
ATHLONE 🕾 (0902) 72626 72 ⇆ 🐾

CO WEXFORD

COURTOWN HARBOUR   Map 01 D3

Courtown 🕾 (055) 25166
Treelined fairways and views of the sea make this 18-hole
parkland course attractive. There are 4 excellent Par 3's, one
of which is the 18th played over a large pond.
18 holes, 5852mtrs, Par 71, SSS 70.
Visitors may not play on competition days.
Societies contact for details.
Green Fees IR£15 (IR£20 weekends).
Facilities restaurant ♀ 🛈 John Coone.
Location Kiltennel, Gorey
Hotel ★★69% Courtown Hotel, COURTOWN
HARBOUR 🕾 (055) 25210 & 25108 21 ⇆ 🐾

ENNISCORTHY   Map 01 D3

Enniscorthy 🕾 (054) 33191
A pleasant course suitable for all levels of ability.
18 holes, 5697mtrs, Par 70, SSS 70.
Club membership 650.
Visitors preferred on weekdays. Must contact in advance.
Societies must book in advance.
Green Fees IR£10 per day (IR£12 weekends & bank holidays).
Facilities ⊗ & 〗⫪ by prior arrangement ⤶ ♥ ♀ ⚘
Location Knockmarshall (2m from town on New Ross road)
Hotel ★★58% Murphy-Flood's Hotel, Market Square,
ENNISCORTHY 🕾 (054) 33413 21rm(5 ⇆13 🐾)

GOREY   Map 01 D3

Courtown ☎ (055) 25166
A pleasant parkland course which is well wooded and
enjoys views across the Irish Sea near Courtown Harbour.
18 holes, 5852mtrs, Par 71, SSS 70.
Club membership 700.

Visitors	Not competition days or 5-7pm Jul & Aug.
Societies	must contact in advance.
Green Fees	IR£13-IR£15 (IR£17-IR£20 weekends).
Facilities	⊗ by prior arrangement ⫰ ⌷ ☲ ♀ ⏃ 🏠 ⸙⏃ 𝄐 John Coone.
Leisure	caddy car hire.
Location	Kiltennel (Off Courtown Road)
Hotel	★★★(red)🏌 Marlfield House Hotel, GOREY ☎ (055) 21124 19 ⇋ ⟆

NEW ROSS   Map 01 C3

New Ross ☎ (051) 21433
A well kept 9-hole parkland course. Straight hitting and
careful placing of shots is very important. A further 9 holes
are to be developed during 1994 and 1995.
9 holes, 6160yds, Par 70, SSS 69.
Club membership 546.

Visitors	no green fees after 2pm on Tue, limited on Wed, contact the secretary/manager.
Societies	apply to secretary/manager.
Green Fees	IR£8 (IR£12 weekends & bank holidays).
Facilities	⌷ ☲ ♀ ⏃
Leisure	caddy cars for hire.
Location	Tinneranny (3m from town centre)
Hotel	★★★★🏌75% Mount Juliet Hotel, THOMASTOWN ☎ (056) 24455 32 ⇋

ROSSLARE   Map 01 D2

Rosslare ☎ (053) 32203 & 32238
This traditional links course is a great favourite with
visitors and the Irish too. Many of the greens are sunken
and are always in beautiful condition, but the semi-blind
approaches are among features of this course which
provide a healthy challenge.
*Old Course: 18 holes, 6554yds, Par 72, SSS 71, Course
record 68.*
New Course: 9 holes, 3153yds, Par 70, SSS 70.
Club membership 900.

Visitors	book in advance.
Societies	apply in writing/telephone.
Green Fees	Old: IR£18 per day (IR£23 weekends). New: IR£12 per 18 holes, IR£8 per 9 holes.
Facilities	⊗ ⫰ ⌷ ☲ ♀ ⏃ 🏠 ⸙⏃ 𝄐 Austin Skerritt.
Leisure	snooker, caddy cars for hire.
Location	Rosslare Strand (6m N of Rosslare Ferry Terminal)
Hotel	★★★(red) Kelly's Strand Hotel, ROSSLARE ☎ (053) 32114 Annexe99 ⇋ ⟆

St Helen's Bay Golf & Country Club
☎ (053) 33234 & 33669
A championship-standard golf course designed by Philip
Walton. Parkland with water hazards, bunkers and trees.
18 holes, 6213mtrs, Par 72, SSS 70, Course record 69.
Club membership 300.

Visitors	advisable to contact in advance.
Societies	advisable to book.
Green Fees	IR£15-IR£17 (IR£18-IR£22 weekends).
Facilities	⊗ ⫰ ⌷ ☲ ♀ ⏃ 🏠 ⸙⏃ ⟿
Leisure	caddy cars.
Location	St Helens, Kilrane
Hotel	★★★56% Hotel Rosslare, ROSSLARE HARBOUR ☎ (053) 33110 & 33312 25rm(22 ⇋ ⟆)

WEXFORD   Map 01 D3

Wexford ☎ (053) 42238
Parkland course with panoramic view of the Wexford
coastline and mountains.
18 holes, 6100yds, Par 71, SSS 69.
Club membership 800.

Visitors	contact in advance. Not Thu & weekends.
Societies	must contact in writing.
Green Fees	not confirmed.
Facilities	⊗ & ⫰ by prior arrangement ⌷ ☲ ♀ ⏃ 🏠 𝄐 G Ronayne.
Leisure	pool table.
Location	Mulgannon
Hotel	★★★69% Talbot Hotel, Trinity St, WEXFORD ☎ (053) 22566 100 ⇋ ⟆

CO WICKLOW

ARKLOW   Map 01 D3

Arklow ☎ (0402) 32492
Scenic links course.
18 holes, 5404mtrs, Par 68, SSS 67, Course record 66.
Club membership 450.

Visitors	may play Mon-Fri.
Societies	must apply in writing.
Green Fees	not confirmed.
Facilities	⊗ & ⫰ by prior arrangement ⌷ ☲ ♀ ⏃ 🏠
Location	Abbeylands (0.5m from town centre)
Hotel	★★★(red)🏌 Marlfield House Hotel, GOREY ☎ (055) 21124 19 ⇋ ⟆

BALTINGLASS   Map 01 D3

Baltinglass ☎ (0508) 81350
On the banks of the River Slaney, the 9-hole course has 4 Par-
4s over 400 yards which have to be played twice.
9 holes, 5554mtrs, Par 68, SSS 68, Course record 66.
Club membership 380.

Visitors	best days for visitors are Mon, Tue & Fri.
Societies	apply in writing or by telephone.
Green Fees	IR£10 (IR£12 weekends & bank holidays).
Facilities	⌷ (full catering on Sat) ♀ ⏃
Leisure	snooker.
Hotel	★★52% Royal Hotel, CARLOW ☎ (0503) 31621 34 ⇋ ⟆

BLAINROE   Map 01 D3

Blainroe ☎ (0404) 68168
Parkland course overlooking the sea on the east coast.
18 holes, 6159mtrs, Par 72, SSS 72. ▶

Club membership 700.
Visitors restricted Mon and weekends. Must contact in advance.
Societies must apply in writing.
Green Fees not confirmed.
Facilities ⊗ 🎿 🏌 💺 ♀ ☂ 🏠 🍴 John McDonald.
Location S of Wicklow, on coast road
Hotel ★★★(red)▲▲ Tinakilly Country House & Restaurant, RATHNEW
☎ (0404) 69274 29 ⇆ 🐾

BLESSINGTON Map 01 D3

Tulfarris Hotel & Country Club
☎ Naas (045) 64574 & 51219
Designed by Eddie Hachett, this course is on the Blessington lakeshore with the Wicklow Mountains as a backdrop.
9 holes, 2806mtrs, Par 36, SSS 69, Course record 74.
Club membership 150.
Visitors booking advisable; not Sun 8-12.30pm.
Societies must contact in writing or telephone in advance.
Green Fees IR£10 per round (IR£13.50 weekends & bank holidays).
Facilities ⊗ 🎿 🏌 💺 (catering by arrangement) ♀ ☂ 🏠 🍴 ⛴
Leisure hard tennis courts, heated indoor swimming pool, fishing, sauna, gymnasium, caddy cars.
Location Via N81, 2m from Blessington village
Hotel ★★★56% Downshire House Hotel, BLESSINGTON
☎ (045) 65199 14 ⇆ 🐾Annexe11 ⇆ 🐾

BRAY Map 01 D2

Bray ☎ (01) 2862484
A 9-hole parkland course with plenty of trees and bunkers.
9 holes, 5761mtrs, Par 70, SSS 70.
Visitors welcome during week.
Societies contact for details.
Green Fees IR£17.
Facilities snacks ♀🍴 Michael Wallby.
Location Ravenswell Rd
Hotel ★★★60% Royal Hotel, Main St, BRAY
☎ (01) 2862935 73rm(72 ⇆ 🐾)

Old Conna ☎ (01) 2826055 & 2826766
Fairly young but interesting course.
18 holes, 6551yds, Par 72, SSS 71.
Club membership 900.
Visitors may not play 12.30-2pm or at weekends unless with member. Must contact in advance.
Societies must telephone well in advance.
Green Fees IR£20 per round.
Facilities ⊗ 🎿 🏌 💺 ♀ ☂ 🏠 🍴 Niall Murray.
Leisure snooker, caddy cars.
Location Ferndale Rd
Hotel ★★★60% Royal Hotel, Main St, BRAY
☎ (01) 2862935 73rm(72 ⇆ 🐾)

Woodbrook ☎ Dublin (01) 2824799
Pleasant parkland with magnificent views and bracing sea breezes which has hosted a number of events. A testing finish is provided by an 18th hole with out of bounds on both sides.
18 holes, 5996mtrs, Par 72, SSS 71, Course record 65.
Club membership 960.

Visitors must contact in advance and have a handicap certificate.
Societies must contact in advance.
Green Fees not confirmed.
Facilities ⊗ 🎿 🏌 💺 ♀ ☂ 🏠 🍴 Billy Kinsella.
Leisure snooker.
Location Dublin Rd (11m S of Dublin on N11)
Hotel ★★★60% Royal Hotel, Main St, BRAY
☎ (01) 2862935 73rm(72 ⇆ 🐾)

BRITTAS BAY Map 01 D3

The European Club ☎ (0404) 47415
A major new links course 30 miles south of Dublin, the course runs through a large dunes system. No 7 in Ireland's 30 greatest golf courses of the Irish Golf Institute in 1994.
18 holes, 6729yds, Par 71, SSS 71.
Club membership 120.
Visitors welcome any day but advisable to book.
Societies advisable to book by telephone.
Green Fees IR£20 (IR£25 weekends).
Facilities ⊗ 🎿 🏌 💺 ♀ ☂ 🏠
Leisure caddy cars, practice tee.
Hotel ★★★(red)▲▲ Tinakilly Country House & Restaurant, RATHNEW
☎ (0404) 69274 29 ⇆ 🐾

DELGANY Map 01 D3

Delgany ☎ (01) 2874536
An undulating parkland course amidst beautiful scenery.
18 holes, 5414mtrs, Par 69, SSS 67, Course record 63.
Club membership 800.
Visitors preferred on Mon, Thu & Fri.
Societies normally Mon & Thu.
Green Fees IR£17 (IR£20 weekends & bank holidays).
Facilities ⊗ (ex Mon & Tue) 🎿 & 🏌 (ex Mon) 💺 ♀ ☂ 🏠 🍴 Paul Thompson.
Leisure snooker, buggies, caddy cars.
Location 0.75m from village
Hotel ★★★60% Royal Hotel, Main St, BRAY
☎ (01) 2862935 73rm(72 ⇆ 🐾)

GREYSTONES Map 01 D3

Charlesland Golf & Country Club Hotel ☎ (01) 2876764
Championship length, Par 72 course with a double dog-leg at the 9th and 18th. Water hazards at the 3rd and 11th.
18 holes, 5907mtrs, Par 72, SSS 72.
Club membership 600.
Visitors no visitors on Sat, limited on Sun.
Societies apply in advance by telephone or in writing.
Green Fees IR£23 (IR£28 weekends & bank holidays).
Facilities ⊗ 🎿 🏌 💺 ♀ ☂ 🏠 🍴 ⛴ Paul Heeney.
Leisure sauna, caddy cars, electric buggies, golf tuition.
Hotel ★★★(red)▲▲ Tinakilly Country House & Restaurant, RATHNEW
☎ (0404) 69274 29 ⇆ 🐾

Greystones ☎ (01) 2876624 & 2874136
A part level and part hilly parkland course.
18 holes, 5401mtrs, Par 69, SSS 68.
Club membership 941.
Visitors only Mon, Tue & Fri a.m. Contact in advance.

Societies   must contact in writing.
Green Fees IR£20 per round.
Facilities ⊗ ⅋⅊⅋ ⅋ ⅊ ⅋ ⅋ ⅊
Hotel   ★★★(red)⚑ Tinakilly Country House &
            Restaurant, RATHNEW
            ☎ (0404) 69274 29 ⇆ ⁀

KILCOOLE   Map 01 D3

Kilcoole ☎ (01) 2872066
9 holes, 5506mtrs, Par 70, SSS 69.
Club membership 250.
Visitors   restricted Sat & Sun 8-10am.
Societies apply in writing or telephone.
Green Fees IR£10 per 18 holes (IR£12 weekends).
Facilities ⊗ ⅋ ⅊ ⅋ ⅊ ⅋
Leisure   caddy cars.
Location   Ballyfillop (N11 Kilcoole/Newcastle)
Hotel   ★★70% Hunter's Hotel, RATHNEW
               ☎ (0404) 40106 18rm(10 ⇆ ⁀)

SHILLELAGH   Map 01 D3

Coollattin ☎ (055) 26302
Plenty of trees on this 9-hole parkland course.
9 holes, 5672mtrs, Par 70, SSS 70.
Visitors   may not play weekends.
Societies contact for details.
Green Fees IR£10.
Facilities catering by arrangement ⅊
Location   Coollattin

Hotel   ★★★(red)⚑ Marlfield House Hotel, GOREY
            ☎ (055) 21124 19 ⇆ ⁀

WICKLOW   Map 01 D3

Wicklow ☎ (0404) 67379
Partly links, partly meadow, the Wicklow course does not
have any trees. It was extended to 18-holes in spring 1994.
9 holes, 5556mtrs, Par 70, SSS 67.
Visitors   welcome, must book for weekends.
Societies contact for details.
Green Fees IR£15.
Facilities catering available ⅊ David Daly.
Location   Dunbur Rd
Hotel   ★★★(red)⚑ Tinakilly Country House &
               Restaurant, RATHNEW
               ☎ (0404) 69274 29 ⇆ ⁀

WOODENBRIDGE   Map 01 D3

Woodenbridge ☎ (0402) 35202
Expanded to 18 holes in summer of 1994, this course is in a
lovely wooded valley - the Vale of Avoca.
9 holes, 5582mtrs, Par 70, SSS 68.
Visitors   welcome.
Societies no details given.
Green Fees IR£15.
Facilities restaurant
Location   Arklow
Hotel   ★★60% Woodenbridge Inn, WOODEN
               BRIDGE ☎ (0402) 35146 11 ⇆ ⁀

Index

Where the location is
different from the course
name, it is printed in
italics

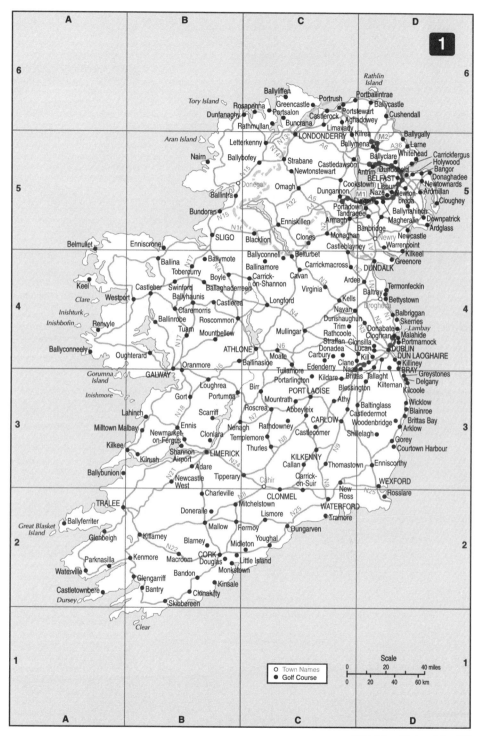

© The Automobile Association 1994

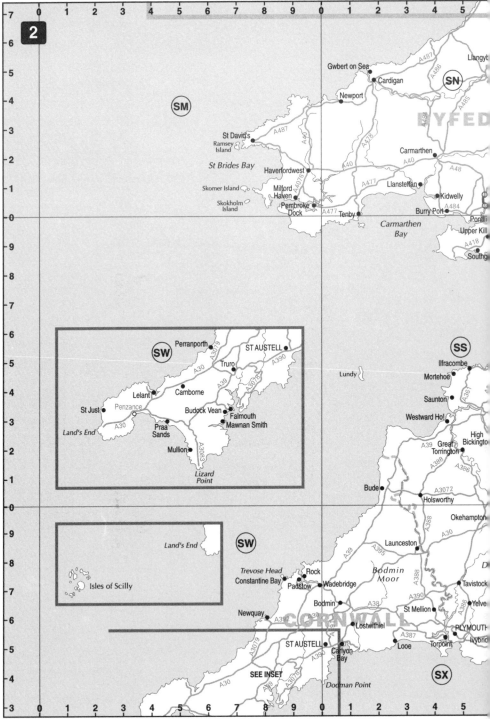

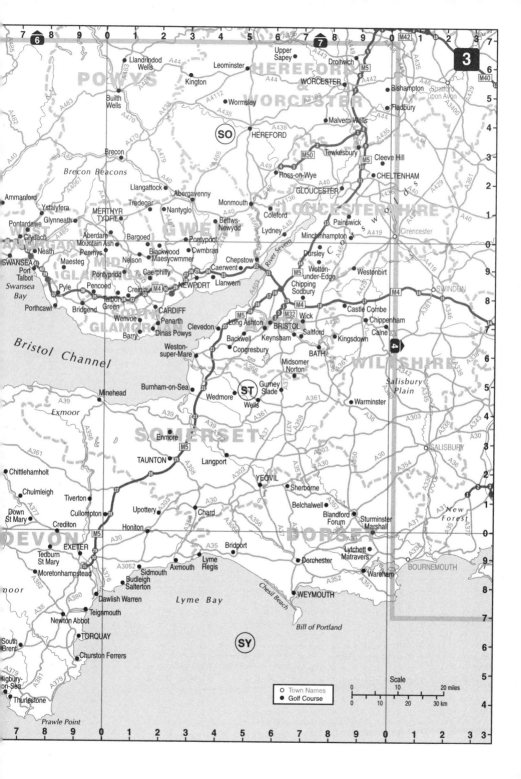

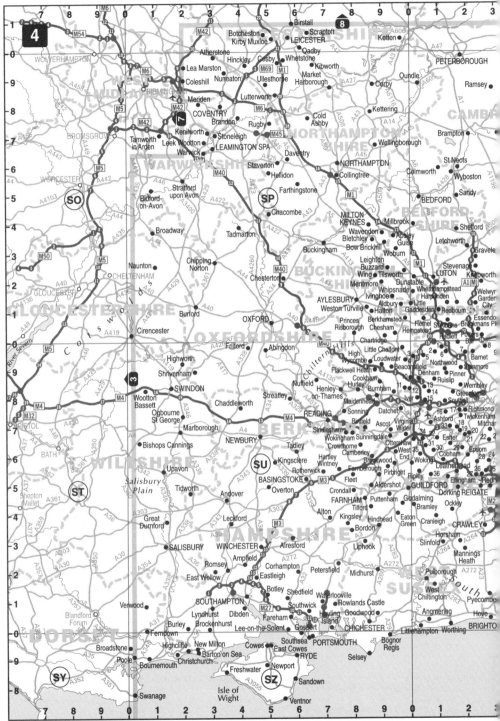

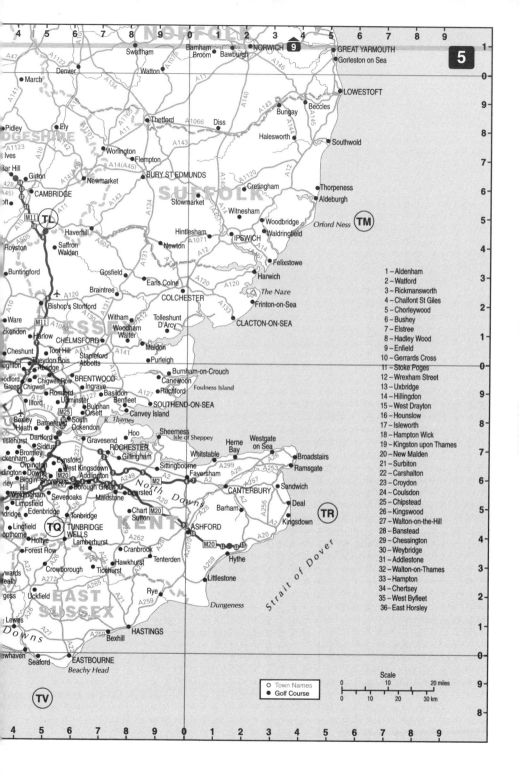

5

1 – Aldenham
2 – Watford
3 – Rickmansworth
4 – Chalfont St Giles
5 – Chorleywood
6 – Bushey
7 – Elstree
8 – Hadley Wood
9 – Enfield
10 – Gerrards Cross
11 – Stoke Poges
12 – Wrexham Street
13 – Uxbridge
14 – Hillingdon
15 – West Drayton
16 – Hounslow
17 – Isleworth
18 – Hampton Wick
19 – Kingston upon Thames
20 – New Malden
21 – Surbiton
22 – Carshalton
23 – Croydon
24 – Coulsdon
25 – Chipstead
26 – Kingswood
27 – Walton-on-the-Hill
28 – Banstead
29 – Chessington
30 – Weybridge
31 – Addlestone
32 – Walton-on-Thames
33 – Hampton
34 – Chertsey
35 – West Byfleet
36 – East Horsley

Scale

○ Town Names
● Golf Course

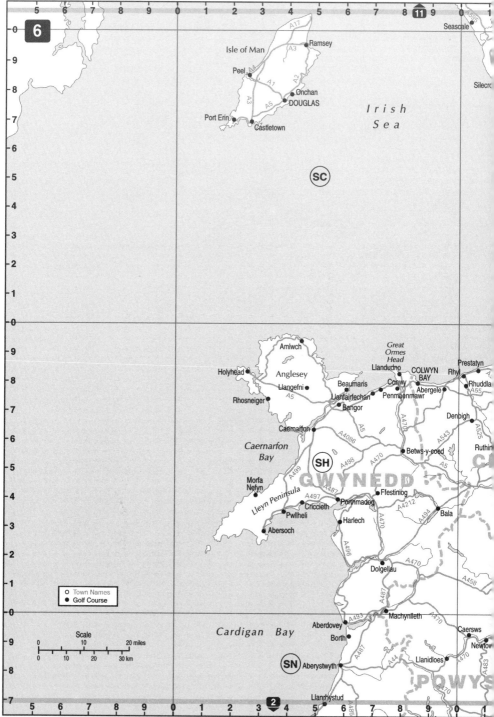

Isle of Man

Ramsey

Peel

Onchan
DOUGLAS

Port Erin

Castletown

Irish Sea

SC

Seascale

Silecr

Great
Ormes
Head

Amlwch

Holyhead

Anglesey

Llangefni

Rhosneiger

Llandudno

Beaumaris

Conwy

Penmaenmawr

Llanfairfechan

Bangor

Caernarfon

COLWYN
BAY

Abergele

Rhyl

Prestatyn

Rhuddla

Denbigh

Ruthir

C

Betws-y-coed

Caernarfon Bay

SH

GWYNEDD

Morfa
Nefyn

Lleyn Peninsula

Criccieth

Pwllheli

Abersoch

Porthmadog

Harlech

Ffestiniog

Bala

Dolgellau

○ Town Names
● Golf Course

Scale
0   10   20 miles
0   10   20   30 km

Cardigan Bay

Aberdovey

Borth

SN Aberystwyth

Machynlleth

Caersws

Newtov

Llanidloes

POWYS

Llanrhystud

2

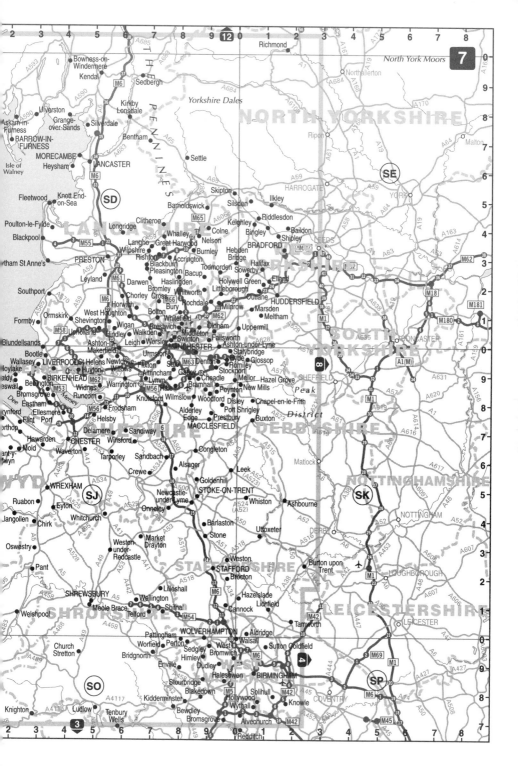

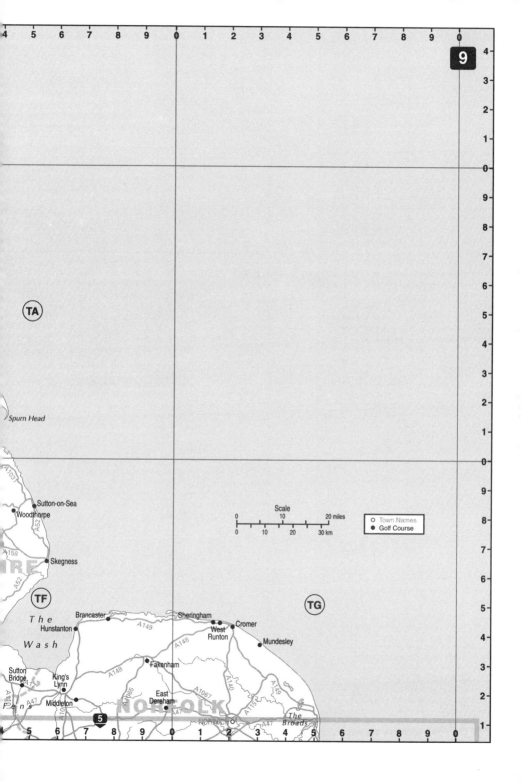

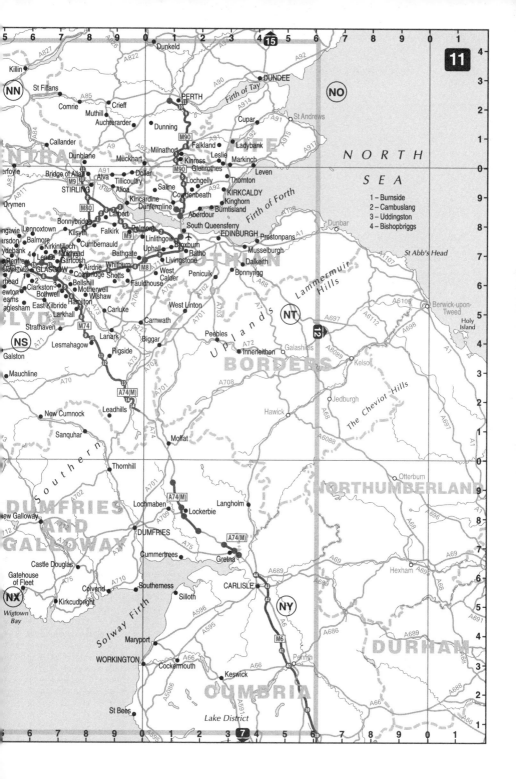

12

NO · SN · NT · NU · NY · NZ

Arbroath
Carnoustie
Monifieth
DUNDEE
Barry
Tayport
Firth of Tay
Leuchars
St Andrews
PERTH
A90
M90
FIFE
Crail
Anstruther
GLENROTHES
Lundin Links
Elie

NORTH SEA

Dunfermline
Firth of Forth
North Berwick
Gullane
Aberlady
Longniddry
Dunbar
EDINBURGH
Haddington
St Abb's Head
Gifford
Eyemouth
LOTHIAN
Lammermuir Hills
Peebles
Duns
Berwick-upon-Tweed
Lauder
Holy Island
Galashiels
Coldstream
Bamburgh
BORDERS
Melrose
Kelso
Belford
Seahouses
St Boswells
Wooler
Moffat
Selkirk
Embleton
Minto
Jedburgh
Hawick
The Cheviot Hills
Alnwick
Alnmouth
Warkworth
Rothbury

Scale
0   10   20 miles
0   10   20   30 km

○ Town Names
● Golf Course

Newcastleton
NORTHUMBERLAND
Newbiggin-by-the-Sea
Morpeth
Bedlington
Bellingham
Blyth
A74(M)
Cramlington
Whitley Bay
Ponteland
Backworth
Tynemouth
Gosforth
Wallsend
South Shields
Hexham
Prudhoe
Ryton
NEWCASTLE UPON TYNE
Brampton
Stocksfield
Whickham
Gateshead
Felling
Boldon
Crosby-on-Eden
Chopwell
Birtley
Washington
Sunderland
CARLISLE
Allendale
Burnopfield
Beamish
Seaham
NY
Consett
Stanley
Houghton-le-Spring
NZ
Alston
Chester-le-Street
DURHAM
Penrith
Crook
A1(M)
8
HARTLEPOOL
Keswick
CUMBRIA
Crook
DURHAM
MIDDLESBROUGH
Appleby-in-Westmorland
Barnard Castle
CLEVELAND
Lake District
DARLINGTON

7

For continuation pages refer to numbered arrows

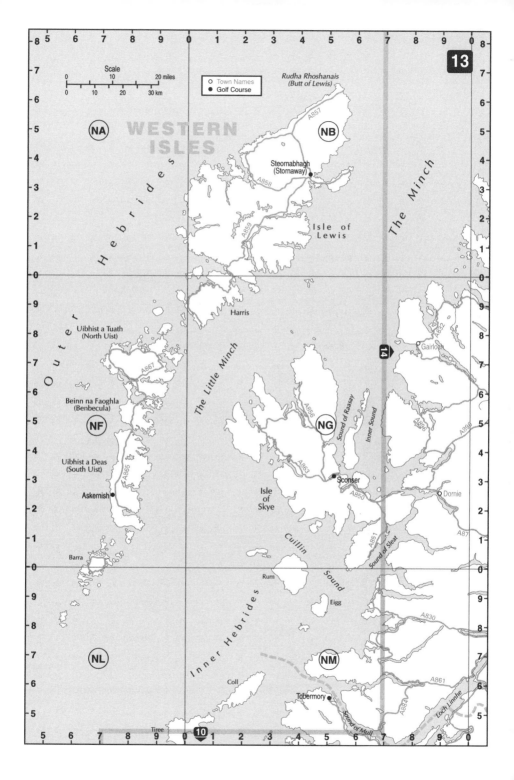

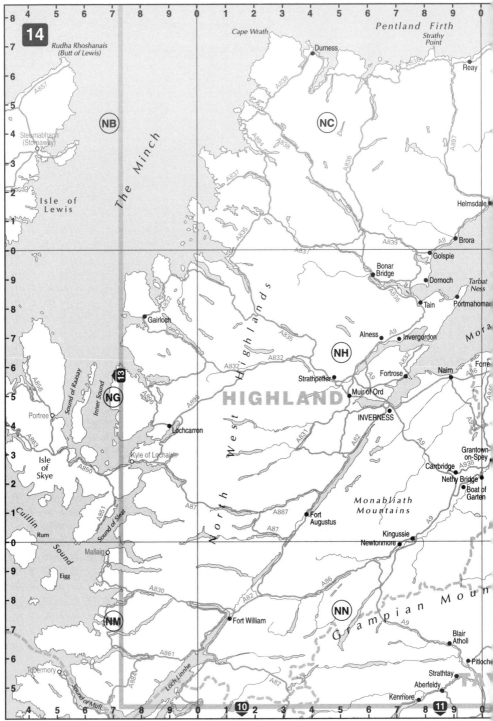

Pentland Firth

Strathy Point

Cape Wrath

Durness

Reay

Rudha Rhoshanais
(Butt of Lewis)

A857

NB

NC

A838

A836

A838

A894

A837

A836

A897

Helmsdale

The Minch

Steòrnabhagh
(Stornoway)

A859

A835

A839

Brora

Golspie

Isle of
Lewis

A837

Bonar
Bridge

Dornoch

Tarbat
Ness

Tain

A836

Portmahomack

A832

A835

Mora

Gairloch

A9

Alness

A9

Invergordon

NH

Strathpeffer

A832

A832

Fortrose

Nairn

Forre

A96

HIGHLAND

A832

A890

Muir of Ord

A9

Portree

Sound of Raasay

Inner Sound

13

NG

A896

INVERNESS

A862

Grantown-
on-Spey

A938

Isle
of
Skye

A863

Lochcarron

A890

A831

A82

Carrbridge

Nethy Bridge

Boat of
Garten

A850

Kyle of Lochalsh

A87

A9

Cuillin

A851

Rum

Sound of Sleat

North
West
Highlands

A887

A87

Fort
Augustus

Monabhliath
Mountains

Kingussie

Newtonmore

A9

A830

Mallaig

A86

Eigg

Grampian
Moun

A861

NM

A82

A9

NN

Fort William

Blair
Atholl

Pitlochr

Tobermory

A848

Strathtay

Aberfeldy

Loch Linnhe

Sound of Mull

A82

Kenmore

TA

10

11

For continuation pages refer to numbered arrows

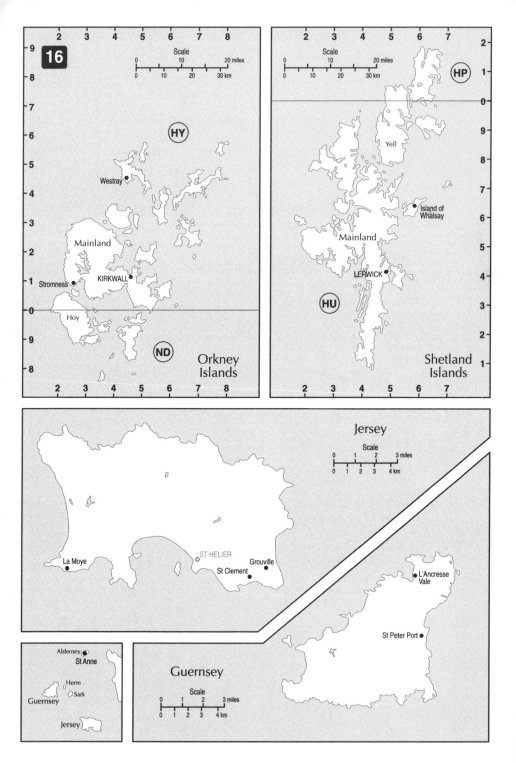

16

Scale
0   10   20 miles
0 10 20 30 km

HY

Westray

Mainland

Stromness KIRKWALL

Hoy

ND

Orkney
Islands

Scale
0   10   20 miles
0 10 20 30 km

HP

Yell

Island of
Whalsay

Mainland

LERWICK

HU

Shetland
Islands

Jersey

Scale
0   1   2   3 miles
0 1 2 3 4 km

ST HELIER

La Moye

Grouville
St Clement

L'Ancresse
Vale

St Peter Port

Alderney
St Anne

Herm
Sark
Guernsey

Jersey

Guernsey

Scale
0   1   2   3 miles
0 1 2 3 4 km

READERS' RECOMMENDATIONS

We make every effort to include as many courses as possible in our guide, but with the present popularity of golf and the opening of so many new courses, it is not always possible to contact every one. If you know of a golf course that is not included in this book, we would be delighted to hear from you with contact details.

Also, if you know of a course that is particularly noteworthy or fun to play and could be considered for highlighting - or indeed one that should not continue to be highlighted - we would be delighted to consider your recommendation.

YOUR NAME AND ADDRESS ....

....

....

NAME AND ADDRESS OF THE COURSE ....

....

....

TELEPHONE NUMBER...

YOUR COMMENTS ....

....

....

....

....

....

....

....

....

....

....

....

....

....

....

READERS' RECOMMENDATIONS

We make every effort to include as many courses as possible in our guide, but with the present popularity of golf and the opening of so many new courses, it is not always possible to contact every one. If you know of a golf course that is not included in this book, we would be delighted to hear from you with contact details.

Also, if you know of a course that is particularly noteworthy or fun to play and could be considered for highlighting - or indeed one that should not continue to be highlighted - we would be delighted to consider your recommendation.

YOUR NAME AND ADDRESS ....

....

....

NAME AND ADDRESS OF THE COURSE ....

....

....

TELEPHONE NUMBER...

YOUR COMMENTS ....

....

....

....

....

....

....

....

....

....

....

....

....